PEARSON   ALWAYS LEARNING

James T. McClave • P. George Benson • Terry Sincich

Statistics for Business and Economics

Third Custom Edition for New York University

Taken from:
Statistics for Business and Economics, Twelfth Edition
by James T. McClave, P. George Benson, and Terry Sincich

Pearson Learning Solutions, 501 Boylston Street, Suite 900, Boston, MA 02116
A Pearson Education Company
www.pearsoned.com

Printed in the United States of America

1 2 3 4 5 6 7 8 9 10 V0UD 17 16 15 14

000200010271888945

RD

ISBN 10: 1-269-90795-6
ISBN 13: 978-1-269-90795-8

Contents

4 Random Variables and Probability Distributions   184

5 Sampling Distributions   265

6 Inferences Based on a Single Sample: Estimation with Confidence Intervals   299

7 Inferences Based on a Single Sample: Tests of Hypotheses   355

8 Inferences Based on Two Samples: Confidence Intervals and Tests of Hypotheses   419

11 Simple Linear Regression   601

12 Multiple Regression and Model Building   666

14 Time Series: Descriptive Analyses, Models, and Forecasting   14-1

☐ Preface

This twelfth edition of *Statistics for Business and Economics* is an introductory text emphasizing inference, with extensive coverage of data collection and analysis as needed to evaluate the reported results of statistical studies and make good decisions. As in earlier editions, the text stresses the development of statistical thinking, the assessment of credibility, and the value of the inferences made from data, both by those who consume and those who produce them. It assumes a mathematical background of basic algebra.

The text incorporates the following features, developed from the American Statistical Association (ASA)–sponsored conferences on *Making Statistics More Effective in Schools of Business* (MSMESB) and the ASA's Guidelines for Assessment and Instruction in Statistics Education (GAISE) Project:

- Emphasize statistical literacy and develop statistical thinking
- Use real data in applications
- Use technology for developing conceptual understanding and analyzing data
- Foster active learning in the classroom
- Stress conceptual understanding rather than mere knowledge of procedures
- Emphasize intuitive concepts of probability

New in the Twelfth Edition

- **More than 1,200 Exercises, with Revisions and Updates to 30 Percent of Them.** Many new and updated exercises, based on contemporary business-related studies and real data, have been added. Most of these exercises foster and promote critical thinking skills.

- **Updated Technology.** All printouts from statistical software (Excel/XLSTAT, SPSS, Minitab, and the TI-84 graphing calculator) and corresponding instructions for use have been revised to reflect the latest versions of the software.

- **New Statistics in Action Cases.** Four of the 14 Statistics in Action cases are new, each based on real data from a recent business study.

- **Continued Emphasis on Ethics.** Where appropriate, boxes have been added emphasizing the importance of ethical behavior when collecting, analyzing, and interpreting data with statistics.

Content-Specific Changes to This Edition

- **Chapter 1 (Statistics, Data, and Statistical Thinking).** Material on all basic sampling concepts (e.g., random sampling and sample survey designs) has been streamlined and moved to Section 1.6 (Collecting Data: Sampling and Related Issues).

- **Chapter 2 (Methods for Describing Sets of Data).** The section on summation notation has been moved to the appendix (Appendix A). Also, recent examples of misleading graphics have been added to Section 2.10 (Distorting the Truth with Descriptive Techniques).

- **Chapter 4 (Random Variables and Probability Distributions).** Use of technology for computing probabilities of random variables with known probability distributions (e.g., binomial, Poisson, normal, and exponential distributions) has been incorporated into the relevant sections of this chapter. Also, the section on approximating a binomial distribution with a normal distribution has been incorporated into Section 4.6 (The Normal Distribution).

- **Chapter 5 (Sampling Distributions).** Material on the sampling distribution of the sample mean (originally in Part III of Chapter 4) has been moved to create this new chapter. Also, two new sections have been added, Section 5.2 (Properties of Sampling Distributions: Unbiasedness and Minimum Variance) and Section 5.4 (The Sampling Distribution of the Sample Proportion).

- **Chapter 6 (Inferences Based on a Single Sample: Estimation with Confidence Intervals).** An optional section (Section 6.7) on estimating a population variance has been added.

- **Chapter 7 (Inferences Based on a Single Sample: Tests of Hypotheses).** The section on *p*-values in hypothesis testing (Section 7.3) has been moved up to emphasize the importance of their use in business-related studies. Throughout the remainder of the text, conclusions from a test of hypothesis are based on *p*-values.

- **Chapter 10 (Categorical Data Analysis).** A subsection on contingency tables with fixed marginals has been added to Section 10.3.

Hallmark Strengths

We have maintained the pedagogical features of *Statistics for Business and Economics* that we believe make it unique among introductory business statistics texts. These features, which assist the student in achieving an overview of statistics and an understanding of its relevance in both the business world and everyday life, are as follows:

- **Use of Examples as a Teaching Device** Almost all new ideas are introduced and illustrated by data-based applications and examples. We believe that students better understand definitions, generalizations, and theoretical concepts *after* seeing an application. All examples have three components: (1) Problem, (2) Solution, and (3) Look Back (or Look Ahead). This step-by-step process provides students with a defined structure by which to approach problems and enhances their problem-solving skills. The Look Back/Look Ahead feature often gives helpful hints to solving the problem and/or provides a further reflection or insight into the concept or procedure that is covered.

- **Now Work Exercises** A *Now Work* exercise suggestion follows most examples. The *Now Work* exercise (marked with the NW icon in the exercise sets) is similar in style and concept to the text example. This provides the student with an opportunity to immediately test and confirm his or her understanding.

- **Real Data-Based Exercises** The text includes more than 1,200 exercises based on applications in a variety of business disciplines and research areas. All the applied exercises employ the use of current real data extracted from current publications (e.g., newspapers, magazines, journals, and the Internet). Some students have difficulty learning the mechanics of statistical techniques when all problems are couched in terms of realistic applications. For this reason, we have six types of exercises:

  Learning the Mechanics. Designed as straightforward applications of new concepts, these exercises allow students to test their ability to comprehend a mathematical concept or a definition.

  Applying the Concepts—Basic. Based on applications taken from a wide variety of business journals, newspapers, and other sources, these short exercises help students begin developing the skills necessary to diagnose and analyze real-world problems.

  Applying the Concepts—Intermediate. Based on more detailed real-world applications, these exercises require students to apply their knowledge of the technique presented in the section.

Applying the Concepts—Advanced. These more difficult real-data exercises require students to utilize their critical thinking skills.

Critical Thinking Challenges. Placed at the end of the Supplementary Exercises section only, students are presented with one or two challenging business problems.

Applet Exercises. In addition to the six types of exercises, we also have exercises based on the applets (short JAVA computer programs) included on the CD, which accompanies the text. These point-and-click applets allow students to easily run simulations that visually demonstrate some of the more difficult statistical concepts (e.g., sampling distributions and confidence intervals). Most chapters contain several optional applet exercises in the exercise sets. They are denoted with the following Applet icon ◌.

□ **Statistics in Action Cases** Each chapter begins with a case study based on an actual contemporary, controversial, or high-profile issue in business. Relevant research questions and data from the study are presented and the proper analysis demonstrated in short *Statistics in Action Revisited* sections throughout the chapter. These motivate students to critically evaluate the findings and think through the statistical issues involved.

□ **Making Business Decisions Cases** Seven extensive real-world business problem-solving cases, with real data and assignments for the student, serve as a good capstone and review of the material that precedes it. Typically, these cases follow two or three chapters and require the student to apply the methods presented in these chapters.

□ **Hands-On Activities** At the end of each chapter, students are provided with an opportunity to participate in hands-on classroom activities, ranging from real data collection to formal statistical analysis. These Activities are designed to be performed by students individually or as a class.

□ **Biographies** Brief descriptions of famous statisticians and their achievements are presented in side boxes. With these profiles, students will develop an appreciation of the statistician's efforts and the discipline of statistics as a whole.

□ **Exploring Data with Statistical Software** Each statistical analysis method presented is demonstrated using output from Excel/XLSTAT, SPSS, Minitab, and the TI-84 graphing calculator. Students are exposed early and often to computer printouts they will encounter in today's high-tech business world.

□ **Using Technology Tutorials** At the end of each chapter are statistical software tutorials with point-and-click instructions (with screen shots) for Minitab, SPSS, and Excel/XLSTAT. These tutorials are easily located and show students how to best use and maximize statistical software. In addition, output and keystroke instructions for the TI-84 graphing calculator are presented.

□ **Data and Applet CD** The text is accompanied by a resource CD that contains files for all of the data sets marked with a CD icon in the text. These include data sets for text examples, exercises, Statistics in Action, and Making Business Decisions. All data files are saved in multiple formats. This CD also contains the applets that are used to illustrate statistical concepts and Chapter 13 (Methods for Quality Improvement: Statistical Process Control), Chapter 14 (Descriptive Analyses, Models, and Forecasting), and Chapter 15 (Nonparametric Statistics).

Flexibility in Coverage

The text is written to allow the instructor flexibility in coverage of topics. Suggestions for two topics, probability and regression, are given below.

□ **Probability and Counting Rules** One of the most troublesome aspects of an introductory statistics course is the study of probability. Probability poses a challenge for instructors because they must decide on the level of presentation, and students find it a difficult subject to comprehend. We believe that one cause for these problems is the mixture of probability and counting rules that occurs in most introductory texts. Consequently, we have included the counting rules (with examples) in an appendix (Appendix B) rather than in the body of Chapter 3. Thus, the instructor can control the level of coverage of probability covered.

- **Multiple Regression and Model Building** This topic represents one of the most useful statistical tools for the solution of applied problems. Although an entire text could be devoted to regression modeling, we believe that we have presented coverage that is understandable, usable, and much more comprehensive than the presentations in other introductory statistics texts. We devote two full chapters to discussing the major types of inferences that can be derived from a regression analysis, showing how these results appear in the output from statistical software, and, most important, selecting multiple regression models to be used in an analysis. Thus, the instructor has the choice of a one-chapter coverage of simple linear regression (Chapter 11), a two-chapter treatment of simple and multiple regression (excluding the sections on model building in Chapter 12), or complete coverage of regression analysis, including model building and regression diagnostics. This extensive coverage of such useful statistical tools will provide added evidence to the student of the relevance of statistics to real-world problems.

- **Role of Calculus in Footnotes** Although the text is designed for students with a noncalculus background, footnotes explain the role of calculus in various derivations. Footnotes are also used to inform the student about some of the theory underlying certain methods of analysis. These footnotes allow additional flexibility in the mathematical and theoretical levels at which the material is presented.

◻ Supplements

Student Resources

Student's Solutions Manual, by Nancy Boudreau (Bowling Green State University), provides detailed, worked-out solutions to all odd-numbered text exercises. (ISBN-10: 0-321-82629-9; ISBN-13: 978-0-321-82629-9)

Excel Technology Manual, by Mark Dummeldinger (University of South Florida), provides tutorial instruction and worked-out text examples for Excel. The *Excel Technology Manual* is available for download at pearsonhighered .com/mathstatresrouces or within MyStatLab.

Business Insight Videos. This series of ten 4- to 7-minute videos, each about a well-known business and the challenges it faces, focuses on statistical concepts as they pertain to the real world. The videos can be downloaded from within MyStatLab. Assessment questions to check students' understanding of the videos and answers are available. Contact your Pearson representative for details.

Study Cards for Business Statistics Software. This series of study cards, available for Excel® with XLSTAT™, Excel® 2010, Minitab®, JMP®, SPSS®, R®, StatCrunch™, and TI-83/84 graphing calculators, provides students with easy, step-by-step guides to the most common business statistics software. Available at www.myPearsonStore.com.

For the Instructor

Annotated Instructor's Edition contains answers to text exercises. Annotated marginal notes include Teaching Tips, suggested exercises to reinforce the statistical concepts discussed in the text, and short answers to the exercises within the exercise sets.(ISBN-10:0-321-82642-6; ISBN-13: 978-0-321-82642-8)

Instructor's Solutions Manual, by Nancy Boudreau (Bowling Green State University), provides detailed, worked-out solutions to all of the book's exercises. Careful attention has been paid to ensure that all methods of solution and notation are consistent with those used in the core text. Available for download at www. pearsonhighered.com/irc.

TestGen® (www.pearsonhighered.com/testgen) enables instructors to build, edit, print, and administer tests using a computerized bank of questions developed to cover all the objectives of the text. TestGen is algorithmically based, allowing instructors to create multiple but equivalent versions of the same question or test with the click of a button. Instructors can also modify test bank questions or add new questions. Tests can be printed or administered online. The software and test bank are available for download from Pearson Education's online catalog (www.pearsonhighered.com/irc).

Technology Resources

On the Companion CD-ROM:
- Data sets in multiple formats for text examples, exercises, Statistics in Action, and Making Business Decisions
- Applets
- Chapter 13: Methods for Quality Improvement: Statistical Process Control
- Chapter 14: Descriptive Analyses, Models, and Forecasting
- Chapter 15: Nonparametric Statistics

MyStatLab™ Online Course (access code required)
MyStatLab is a course management system that delivers **proven results** in helping individual students succeed.

- MyStatLab can be successfully implemented in any environment—lab-based, hybrid, fully online, traditional—and demonstrates the quantifiable difference that integrated usage has on student retention, subsequent success, and overall achievement.
- MyStatLab's comprehensive online gradebook automatically tracks students' results on tests, quizzes, homework, and in the study plan. Instructors can use the gradebook to provide positive feedback or intervene if students have trouble. Gradebook data can be easily exported to a variety of spreadsheet programs, such as Microsoft Excel. You can determine which points of data you want to export, and then analyze the results to determine success.

MyStatLab provides **engaging experiences** that personalize, stimulate, and measure learning for each student. In addition to the resources below, each course includes a full interactive online version of the accompanying textbook.

- ***Tutorial Exercises with Multimedia Learning Aids:*** The homework and practice exercises in MyStatLab align with the exercises in the textbook, and they regenerate algorithmically to give students unlimited opportunity for practice and mastery. Exercises offer immediate helpful feedback, guided solutions, sample problems, animations, videos, and eText clips for extra help at point-of-use.
- ***StatTalk Videos:*** *24 Conceptual Videos to Help You Actually Understand Statistics.* Fun-loving statistician Andrew Vickers takes to the streets of Brooklyn, NY, to demonstrate important statistical concepts through interesting stories and real-life events. These fun and engaging videos will help students actually understand statistical concepts. Available with an instructors user guide and assessment questions.
- ***Getting Ready for Statistics:*** A library of questions now appears within each MyStatLab course to offer the developmental math topics students need for the course.

These can be assigned as a prerequisite to other assignments, if desired.

- *Conceptual Question Library:* In addition to algorithmically regenerated questions that are aligned with your textbook, there is a library of one thousand Conceptual Questions available in the assessment manager that require students to apply their statistical understanding.
- *StatCrunch™:* MyStatLab integrates the Web-based statistical software, StatCrunch, within the online assessment platform so that students can easily analyze data sets from exercises and the text. In addition, MyStatLab includes access to www.StatCrunch.com, a Web site where users can access more than 15,000 shared data sets, conduct online surveys, perform complex analyses using the powerful statistical software, and generate compelling reports.
- *Statistical Software Support:* Knowing that students often use external statistical software, we make it easy to copy our data sets, both from the ebook and the MyStatLab questions, into software such as StatCrunch, Minitab, Excel, and more. Students have access to a variety of support tools—Technology Tutorial Videos, Technology Study Cards, and Technology Manuals for select titles—to learn how to effectively use statistical software.
- *Expert Tutoring:* Although many students describe the whole of MyStatLab as "like having your own personal tutor," students also have access to live tutoring from Pearson. Qualified statistics instructors provide tutoring sessions for students via MyStatLab.

And MyStatLab comes from a **trusted partner** with educational expertise and an eye on the future.

- Knowing that you are using a Pearson product means knowing that you are using quality content. That means that our eTexts are accurate and our assessment tools work. Whether you are just getting started with MyStatLab, or have a question along the way, we're here to help you learn about our technologies and how to incorporate them into your course. To learn more about how MyStatLab combines proven learning applications with powerful assessment, visit www.mystatlab.com or contact your Pearson representative.

MyStatLab™ Ready to Go Course
(access code required)

These new Ready to Go courses provide students with all the same great MyStatLab features that you're used to, but make it easier for instructors to get started. Each course includes pre-assigned homeworks and quizzes to make creating your course even simpler. Ask your Pearson representative about the details for this particular course or to see a copy of this course.

MathXL® for Statistics Online Course
(access code required)

MathXL® is the homework and assessment engine that runs MyStatLab. (MyStatLab is MathXL plus a learning management system.)

With MathXL for Statistics, instructors can:

- Create, edit, and assign online homework and tests using algorithmically generated exercises correlated at the objective level to the textbook.
- Create and assign their own online exercises and import TestGen tests for added flexibility.
- Maintain records of all student work, tracked in MathXL's online gradebook.

With MathXL for Statistics, students can:

- Take chapter tests in MathXL and receive personalized study plans and/or personalized homework assignments based on their test results.
- Use the study plan and/or the homework to link directly to tutorial exercises for the objectives they need to study.
- Students can also access supplemental animations and video clips directly from selected exercises.
- Knowing that students often use external statistical software, we make it easy to copy our data sets, both from the ebook and the MyStatLab questions, into software like StatCrunch™, Minitab, Excel and more.

MathXL for Statistics is available to qualified adopters. For more information, visit our Web site at www.mathxl.com or contact your Pearson representative.

StatCrunch™

StatCrunch is powerful Web-based statistical software that allows users to perform complex analyses, share data sets, and generate compelling reports of their data. The vibrant online community offers more than 15,000 data sets for students to analyze.

- **Collect.** Users can upload their own data to StatCrunch or search a large library of publicly shared data sets, spanning almost any topic of interest. Also, an online survey tool allows users to quickly collect data via Web-based surveys.
- **Crunch.** A full range of numerical and graphical methods allows users to analyze and gain insights from any data set. Interactive graphics help users understand statistical concepts, and are available for export to enrich reports with visual representations of data.
- **Communicate.** Reporting options help users create a wide variety of visually appealing representations of their data.

Full access to StatCrunch is available with a MyStatLab kit, and StatCrunch is available by itself to qualified adopters. StatCrunch Mobile now available to access from your mobile device. For more information, visit our Web site at www.StatCrunch.com or contact your Pearson representative.

StatCrunch™ eBook

This interactive online textbook includes StatCrunch, a powerful Web-based statistical software. Embedded StatCrunch buttons allow users to open all data sets and tables from the book with the click of a button and immediately perform an analysis using StatCrunch.

PowerPoint® Lecture Slides provide an outline to use in a lecture setting, presenting definitions, key concepts, and figures from the text. These slides are available within MyStatLab or at www.pearsonhighered.com/irc.

The Student Edition of Minitab® is a condensed edition of the professional release of Minitab statistical software. It offers the full range of statistical methods and graphical capabilities, along with worksheets that can include up to 10,000 data points. Individual copies of the software can be bundled with the text. (ISBN-10: 0-321-11313-6; ISBN-13: 978-0-321-11313-9)

JMP Student Edition is an easy-to-use, streamlined version of JMP desktop statistical discovery software from AS Institute, Inc., and is available for bundling with the text. (ISBN-10: 0-321-89164-3; ISBN-13: 978-0-321-89164-8)

XLSTAT™ for Pearson. Used by leading businesses and universities, XLSTAT is an Excel® add-in that offers a wide variety of functions to enhance the analytical capabilities of Microsoft® Excel® making it the ideal tool for your everyday data analysis and statistics requirements. XLSTAT™ is compatible with all Excel versions (except Mac 2008). Available for bundling with the text. (ISBN-10: 0-321-75932-X; ISBN-13: 978-0-321-75932-0)

☐ Acknowledgments

This book reflects the efforts of a great many people over a number of years. First, we would like to thank the following professors, whose reviews and comments on this and prior editions have contributed to the twelfth edition:

Reviewers of the Twelfth Edition of *Statistics for Business and Economics*

Christine Ebert	*University of Delaware*
Laura Reisert	*Florida International University*
Bernard Dickman	*Hofstra University*
Daniel Sirvent	*Vanguard University*
Arunas Dagys	*St. Xavier University*
Rick Gibson	*American University*
L. Douglas Smith	*University of Missouri–St. Louis*
Karen Smith	*West Georgia University*
Remus Osan	*Boston University*
Steve Huchendorf	*University of Minnesota*

Reviewers of Previous Editions

CALIFORNIA Joyce Curley-Daly, Jim Daly, Robert K. Smidt, *California Polytechnic State University* • Jim Davis, *Golden Gate University* • Carol Eger, *Stanford University* • Paul W. Guy, *California State University, Chico* • Judd Hammack, P. Kasliwal, *California State University, Los Angeles* • Mabel T. King, *California State University, Fullerton* • James Lackritz, *California State University, San Diego* • Beth Rose, *University of Southern California* **COLORADO** Rick L. Edgeman, Charles F. Warnock, *Colorado State University* • Eric Huggins, *Fort Lewis College* • William J. Weida, *United States Air Force Academy* **CONNECTICUT** Alan E. Gelfand, Joseph Glaz, Timothy 'J. Killeen, *University of Connecticut* **DISTRICT OF COLUMBIA** Phil Cross, Jose Luis Guerrero-Cusumano, *Georgetown University* • Gaminie Meepagala, *Howard University* **FLORIDA** John M. Charnes, *University of Miami* • C. Brad Davis, *Clearwater Christian College* • Fred Leysieffer, Pi-Erh Lin, Doug Zahn, *Florida State University* • P. V. Rao, *University of Florida* • Jeffrey W. Steagall, *University of North Florida* • Edna White, *Florida Atlantic University* **GEORGIA** Robert Elrod, *Georgia State University* **HAWAII** Steve Hora, *University of Hawaii, Hilo* **ILLINOIS** Edward Minieka, *University of Illinois at Chicago* • Don Robinson, *Illinois State University* • Chipei Tseng, *Northern Illinois University* • Pankaj Vaish, *Arthur Andersen & Company* **IOWA** Dileep Dhavale, *University of Northern Iowa* • William Duckworth II, William Q. Meeker, *Iowa State University* • Tim E. McDaniel, *Buena Vista University* **KANSAS** Paul I. Nelson, *Kansas State University* • Lawrence A. Sherr, *University of Kansas* **KENTUCKY** Richard N. McGrath, *Bowling Green State University* **LOUISIANA** James Willis, *Louisiana State University* **MARYLAND** John F. Beyers, Michael Kulansky, *University of Maryland–University College* • Glenn J. Browne, Mary C. Christman, *University of Maryland* **MASSACHUSETTS** Warren M. Holt, *Southeastern Massachusetts University* **MICHIGAN** Atul Agarwal, Petros Ioannatos, *GMI Engineering and Management Institute* • Richard W. Andrews, Peter Lenk, Benjamin Lev, *University of Michigan* • Leszek Gawarecki, *Kettering University* • Toni M. Somers, *Wayne State University* • William Welch, *Saginaw Valley State University* • T. J. Wharton, *Oakland University* **MINNESOTA** Gordon J. Alexander, Donald W. Bartlett, David M. Bergman, Atul Bhatia, Benny Lo, Karen Lundquist, Vijay Pisharody, Donald N. Steinnes, Robert W. Van Cleave, Steve Wickstrom, *University of Minnesota* • Daniel G. Brick, Leigh Lawton, *University of St. Thomas* • Susan Flach, *General Mills, Inc.* • David D. Krueger, Ruth K. Meyer, Jan Saraph, Gary Yoshimoto, *St. Cloud State University* • Paula M. Oas,

General Office Products • Fike Zahroom, *Moorhead State University* **MISSISSIPPI** Eddie M. Lewis, *University of Southern Mississippi* • Alireza Tahai, *Mississippi State University* **MISSOURI** James Holstein, Lawrence D. Ries, *University of Missouri, Columbia* • Marius Janson, *University of Missouri, St. Louis* • Farroll Tim Wright, *University of Missouri* **NEBRASKA** James Wright, *Chadron State College* **NEW HAMPSHIRE** Ken Constantine, *University of New Hampshire* **NEW JERSEY** Lewis Coopersmith, Cengiz Haksever, *Rider University* • Lei Lei, Xuan Li, Zina Taran, *Rutgers University* • Philip Levine, Leonard Presby, *William Paterson University* **NEW MEXICO** S. Howard Kraye, *University of New Mexico* **NEW YORK** James Czachor, *Fordham-Lincoln Center, AT&T* • Bernard Dickman, *Hofstra University* • Joshua Fogel, *Brooklyn College of City University of New York* • Martin Labbe, *State University of New York, College at New Paltz* • Kenneth Leong, *College of New Rochelle* • Mark R. Marino, *Niagara University/Erie Community College* • G. E. Martin, *Clarkson University* • Thomas J. Pfaff, *Ithaca College* • Gary Simon, *New York University, Stern School of Business* • Rungrudee Suetorsak, *SUNY-Fredonia* **NORTH CAROLINA** Golam Azam, *North Carolina Agricultural & Technical University* • Edward Carlstein, Douglas A. Elvers, *University of North Carolina at Chapel Hill* • Barry P. Cuffe, *Wingate University* • Don Holbert, *East Carolina University* • J. Morgan Jones, *University of North Carolina* • Douglas S. Shafer, *University of North Carolina, Charlotte* **OHIO** William H. Beyer, *University of Akron* • Michael Broida, Tim Krehbiel, *Miami University of Ohio* • Chih-Hsu Cheng, Douglas A. Wolfe, *Ohio State University* • Ronald L. Coccari, *Cleveland State University* • Richard W. Culp, *Wright-Patterson AFB, Air Force Institute of Technology* **OKLAHOMA** Larry Claypool, Brenda Masters, Rebecca Moore, *Oklahoma State University* • Robert Curley, *University of Central Oklahoma* **PENNSYLVANIA** Mohammed Albohali, Douglas H. Frank, *Indiana University of Pennsylvania* • Sukhwinder Bagi, *Bloomsburg University* • Carl Bedell, *Philadelphia College of Textiles and Science* • Ann Hussein, *Philadelphia University* • Behnam Nakhai, *Millersville University* • Rose Prave, *University of Scranton* • Farhad Saboori, *Albright College* • Kathryn Szabet, *LaSalle University* • Christopher J. Zappe, *Bucknell University* **SOUTH CAROLINA** Iris Fetta, Robert Ling, *Clemson University* • Kathleen M. Whitcomb, *University of South Carolina* **TENNESSEE** Francis J. Brewerton, *Middle Tennessee State University* **TEXAS** Larry M. Austin, *Texas Tech University* • Jim Branscome, Robert W. Brobst, Mark Eakin, Grace Esimai, Michael E. Hanna, Craig W. Slinkman, *University of Texas at Arlington* • Katarina Jegdic, *University of Houston–Downtown* • Virgil F. Stone, *Texas A & M University* **VIRGINIA** Edward R. Clayton, *Virginia Polytechnic Institute and State University* **WASHINGTON** June Morita, Kim Tamura, *University of Washington* **WISCONSIN** Ross H. Johnson, *Madison College* **WASHINGTON, D.C.** Keith Ord, *Georgetown University* **CANADA** Clarence Bayne, *Concordia University* • Edith Gombay, *University of Alberta* **TURKEY** Dilek Onkal, *Bilkent University, Ankara* **OTHER** Michael P. Wegmann, *Keller Graduate School of Management*

Other Contributors

Special thanks are due to our supplements authors, Nancy Boudreau and Mark Dummeldinger, who have worked with us for many years. C. Brad Davis provided the excellent student activities and applet exercises, while accuracy checkers Cathleen Zucco-Teveloff and Engin Sungur helped ensure a highly accurate, clean text. The source material for many of the interesting and updated data-based exercises was provided by student researchers Demelza Hays and Charles Favreau. Finally, the Pearson Education staff of Deirdre Lynch, Marianne Stepanian, Tracy Patruno, Chere Bemelmans, Dana Bettez, Sonia Ashraf, Erin Lane, Kathleen DeChavez, Barbara Atkinson, Marielle Guiney, Jean Choe, Linda Cox, Ginny Michaud, and Integra-Chicago's Amanda Zagnoli helped greatly with all phases of the text development, production, and marketing effort.

1

Where We're Going

- Introduce the field of statistics (1.1)
- Demonstrate how statistics applies to business (1.2)
- Introduce the language of statistics and the key elements of any statistical problem (1.3)
- Differentiate between population and sample data (1.3)
- Differentiate between descriptive and inferential statistics (1.3)
- Introduce the key elements of a process (1.4)
- Identify the different types of data and data-collection methods (1.5–1.6)
- Discover how critical thinking through statistics can help improve our quantitative literacy (1.7)

▢ Statistics, Data, and Statistical Thinking

STATISTICS in ACTION   ## A *20/20* View of Surveys: Fact or Fiction?

"Did you ever notice that, no matter where you stand on popular issues of the day, you can always find statistics or surveys to back up your point of view–whether to take vitamins, whether daycare harms kids, or what foods can hurt you or save you? There is an endless flow of information to help you make decisions, but is this information accurate, unbiased? John Stossel decided to check that out, and you may be surprised to learn if the picture you're getting doesn't seem quite right, maybe it isn't."

Barbara Walters gave this introduction to a segment of the popular prime-time ABC television program *20/20*. The story was titled "Fact or Fiction?—Exposés of So-Called Surveys." One of the surveys investigated by ABC correspondent John Stossel compared the discipline problems experienced by teachers in the 1940s and those experienced today. The results: In the 1940s, teachers worried most about students talking in class, chewing gum, and running in the halls. Today, they worry most about being assaulted! This information was highly publicized in the print media—in daily newspapers, weekly magazines, gossip columns, the *Congressional Quarterly*, and the *Wall Street Journal*, among others—and referenced in speeches by a variety of public figures, including former first lady Barbara Bush and former Education Secretary William Bennett.

    "Hearing this made me yearn for the old days when life was so much simpler and gentler, but was life that simple then?" asks Stossel. "Wasn't there juvenile delinquency [in the 1940s]? Is the survey true?" With the help of a Yale School of Management professor, Stossel found the original source of the teacher survey—Texas oilman T. Colin Davis—and discovered it wasn't a survey at all! Davis had simply identified certain disciplinary problems encountered by teachers in a conservative newsletter—a list he admitted was not obtained from a statistical survey, but

STATISTICS
in ACTION
CONTINUED

from Davis's personal knowledge of the problems in the 1940s. ("I was in school then") and his understanding of the problems today ("I read the papers").

Stossel's critical thinking about the teacher "survey" led to the discovery of research that is misleading at best and unethical at worst. Several more misleading (and possibly unethical) surveys, conducted by businesses or special interest groups with specific objectives in mind, were presented on the ABC program. These are listed below. Two other studies are also discussed.

The *20/20* segment ended with an interview of Cynthia Crossen, author of *Tainted Truth: The Manipulation of Fact in America,* an exposé of misleading and biased surveys. Crossen warns, "If everybody is misusing numbers and scaring us with numbers to get us to do something, however good [that something] is, we've lost the power of numbers. Now, we know certain things from research. For example, we know that smoking cigarettes is hard on your lungs and heart, and because we know that, many people's lives have been extended or saved. We don't want to lose the power of information to help us make decisions, and that's what I worry about."

Reported Information (Source)	Actual Study Information
1. Eating oat bran is a cheap and easy way to reduce your cholesterol. (Quaker Oats)	Diet must consist of nothing but oat bran to reduce your cholesterol count.
2. 150,000 women a year die from anorexia. (Feminist group)	Approximately 1,000 women a year die from problems that were likely caused by anorexia.
3. Domestic violence causes more birth defects than all medical issues combined. (March of Dimes)	No study–false report.
4. Only 29% of high school girls are happy with themselves, compared to 66% of elementary school girls. (American Association of University Women)	Of 3,000 high school girls, 29% responded, "Always true" to the statement "I am happy the way I am." Most answered, "Sort of true" and "Sometimes true."
5. One in four American children under age 12 is hungry or at risk of hunger. (Food Research and Action Center)	Based on responses to questions: "Do you ever cut the size of meals?" "Do you ever eat less than you feel you should?" "Did you ever rely on limited numbers of foods to feed your children because you were running out of money to buy food for a meal?"
6. There is a strong correlation between a CEO's golf handicap and the company's stock performance: The lower the CEO's handicap (i.e., the better the golfer), the better the stock performs. (*New York Times,* May 31, 1998)	Survey sent to CEOs of 300 largest U.S. companies; only 51 revealed their golf handicaps. Data for several top-ranking CEOs were excluded from the analysis.
7. If the federal government's health reform act is passed, 30% of employers are predicted to "definitely" or "probably" stop offering health coverage. (McKinsey & Company Survey, Feb. 2011)	Online survey of 1,329 private-sector employers in the United States. Respondents were asked leading questions that made it logical to stop offering health insurance.

In the following *Statistics in Action Revisited* sections, we discuss several key statistical concepts covered in this chapter that are relevant to misleading surveys like those exposed in the *20/20* program.

STATISTICS in ACTION REVISITED

- ◻ Identifying the population, sample, and inference **(p. 9)**
- ◻ Identifying the data-collection method and data type **(p. 20)**
- ◻ Critically assessing the ethics of a statistical study **(p. 23)**

1.1 The Science of Statistics

What does *statistics* mean to you? Does it bring to mind batting averages? Gallup polls, unemployment figures, or numerical distortions of facts (lying with statistics!)? Or is it simply a college requirement you have to complete? We hope to persuade you that statistics is a meaningful, useful science whose broad scope of applications to business, government, and the physical and social sciences is almost limitless. We also want to show that statistics can lie only when they are misapplied. Finally, we wish to demonstrate the key role statistics play in critical thinking—whether in the classroom, on the job, or in everyday life. Our objective is to leave you with the impression that the time you spend studying this subject will repay you in many ways.

Although the term can be defined in many ways, a broad definition of *statistics* is the science of collecting, classifying, analyzing, and interpreting information. Thus, a statistician isn't just someone who calculates batting averages at baseball games or tabulates the results of a Gallup poll. Professional statisticians are trained in *statistical science*—that is, they are trained in collecting information in the form of **data,** evaluating it, and drawing conclusions from it. Furthermore, statisticians determine what information is relevant in a given problem and whether the conclusions drawn from a study are to be trusted.

> **Statistics** is the science of data. It involves collecting, classifying, summarizing, organizing, analyzing, and interpreting numerical and categorical information.

In the next section, you'll see several real-life examples of statistical applications in business and government that involve making decisions and drawing conclusions.

1.2 Types of Statistical Applications in Business

FLORENCE NIGHTINGALE (1820–1910)
The Passionate Statistician

In Victorian England, the "Lady of the Lamp" had a mission to improve the squalid field hospital conditions of the British army during the Crimean War. Today, most historians consider Florence Nightingale to be the founder of the nursing profession. To convince members of the British Parliament of the need for supplying nursing and medical care to soldiers in the field, Nightingale compiled massive amounts of data from the army files. Through a remarkable series of graphs (which included the first "pie chart"), she demonstrated that most of the deaths in the war were due to illnesses contracted outside the battlefield or long after battle action from wounds that went untreated. Florence Nightingale's compassion and self-sacrificing nature, coupled with her ability to collect, arrange, and present large amounts of data, led some to call her the "Passionate Statistician."

Statistics means "numerical descriptions" to most people. Monthly unemployment figures, the failure rate of startup companies, and the proportion of female executives in a particular industry all represent statistical descriptions of large sets of data collected on some phenomenon. Often the data are selected from some larger set of data whose characteristics we wish to estimate. We call this selection process *sampling*. For example, you might collect the ages of a sample of customers of an online DVD movie rental company to estimate the average age of *all* customers of the company. Then you could use your estimate to target the firm's advertisements to the appropriate age group. Notice that statistics involves two different processes: (1) describing sets of data and (2) drawing conclusions (making estimates, decisions, predictions, etc.) about the sets of data based on sampling. So, the applications of statistics can be divided into two broad areas: *descriptive statistics* and *inferential statistics*.

> **Descriptive statistics** utilizes numerical and graphical methods to explore data, i.e., to look for patterns in a data set, to summarize the information revealed in a data set, and to present the information in a convenient form.

> **Inferential statistics** utilizes sample data to make estimates, decisions, predictions, or other generalizations about a larger set of data.

Although we'll discuss both descriptive and inferential statistics in the following chapters, the primary theme of the text is **inference**.

Let's begin by examining some business studies that illustrate applications of statistics.

Study 1.1 "Best-Selling Girl Scout Cookies" (www.girlscouts.org): Since 1917, the Girl Scouts of America have been selling boxes of cookies. Currently, there are eight varieties for sale: Thin Mints, Samoas, Caramel deLites, Tagalongs, Peanut Butter Patties, Do-si-dos, Peanut Butter Sandwiches, and Trefoils. Each of the approximately 150 million boxes of Girl Scout cookies sold in 2006 was classified by variety. The results are summarized in Figure 1.1. From the graph, you can clearly see that the best-selling variety is Thin Mints (25%), followed by Samoas (19%) and Tagalongs (13%). Since Figure 1.1 *describes* the variety of categories of the boxes of Girl Scout cookies sold, the graphic is an example of *descriptive statistics*.

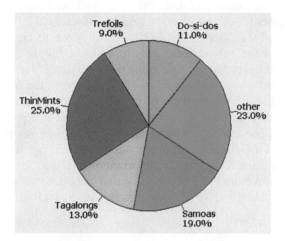

Figure 1.1

Best-selling Girl Scout cookies
Source: "Best-Selling Girl Scout Cookies" www.girlscouts.org.

Study 1.2 "The Executive Compensation Scoreboard" (*Forbes*, April 13, 2011): How much are the top corporate executives in the United States being paid, and are they worth it? To answer these questions, *Forbes* magazine compiles the "Executive Compensation Scoreboard" each year based on a survey of executives at the 500 largest U.S. companies. To determine which executives are worth their pay, *Forbes* also records the performance of shareholders' stock for the CEO's company over the previous 6 years. Based on a comparison of the stock's performance and the CEO's annual salary, each CEO is given an "efficiency" rating—the lower the rating, the more the CEO is worth his/her pay. An analysis of the scoreboard data for the highest-paid CEOs in 2011 is summarized in Table 1.1. The table reveals that CEOs in the business services industry have the lowest average* efficiency rating (4.5), thus, they are the best performers. The CEOs in the telecommunications industry are the worst performers, with the highest efficiency rating (163). Armed with this sample information, *Forbes* might *infer* that, from the shareholders' perspective, typical chief executives in telecommunications are overpaid relative to CEOs in business services. Thus, this study is an example of *inferential statistics*.

Table 1.1	Average Pay-for-Performance Efficiency Ratings of CEOs, by Industry		
Industry	Average Efficiency Rating	Industry	Average Efficiency Rating
Aerospace and Defense	85	Hotels, Restaurants	31
Banking	59	Household Products	110
Business Services	4.5	Insurance	106
Capital Goods	85	Materials	54
Chemicals	131	Media	134
Conglomerates	126	Oil and Gas Operations	91
Construction	144	Retailing	107
Consumer Durables	11	Semiconductors	82
Diversified Financial	106	Software and Services	110
Drugs and Biotechnology	121	Technology Hardware	132
Food, Drink,		Telecommunications	163
and Tobacco	140	Transportation	51
Health Care Equipment	96	Utilities	127

Source: Data from "Executive Compensation Scoreboard," FORBES April 13, 2011.

*Although we will not formally define the term *average* until Chapter 2, *typical* or *middle* can be substituted here without confusion.

Study 1.3 "Does rudeness really matter in the workplace?" (*Academy of Management Journal*, Oct. 2007): Previous studies have established that rudeness in the workplace can lead to retaliatory and counterproductive behavior. However, there has been little research on how rude behaviors influence a victim's task performance. In a recent study, college students enrolled in a management course were randomly assigned to one of two experimental conditions: rudeness condition (45 students) and control group (53 students). Each student was asked to write down as many uses for a brick as possible in 5 minutes; this value (total number of uses) was used as a performance measure for each student. For those students in the rudeness condition, the facilitator displayed rudeness by berating the students in general for being irresponsible and unprofessional (due to a late-arriving confederate). No comments were made about the late-arriving confederate to students in the control group. As you might expect, the researchers discovered that the performance levels for students in the rudeness condition were generally lower than the performance levels for students in the control group; thus, they concluded that rudeness in the workplace negatively effects job performance. As in Study 1.2, this study is an example of the use of inferential statistics. The researchers used data collected on 98 college students in a simulated work environment to make an inference about the performance levels of all workers exposed to rudeness on the job.

These studies provide three real-life examples of the uses of statistics in business, economics, and management. Notice that each involves an analysis of data, either for the purpose of describing the data set (Study 1.1) or for making inferences about a data set (Studies 1.2 and 1.3).

1.3 Fundamental Elements of Statistics

Statistical methods are particularly useful for studying, analyzing, and learning about *populations* of *experimental units*.

> An **experimental (or observational) unit** is an object (e.g., person, thing, transaction, or event) upon which we collect data.

> A **population** is a set of units (usually people, objects, transactions, or events) that we are interested in studying.

For example, populations may include (1) *all* employed workers in the United States, (2) *all* registered voters in California, (3) *everyone* who has purchased a particular brand of cellular telephone, (4) *all* the cars produced last year by a particular assembly line, (5) the *entire* stock of spare parts at United Airlines' maintenance facility, (6) *all* sales made at the drive-through window of a McDonald's restaurant during a given year, and (7) the set of *all* accidents occurring on a particular stretch of interstate during a holiday period. Notice that the first three population examples (1–3) are sets (groups) of people, the next two (4–5) are sets of objects, the next (6) is a set of transactions, and the last (7) is a set of events. Also notice that *each set includes all the experimental units in the population* of interest.

In studying a population, we focus on one or more characteristics or properties of the experimental units in the population. We call such characteristics *variables*. For example, we may be interested in the variables age, gender, income, and/or the number of years of education of the people currently unemployed in the United States.

> A **variable** is a characteristic or property of an individual experimental (or observational) unit.

The name *variable* is derived from the fact that any particular characteristic may vary among the experimental units in a population.

In studying a particular variable, it is helpful to be able to obtain a numerical representation for it. Often, however, numerical representations are not readily available, so the process of measurement plays an important supporting role in statistical studies. **Measurement** is the process we use to assign numbers to variables of individual population units. We might, for instance, measure the preference for a food product by asking a consumer to rate the product's taste on a scale from 1 to 10. Or we might measure workforce age by simply asking each worker, "How old are you?" In other cases, measurement involves the use of instruments such as stopwatches, scales, and calipers.

If the population we wish to study is small, it is possible to measure a variable for every unit in the population. For example, if you are measuring the starting salary for all University of Michigan MBA graduates last year, it is at least feasible to obtain every salary. When we measure a variable for every experimental unit of a population, the result is called a **census** of the population. Typically, however, the populations of interest in most applications are much larger, involving perhaps many thousands or even an infinite number of units. Examples of large populations include the seven listed above, as well as all invoices produced in the last year by a *Fortune* 500 company, all potential buyers of a new iPad, and all stockholders of a firm listed on the New York Stock Exchange. For such populations, conducting a census would be prohibitively time-consuming and/or costly. A reasonable alternative would be to select and study a *subset* (or portion) of the units in the population.

> A **sample** is a subset of the units of a population.

For example, suppose a company is being audited for invoice errors. Instead of examining all 15,472 invoices produced by the company during a given year, an auditor may select and examine a sample of just 100 invoices (see Figure 1.2). If he is interested in the variable "invoice error status," he would record (measure) the status (error or no error) of each sampled invoice.

After the variable(s) of interest for every experimental unit in the sample (or population) is measured, the data are analyzed, either by descriptive or inferential statistical methods. The auditor, for example, may be interested only in *describing* the error rate in

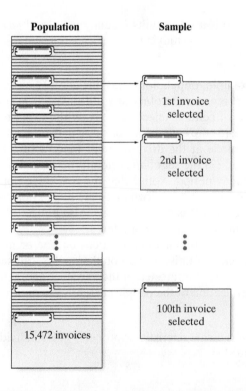

Figure 1.2

A sample of all company invoices

the sample of 100 invoices. More likely, however, he will want to use the information in the sample to make *inferences* about the population of all 15,472 invoices.

> A **statistical inference** is an estimate or prediction or some other generalization about a population based on information contained in a sample.

*That is, we use the information contained in the sample to learn about the larger population.** Thus, from the sample of 100 invoices, the auditor may estimate the total number of invoices containing errors in the population of 15,472 invoices. The auditor's inference about the quality of the firm's invoices can be used in deciding whether to modify the firm's billing operations.

Example 1.1	

Key Elements of a Statistical Problem—Ages of TV Viewers

Problem According to *Variety* (Aug. 10, 2010), the average age of viewers of television programs broadcast on CBS, NBC, and ABC is 51 years. Suppose a rival network (e.g., FOX) executive hypothesizes that the average age of FOX viewers is less than 51. To test her hypothesis, she samples 200 FOX viewers and determines the age of each.

a. Describe the population.
b. Describe the variable of interest.
c. Describe the sample.
d. Describe the inference.

Solution

a. The population is the set of units of interest to the TV executive, which is the set of all FOX viewers.
b. The age (in years) of each viewer is the variable of interest.
c. The sample must be a subset of the population. In this case, it is the 200 FOX viewers selected by the executive.
d. The inference of interest involves the *generalization* of the information contained in the sample of 200 viewers to the population of all FOX viewers. In particular, the executive wants to *estimate* the average age of the viewers in order to determine whether it is less than 51 years. She might accomplish this by calculating the average age in the sample and using the sample average to estimate the population average.

Look Back A key to diagnosing a statistical problem is to identify the data set collected (in this example, the ages of the 200 FOX TV viewers) as a population or sample.

Example 1.2	

Key Elements of a Statistical Problem— Pepsi vs. Coca-Cola

Problem *Cola wars* is the popular term for the intense competition between Coca-Cola and Pepsi displayed in their marketing campaigns. Their campaigns have featured movie and television stars, rock videos, athletic endorsements, and claims of consumer preference based on taste tests. Suppose, as part of a Pepsi marketing campaign, 1,000 cola consumers are given a blind taste test (i.e., a taste test in which the two brand names are disguised). Each consumer is asked to state a preference for brand A or brand B.

---

*The terms *population* and *sample* are often used to refer to the sets of measurements themselves, as well as to the units on which the measurements are made. When a single variable of interest is being measured, this usage causes little confusion. But when the terminology is ambiguous, we'll refer to the measurements as *population data sets* and *sample data sets,* respectively.

a. Describe the population.

b. Describe the variable of interest.

c. Describe the sample.

d. Describe the inference.

Solution

a. Because we are interested in the responses of cola consumers in a taste test, a cola consumer is the experimental unit. Thus, the population of interest is the collection or set of all cola consumers.

b. The characteristic that Pepsi wants to measure is the consumer's cola preference as revealed under the conditions of a blind taste test, so cola preference is the variable of interest.

c. The sample is the 1,000 cola consumers selected from the population of all cola consumers.

d. The inference of interest is the *generalization* of the cola preferences of the 1,000 sampled consumers to the population of all cola consumers. In particular, the preferences of the consumers in the sample can be used to *estimate* the percentage of all cola consumers who prefer each brand.

Look Back In determining whether the statistical application is inferential or descriptive, we assess whether Pepsi is interested in the responses of only the 1,000 sampled customers (descriptive statistics) or in the responses for the entire population of consumers (inferential statistics).

◘ **Now Work Exercise 1.15b**

The preceding definitions and examples identify four of the five elements of an inferential statistical problem: a population, one or more variables of interest in a sample, and an inference. But making the inference is only part of the story. We also need to know its **reliability**–that is, how good the inference is. The only way we can be certain that an inference about a population is correct is to include the entire population in our sample. However, because of *resource constraints* (e.g., insufficient time and/or money), we usually can't work with whole populations, so we base our inferences on just a portion of the population (a sample). Consequently, whenever possible, it is important to determine and report the reliability of each inference made. Reliability, then, is the fifth element of inferential statistical problems.

The measure of reliability that accompanies an inference separates the science of statistics from the art of fortune-telling. A palm reader, like a statistician, may examine a sample (your hand) and make inferences about the population (your life). However, unlike statistical inferences, the palm reader's inferences include no measure of reliability.

Suppose, like the TV executive in Example 1.1, we are interested in the *error of estimation* (i.e., the difference between the average age of the population of TV viewers and the average age of a sample of TV viewers). Using statistical methods, we can determine a *bound on the estimation error*. This bound is simply a number that our estimation error (the difference between the average age of the sample and the average age of the population) is not likely to exceed. We'll see in later chapters that this bound is a measure of the uncertainty of our inference. The reliability of statistical inferences is discussed throughout this text. For now, we simply want you to realize that an inference is incomplete without a measure of its reliability.

A **measure of reliability** is a statement (usually quantified) about the degree of uncertainty associated with a statistical inference.

Let's conclude this section with a summary of the elements of both descriptive and inferential statistical problems and an example to illustrate a measure of reliability.

Four Elements of Descriptive Statistical Problems

1. The population or sample of interest
2. One or more variables (characteristics of the population or experimental units) that are to be investigated
3. Tables, graphs, or numerical summary tools
4. Identification of patterns in the data

Five Elements of Inferential Statistical Problems

1. The population of interest
2. One or more variables (characteristics of the population or experimental units) that are to be investigated
3. The sample of population units
4. The inference about the population based on information contained in the sample
5. A measure of reliability for the inference

Example   1.3

Reliability of an Inference—Pepsi vs. Coca-Cola

Problem Refer to Example 1.2, in which the cola preferences of 1,000 consumers were indicated in a taste test. Describe how the reliability of an inference concerning the preferences of all cola consumers in the Pepsi bottler's marketing region could be measured.

Solution When the preferences of 1,000 consumers are used to estimate the preferences of all consumers in the region, the estimate will not exactly mirror the preferences of the population. For example, if the taste test shows that 56% of the 1,000 consumers chose Pepsi, it does not follow (nor is it likely) that exactly 56% of all cola drinkers in the region prefer Pepsi. Nevertheless, we can use sound statistical reasoning (which is presented later in the text) to ensure that our sampling procedure will generate estimates that are almost certainly within a specified limit of the true percentage of all consumers who prefer Pepsi. For example, such reasoning might assure us that the estimate of the preference for Pepsi from the sample is almost certainly within 5% of the actual population preference. The implication is that the actual preference for Pepsi is between 51% [i.e., $(56 - 5)\%$] and 61% [i.e., $(56 + 5)\%$]—that is, $(56 \pm 5)\%$. This interval represents a measure of reliability for the inference.

Look Back The interval 56 ± 5 is called a *confidence interval*, because we are "confident" that the true percentage of customers who prefer Pepsi in a taste test falls into the range $(51, 61)$. In Chapter 6, we learn how to assess the degree of confidence (e.g., 90% or 95% confidence) in the interval.

STATISTICS in ACTION REVISITED

Identifying the Population, Sample, and Inference

Consider the study on the link between a CEO's golf handicap and the company's stock performance, reported in the *New York Times* (May 31, 1998). The newspaper gathered information on golf handicaps of corporate executives obtained from a *Golf Digest* survey sent to CEOs of the 300 largest U.S. companies. (A golf handicap is a numerical "index" that allows golfers to compare skills; the lower the handicap, the better the golfer.) For the 51 CEOs who reported their handicaps, the *New York Times*

STATISTICS in ACTION REVISITED CONTINUED

then determined each CEO's company stock market performance over a 3-year period (measured as a rate-of-return index, from a low value of 0 to a high value of 100). Thus, the experimental unit for the study is a corporate executive, and the two variables measured are golf handicap and stock performance index. Also, the data for the 51 CEOs represent a sample selected from the much larger population of all corporate executives in the United States. (These data are available in the **GLFCEO** file.)

The *New York Times* discovered a "statistical correlation" (a method discussed in Chapter 11) between golf handicap and stock performance. Thus, the newspaper inferred that the better the CEO is at golf, the better the company's stock performance.

Data Set: GLFCEO

1.4 Processes*

Sections 1.2 and 1.3 focused on the use of statistical methods to analyze and learn about populations, which are sets of *existing* units. Statistical methods are equally useful for analyzing and making inferences about *processes*.

> A **process** is a series of actions or operations that transforms inputs to outputs. A process produces or generates output over time.

The most obvious processes of interest to businesses are those of production or manufacturing. A manufacturing process uses a series of operations performed by people and machines to convert inputs, such as raw materials and parts, to finished products (the outputs). Examples include the process used to produce the paper on which these words are printed, automobile assembly lines, and oil refineries.

Figure 1.3 presents a general description of a process and its inputs and outputs. In the context of manufacturing, the process in the figure (i.e., the transformation process) could be a depiction of the overall production process or it could be a depiction of one of the many processes (sometimes called *subprocesses*) that exist within an overall production process. Thus, the output shown could be finished goods that will be shipped to an external customer or merely the output of one of the steps or subprocesses of the overall process. In the latter case, the output becomes input for the next subprocess. For example, Figure 1.3 could represent the overall automobile assembly process, with its output being fully assembled cars ready for shipment to dealers. Or, it could depict the windshield assembly subprocess, with its output of partially assembled cars with windshields ready for "shipment" to the next subprocess in the assembly line.

Besides physical products and services, businesses and other organizations generate streams of numerical data over time that are used to evaluate the performance of the organization. Examples include weekly sales figures, quarterly earnings, and yearly profits. The U.S. economy (a complex organization) can be thought of as generating streams of data that include the gross domestic product (GDP), stock prices, and the Consumer Price Index. Statisticians and other analysts conceptualize these data streams

Figure 1.3

Graphical depiction of a manufacturing process

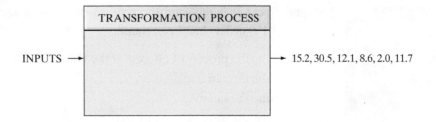

Figure 1.4
A black box process with numerical output

as being generated by processes. Typically, however, the series of operations or actions that cause particular data to be realized are either unknown or so complex (or both) that the processes are treated as *black boxes*.

A process whose operations or actions are unknown or unspecified is called a **black box**.

Frequently, when a process is treated as a black box, its inputs are not specified either. The entire focus is on the output of the process. A black box process is illustrated in Figure 1.4.

In studying a process, we generally focus on one or more characteristics, or properties, of the output. For example, we may be interested in the weight or the length of the units produced or even the time it takes to produce each unit. As with characteristics of population units, we call these characteristics *variables*. In studying processes whose output is already in numerical form (i.e., a stream of numbers), the characteristic, or property, represented by the numbers (e.g., sales, GDP, or stock prices) is typically the variable of interest. If the output is not numeric, we use *measurement processes* to assign numerical values to variables.* For example, if in the automobile assembly process the weight of the fully assembled automobile is the variable of interest, a measurement process involving a large scale will be used to assign a numerical value to each automobile.

As with populations, we use sample data to analyze and make inferences (estimates, predictions, or other generalizations) about processes. But the concept of a sample is defined differently when dealing with processes. Recall that a population is a set of existing units and that a sample is a subset of those units. In the case of processes, however, the concept of a set of existing units is not relevant or appropriate. Processes generate or create their output *over time*—one unit after another. For example, a particular automobile assembly line produces a completed vehicle every 4 minutes. We define a sample from a process in the box.

Any set of output (object or numbers) produced by a process is also called a **sample**.

Thus, the next 10 cars turned out by the assembly line constitute a sample from the process, as do the next 100 cars or every fifth car produced today.

Example 1.4	
Key Elements of a Process—Waiting Time at a Fast-Food Window	**Problem** A particular fast-food restaurant chain has 6,289 outlets with drive-through windows. To attract more customers to its drive-through services, the company is considering offering a 50% discount to customers who wait more than a specified number of minutes to receive their order. To help determine what the time limit should be, the company decided to estimate the average waiting time at a particular drive-through window in Dallas, Texas. For 7 consecutive days, the worker taking customers' orders recorded the time that every order was placed. The worker who handed the order to the customer recorded the time of delivery. In both cases, workers used synchronized

*A process whose output is already in numerical form necessarily includes a measurement process as one of its subprocesses.

digital clocks that reported the time to the nearest second. At the end of the 7-day period, 2,109 orders had been timed.

a. Describe the process of interest at the Dallas restaurant.

b. Describe the variable of interest.

c. Describe the sample.

d. Describe the inference of interest.

e. Describe how the reliability of the inference could be measured.

Solution

a. The process of interest is the drive-through window at a particular fast-food restaurant in Dallas, Texas. It is a process because it "produces," or "generates," meals over time—that is, it services customers over time.

b. The variable the company monitored is customer waiting time, the length of time a customer waits to receive a meal after placing an order. Because the study is focusing only on the output of the process (the time to produce the output) and not the internal operations of the process (the tasks required to produce a meal for a customer), the process is being treated as a black box.

c. The sampling plan was to monitor every order over a particular 7-day period. The sample is the 2,109 orders that were processed during the 7-day period.

d. The company's immediate interest is in learning about the drive-through window in Dallas. They plan to do this by using the waiting times from the sample to make a statistical inference about the drive-through process. In particular, they might use the average waiting time for the sample to estimate the average waiting time at the Dallas facility.

e. As for inferences about populations, measures of reliability can be developed for inferences about processes. The reliability of the estimate of the average waiting time for the Dallas restaurant could be measured by a bound on the error of estimation—that is, we might find that the average waiting time is 4.2 minutes, with a bound on the error of estimation of 0.5 minutes. The implication would be that we could be reasonably certain that the true average waiting time for the Dallas process is between 3.7 and 4.7 minutes.

Look Back Notice that there is also a population described in this example: the company's 6,289 existing outlets with drive-through facilities. In the final analysis, the company will use what it learns about the process in Dallas and, perhaps, similar studies at other locations to make an inference about the waiting times in its population of outlets.

━■ **Now Work Exercise 1.36**

Note that output already generated by a process can be viewed as a population. Suppose a soft-drink canning process produced 2,000 twelve-packs yesterday, all of which were stored in a warehouse. If we were interested in learning something about those 2,000 twelve-packs—such as the percentage with defective cardboard packaging—we could treat the 2,000 twelve-packs as a population. We might draw a sample from the population in the warehouse, measure the variable of interest, and use the sample data to make a statistical inference about the 2,000 twelve-packs, as described in Sections 1.2 and 1.3.

In this optional section, we have presented a brief introduction to processes and the use of statistical methods to analyze and learn about processes. In Chapters 13 and 14 we present an in-depth treatment of these subjects.

1.5 Types of Data

You have learned that statistics is the science of data and that data are obtained by measuring the values of one or more variables on the units in the sample (or population). All data (and hence the variables we measure) can be classified as one of two general types: *quantitative* and *qualitative*.

Quantitative data are data that are measured on a naturally occurring numerical scale.* The following are examples of quantitative data:

1. The temperature (in degrees Celsius) at which each unit in a sample of 20 pieces of heat-resistant plastic begins to melt
2. The current unemployment rate (measured as a percentage) for each of the 50 states
3. The scores of a sample of 150 MBA applicants on the GMAT, a standardized business graduate school entrance exam administered nationwide
4. The number of female executives employed in each of a sample of 75 manufacturing companies

> **Quantitative data** are measurements that are recorded on a naturally occurring numerical scale.

In contrast, qualitative data cannot be measured on a natural numerical scale; they can only be classified into categories.† Examples of qualitative data are as follows:

1. The political party affiliation (Democrat, Republican, or Independent) in a sample of 50 CEOs
2. The defective status (defective or not) of each of 100 computer chips manufactured by Intel
3. The size of a car (subcompact, compact, midsize, or full-size) rented by each of a sample of 30 business travelers
4. A taste tester's ranking (best, worst, etc.) of four brands of barbecue sauce for a panel of 10 testers

Often, we assign arbitrary numerical values to qualitative data for ease of computer entry and analysis. But these assigned numerical values are simply codes: They cannot be meaningfully added, subtracted, multiplied, or divided. For example, we might code Democrat = 1, Republican = 2, and Independent = 3. Similarly, a taste tester might rank the barbecue sauces from 1 (best) to 4 (worst). These are simply arbitrarily selected numerical codes for the categories and have no utility beyond that.

> **Qualitative data** are measurements that cannot be measured on a natural numerical scale; they can only be classified into one of a group of categories.

Example 1.5

Types of Data—Study of a River Contaminated by a Chemical Plant

Problem Chemical and manufacturing plants sometimes discharge toxic-waste materials such as DDT into nearby rivers and streams. These toxins can adversely affect the plants and animals inhabiting the river and the riverbank. The U.S. Army Corps of Engineers conducted a study of fish in the Tennessee River (in Alabama) and its three tributary creeks: Flint Creek, Limestone Creek, and Spring Creek. A total of 144 fish were captured, and the following variables were measured for each:

1. River/creek where each fish was captured
2. Species (channel catfish, largemouth bass, or smallmouth buffalo fish)
3. Length (centimeters)
4. Weight (grams)
5. DDT concentration (parts per million)

*Quantitative data can be subclassified as either *interval* or *ratio*. For ratio data, the origin (i.e., the value 0) is a meaningful number. But the origin has no meaning with interval data. Consequently, we can add and subtract interval data, but we can't multiply and divide them. Of the four quantitative data sets listed, (1) and (3) are interval data, while (2) and (4) are ratio data.

†Qualitative data can be subclassified as either *nominal* or *ordinal*. The categories of an ordinal data set can be ranked or meaningfully ordered, but the categories of a nominal data set can't be ordered. Of the four qualitative data sets listed, (1) and (2) are nominal and (3) and (4) are ordinal.

These data are saved in the **DDT** file. Classify each of the five variables measured as quantitative or qualitative.

Solution The variables length, weight, and DDT are quantitative because each is measured on a numerical scale: length in centimeters, weight in grams, and DDT in parts per million. In contrast, river/creek and species cannot be measured quantitatively: They can only be classified into categories (e.g., channel catfish, largemouth bass, and smallmouth buffalo fish for species). Consequently, data on river/creek and species are qualitative.

Look Back It is essential that you understand whether data are quantitative or qualitative in nature because the statistical method appropriate for describing, reporting, and analyzing the data depends on the data type (quantitative or qualitative).

■ **Now Work Exercise 1.18**

We demonstrate many useful methods for analyzing quantitative and qualitative data in the remaining chapters of the text. But first, we discuss some important ideas on data collection.

1.6 Collecting Data: Sampling and Related Issues

Once you decide on the type of data—quantitative or qualitative—appropriate for the problem at hand, you'll need to collect the data. Generally, you can obtain the data in three different ways:

1. Data from a *published source*
2. Data from a *designed experiment*
3. Data from an *observational study* (e.g., a *survey*)

Sometimes, the data set of interest has already been collected for you and is available in a **published source,** such as a book, journal, newspaper, or Web site. For example, you may want to examine and summarize the unemployment rates (i.e., percentages of eligible workers who are unemployed) in the 50 states of the United States. You can find this data set (as well as numerous other data sets) at your library in the *Statistical Abstract of the United States,* published annually by the U.S. government. Similarly, someone who is interested in monthly mortgage applications for new home construction would find this data set in the *Survey of Current Business,* another government publication. Other examples of published data sources include the *Wall Street Journal* (financial data) and the *The Sporting News* (sports information).* The Internet (World Wide Web) now provides a medium by which data from published sources are readily available.

A second method of collecting data involves conducting a **designed experiment,** in which the researcher exerts strict control over the units (people, objects, or events) in the study. For example, an often-cited medical study investigated the potential of aspirin in preventing heart attacks. Volunteer physicians were divided into two groups—the *treatment* group and the *control* group. In the treatment group, each physician took one aspirin tablet a day for 1 year, while each physician in the control group took an aspirin-free placebo (no drug) made to look like an aspirin tablet. The researchers, not the physicians under study, controlled who received the aspirin (the treatment) and who received the placebo. As you will learn in Chapter 9, a properly designed experiment allows you to extract more information from the data than is possible with an uncontrolled study.

Finally, observational studies can be employed to collect data. In an **observational study,** the researcher observes the experimental units in their natural setting and records the variable(s) of interest. For example, a company psychologist might observe and record the level of "Type A" behavior of a sample of assembly line workers. Similarly, a

---

*With published data, we often make a distinction between the *primary source* and *secondary source.* If the publisher is the original collector of the data, the source is primary. Otherwise, the data are secondary source.

finance researcher may observe and record the closing stock prices of companies that are acquired by other firms on the day prior to the buyout and compare them to the closing prices on the day the acquisition is announced. Unlike a designed experiment, an observational study is one in which the researcher makes no attempt to control any aspect of the experimental units.

The most common type of observational study is a **survey,** where the researcher samples a group of people, asks one or more questions, and records the responses. Probably the most familiar type of survey is the political poll, conducted by any one of a number of organizations (e.g., Harris, Gallup, Roper, and CNN) and designed to predict the outcome of a political election. Another familiar survey is the Nielsen survey, which provides the major television networks with information on the most watched TV programs. Surveys can be conducted through the mail, with telephone interviews, or with in-person interviews. Although in-person interviews are more expensive than mail or telephone surveys, they may be necessary when complex information must be collected.

Regardless of the data-collection method employed, it is likely that the data will be a sample from some population. And if we wish to apply inferential statistics, we must obtain a *representative sample*.

> A **representative sample** exhibits characteristics typical of those possessed by the population of interest.

For example, consider a political poll conducted during a presidential election year. Assume the pollster wants to estimate the percentage of all 145 million registered voters in the United States who favor the incumbent president. The pollster would be unwise to base the estimate on survey data collected for a sample of voters from the incumbent's own state. Such an estimate would almost certainly be *biased* high; consequently, it would not be very reliable.

The most common way to satisfy the representative sample requirement is to select a simple random sample. A **simple random sample** ensures that every subset of fixed size in the population has the same chance of being included in the sample. If the pollster samples 1,500 of the 145 million voters in the population so that every subset of 1,500 voters has an equal chance of being selected, she has devised a simple random sample.

> A **simple random sample** of n experimental units is a sample selected from the population in such a way that every different sample of size n has an equal chance of selection.

The procedure for selecting a simple random sample typically relies on a **random number generator**. Random number generators are available in table form, online,* and in most statistical software packages. The Excel/XLSTAT, Minitab, and SPSS statistical software packages all have easy-to-use random number generators for creating a random sample. The next two examples illustrate the procedure.

Example 1.6 **Generating a Simple Random Sample—Selecting Households for a Feasibility Study**	**Problem** Suppose you wish to assess the feasibility of building a new high school. As part of your study, you would like to gauge the opinions of people living close to the proposed building site. The neighborhood adjacent to the site has 711 homes. Use a random number generator to select a simple random sample of 20 households from the neighborhood to participate in the study. **Solution** In this study, your population of interest consists of the 711 households in the adjacent neighborhood. To ensure that every possible sample of 20 households selected from the 711 has an equal chance of selection (i.e., to ensure a simple random sample), first assign a number from 1 to 711 to each of the households in the population. These numbers were entered into an Excel worksheet. Now, apply the random number

*One of many free online random number generators is available at www.randomizer.org.

generator of Excel/ XLSTAT, requesting that 20 households be selected without replacement. Figure 1.5 shows the output from XLSTAT. You can see that households numbered 40, 63, 108, . . . , 636 are the households to be included in your sample.

	A	B	C	D	E	F	G	H	I	J	K
1		XLSTAT 2011.4.02 - Data sampling - on 11/4/2011 at 10:17:05 AM									
2		Data: Workbook = HOUSEHOLDS.xlsx / Sheet = Sheet1 / Range = Sheet1!$A:$A / 711 rows and 1 column									
3		Sampling method: Random without replacement									
4		Number of samples: 1									
5		Sample size: 20									
6		Seed (random numbers): 4186805									
7											
8											
9		Sampled data:									
10											
11		HOUSEHOLD									
12		40									
13		63									
14		108									
15		153									
16		190									
17		227									
18		283									
19		302									
20		309									
21		371									
22		379									
23		419									
24		434									
25		457									
26		463									
27		489									
28		536									
29		537									
30		560									
31		636									
32											

Figure 1.5

Random selection of
20 households using XLSTAT

Look Back It can be shown (proof omitted) that there are over 3×10^{38} possible samples of size 20 that can be selected from the 711 households. Random number generators guarantee (to a certain degree of approximation) that each possible sample has an equal chance of being selected.

▬■ **Now Work Exercise 1.14**

The notion of random selection and randomization is also key to conducting good research with a designed experiment. The next example illustrates a basic application.

Example   **1.7**

Randomization in a Designed Experiment— A Clinical Trial

Problem A designed experiment in the medical field involving human subjects is referred to as a *clinical trial*. One recent clinical trial was designed to determine the potential of using aspirin in preventing heart attacks. Volunteer physicians were randomly divided into two groups—the *treatment* group and the *control* group. Each physician in the treatment group took one aspirin tablet a day for one year, while the physicians in the control group took an aspirin-free placebo made to look identical to an aspirin tablet. Because the physicians did not know which group, treatment or control, they were assigned to, the clinical trial is called a *blind study*. Assume 20 physicians volunteered for the study. Use a random number generator to randomly assign half of the physicians to the treatment group and half to the control group.

Solution Essentially, we want to select a random sample of 10 physicians from the 20. The first 10 selected will be assigned to the treatment group; the remaining 10 will be assigned to the control group. (Alternatively, we could randomly assign each physician,

⊞ ASPIRIN-STUDY.MTW ***		
↓	C1	C2	C3
	Physician	Treatment	
1	1	3	
2	2	11	
3	3	10	
4	4	14	
5	5	2	
6	6	7	
7	7	6	
8	8	16	
9	9	17	
10	10	9	
11	11		
12	12		
13	13		
14	14		
15	15		
16	16		
17	17		
18	18		
19	19		
20	20		
21			

Figure 1.6

Minitab worksheet with random assignment of physicians

one by one, to either the treatment or control group. However, this would not guarantee exactly 10 physicians in each group.)

The Minitab random sample procedure was employed, producing the printout shown in Figure 1.6. Numbering the physicians from 1 to 20, we see that physicians 3, 11, 10, 14, 2, 7, 6, 16, 17, and 9 are assigned to receive the aspirin (treatment). The remaining physicians are assigned the placebo (control).

◾ **Now Work Exercise 1.33e**

In addition to simple random samples, there are more complex random sampling designs that can be employed. These include (but are not limited to) **stratified random sampling, cluster sampling, systematic sampling,** and **randomized response sampling**. Brief descriptions of each follow. (For more details on the use of these sampling methods, consult the References at the end of this chapter.)

Stratified random sampling is typically used when the experimental units associated with the population can be separated into two or more groups of units, called *strata*, where the characteristics of the experimental units are more similar within strata than across strata. Random samples of experimental units are obtained for each strata; then the units are combined to form the complete sample. For example, if you are gauging opinions of voters on a polarizing issue, like government-sponsored health care, you may want to stratify on political affiliation (Republicans and Democrats), making sure that representative samples of both Republicans and Democrats (in proportion to the number of Republicans and Democrats in the voting population) are included in your survey.

Sometimes it is more convenient and logical to sample natural groupings (*clusters*) of experimental units first, and then collect data from all experimental units within each cluster. This involves the use of *cluster sampling*. For example, suppose a marketer for a large upscale restaurant chain wants to find out whether customers like the new menu. Rather than collect a simple random sample of all customers (which would be very difficult and costly to do), the marketer will randomly sample 10 of the 150 restaurant locations (clusters), and then interview all customers eating at each of the 10 locations on a certain night.

Another popular sampling method is *systematic sampling*. This method involves systematically selecting every *k*th experimental unit from a list of all experimental units. For example, every fifth person who walks into a shopping mall could be asked his or her opinion on a business topic of interest. Or, a quality control engineer at a manufacturing plant may select every 10th item produced on an assembly line for inspection.

A fourth alternative to simple random sampling is *randomized response sampling*. This design is particularly useful when the questions of the pollsters are likely to elicit false answers. For example, suppose each person in a sample of wage earners is asked whether he or she ever cheated on an income tax return. A cheater might lie, thus biasing an estimate of the true likelihood of someone cheating on his or her tax return. To circumvent this problem, each person is presented with two questions, one being the object of the survey and the other an innocuous question, such as:

1. Did you ever cheat on your federal income tax return?

2. Did you drink coffee this morning?

One of the questions is chosen at random to be answered by the wage earner by flipping a coin; however, which particular question is answered is unknown to the interviewer. In this way, the random response method attempts to elicit an honest response to a sensitive question. Sophisticated statistical methods are then employed to derive an estimate of the percentage of "yes" responses to the sensitive question.

No matter what type of sampling design you employ to collect the data for your study, be careful to avoid *selection bias*. Selection bias occurs when some experimental units in the population have less chance of being included in the sample than others. This results in samples that are not representative of the population. Consider an opinion poll that employs either a telephone survey or mail survey.

After collecting a random sample of phone numbers or mailing addresses, each person in the sample is contacted via telephone or the mail and a survey conducted. Unfortunately, these types of surveys often suffer from selection bias due to *nonresponse*. Some individuals may not be home when the phone rings, or others may refuse to answer the questions or mail back the questionnaire. As a consequence, no data are obtained for the nonrespondents in the sample. If the nonrespondents and respondents differ greatly on an issue, then *nonresponse bias* exits. For example, those who choose to answer a question on a school board issue may have a vested interest in the outcome of the survey—say, parents with children of school age, schoolteachers whose jobs may be in jeopardy, or citizens whose taxes might be substantially affected. Others with no vested interest may have an opinion on the issue but might not take the time to respond.

> **Selection bias** results when a subset of experimental units in the population has little or no chance of being selected for the sample.

> **Nonresponse bias** is a type of selection bias that results when data on all experimental units in a sample are not obtained.

Finally, even if your sample is representative of the population, the data collected may suffer from *measurement error*. That is, the values of the data (quantitative or qualitative) may be inaccurate. In sample surveys, opinion polls, etc., measurement error often results from *ambiguous* or *leading questions*. Consider the survey question: "How often did you change the oil in your car last year?" It is not clear whether the researcher wants to know how often you personally changed the oil in your car or how often you took your car into a service station to get an oil change. The ambiguous question may lead to inaccurate responses. On the other hand, consider the question: "Does the new health plan offer more comprehensive medical services at less cost than the old one?" The way the question is phrased *leads* the reader to believe that the new plan is better and to a "yes" response—a response that is more desirable to the researcher. A better, more neutral way to phrase the question is: "Which health plan offers more comprehensive medical services at less cost, the old one or the new one?"

> **Measurement error** refers to inaccuracies in the values of the data collected. In surveys, the error may be due to ambiguous or leading questions and the interviewer's effect on the respondent.

We conclude this section with two examples involving actual sampling studies.

Example 1.8

Method of Data Collection—Survey of Online Shoppers

Problem How do consumers feel about using the Internet for online shopping? To find out, a customer-experience software company recently commissioned a nationwide survey of 1,859 U.S. adults who had conducted at least one online transaction at a banking, shopping, travel, or insurance Web site in the past year. The findings, reported on *BusinessWeek.com*, revealed that 1,655 respondents, or 89%, experienced technical problems with an online transaction. Also, more than one-third of the consumers go to a competitor's Web site when a glitch in the online transaction occurs.

a. Identify the data-collection method.

b. Identify the target population.

c. Are the sample data representative of the population?

Solution

a. The data-collection method is a survey: 1,859 adults completed the questionnaire.

b. Presumably, the software company who commissioned the survey is interested in all consumers who have made at least one online transaction in the past year. Consequently, the target population is *all* consumers who use the Internet for online transactions.

c. Because the 1,859 respondents clearly make up a subset of the target population, they do form a sample. Whether or not the sample is representative is unclear because *BusinessWeek.com* provided no detailed information on how the 1,859 respondents were selected. If the respondents were obtained using, say, random-digit telephone dialing, then the sample is likely to be representative because it is a random sample. However, if the questionnaire was made available to anyone surfing the Internet, then the respondents are *self-selected* (i.e., each Internet user who saw the survey chose whether or not to respond to it). Such a survey often suffers from *nonresponse* bias. It is possible that many Internet users who chose not to respond (or who never saw the questionnaire) would have answered the questions differently, leading to a lower (or higher) sample percentage.

Look Back Any inferences based on survey samples that employ self-selection are suspect due to potential nonresponse bias.

■ **Now Work Exercise 1.25**

Example 1.9

Representative Data— Price Promotion Study

Problem Marketers use wording such as "was $100, now $80" to indicate a price promotion. The promotion is typically compared to the retailer's previous price or to a competitor's price. A study in the *Journal of Consumer Research* investigated whether between-store comparisons result in greater perceptions of value by consumers than within-store comparisons. Suppose 50 consumers were randomly selected from all consumers in a designated market area to participate in the study. The researchers randomly assigned 25 consumers to read a within-store price promotion advertisement ("was $100, now $80") and 25 consumers to read a between-store price promotion ("$100 there, $80 here"). The consumers then gave their opinion on the value of the discount offer on a 10-point scale (where 1 = lowest value and 10 = highest value). The value opinions of the two groups of consumers were compared.

a. Identify the data-collection method.

b. Are the sample data representative of the target population?

Solution

a. Here, the experimental units are the consumers. Because the researchers controlled which price promotion ad—"within-store" or "between-store"—the experimental units (consumers) were assigned to, a designed experiment was used to collect the data.

b. The sample of 50 consumers was randomly selected from all consumers in the designated market area. If the target population is all consumers in this market, it is likely that the sample is representative. However, the researchers warn that the sample data should not be used to make inferences about consumer behavior in other, dissimilar markets.

Look Back By using randomization in a designed experiment, the researcher is attempting to eliminate different types of bias, including self-selection bias.

■ **Now Work Exercise 1.17**

Identifying the Data-Collection Method and Data Type

Refer to the *New York Times* study on the link between a CEO's golf handicap and the company's stock performance. Recall that the newspaper gathered information on golf handicaps of corporate executives obtained from a *Golf Digest* survey that was sent to 300 corporate executives. Thus, the data-collection method is a survey. In addition to golf handicap (a numerical "index" that allows golfers to compare skills), the *Times* measured the CEO's company stock market performance over a 3-year period on a scale of 0 to 100. Because both variables, golf handicap and stock performance, are numerical in nature, they are quantitative data.

🔘 *Data Set:* GLFCEO

1.7 Critical Thinking with Statistics

According to H. G. Wells, author of such science-fiction classics as *The War of the Worlds* and *The Time Machine*, "*Statistical thinking* will one day be as necessary for efficient citizenship as the ability to read and write." Written more than a hundred years ago, Wells's prediction is proving true today.

H. G. WELLS (1866–1946)
Writer and Novelist

English-born Herbert George Wells published his first novel, *The Time Machine,* in 1895 as a parody of the English class division and as a satirical warning that human progress is inevitable. Although most famous as a science-fiction novelist, Wells was a prolific writer as a journalist, sociologist, historian, and philosopher. Wells's prediction about statistical thinking (see above) is just one of a plethora of observations he made about life on this world. Here are a few more of H. G. Wells's more famous quotes:

"Advertising is legalized lying."

"Crude classification and false generalizations are the curse of organized life."

"The crisis of today is the joke of tomorrow."

"Fools make researchers and wise men exploit them."

"The only true measure of success is the ratio between what we might have done and what we might have been on the one hand, and the thing we have made and the things we have made of ourselves on the other."

The growth in data collection associated with scientific phenomena, business operations, and government activities (quality control, statistical auditing, forecasting, etc.) has been remarkable in the past several decades. Every day the media present us with the published results of political, economic, and social surveys. In increasing government emphasis on drug and product testing, for example, we see vivid evidence of the need for **quantitative literacy,** i.e., the ability to evaluate data intelligently. Consequently, each of us has to develop a discerning sense—an ability to use rational thought to interpret and understand the meaning of data. Quantitative literacy can help you make intelligent decisions, inferences, and generalizations; that is, it helps you *think critically* using statistics.

Statistical thinking involves applying rational thought and the science of statistics to critically assess data and inferences. Fundamental to the thought process is that variation exists in populations and process data.

To gain some insight into the role statistics plays in critical thinking, we present two examples of some misleading or faulty surveys.

Example 1.10 **Biased Sample— Motorcycle Helmet Law**	**Problem** An article in the *New York Times* considered the question of whether motorcyclists should be required by law to wear helmets. In supporting his argument for no helmets, the editor of a magazine for Harley-Davidson bikers presented the results of one study that claimed "nine states without helmet laws had a lower fatality rate (3.05 deaths per 10,000 motorcycles) than those that mandated helmets (3.38)" and a survey that found "of 2,500 bikers at a rally, 98% of the respondents opposed such laws." Based on this information, do you think it is safer to ride a motorcycle without a helmet? What further statistical information would you like?

Solution You can use statistical thinking to help you critically evaluate the study. For example, before you can evaluate the validity of the 98% estimate, you would want to know how the data were collected. If a survey was, in fact, conducted, it's possible that the 2,500 bikers in the sample were not selected at random from the target population of all bikers, but rather were "self-selected." (Remember, they were all attending a rally—a rally likely for bikers who oppose the law.) If the respondents were likely to have strong opinions regarding the helmet law (e.g., strongly oppose the law), the resulting estimate is probably biased high. Also, if the selection bias in the sample was intentional, with the sole purpose to mislead the public, the researchers would be guilty of **unethical statistical practice**.

ETHICS in STATISTICS

Intentionally selecting a biased sample in order to produce misleading statistics is considered unethical statistical practice.

You would also want more information about the study comparing the motorcycle fatality rate of the nine states without a helmet law to those states that mandate helmets. Were the data obtained from a published source? Were all 50 states included in the study, or were only certain states selected? That is, are you seeing sample data or population data? Furthermore, do the helmet laws vary among states? If so, can you really compare the fatality rates?

Look Back Questions such as these led a group of mathematics and statistics teachers attending an American Statistical Association course to discover a scientific and statistically sound study on helmets. The study reported a dramatic *decline* in motorcycle crash deaths after California passed its helmet law.

Example 1.11 **Manipulative or Ambiguous Survey Questions—Satellite Radio Survey**	**Problem** Talk-show host Howard Stern moved his controversial radio program from free, over-the-air (AM/FM) radio to Sirius XM satellite radio. The move was perceived in the industry to boost satellite radio subscriptions. This led American Media Services, a developer of AM/FM radio properties, to solicit a nationwide random-digit dialing phone survey of 1,008 people. The purpose of the survey was to determine how much interest Americans really have in buying satellite radio service. After providing some background on Howard Stern's controversial radio program, one of the questions asked, "How likely are you to purchase a subscription to satellite radio after Howard Stern's move to Sirius?" The result: 86% of the respondents stated that they aren't likely to buy satellite radio because of Stern's move. Consequently, American Media Services concluded that "the Howard Stern Factor is overrated" and that "few Americans expect to purchase satellite radio"—claims that made the headlines of news reports and Web blogs. Do you agree?

Solution First, we need to recognize that American Media Services had a vested interest in the outcome of the survey—the company makes its money from over-the-air broadcast radio stations. Second, although the phone survey was conducted using random-digit dialing, there is no information provided on the response rate. It's possible that nonrespondents (people who were not home or refused to answer the survey questions) tend to be people who use cell phones more than their landline phone, and, consequently, are more likely to use the latest in electronic technology, including satellite radio. Finally, the survey question itself is ambiguous. Do the respondents have negative feelings about satellite radio, Howard Stern, or both? If not for Howard Stern's program, would the respondents be more likely to buy satellite radio? To the critical thinker, it's unclear what the results of the survey imply.

Look Back Examining the survey results from the perspective of satellite radio providers, 14% of the respondents indicated that they would be likely to purchase satellite radio. Projecting the 14% back to the population of all American adults, this figure represents about 50 million people; what is interpreted as "few Americans" by American Media Services could be music to the ears of satellite radio providers.

ETHICS in STATISTICS

Intentionally selecting a nonrandom sample in an effort to support a particular viewpoint is considered *unethical statistical practice.*

As with many statistical studies, both the motorcycle helmet study and satellite radio study are based on survey data. Most of the problems with these surveys result from the use of *nonrandom* samples. These samples are subject to potential errors, such as *selection bias, nonresponse bias,* and *measurement error.* Researchers who are aware of these problems and continue to use the sample data to make inferences are practicing *unethical statistics.*

Successful managers rely heavily on statistical thinking to help them make decisions. The role statistics can play in managerial decision making is displayed in the flow diagram in Figure 1.7. Every managerial decision-making problem begins with a real-world problem. This problem is then formulated in managerial terms and framed as a managerial question. The next sequence of steps (proceeding counterclockwise around the flow diagram) identifies the role that statistics can play in this process. The managerial question is translated into a statistical question, the sample data are collected and analyzed, and the statistical question is answered. The next step in the process is using the answer to the statistical question to reach an answer to the managerial question. The answer to the managerial question may suggest a reformulation of the original managerial problem, suggest a new managerial question, or lead to the solution of the managerial problem.

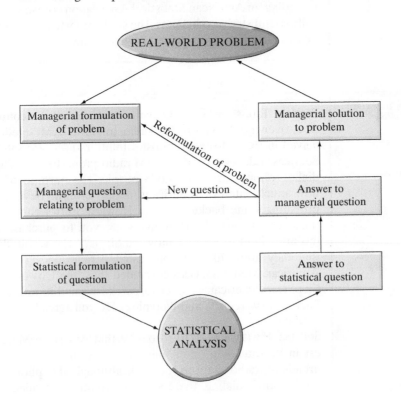

Figure 1.7

Flow diagram showing the role of statistics in managerial decision making
Source: Reprinted with permission from the American Statistician. © 1980 by the American Statistical Association. All rights reserved.

One of the most difficult steps in the decision-making process—one that requires a cooperative effort among managers and statisticians—is the translation of the managerial question into statistical terms (for example, into a question about a population). This statistical question must be formulated so that, when answered, it will provide the key to the answer to the managerial question. Thus, as in the game of chess, you must formulate the statistical question with the end result, the solution to the managerial question, in mind.

In the remaining chapters of the text, you'll become familiar with the tools essential for building a firm foundation in statistics and statistical thinking.

STATISTICS in ACTION REVISITED

Critically Assessing the Ethics of a Statistical Study

The *New York Times* reported a strong link between a corporate executive's golf handicap and his/her company's stock performance. Thus, the newspaper inferred that the better the CEO is at golf, the better the company's stock performance will be. To critically assess this study, consider the following facts:

1. *Golf Digest* sent surveys to the CEOs at the 300 largest U.S. firms. Only 74 executives agreed to reveal their golf handicaps. Of these 74 CEOs, the *Times* collected data on stock performance for only 51 of the companies. (The other 23 CEOs were not in the stock performance database used by the newspaper.)

2. The *New York Times* researcher who performed the analysis of the data stated that "for all the different factors I've tested as possible links to predicting which CEOs are going to perform well or poorly, [golf handicap] is certainly one of the . . . strongest."

3. According to the *Times,* the researcher "scientifically sifted out a handful of CEOs because of their statistical extremes," in effect "removing seven CEOs from the final analysis because [their data] destroyed the trend lines."

These observations lead a critical thinker to doubt the validity of the inference made by the *New York Times* researcher. Consider first that the sample of CEOs analyzed was not randomly selected from all CEOs in the United States. In fact, it was self-selected—only those CEOs who chose to report their golf handicap were included in the study. (Not even all these "self-reporters" were included; some were eliminated because the newspaper did not have information on their company's stock performance in the database.) Thus, the potential for selection and/or nonresponse bias is extremely high.

Second, based on fact #2, it is likely that the researcher tested a multitude of factors and found only one (golf handicap) that had a link to stock performance. We will learn in subsequent chapters that when a plethora of irrelevant variables are tested statistically, by chance one or more of the variables will be found "statistically significant."

Finally, the researcher removed the data for seven CEOs based on their "statistical extremes." In the next chapter, we learn about statistical "outliers"—how to detect them and how to treat them when discovered. However, it can be shown (using the methods outlined in the text) that these seven data points are not outliers. If the data points are included in the analysis, the link between golf handicap and stock performance is found to be weak, at best.

Data Set: GLFCEO □

▫ Chapter Notes

Key Terms

Note: Starred (*) terms are from the optional section in this chapter.

*Black box 11
Census 6
Cluster sampling 17
Data 3
Descriptive statistics 3
Designed experiment 14
Experimental (or
   observational) unit 5
Inference 3
Inferential statistics 3
Measurement 6
Measurement error 18
Measure of reliability 8
Nonresponse bias 18
Observational study 14
Population 5
*Process 10
Published source 14
Qualitative data 13

Quantitative data 13
Quantitative literacy 20
Randomized response
   sampling 17
Random number generator 15
Reliability 8
Representative sample 15
Sample 6
Selection bias 18
Simple random sample 15
Statistical inference 7
Statistical thinking 20
Statistics 3
Stratified random sampling 17
Survey 15
Systematic sampling 17
Unethical statistical
   practice 21
Variable 5

Key Ideas

Types of Statistical Applications

Descriptive
1. Identify **population** or **sample** (collection of **experimental units**)
2. Identify **variable(s)**

3. Collect **data**
4. **Describe** data

Inferential
1. Identify **population** (collection of *all* **experimental units**)
2. Identify **variable(s)**
3. Collect **sample** data (*subset* of population)
4. **Inference** about population based on sample
5. **Measure of reliability** for inference

Types of Data
1. **Quantitative** (numerical in nature)
2. **Qualitative** (categorical in nature)

Data-Collection Methods
1. **Observational** (e.g., survey)
2. **Published source**
3. **Designed experiment**

Types of Random Samples
1. **Simple random sample**
2. **Stratified random sample**
3. **Cluster sample**
4. **Systematic sample**
5. **Random response sample**

Problems with Nonrandom Samples
1. **Selection bias**
2. **Nonresponse bias**
3. **Measurement error**

Exercises 1.1–1.39

Note: Starred (*) exercises are from the optional section in this chapter.

Learning the Mechanics

1.1 What is statistics?

1.2 Explain the difference between descriptive and inferential statistics.

1.3 List and define the four elements of a descriptive statistics problem.

1.4 List and define the five elements of an inferential statistical analysis.

1.5 List the three major methods of collecting data and explain their differences.

1.6 Explain the difference between quantitative and qualitative data.

1.7 Explain how populations and variables differ.

1.8 Explain how populations and samples differ.

1.9 What is a representative sample? What is its value?

1.10 Why would a statistician consider an inference incomplete without an accompanying measure of its reliability?

*1.11 Explain the difference between a population and a process.

1.12 Define *statistical thinking*.

1.13 Suppose you're given a data set that classifies each sample unit into one of four categories: A, B, C, or D. You plan to create a computer database consisting of these data, and you decide to code the data as A = 1, B = 2, C = 3, and D = 4. Are the data consisting of the classifications A, B, C, and D qualitative or quantitative? After the data are input as 1, 2, 3, or 4, are they qualitative or quantitative? Explain your answers.

1.14 Suppose that a population contains 200,000 experimental units. Use a random number generator to select a simple random sample of $n = 10$ units from the population.

⚙ Applet Exercise 1.1

The *Random Numbers* applet generates a list of n random numbers from 1 to N, where n is the size of the sample and N is the size of the population. The list generated often contains repetitions of one or more numbers.

    a. Using the applet *Random Numbers*, enter 1 for the minimum value, 10 for the maximum value, and 10 for the sample size. Then click on *Sample*. Look at the results and list any numbers that are repeated and the number of times each of these numbers occurs.

b. Repeat part **a,** changing the maximum value to 20 and keeping the size of the sample fixed at 10. If you still have repetitions, repeat the process, increasing the maximum value by 10 each time but keeping the size of the sample fixed. What is the smallest maximum value for which you had no repetitions?

c. Describe the relationship between the population size (maximum value) and the number of repetitions in the list of random numbers as the population size increases and the sample size remains the same. What can you conclude about using a random number generator to choose a relatively small sample from a large population?

◉ Applet Exercise 1.2

The *Random Numbers* applet can be used to select a random sample from a population, but can it be used to simulate data? In parts **a** and **b,** you will use the applet to create data sets. Then you will explore whether those data sets are realistic.

a. In the activity *Keep the Change* on page 29, a data set called *Amounts Transferred* is described. Use the *Random Numbers* applet to simulate this data set by setting the minimum value equal to 0, the maximum value equal to 99, and the sample size equal to 30. Explain what the numbers in the list produced by the applet represent in the context of the activity. (You may need to read the activity.) Do the numbers produced by the applet seem reasonable? Explain.

b. Use the *Random Numbers* applet to simulate grades on a statistics test by setting the minimum value equal to 0, the maximum value equal to 100, and the sample size equal to 30. Explain what the numbers in the list produced by the applet represent in this context. Do the numbers produced by the applet seem reasonable? Explain.

c. Referring to parts **a** and **b,** why do the randomly generated data seem more reasonable in one situation than in the other? Comment on the usefulness of using a random number generator to produce data.

Applying the Concepts—Basic

1.15 **Zillow.com estimates of home values.** Zillow.com is a
NW   real estate Web site that provides free estimates of the market value of homes. A trio of University of Texas at San Antonio professors compared *Zillow* estimates to actual sale prices of homes and published their results in *The Appraisal Journal* (Winter 2010). The analysis was based on data collected for 2,045 single-family residential properties in Arlington, Texas, that sold during the last 6 months of 2006. Sale price and *Zillow* estimated value (in dollars) were measured for each property. *Zillow* claims that this market has one of its highest-accuracy ratings. However, the research revealed that *Zillow* overestimated the market value by more than 10% for nearly half of the properties.

a. What is the experimental unit for this study?

b. Describe the variables measured in the study. Do these variables produce quantitative or qualitative data?

c. Give a scenario where the 2,045 properties represent a population.

d. If the 2,045 properties represent a representative sample from a population, describe the population.

e. Suppose the relevant population is all single-family residential properties in the United States. Do you believe the 2,045 properties are representative of this population? Explain.

1.16 **Drafting NFL quarterbacks.** The National Football League (NFL) is a lucrative business, generating an annual revenue of about $8 million. One key to becoming a financially successful NFL team is drafting a good quarterback (QB) out of college. The NFL draft allows the worst-performing teams in the previous year the opportunity of selecting the best quarterbacks coming out of college. The *Journal of Productivity Analysis* (Vol. 35, 2011) published a study of how successful NFL teams are in drafting productive quarterbacks. Data were collected for all 331 quarterbacks drafted between 1970 and 2007. Several variables were measured for each QB, including draft position (one of the top 10 players picked, selection between picks 11–50, or selected after pick 50), NFL winning ratio (percentage of games won), and QB production score (higher scores indicate more productive QBs). The researchers discovered that draft position is only weakly related to a quarterback's performance in the NFL. They concluded that "quarterbacks taken higher [in the draft] do not appear to perform any better."

a. What is the experimental unit for this study?

b. Identify the type (quantitative or qualitative) of each variable measured.

c. Suppose you want to use this study to project the performance of future NFL QBs. Is this an application of descriptive or inferential statistics? Explain.

1.17 **Opinion polls.** Pollsters regularly conduct opinion polls to
NW   determine the popularity rating of the current president. Suppose a poll is to be conducted tomorrow in which 2,000 individuals will be asked whether the president is doing a good or bad job. The 2,000 individuals will be selected by random-digit telephone dialing and asked the question over the phone.

a. What is the relevant population?

b. What is the variable of interest? Is it quantitative or qualitative?

c. What is the sample?

d. What is the inference of interest to the pollster?

e. What method of data collection is employed?

f. How likely is the sample to be representative?

1.18 **College application data.** Colleges and universities are
NW   requiring an increasing amount of information about applicants before making acceptance and financial aid decisions. Classify each of the following types of data required on a college application as quantitative or qualitative.

a. High school GPA

b. Honors, awards

c. Applicant's score on the SAT or ACT

d. Gender of applicant

e. Parents' income

f. Age of applicant

1.19 **Microsoft survey of Windows.** Windows is a computer software product made by Microsoft Corporation. In designing a new version of Windows, Microsoft telephoned thousands of users of an earlier version of Windows and asked them how the product could be improved. Assume customers were asked the following questions:

a. Are you the most frequent user of Windows in your household?

b. What is your age?

c. Are the tutorial instructions that accompany Windows helpful?

d. When using a printer with Windows, do you most frequently use a laser printer or another type of printer?

e. If the speed of Windows could be changed, which one of the following would you prefer: slower, unchanged, or faster?

f. How many people in your household have used Windows at least once?

Each of these questions defines a variable of interest to the company. Classify the data generated for each variable as quantitative or qualitative. Justify your classification.

1.20 **Going online for health information.** A *cyberchondriac* is defined as a person who regularly searches the Web for health care information. Each year a Harris Poll is conducted to determine the number of cyberchondriacs in the United States. In 2011, the Harris Poll surveyed 1,019 U.S. adults by telephone and asked the following questions:

   1. Have you ever gone online to look for health care information?

   2. How many times per month do you look for health care information online?

   3. In the past year, have you ever discussed with your doctor the information you found online?

a. For each question, determine whether the type of data collected is quantitative or qualitative.

b. Do the data collected for the 1,019 adults represent a sample or a population? Explain.

1.21 **The executive compensation scoreboard.** Each year, *Forbes* publishes its Executive Compensation Scoreboard. (See Study 1.2, p. 4) For the 2011 scoreboard, data were collected for chief executive officers at the 500 largest U.S. companies and the following variables were measured for each CEO: (1) the industry type of the CEO's company (e.g., banking, retailing, etc.), (2) the CEO's total compensation ($ millions) for the year, (3) the CEO's total compensation ($ millions) over the previous 5 years, (4) the number of company stock shares (millions) held, (5) the CEO's age (years), and (6) the CEO's efficiency rating.

a. Are the data for the 500 CEOs in the 2011 Executive Compensation Scoreboard a population or sample? Explain.

b. Identify the type (quantitative or qualitative) of each variable measured.

1.22 **Annual survey of computer crimes.** The Computer Security Institute (CSI) conducts an annual survey of computer crime at U.S. businesses. CSI sends survey questionnaries to computer security personnel at all U.S. corporations and government agencies. The 2010 CSI survey was sent by post or e-mail to 5,412 firms, and 351 organizations responded. Forty-one percent of the respondents admitted unauthorized use of computer systems at their firms

during the year. (*CSI Computer Crime and Security Survey, 2010/2011*)

a. Identify the population of interest to CSI.

b. Identify the data-collection method used by CSI. Are there any potential biases in the method used?

c. Describe the variable measured in the CSI survey. Is it quantitative or qualitative?

d. What inference can be made from the study result?

1.23 **Treasury deficit prior to the Civil War.** In *Civil War History* (June 2009), historian Jane Flaherty researched the condition of the U.S. Treasury on the eve of the Civil War in 1861. Between 1854 and 1857 (under President Franklin Pierce), the annual surplus/deficit was +18.8, +6.7, +5.3, and +1.3 million dollars, respectively. In contrast, between 1858 and 1861 (under President James Buchanan), the annual surplus/deficit was −27.3, −16.2, −7.2, and −25.2 million dollars, respectively. Flaherty used these data to aid in portraying the exhausted condition of the U.S. Treasury when Abraham Lincoln took office in 1861. Does this study represent a descriptive or inferential statistical study? Explain.

1.24 **The "lucky store effect" in lottery ticket sales.** In the *American Economic Review* (Vol. 98, 2008), University of Chicago researchers investigated the *lucky store effect* theory in lottery ticket sales, i.e., the theory that a lottery retail store that sold a large-prize-winning ticket will experience greater ticket sales the following week. The researchers examined the weekly ticket sales between January 2000 and June 2002 of all 24,400 active lottery retailers in Texas. Specifically, they focused on sales of the Lotto Texas ticket, with jackpots ranging from $1 to $50 million. The analysis showed that "the week following the sale of [a winning Lotto Texas ticket], the winning store experiences a 12 to 38 percent relative sales increase. . . ." Consequently, the researchers project that future winning lottery retail stores will experience the *lucky store effect*. Is this study an example of descriptive statistics or inferential statistics? Explain.

Applying the Concepts—Intermediate

1.25 **The economic return to earning an MBA.** What are the economic rewards (e.g., higher salary) to obtaining an MBA degree? This was the question of interest in an article published in the *International Economic Review* (August 2008). The researchers made inferences based on wage data collected for a sample of 3,244 individuals who sat for the Graduate Management Admissions Test (GMAT). (The GMAT exam is required for entrance into most MBA programs.) The following sampling scheme was employed. All those who took the GMAT exam in any of four selected time periods (Jan. 1990, Sep. 1991, Jan. 1993, and Jan. 1997) were mailed a questionnaire. Those who responded to the questionnaire were then sent three follow-up surveys (one survey every 3 months). The final sample of 3,244 represents only those individuals who responded to all four surveys. (For example, about 5,600 took the GMAT in Jan. 1990; of these, only about 800 responded to all four surveys.)

a. For this study, describe the population of interest.

b. What method was used to collect the sample data?

c. Do you think the final sample is representative of the population? Who or why not? Comment on potential biases in the sample.

1.26 Corporate sustainability and firm characteristics. *Corporate sustainability* refers to business practices designed around social and environmental considerations (e.g., "going green"). *Business and Society* (March 2011) published a paper on how firm size and firm type impact sustainability behaviors. The researchers added questions on sustainability to a quarterly survey of Certified Public Accountants (CPAs). The survey was sent to approximately 23,500 senior managers at CPA firms, of which 1,293 senior managers responded. (*Note:* It is not clear how the 23,500 senior managers were selected.) Due to missing data (incomplete survey answers), only 992 surveys were analyzed. These data were used to infer whether larger firms are more likely to report sustainability policies than smaller firms and whether public firms are more likely to report sustainability policies than private firms.
a. Identify the population of interest to the researchers.
b. What method was used to collect the sample data?
c. Comment on the representativeness of the sample.
d. How will your answer to part **c** impact the validity of the inferences drawn from the study?

1.27 Inspection of highway bridges. All highway bridges in the United States are inspected periodically for structural deficiency by the Federal Highway Administration (FHWA). Data from the FHWA inspections are compiled into the National Bridge Inventory (NBI). Several of the nearly 100 variables maintained by the NBI are listed below. Classify each variable as quantitative or qualitative.
a. Length of maximum span (feet)
b. Number of vehicle lanes
c. Toll bridge (yes or no)
d. Average daily traffic
e. Condition of deck (good, fair, or poor)
f. Bypass or detour length (miles)
g. Route type (interstate, U.S., state, county, or city)

1.28 Structurally deficient highway bridges. Refer to Exercise 1.27. The 2009 NBI data were analyzed and the results made available at the FHWA Web site (www.fhwa.dot.gov). Using the FHWA inspection ratings, each of the 608,272 highway bridges in the United States was categorized as structurally deficient, functionally obsolete, or safe. About 13.5% of the bridges were found to be structurally deficient, while 3.5% were functionally obsolete.
a. What is the variable of interest to the researchers?
b. Is the variable of part a quantitative or qualitative?
c. Is the data set analyzed a population or a sample? Explain.
d. How did the NBI obtain the data for the study?

*1.29 Monitoring product quality. The Wallace Company of Houston is a distributor of pipes, valves, and fittings to the refining, chemical, and petrochemical industries. The company was a recent winner of the Malcolm Baldrige National Quality Award. One of the steps the company takes to monitor the quality of its distribution process is to send out a survey twice a year to a subset of its current customers, asking the customers to rate the speed

of deliveries, the accuracy of invoices, and the quality of the packaging of the products they have received from Wallace.
a. Describe the process studied.
b. Describe the variables of interest.
c. Describe the sample.
d. Describe the inferences of interest.
e. What are some of the factors that are likely to affect the reliability of the inferences?

1.30 Guilt in decision making. The effect of guilt emotion on how a decision maker focuses on the problem was investigated in the *Journal of Behavioral Decision Making* (January 2007). A total of 171 volunteer students participated in the experiment, where each was randomly assigned to one of three emotional states (guilt, anger, or neutral) through a reading/writing task. Immediately after the task, the students were presented with a decision problem (e.g., whether or not to spend money on repairing a very old car). The researchers found that a higher proportion of students in the guilty-state group chose to repair the car than those in the neutral-state and anger-state groups.
a. Identify the population, sample, and variables measured for this study.
b. Identify the data-collection method used.
c. What inference was made by the researcher?
d. In later chapters you will learn that the reliability of an inference is related to the size of the sample used. In addition to sample size, what factors might affect the reliability of the inference drawn in this study?

1.31 Accounting and Machiavellianism. *Behavioral Research in Accounting* (January 2008) published a study of Machiavellian traits in accountants. *Machiavellian* describes negative character traits that include manipulation, cunning, duplicity, deception, and bad faith. A questionnaire was administered to a random sample of 700 accounting alumni of a large southwestern university; however, due to nonresponse and incomplete answers, only 198 questionnaires could be analyzed. Several variables were measured, including age, gender, level of education, income, job satisfaction score, and Machiavellian ("Mach") rating score. The research findings suggest that Machiavellian behavior is not required to achieve success in the accounting profession.
a. What is the population of interest to the researcher?
b. What type of data (quantitative or qualitative) is produced by each of the variables measured?
c. Identify the sample.
d. Identify the data-collection method used.
e. What inference was made by the researcher?
f. How might the nonresponses impact the inference?

1.32 Sampling stocks on the NYSE. The results of the previous business day's transactions for stocks traded on the New York Stock Exchange (NYSE) and five regional exchanges—the Chicago, Pacific, Philadelphia, Boston, and Cincinnati stock exchanges—are summarized each business day in the NYSE—Composite Transactions table in the *Wall Street Journal*.
a. Examine the NYSE—Composite Transactions table in a recent issue of the *Wall Street Journal* and explain how to draw a simple random sample of stocks from the table.

b. Use the procedure you described in part **a** to draw a simple random sample of 20 stocks from a recent NYSE—Composite Transactions table. For each stock in the sample, list its name (i.e., the abbreviation given in the table), its sales volume, and its closing price.

1.33 **Can money spent on gifts buy love?** Is the gift you purchased for that special someone really appreciated? This was the question of interest to business professors at Stanford University. Their research was published in the *Journal of Experimental Social Psychology* (Vol. 45, 2009). In one study, the researchers investigated the link between engagement ring price (dollars) and level of appreciation of the recipient (measured on a 7-point scale where 1 = "not at all" and 7 = "to a great extent"). Participants for the study were those who used a popular Web site for engaged couples. The Web site's directory was searched for those with "average" American names (e.g., "John Smith," "Sara Jones"). These individuals were then invited to participate in an online survey in exchange for a $10 gift certificate. Of the respondents, those who paid really high or really low prices for the ring were excluded, leaving a sample size of 33 respondents.

a. Identify the experimental units for this study.

b. What are the variables of interest? Are they quantitative or qualitative in nature?

c. Describe the population of interest.

d. Do you believe the sample of 33 respondents is representative of the population? Explain.

e. In a second designed study, the researchers investigated whether the link between gift price and level of appreciation is stronger for birthday gift-givers than for birthday gift-receivers. The participants were randomly assigned to play the role of gift-giver or gift-receiver. Assume that the sample consists of 50 individuals. Use a random number generator to randomly assign 25 individuals to play the gift-receiver role and 25 to play the gift-giver role.

Applying the Concepts—Advanced

1.34 **Random-digit dialing.** To ascertain the effectiveness of their advertising compaigns, firms frequently conduct telephone interviews with consumers using *random-digit dialing*. With this approach, a random number generator mechanically creates the sample of phone numbers to be called. Each digit in the phone number is randomly selected from the possible digits 0, 1, 2, ..., 9. Use the procedure to generate five seven-digit telephone numbers whose first three digits (area code) are 373.

1.35 **Bank corporate mergers.** *Corporate merger* is a means through which one firm (the bidder) acquires control of the assets of another firm (the target). Recently, there was a frenzy of bank mergers in the United States, as the banking industry consolidated into more efficient and more competitive units.

a. Construct a brief questionnaire (two or three questions) that could be used to query a sample of bank presidents concerning their opinions of why the industry is consolidating and whether it will consolidate further.

b. Describe the population about which inferences could be made from the results of the survey.

c. Discuss the pros and cons of sending the questionnaire to all bank presidents versus a sample of 200.

1.36 **Monitoring the production of soft-drink cans.** The Wakefield plant of Coca-Cola and Schweppes Beverages Limited (CCSB) can produce 4,000 cans of soft drink per minute. The automated process consists of measuring and dispensing the raw ingredients into storage vessels to create the syrup, and then injecting the syrup, along with carbon dioxide, into the beverage cans. In order to monitor the subprocess that adds carbon dioxide to the cans, five filled cans are pulled off the line every 15 minutes, and the amount of carbon dioxide in each of these five cans is measured to determine whether the amounts are within prescribed limits.

a. Describe the process studied.

b. Describe the variable of interest.

c. Describe the sample.

d. Describe the inference of interest.

e. *Brix* is a unit for measuring sugar concentration. If a technician is assigned the task of estimating the average brix level of all 240,000 cans of beverage stored in a warehouse near Wakefield, will the technician be examining a process or a population? Explain.

1.37 **Current population survey.** The employment status (employed or unemployed) of each individual in the U.S. workforce is a set of data that is of interest to economists, businesspeople, and sociologists. To obtain information about the employment status of the workforce, the U.S. Bureau of the Census conducts what is known as the *Current Population Survey*. Each month interviewers visit about 50,000 of the 117 million households in the United States and question the occupants over 14 years of age about their employment status. Their responses enable the Bureau of the Census to *estimate* the percentage of people in the labor force who are unemployed (the *unemployment rate*).

a. Define the population of interest to the Census Bureau.

b. What variable is being measured? Is it quantitative or qualitative?

c. Is the problem of interest to the Census Bureau descriptive or inferential?

d. In order to monitor the rate of unemployment, it is essential to have a definition of *unemployed*. Different economists and even different countries define it in various ways. Develop your own definition of an "unemployed person." Your definition should answer such questions as: Are students on summer vacation unemployed? Are college professors who do not teach summer school unemployed? At what age are people considered to be eligible for the workforce? Are people who are out of work but not actively seeking a job unemployed?

1.38 **Sampling TV markets for a court case.** A recent court case involved a claim of satellite television subscribers obtaining illegal access to local TV stations. The defendant (the satellite TV company) wanted to sample TV markets nationwide and determine the percentage of its subscribers in each sampled market who have illegal access to local TV stations. To do this, the defendant's expert witness drew a rectangular grid over the continental United States, with horizontal and vertical grid lines every .02 degrees of latitude and longitude, respectively. This created a total of

500 rows and 1,000 columns, or $(500)(1,000) = 500,000$ intersections. The plan was to randomly sample 900 intersection points and include the TV market at each intersection in the sample. Explain how you could use a random number generator to obtain a random sample of 900 intersections. Develop at least two plans: one that numbers the intersections from 1 to 500,000 prior to selection and another that selects the row and column of each sampled intersection (from the total of 500 rows and 1,000 columns).

Critical Thinking Challenge

1.39 *20/20* **survey exposé.** Refer to the "Statistics in Action" box of this chapter (p. 1). Recall that the popular prime-time ABC television program *20/20* presented several misleading (and possibly unethical) surveys in a segment titled "Fact or Fiction?—Exposés of So-Called Surveys." The information reported from four of these surveys and a more recent survey are reproduced here (actual survey facts are provided in parentheses).

- *Quaker Oats study:* Eating oat bran is a cheap and easy way to reduce your cholesterol count. (Fact: Diet must consist of nothing but oat bran to achieve a slightly lower cholesterol count.)
- *March of Dimes report:* Domestic violence causes more birth defects than all medical issues combined. (Fact: No study—false report.)
- *American Association of University Women (AAUW) study:* Only 29% of high school girls are happy with themselves, compared to 66% of elementary school girls. (Fact: Of 3,000 high school girls, 29% responded, "Always true" to the statement "I am happy the way I am." Most answered, "Sort of true" and "Sometimes true.")
- *Food Research and Action Center study:* One in four American children under age 12 is hungry or at risk of hunger. (Fact: Based on responses to questions: "Do

you ever cut the size of meals?" and "Do you ever eat less than you feel you should?" and "Did you ever rely on limited numbers of foods to feed your children because you were running out of money to buy food for a meal?")

- *McKinsey survey on the health reform act:* Thirty percent of employers would "definitely" or "probably" stop offering health coverage to their employees if the government-sponsored act is passed. (Fact: Employers were asked leading questions that made it seem logical for them to stop offering insurance. For example, respondents were told that the new health insurance exchanges would become "an easy, affordable way for individuals to obtain health insurance" outside the company. Then they were given examples of how little their workers would pay for this insurance. Only then were they asked how likely they would be to stop offering health insurance.)

a. Refer to the Quaker Oats study relating oat bran to cholesterol levels. Discuss why it is unethical to report the results as stated.

b. Consider the false March of Dimes report on domestic violence and birth defects. Discuss the type of data required to investigate the impact of domestic violence on birth defects. What data-collection method would you recommend?

c. Refer to the AAUW study of self-esteem of high school girls. Explain why the results of the study are likely to be misleading. What data might be appropriate for assessing the self-esteem of high school girls?

d. Refer to the Food Research and Action Center study of hunger in America. Explain why the results of the study are likely to be misleading. What data would provide insight into the proportion of hungry American children?

e. Refer to the McKinsey survey on the health reform act. Explain what a "leading question" is and why it might produce responses that bias the results.

| Activity | 1.1 | *Keep the Change:* Collecting Data |

Bank of America has a savings program called *Keep the Change*. Each time a customer enrolled in the program uses his or her debit card to make a purchase, the difference between the purchase total and the next higher dollar amount is transferred from the customer's checking account to a savings account. For example, if you were enrolled in the program and used your debit card to purchase a latte for $3.75, then $0.25 would be transferred from your checking to your savings account. For the first 90 days that a customer is enrolled in the program, Bank of America matches the amounts transferred up to $250. In this and subsequent activities, we will investigate the potential benefit to the customer and cost to the bank.

1. Simulate the program by keeping track of all purchases that you make during one week that could be made with a debit card, even if you use a different form of payment. For each purchase, record both the purchase

total and the amount that would be transferred from checking to savings with the *Keep the Change* program.

2. You now have two sets of data: *Purchase Totals* and *Amounts Transferred*. Both sets contain quantitative data. For each data set, identify the corresponding naturally occurring numerical scale. Explain why each set has an obvious lower bound but only one set has a definite upper bound.

3. Find the total of the amounts transferred for the one-week period. Because 90 days is approximately 13 weeks, multiply the total by 13 to estimate how much the bank would have to match during the first 90 days. Form a third data set, *Bank Matching,* by collecting the 90-day estimates of all the students in your class. Identify the naturally occurring scale, including bounds, for this set of data.

Keep the data sets from this activity for use in other activities. We suggest you save the data using statistical software (e.g., Minitab) or a graphing calculator.

| Activity | 1.2 | **Identifying Misleading Statistics** |

In the *Statistics in Action* feature at the beginning of this chapter, several examples of false or misleading statistics were discussed. Claims such as *One in four American children under age 12 is hungry or at risk of hunger* are often used to persuade the public or the government to donate or allocate more money to charitable groups that feed the poor. Researchers sometimes claim a relationship exists between two seemingly unrelated quantities such as a CEO's golf handicap and the company's stock performance; such relationships are often weak at best and of little practical importance. Read the *Statistics in Action* and *Statistics in Action Revisited* features in this chapter before completing this activity.

1. Look for an article in a newspaper or on the Internet in which a large proportion or percentage of a population is purported to be "at risk" of some calamity, as in the childhood hunger example. Does the article cite a source or provide any information to support the proportion or percentage reported? Is the goal of the article to persuade some individual or group to take some action? If so, what action is being requested? Do you believe that the writer of the article may have some motive for exaggerating the problem? If so, give some possible motives.

2. Look for another article in which a relationship between two seemingly unrelated quantities is purported to exist, as in the CEO golf handicap and stock performance study. Select an article that contains some information on how the data were collected. Identify the target population and the data-collection method. Based on what is presented in the article, do you believe that the data are representative of the population? Explain. Is the purported relationship of any practical interest? Explain.

References

Careers in Statistics, American Statistical Association, 2011 (www.amstat.org)

Cochran, W. G. *Sampling Techniques,* 3rd ed. New York: Wiley, 1977.

Deming, W. E. *Sample Design in Business Research.* New York: Wiley, 1963.

Dillman, D. A., Smyth, J. D., and Christian, L. M. *Internet, Mail, and Mixed-Mode Surveys: The Tailored Design Method.* New York: Wiley, 2008.

Ethical Guidelines for Statistical Practice, American Statistical Association, 1999 (www.amstat.org).

Hahn, G. J. and Doganaksoy, N. *The Role of Statistics in Business and Industry.* New York: Wiley, 2008.

Huff, D. *How to Lie with Statistics.* New York: Norton, 1982 (paperback 1993).

Hoerl, R. and Snee, R. *Statistical Thinking: Improving Business Performance.* Boston: Duxbury, 2002.

Kish, L. *Survey Sampling.* New York: Wiley, 1965 (paperback, 1995).

Peck, R., Casella, G., Cobb, G., Hoerl, R., Nolan, D., Starbuck, R., and Stern, H. *Statistics: A Guide to the Unknown,* 4th ed. Cengage Learning, 2005.

Scheaffer, R., Mendenhall, W., and Ott, R. L. *Elementary Survey Sampling,* 6th ed. Boston: Duxbury, 2005.

What Is a Survey? American Statistical Association (F. Scheuren, editor), 2nd ed., 2005 (www.amstat.org).

| USING TECHNOLOGY | Technology images shown here are taken from SPSS Statistics Professional 20.0, Minitab 16, XLSTAT for Pearson, and Excel 2010. |

SPSS: Accessing and Listing Data

When you start an SPSS session, you will see a screen similar to Figure 1.S.1. The main portion of the screen is an empty spreadsheet, with columns representing variables and rows representing observations (or cases). The very top of the screen is the SPSS main menu bar, with buttons for the different functions and procedures available in SPSS. Once you have entered data into the spreadsheet, you can analyze the data by clicking the appropriate menu buttons.

Figure 1.S.1 Initial screen viewed by the SPSS user

Entering Data

Step 1 To create an SPSS data file, enter data directly into the spreadsheet. See Figure 1.S.2 which shows data entered on a variable called "GPA."

Figure 1.S.2 Data entered into the SPSS spreadsheet

Step 2 Name the variables (columns) by selecting the "Variable View" button at the bottom of the screen and typing in the name of each variable.

Opening an SPSS Data File

If the data have been previously saved as an SPSS (.sav) file, access the data as follows.

Step 1 Click the "File" button on the menu bar, and then click "Open" and "Data," as shown in Figure 1.S.3. A dialog box similar to Figure 1.S.4 will appear.

Figure 1.S.3 Options for opening an SPSS data file

Step 2 Specify the location (folder) that contains the data, click on the SPSS data file, and then click "Open" (see Figure 1.S.4). The data will appear in the SPSS spreadsheet, as shown in Figure 1.S.5.

Figure 1.S.4 Selecting the SPSS data file to open

Figure 1.S.5 The SPSS spreadsheet showing the opened SPSS data file

Accessing External Data from a File

If the data are saved in an external data file, you can access the data using the options available in SPSS.

Step 1 Click the "File" button on the menu bar, and then click "Read Text Data," as shown in Figure 1.S.6. A dialog box similar to Figure 1.S.7 will appear.

Figure 1.S.6 SPSS options for reading data from an external file

Step 2 Specify the location (folder) that contains the data file, click on the data file, and then click "Open," as shown in Figure 1.S.7. The SPSS Text Import Wizard Opens.

Figure 1.S.7 Selecting the external data file in SPSS

Step 3 The Text Import Wizard is a series of six screen menus. Make the appropriate selections on the screen, and click "Next" to go to the next screen.

Step 4 When finished, click "Finish." The SPSS spreadsheet will reappear with the data from the external data file.

Reminder: The variable (columns) can be named by selecting the "Variable View" button at the bottom of the spreadsheet screen and typing in the name of each variable.

Listing (Printing) Data

Step 1 Click on the "Analyze" button on the SPSS main menu bar, then click on "Reports," and then on "Report Summaries in Rows" (see Figure 1.S.8). The resulting menu, or dialog box, appears as in Figure 1.S.9.

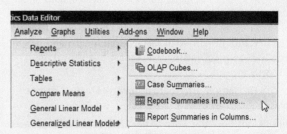

Figure 1.S.8 SPSS menu options for obtaining a data listing

Step 2 Enter the names of the variables you want to print in the "Data Columns" box (you can do this by simply clicking on the variables), check the "Display cases" box at the bottom left, and then click "OK." The printout will show up on your screen.

Figure 1.S.9 SPSS data report dialog box

SPSS: Generating a Random Sample

Step 1 Click on are "Data" button on the SPSS menu bar and then click on "Select Cases" as shown in Figure 1.S.10. The resulting menu list appears as shown in Figure 1.S.11.

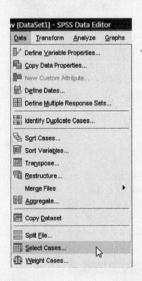

Figure 1.S.10 SPSS menu options for sampling from a data set

Step 2 Select "Random sample of cases" from the list and then click on the "Sample" button. The dialog box shown in Figure 1.S.12 will appear.

Step 3 Specify the sample size there as a percentage of cases or a raw number.

Step 4 Click "Continue" to return to the "Select Cases" dialog box (Figure 1.S.11) and then click "OK." The SPSS spreadsheet will reappear with the selected (sampled) cases.

Figure 1.S.11 SPSS options for selecting a random sample

Figure 1.S.12 SPSS random sample dialog box

Minitab: Accessing and Listing Data

When you start a Minitab session, you will see a screen similar to Figure 1.M.1. The bottom portion of the screen is an empty spreadsheet—called a Minitab worksheet—with columns representing variables and rows representing observations (or cases). The very top of the screen is the Minitab main menu bar, with buttons for the different functions and procedures available in Minitab. Once you have entered data into the spreadsheet, you can analyze the data by clicking the appropriate menu buttons. The results will appear in the Session window.

Figure 1.M.1 Initial screen viewed by the Minitab user

Entering Data

Create a Minitab data file by entering data directly into the worksheet. Figure 1.M.2 shows data entered for a variable called "GPA." Name the variables (columns) by typing in the name of each variable in the box below the column number.

Figure 1.M.2 Data entered into the Minitab worksheet

Opening a Minitab Data File

If the data have been previously saved as a Minitab (.mtw) file, access the data as follows.

Step 1 Click the "File" button on the menu bar, and then click "Open Worksheet," as shown in Figure 1.M.3. A dialog box similar to Figure 1.M.4 will appear.

Figure 1.M.3 Options for opening a Minitab data file

Figure 1.M.4 Selecting the Minitab data file to open

Step 2 Specify the location (folder) that contains the data, click on the Minitab data file, and then click "Open" (see Figure 1.M.4). The data will appear in the Minitab worksheet, as shown in Figure 1.M.5 at bottom of the page.

Accessing External Data from a File

Step 1 Click the "File" button on the menu bar, and then click "Open Worksheet" as shown in Figure 1.M.3. A dialog box similar to Figure 1.M.6 will appear.

Figure 1.M.6 Selecting the external data file in Minitab

Step 2 Specify the location (folder) that contains the external data file and the file type, and then click on the file name, as shown in Figure 1.M.6.

Step 3 If the data set contains qualitative data or data with special characters, click on the "Options" button as shown in Figure 1.M.6. The Options dialog box, shown in Figure 1.M.7, will appear.

Figure 1.M.7 Selecting the Minitab data input options

CEOPAY2011.MTW ***

	C1	C2-T	C3-T	C4	C5
	Rank	Name	Company	Pay ($mil)	5-Yr Pay ($mil)
1	1	Hemsley, Stephen JStephen J Hemsley	UnitedHealth Group	101.965	120.472
2	2	Mueller, Edward AEdward A Mueller	Qwest Communications	65.800	75.003
3	3	Iger, Robert ARobert A Iger	Walt Disney	53.320	147.080
4	4	Paz, GeorgeGeorge Paz	Express Scripts	51.520	100.210
5	5	Frankfort, LewLew Frankfort	Coach	49.450	137.870
6	6	Lauren, RalphRalph Lauren	Polo Ralph Lauren	43.000	155.250

Figure 1.M.5 The Minitab worksheet showing the opened Minitab data file

Step 4 Specify the appropriate options for the data set, and then click "OK" to return to the "Open Worksheet" dialog box (Figure 1.M.6).

Step 5 Click "Open" and the Minitab worksheet will appear with the data from the external data file.

Reminder: The variables (columns) can be named by typing in the name of each variable in the box under the column number.

Listing (Printing) Data

Step 1 Click on the "Data" button on the Minitab main menu bar, and then click on "Display Data." (See Figure 1.M.8.) The resulting menu, or dialog box, appears as in Figure 1.M.9.

Figure 1.M.8 Minitab options for displaying data

Figure 1.M.9 Minitab Display Data dialog box

Step 2 Enter the names of the variables you want to print in the "Columns, constants, and matrices to display" box (you can do this by simply double clicking on the variables), and then click "OK." The printout will show up on your Minitab session screen.

Minitab: Generating a Random Sample

Step 1 Click on the "Calc" button on the Minitab menu bar and then click on "Random Data," and finally, click on "Sample From Columns," as shown in Figure 1.M.10. The resulting dialog box appears as shown in Figure 1.M.11.

Figure 1.M.10 Minitab menu options for sampling from a data set

Figure 1.M.11 Minitab options for selecting a random sample from worksheet columns

Step 2 Specify the sample size (i.e., number of rows), the variable(s) to be sampled, and the column(s) where you want to save the sample.

Step 3 Click "OK" and the Minitab worksheet will reappear with the values of the variable for the selected (sampled) cases in the column specified.

In Minitab, you can also generate a sample of case numbers.

Step 1 From the Minitab menu, click on the "Calc" button and then click on "Random Data," and finally, click on the "Uniform" option (see Figure 1.M.10).

Step 2 In the resulting dialog box (shown in Figure 1.M.12), specify the number of cases (rows, i.e., the sample size), and the column where the case numbers selected will be stored.

Figure 1.M.12 Minitab options for selecting a random sample of cases

Step 3 Click "OK" and the Minitab worksheet will reappear with the case numbers for the selected (sampled) cases in the column specified.

[*Note:* If you want the option of generating the same (identical) sample multiple times from the data set, then first click on the "Set Base" option shown in Figure 1.M.10. Specify an integer in the resulting dialog box. If you always select the same integer, Minitab will select the same sample when you choose the random sampling options.]

Excel: Accessing and Listing Data

When you open Excel, you will see a screen similar to Figure 1.E.1. The majority of the screen window is a spreadsheet—called an Excel workbook—with columns (labeled A, B, C, etc.) representing variables, and rows representing observations (or cases). The very top of the screen is the Excel main menu bar, with buttons for the different functions and procedures available in Excel. Once you have entered data into the spreadsheet, you can analyze the data by clicking the appropriate menu buttons. The results will appear in a new workbook.

Figure 1.E.1 Initial screen viewed by Excel user

Entering Data

Enter data directly into the appropriate row and column of the spreadsheet. Figure 1.E.2 shows data entered in the first (A) column. Optionally, you can add names for the variables (columns) in the first row of the workbook.

Figure 1.E.2 Data entered into the Excel workbook

Opening an Excel File

If the data have been previously saved as an Excel (.xls) file, access the data as follows.

Step 1 Click the round Office button at the far left of the menu bar, and then click "Open," as shown in Figure 1.E.3. A dialog box similar to Figure 1.E.4 will appear.

Figure 1.E.3 Options for opening an Excel file

Figure 1.E.4 Selecting the Excel file to open

Step 2 Specify the location (folder) that contains the data, click on the Excel file, and then click "Open" (see Figure 1.E.4). The data will appear in the Excel spreadsheet as shown in Figure 1.E.5.

	A	B	C	D	E	F
1	RIVER	MILE	SPECIES	LENGTH	WEIGHT	DDT
2	FCM	5	CCATFISH	42.5	732	10
3	FCM	5	CCATFISH	44	795	16
4	FCM	5	CCATFISH	41.5	547	23
5	FCM	5	CCATFISH	39	465	21
6	FCM	5	CCATFISH	50.5	1252	50

Figure 1.E.5 The Excel spreadsheet showing the opened Excel file

Accessing External Data from a File

Step 1 Click the "Office" button on the menu bar, and then click "Open," as shown in Figure 1.E.3. A dialog box similar to Figure 1.E.6 will appear.

Figure 1.E.6 Selecting the external data file in Excel

Step 2 Specify the location (folder) that contains the external data file and the file type, and then click on the file name and click on "Open," as shown in Figure 1.E.6. The Excel Text Import Wizard opens (Figure 1.E.7).

Figure 1.E.7 Excel Text Import Wizard, Screen 1

Step 3 Make the appropriate selections on the screen, and click "Next" to go to the next screen; then click "Next" again.

Step 4 When finished, click "Finish." The Excel workbook will reappear with the data from the external data file.

Naming Variables

Step 1 Select "Insert" from the Excel main menu, and then select "Rows." A blank (empty) row will be added in the first row of the spreadsheet.

Step 2 Type the name of each variable in the first row under the appropriate column.

Listing (Printing) Data

Step 1 Click on the "Office" button on the Excel main menu bar.

Step 2 Click on "Print."

Excel: Generating a Random Sample

To obtain a random sample of numbers in Excel, perform the following:

Step 1 Select "Data," and then "Data Analysis" from the Excel main menu bar, as shown in Figure 1.E.8 at bottom of the page.

Step 2 Select "Random Number Generation" from the Data Analysis dialog box and then click "OK," as shown in Figure 1.E.9.

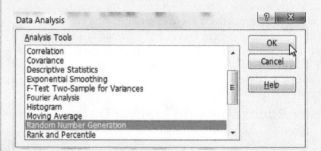

Figure 1.E.9 Excel data analysis tools options: Random number generation

Step 3 In the resulting menu (shown in Figure 1.E.10), specify the number of variables and number of random numbers you want to generate and select "Uniform" for the distribution. Click "OK" to generate the random numbers.

Figure 1.E.10 Excel random number generation dialog box

Figure 1.E.8 Excel menu options for generating a random sample of numbers

2

Where We've Been

- Examined the difference between inferential and descriptive statistics
- Described the key elements of a statistical problem
- Learned about the two types of data–quantitative and qualitative
- Discussed the role of statistical thinking in managerial decision making

Where We're Going

- Describe qualitative data using graphs (2.1)
- Describe quantitative data using graphs (2.2)
- Describe quantitative data using numerical measures (2.3–2.7)
- Describe the relationship between two quantitative variables using graphs (2.8–2.9)
- Detecting descriptive methods that distort the truth (2.10)

▢ Methods for Describing Sets of Data

STATISTICS in ACTION **Can Money Buy Love?**

*Every day, millions of shoppers hit the stores in full force—both online and on foot—searching frantically for the perfect gift.... Americans [spend] over $30 billion at retail stores in the month of December alone. [Yet] many dread the thought of buying gifts; they worry that their purchases will disappoint rather than delight the intended recipients.**

With this paragraph, Stanford University Graduate School of Business researchers Francis J. Flynn and Gabrielle S. Adams introduce their study "Money Can't Buy Love: Asymmetric Beliefs about Gift Price and Feelings of Appreciation," published in the *Journal of Experimental Social Psychology* (Vol. 45, 2009). The researchers investigated the relationship between the price paid for a gift and the level of appreciation felt by the recipient. Gift-givers who spend more money on a gift often do so in order to send a strong signal of their love to the recipient. The researchers theorized that these gift-givers would expect the recipient to express a high level of appreciation for the gift. However, the researchers did not expect gift-recipients to associate a greater level of appreciation with a higher gift price. That is, "The link between gift price and feelings of appreciation will be stronger for gift-givers than for gift-recipients."

In order to test this theory, the researchers conducted an experimental study involving a representative sample of 237 adults from across the nation. Each subject completed an online survey in exchange for a $5 gift certificate to a major online retailer. The survey asked questions about a birthday gift that the subject either received or gave. The participants were randomly assigned to the role of

*Source: "Money Can't Buy Love: Asymmetric Beliefs About Gift Price and Feelings of Appreciation" by Francis J. Flynn and Gabrielle S. Adams, from JOURNAL OF EXPERIMENTAL SOCIAL PSYCHOLOGY, February 2009, Volume 45(2).

STATISTICS in ACTION CONTINUED

either gift-giver or gift-receiver. (In other words, gift-givers were asked about a birthday gift they recently gave, while gift-recipients were asked about a birthday gift they recently received.) Gifts of cash, gift cards, or gift certificates were excluded from the study. Data were collected on the following variables measured for each participant:

1. *Role* (gift-giver or gift-recipient)
2. *Gender* (male or female)
3. *Gift price* (measured in dollars)
4. *Feeling of appreciation* (measured on a 7-point scale in response to the question: "To what extent do you or does the recipient appreciate this gift?," where 1 = "Not at all," 2 = "A little," 3 = "More than a little," 4 = "Somewhat," 5 = "Moderately so," 6 = "Very much," and 7 = "To a great extent")
5. *Feeling of gratefulness* (measured on a 7-point scale in response to the question: "To what extent do you or does the recipient feel grateful for this gift?," where 1 = "Not at all," 2 = "A little," 3 = "More than a little," 4 = "Somewhat," 5 = "Moderately so," 6 = "Very much," and 7 = "To a great extent")
6. *Overall level of appreciation* (measured as the sum of the two 7-point scales—possible values are 2, 3, 4,…, 13, and 14)

These data are saved in the **BUYLOV** file.

The Stanford University researchers' analysis of the data led them to conclude that "gift-givers and gift-receivers disagree about the link between gift price and gift-recipients' feelings of appreciation. Givers anticipated that recipients would appreciate more expensive gifts, but gift-recipients did not base their feelings of appreciation on how much the gift cost."

In the following *Statistics in Action Revisited* sections, we apply the graphical and numerical descriptive techniques of this chapter to the **BUYLOV** data to demonstrate the conclusions reached by the Stanford University researchers.

STATISTICS in ACTION REVISITED

- ◻ Interpreting pie charts and bar graphs **(p. 44)**
- ◻ Interpreting histograms **(p. 57)**
- ◻ Interpreting numerical descriptive measures **(p. 83)**
- ◻ Detecting outliers **(p. 97)**
- ◻ Interpreting scatterplots **(p. 103)**

Data Set: BUYLOVE ◻

Suppose you wish to evaluate the managerial capabilities of a class of 400 MBA students based on their Graduate Management Aptitude Test (GMAT) scores. How would you describe these 400 measurements? Characteristics of the data set include the typical or most frequent GMAT score, the variability in the scores, the highest and lowest scores, the "shape" of the data, and whether or not the data set contains any unusual scores. Extracting this information by "eye-balling" the data isn't easy. The 400 scores may provide too many bits of information for our minds to comprehend. Clearly, we need some formal methods for summarizing and characterizing the information in such a data set. Methods for describing data sets are also essential for statistical inference. Most populations make for large data sets. Consequently, we need methods for describing a sample data set that let us make statements (inferences) about the population from which the sample was drawn.

Two methods for describing data are presented in this chapter, one *graphical* and the other *numerical*. Both play an important role in statistics. Section 2.1 presents both graphical and numerical methods for describing qualitative data. Graphical methods for describing quantitative data are presented in Sections 2.2, 2.7, 2.9, and optional Section 2.8; numerical descriptive methods for quantitative data are presented in Sections 2.3–2.6. We end this chapter with a section on the *misuse* of descriptive techniques.

2.1 Describing Qualitative Data

Recall the "Executive Compensation Scoreboard" tabulated annually by *Forbes* (see Study 1.2 in Section 1.2). In addition to salary information, *Forbes* collects and reports personal data on the CEOs, including level of education. Do most CEOs have advanced degrees, such as master's degrees or doctorates? To answer this question, Table 2.1 gives the highest college degree obtained (bachelor's, MBA, master's, law, PhD, or none) for each of the 40 best-paid CEOs in 2011.

For this study, the variable of interest, highest college degree obtained, is qualitative in nature. Qualitative data are nonnumerical; thus, the value of a qualitative variable can be classified only into categories called *classes*. The possible degree types— bachelor's, MBA, master's, law, PhD, or none—represent the classes for this qualitative variable. We can summarize such data numerically in two ways: (1) by computing the *class frequency*—the number of observations in the data set that fall into each class; or (2) by computing the *class relative frequency*—the proportion of the total number of observations falling into each class.

Table 2.1	Data on 40 Best-Paid Executives				
	CEO	Company	Salary ($ millions)	Age	Degree
1	Hemsley, Stephen	UnitedHealth Group	101.96	58	Bachelor's
2	Mueller, Edward	Qwest Communications	65.80	64	MBA
3	Iger, Robert	Walt Disney	53.32	60	Bachelor's
4	Paz, George	Express Scripts	51.52	56	Bachelor's
5	Frankfort, Lew	Coach	49.45	65	MBA
6	Lauren, Ralph	Polo Ralph Lauren	43.00	71	None
7	Martin, John	Gilead Sciences	42.72	59	PhD
8	Hackett, James	Anadarko Petroleum	38.94	57	MBA
9	Chambers, John	Cisco Systems	37.90	61	MBA
10	Seidenberg, Ivan	Verizon Commun	36.75	64	MBA
11	Pyott, David	Allergan	33.76	58	Master's
12	Lucier, Gregory	Life Technologies	33.75	46	MBA
13	Davidson, Charles	Noble Energy	33.44	61	Master's
14	Hammergren, John	McKesson	32.46	52	MBA
15	Tucci, Joseph	EMC	31.63	63	MBA
16	Huang, Jen-Hsun	Nvidia	31.41	48	Master's
17	Boyce, Gregory	Peabody Energy	30.66	56	Bachelor's
18	Merelli, F H	Cimarex Energy	30.53	75	None
19	Palmisano, Samuel	IBM	30.32	59	Bachelor's
20	Camilleri, Louis	Philip Morris Intl	30.09	56	Bachelor's
21	Watford, Michael	Ultra Petroleum	30.04	57	MBA
22	Schultz, Howard	Starbucks	29.73	57	Bachelor's
23	Novak, David	Yum Brands	29.67	58	Bachelor's
24	Thiry, Kent	DaVita	29.52	55	MBA
25	Farr, David	Emerson Electric	28.93	56	MBA
26	Cutler, Alexander	Eaton	28.47	59	MBA
27	Solomon, Howard	Forest Labs	27.10	83	Law
28	Moonves, Leslie	CBS	26.42	62	Bachelor's
29	Adkerson, Richard	Freeport Copper	25.30	64	MBA
30	Swanson, William	Raytheon	24.89	62	Bachelor's
31	Boyd, Jeffery	Priceline.com	24.39	54	None
32	Chenevert, Louis	United Technologies	23.97	53	Bachelor's
33	Washkewicz, Donald	Parker-Hannifin	23.88	60	MBA
34	Rose, Peter	Expeditors Intl	23.63	68	None
35	Buckley, George	3M	23.22	64	PhD
36	Daane, John	Altera	23.19	47	Bachelor's
37	Young, James	Union Pacific	23.06	59	Bachelor's
38	Larsen, Marshall	Goodrich	22.43	62	Master's
39	Hugin, Robert	Celgene	22.40	56	MBA
40	Snow, David	Medco Health	22.19	56	Master's

Source: Data from "America's Highest Paid Chief Executives," FORBES, April 13, 2011.   ◉ *Data Set:* FRBS40

> A **class** is one of the categories into which qualitative data can be classified.

> The **class frequency** is the number of observations in the data set falling into a particular class.

> The **class relative frequency** is the class frequency divided by the total number of observations in the data set; that is,
>
> $$\text{class relative frequency} = \frac{\text{class frequency}}{n}$$

Examining Table 2.1, we observe that 4 of the 40 best-paid CEOs did not obtain a college degree, 13 obtained bachelor's degrees, 15 MBAs, 5 master's degrees, 2 PhDs, and 1 law degree. These numbers—4, 13, 15, 5, 2, and 1—represent the class frequencies for the six classes and are shown in the summary table, Figure 2.1, produced using SPSS.

> The **class percentage** is the class relative frequency multiplied by 100; that is,
>
> $$\text{class percentage} = (\text{class relative frequency}) \times 100$$

Figure 2.1 also gives the relative frequency of each of the five degree classes. We know that we calculate the relative frequency by dividing the class frequency by the total number of observations in the data set. Thus, the relative frequencies for the five degree types are

$$\text{Bachelor's: } \frac{13}{40} = .325$$

$$\text{Law: } \frac{1}{40} = .025$$

$$\text{Master's: } \frac{5}{40} = .125$$

$$\text{MBA: } \frac{15}{40} = .375$$

$$\text{None: } \frac{4}{40} = .10$$

$$\text{PhD: } \frac{2}{40} = .05$$

These values, expressed as a percentage, are shown in the "Percent" column in the SPSS summary table, Figure 2.1. If we sum the relative frequencies for MBA, master's,

DEGREE

		Frequency	Percent	Valid Percent	Cumulative Percent
Valid	Bachelors	13	32.5	32.5	32.5
	Law	1	2.5	2.5	35.0
	Masters	5	12.5	12.5	47.5
	MBA	15	37.5	37.5	85.0
	None	4	10.0	10.0	95.0
	PhD	2	5.0	5.0	100.0
	Total	40	100.0	100.0	

Figure 2.1

SPSS summary table for degrees of 40 CEOs

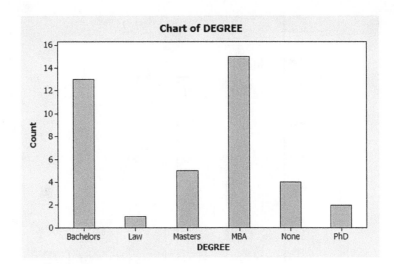

Figure 2.2

Minitab bar graph for degrees of 40 CEOs

**VILFREDO PARETO
(1843–1923)**

The Pareto Principle

Born in Paris to an Italian aristocratic family, Vilfredo Pareto was educated at the University of Turin, where he studied engineering and mathematics. After the death of his parents, Pareto quit his job as an engineer and began writing and lecturing on the evils of the economic policies of the Italian government. While at the University of Lausanne in Switzerland in 1896, he published his first paper, "Cours d'economie politique." In the paper, Pareto derived a complicated mathematical formula to prove that the distribution of income and wealth in society is not random but that a consistent pattern appears throughout history in all societies. Essentially, Pareto showed that approximately 80% of the total wealth in a society lies with only 20% of the families. This famous law about the "vital few and the trivial many" is widely known as the Pareto principle in economics.

law, and PhD, we obtain .375 + .125 + .025 + .05 = .575. Therefore, 57.5% of the 40 best-paid CEOs obtained at least a master's degree (MBA, master's, law, or PhD).

Although the summary table in Figure 2.1 adequately describes the data in Table 2.1, we often want a graphical presentation as well. Figures 2.2 and 2.3 show two of the most widely used graphical methods for describing qualitative data—**bar graphs** and **pie charts.** Figure 2.2 is a bar graph for "highest degree obtained" produced with Minitab. Note that the height of the rectangle, or "bar," over each class is equal to the class frequency. (Optionally, the bar heights can be proportional to class relative frequencies.) In contrast, Figure 2.3 (also created using Minitab) shows the relative frequencies (expressed as a percentage) of the six degree types in a *pie chart*. Note that the pie is a circle (spanning 360°), and the size (angle) of the "pie slice" assigned to each class is proportional to the class relative frequency. For example, the slice assigned to the MBA degree is 37.5% of 360°, or (.375)(360°) = 135°.

Before leaving the data set in Table 2.1, consider the bar graph shown in Figure 2.4, produced using SPSS with annotations. Note that the bars for the CEO degree categories are arranged in descending order of height from left to right across the horizontal axis—that is, the tallest bar (MBA) is positioned at the far left and the shortest bar is at the far right. This rearrangement of the bars in a bar graph is called a *Pareto diagram*. One goal of a Pareto diagram (named for the Italian economist Vilfredo Pareto) is to make it easy to locate the "most important" categories—those with the largest frequencies. For the 40 best-paid CEOs in 2011, an MBA degree was the highest degree obtained by the most CEOs (37.5%).

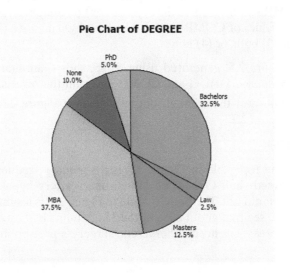

Figure 2.3

Minitab pie chart for degrees of 40 CEOs

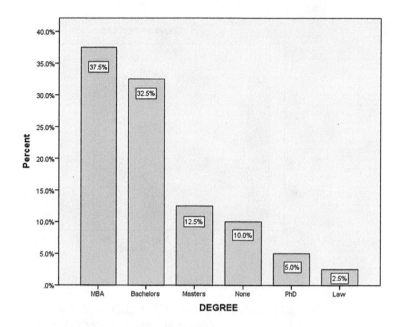

Figure 2.4

SPSS Pareto diagram for degrees
of 40 CEOs

Summary of Graphical Descriptive Methods for Qualitative Data

Bar graph: The categories (classes) of the qualitative variable are represented by bars, where the height of each bar is either the class frequency, class relative frequency, or class percentage.

Pie chart: The categories (classes) of the qualitative variable are represented by slices of a pie (circle). The size of each slice is proportional to the class relative frequency.

Pareto diagram: A bar graph with the categories (classes) of the qualitative variable (i.e., the bars) arranged by height in descending order from left to right.

Let's look at a practical example that requires interpretation of the graphical results.

Example 2.1

Graphing and Summarizing Qualitative Data—Blood Loss Study

Problem A group of cardiac physicians in southwest Florida have been studying a new drug designed to reduce blood loss in coronary artery bypass operations. Blood loss data for 114 coronary artery bypass patients (some who received a dosage of the drug and others who did not) are saved in the **BLOOD** file. Although the drug shows promise in reducing blood loss, the physicians are concerned about possible side effects and complications. So their data set includes not only the qualitative variable, DRUG, which indicates whether or not the patient received the drug, but also the qualitative variable, COMP, which specifies the type (if any) of complication experienced by the patient. The four values of COMP recorded by the physicians are (1) redo surgery, (2) post-op infection, (3) both, or (4) none.

a. Figure 2.5, generated using SPSS, shows summary tables for the two qualitative variables, DRUG and COMP. Interpret the results.

b. Interpret the Minitab output shown in Figure 2.6 and the SPSS output shown in Figure 2.7.

Solution

a. The top table in Figure 2.5 is a summary frequency table for DRUG. Note that exactly half (57) of the 114 coronary artery bypass patients received the drug and half did not. The bottom table in Figure 2.5 is a summary frequency table for COMP. We see that about 69% of the 114 patients had no complications, leaving about 31% who experienced either a redo surgery, a post-op infection, or both.

DRUG

		Frequency	Percent	Valid Percent	Cumulative Percent
Valid	NO	57	50.0	50.0	50.0
	YES	57	50.0	50.0	100.0
	Total	114	100.0	100.0	

COMP

		Frequency	Percent	Valid Percent	Cumulative Percent
Valid	BOTH	6	5.3	5.3	5.3
	INFECT	15	13.2	13.2	18.4
	NONE	79	69.3	69.3	87.7
	REDO	14	12.3	12.3	100.0
	Total	114	100.0	100.0	

Figure 2.5

SPSS summary tables for DRUG and COMP

b. Figure 2.6 is a Minitab side-by-side bar graph for the data. The four bars on the left represent the frequencies of COMP for the 57 patients who did not receive the drug; the four bars on the right represent the frequencies of COMP for the 57 patients who did receive a dosage of the drug. The graph clearly shows that patients who did not get the drug suffered fewer complications. The exact percentages are displayed in the SPSS summary tables of Figure 2.7. About 56% of the patients who got the drug had no complications, compared to about 83% for the patients who did not get the drug.

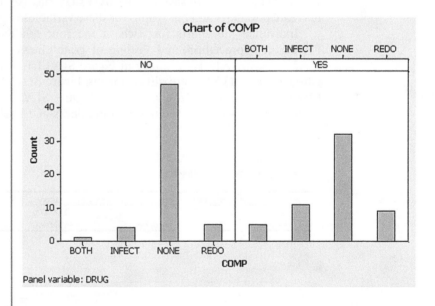

Figure 2.6

Minitab side-by-side bar graphs for COMP, by value of DRUG

COMP

DRUG			Frequency	Percent	Valid Percent	Cumulative Percent
NO	Valid	BOTH	1	1.8	1.8	1.8
		INFECT	4	7.0	7.0	8.8
		NONE	47	82.5	82.5	91.2
		REDO	5	8.8	8.8	100.0
		Total	57	100.0	100.0	
YES	Valid	BOTH	5	8.8	8.8	8.8
		INFECT	11	19.3	19.3	28.1
		NONE	32	56.1	56.1	84.2
		REDO	9	15.8	15.8	100.0
		Total	57	100.0	100.0	

Figure 2.7

SPSS summary tables for COMP by value of DRUG

Look Back Although these results show that the drug may be effective in reducing blood loss, Figures 2.6 and 2.7 imply that patients on the drug may have a higher risk of complications. But before using this information to make a decision about the drug, the physicians will need to provide a measure of reliability for the inference—that is, the physicians will want to know whether the difference between the percentages of patients with complications observed in this sample of 114 patients is generalizable to the population of all coronary artery bypass patients.

▪ **Now Work Exercise 2.12**

STATISTICS in ACTION REVISITED

Interpreting Pie Charts and Bar Graphs

In the *Journal of Experimental Social Psychology* (Vol. 45, 2009) study on whether money can buy love, Stanford University researchers measured several qualitative (categorical) variables for each of 237 adults: *Gender* (male or female), *Role* (gift-giver or gift-recipient), *Feeling of appreciation for the gift* (measured on an ordinal 7-point scale), and *Feeling of gratefulness for the gift* (measured on an ordinal 7-point scale). We classify the last two variables listed as qualitative since the numerical values represent distinct response categories (e.g., 1 = "Not at all," 2 = "A little," 3 = "More than a little," 4 = "Somewhat," 5 = "Moderately so," 6 = "Very much," and 7 = "To a great extent") that portray an opinion on how one feels about giving or receiving a gift. Pie charts and bar graphs can be used to summarize and describe the responses for these variables. Recall that the data are saved in the **BUYLOV** file. We used Excel/XLSTAT and SPSS to create pie charts and bar graphs for these variables.

Individual pie charts for each of the four qualitative variables, Role, Gender, Feeling of appreciation, and Feeling of gratefulness, are shown in Figures SIA2.1–SIA2.4, respectively. First, notice in Figure SIA2.1 that of the 237 adults, 56.5% were gift-givers and 43.5% were gift-recipients. Figure SIA2.2 gives the gender breakdown: 62% were females and 38% were males. Figures SIA2.3 and SIA2.4 show the summary of the responses for the Feeling of gratefulness and Feeling of appreciation questions,

Descriptive statistics (Qualitative data):

Sample	No. of observations	Category	Frequency per category	Rel. frequency per category (%)
Role	237	Giver	134.0000	56.5401
		Receiver	103.0000	43.4599

Pie charts:

Figure SIA2.1
XLSTAT pie chart for role

Descriptive statistics (Qualitative data):

Sample	No. of observations	Category	Frequency per category	Rel. frequency per category (%)
Gender	237	Female	147.0000	62.0253
		Male	90.0000	37.9747

Pie charts:

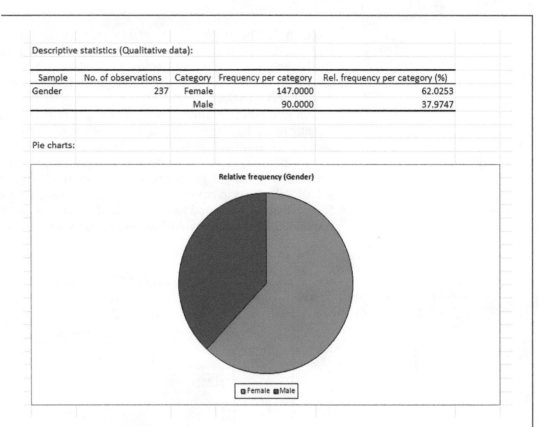

Figure SIA2.2

XLSTAT pie chart for gender

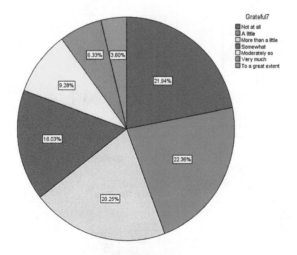

Figure SIA2.3

SPSS pie chart for feeling
of gratefulness

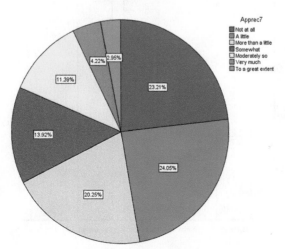

Figure SIA2.4

SPSS pie chart for feeling
of appreciation

STATISTICS
in ACTION
REVISITED
CONTINUED

respectively. The response percentages are very similar. For example, 23.2% of adults responded, "Not at all" to the Feeling of appreciation question compared to 21.9% for the Feeling of gratefulness question. Similarly, 24.0% of adults responded, "To a great extent" to the Feeling of appreciation question compared to 22.4% for the Feeling of gratefulness question.

Of interest in the study is whether gift-givers and gift-recipients would respond differently to the Feeling of gratefulness question. We can gain insight into this question by forming bar graphs of the Feeling of gratefulness responses, one graph for gift-givers and one for gift-recipients. These bar graphs are shown in Figure SIA2.5. You can see that about 32% of the gift-givers responded, "Not at all" (top graph) as compared to about 9% of the gift-recipients (bottom graph). Similarly, 10% of the gift-givers responded, "Somewhat" as compared to about 23% of the gift-recipients, and 2.2% of the gift-givers responded, "To a great extent" as compared to 5.8% of the gift-recipients Thus, it does

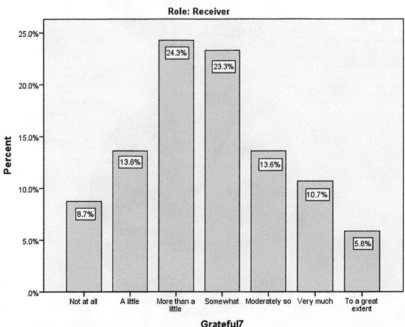

Figure SIA2.5

SPSS bar graphs for feeling
of gratefulness by role

appear that gift-givers and gift-recipients respond differently, with gift-recipients more likely to express a greater level of gratefulness for the gift than what gift-givers perceive.

Also of interest is whether males and females would respond differently to the Feeling of gratefulness question. Figure SIA2.6 is a set of bar graphs of the Feeling of gratefulness responses, one graph for each gender. The bar heights in these graphs look very similar, indicating that males and females responded about the same to the question.

Caution: The information produced in these graphs should be limited to describing the sample of 237 adults who participated in the study. If one is interested in making inferences about the population of all gift-givers and gift-recipients (as were the Stanford University researchers), inferential statistical methods need to be applied to the data. These methods are the topics of later chapters.

Data Set: BUYLOVE

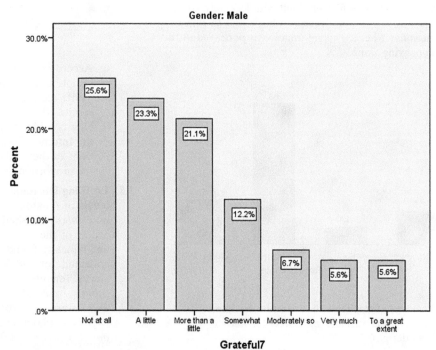

Figure SIA2.6

SPSS bar graphs for feeling of gratefulness by gender

Exercises 2.1–2.17

Learning the Mechanics

2.1 Complete the following table.

Grade on Business Statistics Exam	Frequency	Relative Frequency
A: 90–100	—	.08
B: 80–89	36	—
C: 65–79	90	—
D: 50–64	30	—
F: Below 50	28	—
Total	200	1.00

2.2 A qualitative variable with three classes (X, Y, and Z) is measured for each of 20 units randomly sampled from a target population. The data (observed class for each unit) are listed below.

Y	X	X	Z	X	Y	Y	Y	X	X	Z	X
Y	Y	X	Z	Y	Y	Y	X				

a. Compute the frequency for each of the three classes.
b. Compute the relative frequency for each of the three classes.
c. Display the results, part **a**, in a frequency bar graph.
d. Display the results, part **b**, in a pie chart.

Applying the Concepts—Basic

2.3 **Do social robots walk or roll?** According to the United Nations, social robots now outnumber industrial robots worldwide. A social (or service) robot is designed to entertain, educate, and care for human users. In a paper published by the *International Conference on Social Robotics* (Vol. 6414, 2010), design engineers investigated the trend in the design of social robots. Using a random sample of 106 social robots obtained through a Web search, the engineers found that 63 were built with legs only, 20 with wheels only, 8 with both legs and wheels, and 15 with neither legs nor wheels. This information is portrayed in the accompanying graph.

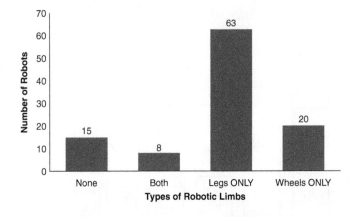

a. What type of graph is used to describe the data?
b. Indentify the variable measured for each of the 106 robot designs.

c. Use the graph to identify the social robot design that is currently used the most.
d. Compute class relative frequencies for the different categories shown in the graph.
e. Use the results from, part **d** to construct a Pareto diagram for the data.

2.4 **Paying for music downloads.** If you use the Internet, have you ever paid to access or download music? This was one of the questions of interest in a recent *Pew Internet & American Life Project Survey* (October 2010). Telephone interviews were conducted on a representative sample of 1,003 adults living in the United States. For this sample, 248 adults stated that they do not use the Internet, 249 revealed that they use the Internet but have never paid to download music, and the remainder (506 adults) admitted that they use the Internet and have paid to download music. The results are summarized in the Minitab pie chart shown.

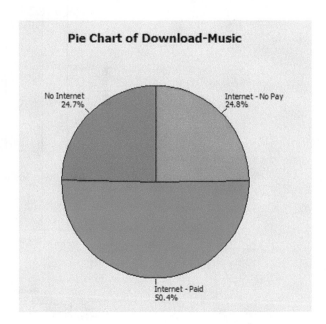

a. According to the pie chart, what proportion of the sample use the Internet and pay to download music? Verify the accuracy of this proportion using the survey results.
b. Now consider only the 755 adults in the sample that use the Internet. Create a graph that compares the proportions of these adults that pay to download music with the proportion that do not pay to download music.

2.5 **Profiling UK rental malls.** An analysis of the retail rental levels of tenants of United Kingdom regional shopping malls was published in *Urban Studies* (June 2011). One aspect of the study involved describing the type of tenant typically found at a UK shopping mall. Data were collected for 148 Shopping malls, which housed 1,821 stores. Tenants were categorized into five different-size groups based on amount of floor space: *anchor tenants* (more than 30,000 square feet), *major space users* (between 10,000 and 30,000 sq. ft.), *large standard tenants* (between 4,000 and 10,000 sq. ft.), *small standard* *tenants* (between 1,500 and 4,000 sq. ft.), and *small tenants* (less than 1,500 sq. ft.). The number of stores in each tenant category was reported as 14, 61, 216, 711, and 819, respectively. Use this information to construct a Pareto diagram for the distribution of tenant groups at UK shopping malls. Interpret the graph.

2.6 **Who is to blame for rising health care costs?** Rising health care costs are of major concern to Americans. A nationwide survey of 2,119 U.S. adults was conducted to elicit opinions on who is to blame for the rising costs (*The Harris Poll,* Oct. 28, 2008). The next table summarizes the responses to the question "When you think of the rising costs of health care, who do you think is most responsible?"

Most Responsible for Rising Health Care Costs	Number Responding
Insurance companies	869
Pharmaceutical companies	339
Government	338
Hospitals	127
Physicians	85
Other	128
Not at all sure	233
Total	2,119

a. Compute the relative frequencies in each response category.
b. Construct a relative frequency bar graph for the data.
c. Convert the relative frequency bar graph into a Pareto diagram. Interpret the graph.

2.7 **PIN pad shipments.** Personal identification number (PIN) pads are devices that connect to point-of-sale electronic cash registers for debit and credit card purchases. The PIN pad allows the customer's card to be accessed and the PIN encrypted before it is sent to the transaction manager. *The Nilson Report* (Oct. 2008) listed the volume of PIN pad shipments by manufacturers worldwide in 2007. For the 12 manufacturers listed in the table, a total of 334,039 PIN pads were shipped in 2007.

Manufacturer	Number Shipped (units)
Bitel	13,500
CyberNet	16,200
Fujian Landi	119,000
Glintt (ParaRede)	5,990
Intelligent	4,562
KwangWoo	42,000
Omron	20,000
Pax Tech.	10,072
ProvencoCadmus	20,000
SZZT Electronics	67,300
Toshiba TEC	12,415
Urmet	3,000

Source: Data from THE NILSON REPORT, No. 912, October 2008, p. 9.

a. One of the 334,039 PIN pads is selected and the manufacturer of the pad is determined. What type of data (quantitative or qualitative) is measured?
b. Construct a frequency bar chart for the data summarized in the table.
c. Convert the frequency bar chart, part **b**, into a Pareto diagram. Interpret the results.

Applying the Concepts—Intermediate

2.8 **The economic return to earning an MBA.** Refer to the *International Economic Review* (August 2008) study on the economic rewards to obtaining an MBA degree, Exercise 1.25 (p. 26). Job status information was collected for a sample of 3,244 individuals who sat for the GMAT in each of four time periods (waves). Summary information (number of individuals) for Wave 1 (at the time of taking the GMAT) and Wave 4 (7 years later) is provided in the accompanying table. Use a graph to compare and contrast the job status distributions of GMAT takers in Wave 1 and Wave 4.

Job Status	Wave 1	Wave 4
Working, No MBA	2,657	1,787
Working, Have MBA	0	1,372
Not Working, Business School	0	7
Not Working, Other Graduate School	36	78
Not Working, 4-Year Institution	551	0
Total	3,244	3,244

Source: Data from P. Arcidiancono, P. Cooley, and A. Hussey, "The economic returns to an MBA," INTERNATIONAL ECONOMIC REVIEW, Vol. 49, No. 3, August 2008, Table 1.

2.9 **Blogs for *Fortune* 500 firms.** Web site communication through blogs and forums is becoming a key marketing tool for companies. The *Journal of Relationship Marketing* (Vol. 7, 2008) investigated the prevalence of blogs and forums at *Fortune* 500 firms with both English and Chinese web sites. Of the firms that provided blogs/forums as a marketing tool, the accompanying table gives a breakdown on the entity responsible for creating the blogs/forums. Use a graphical method to describe the data summarized in the table. Interpret the graph.

Blog/Forum	Percentage of Firms
Created by company	38.5
Created by employees	34.6
Created by third party	11.5
Creator not identified	15.4

Source: Data from K. Mishra and C. Li, "Relationship marketing in FORTUNE 500 U.S. and Chinese web sites," JOURNAL OF RELATIONSHIP MARKETING, Vol. 7, No. 1, 2008.

2.10 **The Executive Compensation Scoreboard.** Refer to the *Forbes* "Executive Compensation Scoreboard" for 2011, described in Chapter 1 and in Exercise 1.21 (p. 26). Recall that the industry type of the CEO's company (e.g., banking, retailing, etc.) was recorded for each of the 175 CEOs with the highest efficiency (pay-for-performance) ratings. (See Table 1.1, p. 4, for a list of the industries.) Access the data file and use a graphical method to describe the frequency of occurrence of the industry types.

2.11 **Doctors and ethics.** For physicians confronted with ethical dilemmas (e.g., end-of-life issues or treatment of patients without insurance), many hospitals provide ethics consultation services. However, not all physicians take advantage of these services and some refuse to use ethics consultation. The extent to which doctors refuse ethics consults was studied in the *Journal of Medical*

Ethics (Vol. 32, 2006). Survey questionnaires were administered to all physicians on staff at a large community hospital in Tampa, Florida, and 118 physicians responded. Several qualitative variables were measured, including *previous use of ethics consultation* ("never used" or "used at least once"), *practitioner specialty* ("medical" or "surgical"), and *future use of ethics consultation* ("yes" or "no").

a. Access the file and generate a graph that describes the level to which the physicians on staff have previously used the ethics consultation services. What proportion of the sampled physicians have never used ethics consultation?

b. Repeat part **a** for *future use of ethics consultation*. What proportion of the sampled physicians state that they will not use the services in the future?

c. Generate side-by-side graphs that illustrate differences in previous use of ethics consultation by medical and surgical specialists. What inference can you make from the graphs?

d. Repeat part **c** for *future use of ethics consultation*.

2.12 **History of corporate acquisitions.** A corporate acquisition occurs when one corporation purchases all the stock shares of another, essentially taking over the other. The *Academy of Management Journal* (Aug. 2008) investigated the performance and timing of corporate acquisitions for a large sample of firms over the years 1980 to 2000. The accompanying data table gives the number of firms sampled and number that announced one or more acquisitions during the years 1980, 1990, and 2000. Construct side-by-side bar charts to describe the firms with and without acquisitions in the 3 years. Compare and contrast the bar charts.

Year	Number of Firms Sampled	Number with Acquisitions
1980	1,963	18
1990	2,197	350
2000	2,778	748

Source: Data from D. N. Iyer and K. D. Miller, "Performance feedback, slack, and the timing of acquisitions," ACADEMY OF MANAGEMENT JOURNAL, Vol. 51, No. 4, August 2008, pp. 808–822, Table 1.

2.13 **Motivation and right-oriented bias.** Evolutionary theory suggests that motivated decision makers tend to exhibit a right-oriented bias. (For example, if presented with two equally valued brands of detergent on a supermarket shelf, consumers are more likely to choose the brand on the right.) In *Psychological Science* (November 2011), researchers tested this theory using data on all penalty shots attempted in World Cup soccer matches (a total of 204 penalty shots). The researchers believed that goalkeepers, motivated to make a penalty-shot save but with little time to make a decision, would tend to dive to the right. The results of the study (percentages of dives to the left, middle, or right) are provided in the table. Note that the percentages in each row, corresponding to a certain match situation, add to 100%. Construct side-by-side bar graphs showing the distribution of dives for the three match situations. What inferences can you draw from the graphs?

Match Situation	Dive Left	Stay Middle	Dive Right
Team behind	29%	0%	71%
Tied	48%	3%	49%
Team ahead	51%	1%	48%

Source: Based on M. Roskes, et al., "The right side? Under time pressure, approach motivation leads to right-oriented bias," PSYCHOLOGICAL SCIENCE, Vol. 22, No. 11, November 2011 (adapted from Figure 2).

Applying the Concepts—Advanced

2.14 **Museum management.** What criteria do museums use to evaluate their performance? In a worldwide survey reported in *Museum Management and Curatorship* (June 2010), managers of 30 leading museums of contemporary art were asked to provide the performance measure used most often. A summary of the results is provided in the table. The researcher concluded that "there is a large amount of variation within the museum community with regard to . . . performance measurement and evaluation," Do you agree? Use a graph to support your conclusion.

Performance Measure	Number of Museums
Total visitors	8
Paying visitors	5
Big shows	6
Funds raised	7
Members	4

2.15 **Advertising with reader-response cards.** "Reader-response cards" are used by marketers to advertise their product and obtain sales leads. These cards are placed in magazines and trade publications. Readers detach and mail in the cards to indicate their interest in the product, expecting literature or a phone call in return. How effective are these cards (called "bingo cards" in the industry) as a marketing tool? Performark, a Minneapolis business that helps companies close on sales leads, attempted to answer this question by responding to 17,000 card-advertisements placed by industrial marketers in a wide variety of trade publications over a 6-year period. Performark kept track of how long it took for each advertiser to respond. A summary of the response times is given in the following table.

Advertiser's Response Time	Percentage
Never responded	21
13–59 days	33
60–120 days	34
More than 120 days	12
Total	100

a. Describe the variable measured by Performark.

b. These results were displayed in the form of a pie chart. Reconstruct the pie chart from the information given in the table.

c. How many of the 17,000 advertisers never responded to the sales lead?

d. Advertisers typically spend at least a million dollars on a reader-response card marketing campaign. Many industrial marketers feel these "bingo cards" are not worth their expense. Does the information in the pie chart, part **b**, support this contention? Explain why or why not. If not, what information can be gleaned from the pie chart to help potential "bingo card" campaigns?

2.16 **Stewardship at MBA programs.** *Business Ethics* (Fall 2005) reported on a survey designed to rank master in business administration (MBA) programs worldwide on how well they prepare students for social and environmental stewardship. Each business school was ranked according to four criteria: *student exposure* (class time dedicated to social and environmental issues), *student opportunity* (courses with social and environmental content), *course content* (courses emphasize business as a force for positive social and environmental change), and *faculty research* (published articles that examine business in a social/environmental context). Each area was rated from 1 star (lowest rating) to 5 stars (highest rating). Overall, Stanford University received the top ranking, followed by ESADE (Spain), York University (Canada), Monterrey Technical Institute (Mexico), and the University of Notre Dame. A summary of the rankings (star ratings) for the top 30 MBA programs is shown in the table.

Criteria	5 Stars	4 Stars	3 Stars	2 Stars	1 Star	Total
Student Exposure	2	9	14	5	0	30
Student Opportunity	3	10	14	3	0	30
Course Content	3	9	17	1	0	30
Faculty Research	3	10	11	4	0	28

Source: Data from Stewardship at MBA programs, D. Biello, "MBA Programs for Social and Environmental Stewardship," BUSINESS ETHICS, Fall 2005, p. 25.

a. Illustrate the differences and similarities of the star-ranking distributions for the four different criteria.

b. Give a plausible reason why there were no 1-star ratings for the 30 MBA programs.

2.17 **Groundwater contamination in wells.** In New Hampshire, about half the counties mandate the use of reformulated gasoline. This has led to an increase in the contamination of groundwater with methyl *tert*-butyl ether (MTBE).

Environmental Science & Technology (Jan. 2005) reported on the factors related to MTBE contamination in public and private New Hampshire wells. Data were collected for a sample of 223 wells. Three of the variables are qualitative in nature: well class (public or private), aquifer (bedrock or unconsolidated), and detectible level of MTBE (below limit or detect). [*Note:* A detectible level of MTBE occurs if the MTBE value exceeds .2 micrograms per liter.] The data for 11 selected wells are shown in the accompanying table.

Well Class	Aquifer	Detect MTBE
Private	Bedrock	Below Limit
Private	Bedrock	Below Limit
Public	Unconsolidated	Detect
Public	Unconsolidated	Below Limit
Public	Unconsolidated	Below Limit
Public	Unconsolidated	Below Limit
Public	Unconsolidated	Detect
Public	Unconsolidated	Below Limit
Public	Unconsolidated	Below Limit
Public	Bedrock	Detect
Public	Bedrock	Detect

Source: Based on Ayotte, J. D., Argue, D. M., and McGarry, F. J. "Methyl tert-Butyl Ether Occurrence and Related Factors in Public and Private Wells in Southeast New Hampshire." ENVIRONMENTAL SCIENCE & TECHNOLOGY, Vol. 39, No. 1, Jan. 2005, pp. 9–16.

a. Use graphical methods to describe each of the three qualitative variables for all 223 wells.

b. Use side-by-side bar charts to compare the proportions of contaminated wells for private and public well classes.

c. Use side-by-side bar charts to compare the proportions of contaminated wells for bedrock and unconsolidated aquifers.

d. What inferences can be made from the bar charts, parts **a–c**?

2.2 Graphical Methods for Describing Quantitative Data

Recall from Section 1.5 that quantitative data sets consist of data that are recorded on a meaningful numerical scale. For describing, summarizing, and detecting patterns in such data, we can use three graphical methods: **dot plots, stem-and-leaf displays,** and **histograms.** Because almost all statistical software packages can produce these graphs, we'll focus here on their interpretations rather than their construction.

For example, suppose a financial analyst is interested in the amount of resources spent by computer hardware and software companies on research and development (R&D). She samples 50 of these high-technology firms and calculates the amount each spent last year on R&D as a percentage of their total revenue. The results are given in Table 2.2. As numerical measurements made on the sample of 50 units (the firms), these percentages represent quantitative data. The analyst's initial objective is to summarize and describe these data in order to extract relevant information.

A visual inspection of the data indicates some obvious facts. For example, the smallest R&D percentage is 5.2% (company 45) and the largest is 13.5% (companies 1 and 16). But it is difficult to provide much additional information on the 50 R&D percentages without resorting to some method of summarizing the data. One such method is a dot plot.

Table 2.2	Percentage of Revenues Spent on Research and Development						
Company	Percentage	Company	Percentage	Company	Percentage	Company	Percentage
1	13.5	14	9.5	27	8.2	39	6.5
2	8.4	15	8.1	28	6.9	40	7.5
3	10.5	16	13.5	29	7.2	41	7.1
4	9.0	17	9.9	30	8.2	42	13.2
5	9.2	18	6.9	31	9.6	43	7.7
6	9.7	19	7.5	32	7.2	44	5.9
7	6.6	20	11.1	33	8.8	45	5.2
8	10.6	21	8.2	34	11.3	46	5.6
9	10.1	22	8.0	35	8.5	47	11.7
10	7.1	23	7.7	36	9.4	48	6.0
11	8.0	24	7.4	37	10.5	49	7.8
12	7.9	25	6.5	38	6.9	50	6.5
13	6.8	26	9.5				

Data Set: R&D

Dot Plots

A **dot plot** for the 50 R&D percentages, produced using Minitab, is shown in Figure 2.8. The horizontal axis of Figure 2.8 is a scale for the quantitative variable, percent. The numerical value of each measurement in the data set is located on the horizontal scale by a dot. When data values repeat, the dots are placed above one another, forming a pile at that particular numerical location. As you can see, this dot plot shows that almost all of the R&D percentages are between 6% and 12%, with most falling between 7% and 9%.

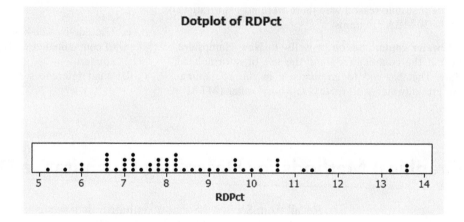

Figure 2.8

Minitab dot plot for 50 R&D percentages

Stem-and-Leaf Display

We used XLSTAT to generate another graphical representation of these same data, a **stem-and-leaf display,** in Figure 2.9. In this display the *stem* is the portion of the measurement (percentage) to the left of the decimal point, while the remaining portion to the right of the decimal point is the *leaf.*

    The stems for the data set are listed in the first column of Figure 2.9 from the smallest (5) to the largest (13). Then the leaf for each observation is recorded in the row of the display corresponding to the observation's stem. For example, the leaf 5 of the first observation (13.5) in Table 2.2 is placed in the row corresponding to the stem 13. Similarly, the leaf 4 for the second observation (8.4) in Table 2.2 is recorded in the row corresponding to the stem 8, while the leaf 5 for the third observation (10.5) is recorded in the row corresponding to the stem 10. (The leaves for these first three observations are shaded in Figure 2.9.) Typically, the leaves in each row are ordered as shown in Figure 2.9.

Stem-and-leaf plot (RDPct):

Unit: **1**

```
      5 269
      6 055568999
      7 11224557789
      8 001222458
      9 02455679
     10 1556
     11 137
     12
     13 255
```

Figure 2.9

XLSTAT stem-and-leaf display for 50 R&D percentages

The stem-and-leaf display presents another compact picture of the data set. You can see at a glance that most of the sampled computer companies (37 of 50) spent between 6.0% and 9.9% of their revenues on R&D, and 11 of them spent between 7.0% and 7.9%. Relative to the rest of the sampled companies, three spent a high percentage of revenues on R&D—in excess of 13%.

The definitions of the stem and leaf can be modified to alter the graphical display. For example, suppose we had defined the stem as the tens digit for the R&D percentage data, rather than the ones and tens digits. With this definition, the stems and leaves corresponding to the measurements 13.5 and 8.4 would be as follows:

Stem	Leaf		Stem	Leaf
1	3		0	8

Note that the decimal portion of the numbers has been dropped. Generally, only one digit is displayed in the leaf.

If you look at the data, you'll see why we didn't define the stem this way. All the R&D measurements fall below 13.5, so all the leaves would fall into just two stem rows—1 and 0—in this display. The picture resulting from using only a few stems would not be nearly as informative as Figure 2.9.

Histograms

A **Minitab histogram** for these 50 R&D measurements is displayed in Figure 2.10. The horizontal axis for Figure 2.10, which gives the percentage amounts spent on R&D for each company, is divided into **class intervals** commencing with the interval (5.0−6.0) and proceeding in intervals of equal size to (13.0−14.0). The vertical axis gives the number (or *frequency*) of the 50 measurements that fall in each class interval. You can see that the class interval (7.0−8.0) (i.e., the class with the highest bar) contains the largest frequency of 11 R&D percentage measurements; the remaining class intervals tend to contain a smaller number of measurements as R&D percentage gets smaller or larger.

Histograms can be used to display either the *frequency* or *relative frequency* of the measurements falling into the class intervals. The class intervals, frequencies, and relative frequencies for the 50 R&D measurements are shown in Table 2.3.* By summing the

Figure 2.10

Minitab histogram for 50 R&D percentages

*Minitab, like many statistical software packages, will classify an observation that falls on the borderline of a class interval into the next highest class interval. For example, the R&D measurement of 8.0, which falls on the border between the intervals (7.0−8.0) and (8.0−9.0), is classified into the (8.0−9.0) interval. The frequencies in Table 2.3 reflect this convention.

JOHN TUKEY (1915–2000)
The Picasso of Statistics

Like the legendary artist Pablo Picasso, who mastered and revolutionized a variety of art forms during his lifetime, John Tukey is recognized for his contributions to many subfields of statistics. Born in Massachusetts, Tukey was home-schooled, graduated with his bachelor's and master's degrees in chemistry from Brown University, and received his PhD in mathematics from Princeton University. While at Bell Telephone Laboratories in the 1960s and early 1970s, Tukey developed "exploratory data analysis," a set of graphical descriptive methods for summarizing and presenting huge amounts of data. Many of these tools, including the stem-and-leaf display and the box plot (see Section 2.7), are now standard features of modern statistical software packages. (In fact, it was Tukey himself who coined the term *software* for computer programs.)

Table 2.3	Class Intervals, Frequencies, and Relative Frequencies for the 50 R&D Measurements		
Class	Class Interval	Class Frequency	Class Relative Frequency
1	5.0–6.0	3	3/50 = .06
2	6.0–7.0	9	9/50 = .18
3	7.0–8.0	11	11/50 = .22
4	8.0–9.0	9	9/50 = .18
5	9.0–10.0	8	8/50 = .16
6	10.0–11.0	4	4/50 = .08
7	11.0–12.0	3	3/50 = .06
8	12.0–13.0	0	0/50 = .00
9	13.0–14.0	3	3/50 = .06
Totals		50	1.00

relative frequencies in the intervals (6.0–7.0), (7.0–8.0), (8.0–9.0), (9.0–10.0), and (10.0–11.0), we find that .18 + .22 + .18 + .16 + .08 = .82, or 82%, of the R&D measurements are between 6.0 and 11.0. Similarly, summing the relative frequencies in the last two intervals, (12.0–13.0) and (13.0–14.0), we find that 6% of the companies spent over 12.0% of their revenues on R&D. Many other summary statements can be made by further study of the histogram. Note that the sum of all class frequencies will always equal the sample size n.

When interpreting a histogram, consider two important facts. First, the proportion of the total area under the histogram that falls above a particular interval of the horizontal axis is equal to the relative frequency of measurements falling in the interval. For example, the relative frequency for the class interval 7.0–8.0 in Figure 2.10 is .22. Consequently, the rectangle above the interval contains 22% of the total area under the histogram.

Second, imagine the appearance of the relative frequency histogram for a very large set of data (say, a population). As the number of measurements in a data set is increased, you can obtain a better description of the data by decreasing the width of the class intervals. When the class intervals become small enough, a relative frequency histogram will (for all practical purposes) appear as a smooth curve (see Figure 2.11). Some recommendations for selecting the number of intervals in a histogram for smaller data sets are given in the box below Figure 2.11.

While histograms provide good visual descriptions of data sets–particularly very large ones–they do not let us identify individual measurements. In contrast, each of the original measurements is visible to some extent in a dot plot and clearly visible in a stem-and-leaf display. The stem-and-leaf display arranges the data in ascending order, so it's easy to locate the individual measurements. For example, in Figure 2.9, we can easily see that three of the R&D measurements are equal to 8.2, but we can't see that fact by inspecting the histogram in Figure 2.10. However, stem-and-leaf displays can become unwieldy for very large data sets. A very large number of stems and leaves causes the vertical and horizontal dimensions of the display to become cumbersome, diminishing the usefulness of the visual display.

Figure 2.11

Effect of the size of a data set on the outline of a histogram

a. Small data set   b. Larger data set   c. Very large data set

Determining the Number of Classes in a Histogram

Number of Observations in Data Set	Number of Classes
Less than 25	5–6
25–50	7–14
More than 50	15–20

Example   2.2

Graphs for a Quantitative Variable— Lost Price Quotes

Problem A manufacturer of industrial wheels suspects that profitable orders are being lost because of the long time the firm takes to develop price quotes for potential customers. To investigate this possibility, 50 requests for price quotes were randomly selected from the set of all quotes made last year, and the processing time was determined for each quote. The processing times are displayed in Table 2.4, and each quote was classified according to whether the order was "lost" or not (i.e., whether or not the customer placed an order after receiving a price quote).

a. Use a statistical software package to create a frequency histogram for these data. Then shade the area under the histogram that corresponds to lost orders. Interpret the result.

b. Use a statistical software package to create a stem-and-leaf display for these data. Then shade each leaf of the display that corresponds to a lost order. Interpret the result.

Solution

a. We used SPSS to generate the frequency histogram in Figure 2.12. Note that 20 classes were formed by the SPSS program. The class intervals are (1.0–2.0), (2.0–3.0),..., (20.0–21.0). This histogram clearly shows the clustering of the measurements in the

Table 2.4	Price Quote Processing Time (Days)				
Request Number	Processing Time	Lost?	Request Number	Processing Time	Lost?
1	2.36	No	26	3.34	No
2	5.73	No	27	6.00	No
3	6.60	No	28	5.92	No
4	10.05	Yes	29	7.28	Yes
5	5.13	No	30	1.25	No
6	1.88	No	31	4.01	No
7	2.52	No	32	7.59	No
8	2.00	No	33	13.42	Yes
9	4.69	No	34	3.24	No
10	1.91	No	35	3.37	No
11	6.75	Yes	36	14.06	Yes
12	3.92	No	37	5.10	No
13	3.46	No	38	6.44	No
14	2.64	No	39	7.76	No
15	3.63	No	40	4.40	No
16	3.44	No	41	5.48	No
17	9.49	Yes	42	7.51	No
18	4.90	No	43	6.18	No
19	7.45	No	44	8.22	Yes
20	20.23	Yes	45	4.37	No
21	3.91	No	46	2.93	No
22	1.70	No	47	9.95	Yes
23	16.29	Yes	48	4.46	No
24	5.52	No	49	14.32	Yes
25	1.44	No	50	9.01	No

Data Set: QUOTES

Figure 2.12

SPSS frequency histogram for price quote data

lower end of the distribution (between approximately 1 and 8 days), and the relatively few measurements in the upper end of the distribution (greater than 12 days). The shading of the area of the frequency histogram corresponding to lost orders (green bars) clearly indicates that they lie in the upper tail of the distribution.

b. We used Minitab to generate the stem-and-leaf display in Figure 2.13. Note that the stem (the second column of the printout) consists of the number of whole days (digits to the left of the decimal). The leaf (the third column of the printout) is the tenths digit (first digit after the decimal) of each measurement. Thus, the leaf 2 in the stem 20 (the last row of the printout) represents the time of 20.23 days. Like the histogram, the stem-and-leaf display shows the shaded "lost" orders in the upper tail of the distribution.

Look Back As is usually the case for data sets that are not too large (say, fewer than 100 measurements), the stem-and-leaf display provides more detail than the histogram without being unwieldy. For instance, the stem-and-leaf display in Figure 2.13 clearly indicates that the lost orders are associated with high processing times (as does the histogram in Figure 2.12), and exactly which of the times correspond to lost orders. Histograms are most useful for displaying very large data sets, when the overall shape of the distribution of measurements is more important than the identification of individual measurements. Nevertheless, the message of both graphical displays is clear: Establishing processing time limits may well result in fewer lost orders.

■ **Now Work Exercise 2.22**

```
Stem-and-leaf of TIME  N  = 50
Leaf Unit = 0.10

   5    1   24789
  10    2   03569
  18    3   23344699
  24    4   034469
  (6)   5   114579
  20    6   01467
  15    7   24557
  10    8   2
   9    9   049
   6   10   0
   5   11
   5   12
   5   13   4
   4   14   03
   2   15
   2   16   2
   1   17
   1   18
   1   19
   1   20   2
```

Figure 2.13

Minitab stem-and-leaf display for price quote data

Most statistical software packages can be used to generate histograms, stem-and-leaf displays, and dot plots. All three are useful tools for graphically describing data sets. We recommend that you generate and compare the displays whenever you can. You'll find that histograms are generally more useful for very large data sets, while stem-and-leaf displays and dot plots provide useful detail for smaller data sets.

> **Summary of Graphical Descriptive Methods for Quantitative Data**
>
> **Dot plot:** The numerical value of each quantitative measurement in the data set is represented by a dot on a horizontal scale. When data values repeat, the dots are placed above one another vertically.
>
> **Stem-and-leaf display:** The numerical value of the quantitative variable is partitioned into a "stem" and a "leaf." The possible stems are listed in order in a column. The leaf for each quantitative measurement in the data set is placed in the corresponding stem row. Leaves for observations with the same stem value are listed in increasing order horizontally.
>
> **Histogram:** The possible numerical values of the quantitative variable are partitioned into class intervals, where each interval has the same width. These intervals form the scale of the horizontal axis. The frequency or relative frequency of observations in each class interval is determined. A horizontal bar is placed over each class interval, with height equal to either the class frequency or class relative frequency.

STATISTICS in ACTION REVISITED

Interpreting Histograms

In the *Journal of Experimental Social Psychology* (Vol. 45, 2009) study on whether money can buy love (p. 37), the researchers randomly assigned participants to the role of either gift-giver or gift-receiver. (Gift-givers, recall, were asked about a birthday gift they recently gave, while gift-recipients were asked about a birthday gift they recently received.) Two quantitative variables were measured for each of the 237 participants: *gift price* (measured in dollars) and *overall level of appreciation for the gift* (measured as the sum of the two 7-point appreciation scales, with higher values indicating a higher level of appreciation). One of the objectives of the research was to investigate whether givers and receivers differ on the price of the gift reported and on the level of appreciation reported. We can explore this phenomenon graphically by forming side-by-side histograms for the quantitative variables, one histogram for gift-givers and one for gift-recipients. These histograms, produced from a Minitab analysis of the data in the **BUYLOV** file, are shown in Figures SIA2.7a and SIA2.7b.

First, examine the histograms for birthday gift price (Figure SIA2.7a). The prices reported by gift-recipients tended to be higher than the prices reported by gift-givers. For example, receivers reported more birthday gift prices of at least $300 than givers, while givers reported more prices of $100 or less than receivers.

Next, examine the histograms for overall level of appreciation (Figure SIA2.7b). For gift-givers, the histogram of appreciation scores is centered around 5 points, while

Figure SIA2.7a

Side-by-side histograms for birthday gift price

Figure SIA2.7b

Side-by-side histograms for overall level of appreciation

for gift-recipients the histogram is centered higher, at about 8 points. Also from the histograms you can see that about 65% of the givers reported an appreciation level of less than 6 compared to about 28% for gift-recipients. As with the bar graphs in the previous Statistics in Action Revisited, it appears that gift-givers and gift-recipients respond differently, with gift-recipients more likely to express a greater level of appreciation for the gift than what gift-givers perceive. In later chapters, we'll learn how to attach a measure of reliability to such an inference.

Data Set: BUYLOV

Exercises 2.18–2.34

Learning the Mechanics

2.18 Graph the relative frequency histogram for the 500 measurements summarized in the accompanying relative frequency table.

Measurement Class	Relative Frequency
.5–2.5	.10
2.5–4.5	.15
4.5–6.5	.25
6.5–8.5	.20
8.5–10.5	.05
10.5–12.5	.10
12.5–14.5	.10
14.5–16.5	.05

2.19 Refer to Exercise 2.18. Calculate the number of the 500 measurements falling into each of the measurement classes. Then graph a frequency histogram for these data.

2.20 Consider the stem-and-leaf display shown here.

Stem	Leaf
5	1
4	457
3	00036
2	1134599
1	2248
0	012

a. How many observations were in the original data set?

b. In the bottom row of the stem-and-leaf display, identify the stem, the leaves, and the numbers in the original data set represented by this stem and its leaves.

c. Re-create all the numbers in the data set and construct a dot plot.

2.21 Minitab was used to generate the following histogram:

a. Is this a frequency histogram or a relative frequency histogram? Explain.

b. How many measurement classes were used in the construction of this histogram?

c. How many measurements are in the data set described by this histogram?

Applying the Concepts—Basic

2.22 **Annual survey of computer crimes.** Refer to the 2010 *CSI Computer Crime and Security Survey,* Exercise 1.22 (p. 26). Recall that 351 organizations responded on unauthorized use of computer systems. One of the survey questions asked respondents to indicate the percentage of monetary losses attributable to malicious actions by individuals within the organization (i.e., malicious insider actions). The following XLSTAT histogram summarizes the data for the 144 firms who experienced some monetary loss due to malicious insider actions.

a. Which measurement class contains the highest proportion of respondents?

b. What is the approximate proportion of the 144 organizations that reported a percentage monetary loss from malicious insider actions less than 20%?

c. What is the approximate proportion of the 144 organizations that reported a percentage monetary loss from malicious insider actions greater than 60%?

d. About how many of the 144 organizations reported a percentage monetary loss from malicious insider actions between 20% and 30%?

2.23 **Corporate sustainability of CPA firms.** Refer to the *Business and Society* (March 2011) study on the sustainability behaviors of CPA corporations, Exercise 1.26 (p. 27). *Corporate sustainability,* recall, refers to business practices designed around social and environmental considerations. Data on the level of support for corporate sustainability were obtained for 992 senior managers. Level of support was measured quantitatively. Simulation was used to convert the data from the study to a scale ranging from 0 to 160 points, where higher point values indicate a higher level of support for sustainability.

a. A histogram for level of support for sustainability is shown next. What type of histogram is produced, frequency or relative frequency?

b. Use the graph to estimate the percentage of the 992 senior managers who reported a high (100 points or greater) level of support for corporate sustainability.

Minitab histogram for Exercise 2.23

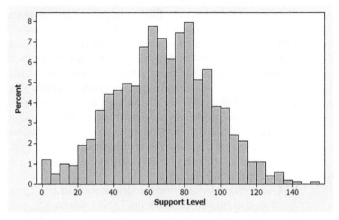

2.24 **Sanitation inspection of cruise ships.** To minimize the potential for gastrointestinal disease outbreaks, all passenger cruise ships arriving at U.S. ports are subject to unannounced sanitation inspections. Ships are rated on a 100-point scale by the Centers for Disease Control and Prevention. A score of 86 or higher indicates that the ship is providing an accepted standard of sanitation. The latest (as of Jan. 2010) sanitation scores for 186 cruise ships are saved in the accompanying file. The first five and last five observations in the data set are listed in the accompanying table.

Ship Name	Sanitation Score
Adventure of the Seas	98
AIDAaura	100
Albatross	69
Amadea	84
Amsterdam	99
⋮	⋮
Westerdam	99
Wind Spirit	97
Wind Surf	95
Zaandam	99
Zuiderdam	95

Source: Data from U.S. Department of Health and Human Services, Centers for Disease Control and Prevention/National Center for Environmental Health and Agency for Toxic Substances and Disease Registry, January 6, 2010.

a. Generate both a stem-and-leaf display and histogram of the data.

b. Use the graphs to estimate the proportion of ships that have an accepted sanitation standard. Which graph did you use?

c. Locate the inspection score of 69 (*Albatross*) on the graph. Which graph did you use?

2.25 **History of corporate acquisitions.** Refer to the *Academy of Management Journal* (Aug. 2008) study of corporate acquisitions from 1980 to 2000, Exercise 2.12 (p. 50). The data file includes the number of firms with at least one acquisition each year.

a. Construct either a dot plot or a stem-and-leaf display for the annual number of firms with at least one acquisition.

b. On the graph, part **a**, highlight (or circle) the values for the years 1996–2000. Do you detect a pattern? If so, what conclusion can you draw from the data?

Applying the Concepts—Intermediate

2.26 Most valuable NFL teams. Each year *Forbes* reports on the
value of all teams in the National Football League. Although
England's soccer team, Manchester United, is the most valuable team in the world ($1.8 billion), the NFL now has 15
teams worth at least $1 billion. For 2011, *Forbes* reports that
the Dallas Cowboys are the most valuable team in the NFL,
worth $1.85 billion. The current values (in $ millions) of all
32 NFL teams, as well as the percentage changes in values
from 2010 to 2011, debt-to-value ratios, annual revenues, and
operating incomes are listed in the first table below.
  a. Use a graph to describe the distribution of current values for the 32 NFL teams.
  b. Use a graph to describe the distribution of the 1-year
  change in current value for the 32 NFL teams.
  c. Use a graph to describe the distribution of debt-to-
  value ratios for the 32 NFL teams.

  d. Use a graph to describe the distribution of the annual
  revenues for the 32 NFL teams.
  e. Use a graph to describe the distribution of operating
  incomes for the 32 NFL teams.
  f. Compare and contrast the graphs, parts **a–e.**

2.27 State SAT scores. Educators are constantly evaluating
the efficacy of public schools in the education and training of American students. One quantitative assessment of
change over time is the difference in scores on the SAT,
which has been used for decades by colleges and universities as one criterion for admission. Originally, the SAT
provided scores in reading and mathematics. Now, three
scores are provided: reading, mathematics, and critical
writing. SAT scores for each of the 50 states and District of
Columbia for the years 2011, 2010, and 2001 are saved in
the accompanying file. Data for the first five and last two
states are shown in the second table below.

Rank	Team	Current Value ($ mil)	1-Yr Value Change (%)	Debt/Value (%)	Revenue ($ mil)	Operating Income ($ mil)
1	Dallas Cowboys	1,850	2	18	406	119
2	Washington Redskins	1,555	0	26	352	65.6
3	New England Patriots	1,400	2	19	333	42.9
4	New York Giants	1,300	10	50	293	40.6
5	New York Jets	1,223	7	61	285	25.1
6	Houston Texans	1,202	3	17	283	41
7	Philadelphia Eagles	1,164	4	9	274	28.9
8	Chicago Bears	1,093	2	11	266	43.4
9	Green Bay Packers	1,089	7	2	259	12
10	Baltimore Ravens	1,088	1	25	262	24.9
11	Indianapolis Colts	1,057	2	4	252	32.8
12	Denver Broncos	1,046	0	14	255	28.5
13	Pittsburgh Steelers	1,018	2	25	255	28.3
14	Miami Dolphins	1,012	0	40	253	12.9
15	Carolina Panthers	1,002	−3	19	257	31.2
16	Seattle Seahawks	997	1	12	249	7.8
17	San Francisco 49ers	990	7	14	234	1.5
18	Kansas City Chiefs	986	2	14	252	14.5
19	Tampa Bay Buccaneers	981	−5	18	245	50.8
20	Cleveland Browns	977	−4	15	247	−2.9
21	New Orleans Saints	965	1	13	261	28.9
22	Tennessee Titans	964	−3	13	250	21.8
23	San Diego Chargers	920	1	14	241	34.2
24	Arizona Cardinals	901	−2	17	240	56.4
25	Cincinnati Bengals	875	−3	11	236	44.7
26	Detroit Lions	844	3	33	228	−7.7
27	Atlanta Falcons	814	−2	34	233	27.2
28	Minnesota Vikings	796	3	41	227	3.7
29	Buffalo Bills	792	−1	16	236	40.9
30	St. Louis Rams	775	−1	15	228	24.6
31	Oakland Raiders	761	0	16	217	23
32	Jacksonville Jaguars	725	0	17	236	32.8

Source: Based on Kurt Badenhausen, "The NFL's Most Valuable Teams," FORBES, September 7, 2011.

Data for Exercise 2.27

State	2011			2010			2001	
	Read	Math	Write	Read	Math	Write	Read	Math
Alabama	546	541	536	556	550	543	559	554
Alaska	515	511	487	516	513	489	514	510
Arizona	517	523	499	518	524	498	523	525
Arkansas	568	570	554	564	564	550	562	550
California	499	515	499	501	516	500	498	517
Wisconsin	590	602	575	593	603	578	584	596
Wyoming	572	569	551	568	565	543	547	545

Source: Data from "SAT Trends: Background on the SAT Takers in the Class of 2011," The College Board, 2011.

a. Use graphs to display the SAT mathematics score distributions in 2011 and 2010. How did the distributions of state scores change over the year?

b. Repeat part **a,** but compare the distribution in 2011 with the one in 2001. How did the distributions of state scores change over the past 10 years?

c. As another method of comparing the 2011 and 2001 SAT mathematics scores, compute the *paired difference* by subtracting the 2001 score from the 2011 score for each state. Summarize these differences with a graph. Compare the results to those of part **b.**

d. Based on the graph, part **c,** what is the largest improvement in SAT mathematics score? Identify the state associated with this improvement.

2.28 Items arriving and departing a work center. In a manufacturing plant, a *work center* is a specific production facility that consists of one or more people and/or machines and is treated as one unit for the purposes of capacity requirements for planning and job scheduling. If jobs arrive at a particular work center at a faster rate than they depart, the work center impedes the overall production process and is referred to as a *bottleneck*. The data in the table at the bottom of the page were collected by an operations manager for use in investigating a potential bottleneck work center. Construct dot plots for the two sets of data. Do the dot plots suggest that the work center may be a bottleneck? Explain.

2.29 Crude oil biodegradation. In order to protect their valuable resources, oil companies spend millions of dollars researching ways to prevent biodegradation of crude oil. The *Journal of Petroleum Geology* (April 2010) published a study of the environmental factors associated with biodegradation in crude oil reservoirs. Sixteen water specimens were randomly selected from various locations in a reservoir on the floor of a mine. Two of the variables measured were (1) the amount of dioxide (milligrams/liter) present in the water specimen and (2) whether or not oil was present in the water specimen. These data are listed in the accompanying table in the left column. Construct a stem-and-leaf display for the dioxide data. Locate the dioxide levels associated with water specimens that contain oil. Highlight these data points on the stem-and-leaf display. Is there a tendency for crude oil to be present in water with lower levels of dioxide?

2.30 Is honey a cough remedy? Coughing at night is a common symptom of an upper respiratory tract infection, yet there is no accepted therapeutic cure. Does a teaspoon of honey before bed really calm a child's cough? To test the folk remedy, pediatric researchers at Pennsylvania State University carried out a designed study conducted over two nights (*Archives of Pediatrics and Adolescent Medicine*, Dec. 2007). A sample of 105 children who were ill with an upper respiratory tract infection and their parents participated in the study. On the first night, the parents rated their children's cough symptoms on a scale from 0 (no problems at all) to 6 (extremely severe) in five different areas. The total symptoms score (ranging from 0 to 30 points) was the variable of interest for the 105 patients. On the second night, the parents were instructed to give their sick child a dosage of liquid "medicine" prior to bedtime. Unknown to the parents, some were given a dosage of dextromethorphan (DM)—an over-the-counter cough medicine—while others were given a similar dose of honey. Also, a third group of parents (the control group) gave their sick children no dosage at all. Again, the parents rated their children's cough symptoms, and the improvement in total cough symptoms score was determined for each child. The data (improvement scores) for the study are shown in the table on the next page, followed by a Minitab dot plot of the data. Notice that the green dots represent the children who received a dose of honey, the red dots represent those who got the DM dosage, and the black dots represent the children in the control group. What conclusions can pediatric researchers draw from the graph? Do you agree with the statement (extracted from the article), "Honey may be a preferable treatment for the cough and sleep difficulty associated with childhood upper respiratory tract infection"?

Dioxide Amount	Crude Oil Present
3.3	No
0.5	Yes
1.3	Yes
0.4	Yes
0.1	No
4.0	No
0.3	No
0.2	Yes
2.4	No
2.4	No
1.4	No
0.5	Yes
0.2	Yes
4.0	No
4.0	No
4.0	No

Source: Based on A. Permanyer, J. L. R. Gallego, M. A. Caja, and D. Dessort, "Crude Oil Biodegradation and Environmental Factors at the Riutort Oil Shale Mine, SE Pyrenees." JOURNAL OF PETROLEUM GEOLOGY, Vol. 33, No. 2, April 2010, Table 1.

Data for Exercise 2.28

Number of Items Arriving at Work Center per Hour

155	115	156	150	159	163	172	143	159	166	148	175
151	161	138	148	129	135	140	152	139			

Number of Items Departing Work Center per Hour

156	109	127	148	135	119	140	127	115	122	99	106
171	123	135	125	107	152	111	137	161			

Data for Exercise 2.30

Honey Dosage:	12	11	15	11	10	13	10	4	15	16	9	14
	10	6	10	8	11	12	12	8	9	5	12	
	12	9	11	15	10	15	9	13	8	12	10	8
DM Dosage:	4	6	9	4	7	7	7	9	12	10	11	6	3
	4	9	12	7	6	8	12	12	4	12	10	15	9
	13	7	10	13	9	4	4						
No Dosage (Control):	5	8	6	1	0	8	12	8	7	7	1	6	7
	7	12	7	9	7	9	5	11	9	5	1	4	3
	6	8	8	6	7	10	9	4	8	7	3		

Source: Based on Paul, I. M., et al. "Effect of honey, dextromethorphan, and no treatment on nocturnal cough and sleep quality for coughing children and their parents," *Archives of Pediatrices and Adolescent Medicine,* Vol. 161, No. 12, Dec. 2007 (data simulated).

Applying the Concepts—Advanced

2.31 **Doctors and ethics.** Refer to the *Journal of Medical Ethics* (Vol. 32, 2006) study of physicians' use of ethics consultation, Exercise 2.11 (p. 49). In addition to the qualitative variable, *use of ethics consultation in the future* ("yes" or "no"), one of the quantitative variables measured in the survey of physicians was *length of time in practice* (i.e., years of experience). The medical researchers hypothesized that older, more experienced physicians would be less likely to use ethics consultation in the future. Access the file and generate two graphs to describe the distribution of years of experience—one for physicians who indicated they would use ethics consultation in the future and one for physicians who refused to use ethics consultation. Place the graphs side by side. Is there support for the researchers' assertion? Explain.

2.32 **Time in bankruptcy.** Financially distressed firms can gain protection from their creditors while they restructure by filing for protection under U.S. Bankruptcy Codes. In a *prepackaged bankruptcy,* a firm negotiates a reorganization plan with its creditors prior to filing for bankruptcy. This can result in a much quicker exit from bankruptcy than tradional bankruptcy filings. A study of 49 prepackaged bankruptcies was published in *Financial Management* (Spring, 1995). For each firm, information was collected on the time (in months) in bankruptcy as well as the results of the board of directors' vote on the type of reorganization plan. Three types of plans were studied: "Joint"—a joint exachange offer with prepackaged bankruptcy solicitation; "Prepack"—prepackaged bankruptcy solicitation only; and "None"—no pre-filing vote held. The data for the 49 firms is provided in the accompanying table.

Reorganization Plan	Time in Bankruptcy (months)						
None	3.9	10.1	4.1	3.0	3.2	4.2	
	2.9	2.4	7.8*	2.6*	2.4		
Prepack	1.5	1.0*	1.9	1.3*	4.1	1.1	1.0*
	3.8	1.0*	1.5	1.0	1.4*	1.2*	3.0*
	1.6*	1.4*	1.1*	1.2	1.5*	2.1*	1.4
	1.7	1.4	2.7	1.2	4.1	2.9*	
Joint	1.4	1.2*	1.2	1.5*	1.4	5.2	4.5*
	2.1	3.9*	1.4*	5.4			

Source: Data from B. L. Betker, "An empirical examination of prepackaged bankruptcy," FINANCIAL MANAGEMENT, Vol. 24, No. 1, Spring 1995, p. 6 (Table 2).

a. Construct a stem-and-leaf display for the length of time in bankruptcy for all 49 companies.

b. Summarize the information reflected in the stem-and-leaf display from part **a.** Make a general statement about the length of time in bankruptcy for firms using "prepacks."

c. Select a graphical method that will permit a comparison of the time-in-bankruptcy distributions for the three types or reorganization plans.

d. Firms that were reorganized through a leveraged buyout are identified by an asterisk in the table. Mark these firms on the stem-and-leaf display, part **a,** by circling their bankruptcy times. Do you observe any pattern in the graph? Explain.

2.33 **Phishing attacks to e-mail accounts.** *Phishing* is the term used to describe an attempt to extract personal/financial information (e.g., PIN numbers, credit card information, bank account numbers) from unsuspecting people through fraudulent e-mail. An article in *Chance* (Summer 2007) demonstrates how statistics can help identify phishing attempts and make e-commerce safer. Data from an actual phishing attack against an organization were used to determine whether the attack may have been an "inside job" that originated within the company. The company set up a publicized e-mail account—called a "fraud box"—that enabled employees to notify them if they suspected an e-mail phishing attack. The interarrival times, i.e., the time differences (in seconds), for 267 fraud box e-mail notifications were recorded and saved in the file. *Chance* showed that if there is minimal or no collaboration or collusion from within the company, the interarrival times would have a frequency distribution similar to the one shown in the accompanying figure. Construct a frequency histogram for the interarrival times. Give your opinion on whether the phishing attack against the organization was an "inside job."

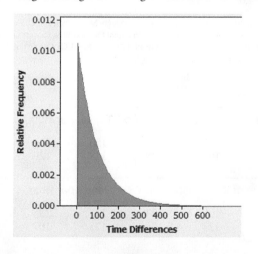

2.34 Made-to-order delivery times. Production processes may be classified as *make-to-stock processes* or *make-to-order processes*. Make-to-stock processes are designed to produce a standardized product that can be sold to customers from the firm's inventory. Make-to-order processes are designed to produce products according to customer specifications (Schroeder, *Operations Management*, 2008). In general, performance of make-to-order processes is measured by delivery time—the time from receipt of an order until the product is delivered to the customer. The accompanying data set is a sample of delivery times (in days) for a particular make-to-order firm last year. The delivery times marked by an asterisk are associated with customers who subsequently placed additional orders with the firm.

50*	64*	56*	43*	64*	82*	65*	49*	32*	63*	44*	71
54*	51*	102	49*	73*	50*	39*	86	33*	95	59*	51*
68											

Concerned that they are losing potential repeat customers because of long delivery times, the management would like to establish a guideline for the maximum tolerable delivery time. Use a graphical method to help suggest a guideline. Explain your reasoning.

2.3 Numerical Measures of Central Tendency

When we speak of a data set, we refer to either a sample or a population. If statistical inference is our goal, we'll wish ultimately to use sample **numerical descriptive measures** to make inferences about the corresponding measures for the population.

As you'll see, a large number of numerical methods are available to describe quantitative data sets. Most of these methods measure one of two data characteristics:

1. The **central tendency** of the set of measurements—that is, the tendency of the data to cluster, or center, about certain numerical values (see Figure 2.14a).
2. The **variability** of the set of measurements—that is, the spread of the data (see Figure 2.14b).

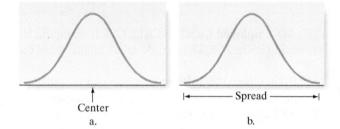

Figure 2.14

Numerical descriptive measures

In this section we concentrate on **measures of central tendency.** In the next section, we discuss measures of variability. The most popular and best-understood measure of central tendency for quantitative data is the arithmetic mean (or simply the mean) of a data set.

> The **mean** of a set of quantitative data is the sum of the measurements divided by the number of measurements contained in the data set.

In everyday terms, the mean is the average value of the data set and is often used to represent a "typical" value. We denote the **mean of a sample** of measurements by $\bar{x}$ (read "x-bar") and represent the formula for its calculation as shown in the box below.

> **Formula for a Sample Mean**
>
> $$\bar{x} = \frac{\sum\limits_{i=1}^{n} x_i}{n}$$
>
> [*Note:* $\sum\limits_{i=1}^{n} x_i = (x_1 + x_2 + \cdots + x_n)$. For more details on this summation notation, see Appendix A.]

Example 2.3	**Problem** Calculate the mean of the following five sample measurements: 5, 3, 8, 5, 6.

Calculating the Sample Mean

Solution Using the definition of sample mean and the summation notation, we find

$$\bar{x} = \frac{\sum_{i=1}^{5} x_i}{5} = \frac{5 + 3 + 8 + 5 + 6}{5} = \frac{27}{5} = 5.4$$

Thus, the mean of this sample is 5.4.

Look Back There is no specific rule for rounding when calculating $\bar{x}$ because $\bar{x}$ is specifically defined to be the sum of all measurements divided by n—that is, it is a specific fraction. When $\bar{x}$ is used for descriptive purposes, it is often convenient to round the calculated value of $\bar{x}$ to the number of significant figures used for the original measurements. When $\bar{x}$ is to be used in other calculations, however, it may be necessary to retain more significant figures.

◼ Now Work Exercise 2.36

Example 2.4	**Problem** Calculate the sample mean for the R&D expenditure percentages of the 50 companies given in Table 2.2 on page 52.

Finding the Mean on a Printout—R&D Expenditures

Solution The mean R&D percentage for the 50 companies is denoted

$$\bar{x} = \frac{\sum_{i=1}^{50} x_i}{50}$$

We employed Excel and XLSTAT to compute the mean. The XLSTAT printout is shown in Figure 2.15. The sample mean, highlighted on the printout, is $\bar{x} = 8.492$.

Look Back Given this information, you can visualize a distribution of R&D percentages centered in the vicinity $\bar{x} = 8.492$. An examination of the relative frequency histogram (Figure 2.10) confirms that $\bar{x}$ does, in fact, fall near the center of the distribution.

Descriptive statistics (Quantitative data):

Statistic	RDPct
No. of observations	50
Minimum	5.2000
Maximum	13.5000
Range	8.3000
1st Quartile	7.1000
Median	8.0500
3rd Quartile	9.5750
Mean	8.4920
Variance (n-1)	3.9228
Standard deviation (n-1)	1.9806

Figure 2.15
XLSTAT numerical descriptive measures for 50 R&D percentages

The sample mean $\bar{x}$ will play an important role in accomplishing our objective of making inferences about populations based on sample information. For this reason, we need to use a different symbol for the *mean of a population*–the mean of the set of measurements on every unit in the population. We use the Greek letter μ (mu) for the population mean.

Symbols for the Sample and Population Mean

In this text, we adopt a general policy of using Greek letters to represent population numerical descriptive measures and Roman letters to represent corresponding descriptive measures for the sample. The symbols for the mean are

$$\bar{x} = \text{Sample mean}$$
$$\mu = \text{Population mean*}$$

We'll often use the sample mean $\bar{x}$ to estimate (make an inference about) the population mean, μ. For example, the percentages of revenues spent on R&D by the population consisting of *all* U.S. companies has a mean equal to some value, μ. Our sample of 50 companies yielded percentages with a mean of $\bar{x} = 8.492$. If, as is usually the case, we don't have access to the measurements for the entire population, we could use $\bar{x}$ as an estimator or approximator for μ. Then we'd need to know something about the reliability of our inference—that is, we'd need to know how accurately we might expect $\bar{x}$ to estimate μ. In Chapter 6, we'll find that this accuracy depends on two factors:

1. The *size of the sample*. The larger the sample, the more accurate the estimate will tend to be.
2. The *variability,* or *spread, of the data*. All other factors remaining constant, the more variable the data, the less accurate the estimate.

Another important measure of central tendency is the *median*.

The **median** of a quantitative data set is the middle number when the measurements are arranged in ascending (or descending) order.

The median is of most value in describing large data sets. If the data set is characterized by a relative frequency histogram (Figure 2.16), the median is the point on the *x*-axis such that half the area under the histogram lies above the median and half lies below. [*Note:* In Section 2.2, we observed that the relative frequency associated with a particular interval on the horizontal axis is proportional to the amount of area under the histogram that lies above the interval.] We denote the *median of a sample* by *m*. Like with the population mean, we use a Greek letter (η) to represent the population median.

Calculating a Sample Median, *m*

Arrange the *n* measurements from smallest to largest.

1. If *n* is odd, *m* is the middle number.
2. If *n* is even, *m* is the mean of the middle two numbers.

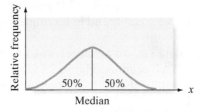

Figure 2.16
Location of the median

---

*The population mean μ is calculated as $\mu = \dfrac{\displaystyle\sum_{i=1}^{N} x_i}{N}$, where N is the population size.

> **Symbols for the Sample and Population Median**
>
> $$m = \text{sample median}$$
>
> $$\eta = \text{population median*}$$

Example 2.5
Computing the Median

Problem Consider the following sample of $n = 7$ measurements: 5, 7, 4, 5, 20, 6, 2.

a. Calculate the median m of this sample.

b. Eliminate the last measurement (the 2) and calculate the median of the remaining $n = 6$ measurements.

Solution

a. The seven measurements in the sample are ranked in ascending order: 2, 4, 5, 5, 6, 7, 20. Because the number of measurements is odd, the median is the middle measurement. Thus, the median of this sample is $m = 5$ (the second 5 listed in the sequence).

b. After removing the 2 from the set of measurements, we rank the sample measurements in ascending order as follows: 4, 5, 5, 6, 7, 20. Now the number of measurements is even, so we average the middle two measurements. The median is $m = (5 + 6)/2 = 5.5$.

Look Back When the sample size n is even and the two middle numbers are different (as in part **b**), exactly half of the measurements will fall below the calculated median m. However, when n is odd (as in part **a**), the percentage of measurements that fall below m is approximately 50%. This approximation improves as n increases.

■ **Now Work Exercise 2.35**

In certain situations, the median may be a better measure of central tendency than the mean. In particular, the median is less sensitive than the mean to extremely large or small measurements. Note, for instance, that all but one of the measurements in part **a** of Example 2.5 center about $x = 5$. The single relatively large measurement, $x = 20$, does not affect the value of the median, 5, but it causes the mean, $\bar{x} = 7$, to lie to the right of most of the measurements.

As another example of data for which the central tendency is better described by the median than the mean, consider the salaries of professional athletes (e.g., National Basketball Association players). The presence of just a few athletes (e.g., LeBron James) with extremely high salaries will affect the mean more than the median. Thus, the median will provide a more accurate picture of the typical salary for the professional league. The mean could exceed the vast majority of the sample measurements (salaries), making it a misleading measure of central tendency.

Example 2.6
Finding the Median on a Printout—R&D Expenditures

Problem Calculate the median for the 50 R&D percentages given in Table 2.2 on page 52. Compare the median to the mean found in Example 2.4.

Solution For this large data set, we again resort to a computer analysis. The median is highlighted on the XLSTAT printout, Figure 2.15. You can see that the median is 8.05. This value implies that half of the 50 R&D percentages in the data set fall below 8.05 and half lie above 8.05.

Note that the mean (8.492) for these data is larger than the median. This fact indicates that the data are **skewed** to the right–that is, there are more extreme

---

*The population median η is calculated like the sample median, but with all N observations in the population arranged from smallest to largest.

measurements in the right tail of the distribution than in the left tail (recall the histogram in Figure 2.10).

Look Back In general, extreme values (large or small) affect the mean more than the median because these values are used explicitly in the calculation of the mean. On the other hand, the median is not affected directly by extreme measurements because only the middle measurement (or two middle measurements) is explicitly used to calculate the median. Consequently, if measurements are pulled toward one end of the distribution (as with the R&D percentages), the mean will shift toward that tail more than the median.

A data set is said to be **skewed** if one tail of the distribution has more extreme observations than the other tail.

A comparison of the mean and the median gives us a general method for detecting skewness in data sets, as shown in the next box. With *rightward skewed* data, the right tail (high end) of the distribution has more extreme observations. These few, but large, measurements tend to pull the mean away from the median toward the right; that is, rightward skewness typically indicates that the mean is greater than the median. Conversely, with *leftward skewed* data, the left tail (low end) of the distribution has more extreme observations. These few, but small, measurements also tend to pull the mean away from the median but toward the left; consequently, leftward skewness typically implies that the mean is smaller than the median.

Detecting Skewness by Comparing the Mean and the Median

If the data set is skewed to the right, then typically the median is less than the mean.

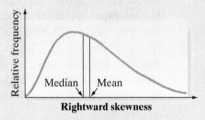

If the data set is symmetric, the mean equals the median.

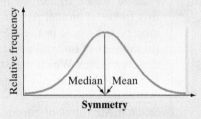

If the data set is skewed to the left, then typically the mean is less than (to the left of) the median.

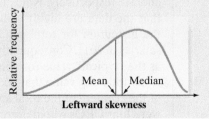

A third measure of central tendency is the *mode* of a set of measurements.

> The **mode** is the measurement that occurs most frequently in the data set.

Example 2.7	
Finding the Mode	**Problem** Each of 10 taste testers rated a new brand of barbecue sauce on a 10-point scale, where 1 = awful and 10 = excellent. Find the mode for the 10 ratings shown below.

8 7 9 6 8 10 9 9 5 7

Solution Because 9 occurs most often, the mode of the 10 taste-ratings is 9.

Look Back Note that the data are actually qualitative in nature (e.g., "awful," "excellent"). The mode is particularly useful for describing qualitative data. The modal category is simply the category (or class) that occurs most often.

■ Now Work Exercise 2.39

Because it emphasizes data concentration, the mode is used with quantitative data sets to locate the region in which much of the data are concentrated. A retailer of men's clothing would be interested in the modal neck size and sleeve length of potential customers. The modal income class of the laborers in the United States is of interest to the Labor Department.

For some quantitative data sets, the mode may not be very meaningful. For example, consider the percentages of revenues spent on R&D by 50 companies, Table 2.2. A reexamination of the data reveals that three of the measurements are repeated three times: 6.5%, 6.9%, and 8.2%. Thus, there are three modes in the sample, and none is particularly useful as a measure of central tendency.

A more meaningful measure can be obtained from a relative frequency histogram for quantitative data. The class interval containing the largest relative frequency is called the **modal class.** Several definitions exist for locating the position of the mode within a modal class, but the simplest is to define the mode as the midpoint of the modal class. For example, examine the relative frequency histogram for the price quote processing times in Figure 2.12. You can see that the modal class is the interval (3.0–4.0). The mode (the midpoint) is 3.5. This modal class (and the mode itself) identifies the area in which the data are most concentrated, and in that sense it is a measure of central tendency. However, for most applications involving quantitative data, the mean and median provide more descriptive information than the mode.

Example 2.8 ◉	
Comparing the Mean, Median, and Mode— CEO Salaries	**Problem** Refer to *Forbes* magazine's "Executive Compensation Scoreboard," which lists the total annual pay for CEOs at the 500 largest U.S. firms. The data for the 2011 scoreboard, saved in the **CEO** file, includes the quantitative variables total annual pay (in millions of dollars) and age (in years). Find the mean, median, and mode for both of these variables. Which measure of central tendency is better for describing the distribution of total annual pay? Age?

Solution Measures of central tendency for the two variables were obtained using SPSS. The means, medians, and modes are displayed at the top of the SPSS printout, Figure 2.17.

For total annual pay, the mean, median, and mode are $9.25 million, $6.10 million, and $0, respectively. Note that the mean is much greater than the median, indicating that the data are highly skewed right. This rightward skewness (graphically shown on the histogram for total pay in Figure 2.17) is due to several exceptionally high CEO salaries in 2011. Consequently, we would probably want to use the median, $6.10 million, as the "typical" value for annual pay for CEOs at the 500 largest firms. The mode of $0 is the total pay value that occurs most often in the data set, but it is not very descriptive of the "center" of the total annual pay distribution. The mode reflects the fact that there were four CEOs who deferred their 2011 pay until the next year.

Statistics

		CEO Pay ($mil)	Age (years)
N	Valid	478	500
	Missing	22	0
Mean		9.24692	56.62
Median		6.10000	56.00
Mode		.000	56

Figure 2.17

SPSS analysis of total 2011 pay and age for 500 CEOs

For age, the mean, median, and mode are 56.6, 56, and 56 years, respectively. All three values are nearly the same, which is typical of symmetric distributions. From the age histogram on the right in Figure 2.17, you can see that the age distribution is nearly symmetric. Consequently, any of the three measures of central tendency could be used to describe the "middle" of the age distribution.

Look Back The choice of which measure of central tendency to use will depend on the properties of the data set analyzed and on the application. Consequently, it is vital that you understand how the mean, median, and mode are computed.

◼ **Now Work Exercise 2.44a, b**

Exercises 2.35–2.55

Learning the Mechanics

2.35 Calculate the mean and median of the following grade point
NW averages:

$$3.2 \quad 2.5 \quad 2.1 \quad 3.7 \quad 2.8 \quad 2.0$$

2.36 Calculate the mean for samples where
NW
a. $n = 10$, $\sum x = 85$
b. $n = 16$, $\sum x = 400$
c. $n = 45$, $\sum x = 35$
d. $n = 18$, $\sum x = 242$

2.37 Explain how the relationship between the mean and median provides information about the symmetry or skewness of the data's distribution.

2.38 Explain the difference between the calculation of the median for an odd and an even number of measurements. Construct one data set consisting of five measurements and another consisting of six measurements for which the medians are equal.

2.39 Calculate the mode, mean, and median of the following data:
NW

$$18 \quad 10 \quad 15 \quad 13 \quad 17 \quad 15 \quad 12 \quad 15 \quad 18 \quad 16 \quad 11$$

2.40 Calculate the mean, median, and mode for each of the following samples:
a. $7, -2, 3, 3, 0, 4$
b. $2, 3, 5, 3, 2, 3, 4, 3, 5, 1, 2, 3, 4$
c. $51, 50, 47, 50, 48, 41, 59, 68, 45, 37$

2.41 Describe how the mean compares to the median for a distribution as follows:
  a. Skewed to the left
  b. Skewed to the right
  c. Symmetric

⚙ Applet Exercise 2.1

Use the applet entitled *Mean versus Median* to find the mean and median of each of the three data sets in Exercise 2.40. For each data set, set the lower limit to a number less than all of the data, set the upper limit to a number greater than all of the data, and then click on *Update*. Click on the approximate location of each data item on the number line. You can get rid of a point by dragging it to the trash can. To clear the graph between data sets, simply click on the trash can.

  a. Compare the means and medians generated by the applet to those you calculated by hand in Exercise 2.40. If there are differences, explain why the applet might give values slightly different from the hand calculations.
  b. Despite providing only approximate values of the mean and median of a data set, describe some advantages of using the applet to find these values.

⚙ Applet Exercise 2.2

Use the applet *Mean versus Median* to illustrate your descriptions in Exercise 2.41. For each part **a, b,** and **c,** create a data set with 10 items that has the given property. Using the applet, verify that the mean and median have the relationship you described in Exercise 2.41.

⚙ Applet Exercise 2.3

Use the applet *Mean versus Median* to study the effect that an extreme value has on the difference between the mean and median. Begin by setting appropriate limits and plotting the given data on the number line provided in the applet.

  0 6 7 7 8 8 8 9 9 10

  a. Describe the shape of the distribution and record the value of the mean and median. Based on the shape of the distribution, do the mean and median have the relationship that you would expect?
  b. Replace the extreme value of 0 with 2, then 4, and then 6. Record the mean and median each time. Describe what is happening to the mean as 0 is replaced by higher numbers. What is happening to the median? How is the difference between the mean and the median changing?
  c. Now replace 0 with 8. What values does the applet give you for the mean and the median? Explain why the mean and the median should be the same.

Applying the Concepts—Basic

2.42 **Performance of stock screeners.** Investment companies provide their clients with automated tools—called *stock screeners*—to help them select a portfolio of stocks to invest in. The American Association of Individual Investors (AAII) provides statistics on stock screeners at its Web site, www.aaii.com. The next table lists the annualized percentage return on investment (as compared to the Standard & Poor's 500 Index) for 13 randomly selected stock screeners. (*Note:* A negative annualized return reflects a stock portfolio that performed worse than the S&P 500.)

9.0 −.1 −1.6 14.6 16.0 7.7 19.9 9.8 3.2 24.8 17.6 10.7 9.1

  a. Compute the mean for the data set. Interpret its value.
  b. Compute the median for the data set. Interpret its value.

2.43 **U.S. wine export markets.** The data in the next table, compiled by the Center for International Trade Development (CITD), provide a listing of the top 30 U.S. export markets for sparkling wines. Descriptive statistics for the amount exported (thousands of dollars) and 3-year percentage change for the 30 countries are shown in the Minitab printout below.

Descriptive Statistics: EXPORT, CHANGE

Variable	N	N*	Mean	StDev	Minimum	Q1	Median	Q3	Maximum	IQR
EXPORT	30	0	653	1113	70	105	231	523	4952	418
CHANGE	28	2	481	1098	−49	21	156	499	5750	478

Top 30 U.S. Sparkling Wine Export Markets

Country	Export ($ Thousands)	3-Year Change (%)
Canada	4952	71.9
Japan	3714	−16.9
Mexico	2104	143.2
Cayman Islands	1576	280.7
United Kingdom	1041	465.8
Netherlands	807	550.8
Germany	645	658.8
Korea	482	20.5
France	449	−48.7
Russia	351	5750
Jamaica	350	21.5
China	339	539.6
Taiwan	309	505.9
Colombia	272	159
Hong Kong	232	114.8
Aruba	229	−31.6
Australia	225	1223.5
Haiti	191	478.8
Switzerland	181	70.8
Trinidad & Tobago	175	1490.9
Costa Rica	170	NA
Panama	126	447.8
Slovenia	106	NA
Neth. Antilles	103	−41.8
Bahamas	92	−20.7
New Zealand	91	193.5
Honduras	74	51
Philippines	72	242.9
Greece	71	153.6
Belgium	70	−16.7

Source: "Best Export Markets for U.S. Wines, 2008," *Center for International Trade Development* (Table 11.A-3). Copyright © 2008 by Center for International Trade Development. Reprinted with permission.

  a. Locate the mean amount exported on the printout and practically interpret its value.
  b. Locate the median amount exported on the printout and practically interpret its value.
  c. Locate the mean 3-year percentage change on the printout and practically interpret its value.
  d. Locate the median 3-year percentage change on the printout and practically interpret its value.

2.44 **Surface roughness of oil field pipe.** Oil field pipes are internally coated in order to prevent corrosion. Researchers at the University of Louisiana, Lafayette, investigated the influence that coating may have on the surface roughness of oil field pipes (*Anti-corrosion Methods and Materials,* Vol. 50, 2003). A scanning probe instrument was used to measure the surface roughness of each in a sample of 20 sections of coated interior pipe. The data (in micrometers) are provided in the table.

1.72	2.50	2.16	2.13	1.06	2.24	2.31	2.03	1.09	1.40
2.57	2.64	1.26	2.05	1.19	2.13	1.27	1.51	2.41	1.95

Source: Farshed, F., & Pesacreta, T. "Coated pipe interior surface roughness as measured by three scanning probe instruments." *Anti-corrosion Methods and Materials.* Vol. 50, No. 1, 2003 (Table III).

NW **a.** Find and interpret the mean of the sample.

NW **b.** Find and interpret the median of the sample.

c. Which measure of central tendency—the mean or the median—best describes the surface roughness of the sampled pipe sections? Explain.

2.45 **Top research universities.** Each year, the Center for Measuring University Performance produces a report on America's top research universities. The total expenditures (in thousands of dollars) for research for the top 20 ranked universities from the *2010 Annual Report* are listed in the table.

RESRCH

Rank	Institution	Expenditures ($ thousands)	Type
1	Johns Hopkins University	1,680,927	Private
2	University of California–San Francisco	885,182	Public
3	University of Wisconsin	881,777	Public
4	University of Michigan	876,390	Public
5	University of California–Los Angeles	871,478	Public
6	University of California–San Diego	842,027	Public
7	Duke University	766,906	Private
8	University of Washington	765,135	Public
9	University of Pennsylvania	708,244	Private
10	Ohio State University	702,592	Public
11	Stanford University	688,225	Private
12	University of Minnesota	682,662	Public
13	Massachusetts Institute of Technology	659,626	Private
14	University of California–Davis	642,519	Public
15	Pennsylvania State University	620,432	Public
16	University of Pittsburgh	595,627	Public
17	University of California–Berkeley	591,770	Public
18	University of Florida	584,170	Public
19	Texas A&M University	582,365	Public
20	Washington University–St. Louis	563,967	Private

Source: Based on Elizabeth D. Capaldi, John V. Lombardi, Craig W. Abbey, and Diane D. Craig, THE TOP AMERICAN RESEARCH UNIVERSITIES: 2010 Annual Report. © The Center for Measuring University Performance.

a. Find the mean of the research expenditures for the top 20 ranked universities. Interpret this value.

b. Find the median of the research expenditures for the top 20 ranked universities. Interpret this value.

c. Consider a university president who is interested in the distribution of research expenditures of all American universities. Would the mean, part **a**, be a good measure of the center of this distribution? Explain.

2.46 **Corporate sustainability of CPA firms.** Refer to the *Business and Society* (March 2011) study on the sustainability behaviors of CPA corporations, Exercise 2.23 (p. 59). Recall that the level of support for corporate sustainability (measured on a quantitative scale ranging from 0 to 160 points) was obtained for each 992 senior managers at CPA firms. Numerical measures of central tendency for level of support are shown in the accompanying Minitab printout.

CORSUS

Descriptive Statistics: Support

```
                                                        N for
Variable    N    Mean  Minimum  Median  Maximum  Mode   Mode
Support    992  67.755   0.000  68.000  155.000    64     20
```

a. Locate the mean on the printout. Comment on the accuracy of the statement: "On average, the level of support for corporate sustainability for the 992 senior managers was 67.76 points."

b. Locate the median on the printout. Comment on the accuracy of the statement: "Half of the 992 senior managers reported a level of support for corporate sustainability below 68 points."

c. Locate the mode on the printout. Comment on the accuracy of the statement: "Most of the 992 senior managers reported a level of support for corporate sustainability below 64 points."

d. Based on the values of the measures of central tendency, make a statement about the type of skewness (if any) that exists in the distribution of 992 support levels. Check your answer by examining the histogram shown in Exercise 2.23.

Applying the Concepts—Intermediate

2.47 **Is honey a cough remedy?** Refer to the *Archives of Pediatrics and Adolescent Medicine* (Dec. 2007) study of honey as a remedy for coughing, Exercise 2.30 (p. 61). Recall that the 105 ill children in the sample were randomly divided into three groups: those who received a dosage of an over-the-counter cough medicine (DM), those who received a dosage of honey (H), and those who received no dosage (control group). The coughing improvement scores (as determined by the children's parents) for the patients are reproduced in the accompanying table.

HCOUGH

a. Find the median improvement score for the honey dosage group.

Honey Dosage:	12 11 15 11 10 13 10 4 15 16 9 14 10 6 10 8 11 12 12 8 12 9 11 15 10 15 9 13 8 12 10 8 9 5 12
DM Dosage:	4 6 9 4 7 7 7 9 12 10 11 6 3 4 9 12 7 6 8 12 12 4 12 13 7 10 13 9 4 4 10 15 9
No Dosage (Control):	5 8 6 1 0 8 12 8 7 7 1 6 7 7 12 7 9 7 9 5 11 9 5 6 8 8 6 7 10 9 4 8 7 3 1 4 3

Source: Based on Paul, I. M., et al. "Effect of honey, dextromethorphan, and no treatment on nocturnal cough and sleep quality for coughing children and their parents." *Archives of Pediatrics and Adolescent Medicine,* Vol. 161, No. 12. Dec. 2007 (data simulated).

b. Find the median improvement score for the DM dosage group.

c. Find the median improvement score for the control group.

d. Based on the results, parts **a–c**, what conclusions can pediatric researchers draw? (We show how to support these conclusions with a measure of reliability in subsequent chapters.)

2.48 **Crude oil biodegradation.** Refer to the *Journal of Petroleum Geology* (April 2010) study of the environmental factors associated with biodegradation in crude oil reservoirs, Exercise 2.29 (p. 61). Recall that amount of dioxide (milligrams/liter) and presence/absence of crude oil was determined for each of 16 water specimens collected from a mine reservoir. The data are repeated in the accompanying table.

BIODEG

Dioxide Amount	Crude Oil Present
3.3	No
0.5	Yes
1.3	Yes
0.4	Yes
0.1	No
4.0	No
0.3	No
0.2	Yes
2.4	No
2.4	No
1.4	No
0.5	Yes
0.2	Yes
4.0	No
4.0	No
4.0	No

Source: Based on A. Permanyer, J. L. R. Gallego, M. A. Caja, and D. Dessort, "Crude Oil Biodegradation and Environmental Factors at the Riutort Oil Shale Mine, SE Pyrenees." JOURNAL OF PETROLEUM GEOLOGY, Vol. 33, No. 2, April 2010, Table 1.

a. Find the mean dioxide level of the 16 water specimens. Interpret this value.

b. Find the median dioxide level of the 16 water specimens. Interpret this value.

c. Find the mode of the 16 dioxide levels. Interpret this value.

d. Find the median dioxide level of the 10 water specimens with no crude oil present.

e. Find the median dioxide level of the 6 water specimens with crude oil present.

f. Compare the results, parts **d** and **e**. Make a statement about the association between dioxide level and presence/absence of crude oil.

2.49 **Symmetric or skewed?** Would you expect the data sets described below to possess relative frequency distributions that are symmetric, skewed to the right, or skewed to the left? Explain.

a. The salaries of all persons employed by a large university

b. The grades on an easy test

c. The grades on a difficult test

d. The amounts of time students in your class studied last week

e. The ages of automobiles on a used-car lot

f. The amounts of time spent by students on a difficult examination (maximum time is 50 minutes)

2.50 **Ranking driving performance of professional golfers.** A group of Northeastern University researchers developed a new method for ranking the total driving performance of golfers on the Professional Golf Association (PGA) tour (*The Sport Journal*, Winter 2007). The method requires knowing a golfer's average driving distance (yards) and driving accuracy (percent of drives that land in the fairway). The values of these two variables are used to compute a driving performance index. Data for the top 40 PGA golfers (as ranked by the new method) are saved in the accompanying file. The first five and last five observations are listed in the table below.

PGA

Rank	Player	Driving Distance (yards)	Driving Accuracy (%)	Driving Performance Index
1	Woods	316.1	54.6	3.58
2	Perry	304.7	63.4	3.48
3	Gutschewski	310.5	57.9	3.27
4	Wetterich	311.7	56.6	3.18
5	Hearn	295.2	68.5	2.82
⋮	⋮	⋮	⋮	⋮
36	Senden	291	66	1.31
37	Mickelson	300	58.7	1.30
38	Watney	298.9	59.4	1.26
39	Trahan	295.8	61.8	1.23
40	Pappas	309.4	50.6	1.17

Source: Based on Frederick Wiseman, Ph.D., Mohamed Habibullah, Ph.D., and Mustafa Yilmaz, Ph.D, "Ranking Driving Performance on the PGA Tour." SPORTS JOURNAL, Vol. 10, No. 1, Winter 2007 (Table 2).

a. Find the mean, median, and mode for the 40 driving performance index values.

b. Interpret each of the measures of central tendency, part **a.**

c. Use the results, part **a,** to make a statement about the type of skewness in the distribution of driving performance indexes. Support your statement with a graph.

2.51 **Semester hours taken by CPA candidates.** In order to become a certified public accountant (CPA), you must pass the Uniform CPA Exam. Many states require a minimum of 150 semester hours of college education before a candidate can sit for the CPA exam. However, traditionally, colleges only require 128 semester hours for an undergraduate degree. A study of whether the "extra" 22 hours of college credit is warranted for CPA candidates was published in the *Journal of Accounting and Public Policy* (Spring 2002). For one aspect of the study, researchers sampled over 100,000 first-time candidates for the CPA exam and recorded the total semester hours of college credit for each candidate. The mean and median for the data set were 141.31 and 140 hours, respectively. Interpret these values. Make a statement about the type of skewness, if any, that exists in the distribution of total semester hours.

2.52 **Doctors and ethics.** Refer to the *Journal of Medical Ethics* (Vol. 32, 2006) study of physicians' use of ethics consultation, Exercise 2.31 (p. 62). In addition to the qualitative variable, *use of ethics consultation in the future* ("yes" or "no"), one of the quantitative variables measured in the survey of physicians was *length of time in practice* (i.e., years of experience). Recall that the medical researchers hypothesized that physicians who refused to use ethics consultation in the future would tend to be older, more experienced physicians.

ETHICS

a. Access the data file and find the mean, median, and mode for the *length of time in practice* (i.e., years of experience) variable. Give a practical interpretation of each of these measures of central tendency.

b. Consider only the physicians who would refuse to use ethics consultation in the future. Find the mean, median, and mode for the *length of time in practice* for these physicians. Practically interpret the results.

c. Repeat part **b** for physicians who would use ethics consultation in the future.

d. Use the results, parts **b** and **c,** to comment on the medical researchers' theory.

Applying the Concepts—Advanced

2.53 Time in bankruptcy. Refer to the *Financial Management* (Spring 1995) study of prepackaged bankruptcy filings, Exercise 2.32 (p. 62). Recall that each of 49 firms that negotiated a reorganization plan with its creditors prior to filing for bankruptcy was classified in one of three categories: joint exchange offer with prepack, prepack solicitation only, and no prefiling vote held. Consider the quantitative variable length of time in bankruptcy (months) saved in the accompanying file. Is it reasonable to use a single number (e.g., mean or median) to describe the center of the time-in-bankruptcy distributions? Or should three "centers" be calculated, one for each of the three categories of prepack firms? Explain.

2.54 Active nuclear power plants. The U.S. Energy Information Administration monitors all nuclear power plants operating in the United States. The next table lists the number of active nuclear power plants operating in each of a sample of 20 states.

a. Find the mean, median, and mode of this data set.

b. Eliminate the largest value from the data set and repeat part **a.** What effect does dropping this measurement have on the measures of central tendency found in part **a**?

c. Arrange the 20 values in the table from lowest to highest. Next, eliminate the lowest two values and the highest two values from the data set and find the mean of the remaining data values. The result is called a *10% trimmed mean,* because it is calculated after removing the highest 10% and the lowest 10% of the data values. What advantages does a trimmed mean have over the regular arithmetic mean?

State	Number of Power Plants	State	Number of Power Plants
Alabama	5	New Hampshire	1
Arizona	2	New York	6
California	4	North Carolina	5
Florida	5	Ohio	3
Georgia	4	Pennsylvania	9
Illinois	11	South Carolina	7
Kansas	1	Tennessee	3
Louisiana	2	Texas	4
Massachusetts	1	Vermont	1
Mississippi	1	Wisconsin	3

Source: Data from STATISTICAL ABSTRACT OF THE UNITED STATES, 2010 (Table 907). U.S. Energy Information Administration, Electric Power Annual.

2.55 Professional athletes' salaries. The salaries of superstar professional athletes receive much attention in the media. The multimillion-dollar long-term contract is now commonplace among this elite group. Nevertheless, rarely does a season pass without negotiations between one or more of the players' associations and team owners for additional salary and fringe benefits for *all* players in their particular sports.

a. If a players' association wanted to support its argument for higher "average" salaries, which measure of central tendency do you think it should use? Why?

b. To refute the argument, which measure of central tendency should the owners apply to the players' salaries? Why?

2.4 Numerical Measures of Variability

Measures of central tendency provide only a partial description of a quantitative data set. The description is incomplete without a **measure of the variability,** or **spread,** of the data set. Knowledge of the data's variability along with its center can help us visualize the shape of a data set as well as its extreme values.

For example, suppose we are comparing the profit margin per construction job (as a percentage of the total bid price) for 100 construction jobs for each of two cost estimators working for a large construction company. The histograms for the two sets of 100 profit margin measurements are shown in Figure 2.18. If you examine the two histograms, you will notice that both data sets are symmetric with equal modes, medians, and means. However, cost estimator A (Figure 2.18a) has profit margins spread with almost equal relative frequency over the measurement classes, while cost estimator B (Figure 2.18b) has profit margins clustered about the center of the distribution. Thus, estimator B's profit margins are *less variable* than estimator A's. Consequently, you can see that we need a measure of variability as well as a measure of central tendency to describe a data set.

Perhaps the simplest measure of the variability of a quantitative data set is its *range*.

Figure 2.18

Profit margin histograms for two cost estimators

a. Cost estimator A

b. Cost estimator B

> The **range** of a quantitative data set is equal to the largest measurement minus the smallest measurement.

The range is easy to compute and easy to understand, but it is a rather insensitive measure of data variation when the data sets are large. This is because two data sets can have the same range and be vastly different with respect to data variation. This phenomenon is demonstrated in Figure 2.18. Although the ranges are equal and all central tendency measures are the same for these two symmetric data sets, there is an obvious difference between the two sets of measurements. The difference is that estimator B's profit margins tend to be more stable—that is, to pile up or to cluster about the center of the data set. In contrast, estimator A's profit margins are more spread out over the range, indicating a higher incidence of some high profit margins but also a greater risk of losses. Thus, even though the ranges are equal, the profit margin record of estimator A is more variable than that of estimator B, indicating a distinct difference in their cost-estimating characteristics.

Let's see if we can find a measure of data variation that is more sensitive than the range. Consider the two samples in Table 2.5: Each has five measurements. (We have ordered the numbers for convenience.)

Note that both samples have a mean of 3 and that we have also calculated the distance and direction, or *deviation*, between each measurement and the mean. What information do these deviations contain? If they tend to be large in magnitude, as in sample 1, the data are spread out, or highly variable, as shown in Figure 2.19a. If the deviations are mostly small, as in sample 2, the data are clustered around the mean, $\bar{x}$, and therefore do not exhibit much variability, as shown in Figure 2.19b. You can see that these deviations provide information about the variability of the sample measurements.

The next step is to condense the information in these deviations into a single numerical measure of variability. Averaging the deviations from $\bar{x}$ won't help because the negative and positive deviations cancel; that is, the sum of the deviations (and thus the average deviation) is always equal to zero.

Table 2.5	Two Hypothetical Data Sets	
	Sample 1	Sample 2
Measurements	$1, 2, 3, 4, 5$	$2, 3, 3, 3, 4$
Mean	$\bar{x} = \dfrac{1 + 2 + 3 + 4 + 5}{5} = \dfrac{15}{5} = 3$	$\bar{x} = \dfrac{2 + 3 + 3 + 3 + 4}{5} = \dfrac{15}{5} = 3$
Deviations of measurement values from $\bar{x}$	$(1 - 3), (2 - 3), (3 - 3), (4 - 3),$ $(5 - 3),$ or $-2, -1, 0, 1, 2$	$(2 - 3), (3 - 3), (3 - 3), (3 - 3),$ $(4 - 3),$ or $-1, 0, 0, 0, 1$

Figure 2.19

Dot plots for two data sets

a. Sample 1   b. Sample 2

Two methods come to mind for dealing with the fact that positive and negative deviations from the mean cancel. The first is to treat all the deviations as though they were positive, ignoring the sign of the negative deviations. We won't pursue this line of thought because the resulting measure of variability (the mean of the absolute values of the deviations) presents analytical difficulties beyond the scope of this text. A second method of eliminating the minus signs associated with the deviations is to square them. The quantity we can calculate from the squared deviations will provide a meaningful description of the variability of a data set and present fewer analytical difficulties in inference making.

To use the squared deviations calculated from a data set, we first calculate the *sample variance*.

> The **sample variance** for a sample of n measurements is equal to the sum of the squared deviations from the mean divided by $(n - 1)$. The symbol s^2 is used to represent the sample variance.

> **Formula for the Sample Variance**
>
> $$s^2 = \frac{\sum_{i=1}^{n}(x_i - \bar{x})^2}{n - 1}$$
>
> *Note:* A shortcut formula for calculating s^2 is
>
> $$s^2 = \frac{\sum_{i=1}^{n}x_i^2 - \frac{\left(\sum_{i=1}^{n}x_i\right)^2}{n}}{n - 1}$$

Referring to the two samples in Table 2.5, you can calculate the variance for sample 1 as follows:

$$s^2 = \frac{(1 - 3)^2 + (2 - 3)^2 + (3 - 3)^2 + (4 - 3)^2 + (5 - 3)^2}{5 - 1}$$

$$= \frac{4 + 1 + 0 + 1 + 4}{4} = 2.5$$

The second step in finding a meaningful measure of data variability is to calculate the *standard deviation* of the data set.

> The **sample standard deviation,** s, is defined as the positive square root of the sample variance, s^2. Thus, $s = \sqrt{s^2}$.

The population variance, denoted by the symbol σ^2 (sigma squared), is the average of the squared distances of the measurements on *all* units in the population from the mean, μ, and σ (sigma) is the square root of this quantity. Because we rarely, if ever, have access to the population data, we do not compute σ^2 or σ. We simply denote these two quantities by their respective symbols.*

*The population variance, σ^2, is calculated as $\sigma^2 = \dfrac{\sum_{i=1}^{N}(x_i - \mu)^2}{N}$, where N is the size of the population.

> **Symbols for Variance and Standard Deviation**
>
> s^2 = Sample variance
>
> s = Sample standard deviation
>
> σ^2 = Population variance
>
> σ = Population standard deviation

Notice that, unlike the variance, the standard deviation is expressed in the original units of measurement. For example, if the original measurements are in dollars, the variance is expressed in the peculiar units "dollars squared," but the standard deviation is expressed in dollars. Consequently, you can think of s as a "typical" distance of an observation x from its mean, $\bar{x}$.

You may wonder why we use the divisor $(n - 1)$ instead of n when calculating the sample variance. Wouldn't using n be more logical so that the sample variance would be the average squared deviation from the mean? The trouble is that using n tends to produce an underestimate of the population variance, σ^2, so we use $(n - 1)$ in the denominator to provide the appropriate correction for this tendency.* Because sample statistics such as s^2 are primarily used to estimate population parameters such as σ^2, $(n - 1)$ is preferred to n when defining the sample variance.

Example 2.9	

Computing Measures of Variation

Problem Calculate the variance and standard deviation of the following sample: 2, 3, 3, 3, 4.

Solution If you calculate the values of s and s^2 using the formula in the box on page 75, you first need to compute $\bar{x}$. From the table below, we see that $\Sigma x = 15$. Thus, $\bar{x} = \dfrac{\Sigma x}{n} = \dfrac{15}{5} = 3$. Now, for each measurement, find $(x - \bar{x})$ and $(x - \bar{x})^2$, as shown.

x	$(x - \bar{x})$	$(x - \bar{x})^2$
2	-1	1
3	0	0
3	0	0
3	0	0
4	1	1
$\Sigma x = 15$		$\Sigma(x - \bar{x})^2 = 2$

Then we use†

$$s^2 = \frac{\sum_{i=1}^{n}(x - \bar{x})^2}{n - 1} = \frac{2}{5 - 1} = \frac{2}{4} = .5$$

$$s = \sqrt{.5} = .71$$

Look Ahead As the sample size n increases, these calculations can become very tedious. As the next example shows, we can use the computer to find s^2 and s.

◼ **Now Work Exercise 2.57**

---

*Appropriate here means that s^2 with the divisor $(n - 1)$ is an *unbiased estimator* of σ^2. We define and discuss *unbiasedness* of estimators in Chapter 5.

†When calculating s^2, how many decimal places should you carry? Although there are no rules for the rounding procedure, it's reasonable to retain twice as many decimal places in s^2 as you ultimately wish to have in s. If you wish to calculate s to the nearest hundredth (two decimal places), for example, you should calculate s^2 to the nearest ten-thousandth (four decimal places).

Example	2.10

Finding Measures of Variation on a Printout— R&D Expenditures

Problem Use the computer to find the sample variance s^2 and the sample standard deviation s for the 50 companies' percentages of revenues spent on R&D, given in Table 2.2 (p. 52).

Solution The XLSTAT printout describing the R&D percentage data is reproduced in Figure 2.20. The variance and standard deviation, highlighted on the printout, are $s^2 = 3.9228$ and $s = 1.9806$. The value $s = 1.98$ represents a typical deviation of an R&D percentage from the sample mean, $\bar{x} = 8.49\%$. We have more to say about the interpretation of s in the next section.

■ **Now Work Exercise 2.67**

Descriptive statistics (Quantitative data):

Statistic	RDPct
No. of observations	50
Minimum	5.2000
Maximum	13.5000
Range	8.3000
1st Quartile	7.1000
Median	8.0500
3rd Quartile	9.5750
Mean	8.4920
Variance (n-1)	3.9228
Standard deviation (n-1)	1.9806

Figure 2.20

XLSTAT numerical descriptive measures for 50 R&D percentages

You now know that the standard deviation measures the variability of a set of data. The larger the standard deviation, the more variable the data. The smaller the standard deviation, the less variable the data. But how can we practically interpret the standard deviation and use it to make inferences? This is the topic of Section 2.5.

Exercises 2.56–2.70

Learning the Mechanics

2.56 Answer the following questions about variability of data sets:
  a. What is the primary disadvantage of using the range to compare the variability of data sets?
  b. Describe the sample variance using words rather than a formula. Do the same with the population variance.
  c. Can the variance of a data set ever be negative? Explain. Can the variance ever be smaller than the standard deviation? Explain.

2.57 Calculate the range, variance, and standard deviation for
  the following samples:
  a. $4, 2, 1, 0, 1$
  b. $1, 6, 2, 2, 3, 0, 3$
  c. $8, -2, 1, 3, 5, 4, 4, 1, 3, 3$
  d. $0, 2, 0, 0, -1, 1, -2, 1, 0, -1, 1, -1, 0, -3, -2, -1, 0, 1$

2.58 Calculate the variance and standard deviation for samples where
  a. $n = 10, \Sigma x^2 = 84, \Sigma x = 20$
  b. $n = 40, \Sigma x^2 = 380, \Sigma x = 100$
  c. $n = 20, \Sigma x^2 = 18, \Sigma x = 17$

2.59 Compute $\bar{x}$, s^2, and s for each of the following data sets. If appropriate, specify the units in which your answer is expressed.
  a. $3, 1, 10, 10, 4$
  b. 8 feet, 10 feet, 32 feet, 5 feet
  c. $-1, -4, -3, 1, -4, -4$
  d. $\frac{1}{5}$ ounce, $\frac{1}{5}$ ounce, $\frac{1}{5}$ ounce, $\frac{2}{5}$ ounce, $\frac{1}{5}$ ounce, $\frac{4}{5}$ ounce

2.60 Calculate the range, variance, and standard deviation for the following samples:
  a. $39, 42, 40, 37, 41$
  b. $100, 4, 7, 96, 80, 3, 1, 10, 2$
  c. $100, 4, 7, 30, 80, 30, 42, 2$

2.61 Using only integers between 0 and 10, construct two data sets with at least 10 observations each that have the same range but different means. Construct a dot plot for each of your data sets, and mark the mean of each data set on its dot diagram.

2.62 Using only integers between 0 and 10, construct two data sets with at least 10 observations each so that the two sets have the same mean but different variances. Construct dot plots for each of your data sets and mark the mean of each data set on its dot diagram.

2.63 Consider the following sample of five measurements: 2, 1, 1, 0, 3.
  a. Calculate the range, s^2, and s.
  b. Add 3 to each measurement and repeat part **a.**
  c. Subtract 4 from each measurement and repeat part **a.**
  d. Considering your answers to parts **a, b,** and **c,** what seems to be the effect on the variability of a data set by adding the same number to or subtracting the same number from each measurement?

⬤ Applet Exercise 2.4

Use the applet entitled *Standard Deviation* to find the standard deviation of each of the four data sets in Exercise 2.57. For each data set, set the lower limit to a number less than all of the data, set the upper limit to a number greater than all of the data, and then click on *Update*. Click on the approximate location of each data item on the number line. You can get rid of a point by dragging it to the trash can. To clear the graph between data sets, simply click on the trash can.
  a. Compare the standard deviations generated by the applet to those you calculated by hand in Exercise 2.57. If there are differences, explain why the applet might give values slightly different from the hand calculations.
  b. Despite providing a slightly different value of the standard deviation of a data set, describe some advantages of using the applet.

Applet Exercise 2.5

Use the applet *Standard Deviation* to study the effect that multiplying or dividing each number in a data set by the same number has on the standard deviation. Begin by setting appropriate limits and plotting the given data on the number line provided in the applet.

$$0 \quad 1 \quad 1 \quad 1 \quad 2 \quad 2 \quad 3 \quad 4$$

a. Record the standard deviation. Then multiply each data item by 2, plot the new data items, and record the standard deviation. Repeat the process, first multiplying each of the original data items by 3 and then by 4. Describe what is happening to the standard deviation as the data items are multiplied by higher numbers. Divide each standard deviation by the standard deviation of the original data set. Do you see a pattern? Explain.

b. Divide each of the original data items by 2, plot the new data, and record the standard deviation. Repeat the process, first dividing each of the original data items by 3 and then by 4. Describe what is happening to the standard deviation as the data items are divided by higher numbers. Divide each standard deviation by the standard deviation of the original data set. Do you see a pattern? Explain.

c. Using your results from parts **a** and **b**, describe what happens to the standard deviation of a data set when each of the data items in the set is multiplied or divided by a fixed number n. Experiment by repeating parts **a** and **b** for other data sets if you need to.

Applet Exercise 2.6

Use the applet *Standard Deviation* to study the effect that an extreme value has on the standard deviation. Begin by setting appropriate limits and plotting the given data on the number line provided in the applet.

$$0 \quad 6 \quad 7 \quad 7 \quad 8 \quad 8 \quad 8 \quad 9 \quad 9 \quad 10$$

a. Record the standard deviation. Replace the extreme value of 0 with 2, then 4, and then 6. Record the standard deviation each time. Describe what is happening to the standard deviation as 0 is replaced by higher numbers.

b. How would the standard deviation of the data set compare to the original standard deviation if the 0 were replaced by 16? Explain.

Applying the Concepts—Basic

2.64 **Performance of stock screeners.** Refer to the American Association of Individual Investors (AAII) statistics on
SCREEN stock screeners, Exercise 2.42 (p. 70). Annualized percentage return on investment (as compared to the Standard & Poor's 500 Index) for 13 randomly selected stock screeners are reproduced in the table.

| 9.0 | −.1 | −1.6 | 14.6 | 16.0 | 7.7 | 19.9 | 9.8 | 3.2 | 24.8 | 17.6 | 10.7 | 9.1 |

a. Find the range of the data for the 13 stock screeners. Give the units of measurement for the range.

b. Find the variance of the data for the 13 stock screeners. If possible, give the units of measurement for the variance.

c. Find the standard deviation of the data for the 13 stock screeners. Give the units of measurement for the standard deviation.

2.65 **U.S. wine export markets.** Refer to the data on the top 30 U.S. export markets for sparkling wines, compiled by
WINEX the Center for International Trade Development (CITD), given in Exercise 2.43 (p. 70). The Minitab descriptive statistics printout for the amount exported (thousands of dollars) and 3-year percentage change for the 30 countries is reproduced below.

Descriptive Statistics: EXPORT, CHANGE

Variable	N	N*	Mean	StDev	Minimum	Q1	Median	Q3	Maximum	IQR
EXPORT	30	0	653	1113	70	105	231	523	4952	418
CHANGE	28	2	481	1098	-49	21	156	499	5750	478

a. Use the information on the printout to find the range of the amount exported.

b. Locate the standard deviation of the amount exported on the printout.

c. Use the result, part **b**, to find the variance of the amount exported.

2.66 **Is honey a cough remedy?** Refer to the *Archives of Pediatrics and Adolescent Medicine* (Dec. 2007) study of
HCOUGH honey as a remedy for coughing, Exercise 2.30 (p. 61). The coughing improvement scores (as determined by the children's parents) for the patients in the over-the-counter cough medicine dosage (DM) group, honey dosage group, and control group are reproduced in the accompanying table.

Honey Dosage:	12	11	15	11	10	13	10	4	15	16	9
	14	10	6	10	8	11	12	12	8		
	12	9	11	15	10	15	9	13	8	12	10
	8	9	5	12							
DM Dosage:	4	6	9	4	7	7	7	9	12	10	11	6
	3	4	9	12	7	6	8	12	12	4	12	
	13	7	10	13	9	4	4	10	15	9		
No Dosage (Control):	5	8	6	1	0	8	12	8	7	7	1	6
	7	7	12	7	9	7	9	5	11	9	5	
	6	8	8	6	7	10	9	4	8	7	3	1	4	3

Source: Based on Paul, I. M., et al. "Effect of honey, dextromethorphan, and no treatment on nocturnal cough and sleep quality for coughing children and their parents," *Archives of Pediatrics and Adolescent Medicine*, Vol. 161, No. 12, Dec. 2007 (data simulated).

a. Find the standard deviation of the improvement scores for the honey dosage group.

b. Find the standard deviation of the improvement scores for the DM dosage group.

c. Find the standard deviation of the improvement scores for the control group.

d. Based on the results, parts **a–c**, which group appears to have the most variability in coughing improvement scores? The least variability?

Applying the Concepts—Intermediate

2.67 **Corporate sustainability of CPA firms.** Refer to the *Business and Society* (March 2011) study on
CORSUS sustainability behaviors of CPA corporations, Exercise 2.46
NW (p. 71). Numerical measures of variation for level of support for the 992 senior managers are shown in the accompanying Minitab printout.

Descriptive Statistics: Support

Variable	N	Mean	StDev	Variance	Minimum	Maximum	Range
Support	992	67.755	26.871	722.036	0.000	155.000	155.000

a. Locate the range on the printout. Comment on the accuracy of the statement: "The difference between the largest and smallest values of level of support for the 992 senior managers is 155 points."

b. Locate the variance on the printout. Comment on the accuracy of the statement: "On average, the level of support for corporate sustainability for the 992 senior managers is 722 points."

c. Locate the standard deviation on the printout. Does the distribution of support levels for the 992 senior managers have more or less variation than another distribution with a standard deviation of 50? Explain.

d. Which measure of variation best describes the distribution of 992 support levels? Explain.

2.68 **Doctors and ethics.** Refer to the *Journal of Medical Ethics* (Vol. 32, 2006) study of physicians' use of ethics consultation, Exercise 2.52 (p. 72). Again, consider an analysis of the quantitative variable, *length of time in practice* (i.e., years of experience).

ETHICS

a. Access the data file and find the range, variance, and standard deviation for the *length of time in practice* (i.e., years of experience) variable. If possible, give a practical interpretation of each of these measures of variation.

b. Consider only the physicians who would refuse to use ethics consultation in the future. Find the standard deviation for the *length of time in practice* for these physicians.

c. Repeat part **b** for physicians who would use ethics consultation in the future.

d. Use the results, parts **b** and **c**, to compare the variation in the length of time in practice distributions for physicians who would use and who would refuse ethics consultation in the future.

2.69 **Active nuclear power plants.** Refer to Exercise 2.54 (p. 73) and the U.S. Energy Information Administration's data on the number of nuclear power plants operating in each of 20 states.

NUKES

a. Find the range, variance, and standard deviation of this data set.

b. Eliminate the largest value from the data set and repeat part **a.** What effect does dropping this measurement have on the measures of variation found in part **a?**

c. Eliminate the smallest and largest value from the data set and repeat part **a.** What effect does dropping both of these measurements have on the measures of variation found in part **a?**

Applying the Concepts—Advanced

2.70 **Estimating production time.** A widely used technique for estimating the length of time it takes workers to produce a product is the **time study.** In a time study, the task to be studied is divided into measurable parts, and each is timed with a stopwatch or filmed for later analysis. For each worker, this process is repeated many times for each subtask. Then the average and standard deviation of the time required to complete each subtask are computed for each worker. A worker's overall time to complete the task under study is then determined by adding his or her subtask-time averages (Gaither and Frazier, *Operations Management*, 2001). The data (in minutes) given in the table are the result of a time study of a production operation involving two subtasks.

TIMES

	Worker A		Worker B	
Repetition	Subtask 1	Subtask 2	Subtask 1	Subtask 2
1	30	2	31	7
2	28	4	30	2
3	31	3	32	6
4	38	3	30	5
5	25	2	29	4
6	29	4	30	1
7	30	3	31	4

a. Find the overall time it took each worker to complete the manufacturing operation under study.

b. For each worker, find the standard deviation of the seven times for subtask 1.

c. In the context of this problem, what are the standard deviations you computed in part **b** measuring?

d. Repeat part **b** for subtask 2.

e. If you could choose workers similar to A or workers similar to B to perform subtasks 1 and 2, which type would you assign to each subtask? Explain your decisions on the basis of your answers to parts **a–d.**

2.5 Using the Mean and Standard Deviation to Describe Data

We've seen that if we are comparing the variability of two samples selected from a population, the sample with the larger standard deviation is the more variable of the two. Thus, we know how to interpret the standard deviation on a relative or comparative basis, but we haven't explained how it provides a measure of variability for a single sample.

To understand how the standard deviation provides a measure of variability of a data set, consider a specific data set and answer the following questions: How many measurements are within 1 standard deviation of the mean? How many measurements are within 2 standard deviations? For a specific data set, we can answer these questions by counting the number of measurements in each of the intervals. However, if we are interested in obtaining a general answer to these questions, the problem is more difficult.

Tables 2.6 and 2.7 give two sets of answers to the questions of how many measurements fall within 1, 2, and 3 standard deviations of the mean. The first, which applies to *any* set of data, is derived from a theorem proved by the Russian mathematician P. L. Chebyshev. The second, which applies to **mound-shaped, symmetric distributions** of data (where the mean, median, and mode are all about the same), is based upon empirical evidence that has accumulated over the years. However, the percentages given for the intervals in Table 2.7 provide remarkably good approximations even when the distribution of the data is slightly skewed or asymmetric. Note that both rules apply to either population data sets or sample data sets.

Table 2.6	Using the Mean and Standard Deviation to Describe Data: Chebyshev's Rule

Chebyshev's Rule applies to any data set, regardless of the shape of the frequency distribution of the data.

   a. No useful information is provided on the fraction of measurements that fall within 1 standard deviation of the mean [i.e., within the interval $(\bar{x} - s, \bar{x} + s)$ for samples and $(\mu - \sigma, \mu + \sigma)$ for populations].

   b. At least $\frac{3}{4}$ will fall within 2 standard deviations of the mean [i.e., within the interval $(\bar{x} - 2s, \bar{x} + 2s)$ for samples and $(\mu - 2\sigma, \mu + 2\sigma)$ for populations].

   c. At least $\frac{8}{9}$ of the measurements will fall within 3 standard deviations of the mean [i.e., within the interval $(\bar{x} - 3s, \bar{x} + 3s)$ for samples and $(\mu - 3\sigma, \mu + 3\sigma)$ for populations].

   d. Generally, for any number k greater than 1, at least $(1 - 1/k^2)$ of the measurements will fall within k standard deviations of the mean [i.e., within the interval $(\bar{x} - ks, \bar{x} + ks)$ for samples and $(\mu - k\sigma, \mu + k\sigma)$ for populations].

Table 2.7	Using the Mean and Standard Deviation to Describe Data: The Empirical Rule

The **Empirical Rule** is a rule of thumb that applies to data sets with frequency distributions that are mound-shaped and symmetric, as shown below.

   a. Approximately 68% of the measurements will fall within 1 standard deviation of the mean [i.e., within the interval $(\bar{x} - s, \bar{x} + s)$ for samples and $(\mu - \sigma, \mu + \sigma)$ for populations].

   b. Approximately 95% of the measurements will fall within 2 standard deviations of the mean [i.e., within the interval $(\bar{x} - 2s, \bar{x} + 2s)$ for samples and $(\mu - 2\sigma, \mu + 2\sigma)$ for populations].

   c. Approximately 99.7% (essentially all) of the measurements will fall within 3 standard deviations of the mean [i.e., within the interval $(\bar{x} - 3s, \bar{x} + 3s)$ for samples and $(\mu - 3\sigma, \mu + 3\sigma)$ for populations].

Example 2.11

Interpreting the Standard Deviation—R&D Expenditures

Problem The 50 companies' percentages of revenues spent on R&D are repeated in Table 2.8. We have previously shown (see Figure 2.20, p. 77) that the mean and standard deviation of these data (rounded) are 8.49 and 1.98, respectively. Calculate the fraction of these measurements that lie within the intervals $\bar{x} \pm s$, $\bar{x} \pm 2s$, and $\bar{x} \pm 3s$ and compare the results with those predicted in Tables 2.6 and 2.7.

Table 2.8	R&D Percentages for 50 Companies								
13.5	9.5	8.2	6.5	8.4	8.1	6.9	7.5	10.5	13.5
7.2	7.1	9.0	9.9	8.2	13.2	9.2	6.9	9.6	7.7
9.7	7.5	7.2	5.9	6.6	11.1	8.8	5.2	10.6	8.2
11.3	5.6	10.1	8.0	8.5	11.7	7.1	7.7	9.4	6.0
8.0	7.4	10.5	7.8	7.9	6.5	6.9	6.5	6.8	9.5

Data Set: R&D

PAFNUTY L. CHEBYSHEV
(1821–1894)
The Splendid Russian
Mathematician

P. L. Chebyshev was educated in mathematical science at Moscow University, eventually earning his master's degree. Following his graduation, Chebyshev joined St. Petersburg (Russia) University as a professor, becoming part of the well-known "Petersburg mathematical school." It was here that Chebyshev proved his famous theorem about the probability of a measurement being within k standard deviations of the mean (Table 2.6). His fluency in French allowed him to gain international recognition in probability theory. In fact, Chebyshev once objected to being described as a "splendid Russian mathematician," saying he surely was a "worldwide mathematician." One student remembered Chebyshev as "a wonderful lecturer" who "was always prompt for class," and "as soon as the bell sounded, he immediately dropped the chalk, and, limping, left the auditorium."

Solution We first form the interval

$$(\bar{x} - s, \bar{x} + s) = (8.49 - 1.98, 8.49 + 1.98) = (6.51, 10.47)$$

A check of the measurements reveals that 34 of the 50 measurements, or 68%, are within 1 standard deviation of the mean.

The next interval of interest,

$$(\bar{x} - 2s, \bar{x} + 2s) = (8.49 - 3.96, 8.49 + 3.96) = (4.53, 12.45),$$

contains 47 of the 50 measurements, or 94%.

Finally, the 3-standard-deviation interval around $\bar{x}$,

$$(\bar{x} - 3s, \bar{x} + 3s) = (8.49 - 5.94, 8.49 + 5.94) = (2.55, 14.43),$$

contains all, or 100%, of the measurements.

In spite of the fact that the distribution of these data is skewed to the right (see Figure 2.10, p. 53), the percentages within 1, 2, and 3 standard deviations (68%, 94%, and 100%) agree very well with the approximations of 68%, 95%, and 99.7% given by the Empirical Rule (Table 2.7).

Look Back You will find that unless the distribution is extremely skewed, the mound-shaped approximations will be reasonably accurate. Of course, no matter what the shape of the distribution, Chebyshev's Rule (Table 2.6) ensures that at least 75% and at least 89% of the measurements will lie within 2 and 3 standard deviations of the mean, respectively.

———◼ **Now Work Exercise 2.74**

Example **2.12**

Check on the Calculation of s — R&D Expenditures

Figure 2.21
The relation between the range and the standard deviation

Problem Chebyshev's Rule and the Empirical Rule are useful as a check on the calculation of the standard deviation. For example, suppose we calculated the standard deviation for the R&D percentages (Table 2.8) to be 3.92. Are there any "clues" in the data that enable us to judge whether this number is reasonable?

Solution The range of the R&D percentages in Table 2.8 is $13.5 - 5.2 = 8.3$. From Chebyshev's Rule and the Empirical Rule we know that most of the measurements (approximately 95% if the distribution is mound-shaped) will be within 2 standard deviations of the mean. And, regardless of the shape of the distribution and the number of measurements, almost all of them will fall within 3 standard deviations of the mean. Consequently, we would expect the range of the measurements to be between 4 (i.e., $\pm 2s$) and 6 (i.e., $\pm 3s$) standard deviations in length (see Figure 2.21).

For the R&D data, this means that s should fall between

$$\frac{\text{Range}}{6} = \frac{8.3}{6} = 1.38 \quad \text{and} \quad \frac{\text{Range}}{4} = \frac{8.3}{4} = 2.08$$

In particular, the standard deviation should not be much larger than $\frac{1}{4}$ of the range, particularly for the data set with 50 measurements. Thus, we have reason to believe that the calculation of 3.92 is too large. A check of our work reveals that 3.92 is the variance s^2, not the standard deviation s (see Example 2.10). We "forgot" to take the square root (a common error); the correct value is $s = 1.98$. Note that this value is between $\frac{1}{6}$ and $\frac{1}{4}$ of the range.

Look Ahead In examples and exercises we'll sometimes use $s \approx \text{range}/4$ to obtain a crude, and usually conservatively large, approximation for s. However, we stress that this is no substitute for calculating the exact value of s when possible.

———◼ **Now Work Exercise 2.75**

In the next example, we use the concepts in Chebyshev's Rule and the Empirical Rule to build the foundation for statistical inference making.

Example   2.13

Making a Statistical Inference—Car Battery Guarantee

Problem A manufacturer of automobile batteries claims that the average length of life for its grade A battery is 60 months. However, the guarantee on this brand is for just 36 months. Suppose the standard deviation of the life length is known to be 10 months, and the frequency distribution of the life-length data is known to be mound-shaped.

a. Approximately what percentage of the manufacturer's grade A batteries will last more than 50 months, assuming the manufacturer's claim is true?

b. Approximately what percentage of the manufacturer's batteries will last less than 40 months, assuming the manufacturer's claim is true?

c. Suppose your battery lasts 37 months. What could you infer about the manufacturer's claim?

Solution If the distribution of life length is assumed to be mound-shaped with a mean of 60 months and a standard deviation of 10 months, it would appear as shown in Figure 2.22. Note that we can take advantage of the fact that mound-shaped distributions are (approximately) symmetric about the mean, so that the percentages given by the Empirical Rule can be split equally between the halves of the distribution on each side of the mean.

For example, because approximately 68% of the measurements will fall within 1 standard deviation of the mean, the distribution's symmetry implies that approximately $\frac{1}{2}(68\%) = 34\%$ of the measurements will fall between the mean and 1 standard deviation on each side. This concept is illustrated in Figure 2.22. The figure also shows that 2.5% of the measurements lie beyond 2 standard deviations in each direction from the mean. This result follows from the fact that if approximately 95% of the measurements fall within 2 standard deviations of the mean, then about 5% fall outside 2 standard deviations; if the distribution is approximately symmetric, then about 2.5% of the measurements fall beyond 2 standard deviations on each side of the mean.

a. It is easy to see in Figure 2.22 that the percentage of batteries lasting more than 50 months is approximately 34% (between 50 and 60 months) plus 50% (greater than 60 months). Thus, approximately 84% of the batteries should have life length exceeding 50 months.

b. The percentage of batteries that last less than 40 months can also be easily determined from Figure 2.22. Approximately 2.5% of the batteries should fail prior to 40 months, assuming the manufacturer's claim is true.

c. If you are so unfortunate that your grade A battery fails at 37 months, you can make one of two inferences: either your battery was one of the approximately 2.5% that fail prior to 40 months, or something about the manufacturer's claim is not true. Because the chances are so small that a battery fails before 40 months, you would have good reason to have serious doubts about the manufacturer's claim. A mean smaller than 60 months and/or a standard deviation longer than 10 months would both increase the likelihood of failure prior to 40 months.*

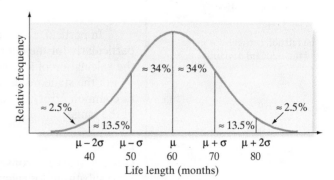

Figure 2.22
Battery life-length distribution:
Manufacturer's claim assumed true

*The assumption that the distribution is mound-shaped and symmetric may also be incorrect. However, if the distribution were skewed to the right, as life-length distributions often tend to be, the percentage of measurements more than 2 standard deviations *below* the mean would be even less than 2.5%.

Look Back The approximations given in Figure 2.22 are more dependent on the assumption of a mound-shaped distribution than those given by the Empirical Rule (Table 2.7) because the approximations in Figure 2.22 depend on the (approximate) symmetry of the mound-shaped distribution. We saw in Example 2.11 that the Empirical Rule can yield good approximations even for skewed distributions. This will *not* be true of the approximations in Figure 2.22; the distribution *must* be mound-shaped and approximately symmetric.

Example 2.13 is our initial demonstration of the statistical inference-making process. At this point you should realize that we'll use sample information (in Example 2.13, your battery's failure at 37 months) to make inferences about the population (in Example 2.13, the manufacturer's claim about the life length for the population of all batteries). We'll build on this foundation as we proceed.

STATISTICS in ACTION REVISITED

Interpreting Numerical Descriptive Measures

We return to the *Journal of Experimental Social Psychology* (Vol. 45, 2009) study on whether money can buy love for two groups of participants—those assigned the role of gift-giver and those assigned the role of gift-recipient. Recall that the researchers investigated whether givers and receivers differ on the price of the birthday gift reported and on the overall level of appreciation reported. The Minitab descriptive statistics printout for the **BUYLOV** data is displayed in Figure SIA2.8, with means and standard deviations highlighted.

First, we focus on the quantitative variable, *birthday gift price*. The sample mean gift price for givers is \$105.84 compared to \$149.00 for receivers. Our interpretation is that receivers report a higher average gift price than givers—a difference of about \$43.

To interpret the gift price standard deviations (93.47 for givers and 134.5 for receivers), we substitute into the formula, $\bar{x} \pm 2s$, to obtain the following intervals:

Gift-Giver: $\bar{x} \pm 2s = 105.84 \pm 2(93.47) = 105.84 \pm 186.94 = (-81.1, 292.78)$

Gift-Receiver: $\bar{x} + 2s = 149.00 \pm 2(134.50) = 149 \pm 269 = (-120, 418)$

Because gift price cannot have a negative value, the two intervals for givers and receivers are more practically given as (0, 293) and (0, 418), respectively. Since the distributions of gift price are not mound-shaped and symmetric (see Figure SIA2.7a), we apply Chebyshev's Rule (Table 2.6). Thus, we know that at least 75% of the gift-givers in the study reported a gift price between \$0 and \$293, and at least 75% of the gift-recipients reported a gift price between \$0 and \$418. You can see that the upper endpoint of the interval for givers lies below that for receivers. Consequently, we can infer that prices reported by gift-recipients tend to be higher than the prices reported by gift-givers. Also, if a gift price of \$400 is observed, it is much more likely to be reported by a gift-receiver than a gift-giver.

A similar analysis performed for the variable *overall level of appreciation* yielded the following intervals:

Gift-Giver: $\bar{x} \pm 2s = 4.985 \pm 2(2.775) = 4.985 \pm 5.55 = (-.565, 10.535)$

Gift-Receiver: $\bar{x} \pm 2s = 7.165 \pm 2(2.928) = 7.165 \pm 5.856 = (1.309, 13.021)$

Since overall level of appreciation cannot have a value less than 2 and is a whole number, the two intervals for givers and receivers are more practically given as (2, 10) and (2, 13),

Descriptive Statistics: BGiftPrice, OverallApp

Variable	Role	N	Mean	StDev	Variance	Minimum	Median	Maximum
BGiftPrice	Giver	134	105.84	93.47	8736.78	2.00	75.50	431.00
	Receiver	103	149.0	134.5	18083.8	1.0	133.0	548.0
OverallApp	Giver	134	4.985	2.775	7.699	2.000	4.000	13.000
	Receiver	103	7.165	2.928	8.571	2.000	7.000	14.000

Figure SIA2.8

Minitab descriptive statistics for gift price and appreciation level, by role respectively. Applying Chebyshev's Rule, we know that at least 75% of the gift-givers in the study reported an appreciation level between 2 and 10 points, and at least 75% of the gift-recipients reported an appreciation level between 2 and 13 points. Again, the upper endpoint of the interval for givers lies below that for receivers; thus, we infer that overall levels of appreciation reported by gift-recipients tend to be higher than those reported by gift-givers.

Now, how does this information help the researchers determine whether there are "significant" differences in the means for gift-givers and gift-recipients? In Chapters 6 and 7 we present inferential methods that will answer such a question and provide a measure of reliability for the inference.

Data Set: BUYLOVE

Exercises 2.71–2.89

Learning the Mechanics

2.71 The output from a statistical software package indicates that the mean and standard deviation of a data set consisting of 200 measurements are $1,500 and $300, respectively.
  a. What are the units of measurement of the variable of interest? Based on the units, what type of data is this: quantitative or qualitative?
  b. What can be said about the number of measurements between $900 and $2,100? Between $600 and $2,400? Between $1,200 and $1,800? Between $1,500 and $2,100?

2.72 For any set of data, what can be said about the percentage of the measurements contained in each of the following intervals?
  a. $\bar{x} - s$ to $\bar{x} + s$
  b. $\bar{x} - 2s$ to $\bar{x} + 2s$
  c. $\bar{x} - 3s$ to $\bar{x} + 3s$

2.73 For a set of data with a mound-shaped relative frequency distribution, what can be said about the percentage of the measurements contained in each of the intervals specified in Exercise 2.72?

2.74 The following is a sample of 25 measurements:

| 7 | 6 | 6 | 11 | 8 | 9 | 11 | 9 | 10 | 8 | 7 | 7 |
| 5 | 9 | 10 | 7 | 7 | 7 | 7 | 9 | 12 | 10 | 10 | 8 | 6 |

  a. Compute $\bar{x}$, s^2, and s for this sample.
  b. Count the number of measurements in the intervals $\bar{x} \pm s$, $\bar{x} \pm 2s$, $\bar{x} \pm 3s$. Express each count as a percentage of the total number of measurements.
  c. Compare the percentages found in part **b** to the percentages given by the Empirical Rule and Chebyshev's Rule.
  d. Calculate the range and use it to obtain a rough approximation for s. Does the result compare favorably with the actual value for s found in part **a?**

2.75 Given a data set with a largest value of 760 and a smallest value of 135, what would you estimate the standard deviation to be? Explain the logic behind the procedure you used to estimate the standard deviation. Suppose the standard deviation is reported to be 25. Is this feasible? Explain.

Applying the Concepts—Basic

2.76 **Do social robots walk or roll?** Refer to the *International Conference on Social Robotics* (Vol. 6414, 2010) study on the current trend in the design of social robots, ROBOTS

Exercise 2.3 (p. 48). Recall that in a random sample of social robots obtained through a Web search, 28 were built with wheels. The number of wheels on each of the 28 robots is listed in the accompanying table.

| 4 | 4 | 3 | 3 | 3 | 6 | 4 | 2 | 2 | 2 | 1 | 3 | 3 | 3 |
| 3 | 4 | 4 | 3 | 2 | 8 | 2 | 2 | 3 | 4 | 3 | 3 | 4 | 2 |

Source: Based on Chew, S., et al. "Do social robots walk or roll?," *International Conference on Social Robotics,* Vol. 6414, 2010 (adapted from Figure 2).

  a. Generate a histogram for the sample data set. Is the distribution of number of wheels mound-shaped and symmetric?
  b. Find the mean and standard deviation for the sample data set.
  c. Form the interval, $\bar{x} \pm 2s$.
  d. According to Chebychev's rule, what proportion of sample observations will fall within the interval, part **c?**
  e. According to the Empirical Rule, what proportion of sample observations will fall within the interval, part **c?**
  f. Determine the actual proportion of sample observations that fall within the interval, part **c.** Even though the histogram, part **a,** is not perfectly symmetric, does the Empirical Rule provide a good estimate of the proportion?

2.77 **College dropout study.** The *American Economic Review* (Dec. 2008) published a study on whether the removal of credit constraints would impact the likelihood of a student dropping out of college. As part of the investigation, the researchers looked for factors other than credit constraints that would influence the college dropout decision. One factor of interest was expected GPA for a college student who studied 3 hours per day. In a representative sample of 307 college students, the researchers reported the following summary statistics for the expected GPA of those who studied 3 hours per day: $\bar{x} = 3.11$, $s = .66$.
  a. Give an interval that will contain most (at least 75% to approximately 95%) of the 307 GPAs.
  b. If you observe a GPA of 1.25, is it likely that this college student studied 3 hours per day? Explain.

2.78 **Blogs for *Fortune* 500 firms.** Refer to the *Journal of Relationship Marketing* (Vol. 7, 2008) study of the prevalence of blogs and forums at *Fortune* 500 firms with both English and Chinese Web sites, Exercise 2.9 (p. 49). In a sample of firms that provide blogs and forums as marketing tools, the mean number of blogs/forums per site was 4.25, with a standard deviation of 12.02.

a. Provide an interval that is likely to contain the number of blogs/forums per site for at least 75% of the *Fortune 500* firms in the sample.

b. Do you expect the distribution of the number of blogs/forums to be symmetric, skewed right, or skewed left? Explain.

2.79 **Semester hours taken by CPA candidates.** Refer to the *Journal of Accounting and Public Policy* (Spring 2002) study of 100,000 first-time candidates for the CPA exam, Exercise 2.51 (p. 72). Recall that the mean number of semester hours of college credit taken by the candidates was 141.31 hours. The standard-deviation was reported to be 17.77 hours.

a. Compute the 2-standard-deviation interval around the mean.

b. Make a statement about the proportion of first-time candidates for the CPA exam who have total college credit hours within the interval, part **a.**

c. For the statement, part **b,** to be true, what must be known about the shape of the distribution of total semester hours?

2.80 **Motivation of drug dealers.** Researchers at Georgia State University investigated the personality characteristics of drug dealers in order to shed light on their motivation for participating in the illegal drug market (*Applied Psychology in Criminal Justice*, Sep. 2009). The sample consisted of 100 convicted drug dealers who attended a court-mandated counseling program. Each dealer was scored on the Wanting Recognition (WR) Scale, which provides a quantitative measure of a person's level of need for approval and sensitivity to social situations. (Higher scores indicate a greater need for approval.) The sample of drug dealers had a mean WR score of 39, with a standard deviation of 6. Assume the distribution of WR scores for drug dealers is mound-shaped and symmetric.

a. Give a range of WR scores that will contain about 95% of the scores in the drug dealer sample.

b. What proportion of the drug dealers had WR scores above 51?

c. Give a range of WR sores that contain nearly all the scores in the drug dealer sample.

Applying the Concepts—Intermediate

2.81 **Sanitation inspection of cruise ships.** Refer to the Centers for Disease Control and Prevention listing of the Jan. 2010 sanitation scores for 186 cruise ships, Exercise 2.24 (p. 59).

SANIT

a. Find the mean and standard deviation of the sanitation scores.

b. Calculate the intervals $\bar{x} \pm s, \bar{x} \pm 2s, \bar{x} \pm 3s$.

c. Find the percentage of measurements in the data set that fall within each of the intervals, part **b.** Do these percentages agree with Chebyshev's Rule? The Empirical Rule?

2.82 **Laptop use in middle school.** Many middle schools have initiated a program that provides every student with a free laptop (notebook) computer. Student usage of laptops at a middle school that participates in the initiative was investigated in *American Secondary Education* (Fall 2009). In a sample of 106 students, the researchers reported the following statistics on how many minutes per

day each student used his or her laptop for taking notes: $\bar{x} = 13.2, s = 19.5$.

a. Compute the interval, $\bar{x} \pm 2s$.

b. Explain why the distribution of laptop usage for taking notes for these 106 students cannot be symmetric.

c. Given your answer to part **b,** what percentage of the 106 students have laptop usages that fall within the $\bar{x} \pm 2s$ interval?

2.83 **Bearing strength of concrete FRP strips.** Fiber reinforced polymer (FRP) composite materials are the standard for strengthening, retrofitting, and repairing concrete structures. Typically, FRP strips are fastened to the concrete with epoxy adhesive. Engineers at the University of Wisconsin-Madison have developed a new method of fastening the FRP strips using mechanical anchors (*Composites Fabrication Magazine*, Sep. 2004). To evaluate the new fastening method, 10 specimens of pultruded FRP strips mechanically fastened to highway bridges were tested for bearing strength. The strength measurements (recorded in mega pascal units, Mpa) are shown in the table. Use the sample data to find an interval that is likely to contain the bearing strength of a pultruded FRP strip.

FRP

240.9	248.8	215.7	233.6	231.4	230.9	225.3	247.3	235.5	238.0

Source: Based on summary information provided in COMPOSITES FABRICATION MAGAZINE, September 2004, p. 32, Table 1.

2.84 **Time in bankruptcy.** Refer to the *Financial Management* (Spring 1995) study of 49 firms filing for prepackaged bankruptcy, Exercise 2.32 (p. 62). Data on the variable of interest, length of time (months) in bankruptcy for each firm, are saved in the accompanying file.

BNKRPT

a. Construct a histogram for the 49 bankruptcy times. Comment on whether the Empirical Rule is applicable for describing the bankruptcy time distribution for firms filing for prepackaged bankruptcy.

b. Find numerical descriptive statistics for the data set. Use this information to construct an interval that captures at least 75% of the bankruptcy times.

c. Count the number of the 49 bankruptcy times that fall within the interval, part **b,** and convert the result to a percentage. Does the result agree with Chebyshev's Rule? The Empirical Rule?

d. A firm is considering filing a prepackaged bankruptcy plan. Estimate the length of time the firm will be in bankruptcy.

2.85 **Shopping vehicle and judgment.** While shopping at the grocery store, are you more likely to buy a vice product (e.g., a candy bar) when pushing a shopping cart or when carrying a shopping basket? This was the question of interest in a study published in the *Journal of Marketing Research* (Dec. 2011). The researchers believe that when your arm is flexed (as when carrying a basket), you are more likely to choose a vice product than when your arm is extended (as when pushing a cart). To test this theory in a laboratory setting, the researchers recruited 22 consumers and asked each to push his or her hand against a table while being asked a serious of shopping questions. Half of the consumers were told to put their arms in a flex position (similar to a shopping basket) and the other half were told to put their arms in an extended position (similar to a shopping cart). Participants were offered several choices between a vice and a virtue (e.g., a movie ticket vs. a shopping coupon, paying later with a larger amount vs. paying now), and a choice score (on a scale of 0 to 100) was determined for each. (Higher scores indicate a greater preference for vice options.) The average choice score for consumers with a flexed arm was 59, while the average for consumers with an extended arm was 43.

a. Suppose the standard deviations of the choice scores for the flexed arm and extended arm conditions are 4 and 2, respectively. Does this information support the researchers' theory? Explain.

b. Suppose the standard deviations of the choice scores for the flexed arm and extended arm conditions are 10 and 15, respectively. Does this information support the researchers' theory? Explain.

2.86 Buy-side vs. sell-side analysts' earnings forecasts. Financial analysts are hired by investment companies to make forecasts of stock prices and recommendations about whether to buy, sell, or hold specific securities. These analysts can be categorized as either "buy-side" analysts or "sell-side" analysts based on a variety of factors, including scope of industry coverage, sources of information used, and target audience. A group of Harvard Business School professors compared earnings forecasts of buy-side and sell-side analysts (*Financial Analysts Journal*, Jul/Aug 2008). Data were collected on 3,526 forecasts made by buy-side analysts and 58,562 forecasts made by sell-side analysts, and the relative absolute forecast error was determined for each.

a. Frequency distributions for buy-side and sell-side analysts forecast errors (with the sell-side distribution superimposed over the buy-side distribution) are shown in the accompanying figure. Based on the figure, the researchers concluded "that absolute forecast errors for buy-side analysts have a higher mean and variance than those for the sell-side analysts." Do you agree? Explain.

b. The mean and standard deviation of forecast errors for both buy-side and sell-side analysts are given in the following table. For each type of analyst, provide an interval that will contain approximately 95% of the forecast errors. Compare these intervals. Which type of analyst is likely to have a relative forecast error of +2.00 or higher?

	Buy-Side Analysts	Sell-Side Analysts
Mean	0.85	−0.05
Standard deviation	1.93	0.85

Source: Based on Groysberg, B., Healy, P., & Chapman, C. *Financial Analysis Journal*, Vol. 64, No. 4. Jul/Aug. 2008 (Table 2).

Applying the Concepts—Advanced

2.87 Land purchase decision. A buyer for a lumber company must decide whether to buy a piece of land containing 5,000 pine trees. If 1,000 of the trees are at least 40 feet tall,

the buyer will purchase the land; otherwise, he won't. The owner of the land reports that the height of the trees has a mean of 30 feet and a standard deviation of 3 feet. Based on this information, what is the buyer's decision?

2.88 Improving SAT scores. The National Education Longitudinal Survey (NELS) tracks a nationally representative sample of U.S. students from eighth grade through high school and college. Research published in *Chance* (Winter 2001) examined the Standardized Assessment Test (SAT) scores of 265 NELS students who paid a private tutor to help them improve their scores. The table summarizes the changes in both the SAT–Mathematics and SAT–Verbal scores for these students.

	SAT–Math	SAT–Verbal
Mean change in score	19	7
Standard deviation of score changes	65	49

a. Suppose one of the 265 students who paid a private tutor is selected at random. Give an interval that is likely to contain this student's change in the SAT–Math score.

b. Repeat part **a** for the SAT–Verbal score.

c. Suppose the selected student increased his score on one of the SAT tests by 140 points. Which test, the SAT–Math or SAT–Verbal, is the one most likely to have the 140-point increase? Explain.

2.89 Monitoring weights of flour bags. When it is working properly, a machine that fills 25-pound bags of flour dispenses an average of 25 pounds per fill; the standard deviation of the amount of fill is .1 pound. To monitor the performance of the machine, an inspector weighs the contents of a bag coming off the machine's conveyor belt every half hour during the day. If the contents of two consecutive bags fall more than 2 standard deviations from the mean (using the mean and standard deviation given above), the filling process is said to be out of control, and the machine is shut down briefly for adjustments. The data given in the following table are the weights measured by the inspector yesterday. Assume the machine is never shut down for more than 15 minutes at a time. At what times yesterday was the process shut down for adjustment? Justify your answer.

Time	Weight (pounds)
8:00 A.M.	25.10
8:30	25.15
9:00	24.81
9:30	24.75
10:00	25.00
10:30	25.05
11:00	25.23
11:30	25.25
12:00	25.01
12:30 P.M.	25.06
1:00	24.95
1:30	24.80
2:00	24.95
2:30	25.21
3:00	24.90
3:30	24.71
4:00	25.31
4:30	25.15
5:00	25.20

2.6 Numerical Measures of Relative Standing

We've seen that numerical measures of central tendency and variability describe the general nature of a quantitative data set (either a sample or a population). In addition, we may be interested in describing the *relative* quantitative location of a particular measurement within a data set. Descriptive measures of the relationship of a measurement to the rest of the data are called **measures of relative standing.**

One measure of the relative standing of a measurement is its **percentile ranking,** or **percentile score.** For example, if oil company A reports that its yearly sales are in the 90th percentile of all companies in the industry, the implication is that 90% of all oil companies have yearly sales less than company A's, and only 10% have yearly sales exceeding company A's. This is demonstrated in Figure 2.23. Similarly, if the oil company's yearly sales are in the 50th percentile (the median of the data set), 50% of all oil companies would have lower yearly sales and 50% would have higher yearly sales.

Percentile rankings are of practical value only for large data sets. Finding them involves a process similar to the one used in finding a median. The measurements are ranked in order, and a rule is selected to define the location of each percentile. Because we are primarily interested in interpreting the percentile rankings of measurements (rather than finding particular percentiles for a data set), we define the *pth percentile* of a data set.

Figure 2.23

Location of 90th percentile for yearly sales of oil companies

> For any set of *n* measurements (arranged in ascending or descending order), the ***pth* percentile** is a number such that *p*% of the measurements fall below the *pth* percentile and $(100 - p)$% fall above it.

Example 2.14

Finding and Interpreting Percentiles—R&D Expenditures

Problem Refer to the percentages spent on R&D by the 50 high-technology firms listed in Table 2.8 (p. 80). A portion of the SPSS descriptive statistics printout is shown in Figure 2.24. Locate the 25th percentile and 95th percentile on the printout and interpret these values.

Solution Both the 25th percentile and 95th percentile are highlighted on the SPSS printout, Figure 2.24. These values are 7.05 and 13.335, respectively. Our interpretations are as follows: 25% of the 50 R&D percentages fall below 7.05 and 95% of the R&D percentages fall below 13.335.

Look Back The method for computing percentiles with small data sets varies according to the software used. As the sample size increases, these percentile values from the different software packages will converge to a single number.

Statistics

RDPCT

N	Valid	50
	Missing	0
Percentiles	5	5.765
	10	6.500
	25	7.050
	50	8.050
	75	9.625
	90	11.280
	95	13.335

Figure 2.24

SPSS percentiles for 50 R&D percentages

■ Now Work Exercise 2.91

Figure 2.25

The quartiles for a data set

Percentiles that partition a data set into four categories, each category containing exactly 25% of the measurements, are called **quartiles.** The *lower quartile* (Q_L) is the 25th percentile, the *middle quartile* (Q_M) is the median or 50th percentile, and the *upper quartile* (Q_U) is the 75th percentile, as shown in Figure 2.25. Therefore, in Example 2.14, we have (from the SPSS printout, Figure 2.24), $Q_L = 7.05$, $Q_M = 8.05$, and $Q_U = 9.625$. Quartiles will prove useful in finding unusual observations in a data set (Section 2.7).

> The **lower quartile (Q_L)** is the 25th percentile of a data set. The **middle quartile (Q_M)** is the median or 50th percentile. The **upper quartile (Q_U)** is the 75th percentile.

Another measure of relative standing in popular use is the *z-score*. As you can see in the definition of *z*-score below, the *z*-score makes use of the mean and standard deviation of the data set in order to specify the relative location of a measurement. Note that the *z*-score is calculated by subtracting $\bar{x}$ (or μ) from the measurement x and then dividing the result by s (or σ). The final result, the *z*-score, represents the distance between a given measurement x and the mean, expressed in standard deviations.

> The **sample *z*-score** for a measurement x is
>
> $$z = \frac{x - \bar{x}}{s}$$
>
> The **population *z*-score** for a measurement x is
>
> $$z = \frac{x - \mu}{\sigma}$$

Example   2.15

Finding a *z*-Score—GMAT Results

Problem A random sample of 2,000 students who sat for the Graduate Management Admission Test (GMAT) is selected. For this sample, the mean GMAT score is $\bar{x} = 540$ points and the standard deviation is $s = 100$ points. One student from the sample, Kara Smith, had a GMAT score of $x = 440$ points. What is Kara's sample *z*-score?

Solution First, note that Kara's GMAT score lies below the mean score for the 2,000 students (see Figure 2.26). Now we compute

$$z = (x - \bar{x})/s = (440 - 540)/100 = -100/100 = -1.0$$

This *z*-score implies that Kara Smith's GMAT score is 1.0 standard deviations below the sample mean GMAT score, or, in short, her sample *z*-score is −1.0.

Look Back The numerical value of the *z*-score reflects the relative standing of the measurement. A large positive *z*-score implies that the measurement is larger than almost all other measurements, whereas a large (in magnitude) negative *z*-score indicates that the measurement is smaller than almost every other measurement. If a *z*-score is 0 or near 0, the measurement is located at or near the mean of the sample or population.

Figure 2.26

GMAT scores of a sample of test takers

			GMAT Score
240	440	540	840
$\bar{x} - 3s$	Kara Smith's GMAT	$\bar{x}$	$\bar{x} + 3s$

■ **Now Work Exercise 2.90**

If we know that the frequency distribution of the measurements is mound-shaped, the following interpretation of the z-score can be given.

> **Interpretation of z-Scores for Mound-Shaped Distributions of Data**
>
> **1.** Approximately 68% of the measurements will have a z-score between -1 and 1.
>
> **2.** Approximately 95% of the measurements will have a z-score between -2 and 2.
>
> **3.** Approximately 99.7% (almost all) of the measurements will have a z-score between -3 and 3.

Note that this interpretation of z-scores is identical to that given by the Empirical Rule for mound-shaped distributions (Table 2.7). The statement that a measurement falls in the interval $(\mu - \sigma)$ to $(\mu + \sigma)$ is equivalent to the statement that a measurement has a population z-score between -1 and 1 because all measurements between $(\mu - \sigma)$ and $(\mu + \sigma)$ are within 1 standard deviation of μ. These z-scores are displayed in Figure 2.27.

Figure 2.27
Population z-scores for a mound-shaped distribution

Exercises 2.90–2.105

Learning the Mechanics

2.90 Compute the z-score corresponding to each of the following
NW values of x:
  a. $x = 40, s = 5, \bar{x} = 30$
  b. $x = 90, \mu = 89, \sigma = 2$
  c. $\mu = 50, \sigma = 5, x = 50$
  d. $s = 4, x = 20, \bar{x} = 30$
  e. In parts **a–d**, state whether the z-score locates x within a sample or a population.
  f. In parts **a–d**, state whether each value of x lies above or below the mean and by how many standard deviations.

2.91 Give the percentage of measurements in a data set that are
NW above and below each of the following percentiles:
  a. 75th percentile
  b. 50th percentile
  c. 20th percentile
  d. 84th percentile

2.92 In terms of percentiles, define Q_L, Q_M, and Q_U.

2.93 Compare the z-scores to decide which of the following x values lie the greatest distance above the mean and the greatest distance below the mean.

  a. $x = 100, \mu = 50, \sigma = 25$
  b. $x = 1, \mu = 4, \sigma = 1$
  c. $x = 0, \mu = 200, \sigma = 100$
  d. $x = 10, \mu = 5, \sigma = 3$

2.94 Suppose that 40 and 90 are two elements of a population data set and that their z-scores are -2 and 3, respectively. Using only this information, is it possible to determine the population's mean and standard deviation? If so, find them. If not, explain why it's not possible.

Applying the Concepts—Basic

2.95 **Mathematics assessment test scores.** According to the National Center for Education Statistics (2009), scores on a mathematics assessment test for U.S. eighth graders have a mean of 283, a 25th percentile of 259, a 75th percentile of 308, and a 90th percentile of 329. Interpret each of these numerical descriptive measures.

2.96 **Motivation of drug dealers.** Refer to the *Applied Psychology in Criminal Justice* (Sep. 2009) study of convicted drug dealers' motivations, Exercise 2.80 (p. 85). Recall that the sample of drug dealers had a mean Wanting Recognition (WR) score of 39 points, with a standard deviation of 6 points.

a. Find and interpret the z-score for a drug dealer with a WR score of 30 points.

b. What proportion of the sampled drug dealers had WR scores below 39 points? (Assume the distribution of WR scores is mound-shaped and symmetric.)

c. If 5% of convicted drug dealers have WR scores above 49 points, give a percentile ranking for the WR score of 49.

2.97 Starting and mid-career salaries of bachelor's degree graduates. PayScale, Inc., an online provider of global compensation data, recently conducted a survey of 1.2 million bachelor's degree graduates with a minimum of 10 years of work experience. Three of the many variables measured by PayScale were the graduate's starting salary, mid-career salary, and the college or university where they obtained their degree. A summary of the starting and mid-career salary data was reported in *the Wall Street Journal* (July 31, 2008). Descriptive statistics were provided for each of the over 300 colleges and universities that graduates attended. For example, graduates of the University of South Florida (USF) had a median starting salary of $41,100, a median mid-career salary of $71,100, and a mid-career 90th percentile salary of $131,000. Describe the salary distribution of USF bachelor's degree graduates by interpreting each of these summary statistics.

2.98 Sanitation inspection of cruise ships. Refer to the Jan. 2010 sanitation levels of cruise ships, Exercise 2.81 (p. 85).
SANIT
a. Give a measure of relative standing for the *Nautilus Explorer* score of 74. Interpret the result.

b. Give a measure of relative standing for the *Rotterdam's* score of 92. Interpret the result.

Applying the Concepts—Intermediate

2.99 Lead in drinking water. The U.S. Environmental Protection Agency (EPA) sets a limit on the amount of lead permitted in drinking water. The EPA *Action Level* for lead is .015 milligrams per liter (mg/L) of water. Under EPA guidelines, if 90% of a water system's study samples have a lead concentration less than .015 mg/L, the water is considered safe for drinking. I (coauthor Sincich) received a recent report on a study of lead levels in the drinking water of homes in my subdivision. The 90th percentile of the study sample had a lead concentration of .00372 mg/L. Are water customers in my subdivision at risk of drinking water with unhealthy lead levels? Explain.

2.100 Corporate sustainability of CPA firms. Refer to the *Business and Society* (March 2011) study on the sustainability behaviors of CPA corporations, Exercise 2.67 (p. 78).
CORSUS
Numerical descriptive measures for level of support for corporate sustainability for the 992 senior managers are repeated in the accompanying Minitab printout. One of the managers reported a support level of 155 points. Would you consider this support level to be typical of the study sample? Explain.

Descriptive Statistics: Support

Variable	N	Mean	StDev	Variance	Minimum	Median	Maximum
Support	992	67.755	26.871	722.036	0.000	68.000	155.000

2.101 Hazardous waste cleanup in Arkansas. The Superfund Act was passed by Congress to encourage state participation
SPRFND in the implementation of a law relating to the release and cleanup of hazardous substances. Hazardous waste sites financed by the Superfund Act are called *Superfund sites*. A total of 393 Superfund sites are operated by waste management companies in Arkansas (Tabor and Stanwick, *Arkansas Business and Economic Review*, Summer 1995). The numbers of these Superfund sites in each of Arkansas's 75 counties are shown in the next table.

3	3	2	1	2	0	5	3	5	2	1	8	2
12	3	5	3	1	3	0	8	0	9	6	8	6
2	16	0	6	0	5	5	0	1	25	0	0	0
6	2	10	12	3	10	3	17	2	4	2	1	21
4	2	1	11	5	2	2	7	2	3	1	8	2
0	0	0	2	3	10	2	3	48	21			

Source: Based on Tabor. R. H., & Stanwick, S. D. "Arkansas: An environmental perspective." Arkansas Business and Economic Review. Vol. 28, No. 2. Summer 1995, pp. 22–32 (Table 4).

a. Find the 10th percentile of the data set. Interpret the result.

b. Find the 95th percentile of the data set. Interpret the result.

c. Find the mean and standard deviation of the data; then use these values to calculate the z-score for an Arkansas county with 48 Superfund sites.

d. Based on your answer to part **c**, would you classify 48 as an extreme number of Superfund sites?

2.102 Blue- vs. red-colored exam study. In a study of how external clues influence performance, professors at the University of Alberta and Pennsylvania State University gave two different forms of a midterm examination to a large group of introductory students. The questions on the exam were identical and in the same order, but one exam was printed on blue paper and the other on red paper (*Teaching Psychology*, May 1998). Grading only the difficult questions on the exam, the researchers found that scores on the blue exam had a distribution with a mean of 53% and a standard deviation of 15%, while scores on the red exam had a distribution with a mean of 39% and a standard deviation of 12%. (Assume that both distributions are approximately mound-shaped and symmetric.)

a. Give an interpretation of the standard deviation for the students who took the blue exam.

b. Give an interpretation of the standard deviation for the students who took the red exam.

c. Suppose a student is selected at random from the group of students who participated in the study and the student's score on the difficult questions is 20%. Which exam form is the student more likely to have taken, the blue or the red exam? Explain.

2.103 Ranking PhD programs in economics. Thousands of students apply for admission to graduate schools in eco-
ECOPHD nomics each year with the intention of obtaining a PhD. The *Southern Economic Journal* (Apr. 2008) published a guide to graduate study in economics by ranking the PhD programs at 129 colleges and universities. Each program was evaluated according to the number of publications published by faculty teaching in the PhD program and by the quality of the publications. Data obtained from the Social Science Citation Index (SSCI) were used to

calculate an overall productivity score for each PhD program. The mean and standard deviation of these 129 productivity scores were then used to compute a z-score for each economics program. Harvard University had the highest z-score (z = 5.08) and, hence, was the top-ranked school; Howard University was ranked last because it had the lowest z-score (z = −0.81). The data (z-scores) for all 129 economic programs are saved in the data file.

a. Interpret the z-score for Harvard University.

b. Interpret the z-score for Howard University.

c. The authors of the *Southern Economic Journal* article note that "only 44 of the 129 schools have positive z-scores, indicating that the distribution of overall productivity is skewed to the right." Do you agree? (Check your answer by constructing a histogram for the z-scores in the file.)

Applying the Concepts—Advanced

2.104 Using z-scores for grades. At one university, the students are given z-scores at the end of each semester rather than the traditional GPAs. The mean and standard deviation of all students' cumulative GPAs, on which the z-scores are based, are 2.7 and .5, respectively.

a. Translate each of the following z-scores to the corresponding GPA: $z = 2.0$, $z = -1.0$, $z = .5$, $z = -2.5$.

b. Students with z-scores below −1.6 are put on probation. What is the corresponding probationary GPA?

c. The president of the university wishes to graduate the top 16% of the students with *cum laude* honors and the top 2.5% with *summa cum laude* honors. Where (approximately) should the limits be set in terms of z-scores? In terms of GPAs? What assumption, if any, did you make about the distribution of the GPAs at the university?

2.105 Ranking PhD programs in economics (cont'd). Refer to the *Southern Economic Journal* (Apr. 2008) study of PhD programs in economics, Exercise 2.103. The authors also made the following observation: "A noticeable feature of this skewness is that distinction between schools diminishes as the rank declines. For example, the top-ranked school, Harvard, has a z-score of 5.08, and the fifth-ranked school, Yale, has a z-score of 2.18, a substantial difference. However,…,the 70th-ranked school, the University of Massachusetts, has a z-score of –0.43, and the 80th-ranked school, the University of Delaware, has a z-score of –0.50, a very small difference. [Consequently] the ordinal rankings presented in much of the literature that ranks economics departments miss the fact that below a relatively small group of top programs, the differences in [overall] productivity become fairly small." Do you agree?

2.7 Methods for Detecting Outliers: Box Plots and z-Scores

Sometimes it is important to identify inconsistent or unusual measurements in a data set. An observation that is unusually large or small relative to the data values we want to describe is called an *outlier.*

Outliers are often attributable to one of several causes. First, the measurement associated with the outlier may be invalid. For example, the experimental procedure used to generate the measurement may have malfunctioned, the experimenter may have misrecorded the measurement, or the data might have been coded incorrectly in the computer. Second, the outlier may be the result of a misclassified measurement—that is, the measurement belongs to a population different from which the rest of the sample was drawn. Finally, the measurement associated with the outlier may be recorded correctly and be from the same population as the rest of the sample but represent a rare (chance) event. Such outliers occur most often when the relative frequency distribution of the sample data is extremely skewed because such a distribution has a tendency to include extremely large or small observations relative to the others in the data set.

> An observation (or measurement) that is unusually large or small relative to the other values in a data set is called an **outlier.** Outliers typically are attributable to one of the following causes:
>
> **1.** The measurement is observed, recorded, or entered into the computer incorrectly.
>
> **2.** The measurement comes from a different population.
>
> **3.** The measurement is correct but represents a rare (chance) event.

Two useful methods for detecting outliers, one graphical and one numerical, are **box plots** and z-scores. The box plot is based on the *quartiles* (defined in Section 2.6) of a data set. Specifically, a box plot is based on the *interquartile range* (IQR), the distance between the lower and upper quartiles:

$$IQR = Q_U - Q_L$$

> The **interquartile range (IQR)** is the distance between the lower and upper quartiles:
>
> $$IQR = Q_U - Q_L$$

An annotated Minitab box plot for the 50 companies' percentages of revenues spent on R&D (Table 2.2) is shown in Figure 2.28.* Note that a rectangle (the box) is drawn, with the top and bottom sides of the rectangle (the **hinges**) drawn at the quartiles Q_L and Q_U, respectively. Recall that Q_L represents the 25th percentile and Q_U represents the 75th percentile. By definition, then, the "middle" 50% of the observations—those between Q_L and Q_U—fall inside the box. For the R&D data, these quartiles are at 7.05 and 9.625 (see Figure 2.24, p. 87). Thus,

$$IQR = 9.625 - 7.05 = 2.575$$

The median is shown at 8.05 by a horizontal line within the box.

Figure 2.28

Annotated Minitab box plot for 50 R&D percentages

To guide the construction of the "tails" of the box plot, two sets of limits, called **inner fences** and **outer fences,** are used. Neither set of fences actually appears on the box plot. Inner fences are located at a distance of 1.5(IQR) from the hinges. Emanating from the hinges of the box are vertical lines called the **whiskers.** The two whiskers extend to the most extreme observation inside the inner fences. For example, the inner fence on the lower side (bottom) of the R&D percentage box plot is

$$\text{Lower inner fence} = \text{Lower hinge} - 1.5(IQR)$$
$$= 7.05 - 1.5(2.575)$$
$$= 7.05 - 3.863 = 3.187$$

The smallest measurement in the data set is 5.2, which is well inside this inner fence. Thus, the lower whisker extends to 5.2. Similarly, the upper whisker extends to the most extreme observation inside the upper inner fence, where

$$\text{Upper inner fence} = \text{Upper hinge} + 1.5(IQR)$$
$$= 9.625 + 1.5(2.575)$$
$$= 9.625 + 3.863 = 13.488$$

The largest measurement inside this fence is the third largest measurement, 13.2. Note that the longer upper whisker reveals the rightward skewness of the R&D distribution.

Values that are beyond the inner fences are deemed *potential outliers* because they are extreme values that represent relatively rare occurrences. In fact, for mound-shaped distributions, fewer than 1% of the observations are expected to fall outside the inner fences. Two of the 50 R&D measurements, both at 13.5, fall outside the upper inner fence. Each of these potential outliers is represented by the asterisk (*) at 13.5.

*Although box plots can be generated by hand, the amount of detail required makes them particularly well suited for computer generation. We use computer software to generate the box plots in this section.

The other two imaginary fences, the outer fences, are defined at a distance 3(IQR) from each end of the box. Measurements that fall beyond the outer fence are represented by 0s (zeros) and are very extreme measurements that require special analysis. Because less than one-hundredth of 1% (.01% or .0001) of the measurements from mound-shaped distributions are expected to fall beyond the outer fence, these measurements are considered to be *outliers*. No measurement in the R&D percentage box plot (Figure 2.28) is represented by a 0; thus there are no outliers.

Recall that outliers are extreme measurements that stand out from the rest of the sample and may be faulty: They may be incorrectly recorded observations, members of a population different from the rest of the sample, or, at the least, very unusual measurements from the same population. For example, the two R&D measurements at 13.5 (identified by an asterisk) may be considered outliers. When we analyze these measurements, we find that they are correctly recorded. However, it turns out that both represent R&D expenditures of relatively young and fast-growing companies. Thus, the outlier analysis may have revealed important factors that relate to the R&D expenditures of high-tech companies: their age and rate of growth. Outlier analysis often reveals useful information of this kind and therefore plays an important role in the statistical inference-making process.

In addition to detecting outliers, box plots provide useful information on the variation in a data set. The elements (and nomenclature) of box plots are summarized in the next box. Some aids to the interpretation of box plots are also given.

Elements of a Box Plot

1. A rectangle (the **box**) is drawn with the ends (the **hinges**) drawn at the lower and upper quartiles (Q_L and Q_U). The median (Q_M) of the data is shown in the box, usually by a line or a symbol (such as "+").

2. The points at distances 1.5(IQR) from each hinge define the **inner fences** of the data set. Lines (the **whiskers**) are drawn from each hinge to the most extreme measurement inside the inner fence. Thus,

$$\text{Lower inner fence} = Q_L - 1.5(\text{IQR})$$
$$\text{Upper inner fence} = Q_U + 1.5(\text{IQR})$$

3. A second pair of fences, the **outer fences,** are defined at a distance of 3 interquartile ranges, 3(IQR) from the hinges. One symbol (usually "*") is used to represent measurements falling between the inner and outer fences, and another (usually "0") is used to represent measurements beyond the outer fences. Outer fences are not shown unless one or more measurements lie beyond them:

$$\text{Lower outer fence} = Q_L - 3(\text{IQR})$$
$$\text{Upper outer fence} = Q_U + 3(\text{IQR})$$

4. The symbols used to represent the median and the extreme data points (those beyond the fences) will vary depending on the software you use to construct the box plot. (You may use your own symbols if you are constructing a box plot by hand.) You should consult the program's documentation to determine exactly which symbols are used.

Aids to the Interpretation of Box Plots

1. The line (median) inside the box represents the "center" of the distribution of data.

2. Examine the length of the box. The IQR is a measure of the sample's variability and is especially useful for the comparison of two samples (see Example 2.17).

3. Visually compare the lengths of the whiskers. If one is clearly longer, the distribution of the data is probably skewed in the direction of the longer whisker.

4. Analyze any measurements that lie beyond the fences. Fewer than 5% should fall beyond the inner fences, even for very skewed distributions. Measurements beyond the outer fences are probably outliers, with one of the following explanations:

    a. The measurement is incorrect. It may have been observed, recorded, or entered into the computer incorrectly.
    b. The measurement belongs to a population different from the population that the rest of the sample was drawn from (see Example 2.17).
    c. The measurement is correct *and* from the same population as the rest. Generally, we accept this explanation only after carefully ruling out all others.

Example	2.16

Interpreting a Box Plot— Lost Price Quotes

Problem In Example 2.2 (p. 55) we analyzed 50 processing times (listed in Table 2.4) for the development of price quotes by the manufacturer of industrial wheels. The intent was to determine whether the success or failure in obtaining the order was related to the amount of time to process the price quotes. Each quote that corresponds to "lost" business was so classified. Use a statistical software package to draw a box plot for all 50 processing times. What does the box plot reveal about the data? Identify any outliers in the data set.

Solution The Minitab box plot printout for these data is shown in Figure 2.29. Note that the upper whisker is much longer than the lower whisker, indicating rightward skewness of the data. However, the most important feature of the data is made very obvious by the box plot: There are four measurements (indicated by asterisks) that are beyond the upper inner fence. Thus, the distribution is extremely skewed to the right, and several measurements—or outliers—need special attention in our analysis. Examination of the data reveals that these four outliers correspond to processing times 14.06, 14.32, 16.29, and 20.23 days.

Look Back Before removing outliers from the data set, a good analyst will make a concerted effort to find the cause of the outliers. We offer an explanation for these processing time outliers in the next example.

Figure 2.29

Minitab box plot for processing time data

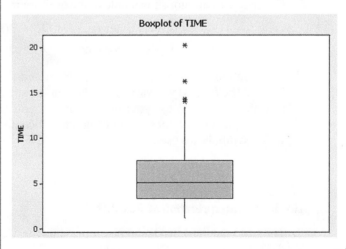

■ **Now Work Exercise 2.108**

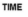

Example 2.17

Comparing Box Plots— Lost Price Quotes

Problem Refer to Example 2.16. The box plot for the 50 processing times (Figure 2.29) does not explicitly reveal the differences, if any, between the set of times corresponding to the success and the set of times corresponding to the failure to obtain the business. Box plots corresponding to the 39 "won" and 11 "lost" bids were generated using SPSS and are shown in Figure 2.30. Interpret them.

Solution The division of the data set into two parts, corresponding to won and lost bids, eliminates any observations that are beyond the inner fences. Furthermore, the skewness in the distributions has been reduced, as evidenced by the fact that the up-

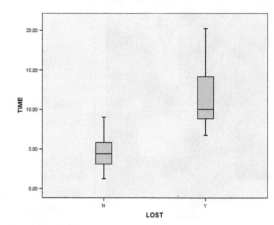

Figure 2.30
SPSS box plots of processing times for won and lost bids

per whiskers are only slightly longer than the lower. The box plots also reveal that the processing times corresponding to the lost bids tend to exceed those of the won bids. A plausible explanation for the outliers in the combined box plot (Figure 2.29) is that they are from a different population than the bulk of the times. In other words, there are two populations represented by the sample of processing times—one corresponding to lost bids and the other to won bids.

Look Back The box plots lend support to the conclusion that the price quote processing time and the success of acquiring the business are related. However, whether the visual differences between the box plots generalize to inferences about the populations corresponding to these two samples is a matter for inferential statistics, not graphical descriptions. We'll discuss how to use samples to compare two populations using inferential statistics in Chapter 8.

■ **Now Work Exercise 2.110**

The following example illustrates how *z*-scores can be used to detect outliers and make inferences.

Example 2.18

Inference Using *z*-Scores—Salary Discrimination

Problem Suppose a female bank employee believes that her salary is low as a result of sex discrimination. To substantiate her belief, she collects information on the salaries of her male counterparts in the banking business. She finds that their salaries have a mean of \$64,000 and a standard deviation of \$2,000. Her salary is \$57,000. Does this information support her claim of sex discrimination?

Solution The analysis might proceed as follows: First, we calculate the *z*-score for the woman's salary with respect to those of her male counterparts. Thus,

$$z = \frac{\$57,000 - \$64,000}{\$2,000} = -3.5$$

The implication is that the woman's salary is 3.5 standard deviations *below* the mean of the male salary distribution. Furthermore, if a check of the male salary data shows that the frequency distribution is mound-shaped, we can infer that very few salaries in this distribution should have a *z*-score less than −3, as shown in Figure 2.31. Clearly, a *z*-score of −3.5 represents an outlier. Either this female's salary is from a distribution different from the male salary distribution, or it is a very unusual (highly improbable) measurement from a distribution that is no different from the male salary distribution.

Figure 2.31
Male salary distribution

Look Back Which of the two situations do you think prevails? Statistical thinking would lead us to conclude that her salary does not come from the male salary distribution, lending support to the female bank employee's claim of sex discrimination. A careful investigator should aquire more information before inferring sex discrimination as the cause. We would want to know more about the data-collection technique the woman used and more about her competence at her job. Also, perhaps other factors such as length of employment should be considered in the analysis.

■ **Now Work Exercise 2.106**

Examples 2.17 and 2.18 exemplify an approach to statistical inference that might be called the **rare-event approach.** An experimenter hypothesizes a specific frequency distribution to describe a population of measurements. Then a sample of measurements is drawn from the population. If the experimenter finds it unlikely that the sample came from the hypothesized distribution, the hypothesis is concluded to be false. Thus, in Example 2.18 the woman believes her salary reflects discrimination. She hypothesizes that her salary should be just another measurement in the distribution of her male counterparts' salaries if no discrimination exists. However, it is so unlikely that the sample (in this case, her salary) came from the male frequency distribution that she rejects that hypothesis, concluding that the distribution from which her salary was drawn is different from the distribution for the men.

This rare-event approach to inference-making is discussed further in later chapters. Proper application of the approach requires a knowledge of probability, the subject of our next chapter.

We conclude this section with some rules of thumb for detecting outliers.

Rules of Thumb for Detecting Outliers*

Box Plots: Observations falling between the inner and outer fences are deemed *suspect outliers.* Observations falling beyond the outer fence are deemed *highly suspect outliers.*

Suspect Outliers	Highly Suspect Outliers
Between $Q_L - 1.5(IQR)$ and $Q_L - 3(IQR)$ or Between $Q_U + 1.5(IQR)$ and $Q_U + 3(IQR)$	Below $Q_L - 3(IQR)$ or Above $Q_U + 3(IQR)$

z-scores: Observations with z-scores greater than 3 in absolute value are considered outliers. For some highly skewed data sets, observations with z-scores greater than 2 in absolute value may be outliers.

Possible Outliers	Outliers
$|z| > 2$	$|z| > 3$

---

*The z-score and box plot methods both establish rule-of-thumb limits outside of which a measurement is deemed to be an outlier. Usually, the two methods produce similar results. However, the presence of one or more outliers in a data set can inflate the computed value of s. Consequently, it will be less likely that an errant observation would have a z-score larger than 3 in absolute value. In contrast, the values of the quartiles used to calculate the intervals for a box plot are not affected by the presence of outliers.

Detecting Outliers

In the *Journal of Experimental Social Psychology* (Vol. 45, 2009) study on whether money can buy love, recall that the researchers measured the quantitative variable *birthday gift price* (dollars) for each of the 237 participants. Are there any unusual reported prices in the **BUYLOV** data set? We will apply both the box plot and z-score methods to aid in identifying any outliers in the data. Since from previous analyses, there appears to be a difference in the distribution of reported prices for gift-givers and gift-recipients, we will analyze the data by role.

z-Score Method: To employ the z-score method, we require the mean and standard deviation of the data for each role type. These values were already computed in the previous Statistics in Action Revisited section. For gift-givers, $\bar{x} = \$105.84$ and $s = \$93.47$; for gift-recipients, $\bar{x} = \$149.00$ and $s = \$134.50$ (see Figure SIA2.8). Then, the 3-standard-deviation interval for each role is calculated as follows:

$$Givers: \quad \bar{x} \pm 3s = 105.84 \pm 3(93.47) = 105.84 \pm 280.41 = (0, 386.25)$$
$$Receivers: \quad \bar{x} \pm 3s = 149.00 \pm 3(134.50) = 149.00 \pm 403.50 = (0, 552.50)$$

(*Note:* Since price cannot be negative, we replaced negative lower endpoints with 0.) If you examine the gift prices for givers reported in the data set, you will find that only one ($431) falls beyond the 3-standard-deviation interval. None of the prices for receivers fall outside the 3-standard-deviation interval. Consequently, if we use the z-score approach, there is only one highly suspect outlier in the gift price data.

Box Plot Method: Box plots for the data are shown in Figure SIA2.9. Although several suspect outliers (asterisks) are shown on the box plot for each role type, there are no highly suspect outliers (zeros) shown. That is, no gift prices fall beyond the outer fences of the box plots.

Figure SIA2.9

Minitab box plots for birthday gift price by role

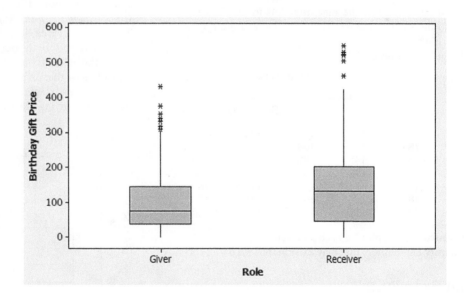

Although not detected by the box plot method, the z-score method did detect one highly suspect outlier—the gift price of $431 reported by a birthday gift-giver. The researchers should investigate whether or not to include this observation in any analysis that leads to an inference about the population of gift-givers. Is the outlier a legitimate value (in which case it will remain in the data set for analysis), or is the outlier associated with a gift-giver who is not a member of the population of interest—say, a person who mistakenly reported on the price of a wedding gift rather than a birthday gift (in which case it will be removed from the data set prior to analysis)?

Data Set: BUYLOVE

Exercises 2.106–2.120

Learning the Mechanics

2.106 A sample data set has a mean of 57 and a standard deviation of 11. Determine whether each of the following sample measurements are outliers.

    a. 65
    b. 21
    c. 72
    d. 98

2.107 Suppose a data set consisting of exam scores has a lower quartile $Q_L = 60$, a median $Q_M = 75$, and an upper quartile $Q_U = 85$. The scores on the exam range from 18 to 100. Without having the actual scores available to you, construct as much of the box plot as possible.

2.108 Consider the horizontal box plot shown below.

    a. What is the median of the data set (approximately)?
    b. What are the upper and lower quartiles of the data set (approximately)?
    c. What is the interquartile range of the data set (approximately)?
    d. Is the data set skewed to the left, skewed to the right, or symmetric?
    e. What percentage of the measurements in the data set lie to the right of the median? To the left of the upper quartile?
    f. Identify any outliers in the data.

2.109 Consider the following two sample data sets.

L02109

Sample A			Sample B		
121	171	158	171	152	170
173	184	163	168	169	171
157	85	145	190	183	185
165	172	196	140	173	206
170	159	172	172	174	169
161	187	100	199	151	180
142	166	171	167	170	188

    a. Construct a box plot for each data set.
    b. Identify any outliers that may exist in the two data sets.

⚙ Applet Exercise 2.7

Use the applet *Standard Deviation* to determine whether an item in a data set may be an outlier. Begin by setting appropriate limits and plotting the data below on the number line provided in the applet.

10 80 80 85 85 85 85 90 90 90 90 90 95 95 95 95 100 100

    a. The green arrow shows the approximate location of the mean. Multiply the standard deviation given by the applet by 3. Is the data item 10 more than 3 standard deviations away from the green arrow (the mean)? Can you conclude that the 10 is an outlier?
    b. Using the mean and standard deviation from part **a**, move the point at 10 on your plot to a point that appears to be about 3 standard deviations from the mean. Repeat the process in part **a** for the new plot and the new suspected outlier.
    c. When you replaced the extreme value in part **a** with a number that appeared to be within 3 standard deviations of the mean, the standard deviation got smaller and the mean moved to the right, yielding a new data set where the extreme value was not within 3 standard deviations of the mean. Continue to replace the extreme value with higher numbers until the new value is within 3 standard deviations of the mean in the new data set. Use trial and error to estimate the smallest number that can replace the 10 in the original data set so that the replacement is not considered to be an outlier.

Applying the Concepts—Basic

2.110 Treating psoriasis with the "Doctorfish of Kangal." Psoriasis is a skin disorder with no known cure and no proven effective pharmacological treatment. An alternative treatment for psoriasis is ichthyotherapy, also known as therapy with the "Doctorfish of Kangal." Fish from the hot pools of Kangal, Turkey, feed on the skin scales of bathers, reportedly reducing the symptoms of psoriasis. In one study, 67 patients diagnosed with psoriasis underwent 3 weeks of ichthyotherapy (*Evidence-Based Research in Complementary and Alternative Medicine,* Dec. 2006). The Psoriasis Area Severity Index (PASI) of each patient was measured both before and after treatment. (The lower the PASI score, the better is the skin condition.) Box plots of the PASI scores, both before (baseline) and after 3 weeks of ichthyotherapy treatment, are shown in the accompanying diagram.

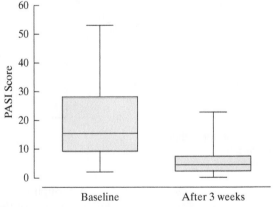

Source: Based on "Ichthyotherapy as alternative treatment for patients with psoriasis: A pilot study" by M. Grassberger and W. Hoch, from EVIDENCE-BASED RESEARCH IN COMPLEMENTARY AND ALTERNATIVE MEDICINE, December 2006, Volume 3(4).

    a. Find the approximate 25th percentile, the median, and the 75th percentile for the PASI scores before treatment.

b. Find the approximate 25th percentile, the median, and the 75th percentile for the PASI scores after treatment.

c. Comment on the effectiveness of ichthyotherapy in treating psoriasis.

2.111 Budget lapsing at army hospitals. Accountants use the term *budget lapsing* to describe the situation that occurs when unspent funds do not carry over from one budgeting period to the next. Due to budget lapsing, U.S. army hospitals tend to stockpile pharmaceuticals and other supplies toward the end of the fiscal year, leading to a spike in expenditures. This phenomenon was investigated in the *Journal of Management Accounting Research* (Vol. 19, 2007). Data on expenses per full-time equivalent employees for a sample of 1,751 army hospitals yielded the following summary statistics: $\bar{x} = \$6,563$, $m = \$6,232$, $s = \$2,484$, $Q_L = \$5,309$, and $Q_U = \$7,216$.

a. Interpret, practically, the measures of relative standing.

b. Compute the interquartile range, IQR, for the data.

c. What proportion of the 1,751 army hospitals have expenses between \$5,309 and \$7,216?

2.112 Salary offers to MBAs. Consider the top salary offer (in thousands of dollars) received by each member of a sample of 50 MBA students who graduated from the Graduate School of Management at Rutgers, the state university of New Jersey. Descriptive statistics and a box plot for the data are shown on the XLSTAT printouts below.

Statistic	SALARY
No. of observations	50
Minimum	35.0000
Maximum	75.0000
Range	40.0000
1st Quartile	45.7250
Median	51.0000
3rd Quartile	58.9000
Mean	52.3340
Variance (n-1)	85.0851
Standard deviation (n-1)	9.2242

Box plots:

Box plot (SALARY)

a. Find and interpret the z-score associated with the highest salary offer, the lowest salary offer, and the mean salary offer. Would you consider the highest offer to be unusually high? Why or why not?

b. Based on the box plot for this data set, which salary offers (if any) are suspect or highly suspect outliers?

2.113 Semester hours taken by CPA candidates. Refer to the *Journal of Accounting and Public Policy* (Spring 2002) study of 100,000 first-time candidates for the CPA exam, Exercise 2.51 (p. 72). The number of semester hours of college credit earned by the candidates had a mean of 141.31 hours and a standard deviation of 17.77 hours.

a. Find the z-score for a first-time candidate for the CPA exam who earned 160 semester hours of college credit. Is this observation considered an outlier?

b. Give a value of the number of semester hours that would, in fact, be considered an outlier in this data set.

Applying the Concepts—Intermediate

2.114 Corporate sustainability of CPA firms. Refer to the *Business and Society* (March 2011) study on the sustainability behaviors of CPA corporations, Exercise 2.100 (p. 91). Recall that data on the level of support for corporate sustainability were recorded for each of 992 senior managers. One of the managers reported a support level of 155 points. Use both a graph and a numerical technique to determine if this observation is an outlier.

2.115 Time in bankruptcy. Refer to the *Financial Management* (Spring 1995) study of 49 firms filing for prepackaged bankruptcies, Exercise 2.32 (p. 62). Recall that three types of "prepack" firms exist: (1) those who hold no prefiling vote, (2) those who vote their preference for a joint solution; and (3) those who vote their preference for a prepack.

a. Construct a box plot for the time in bankruptcy (months) for each type of firm.

b. Find the median bankruptcy times for the three types.

c. How do the variabilities of the bankruptcy times compare for the three types?

d. The standard deviations of the bankruptcy times are 2.47 for "none," 1.72 for "joint," and 0.96 for "prepack." Do the standard deviations agree with the interquartile ranges with regard to the comparison of the variabilities of the bankruptcy times?

e. Is there evidence of outliers in any of the three distributions?

2.116 Hazardous waste cleanup in Arkansas. Refer to Exercise 2.101 (p. 90) and the data on the number of Superfund sites in each of 75 Arkansas counties.

a. There is at least one outlier in the data. Use the methods of this chapter to detect the outliers.

b. Delete the outlier(s) found in part **a** from the data set and recalculate measures of central tendency and variation. Which measures are most affected by the removal of the outlier(s)?

2.117 Sanitation inspection of cruise ships. Refer to Exercise 2.81 (p. 85) and the data on the sanitation levels of passenger cruise ships.

a. Use the box plot method to detect any outliers in the data set.

b. Use the z-score method to detect any outliers in the data set.

c. Do the two methods agree? If not, explain why.

2.118 Network server downtime. A manufacturer of network computer server systems is interested in improving its customer support services. As a first step, its marketing department has been charged with the responsibility of summarizing the extent of customer problems in terms of system downtime. The 40 most recent customers were surveyed to determine the amount of downtime (in hours) they had experienced during the previous month. These data are listed in the table.

Customer Number	Downtime	Customer Number	Downtime
230	12	250	4
231	16	251	10
232	5	252	15
233	16	253	7
234	21	254	20
235	29	255	9
236	38	256	22
237	14	257	18
238	47	258	28
239	0	259	19
240	24	260	34
241	15	261	26
242	13	262	17
243	8	263	11
244	2	264	64
245	11	265	19
246	22	266	18
247	17	267	24
248	31	268	49
249	10	269	50

a. Construct a box plot for these data. Use the information reflected in the box plot to describe the frequency distribution of the data set. Your description should address central tendency, variation, and skewness.

b. Use your box plot to determine which customers are having unusually lengthy downtimes.

c. Find and interpret the z-scores associated with the customers you identified in part **b**.

Applying the Concepts—Advanced

2.119 Made-to-order delivery times. Refer to the data on delivery times for a made-to-order product, Exercise 2.34 (p. 63). The delivery times (in days) for a sample of 25 orders are repeated in the accompanying table. (Times marked by an asterisk are associated with customers who subsequently placed additional orders with the company.) Identify any unusual observations (outliers) in the data set, and then use the results to comment on the claim that repeat customers tend to have shorter delivery times than one-time customers.

50*	64*	56*	43*	64*	82*	65*	49*	32*	63*	44*	71	54*
51*	102	49*	73*	50*	39*	86	33*	95	59*	51*	68	

2.120 Sensor motion of a robot. Researchers at Carnegie Mellon University developed an algorithm for estimating the sensor motion of a robotic arm by mounting a camera with inertia sensors on the arm (*International Journal of Robotics Research*, Dec. 2004). One variable of interest is the error of estimating arm translation (measured in centimeters). Data for 10 experiments are listed in the following table. In each experiment, the perturbation of camera intrinsics and projections were varied. Suppose a trial resulted in a translation error of 4.5 cm. Is this value an outlier for trials with perturbed intrinsics but no perturbed projections? For trials with perturbed projections but no perturbed intrinsics? What type of camera perturbation most likely occurred for this trial?

Trial	Perturbed Intrinsics	Perturbed Projections	Translation Error (cm)
1	Yes	No	1.0
2	Yes	No	1.3
3	Yes	No	3.0
4	Yes	No	1.5
5	Yes	No	1.3
6	No	Yes	22.9
7	No	Yes	21.0
8	No	Yes	34.4
9	No	Yes	29.8
10	No	Yes	17.7

Source: Strelow. D., & Singh, S. "Motion estimation form image and intertial measurements," *International Journal of Robotics Research*, Vol. 23, No. 12, Dec. 2004 (Table 4). Dennis Strelow, © November 2004. Reprinted by permission of the author.

2.8 Graphing Bivariate Relationships*

The claim is often made that the crime rate and the unemployment rate are "highly correlated." Another popular belief is that the gross domestic product (GDP) and the rate of inflation are "related." Some people even believe that the Dow Jones Industrial Average and the lengths of fashionable skirts are "associated." The words *correlated*, *related*, and *associated* imply a relationship between two variables—in the examples above, two *quantitative* variables.

One way to describe the relationship between two quantitative variables–called a **bivariate relationship**—is to plot the data in a **scatterplot.** A scatterplot is a two-dimensional graph, with one variable's values plotted along the vertical axis and the other variable's values plotted along the horizontal axis. For example, Figure 2.32 is a

Figure 2.32

Scatterplot of cost vs. floor area

scatterplot relating (1) the cost of mechanical work (heating, ventilating, and plumbing) to (2) the floor area of the building for a sample of 26 factory and warehouse buildings. Note that the scatterplot suggests a general tendency for mechanical cost to increase as building floor area increases.

When an increase in one variable is generally associated with an increase in the second variable, we say that the two variables are "positively related" or "positively correlated."* Figure 2.32 implies that mechanical cost and floor area are positively correlated. Alternatively, if one variable has a tendency to decrease as the other increases, we say the variables are "negatively correlated." Figure 2.33 shows hypothetical scatterplots that portray a positive bivariate relationship (Figure 2.33a), a negative bivariate relationship (Figure 2.33b), and a situation where the two variables are unrelated (Figure 2.33c).

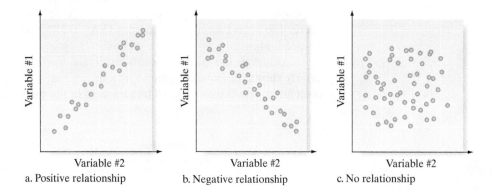

Figure 2.33

Hypothetical bivariate relationship

a. Positive relationship   b. Negative relationship   c. No relationship

Example **2.19**

Graphing Bivariate Data—Hospital Length of Stay

Problem A medical item used to treat a hospital patient is called a *factor*. For example, factors can be intravenous (IV) tubing, IV fluid, needles, shave kits, bedpans, diapers, dressings, medications, and even code carts. The coronary care unit at Bayonet Point Hospital (St. Petersburg, Florida) recently investigated the relationship between the number of factors used per patient and the patient's length of stay (in days). Data on

*A formal definition of correlation is given in Chapter 11. We will learn that correlation measures the strength of the linear (or straight-line) relationship between two quantitative variables.

these two variables for a sample of 50 coronary care patients are given in Table 2.9. Use a scatterplot to describe the relationship between the two variables of interest: number of factors and length of stay.

Table 2.9	Data on Patient's Factors and Length of Stay		
Number of Factors	Length of Stay (days)	Number of Factors	Length of Stay (days)
231	9	354	11
323	7	142	7
113	8	286	9
208	5	341	10
162	4	201	5
117	4	158	11
159	6	243	6
169	9	156	6
55	6	184	7
77	3	115	4
103	4	202	6
147	6	206	5
230	6	360	6
78	3	84	3
525	9	331	9
121	7	302	7
248	5	60	2
233	8	110	2
260	4	131	5
224	7	364	4
472	12	180	7
220	8	134	6
383	6	401	15
301	9	155	4
262	7	338	8

Source: Based on Bayonet Point Hospital, Coronary Care Unit.   *Data Set:* MEDFAC

Solution Rather than construct the plot by hand, we resort to a statistical software package. The XLSTAT plot of the data in Table 2.9, with length of stay (LOS) on the vertical axis and number of factors (FACTORS) on the horizontal axis, is shown in Figure 2.34.

Although the plotted points exhibit a fair amount of variation, the scatterplot clearly shows an increasing trend. It appears that a patient's length of stay is positively correlated with the number of factors used in the patient's care.

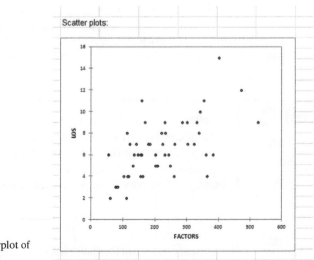

Figure 2.34

XLSTAT scatterplot of data in Table 2.9

Look Back If hospital administrators can be confident that the sample trend shown in Figure 2.34 accurately describes the trend in the population, then they may use this information to improve their forecasts of lengths of stay for future patients.

■ Now Work Exercise 2.123

The scatterplot is a simple but powerful tool for describing a bivariate relationship. However, keep in mind that it is only a graph. No measure of reliability can be attached to inferences made about bivariate populations based on scatterplots of sample data. The statistical tools that enable us to make inferences about bivariate relationships are presented in Chapter 11.

STATISTICS in ACTION REVISITED

Interpreting Scatterplots

Refer, again, to the *Journal of Experimental Social Psychology* (Vol. 45, 2009) study on whether money can buy love. Two quantitative variables of interest to the Stanford University researchers were *birthday gift price* (dollars) and *overall level of appreciation for the gift* (measured on a scale from 2 to 14). To investigate a possible relationship between these two variables, we created a scatterplot for the data collected for each of the 237 participants. The Minitab scatterplot is displayed in Figure SIA2.10a.

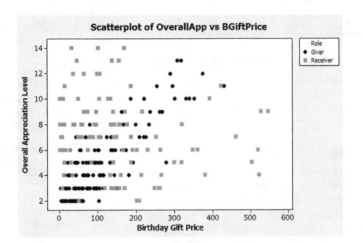

Figure SIA2.10a

Minitab scatterplot of appreciation level vs. gift price

At first glance, the graph appears to show little or no association between appreciation level and gift price. However, if you look closely you will see that the data points associated with gift-givers are plotted with a different symbol (black circle) than the data points associated with gift-recipients (red square). Focusing on just the black circles, a fairly strong positive trend is apparent. To see this trend more clearly, we generated side-by-side scatterplots for the data, one plot for givers and one for receivers. This graph is shown in Figure SIA2.10b.

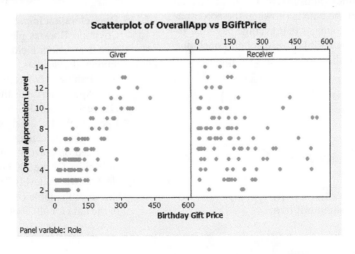

Figure SIA2.10b

Minitab side-by-side scatterplots for the study

STATISTICS in ACTION REVISITED CONTINUED

The left panel of Figure SIA2.10b shows a fairly strong positive association between appreciation level and gift price for gift-givers. As gift price increases, the gift-giver anticipates that the level of appreciation for the gift will increase. Conversely, the right panel of Figure SIA2.10b shows little or no association between appreciation level and gift price for gift-recipients. This type of analysis led the Stanford University researchers to conclude that "gift-givers and gift-receivers disagree about the link between gift price and gift-recipients' feelings of appreciation. Givers anticipated that recipients would appreciate more expensive gifts, but gift-recipients did not base their feelings of appreciation on how much the gift cost."

In Chapter 11, we show how to attach a measure of reliability to these conclusions. ◻

Exercises 2.121–2.132

Learning the Mechanics

2.121 Construct a scatterplot for the data in the following table.

Variable 1:	5	1	1.5	2	2.5	3	3.5	4	4.5	5
Variable 2:	2	1	3	4	6	10	9	12	17	17

2.122 Construct a scatterplot for the data in the following table.

Variable 1:	5	3	−1	2	7	6	4	0	8
Variable 2:	14	3	10	1	8	5	3	2	12

Applying the Concepts—Basic

2.123 In business, do nice guys really finish last? In baseball, there is an old saying that "nice guys finish last." Is this true in the competitive corporate world? Researchers at Harvard University attempted to answer this question and reported their results in *Nature* (March 20, 2008). In the study, Boston-area college students repeatedly played a version of the game "prisoner's dilemma," where competitors choose cooperation, defection, or costly punishment. (Cooperation meant paying 1 unit for the opponent to receive 2 units; defection meant gaining 1 unit at a cost of 1 unit for the opponent; and punishment meant paying 1 unit for the opponent to lose 4 units.) At the conclusion of the games, the researchers recorded the average payoff and the number of times punishment was used against each player. A graph of the data is shown in the accompanying scatterplot. Does it appear that average payoff is associated with punishment use? The researchers concluded that "winners don't punish." Do you agree? Explain.

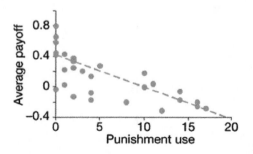

2.124 Lobster trap placement. Strategic placement of lobster traps is one of the keys for a successful lobster fisherman. An observational study of teams fishing for the red spiny lobster in Baja California Sur, Mexico, was conducted and the results published in *Bulletin of Marine Science* (April 2010). Two variables measured for each of eight teams from the Punta Abreojos (PA) fishing cooperative were y = total catch of lobsters (in kilograms) during the season and x = average percentage of traps allocated per day to exploring areas of unknown catch (called *search frequency*). These data are listed in the accompanying table. Graph the data in a scatterplot. What type of trend, if any, do you observe?

Lobster Fishing Study Data

Total Catch	Search Frequency
2,785	35
6,535	21
6,695	26
4,891	29
4,937	23
5,727	17
7,019	21
5,735	20

Source: Based on Shester, G. G. "Explaining catch variation among Baja California lobster fishers through spatial analysis of trap-placement decisions," *Bulletin of Marine Science*, Vol. 86, No. 2, April 2010 (Table 1), pp. 479–498.

2.125 Does elevation impact hitting performance in baseball? The Colorado Rockies play their Major League home baseball games at Coors Field, Denver. Each year, the Rockies are among the leaders in team batting statistics (e.g., home runs, batting average, and slugging percentage). Many baseball experts attribute this phenomenon to the "thin air" of Denver—called the "mile-high" city due to its elevation. *Chance* (Winter 2006) investigated the effects of elevation on slugging percentage in Major League Baseball. Data were compiled on players' composite slugging percentage at each of 29 cities for the 2003 season, as well as each city's elevation (feet above sea level). The data for selected observations are shown in the table on the next page. Construct a scatterplot of the data for all 29 cities. Do you detect a trend?

Data for Exercise 2.125

City	Slug Pct.	Elevation
Anaheim	.480	160
Arlington	.605	616
Atlanta	.530	1,050
Baltimore	.505	130
Boston	.505	20
⋮	⋮	⋮
Denver	.625	5,277
⋮	⋮	⋮
Seattle	.550	350
San Francisco	.510	63
St. Louis	.570	465
Tampa	.500	10
Toronto	.535	566

Source: Schaffer, J., & Heiny. E. L. "The effects of elevation on slugging percentage in Major League Baseball." *Chance,* Vol. 19, No. 1. Winter 2006 (adapted from Figure 2, p. 30).

2.126 State SAT scores. Refer to Exercise 2.27 (p. 60) and the data on state SAT scores. Construct a scatterplot for the SATMAT data, with 2001 Math SAT score on the horizontal axis and 2011 Math SAT score on the vertical axis. What type of trend do you detect?

2.127 Are geography journals worth their cost? In *Geoforum* (Vol. 37, 2006), Simon Fraser University professor Nicholas GEOJRN Blomley assessed whether the price of a geography journal is correlated with quality. He collected pricing data (cost for a 1-year subscription in U.S. dollars) for a sample of 28 geography journals. In addition to cost, three other variables were measured: Journal Impact Factor (JIF), defined as

Journal	Cost ($)	JIF	Cites	RPI
J. Econ. Geogr.	468	3.139	207	1.16
Prog. Hum. Geog.	624	2.943	544	0.77
T. I. Brit. Geogr.	499	2.388	249	1.11
Econ. Geogr.	90	2.325	173	0.30
A. A. A. Geogr.	698	2.115	377	0.93
Antipode	717	1.922	333	0.96
Reg. Stud.	1,312	1.652	445	1.49
Environ. Plan A	1,297	1.622	773	0.91
Environ. Plan D	479	1.591	297	0.99
Geoforum	1,118	1.560	298	1.58
Area	242	1.475	215	0.53
Polit. Geogr.	1,099	1.316	282	1.92
Int. J. Geogr. IS	1,733	1.234	240	3.42
Landscape. Ur. Plan	1,619	1.204	446	1.56
Sing. J. Trop. Geo.	197	1.029	62	1.13
Aust. Geogr.	345	0.947	72	1.83
Eur. Geogr. Eco.	499	0.780	62	1.99
Urban. Geogr.	530	0.667	135	1.81
J. Hist. Geogr.	388	0.661	96	1.44
Tij. Eco. Soc. Geo	343	0.518	99	1.00
Cult. Geogr.	538	0.500	24	NA
Pap. Reg. Sci.	397	0.481	89	1.36
Can. Geo. Can.	253	0.429	74	1.05
J. Geo. High. Ed.	1,115	0.413	79	4.33
Cartogr. J.	266	0.295	18	3.11
Geogr. Anal.	213	0.902	106	0.88
Geogr. J.	223	0.857	81	0.94
Appl. Geogr.	646	0.853	74	3.38

Source: Data from Blomley, N. "Is this journal worth US$1118?. "*Geoforum,* Vol. 37, 2006.

the average number of times articles from the journal have been cited; number of citations for a journal over the past 5 years; and Relative Price Index (RPI), a measure developed by economists. [*Note:* A journal with an RPI less than 1.25 is considered a "good value."] The data for the 28 geography journals are listed in the accompanying table.

a. Construct a scatterplot for the variables JIF and cost. Do you detect a trend?

b. Construct a scatterplot for the variables number of cites and cost. Do you detect a trend?

c. Construct a scatterplot for the variables RPI and cost. Do you detect a trend?

Applying the Concepts—Intermediate

2.128 Spreading rate of spilled liquid. A contract engineer at DuPont Corp. studied the rate at which a spilled volatile LSPILL liquid will spread across a surface (*Chemical Engineering Progress,* Jan. 2005). Assume 50 gallons of methanol spills onto a level surface outdoors. The engineer used derived empirical formulas (assuming a state of turbulent-free convection) to calculate the mass (in pounds) of the spill after a period of time ranging from 0 to 60 minutes. The calculated mass values are given in the table. Is there evidence to indicate that the mass of the spill tends to diminish as time increases? Support your answer with a scatterplot.

Time (minutes)	Mass (pounds)
0	6.64
1	6.34
2	6.04
4	5.47
6	4.94
8	4.44
10	3.98
12	3.55
14	3.15
16	2.79
18	2.45
20	2.14
22	1.86
24	1.60
26	1.37
28	1.17
30	0.98
35	0.60
40	0.34
45	0.17
50	0.06
55	0.02
60	0.00

Source: Based on Barry. J. "Estimating rates of spreading and evaporation of volatile liquids." *Chemical Engineering Progress,.* Vol. 101, No. 1. Jan. 2005, p. 38.

2.129 Performance ratings of government agencies. The U.S. Office of Management and Budget (OMB) requires government agencies to produce annual performance and PARS accounting reports (PARS) each year. A research team at George Mason University evaluated the quality of the PARS for 24 government agencies (*The Public Manager,* Summer 2008). Evaluation scores ranged from 12 (lowest) to 60 (highest). The PARS evaluation scores for two consecutive years are shown in the next table.

Data for Exercise 2.129

Agency	Year 1	Year 2
Transportation	55	53
Labor	53	51
Veterans	51	51
NRC	39	34
Commerce	37	36
HHS	37	35
DHS	37	30
Justice	35	37
Treasury	35	35
GSA	34	40
Agriculture	33	35
EPA	33	36
Social Security	33	33
USAID	32	42
Education	32	36
Interior	32	31
NASA	32	32
Energy	31	34
HUD	31	30
NSF	31	31
State	31	50
OPM	27	28
SBA	22	31
Defense	17	32

Source: "Performance ratings of government agencies," by J. Ellig and H. Wray, from Measuring Performance Reporting Quality. THE PUBLIC MANAGER, Vol. 37.2, Summer 2008, p. 68. Copyright © 2008 by Jerry Ellig. Reprinted with permission.

a. Construct a scatterplot for the data. Do you detect a trend in the data?

b. Based on the graph, identify one or two agencies that had greater than expected PARS evaluation scores for year 2.

2.130 Most valuable NFL teams. Refer to the *Forbes* listing of the 2011 values of the 32 teams in the National Football League (NFL), Exercise 2.26 (p. 60). Construct a scatterplot to investigate the relationship between 2011 value ($ millions) and operating income ($ millions). Would you recommend that an NFL executive use operating income to predict a team's current value? Explain.

2.131 Doctors and ethics. Refer to the *Journal of Medical Ethics* (Vol. 32, 2006) study of physicians' use of ethics consultation, Exercise 2.68 (p. 79). In addition to *length of time in practice* (i.e., years of experience), the researchers also measured the *amount of exposure to ethics in medical school* (number of hours) for the sample of 118 physicians.

a. Use data from the accompanying file to create a scatterplot for these two variables. Plot years of experience on the vertical axis and amount of exposure to ethics in medical school on the horizontal axis. Comment on the strength of the association between these two variables.

b. Conduct an outlier analysis of the data for the variable *amount of exposure to ethics in medical school.* Identify the highly suspect outlier in the data set.

c. Remove the outlier, part **b,** from the data set and re-create the scatterplot of part **a.** What do you observe?

Applying the Concepts—Advanced

2.132 Ranking driving performance of professional golfers. Refer to *The Sport Journal* (Winter 2007) analysis of a new method for ranking the total driving performance of golfers on the PGA tour, Exercise 2.50 (p. 72). Recall that the method uses both the average driving distance (yards) and driving accuracy (percent of drives that land in the fairway). Data on these two variables for the top 40 PGA golfers are saved in the accompanying file. A professional golfer is practicing a new swing to increase his average driving distance. However, he is concerned that his driving accuracy will be lower. Is his concern a valid one? Explain.

2.9 The Time Series Plot*

Each of the previous sections has been concerned with describing the information contained in a sample or population of data. Often these data are viewed as having been produced at essentially the same point in time. Thus, time has not been a factor in any of the graphical methods described so far.

Data of interest to managers are often produced and monitored over time. Examples include the daily closing price of their company's common stock, the company's weekly sales volume and quarterly profits, and characteristics—such as weight and length—of products produced by the company.

> Data that are produced and monitored over time are called **time series data.**

Recall from Section 1.4 that a process is a series of actions or operations that generates output over time. Accordingly, measurements taken of a sequence of units produced by a process–such as a production process—are time series data. In general, any sequence of numbers produced over time can be thought of as being generated by a process.

When measurements are made over time, it is important to record both the numerical value and the time or the time period associated with each measurement. With this information, a **time series plot**—sometimes called a **run chart**—can be constructed to describe the time series data and to learn about the process that generated the data.

A time series plot is simply a scatterplot with the measurements on the vertical axis and time or the order in which the measurements were made on the horizontal axis. The plotted points are usually connected by straight lines to make it easier to see the changes and movement in the measurements over time. For example, Figure 2.35 is a time series plot of a particular company's monthly sales (number of units sold per month). And Figure 2.36 is a time series plot of the weights of 30 one-gallon paint cans that were consecutively filled by the same filling head. Notice that the weights are plotted against the order in which the cans were filled rather than some unit of time. When monitoring production processes, it is often more convenient to record the order rather than the exact time at which each measurement was made.

Time series plots reveal the movement (trend) and changes (variation) in the variable being monitored. Notice how sales trend upward in the summer and how the variation in the weights of the paint cans increases over time. This kind of information would not be revealed by stem-and-leaf displays or histograms, as the following example illustrates.

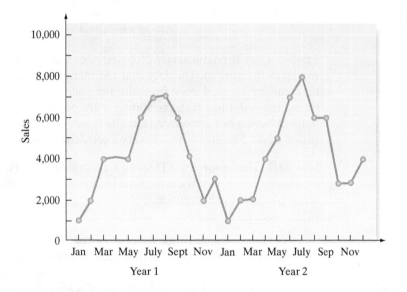

Figure 2.35

Time series plot of company sales

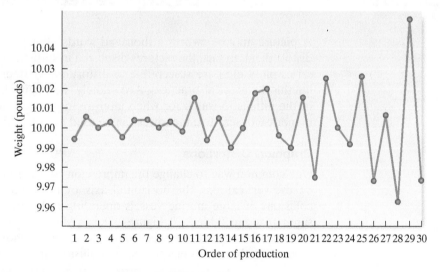

Figure 2.36

Time series plot of paint can weights

Example **2.20**

Time Series Plot vs. a Histogram—Deming's Example

Problem W. Edwards Deming was one of America's most famous statisticians. He was best known for the role he played after World War II in teaching the Japanese how to improve the quality of their products by monitoring and continually improving their production processes. In his book *Out of the Crisis* (1986), Deming warned against the knee-jerk (i.e., automatic) use of histograms to display and extract information from data. As evidence, he offered the following example.

Fifty camera springs were tested in the order in which they were produced. The elongation of each spring was measured under the pull of 20 grams. Both a time series plot and a histogram were constructed from the measurements. They are shown in Figure 2.37, which has been reproduced from Deming's book. If you had to predict the elongation measurement of the next spring to be produced (i.e., spring 51) and could use only one of the two plots to guide your prediction, which would you use? Why?

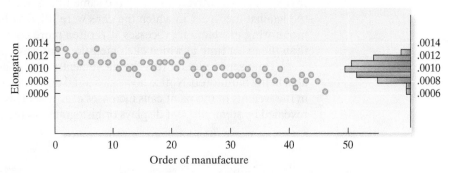

Figure 2.37

Deming's time series plot and histogram

Solution Only the time series plot describes the behavior *over time* of the process that produces the springs. The fact that the elongation measurements are decreasing over time can be gleaned only from the time series plot. Because the histogram does not reflect the order in which the springs were produced, it in effect represents all observations as having been produced simultaneously. Using the histogram to predict the elongation of the 51st spring would very likely lead to an overestimate.

Look Back The lesson from Deming's example is this: For displaying and analyzing data that have been generated over time by a process, the primary graphical tool is the time series plot, not the histogram.

We cover many other aspects of the statistical analysis of time series data in Chapter 14 (available on a CD that accompanies the text).

2.10 Distorting the Truth with Descriptive Techniques

A picture may be "worth a thousand words," but pictures can also color messages or distort them. In fact, the pictures displayed in statistics (e.g., histograms, bar charts, time series plots, etc.) are susceptible to distortion, whether unintentional or as a result of unethical statistical practices. Accordingly, we begin this section by mentioning a few of the pitfalls to watch for when interpreting a chart or a graph. Then we discuss how numerical descriptive measures can be used to distort the truth.

Graphical Distortions

One common way to change the impression conveyed by a graph is to change the scale on the vertical axis, the horizontal axis, or both. For example, consider the data on collisions of large marine vessels operating in European waters over a 5-year period summarized in Table 2.10. Figure 2.38 is a Minitab bar graph showing the frequency of collisions for each of the three locations. The graph shows that "in port" collisions occur more often than collisions "at sea" or collisions in "restricted waters."

Table 2.10	Collisions of Marine Vessels by Location
Location	Number of Ships
At sea	376
Restricted waters	273
In port	478
TOTAL	1,127

 Data Set: MARINE

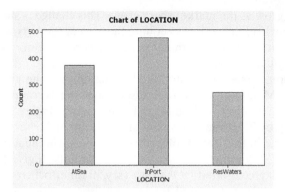

Figure 2.38

Minitab bar graph of vessel collisions by location

Suppose you want to use the same data to exaggerate the difference between the number of "in port" collisions and the number of collisions in "restricted waters." One way to do this is to increase the distance between successive units on the vertical axis—that is, to *stretch* the vertical axis by graphing only a few units per inch. A telltale sign of stretching is a long vertical axis, but this is often hidden by starting the vertical axis at some point above the origin, 0. Such a graph is shown in the SPSS printout, Figure 2.39. By starting the bar chart at 250 collisions (instead of at 0), it appears that the frequency of "in port" collisions is many times larger than the frequency of collisions in "restricted waters."

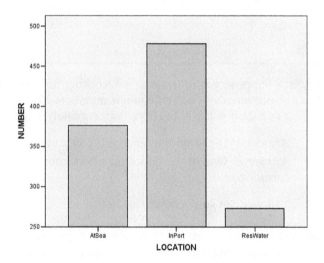

Figure 2.39

SPSS bar graph of vessel collisions by location—adjusted vertical axis

ETHICS in STATISTICS

Intentionally distorting a graph to portray a particular viewpoint is considered *unethical statistical practice*.

Another method of achieving visual distortion with bar graphs is by making the width of the bars proportional to the height. For example, look at the bar chart in Figure 2.40a, which depicts the percentage of a year's total automobile sales attributable to each of four major manufacturers. Now suppose we make both the width and the

Figure 2.40

Relative share of the automobile market for each of four major manufacturers

a. Bar chart   b. Width of bars grows with height

Production declines again

a.

2012: 2nd best year for production

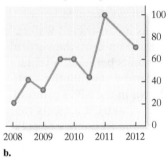

b.

Figure 2.41

Changing the verbal description to change a viewer's interpretation

height grow as the market share grows. This change is shown in Figure 2.40b. The distortion may lead the reader to equate the *area* of the bars with the relative market share of each manufacturer. But the fact is the true relative market share is proportional only to the *height* of the bars.

Sometimes, we do not need to manipulate the graph to distort the impression it creates. Modifying the verbal description that accompanies the graph can change the interpretation that will be made by the viewer. Figure 2.41 provides a good illustration of this ploy. The time series plots show the annual level of production of a firm. The only difference in the two graphs is the headings. The heading "Production declines again" in Figure 2.41a might be used if the firm wants to give the impression that it is underperforming compared to the past (say, in an effort to convince the government that it should not be prosecuted for monopolistic practices). In contrast, the heading "2012: 2nd best year for production" in Figure 2.41b might be intended for stockholders (to give the impression that the firm's stock is a wise investment).

Although we've discussed only a few of the ways that graphs can be used to convey misleading pictures of phenomena, the lesson is clear. Look at all graphical descriptions of data with a critical eye. Particularly, check the axes and the size of the units on each axis. Ignore the visual changes and concentrate on the actual numerical changes indicated by the graph or chart.

Misleading Numerical Descriptive Statistics

The information in a data set can also be distorted by using numerical descriptive measures, as Example 2.21 indicates.

Example 2.21

Misleading Descriptive Statistics — Your Average Salary

Problem Suppose you're considering working for a small law firm—one that currently has a senior member and three junior members. You inquire about the salary you could expect to earn if you join the firm. Unfortunately, you receive two answers:

Answer A: The senior member tells you that an "average employee" earns $107,500.

Answer B: One of the junior members later tells you that an "average employee" earns $95,000.

Which answer can you believe?

Solution The confusion exists because the phrase "average employee" has not been clearly defined. Suppose the four salaries paid are $95,000 for each of the three junior members and $145,000 for the senior member. Thus,

$$\text{Mean} = \frac{3(\$95,000) + \$145,000}{4} = \frac{\$430,000}{4} = \$107,500$$

$$\text{Median} = \$95,000$$

You can now see how the two answers were obtained. The senior member reported the mean of the four salaries, and the junior member reported the median. The information you received was distorted because neither person stated which measure of central tendency was being used.

Look Back Based on our earlier discussion of the mean and median, we would probably prefer the median as the measure that best describes the salary of the "average" employee.

Another distortion of information in a sample occurs when *only* a measure of central tendency is reported. Both a measure of central tendency and a measure of variability are needed to obtain an accurate mental image of a data set.

Suppose you want to buy a new car and are trying to decide which of two models to purchase. Because energy and economy are both important issues, you decide to purchase model A because its EPA mileage rating is 32 miles per gallon in the city, whereas the mileage rating for model B is only 30 miles per gallon in the city.

However, you may have acted too quickly. How much variability is associated with the ratings? As an extreme example, suppose that further investigation reveals that the standard deviation for model A mileages is 5 miles per gallon, whereas that for model B is only 1 mile per gallon. If the mileages form a mound-shaped distribution, they might appear as shown in Figure 2.42. Note that the larger amount of variability associated with model A implies that more risk is involved in purchasing model A—that is, the particular car you purchase is more likely to have a mileage rating that will greatly differ from the EPA rating of 32 miles per gallon if you purchase model A, while a model B car is not likely to vary from the 30-miles-per-gallon rating by more than 2 miles per gallon.

Figure 2.42

Mileage distributions for two car models

We conclude this section with another example on distorting the truth with numerical descriptive measures.

Example 2.22

More Misleading Descriptive Statistics— Delinquent Children

Problem *Children out of School in America* is a report on delinquency of school-age children prepared by the Children's Defense Fund (CDF), a government-sponsored organization. Consider the following three reported results of the CDF survey.

- Reported result 1: 25% of the 16- and 17-year-olds in the Portland, Maine, Bayside East Housing Project were out of school. Fact: *Only eight children were surveyed; two were found to be out of school.*

- Reported result 2: Of all the secondary-school students who had been suspended more than once in census tract 22 in Columbia, South Carolina, 33% had been suspended two times and 67% had been suspended three or more times. Fact: *CDF found only three children in that entire census tract who had been suspended; one child was suspended twice and the other two children, three or more times.*

- Reported result 3: In the Portland Bayside East Housing Project, 50% of all the secondary-school children who had been suspended more than once had been suspended three or more times. Fact: *The survey found two secondary-school children had been suspended in that area; one of them had been suspended three or more times.*

Identify the potential distortions in the results reported by the CDF.

Solution In each of these examples, the reporting of percentages (i.e., relative frequencies) instead of the numbers themselves is misleading. No inference we might draw from the cited examples would be reliable. (We'll see how to measure the reliability of estimated percentages in Chapter 6.) In short, either the report should state the numbers alone instead of percentages, or, better yet, it should state that the numbers were too small to report by region.

Look Back If several regions were combined, the numbers (and percentages) would be more meaningful.

ETHICS in STATISTICS

Purposeful reporting of numerical descriptive statistics in order to mislead the target audience is considered *unethical statistical practice.*

Exercises 2.133–2.136

Applying the Concepts—Intermediate

2.133 **Museum management.** Refer to the *Museum Management and Curatorship* (June 2010) study of how museums evaluate their performance, Exercise 2.14 (p. 50). Recall that managers of 30 museums of contemporary art identified the performance measure used most often. A summary of the results is reproduced in the table. Consider the bar graph shown. Identify two ways in which the bar graph might mislead the viewer by overemphasizing the importance of one of the performance measures.

Performance Measure	Number of Museums	Proportion of Museums
Total visitors	8	.267
Paying visitors	5	.167
Big shows	6	.200
Funds raised	7	.233
Members	4	.133

2.134 **Trend in Iraq War casualties.** While the United States was still actively fighting in the Iraq War, a news media outlet produced a graphic showing a dramatic decline in the annual number of American casualties. The number of deaths for the years 2003, 2004, 2005, and 2006 were (approximately) 475, 850, 820, and 130, respectively.

a. Create a time series plot showing the dramatic decline in the number of American deaths per year.

b. The graphic was based on data collected through February of 2006. Knowing this fact, why is the time series plot misleading?

c. What information would you like to have in order to construct a graph that accurately reflects the trend in American casualties from the Iraq War?

2.135 **Misleading graph.** Consider the following graphic, produced by the *Silicon Alley Insider*, an online publication

for business news. The graph is attempting to show the increasing trend in annual revenue produced by Craigslist as compared to the decrease in newspaper classified ad sales.

a. Why might the graph be misleading? [*Hint:* Focus on the units of measure on the two vertical axes.]

b. Redraw the graph, but use the same units of measure for both Craigslist revenue and newspaper ad sales. What conclusions can you draw from the redrawn graph?

2.136 **BP oil leak.** In the summer of 2010, an explosion on the Deepwater Horizon oil drilling rig caused a leak in one of British Petroleum (BP) Oil Company's wells in the Gulf of Mexico. Crude oil rushed unabated for 3 straight months into the Gulf until BP could fix the leak. During the disaster, BP used suction tubes to capture some of the gushing oil. In May of 2011, in an effort to demonstrate the daily improvement in the process, a BP representative presented a graphic on the daily number of 42-gallon barrels (bbl) of oil collected by the suctioning process. A graphic similar to the one used by BP is shown below.

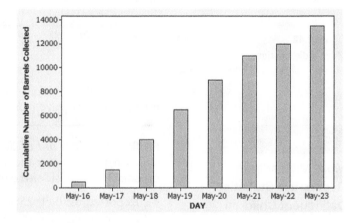

a. Note that the vertical axis represents the "cumulative" number of barrels collected per day. This is calculated by adding the amounts of the previous days' oil collection to the current day's oil collection. Explain why this graph is misleading.

b. Estimates of the actual number of barrels of oil collected per day for each of the 8 days are listed in the accompanying table. Construct a graph for this data that accurately depicts BP's progress in its daily collection of oil. What conclusions can you draw from the graph?

Estimates of Daily Collection of Oil

Day	Number of Barrels (bbl)
May 16	500
May 17	1,000
May 18	3,000
May 19	2,500
May 20	2,500
May 21	2,000
May 22	1,000
May 23	1,500

◻ Chapter Notes

Key Terms

Note: Starred (*) items are from the optional sections in this chapter.

Bar graph 41
*Bivariate relationship 100
Box plots 91
Central tendency 63
Chebyshev's Rule 80
Class 40
Class frequency 40
Class interval 53
Class percentage 40
Class relative frequency 40
Dot plot 51
Empirical Rule 80
Hinges 92
Histogram 51
Inner fences 92
Interquartile range (IQR) 92
Lower quartile 88
Mean 63
Mean of a sample 63
Measures of central
  tendency 63
Measures of relative
  standing 87
Measures of variability 73
Median 65
Middle quartile 88
Minitab histogram 53
Modal class 68
Mode 68
Mound-shaped distribution 80

Numerical descriptive
  measures 63
Outer fences 92
Outliers 91
Pareto diagram 42
Percentile ranking/score 87
Pie chart 41
Population *z*-score 88
pth percentile 87
Quartiles 88
Range 74
Rare-event approach 96
*Run chart 106
Sample standard deviation 75
Sample variance 75
Sample *z*-score 88
*Scatterplot 100
Skewness 67
Spread 73
Standard deviation 76
Stem-and-leaf display 51
Symmetric distribution 80
*Time series data 106
*Time series plot 106
Time study 79
Upper quartile 88
Variability 63
Variance 76
Whiskers 92
z-score 88

Key Symbols

	Sample	Population
Mean:	$\bar{x}$	μ
Variance:	s^2	σ^2
Std. Dev.:	s	σ
Median:	m or Q_M	η
Lower Quartile:	Q_L	
Upper Quartile:	Q_U	
Interquartile Range:	IQR	

Key Ideas

Describing Qualitative Data

1. Identify **category classes**
2. Determine **class frequencies**
3. **Class relative frequency** = (class frequency)/n
4. **Graph** relative frequencies

Pie Chart:

Bar Graph:

Pareto Diagram:

Graphing Quantitative Data

One Variable
1. Identify class intervals
2. Determine **class interval frequencies**
3. **Class interval relative frequency** =
  (class interval frequency)/n
4. **Graph** class interval relative frequencies

Dot Plot:

Stem-and-Leaf Display:

```
1 | 3
2 | 2489
3 | 126678
4 | 37
5 | 2
```

Histogram:

Box Plot:

Two Variables

Scatterplot:

Time series plot:

Time

Numerical Description of Quantitative Data

Central Tendency
Mean: $\bar{x} = (\Sigma x_i)/n$
Median: Middle value when data ranked in order
Mode: Value that occurs most often

Variation
Range: Difference between largest and smallest value
Variance:

$$s^2 = \frac{\Sigma(x_i - \bar{x})^2}{n-1} = \frac{\Sigma x_i^2 - \dfrac{(\Sigma x_i)^2}{n}}{n-1}$$

Std. Dev.: $s = \sqrt{s^2}$
Interquartile Range: $IQR = Q_U - Q_L$

Relative Standing
Percentile Score: Percentage of values that fall below *x*-score
z-score:

$$z = (x - \bar{x})/s$$
$$= (x - \mu)/\sigma$$

Rules for Detecting Quantitative Outliers

Interval	Chebyshev's Rule	Empirical Rule
$\bar{x} \pm s$	At least 0%	$\approx 68\%$
$\bar{x} \pm 2s$	At least 75%	$\approx 95\%$
$\bar{x} \pm 3s$	At least 89%	$\approx$ All

Rules for Detecting Quantitative Outliers

Method	Suspect	Highly Suspect
Box plot:	Values between inner & outer fences	Values beyond outer fences
z-score:	$2 < |z| < 3$	$|z| > 3$

Guide to Selecting the Data Description Method

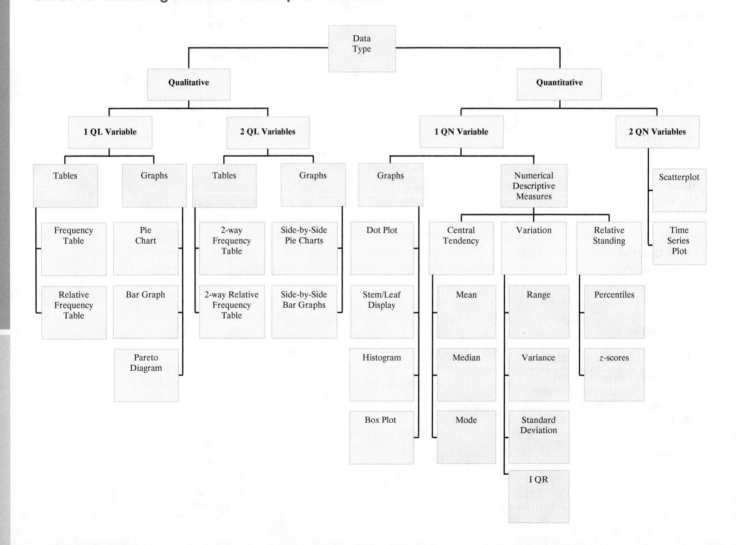

Supplementary Exercises 2.137–2.171

Note: Starred (*) exercises refer to the optional sections in this chapter.

Learning the Mechanics

2.137 Construct a relative frequency histogram for the data summarized in the accompanying table.

Measurement Class	Relative Frequency
.00–.75	.02
.75–1.50	.01
1.50–2.25	.03
2.25–3.00	.05
3.00–3.75	.10
3.75–4.50	.14
4.50–5.25	.19
5.25–6.00	.15
6.00–6.75	.12
6.75–7.50	.09
7.50–8.25	.05
8.25–9.00	.04
9.00–9.75	.01

2.138 Discuss the conditions under which the median is preferred to the mean as a measure of central tendency.

2.139 Consider the following three measurements: 50, 70, 80. Find the z-score for each measurement if they are from a population with a mean and standard deviation equal to
  a. $\mu = 60, \sigma = 10$
  b. $\mu = 50, \sigma = 5$
  c. $\mu = 40, \sigma = 10$
  d. $\mu = 40, \sigma = 100$

2.140 Refer to Exercise 2.139. For parts **a–d,** determine whether the values 50, 70, and 80 are outliers.

2.141 For each of the following data sets, compute $\bar{x}$, s^2, and s:
  a. 13, 1, 10, 3, 3
  b. 13, 6, 6, 0
  c. 1, 0, 1, 10, 11, 11, 15
  d. 3, 3, 3, 3

2.142 For each of the following data sets, compute $\bar{x}$, s^2, and s. If appropriate, specify the units in which your answers are expressed.
  a. 4, 6, 6, 5, 6, 7
  b. −$1, $4, −$3, $0, −$3, −$6
  c. $\frac{3}{5}\%$, $\frac{4}{5}\%$, $\frac{2}{5}\%$, $\frac{1}{5}\%$, $\frac{1}{16}\%$
  d. Calculate the range of each data set in parts **a–c.**

2.143 Explain why we generally prefer the standard deviation to the range as a measure of variability for quantitative data.

2.144 If the range of a set of data is 20, find a rough approximation to the standard deviation of the data set.

*2.145 Construct a scattergram for the data in the following table.

L02145

Variable 1:	174	268	345	119	400	520	190	448	307	252
Variable 2:	8	10	15	7	22	31	15	20	11	9

Applying the Concepts—Basic

2.146 Management system failures. The U.S. Chemical Safety and Hazard Investigation Board (CSB) is responsible for determining the root cause of industrial accidents (*Process*

Safety Progress, Dec. 2004). The accompanying table gives a breakdown of the root causes of 83 incidents caused by management system failures.

Management System Cause Category	Number of Incidents
Engineering & Design	27
Procedures & Practices	24
Management & Oversight	22
Training & Communication	10
Total	83

Source: Based on A. S. Blair, "Management system failures identified in incidents investigated by the U.S. Chemical Safety and Hazard Investigation Board," PROCESS SAFETY PROGRESS, Vol. 23, No. 4, December 2004, pp. 232–236 (Table 1).

  a. Find the relative frequency of the number of incidents for each cause category.
  b. Construct a Pareto diagram for the data.
  c. From the Pareto diagram, identify the cause categories with the highest (and lowest) relative frequency of incidents.

2.147 Business marketing publications. Business-to-business marketing describes the field of marketing between multiple business entities. The *Journal of Business-to-Business Marketing* (Vol. 15, 2008) produced a pie chart describing the number of business-to-business marketing articles published in all journals, by topical area, between 1971 and 2006. The data used to produce the pie chart are shown in the table.

MARPUB

Area	Number
Global Marketing	235
Sales Management	494
Buyer Behavior	478
Relationships	498
Innovation	398
Marketing Strategy	280
Channels/Distribution	213
Marketing Research	131
Services	136
Total	2,863

Source: Based on Peter J. LaPlaca, "Commentary on 'The Essence of Business Marketing...' by Lichtenthal, Mummalaneni, and Wilson: The JBBM Comes of Age," JOURNAL OF BUSINESS-TO-BUSINESS MARKETING, Vol. 15, No. 2, 2008 (Figure 4), p. 187.

  a. Compute the relative frequencies for the nine topical areas shown in the table. Interpret the relative frequency for Buyer Behavior.
  b. Use the relative frequencies, part **a,** to construct a pie chart for the data. Why is the slice for Marketing Research smaller than the slice for Sales Management?

*2.148 A boom in U.S. bankruptcies. The American Bankruptcy Institute and the National Bankruptcy Research Center monitor the number of consumer bankruptcy filings each month. The table on the next page lists the number of bankruptcy filings for each of the first 10 months of a recent year.

FILING

  a. Explain why the data in the table represent time series data.

b. Construct a time series plot for the monthly number of bankruptcy filings.

c. Do you detect a trend in the time series plot? Explain.

Month	Number of bankruptcy filings
January	66,050
February	76,120
March	86,165
April	92,291
May	91,214
June	82,770
July	94,124
August	96,413
September	88,663
October	106,266

2.149 Crash tests on new cars. The National Highway Traffic Safety Administration (NHTSA) crash-tests new car models to determine how well they protect the driver and front-seat passenger in a head-on collision. The NHTSA has developed a "star" scoring system for the frontal crash test, with results ranging from one star (*) to five stars (*****). The more stars in the rating, the better the level of crash protection in a head-on collision. The NHTSA crash test results for 98 cars (in a recent model year) are stored in the accompanying data file. The driver-side star ratings for the 98 cars are summarized in the Minitab printout shown below. Use the information in the printout to form a pie chart. Interpret the graph.

Tally for Discrete Variables: DRIVSTAR

```
DRIVSTAR   Count   Percent
       2       4      4.08
       3      17     17.35
       4      59     60.20
       5      18     18.37
     N=       98
```

2.150 Crash tests on new cars (cont'd). Refer to Exercise 2.149. One quantitative variable recorded by the NHTSA is driver's severity of head injury (measured on a scale from 0 to 1,500). The mean and standard deviation for the 98 driver head-injury ratings are displayed in the Minitab printout below.

Descriptive Statistics: DRIVHEAD

```
Variable   N    Mean    StDev   Minimum     Q1   Median      Q3   Maximum
DRIVHEAD  98   603.7    185.4     216.0  475.0    605.0   724.3    1240.0
```

a. Give a practical interpretation of the mean.

b. Use the mean and standard deviation to make a statement about where most of the head-injury ratings fall.

c. Find the z-score for a driver head-injury rating of 408. Interpret the result.

2.151 Defects in new automobiles. Consider the following data from the automobile industry (adapted from Kane 1989). All cars produced on a particular day were inspected for defects. The 145 defects found were categorized by type as shown in the accompanying table.

Defect Type	Number
Accessories	50
Body	70
Electrical	10
Engine	5
Transmission	10

a. Construct a Pareto diagram for the data. Use the graph to identify the most frequently observed type of defect.

b. All 70 car body defects were further classified as to type. The frequencies are provided in the following table. Form a Pareto diagram for type of body defect. (Adding this graph to the original Pareto diagram of part **a** is called *exploding the Pareto diagram*.) Interpret the result. What type of body defect should be targeted for special attention?

Body Defect	Number
Chrome	2
Dents	25
Paint	30
Upholstery	10
Windshield	3

2.152 Products "Made in the USA." "Made in the USA" is a claim stated in many product advertisements or on product labels. Advertisers want consumers to believe that the product is manufactured with 100% U.S. labor and materials—which is often not the case. What does "Made in the USA" mean to the typical consumer? To answer this question, a group of marketing professors conducted an experiment at a shopping mall in Muncie, Indiana (*Journal of Global Business*, Spring 2002). They asked every fourth adult entrant to the mall to participate in the study. A total of 106 shoppers agreed to answer the question, "'Made in the USA' means what percentage of U.S. labor and materials?" The responses of the 106 shoppers are summarized as follows: "100%" (64 shoppers), "75 to 99%" (20 shoppers), "50 to 74%" (18 shoppers), and "less than 50%" (4 shoppers).

a. What type of data-collection method was used?

b. What type of variable, quantitative or qualitative, is measured?

c. Present the data in graphical form. Use the graph to make a statement about the percentage of consumers who believe "Made in the USA" means 100% U.S. labor and materials.

2.153 Vehicle use of an intersection. For each day of last year, the number of vehicles passing through a certain intersection was recorded by a city engineer. One objective of this study was to determine the percentage of days that more than 425 vehicles used the intersection. Suppose the mean for the data was 375 vehicles per day and the standard deviation was 25 vehicles.

a. What can you say about the percentage of days that more than 425 vehicles used the intersection? Assume you know nothing about the shape of the relative frequency distribution for the data.

b. What is your answer to part **a** if you know that the relative frequency distribution for the data is mound-shaped?

2.154 Drivers stopped by police. According to the Bureau of Justice Statistics (June 2006), 75% of all licensed drivers stopped by police are 25 years or older. Give a percentile ranking for the age of 25 years in the distribution of all ages of licensed drivers stopped by police.

Applying the Concepts—Intermediate

2.155 Environmental failures of Arkansas companies. Failure of a corporation to obey both federal and state environmental regulations may result in irreparable damage to the environment and costly financial penalties to the firm. The accompanying table lists the financial penalties (thousands of dollars) assessed in 38 civil actions filed against Arkansas companies by the U.S. Department of Justice and the Environmnetal Protection Agency. The penalties were assessed for violations of at least one of several different environmental laws, including the Clean Air Act (CAA). (Penalties assessed due to CAA violations are marked with an asterisk in the table.)

ARKAIR

91*	25*	25*	19*	35*	4*	30*	15*	105*	930
10	124	38	138	1000	25	30	100	43	190
15	20	40	20	40	850	35	25	40	15
20	400	85	30	300	25	90	3		

Source: Data from R. H. Tabor and S. D. Stanwick, "Arkansas: An environmental perspective," ARKANSAS BUSINESS AND ECONOMIC REVIEW, Vol. 28, No. 2, Summer 1995 (Table 4).

  a. Construct a stem-and-leaf display for all 38 penalties.

  b. Circle the individual leaves that are associated with penalties imposed for CAA violations.

  c. What does the pattern of circles in part b suggest about the severity of the penalties imposed for CAA violations relative to the other types of violations reported in the table? Explain.

2.156 Color and clarity of diamonds. Diamonds are categorized according to the "four C's": carats, clarity, color, and cut. Each diamond stone that is sold on the open market is provided a certificate by an independent diamond assessor that lists these characteristics. Data for 308 diamonds were extracted from Singapore's *Business Times* (*Journal of Statistics Education*, Vol. 9, No. 1, 2001). Color is classified as D, E, F, G, H, or I, while clarity is classified as IF, VVS1, VVS2, VS1, or VS2. Use a graphical technique to summarize the color and clarity of the 308 diamond stones. What is the color and clarity that occurs most often? Least often?

DIAMND

2.157 Color and clarity of diamonds (cont'd). Refer to Exercise 2.156. In addition to color and clarity, the independent certification group (GIA, HRD, or IGI) and the number of carats were recorded for each of 308 diamonds for sale on the open market.

DIAMND

  a. Use a graphical method to describe the carat distribution of all 308 diamonds.

  b. Use a graphical method to describe the carat distribution of diamonds certified by the GIA group.

  c. Repeat part **b** for the HRD and IGI certification groups.

  d. Compare the three carat distributions, parts **b** and **c**. Is there one particular certification group that appears to be assessing diamonds with higher carats than the others?

  e. Find and interpret the mean of the data set.

  f. Find and interpret the median of the data set.

  g. Find and interpret the mode of the data set.

  h. Which measure of central tendency best describes the 308 carat values? Explain.

  i. Use the mean and standard deviation to form an interval that will contain at least 75% of the carat values in the data set.

*2.158 Characteristics of diamonds sold at retail. Refer to Exercise 2.157. In addition to the number of carats, the asking price for each of the 308 diamonds for sale on the open market was recorded. Construct a scatterplot for the data, with number of carats on the horizontal axis and price on the vertical axis. What type of trend do you detect?

DIAMND

2.159 Hull failures of oil tankers. Owing to several major ocean oil spills by tank vessels, Congress passed the 1990 Oil Pollution Act, which requires all tankers to be designed with thicker hulls. Further improvements in the structural design of a tank vessel have been proposed since then, each with the objective of reducing the likelihood of an oil spill and decreasing the amount of outflow in the event of a hull puncture. To aid in this development, *Marine Technology* (Jan. 1995) reported on the spillage amount (in thousands of metric tons) and cause of puncture for 42 major oil spills from tankers and carriers. [*Note:* Cause of puncture is classified as either collision (C), fire/explosion (FE), hull failure (HF), or grounding (G).] The data are saved in the accompanying file.

HULL

  a. Use a graphical method to describe the cause of oil spillage for the 42 tankers. Does the graph suggest that any one cause is more likely to occur than any other? How is this information of value to the design engineers?

  b. Find and interpret descriptive statistics for the 42 spillage amounts. Use this information to form an interval that can be used to predict the spillage amount of the next major oil spill.

2.160 Software defects. The Promise Software Engineering Repository is a collection of data sets available to serve businesses in building predictive software models. One such data set, saved in the accompanying file, contains information on 498 modules of software code. Each module was analyzed for defects and classified as "true" if it contained defective code and "false" if not. Access the data file and produce a bar graph or a pie chart for the defect variable. Use the graph to make a statement about the likelihood of defective software code.

SWDEF

2.161 Velocity of Winchester bullets. The *American Rifleman* (June 1993) reported on the velocity of ammunition fired from the FEG P9R pistol, a 9 mm gun manufactured in Hungary. Field tests revealed that Winchester bullets fired from the pistol had a mean velocity (at 15 feet) of 936 feet per second and a standard deviation of 10 feet per second. Tests were also conducted with Uzi and Black Hills ammunition.

  a. Describe the velocity distribution of Winchester bullets fired from the FEG P9R pistol.

  b. A bullet, brand unknown, is fired from the FEG P9R pistol. Suppose the velocity (at 15 feet) of the bullet is 1,000 feet per second. Is the bullet likely to be manufactured by Winchester? Explain.

2.162 Time to develop price quotes. A manufacturer of industrial wheels is losing many profitable orders because of the long time it takes the firm's marketing, engineering, and accounting departments to develop price quotes for potential customers. To remedy this problem, the firm's management would like to set guidelines for the length of time each department should spend developing price quotes. To help develop these guidelines, 50 requests for price quotes

WHEELS

were randomly selected from the set of price quotes made last year: the processing time (in days) was determined for each price quote for each department. Several observations are displayed in the table below. The price quotes are also classified by whether or not they were "lost" (i.e., whether or not the customer placed an order after receiving the price quote).

Request Number	Marketing	Engineering	Accounting	Lost?
1	7.0	6.2	.1	No
2	.4	5.2	.1	No
3	2.4	4.6	.6	No
4	6.2	13.0	.8	Yes
5	4.7	.9	.5	No
⋮	⋮	⋮	⋮	⋮
46	6.4	1.3	6.2	No
47	4.0	2.4	13.5	Yes
48	10.0	5.3	.1	No
49	8.0	14.4	1.9	Yes
50	7.0	10.0	2.0	No

a. Construct a stem-and-leaf display for the total processing time for each department. Shade the leaves that correspond to "lost" orders in each of the displays, and interpret each of the displays.

b. Using your results from part **a,** develop "maximum processing time" guidelines for each department that, if followed, will help the firm reduce the number of lost orders.

c. Generate summary statistics for the processing times. Interpret the results.

d. Calculate the z-score corresponding to the maximum processing time guideline you developed in part **b** for each department, and for the total processing time.

e. Calculate the maximum processing time corresponding to a z-score of 3 for each of the departments. What percentage of the orders exceed these guidelines? How does this agree with Chebyshev's Rule and the Empirical Rule?

f. Repeat part **e** using a z-score of 2.

g. Compare the percentage of "lost" quotes with corresponding times that exceed at least one of the guidelines in part **e** to the same percentage using the guidelines in part **f.** Which set of guidelines would you recommend be adopted? Why?

2.163 Misleading advertisement. A time series plot similar to the one shown next appeared in a recent advertisement for a well-known golf magazine. One person might interpret the plot's message as the longer you subscribe to the magazine, the better golfer you should become. Another person might interpret it as indicating that if you subscribe for 3 years, your game should improve dramatically.

Length of subscription
(years)

a. Explain why the plot can be interpreted in more than one way.

b. How could the plot be altered to rectify the current distortion?

*2.164 History of corporate acquisitions. Refer to the *Academy of Management Journal* (Aug. 2008) study of corporate acquisitions from 1980 to 2000, Exercise 2.12 (p. 50).

a. Construct a time series plot of the number of firms with at least one acquisition.

b. For each year, compute the percentage of sampled firms with at least one acquisition. Then construct a time series plot of these percentages.

c. Which time series plot, part **a** or part **b,** is more informative about the history of corporate acquisitions over time? Explain.

2.165 Radiation levels in homes. In some locations, radiation levels in homes are measured at well above normal background levels in the environment. As a result, many architects and builders are making design changes to ensure adequate air exchange so that radiation will not be "trapped" in homes. In one such location, 50 homes' levels were measured, and the mean level was 10 parts per billion (ppb), the median was 8 ppb, and the standard deviation was 3 ppb. Background levels in this location are at about 4 ppb.

a. Based on these results, is the distribution of the 50 homes' radiation levels symmetric, skewed to the left, or skewed to the right? Why?

b. Use both Chebyshev's Rule and the Empirical Rule to describe the distribution of radiation levels. Which do you think is most appropriate in this case? Why?

c. Use the results from part **b** to approximate the number of homes in this sample that have radiation levels above the background level.

d. Suppose another home is measured at a location 10 miles from the one sampled and has a level of 20 ppb. What is the z-score for this measurement relative to the 50 homes sampled in the other location? Is it likely that this new measurement comes from the same distribution of radiation levels as the other 50? Why? How would you go about confirming your conclusion?

2.166 Amount of zinc phosphide in commercial rat poison. A chemical company produces a substance composed of 98% cracked corn particles and 2% zinc phosphide for use in controlling rat populations in sugarcane fields. Production must be carefully controlled to maintain the 2% zinc phosphide because too much zinc phosphide will cause damage to the sugarcane and too little will be ineffective in controlling the rat population. Records from past production indicate that the distribution of the actual percentage of zinc phosphide present in the substance is approximately mound-shaped, with a mean of 2.0% and a standard deviation of .08%.

a. If the production line is operating correctly, approximately what proportion of batches from a day's production will contain less than 1.84% of zinc phosphide?

b. Suppose one batch chosen randomly actually contains 1.80% zinc phosphide. Does this indicate that there is too little zinc phosphide in today's production? Explain your reasoning.

2.167 U.S. peanut production. If not examined carefully, the graphical description of U.S. peanut production shown at the bottom of the page can be misleading.
  a. Explain why the graph may mislead some readers.
  b. Construct an undistorted graph of U.S. peanut production for the given years.

Applying the Concepts—Advanced

2.168 Investigating the claims of weight-loss clinics. The U.S. Federal Trade Commission assesses fines and other penalties against weight-loss clinics that make unsupported or misleading claims about the effectiveness of their programs. Brochures from two weight-loss clinics both advertise "statistical evidence" about the effectiveness of their programs. Clinic A claims that the *mean* weight loss during the first month is 15 pounds; Clinic B claims a *median* weight loss of 10 pounds.
  a. Assuming the statistics are accurately calculated, which clinic would you recommend if you had no other information? Why?
  b. Upon further research, the median and standard deviation for Clinic A are found to be 10 pounds and 20 pounds, respectively, while the mean and standard deviation for Clinic B are found to be 10 and 5 pounds, respectively. Both are based on samples of more than 100 clients. Describe the two clinics' weight-loss distributions as completely as possible given this additional information. What would you recommend to a prospective client now? Why?
  c. Note that nothing has been said about how the sample of clients upon which the statistics are based was selected. What additional information would be important regarding the sampling techniques employed by the clinics?

2.169 Age discrimination study. The Age Discrimination in Employment Act mandates that workers 40 years of age or older be treated without regard to age in all phases of employment (hiring, promotions, firing, etc.). Age discrimination cases are of two types: *disparate treatment* and *disparate impact*. In the former, the issue is whether workers have been intentionally discriminated against. In the latter, the issue is whether employment practices adversely affect the protected class (i.e., workers 40 and over) even though

no such effect was intended by the employer. A small computer manufacturer laid off 10 of its 20 software engineers. The ages of all engineers at the time of the layoff are shown below. Analyze the data to determine whether the company may be vulnerable to a disparate impact claim.

| Not laid off: | 34 | 55 | 42 | 38 | 42 | 32 | 40 | 40 | 46 | 29 |
| Laid off: | 52 | 35 | 40 | 41 | 40 | 39 | 40 | 64 | 47 | 44 |

Critical Thinking Challenges

2.170 No Child Left Behind Act. According to the government, federal spending on K-12 education has increased dramatically over the past 20 years, but student performance has essentially stayed the same. Hence, in 2002, President George Bush signed into law the No Child Left Behind Act, a bill that promised improved student achievement for all U.S. children. *Chance* (Fall 2003) reported on a graphic

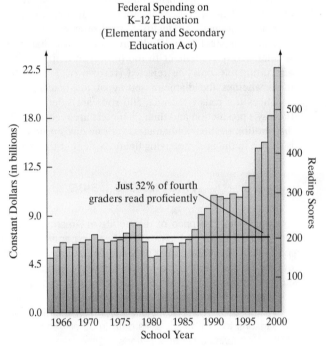

Federal Spending on
K–12 Education
(Elementary and Secondary
Education Act)

Source: Based on U.S. Department of Education.

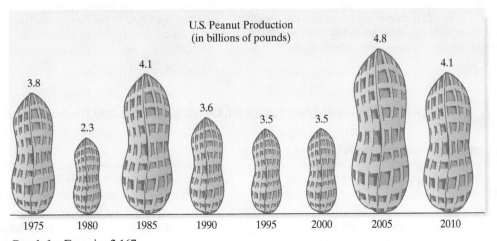

U.S. Peanut Production
(in billions of pounds)

Graph for Exercise 2.167

obtained from the U.S. Department of Education Web site (www.ed.gov) that was designed to support the new legislation. The graphic is reproduced on the previous page. The bars in the graph represent annual federal spending on education, in billions of dollars (left-side vertical axis). The horizontal line represents the annual average fourth-grade children's reading ability score (right-side vertical axis). Critically assess the information portrayed in the graph. Does it, in fact, support the government's position that our children are not making classroom improvements despite federal spending on education? Use the following facts (divulged in the *Chance* article) to help you frame your answer: (1) The U.S. student population has also increased dramatically over the past 20 years, (2) fourth-grade reading test scores are designed to have an average of 250 with a standard deviation of 50, and (3) the reading test scores of seventh and twelfth graders and the mathematics scores of fourth graders did improve substantially over the past 20 years.

2.171 **Steel rod quality.** In his essay "Making Things Right," W. Edwards Deming considered the role of statistics in the quality control of industrial products.* In one example, Deming examined the quality-control process for a manufacturer of steel rods. Rods produced with diameters smaller than 1 centimeter fit too loosely in their bearings and ultimately must be rejected (thrown out). To determine whether the diameter setting of the machine that produces the rods is correct, 500 rods are selected from the day's production and their diameters are recorded. The distribution of the 500 diameters for one day's production is shown in the accompanying figure. Note that the symbol

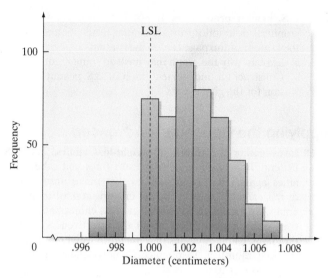

*From Tanur, J., et al., eds. *Statistics: A Guide to the Unknown.* San Francisco: Holden-Day, 1978, pp. 279–81.

LSL in the figure represents the 1-centimeter lower specification limit of the steel rod diameters. There has been speculation that some of the inspectors are unaware of the trouble that an undersized rod diameter would cause later in the manufacturing process. Consequently, these inspectors may be passing rods with diameters that are barely below the lower specification limit and recording them in the interval centered at 1.000 centimeter. According to the figure, is there any evidence to support this claim? Explain.

Activity 2.1   Real Estate Sales

In recent years, the price of real estate in America's major metropolitan areas has skyrocketed. Newspapers usually report recent real estate sales data in their Saturday editions, both hard copies and online. These data usually include the actual prices paid for homes by geographical location during a certain time period, usually a 1-week period 6 to 8 weeks earlier, and some summary statistics, which might include comparisons to real estate sales data in other geographical locations or during other time periods.

1. Locate the real estate sales data in a newspaper for a major metropolitan area. From the information given, identify the time period during which the homes listed were sold. Then describe the way the sales prices are organized. Are they categorized by type of home (single family or condominium), by neighborhood or address, by sales price, etc.?

2. What summary statistics and comparisons are provided with the sales data? Describe several groups of people who might be interested in this data and how each of the summary statistics and comparisons would be helpful to them. Why are the measures of central tendency listed more useful in the real estate market than other measures of central tendency?

3. Based on the lowest and highest sales prices represented in the data, create 10 intervals of equal size and use these intervals to create a relative frequency histogram for the sales data. Describe the shape of the histogram and explain how the summary statistics provided with the data are illustrated in the histogram. Based on the histogram, describe the "typical" home price.

Activity 2.2   *Keep the Change:* Measures of Central Tendency and Variability

In this activity, we continue our study of the Bank of America *Keep the Change* savings program by looking at the measures of central tendency and variability for the three data sets collected in Activity 1.1 (p. 29).

1. Before performing any calculations, explain why you would expect greater variability in the data set *Purchase Totals*

than in *Amounts Transferred*. Then find the mean and median of each of these two data sets. Are the mean and median essentially the same for either of these sets? If so, which one? Can you offer an explanation for these results?

2. Make a histogram for each of the data sets *Amounts Transferred* and *Bank Matching*. Describe any properties

(Continued)

of the data that are evident in the histograms. Explain why it is more likely that *Bank Matching* is skewed to the right than *Amounts Transferred*. Based on your data and histogram, how concerned does Bank of America need to be about matching the maximum amount of $250 for its customers who are college students?

3. Form a fourth data set *Mean Amounts Transferred* by collecting the mean of the data set *Amounts Transferred* for each student in your class. Before performing any

calculations, inspect the new data and describe any trends that you notice. Then find the mean and standard deviation of *Mean Amounts Transferred.* How close is the mean to $0.50? Without performing further calculations, determine whether the standard deviation of *Amounts Transferred* is less than or greater than the standard deviation of *Mean Amounts Transferred.* Explain.

Keep your results from this activity for use in other activities.

References

Deming, W. E. *Out of the Crisis.* Cambridge, Mass.: M.I.T. Center for Advanced Engineering Study, 1986.

Gitlow, H., Oppenheim, A., Oppenheim, R., and Levine, D. *Quality Management,* 3rd ed. Homewood, Ill.: Irwin, 2004.

Huff, D. *How to Lie with Statistics.* New York: Norton, 1954.

Ishikawa, K. *Guide to Quality Control,* 2nd ed. Asian Productivity Organization, 1986.

Juran, J. M. *Juran on Quality by Design: The New Steps for Planning Quality into Goods and Services.* New York: The Free Press, 1992.

Tufte, E. R. *Beautiful Evidence.* Cheshire, Conn.: Graphics Press, 2006.

Tufte, E. R. *Envisioning Information.* Cheshire, Conn.: Graphics Press, 1990.

Tufte, E. R. *Visual Display of Quantiative Information.* Cheshire, Conn.: Graphics Press, 1983.

Tufte, E. R. *Visual Explanations.* Cheshire, Conn.: Graphics Press, 1997.

Tukey, J. *Exploratory Data Analysis.* Reading, Mass.: Addison-Wesley, 1977.

Zabel, S. L. "Statistical Proof of Employment Discrimination." *Statistics: A Guide to the Unknown,* 3rd ed. Pacific Grove, Calif.: Wadsworth, 1989.

USING TECHNOLOGY   Technology images shown here are taken from SPSS Statistics Professional 20.0, Minitab 16, XLSTAT for Pearson, and Excel 2010.

SPSS: Describing Data

Graphing Data

Step 1 Click on the "Graphs" button on the SPSS menu bar and then select "Legacy Dialogs."

Step 2 Click on the graph of your choice (bar, pie, box plot, scatter/dot plot, or histogram) to view the appropriate dialog box. The dialog box for a histogram is shown in Figure 2.S.1.

Figure 2.S.1 SPSS histogram dialog box

Step 3 Make the appropriate variable selections and click "OK" to view the graph.

Stem-and-Leaf Plots

Step 1 Select "Analyze" from the main SPSS menu, then "Descriptive Statistics," and then "Explore."

Step 2 In the "Explore" dialog box, select the variable to be analyzed in the "Dependent List" box, as shown in Figure 2.S.2.

Figure 2.S.2 SPSS explore dialog box

Step 3 Click on either "Both" or "Plots" in the "Display" options and then click "OK" to display the stem-and-leaf graph.

Pareto Diagrams

Step 1 Select "Analyze" from the main SPSS menu, then "Quality Control," and then "Pareto Charts."

Step 2 Click "Define" on the resulting menu and then select the variable to be analyzed and move it to the "Category Axis" box, as shown in Figure 2.S.3.

Figure 2.S.3 SPSS Pareto chart dialog box

Step 3 Click "OK" to display the Pareto diagram.

Numerical Descriptive Statistics

Step 1 Click on the "Analyze" button on the main menu bar and then click on "Descriptive Statistics."

Step 2 Select "Descriptives;" the dialog box is shown in Figure 2.S.4.

Figure 2.S.4 SPSS descriptive statistics dialog box

Step 3 Select the quantitative variables you want to analyze and place them in the "Variable(s)" box. You can control which descriptive statistics appear by clicking the "Options" button on the dialog box and making your selections.

Step 4 Click "OK" to view the descriptive statistics printout.

Percentiles

Step 1 Select "Analyze" on the main menu bar, and then click on "Descriptive Statistics."

Step 2 Select "Explore" from the resulting menu.

Step 3 In the resulting dialog box (see Figure 2.S.2), select the "Statistics" button and check the "Percentiles" box.

Step 4 Return to the "Explore" dialog box and click "OK" to generate the descriptive statistics.

Minitab: Describing Data

Graphing Data

Step 1 Click on the "Graph" button on the Minitab menu bar.

Step 2 Click on the graph of your choice (bar, pie, scatterplot, histogram, dotp lot, or stem-and-leaf) to view the appropriate dialog box. The dialog box for a histogram is shown in Figure 2.M.1.

Figure 2.M.1 Minitab histogram dialog box

Step 3 Make the appropriate variable selections and then click "OK" to view the graph.

Numerical Descriptive Statistics

Step 1 Click on the "Stat" button on the main menu bar, click on "Basic Statistics," and then click on "Display Descriptive Statistics." The resulting dialog box appears in Figure 2.M.2.

Figure 2.M.2 Minitab descriptive statistics dialog box

Step 2 Select the quantitative variables you want to analyze and place them in the "Variables" box. You can control which descriptive statistics appear by clicking the "Statistics" button on the dialog box and making your selections. (As an option, you can create histograms and dot plots for the data by clicking the "Graphs" button and making the appropriate selections.)

Step 3 Click "OK" to view the descriptive statistics printout.

Excel/XLSTAT: Describing Data

Graphing Data

Step 1 Click the "XLSTAT" button on the Excel main menu bar and then click "Visualizing Data."

Step 2 From the resulting menu (see Figure 2.E.1), select the graph of your choice. For bar graphs, pie charts, stem-and-leaf displays, or box plots, select "Univariate plots"; for histograms, select "Histogram"; and for scatterplots, select "Scatter plots."

Figure 2.E.1 XLSTAT menu for graphing data

Step 3 When the resulting dialog box appears, highlight the data column(s) you want to graph so that the column information appears in the appropriate entry (see, for example, Figure 2.E.2).

Figure 2.E.2 XLSTAT graphing univariate plots dialog box

Step 4 For univariate plots only, click the "Charts (1)" option for quantitative data or the "Charts (2)" option for qualitative data, and then select the type of graph (e.g., pie chart, bar graph, stem-and-leaf display, or box plot) you want to display. (See Figure 2.E.3.)

Figure 2.E.3 XLSTAT univariate plots charts options

Step 5 Click "OK," and then "Continue" to display the graph.

Numerical Descriptive Statistics

Step 1 Click the "XLSTAT" button on the Excel main menu bar, click "Describing Data," and then click "Descriptive Statistics."

Step 2 When the resulting dialog box appears, highlight the data column(s) you want to graph so that the column information appears in the quantitative data entry.

Step 3 Click the "Outputs" option, and then select the descriptive statistics you want to produce. (See Figure 2.E.4.)

Figure 2.E.4 XLSTAT descriptive statistics outputs options

Step 5 Click "OK," and then "Continue" to display the summary statistics.

TI-84 Graphing Calculator: Describing Data

Histogram from Raw Data

Step 1 *Enter the data*

- Press **STAT** and select **1:Edit**

Note: If the list already contains data, clear the old data. Use the up arrow to highlight "**L1**." Press **CLEAR ENTER**. Use the arrow and **ENTER** keys to enter the data set into **L1**.

Step 2 *Set up the histogram plot*

- Press **2nd** and press **Y =** for **STAT PLOT**
- Press **1** for **Plot1**
- Set the cursor so that **ON** is flashing
- For **Type,** use the arrow and **ENTER** keys to highlight and select the histogram
- For **Xlist,** choose the column containing the data (in most cases, L1)

Note: Press **2nd 1** for **L1**. **Freq** should be set to 1.

Step 3 *Select your window settings*

- Press **WINDOW** and adjust the settings as follows:

$$X \text{ min} = \text{lowest class boundary}$$
$$X \text{ max} = \text{highest class boundary}$$
$$X \text{ scl} = \text{class width}$$
$$Y \text{ min} = 0$$
$$Y \text{ max} \geq \text{greatest class frequency}$$
$$Y \text{ scl} = 1$$
$$X \text{ res} = 1$$

Step 4 *View the graph*

- Press **GRAPH**

Optional *Read class frequencies and class boundaries*

Step You can press **TRACE** to read the class frequencies and class boundaries. Use the arrow keys to move between bars.

Example The following figures show TI-84 window settings and histogram for the following sample data:

86, 70, 62, 98, 73, 56, 53, 92, 86, 37, 62, 83, 78, 49, 78, 37, 67, 79, 57

Histogram from a Frequency Table

Step 1 *Enter the data*

- Press **STAT** and select **1:Edit**

Note: If a list already contains data, clear the old data. Use the up arrow to highlight the list name, "**L1**" or "**L2**."

- Press **CLEAR ENTER**
- Enter the midpoint of each class into **L1**
- Enter the class frequencies or relative frequencies into **L2**

Step 2 *Set up the histogram plot*

- Press **2nd** and **Y =** for **STAT PLOT**
- Press **1** for **Plot1**
- Set the cursor so that **ON** is flashing
- For **Type,** use the arrow and **ENTER** keys to highlight and select the histogram
- For **Xlist,** choose the column containing the midpoints
- For **Freq,** choose the column containing the frequencies or relative frequencies

Step 3–4 *Follow steps 3–4 given above.*

Note: To set up the Window for relative frequencies, be sure to set **Ymax** to a value that is greater than or equal to the largest relative frequency.

One-Variable Descriptive Statistics

Step 1 *Enter the data*

- Press STAT and select **1:Edit**

Note: If the list already contains data, clear the old data. Use the up arrow to highlight "**L1**." Press **CLEAR ENTER.**

- Use the arrow and **ENTER** keys to enter the data set into L1

Step 2 *Calculate descriptive statistics*

- Press **STAT**
- Press the right arrow key to highlight **CALC**
- Press **ENTER** for **1-Var Stats**

- Enter the name of the list containing your data
- Press **2nd 1** for **L1** (or **2nd 2** for **L2,** etc.)
- Press **ENTER**

You should see the statistics on your screen. Some of the statistics are off the bottom of the screen. Use the down arrow to scroll through to see the remaining statistics. Use the up arrow to scroll back up.

Example The descriptive statistics for the sample data set

86, 70, 62, 98, 73, 56, 53, 92, 86, 37, 62, 83, 78, 49, 78, 37, 67, 79, 57

The output screens for this example are shown below.

Sorting Data (to Find the Mode)

The descriptive statistics do not include the mode. To find the mode, sort your data as follows:

- Press **STAT**
- Press **2** for **SORTA(**
- Enter the name of the list your data are in. If your data are in **L1,** press **2nd 1**
- Press **ENTER**
- The screen will say: **DONE**
- To see the sorted data, press **STAT** and select **1:Edit**
- Scroll down through the list and locate the data value that occurs most frequently

Box Plot

Step 1 *Enter the data*

- Press **STAT** and select **1:Edit**

Note: If the list already contains data, clear the old data. Use the up arrow to highlight "**L1**." Press **CLEAR ENTER.**

- Use the arrow and **ENTER** keys to enter the data set into **L1**

Step 2 *Set up the box plot*

- Press **2nd Y =** for **STAT PLOT**
- Press **1** for **Plot1**
- Set the cursor so that **"ON"** is flashing
- For **TYPE,** use the right arrow to scroll through the plot icons and select the box plot in the middle of the second row
- For **XLIST,** choose **L1**
- Set **FREQ** to 1

Step 3 *View the graph*

- Press **ZOOM** and select **9:ZoomStat**

Optional *Read the five-number summary*

- Press **TRACE**
- Use the left and right arrow keys to move between **minX, Q1, Med, Q3,** and **maxX**

Example Make a box plot for the given data:

$86, 70, 62, 98, 73, 56, 53, 92, 86, 37, 62, 83, 78, 49, 78, 37, 67, 79, 57$

The output screen for this example is shown below.

Scatterplots

Step 1 *Enter the data*

- Press **STAT** and select **1:Edit**

Note: If a list already contains data, clear the old data. Use the up arrow to highlight the list name, "**L1**" or "**L2**."

- Press **CLEAR ENTER**
- Enter your *x*-data in **L1** and your *y*-data in **L2**

Step 2 *Set up the scatterplot*

- Press **2nd Y =** for **STAT PLOT**
- Press **1** for **Plot1**

- Set the cursor so that **ON** is flashing
- For **Type,** use the arrow and **ENTER** keys to highlight and select the scatterplot (first icon in the first row)

- For **Xlist,** choose the column containing the *x*-data
- For **Ylist,** choose the column containing the *y*-data

Step 3 *View the scatterplot*

- Press **ZOOM 9** for **ZoomStat**

Example The figures below show a table of data entered on the T1-84 and the scatterplot of the data obtained using the steps given above.

[PART 1] The Kentucky Milk Case

Many products and services are purchased by governments, cities, states, and businesses on the basis of scaled bids, and contracts are awarded to the lowest bidders. This process works extremely well in competitive markets, but it has the potential to increase the cost of purchasing if the markets are noncompetitive or if collusive practices are present.

An investigation that began with a statistical analysis of bids in the Florida school milk market led to the recovery of more than $33,000,000 from dairies that had conspired to rig the bids there. The investigation spread quickly to other states, and to date, settlements and fines from dairies exceed $100.000,000 for school milk bidrigging in 20 other states. This case concerns a school milk bidrigging investigation in Kentucky.

Each year, the Commonwealth of Kentucky invites bids from dairies to supply half-pint containers of fluid milk products for its school districts. The products include whole white milk, low-fat white milk, and low-fat chocolate milk. In 13 school districts in northern Kentucky, the suppliers (dairies) were accused of "price-fixing"—that is, conspiring to allocate the districts so that the "winner" was predetermined. Because these districts are located in Boone, Campbell, and Kenton counties, the geographic market they represent is designated as the "tri-county" market. Over a 9-year period, two dairies—Meyer Dairy and Trauth Dairy— were the only bidders on the milk contracts in the school districts in the tri-county market. Consequently, these two companies were awarded all the milk contracts in the market. (In contrast, a large number of different dairies won the milk contracts for the school districts in the remainder of the northern Kentucky market—called the "surrounding" market.) The

Commonwealth of Kentucky alleged that Meyer and Trauth conspired to allocate the districts in the tri-county market. To date, one of the dairies (Meyer) has admitted guilt, while the other (Trauth) steadfastly maintains its innocence.

The Commonwealth of Kentucky maintains a database on all bids received from the dairies competing for the milk contracts. Some of these data have been made available to you to analyze to determine whether there is empirical evidence of bid collusion in the tri-county market. The data, saved in the **MILK** file, are described in detail below. Some background information on the data and important economic theory regarding bid collusion is also provided. Use this information to guide your analysis. Prepare a professional document that presents the results of your analysis and gives your opinion regarding collusion.

Background Information

Collusive Market Environment

Certain economic features of a market create an environment in which collusion may be found. These basic features include the following:

1. *Few sellers and high concentration.* Only a few dairies control all or nearly all of the milk business in the market.

2. *Homogeneous products.* The products sold are essentially the same from the standpoint of the buyer (i.e., the school district).

3. *Inelastic demand.* Demand is relatively insensitive to price. (*Note:* The quantity of milk required by a school district is primarily determined by school enrollment, not price.)

4. *Similar costs.* The dairies bidding for the milk contracts face similar cost conditions. (*Note:* Approximately 60% of a dairy's production cost is raw milk, which is federally regulated. Meyer and Trauth are dairies of similar size, and both bought their raw milk from the same supplier.)

Although these market structure characteristics create an environment that makes collusive behavior easier, they do not necessarily indicate the existence of collusion. An analysis of the actual bid prices may provide additional information about the degree of competition in the market.

Variable	Type	Description
YEAR	QN	Year in which milk contract awarded
MARKET	QL	Northern Kentucky Market (TRI-COUNTY or SURROUND)
WINNER	QL	Name of winning dairy
WWBID	QN	Winning bid price of whole white milk (dollars per half-pint)
WWQTY	QN	Quantity of whole white milk purchased (number of half-pints)
LFWBID	QN	Winning bid price of low-fat white milk (dollars per half-pints)
LFWQTY	QN	Quantity of low-fat white milk purchased (number of half-pints)
LFCBID	QN	Winning bid price of low-fat chocolate milk (dollars per half-pint)
LFCQTY	QN	Quantity of low-fat chocolate milk purchased (number of half-pints)
DISTRICT	QL	School district number
KYFMO	QN	FMO minimum raw cost of milk (dollars per half-pint)
MILESM	QN	Distance (miles) from Meyer processing plant to school district
MILEST	QN	Distance (miles) from Trauth processing plant to school district
LETDATE	QL	Date on which bidding on milk contract began (month/day/year)

(Number of observations: 392)

 Data Set: MILK

Collusive Bidding Patterns

The analyses of patterns in sealed bids reveal much about the level of competition, or lack thereof, among the vendors serving the market. Consider the following bid analyses:

1. *Market shares.* A market share for a dairy is the number of milk half-pints supplied by the dairy over a given school year, divided by the total number of half-pints supplied to the entire market. One sign of potential collusive behavior is stable, nearly equal market shares over time for the dairies under investigation.

2. *Incumbency rates.* Market allocation is a common form of collusive behavior in bidrigging conspiracies. Typically, the same dairy controls the same school districts year after year. The incumbency rate for a market in a given school year is defined as the percentage of school districts that are won by the same vendor who won the previous year. An incumbency rate that exceeds 70% has been considered a sign of collusive behavior.

3. *Bid levels and dispersion.* In competitive sealed-bid markets, vendors do not share information about their bids. Consequently, more dispersion or variability among the bids is observed than in collusive markets, where vendors communicate about their bids and have a tendency to submit bids in close proximity to one another in an attempt to make the bidding appear competitive. Furthermore, in competitive markets the bid dispersion tends to be directly proportional to the level of the bid: When bids are submitted at relatively high levels, there is more variability among the bids than when they are submitted at or near marginal cost, which will be approximately the same among dairies in the same geographic market.

4. *Price versus cost/distance.* In competitive markets, bid prices are expected to track costs over time. Thus, if the market is competitive, the bid price of milk should be highly correlated with the raw milk cost. Lack of such a relationship is another sign of collusion. Similarly, bid price should be correlated to the distance the product must travel from the processing plant to the school (due to delivery costs) in a competitive market.

5. *Bid sequence.* School milk bids are submitted over the spring and summer months, generally at the end of one school year and before the beginning of the next. When the bids are examined in sequence in competitive markets, the level of bidding is expected to fall as the bidding season progresses. (This phenomenon is attributable to the learning process that occurs during the season, with bids adjusted accordingly. Dairies may submit relatively high bids early in the season to "test the market," confident that volume can be picked up later if the early high bids lose. But, dairies who do not win much business early in the season are likely to become more aggressive in their bidding as the season progresses, driving price levels down.) Constant or slightly increasing price patterns of sequential bids in a market where a single dairy wins year after year is considered another indication of collusive behavior.

6. *Comparison of average winning bid prices.* Consider two similar markets, one in which bids are possibly rigged and the other in which bids are competitively determined. In theory, the mean winning price in the "rigged" market will be significantly higher than the mean price in the competitive market for each year in which collusion occurs.

3

Where We've Been

- Identified the objective of inferential statistics: to make inferences about a population based on information in a sample.
- Introduced graphical and numerical descriptive measures for both quantitative and qualitative data.

Where We're Going

- Develop probability as a measure of uncertainty (3.1)
- Introduce basic rules for finding probabilities (3.2–3.6)
- Use probability as a measure of reliability for an inference (3.2–3.6)
- Provide an advanced rule for finding probabilities (3.7)

▢ Probability

STATISTICS in ACTION   ## Lotto Buster!

"Welcome to the Wonderful World of Lottery Bu$ters." So began the premier issue of Lottery Buster, *a monthly publication for players of the state lottery games.* Lottery Buster *provides interesting facts and figures on the 42 state lotteries and 2 multistate lotteries currently operating in the United States and, more importantly, tips on how to increase a player's odds of winning the lottery.*

New Hampshire, in 1963, was the first state in modern times to authorize a state lottery as an alternative to increasing taxes. (Prior to this time, beginning in 1895, lotteries were banned in America because of corruption.) Since then, lotteries have become immensely popular for two reasons: (1) They lure you with the opportunity to win millions of dollars with a $1 investment, and (2) when you lose, at least you believe your money is going to a good cause. Many state lotteries, such as Florida's, designate a high percentage of lottery revenues to fund state education.

The popularity of the state lottery has brought with it an avalanche of "experts" and "mathematical wizards" (such as the editors of *Lottery Buster*) who provide advice on how to win the lottery—for a fee, of course! Many offer guaranteed "systems" of winning through computer software products with catchy names such as Lotto Wizard, Lottorobics, Win4d, and Lotto-luck.

For example, most knowledgeable lottery players would agree that the "golden rule" or "first rule" in winning lotteries is *game selection*. State lotteries generally offer three types of games: an Instant (scratch-off tickets or online) game, Daily Numbers (Pick-3 or Pick-4), and a weekly Pick-6 Lotto game.

One version of the Instant game involves scratching off the thin opaque covering on a ticket with the edge of a coin to determine whether you have won or lost. The cost of a ticket ranges from 50¢ to $5, and the amount won ranges from $1 to $100,000 in most states, and to as much as $1 million in others. *Lottery Buster* advises against playing the Instant game because it is "a pure chance play, and you can win only by dumb luck. No skill can be applied to this game."

The Daily Numbers game permits you to choose either a three-digit (Pick-3) or four-digit (Pick-4) number at a cost of $1 per ticket. Each night, the winning number is drawn. If your number matches the winning number, you win a large sum of money, usually $100,000. You do have some control over the Daily Numbers game (because you pick the numbers that you play), and, consequently, there are strategies available to increase your chances of winning. However, the Daily Numbers game, like the Instant game, is not available for out-of-state play.

To play Pick-6 Lotto, you select six numbers of your choice from a field of numbers ranging from 1 to N, where N depends on which state's game you are playing. For example, Florida's current Lotto game involves picking six numbers ranging from 1 to 53. (See Figure SIA3.1.) The cost of a ticket is $1, and the payoff, if your six numbers match the winning numbers drawn, is $7 million or more, depending on the number of tickets purchased. (To date, Florida has had the largest individual state weekly payoff of over $200 million.) In addition to the grand prize, you can win second-, third-, and fourth-prize payoffs by matching five, four, and three of the six numbers drawn, respectively. And you don't have to be a resident of the state to play the state's Lotto game.

In this chapter, several Statistics in Action Revisited examples demonstrate how to use the basic concepts of probability to compute the odds of winning a state lottery game and to assess the validity of the strategies suggested by lottery "experts."

STATISTICS in ACTION REVISITED

Recall that one branch of statistics is concerned with decisions about a population based on sample information. You can see how this is accomplished more easily if you understand the relationship between population and sample—a relationship that becomes clearer if we reverse the statistical procedure of making inferences from sample to population. In this chapter, then, we assume that the population is known and calculate the chances of obtaining various samples from the population. Thus, we show that probability is the reverse of statistics: **In probability, we use the population information to infer the probable nature of the sample.**

Probability plays an important role in inference making. Suppose, for example, you have an opportunity to invest in an oil exploration company. Past records show that out of 10 previous oil drillings (a sample of the company's experiences), all 10 came up dry. What do you conclude? Do you think the chances are better than 50:50 that the company will hit a gusher? Should you invest in this company? Chances are, your answer to these questions will be an emphatic "no." If the company's exploratory prowess is sufficient to hit a producing well 50% of the time, a record of 10 dry wells out of 10 drilled is an event that is just too improbable.

Or suppose you're playing poker with what your opponents assure you is a well-shuffled deck of cards. In three consecutive five-card hands, the person on your right is dealt four aces. Based on this sample of three deals, do you think the cards are being adequately shuffled? Again, your answer is likely to be "no" because dealing three hands of four aces is just too improbable if the cards were properly shuffled.

Note that the decisions concerning the potential success of the oil drilling company and the adequacy of card shuffling both involve knowing the chance–or probability–of a certain sample result. Both situations were contrived so that you could easily conclude that the probabilities of the sample results were small. Unfortunately, the probabilities of many observed sample results are not so easy to evaluate intuitively. For these cases we will need the assistance of a theory of probability.

Events, Sample Spaces, and Probability

Let's begin our treatment of probability with simple examples that are easily described. With the aid of simple examples, we can introduce important definitions that will help us develop the notion of probability more easily.

Suppose a coin is tossed once and the up face is recorded. The result we see and record is called an *observation*, or *measurement*, and the process of making an observation is called an *experiment*. Notice that our definition of *experiment* is broader than the one used in the physical sciences, where you would picture test tubes, microscopes, and other laboratory equipment. Among other things, statistical experiments may include recording an Internet user's preference for a Web browser, recording a change in the Dow Jones Industrial Average from one day to the next, recording the weekly sales of a business firm, and counting the number of errors on a page of an accountant's ledger. The point is that a statistical experiment can be almost any act of observation as long as the outcome is uncertain.

> An **experiment** is an act or process of observation that leads to a single outcome that cannot be predicted with certainty.

Consider another simple experiment consisting of tossing a die and observing the number on the up face. The six basic possible outcomes to this experiment are as follows:

1. Observe a 1
2. Observe a 2
3. Observe a 3
4. Observe a 4
5. Observe a 5
6. Observe a 6

Note that if this experiment is conducted once, *you can observe one and only one of these six basic outcomes, and the outcome cannot be predicted with certainty.* Also, these possibilities cannot be decomposed into more basic outcomes. Because observing the outcome of an experiment is similar to selecting a sample from a population, the basic possible outcomes to an experiment are called *sample points.**

> A **sample point** is the most basic outcome of an experiment.

Example 3.1	**Problem** Two coins are tossed, and their up faces are recorded. List all the sample points for this experiment.

Listing the Sample Points for a Coin–Tossing Experiment

Solution Even for a seemingly trivial experiment, we must be careful when listing the sample points. At first glance, we might expect three basic outcomes: Observe two heads, Observe two tails, or Observe one head and one tail. However, further reflection reveals that the last of these, Observe one head and one tail, can be decomposed into two outcomes: Head on coin 1, Tail on coin 2; and Tail on coin 1, Head on coin 2.

A useful tool for illustrating this notion is a **tree diagram.** Figure 3.1 shows a tree diagram for this experiment. At the top of the "tree," there are two branches, representing the two outcomes (*H* or *T*) for the first tossed coin. Each of these outcomes results in two more branches, representing the two outcomes (*H* or *T*) for the second tossed coin. Consequently, after tossing both coins, you can see that we have four sample points.

1. Observe *HH*   **3.** Observe *TH*
2. Observe *HT*   **4.** Observe *TT*

*Alternatively, the term *simple event* can be used.

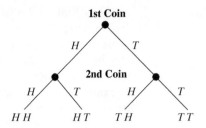

Figure 3.1

Tree diagram for the coin-tossing experiment

where H in the first position means "Head on coin 1," H in the second position means "Head on coin 2," and so on.

Look Back Even if the coins are identical in appearance, there are, in fact, two distinct coins. Thus, the sample points must account for this distinction.

▬▪ **Now Work Exercise 3.7a**

We often wish to refer to the collection of all the sample points of an experiment. This collection is called the *sample space* of the experiment. For example, there are six sample points in the sample space associated with the die-toss experiment. The sample spaces for the experiments discussed thus far are shown in Table 3.1.

> The **sample space** of an experiment is the collection of all its sample points.

Just as graphs are useful in describing sets of data, a pictorial method for presenting the sample space will often be useful. Figure 3.2 shows such a representation for each of the experiments in Table 3.1. In each case, the sample space is shown as a closed figure, labeled S, containing all possible sample points. Each sample point is represented by a solid dot (i.e., a "point") and labeled accordingly. Such graphical representations are called **Venn diagrams.**

Table 3.1	**Experiments and Their Sample Spaces**

Experiment: Observe the up face on a coin.
Sample space: **1.** Observe a head
 2. Observe a tail

This sample space can be represented in set notation as a set containing two sample points:

$$S: \{H, T\}$$

where H represents the sample point Observe a head and T represents the sample point Observe a tail.

Experiment: Observe the up face on a die.
Sample space: **1.** Observe a 1
 2. Observe a 2
 3. Observe a 3
 4. Observe a 4
 5. Observe a 5
 6. Observe a 6

This sample space can be represented in set notation as a set of six sample points:

$$S: \{1, 2, 3, 4, 5, 6\}$$

Experiment: Observe the up faces on two coins.
Sample space: **1.** Observe HH
 2. Observe HT
 3. Observe TH
 4. Observe TT

This sample space can be represented in set notation as a set of four sample points:

$$S: \{HH, HT, TH, TT\}$$

○ H **○** T

S

a. Experiment: Observe the up face on a coin

○1   **○**2   **○**3

○4   **○**5   **○**6

S

b. Experiment: Observe the up face on a die

○ HH **○** HT

○ TH **○** TT

S

c. Experiment: Observe the up faces on two coins

Figure 3.2

Venn diagrams for the three experiments from Table 3.1

Now that we know that an experiment will result in *only one* basic outcome—called a *sample point*—and that the sample space is the collection of all possible sample points, we're ready to discuss the probabilities of the sample points. You've undoubtedly used the term *probability* and have some intuitive idea about its meaning. Probability is generally used synonymously with "chance," "odds," and similar concepts. For example, if a fair coin is tossed, we might reason that both the sample points, Observe a head and Observe a tail, have the same *chance* of occurring. Thus, we might state that "the probability of observing a head is 50%" or "the *odds* of seeing a head are 50:50." Both of these statements are based on an informal knowledge of probability. We'll begin our treatment of probability by using such informal concepts and then later solidify what we mean.

The probability of a sample point is a number between 0 and 1 inclusive that measures the likelihood that the outcome will occur when the experiment is performed. This number is usually taken to be the relative frequency of the occurrence of a sample point in a very long series of repetitions of an experiment.* For example, if we are assigning probabilities to the two sample points (Observe a head and Observe a tail) in the coin-toss experiment, we might reason that if we toss a balanced coin a very large number of times, the sample points Observe a head and Observe a tail will occur with the same relative frequency of .5.

Our reasoning is supported by Figure 3.3. The figure plots the relative frequency of the number of times that a head occurs when simulating (by computer) the toss of a coin N times, where N ranges from as few as 25 tosses to as many as 1,500 tosses of the coin. You can see that when N is large (i.e., $N = 1,500$), the relative frequency is converging to .5. Thus, the probability of each sample point in the coin-tossing experiment is .5.

For some experiments, we may have little or no information on the relative frequency of occurrence of the sample points; consequently, we must assign probabilities to the sample points based on general information about the experiment. For example, if the experiment is to invest in a business venture and to observe whether it succeeds or fails, the sample space would appear as in Figure 3.4.

We are unlikely to be able to assign probabilities to the sample points of this experiment based on a long series of repetitions because unique factors govern each performance of this kind of experiment. Instead, we may consider factors such as the personnel managing the venture, the general state of the economy at the time, the

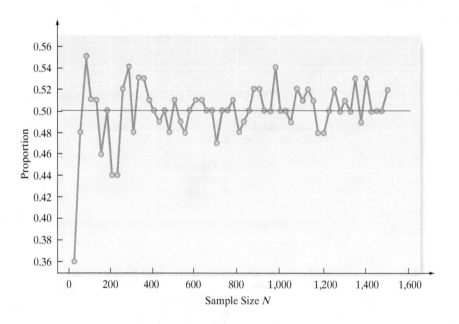

Figure 3.3

Proportion of heads in N coin tosses

*The result derives from an axiom in probability theory called the **Law of Large Numbers**. Phrased informally, this law states that the relative frequency of the number of times that an outcome occurs when an experiment is replicated over and over again (i.e., a large number of times) approaches the theoretical probability of the outcome.

Figure 3.4

Experiment: Invest in a business venture and observe whether it succeeds (*S*) or fails (*F*)

rate of success of similar ventures, and any other pertinent information. If we finally decide that the venture has an 80% chance of succeeding, we assign a probability of .8 to the sample point Success. This probability can be interpreted as a measure of our degree of belief in the outcome of the business venture; that is, it is a subjective probability. Notice, however, that such probabilities should be based on expert information that is carefully assessed. If not, we may be misled on any decisions based on these probabilities or based on any calculations in which they appear. [*Note*: For a text that deals in detail with the subjective evaluation of probabilities, see Winkler (1972) or Lindley (1985).]

No matter how you assign the probabilities to sample points, the probabilities assigned must obey two rules:

Probability Rules for Sample Points

Let p_i represent the probability of sample point *i*.

1. All sample point probabilities *must* lie between 0 and 1 (i.e., $0 \leq p_i \leq 1$).
2. The probabilities of all the sample points within a sample space *must* sum to 1 (i.e., $\sum p_i = 1$).

Assigning probabilities to sample points is easy for some experiments. For example, if the experiment is to toss a fair coin and observe the face, we would probably all agree to assign a probability of $\frac{1}{2}$ to the two sample points, Observe a head and Observe a tail. However, many experiments have sample points whose probabilities are more difficult to assign.

Example	3.2

Sample Point Probabilities—Hotel Water Conservation

Problem *Going Green* is the term used to describe water conservation programs at hotels and motels. Many hotels now offer their guests the option of participating in these Going Green programs by reusing towels and bed linens. Suppose you randomly select one hotel from a registry of all hotels in Orange County, California, and check whether or not the hotel participates in a water conservation program. Show how this problem might be formulated in the framework of an experiment with sample points and a sample space. Indicate how probabilities might be assigned to the sample points.

Solution The experiment can be defined as the selection of an Orange County hotel and the observation of whether or not a water conservation program is offered to guests at the hotel. There are two sample points in the sample space for this experiment:

C: {The hotel offers a water conservation program.}

N: {The hotel does not offer a water conservation program.}

The difference between this and the coin-toss experiment becomes apparent when we attempt to assign probabilities to the two sample points. What probability should we assign to sample point *C*? If you answer .5, you are assuming that the events *C* and *N* occur with equal likelihood, just like the sample points Heads and Tails in the coin-toss experiment. But assigning sample point probabilities for the hotel water conservation experiment is not so easy. In fact, a recent report by the Orange County Water District stated that 70% of the hotels in the county now participate in a water conservation program of some type. In that case, it might be reasonable to approximate the probability of the sample point *C* as .7 and that of the sample point *N* as .3.

Look Back Here we see that sample points are not always equally likely, so assigning probabilities to them can be complicated—particularly for experiments that represent real applications (as opposed to coin- and die-toss experiments).

■ Now Work Exercise 3.9

Although the probabilities of sample points are often of interest in their own right, it is usually probabilities of collections of sample points that are important. Example 3.3 demonstrates this point.

Example	3.3

Probability of a Collection of Sample Points— Die-Tossing Experiment

Problem A fair die is tossed, and the up face is observed. If the face is even, you win $1. Otherwise, you lose $1. What is the probability that you win?

Solution Recall that the sample space for this experiment contains six sample points:

$$S: \{1, 2, 3, 4, 5, 6\}$$

Because the die is balanced, we assign a probability of $\frac{1}{6}$ to each of the sample points in this sample space. An even number will occur if one of the sample points, Observe a 2, Observe a 4, or Observe a 6, occurs. A collection of sample points such as this is called an *event*, which we denote by the letter A. Because the event A contains three sample points—each with probability $\frac{1}{6}$—and because no sample points can occur simultaneously, we reason that the probability of A is the sum of the probabilities of the sample points in A. Thus, the probability of A (i.e., the probability that you will win) is $\frac{1}{6} + \frac{1}{6} + \frac{1}{6} = \frac{1}{2}$.

Look Back Based on our notion of probability, $P(A) = \frac{1}{2}$ implies that, *in the long run*, you will win $1 half the time and lose $1 half the time.

━━━━━━━━━━━━━━━━━━━━━━━━━━━━ ▪ **Now Work Exercise 3.6**

Figure 3.5

Die-toss experiment with event *A:* Observe an even number

Figure 3.5 is a Venn diagram depicting the sample space associated with a die-toss experiment and the event A, Observe an even number. The event A is represented by the closed figure inside the sample space S. This closed figure A contains all the sample points that comprise it.

To decide which sample points belong to the set associated with an event A, test each sample point in the sample space S. If event A occurs, then that sample point is in the event A. For example, the event A, Observe an even number, in the die-toss experiment will occur if the sample point Observe a 2 occurs. By the same reasoning, the sample points Observe a 4 and Observe a 6 are also in event A.

To summarize, we have demonstrated that an event can be defined in words or it can be defined as a specific set of sample points. This leads us to the following general definition of an event:

> An **event** is a specific collection of sample points. Further, a **simple event** contains only a single sample point, while a **compound event** contains two or more sample points.

Example	3.4

The Probability of a Compound Event— Coin-Tossing Experiment

Problem Consider the experiment of tossing two *unbalanced* coins. Because the coins are *not* balanced, their outcomes (H or T) are not equiprobable. Suppose the correct probabilities associated with the sample points are given in the table. [*Note:* The necessary properties for assigning probabilities to sample points are satisfied.]

Consider the events

$$A: \{\text{Observe exactly one head}\}$$

$$B: \{\text{Observe at least one head}\}$$

Calculate the probability of A and the probability of B.

Sample Point	Probability
HH	$\frac{4}{9}$
HT	$\frac{2}{9}$
TH	$\frac{2}{9}$
TT	$\frac{1}{9}$

Solution Event A contains the sample points HT and TH; thus, A is a compound event. Because two or more sample points cannot occur at the same time, we can easily calculate the probability of event A by summing the probabilities of the two sample points. Thus, the probability of observing exactly one head (event A), denoted by the symbol $P(A)$, is

$$P(A) = P(\text{Observe } HT) + P(\text{Observe } TH) = \tfrac{2}{9} + \tfrac{2}{9} = \tfrac{4}{9}$$

Similarly, because B contains the sample points HH, HT, and TH,

$$P(B) = \tfrac{4}{9} + \tfrac{2}{9} + \tfrac{2}{9} = \tfrac{8}{9}$$

Look Back Again, these probabilities should be interpreted *in the long run*. For example, $P(B) = \tfrac{8}{9} \approx .89$ implies that if we were to toss two coins an infinite number of times, we would observe at least 2 heads on about 89% of the tosses.

◼ Now Work Exercise 3.3

The preceding example leads us to a general procedure for finding the probability of an event A:

Probability of an Event

The probability of an event A is calculated by summing the probabilities of the sample points in the sample space for A.

Thus, we can summarize the steps for calculating the probability of any event, as indicated in the next box.

Steps for Calculating Probabilities of Events

Step 1 Define the experiment; that is, describe the process used to make an observation and the type of observation that will be recorded.

Step 2 List the sample points.

Step 3 Assign probabilities to the sample points.

Step 4 Determine the collection of sample points contained in the event of interest.

Step 5 Sum the sample point probabilities to get the event probability.

Example	3.5

Applying the Five Steps to Find a Probability—Diversity Training

Problem Diversity training of employees is the latest trend in U.S. business. *USA Today* reported on the primary reasons businesses give for making diversity training part of their strategic planning process. The reasons are summarized in Table 3.2. Assume that one business is selected at random from all U.S. businesses that use diversity training, and the primary reason is determined.

Table 3.2	Primary Reasons for Diversity Training
Reason	Percentage
Comply with personnel policies (CPP)	7
Increase productivity (IP)	47
Stay competitive (SC)	38
Social responsibility (SR)	4
Other (O)	4
Total	100

a. Define the experiment that generated the data in Table 3.2 and list the sample points.

b. Assign probabilities to the sample points.

c. What is the probability that the primary reason for diversity training is business related, that is, related to competition or productivity?

d. What is the probability that social responsibility is not a primary reason for diversity training?

Figure 3.6

Venn diagram for diversity training survey

Solution

a. The experiment is the act of determining the primary reason for diversity training of employees at a U.S. business. The sample points, the simplest outcomes of the experiment, are the five response categories listed in Table 3.2. These sample points are shown in the Venn diagram in Figure 3.6.

b. If, as in Example 3.1, we were to assign equal probabilities in this case, each of the response categories would have a probability of one-fifth, $\frac{1}{5}$, or .20. But, by examining Table 3.2 you can see that equal probabilities are not reasonable here because the response percentages are not even approximately the same in the five classifications. It is more reasonable to assign a probability equal to the response percentage in each class, as shown in Table 3.3.*

c. Let the symbol B represent the event that the primary reason for diversity training is business related. B is not a sample point because it consists of more than one of the response classifications (the sample points). In fact, as shown in Figure 3.6, B consists of two sample points, IP and SC. The probability of B is defined to be the sum of the probabilities of the sample points in B.

$$P(B) = P(\text{IP}) + P(\text{SC}) = .47 + .38 = .85$$

d. Let NSR represent the event that social responsibility is not a primary reason for diversity training. Then NSR consists of all sample points except SR, and the probability is the sum of the corresponding sample point probabilities:

$$P(NSR) = P(\text{CPP}) + P(\text{IP}) + P(\text{SC}) + P(\text{O})$$
$$= .07 + .47 + .38 + .04 = .96$$

Table 3.3	
Sample Point Probabilities for Diversity Training Survey	
Sample Point	Probability
CPP	.07
IP	.47
SC	.38
SR	.04
O	.04

Look Back The key to solving this problem is to follow the steps outlined in the box. We defined the experiment (Step 1) and listed the sample points (Step 2) in part **a.** The assignment of probabilities to the sample points (Step 3) was done in part **b.** For each probability in parts **c** and **d,** we identified the collection of points in the event (Step 4) and summed their probabilities (Step 5).

◼ **Now Work Exercise 3.15**

Example 3.6

Another Compound Event Probability—Investing in a Successful Venture

Problem You have the capital to invest in two of four ventures, each of which requires approximately the same amount of investment capital. Unknown to you, two of the investments will eventually fail and two will be successful. You research the four ventures because you think that your research will increase your probability of a successful choice over a purely random selection, and you eventually decide on two. If you used none of the information generated by your research and selected two ventures at random, what is the probability that you would select at least one successful venture?

Solution

Step 1: Denote the two successful enterprises as S_1 and S_2 and the two failing enterprises as F_1 and F_2. The experiment involves a random selection of two out of the four ventures, and each possible pair of ventures represents a sample point.

---

*The response percentages were based on a sample of U.S. businesses; consequently, these assigned probabilities are estimates of the true population-response percentages. You'll learn how to measure the reliability of probability estimates in Chapter 6.

Step 2: The six sample points that make up the sample space are

1. (S_1, S_2)
2. (S_1, F_1)
3. (S_1, F_2)
4. (S_2, F_1)
5. (S_2, F_2)
6. (F_1, F_2)

Step 3: Next, we assign probabilities to the sample points. If we assume that the choice of any one pair is as likely as any other, then the probability of each sample point is $\frac{1}{6}$.

Step 4: The event of selecting at least one of the two successful ventures includes all the sample points except (F_1, F_2).

Step 5: Now, we find

$$P(\text{Select at least one success}) = P(S_1, S_2) + P(S_1, F_1) + P(S_1, F_2) +$$
$$P(S_2, F_1) + P(S_2, F_2)$$
$$= \tfrac{1}{6} + \tfrac{1}{6} + \tfrac{1}{6} + \tfrac{1}{6} + \tfrac{1}{6} = \tfrac{5}{6}$$

Therefore, with a random selection, the probability of selecting at least one successful venture out of two is $\frac{5}{6}$.

The preceding examples have one thing in common: The number of sample points in each of the sample spaces was small; hence, the sample points were easy to identify and list. How can we manage this when the sample points run into the thousands or millions? For example, suppose you wish to select five business ventures from a group of 1,000. Then each different group of five ventures would represent a sample point. How can you determine the number of sample points associated with this experiment?

One method of determining the number of sample points for a complex experiment is to develop a counting system. Start by examining a simple version of the experiment. For example, see if you can develop a system for counting the number of ways to select two ventures from a total of four (this is exactly what was done in Example 3.6). If the ventures are represented by the symbols V_1, V_2, V_3, and V_4, the sample points could be listed in the following pattern:

$$(V_1, V_2) \quad (V_2, V_3) \quad (V_3, V_4)$$
$$(V_1, V_3) \quad (V_2, V_4)$$
$$(V_1, V_4)$$

Note the pattern and now try a more complex situation—say, sampling three ventures out of five. List the sample points and observe the pattern. Finally, see if you can deduce the pattern for the general case. Perhaps you can program a computer to produce the matching and counting for the number of samples of five selected from a total of 1,000.

A second method of determining the number of sample points for an experiment is to use **combinatorial mathematics.** This branch of mathematics is concerned with developing counting rules for given situations. For example, there is a simple rule for finding the number of different samples of 5 ventures selected from 1,000. This rule, called the **Combinations Rule,** is given in the box.

Combinations Rule

A sample of n elements is to be drawn from a set of N elements. Then, the number of different samples possible is denoted by $\binom{N}{n}$ and is equal to

$$\binom{N}{n} = \frac{N!}{n!(N-n)!}$$

> where the factorial symbol (!) means that
>
> $$n! = n(n-1)(n-2)\cdots(3)(2)(1)$$
>
> For example, $5! = 5 \cdot 4 \cdot 3 \cdot 2 \cdot 1$. [*Note:* The quantity 0! is defined to be equal to 1.]

Example 3.7

Using the Combinations Rule—Selecting 2 Investments from 4

Problem Refer to Example 3.6, where we selected two ventures from four in which to invest. Use the combinations rule to determine how many different selections can be made.

Solution For this example, $N = 4$, $n = 2$, and

$$\binom{4}{2} = \frac{4!}{2!2!} = \frac{4 \cdot 3 \cdot 2 \cdot 1}{(2 \cdot 1)(2 \cdot 1)} = \frac{4 \cdot 3}{2 \cdot 1} = \frac{12}{2} = 6$$

Look Back You can see that this agrees with the number of sample points obtained in Example 3.6.

◼ **Now Work Exercise 3.5**

Example 3.8

Using the Combinations Rule—Selecting 5 Investments from 20

Problem Suppose you plan to invest equal amounts of money in each of five business ventures. If you have 20 ventures from which to make the selection, how many different samples of five ventures can be selected from the 20?

Solution For this example, $N = 20$ and $n = 5$. Then the number of different samples of 5 that can be selected from the 20 ventures is

$$\binom{20}{5} = \frac{20!}{5!(20-5)!} = \frac{20!}{5!15!}$$

$$= \frac{20 \cdot 19 \cdot 18 \cdot \cdots \cdot 3 \cdot 2 \cdot 1}{(5 \cdot 4 \cdot 3 \cdot 2 \cdot 1)(15 \cdot 14 \cdot 13 \cdot \cdots \cdot 3 \cdot 2 \cdot 1)} = \frac{20 \cdot 19 \cdot 18 \cdot 17 \cdot 16}{5 \cdot 4 \cdot 3 \cdot 2 \cdot 1} = 15{,}504$$

Look Back You can see that attempting to list all the sample points for this experiment would be an extremely tedious and time-consuming, if not practically impossible, task.

◼ **Now Work Exercise 3.20**

The Combinations Rule is just one of a large number of counting rules that have been developed by combinatorial mathematicians. This counting rule applies to situations in which the experiment calls for selecting n elements from a total of N elements, without replacing each element before the next is selected. If you are interested in learning other methods for counting sample points for various types of experiments, you will find a few of the basic counting rules in Appendix B. Others can be found in the chapter references.

STATISTICS in ACTION REVISITED

The Probability of Winning Lotto

In Florida's state lottery game, called Pick-6 Lotto, you select six numbers of your choice from a set of numbers ranging from 1 to 53. We can apply the Combinations Rule to determine the total number of combinations of 6 numbers selected from 53 (i.e., the total number of sample points [or possible winning tickets]). Here, $N = 53$ and $n = 6$; therefore, we have

$$\binom{N}{n} = \frac{N!}{n!(N-n)!} = \frac{53!}{6!47!}$$

$$= \frac{(53)(52)(51)(50)(49)(48)(47!)}{(6)(5)(4)(3)(2)(1)(47!)}$$

$$= 22{,}957{,}480$$

Now, since the Lotto balls are selected at random, each of these 22,957,480 combinations is equally likely to occur. Therefore, the probability of winning Lotto is

$$P(\text{Win } 6/53 \text{ Lotto}) = 1/(22,957,480) = .00000004356$$

This probability is often stated as follows: The odds of winning the game with a single ticket are 1 in 22,957,480, or 1 in approximately 23 million. For all practical purposes, this probability is 0, implying that you have almost no chance of winning the lottery with a single ticket. Yet each week there is almost always a winner in the Florida Lotto. This apparent contradiction can be explained with the following analogy.

Suppose there is a line of Smart cars, front to back, from New York City to Los Angeles, California. Based on the distance between the two cities and the length of a standard minivan, there would be approximately 23 million Smart cars in line. Lottery officials will select, at random, one of the Smart cars and put a check for $10 million dollars in the glove compartment. For a cost of $1, you may roam the country and select one (and only one) Smart car and check the glove compartment. Do you think you will find $10 million in the Smart car you choose? You can be almost certain that you won't. But now permit anyone to enter the lottery for $1 and suppose that 50 million people do so. With such a large number of participants, it is very likely that someone will find the Smart car with the $10 million—but it almost certainly won't be you! (This example illustrates an axiom in statistics called the Law of Large Numbers. See the footnote at the bottom of p. 132.)

Exercises 3.1–3.27

Learning the Mechanics

3.1 An experiment results in one of the following sample points: $E_1, E_2, E_3, E_4,$ or E_5.
  a. Find $P(E_3)$ if $P(E_1) = .1, P(E_2) = .2, P(E_4) = .1,$ and $P(E_5) = .1$.
  b. Find $P(E_3)$ if $P(E_1) = P(E_3), P(E_2) = .1, P(E_4) = .2,$ and $P(E_5) = .1$.
  c. Find $P(E_3)$ if $P(E_1) = P(E_2) = P(E_4) = P(E_5) = .1$.

3.2 The diagram below describes the sample space of a particular experiment and events A and B.

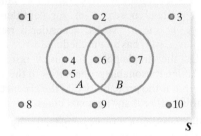

  a. What is this type of diagram called?
  b. Suppose the sample points are equally likely. Find $P(A)$ and $P(B)$.
  c. Suppose $P(1) = P(2) = P(3) = P(4) = P(5) = \frac{1}{20}$ and $P(6) = P(7) = P(8) = P(9) = P(10) = \frac{3}{20}$. Find $P(A)$ and $P(B)$.

3.3 The sample space for an experiment contains five sample
NW points with probabilities as shown in the table. Find the probability of each of the following events:

Sample Points	Probabilities
1	.05
2	.20
3	.30
4	.30
5	.15

  A: {Either 1, 2, or 3 occurs}
  B: {Either 1, 3, or 5 occurs}
  C: {4 does not occur}

3.4 Compute each of the following:
  a. $\binom{9}{4}$ **b.** $\binom{7}{2}$ **c.** $\binom{4}{4}$
  d. $\binom{5}{0}$ **e.** $\binom{6}{5}$

3.5 Compute the number of ways you can select n elements
NW from N elements for each of the following:
  a. $n = 2, N = 5$
  b. $n = 3, N = 6$
  c. $n = 5, N = 20$

3.6 Two fair dice are tossed, and the face on each die is observed.

 a. Use a tree diagram to find the 36 sample points contained in the sample space.

 b. Assign probabilities to the sample points in part **a.**

 c. Find the probability of each of the following events:

 $A = \{3 \text{ showing on each die}\}$

 $B = \{\text{sum of two numbers showing is 7}\}$

 $C = \{\text{sum of two numbers showing is even}\}$

3.7 Two marbles are drawn at random and without replacement from a box containing two blue marbles and three red marbles.

 a. List the sample points for this experiment.

 b. Assign probabilities to the sample points.

 c. Determine the probability of observing each of the following events:

 A: {Two blue marbles are drawn.}

 B: {A red and a blue marble are drawn.}

 C: {Two red marbles are drawn.}

3.8 Simulate the experiment described in Exercise 3.7 using any five identically shaped objects, two of which are one color and three another color. Mix the objects, draw two, record the results, and then replace the objects. Repeat the experiment a large number of times (at least 100). Calculate the proportion of time events *A, B,* and *C* occur. How do these proportions compare with the probabilities you calculated in Exercise 3.7? Should these proportions equal the probabilities? Explain.

⚙ Applet Exercise 3.1

Use the applet *Simulating the Probability of Rolling a 6* to explore the relationship between the proportion of 6s rolled on several rolls of a die and the theoretical probability of rolling a 6 on a fair die.

 a. To simulate rolling a die one time, click on the *Roll* button on the screen while $n = 1$. The outcome of the roll appears in the list at the right, and the cumulative proportion of 6s for one roll is shown above the graph and as a point on the graph corresponding to 1. Click *Reset* and repeat the process with $n = 1$ several times. What are the possible values of the cumulative proportion of 6s for one roll of a die? Can the cumulative proportion of 6s for one roll of a die equal the theoretical probability of rolling a 6 on a fair die? Explain.

 b. Set $n = 10$ and click the *Roll* button. Repeat this several times, resetting after each time. Record the cumulative proportion of 6s for each roll. Compare the cumulative proportions for $n = 10$ to those for $n = 1$ in part **a.** Which tend to be closer to the theoretical probability of rolling a 6 on a fair die?

 c. Repeat part **b** for $n = 1,000$, comparing the cumulative proportions for $n = 1,000$ to those for $n = 1$ in part **a** and for $n = 10$ in part **b.**

 d. Based on your results for parts **a, b,** and **c,** do you believe that we could justifiably conclude that a die is unfair because we rolled it 10 times and didn't roll any 6s? Explain.

⚙ Applet Exercise 3.2

Use the applet *Simulating the Probability of a Head with a Fair Coin* to explore the relationship between the proportion of heads on several flips of a coin and the theoretical probability of getting heads on one flip of a fair coin.

 a. Repeat parts **a–c** of Applet Exercise 3.1 for the experiment of flipping a coin and the event of getting heads.

 b. Based on your results for part **a,** do you believe that we could justifiably conclude that a coin is unfair because we flipped it 10 times and didn't get any heads? Explain.

Applying the Concepts–Basic

3.9 **Colors of M&M's candies.** In 1940, Forrest E. Mars Sr. formed the Mars Corporation to produce chocolate candies with a sugar shell that could be sold throughout the year and wouldn't melt during the summer. Originally, M&M's Plain Chocolate Candies came in only a brown color. Today, M&M's in standard bags come in six colors: brown, yellow, red, blue, orange, and green. According to Mars Corporation, today 24% of all M&M's produced are blue, 20% are orange, 16% are green, 14% are yellow, 13% are brown, and 13% are red. Suppose you purchase a randomly selected bag of M&M's Plain Chocolate Candies and randomly select one of the M&M's from the bag. The color of the selected M&M is of interest.

 a. Identify the outcomes (sample points) of this experiment.

 b. Assign reasonable probabilities to the outcomes, part **a.**

 c. What is the probability that the selected M&M is brown (the original color)?

 d. In 1960, the colors red, green, and yellow were added to brown M&Ms. What is the probability that the selected M&M is either red, green, or yellow?

 e. In 1995, based on voting by American consumers, the color blue was added to the M&M mix. What is the probability that the selected M&M is not blue?

3.10 **Workers' unscheduled absence survey.** Each year CCH, Inc., a firm that provides human resources and employment law information, conducts a survey on absenteeism in the workplace. The latest *CCH Unscheduled Absence Survey* found that of all unscheduled work absences, 34% are due to "personal illness," 22% for "family issues," 18% for "personal needs," 13% for "entitlement mentality," and 13% due to "stress." Consider a randomly selected employee who has an unscheduled work absence.

 a. List the sample points for this experiment.

 b. Assign reasonable probabilities to the sample points.

 c. What is the probability that the absence is due to something other than "personal illness"?

3.11 **Male nannies.** In a survey conducted by the International Nanny Association (INA) and reported at the INA Web site (*www.nanny.org*), 4,176 nannies were placed in a job in a given year. Only 24 of the nannies placed were men. Find the probability that a randomly selected nanny who was placed during the last year is a male nanny (a "mannie").

3.12 **Predicting when a Florida hurricane occurs.** Since the early 1900s, the state of Florida has exceeded $450 million in damages due to destructive hurricanes. Consequently, the value of property insured against windstorm damage in Florida is the highest in the nation. Researchers at Florida State University conducted a comprehensive analysis of damages caused by Florida hurricanes and published the results in *Southeastern Geographer* (Summer 2009). Part of their analysis included estimating the likelihood that a hurricane develops from a tropical storm based on the sequence number of the tropical storm within a season. The researchers discovered that of the 67 Florida hurricanes since 1900, 11 developed from the fifth tropical storm of the season (the sequence with the highest frequency). Also, only 5 hurricanes developed from a tropical storm with a sequence number of 12 or greater.

a. Estimate the probability that a Florida hurricane develops from the fifth tropical storm of the season.

b. Estimate the probability that a Florida hurricane develops before the 12th tropical storm of the season.

3.13 **Going online for health information.** A *cyberchondriac* is defined as a person who regularly searches the Web for health care information (see Exercise 1.20, p. 26). A 2011 Harris Poll surveyed 1,019 U.S. adults by telephone and asked each respondent how often (in the past month) he/she looked for health care information online. The results are summarized in the following table. Consider the response category of a randomly selected person who participated in the Harris Poll.

Response (# per Month)	Percentage of Respondents
None	19
1 or 2	31
3–5	26
6–9	5
10 or more	19
Total	100

Source: Data from *The Harris Poll*, Sept. 15, 2011 (Table 4).

a. List the sample points for the experiment.

b. Assign reasonable probabilities to the sample points.

c. Find the probability that the respondent looks for health care information online more than two times per month.

3.14 **Working on summer vacation.** Is summer vacation a break from work? Not according to an *Adweek/Harris* (July 2011) poll of 3,304 U.S. adults. The poll found that 46% of the respondents work during their summer vacation, 35% do not work at all while on vacation, and 19% were unemployed. Consider the work status during summer vacation of a randomly selected poll respondent.

a. List the sample points for this experiment.

b. Assign reasonable probabilities to the sample points.

c. What is the probability that a randomly selected poll respondent will not work while on summer vacation or is unemployed?

Applying the Concepts—Intermediate

3.15 **Is a product "green"?** A "green" product (e.g., a product
NW built from recycled materials) is one that has minimal impact on the environment and human health. How do consumers determine if a product is "green"? The *2011*

ImagePower Green Brands Survey asked this question of more than 9,000 international consumers. The results are shown in the following table.

Reason for Saying a Product Is Green	Percentage of Consumers
Certification mark on label	45
Packaging	15
Reading information about the product	12
Advertisement	6
Brand Web site	4
Other	18
Total	100

Source: Based on 2011 ImagePower Green Brands Survey.

a. What method is an international consumer most likely to use to identify a green product?

b. Find the probability that an international consumer identifies a green product by a certification mark on the product label or by the product packaging.

c. Find the probability that an international consumer identifies a green product by reading about the product or from information at the brand's Web site.

d. Find the probability that an international consumer does not use advertisements to identify a green product.

3.16 **Museum management.** Refer to the *Museum Management and Curatorship* (June 2010) study of the criteria used
MMC to evaluate museum performance, Exercise 2.14 (p. 50). Recall that the managers of 30 leading museums of contemporary art were asked to provide the performance measure used most often. A summary of the results is reproduced in the table.

Performance Measure	Number of Museums
Total visitors	8
Paying visitors	5
Big shows	6
Funds raised	7
Members	4

a. If one of the 30 museums is selected at random, what is the probability that the museum uses total visitors or funds raised most often as a performance measure?

b. Consider two museums of contemporary art randomly selected from all such museums. Of interest is whether or not the museums use total visitors or funds raised most often as a performance measure. Use a tree diagram to aid in listing the sample points for this problem.

c. Assign reasonable probabilities to the sample points of part **b.** [*Hint:* Use the probability, part **a,** to estimate these probabilities.]

d. Refer to parts **b** and **c.** Find the probability that both museums use total visitors or funds raised most often as a performance measure.

3.17 **USDA chicken inspection.** The U.S. Department of Agriculture (USDA) reports that, under its standard inspection system, one in every 100 slaughtered chickens passes inspection with fecal contamination.

a. If a slaughtered chicken is selected at random, what is the probability that it passes inspection with fecal contamination?

b. The probability of part **a** was based on a USDA study that found that 306 of 32,075 chicken carcasses passed inspection with fecal contamination. Do you agree with the USDA's statement about the likelihood of a slaughtered chicken passing inspection with fecal contamination?

3.18 PIN pad shipments. Personal identification number (PIN) pads are devices that connect to point-of-sale electronic cash registers for debit and credit card purchases. Refer to *The Nilson Report* (Oct. 2008) listing of the volume of PIN pad shipments by manufacturers worldwide, Exercise 2.7 (p. 49). Recall that for the 12 manufacturers listed in the table, a total of 334,039 PIN pads were shipped. Suppose you randomly select one of these PIN pads and identify the manufacturer.

Manufacturer	Number Shipped (units)
Bitel	13,500
CyberNet	16,200
Fujian Landi	119,000
Glintt (ParaRede)	5,990
Intelligent	4,562
KwangWoo	42,000
Omron	20,000
Pax Tech.	10,072
ProvencoCadmus	20,000
SZZT Electronics	67,300
Toshiba TEC	12,415
Urmet	3,000

Source: Data from *The Nilson Report*, No. 912, October 2008 (p. 9).

a. Find the probability that the PIN pad is shipped by either Fujian Landi or SZZT Electronics.

b. Suppose that 1,000 of the PIN pads shipped were found to be defective. Find the probability that the PIN pad selected is one of the defectives.

3.19 Randomization in a study of TV commercials. Gonzaga University professors conducted a study of more than 1,500 television commercials and published their results in the *Journal of Sociology, Social Work and Social Welfare* (Vol. 2, 2008). Commercials from eight networks—ABC, FAM, FOX, MTV, ESPN, CBS, CNN, and NBC—were sampled during an 8-day period, with one network randomly selected each day. The table below shows the actual order determined by random draw:

```
ABC—July 6 (Wed)
FAM—July 7 (Thr)
FOX—July 9 (Sat)
MTV—July 10 (Sun)
ESPN—July 11 (Mon)
CBS—July 12 (Tue)
CNN—July 16 (Sat)
NBC—July 17 (Sun)
```

a. What is the probability that ESPN was selected on Monday, July 11?

b. Consider the four networks chosen for the weekends (Saturday and Sunday). How many ways could the researchers select four networks from the eight for the weekend analysis of commercials? (Assume that the order of assignment for the four weekend days was immaterial to the analysis.)

c. Knowing that the networks were selected at random, what is the probability that ESPN was one of the four networks selected for the weekend analysis of commercials?

3.20 Jai-alai bets. The Quinella bet at the paramutual game of jai-alai consists of picking the jai-alai players that will place first and second in a game *irrespective* of order. In jai-alai, eight players (numbered 1, 2, 3,…,8) compete in every game.
a. How many different Quinella bets are possible?
b. Suppose you bet the Quinella combination of 2–7. If the players are of equal ability, what is the probability that you win the bet?

3.21 Investing in stocks. From a list of 15 preferred stocks recommended by your broker, you will select three to invest in. How many different ways can you select the three stocks from the 15 recommended stocks?

3.22 Groundwater contamination in wells. Refer to the *Environmental Science & Technology* (Jan. 2005) study of methyl *tert*-butyl ether (MTBE) contamination in New Hampshire wells, Exercise 2.17 (p. 51). Data collected for a sample of 223 wells are saved in the accompanying file. Recall that each well was classified according to well class (public or private), aquifer (bedrock or unconsolidated), and detectable level of MTBE (below limit or detect).
a. Consider an experiment in which the well class, aquifer, and detectable MTBE level of a well are observed. List the sample points for this experiment. [*Hint:* One sample point is private/bedrock/below limit.]
b. Use statistical software to find the number of the 223 wells in each sample point outcome. Then use this information to compute probabilities for the sample points.
c. Find and interpret the probability that a well has a detectable level of MTBE.

3.23 Choosing portable grill displays. University of Maryland marketing professor R. W. Hamilton studied how people attempt to influence the choices of others by offering undesirable alternatives (*Journal of Consumer Research*, Mar. 2003). Such a phenomenon typically occurs when family members propose a vacation spot, friends recommend a restaurant for dinner, and realtors show the buyer potential homes. In one phase of the study, the researcher had each of 124 college students select showroom displays for portable grills. Five different displays (representing five different-sized grills) were available, but only three displays would be selected. The students were instructed to select the displays to maximize purchases of Grill #2 (a smaller-sized grill).
a. In how many possible ways can the three grill displays be selected from the five displays? List the possibilities.
b. The table shows the grill display combinations and the number of each selected by the 124 students. Use this information to assign reasonable probabilities to the different display combinations.
c. Find the probability that a student who participated in the study selected a display combination involving Grill #1.

Grill Display Combination	Number of Students
1-2-3	35
1-2-4	8
1-2-5	42
2-3-4	4
2-3-5	1
2-4-5	34

Source: Based on Hamilton, R. W. "Why do people suggest what they do not want? Using context effects to influence others' choices," *Journal of Consumer Research*, Vol. 29, No. 4. Mar. 2003 (Table 1).

3.24 Highest-rated new cars. *Consumer Reports* magazine annually asks readers to evaluate their experiences in buying a new car during the previous year. Analysis of the questionnaires for a recent year revealed that readers were very satisfied with the following three new cars (in no particular order): Hyundai Elantra, Toyota Prius, and Subaru Forrester (*Consumer Reports,* Apr. 2011).

a. List all possible sets of rankings for these top three cars.

b. Assuming that each set of rankings in part **a** is equally likely, what is the probability that readers ranked Toyota Prius first? That readers ranked Hyundai Elantra third? That readers ranked Toyota Prius first and Subaru Forrester second?

Applying the Concepts—Advanced

3.25 Odds of winning a race. Handicappers for greyhound races express their belief about the probabilities that each greyhound will win a race in terms of **odds.** If the probability of event E is $P(E)$, then the *odds in favor of* E are $P(E)$ to $1 - P(E)$. Thus, if a handicapper assesses a probability of .25 that Oxford Shoes will win its next race, the odds in favor of Oxford Shoes are $\frac{25}{100}$ to $\frac{75}{100}$, or 1 to 3. It follows that the *odds against* E are $1 - P(E)$ to $P(E)$, or 3 to 1 against a win by Oxford Shoes. In general, if the odds in favor of event E are a to b, then $P(E) = a/(a + b)$.

a. A second handicapper assesses the probability of a win by Oxford Shoes to be $\frac{1}{3}$. According to the second handicapper, what are the odds in favor of Oxford Shoes winning?

b. A third handicapper assesses the odds in favor of Oxford Shoes to be 1 to 1. According to the third handicapper, what is the probability of Oxford Shoes winning?

c. A fourth handicapper assesses the odds against Oxford Shoes winning to be 3 to 2. Find this handicapper's assessment of the probability that Oxford Shoes will win.

3.26 Lead bullets as forensic evidence. *Chance* (Summer 2004) published an article on the use of lead bullets as forensic evidence in a federal criminal case. Typically, the Federal Bureau of Investigation (FBI) will use a laboratory method to match the lead in a bullet found at the crime scene with unexpended lead cartridges found in possession of the suspect. The value of this evidence depends on the chance of a *false positive* (i.e., the probability that the FBI finds a match given that the lead at the crime scene and the lead in possession of the suspect are actually from two different "melts," or sources). To estimate the false-positive rate, the FBI collected 1,837 bullets that they were confident all came from different melts. The FBI then examined every possible pair of bullets and counted the number of matches using its established criteria. According to *Chance*, the FBI found 693 matches. Use this information to compute the chance of a false positive. Is this probability small enough for you to have confidence in the FBI's forensic evidence?

3.27 Making your vote count. The recent Democratic and Republican presidential state primary elections were highlighted by the difference in the way winning candidates were awarded delegates. In Republican states, the winner is awarded all the state's delegates; conversely, the Democratic state winner is awarded delegates in proportion to the percentage of votes. This led to a *Chance* (Fall 2007) article on making your vote count. Consider the following scenario where you are one of five voters (for example, on a county commission where you are one of the five commissioners voting on an issue).

a. Determine the number of ways the five commissioners can vote, where each commissioner votes either for or against. (These outcomes represent the sample points for the experiment.)

b. Assume each commissioner is equally likely to vote for or against. Assign reasonable probabilities to the sample points, part **a**.

c. Your vote counts (i.e., is the decisive vote) only if the other four voters split, two in favor and two against. Assuming you are commissioner number 5, how many of the sample points in part **a** result in a 2-2 split for the other four commissioners?

d. Use your answers to parts **a–c** to find the probability that your vote counts.

e. Now suppose you convince two other commissioners to "vote in bloc," i.e., you all agree to vote among yourselves first, and whatever the majority decides is the way all three will vote. With only five total voters, this guarantees that the bloc vote will determine the outcome. In this scenario, your vote counts only if the other two commissioners in the bloc split votes, one in favor and one against. Find the probability that your vote counts.

3.2 Unions and Intersections

An event can often be viewed as a composition of two or more other events. Such events, which are called **compound events,** can be formed (composed) in two ways, as defined and illustrated here.

> The **union** of two events A and B is the event that occurs if either A *or* B *or* both occur on a single performance of the experiment. We denote the union of events A and B by the symbol $A \cup B$. $A \cup B$ consists of all the sample points that belong to A *or* B *or both*. (See Figure 3.7a.)

The **intersection** of two events *A and B* is the event that occurs if both *A and B* occur on a single performance of the experiment. We write $A \cap B$ for the intersection of *A* and *B*. $A \cap B$ consists of all the sample points belonging to *both A and B*. (See Figure 3.7b.)

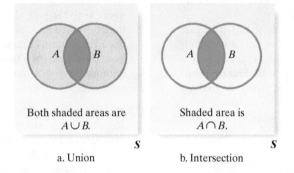

Both shaded areas are
$A \cup B$.

Shaded area is
$A \cap B$.

a. Union

b. Intersection

Figure 3.7

Venn diagrams for union
and intersection

Example 3.9

Probabilities of Unions and Intersections— Die-Toss Experiment

Figure 3.8

Venn diagram for die toss

Problem Consider the die-toss experiment. Define the following events:

A: {Toss an even number}

B: {Toss a number less than or equal to 3}

a. Describe $A \cup B$ for this experiment.

b. Describe $A \cap B$ for this experiment.

c. Calculate $P(A \cup B)$ and $P(A \cap B)$ assuming the die is fair.

Solution Draw the Venn diagram as shown in Figure 3.8.

a. The union of *A* and *B* is the event that occurs if we observe either an even number, a number less than or equal to 3, or both on a single throw of the die. Consequently, the sample points in the event $A \cup B$ are those for which *A* occurs, *B* occurs, or both *A* and *B* occur. Checking the sample points in the entire sample space, we find that the collection of sample points in the union of *A* and *B* is

$$A \cup B = \{1, 2, 3, 4, 6\}$$

b. The intersection of *A* and *B* is the event that occurs if we observe *both* an even number and a number less than or equal to 3 on a single throw of the die. Checking the sample points to see which imply the occurrence of *both* events *A* and *B*, we see that the intersection contains only one sample point:

$$A \cap B = \{2\}$$

In other words, the intersection of *A* and *B* is the sample point Observe a 2.

c. Recalling that the probability of an event is the sum of the probabilities of the sample points of which the event is composed, we have

$$P(A \cup B) = P(1) + P(2) + P(3) + P(4) + P(6)$$

$$= \tfrac{1}{6} + \tfrac{1}{6} + \tfrac{1}{6} + \tfrac{1}{6} + \tfrac{1}{6} = \tfrac{5}{6}$$

and

$$P(A \cap B) = P(2) = \tfrac{1}{6}$$

Look Back Since the six sample points are equally likely, the probabilities in part **c** are simply the number of sample points in the event of interest, divided by 6.

■ **Now Work Exercise 3.31a–d**

Unions and intersections can be defined for more than two events. For example, the event $A \cup B \cup C$ represents the union of three events: *A*, *B*, and *C*. This event, which includes the set of sample points in *A*, *B*, or *C*, will occur if any one (or more) of the events *A*, *B*, and *C* occurs. Similarly, the intersection $A \cap B \cap C$ is the event that all three of the events *A*, *B*, and *C* occur. Therefore, $A \cap B \cap C$ is the set of sample points that are in all three of the events.

Example 3.10

Finding Probabilities in a Two-Way Table — Income vs. age

Problem Many firms undertake direct marketing campaigns to promote their products. The campaigns typically involve mailing information to millions of households. The response rates are carefully monitored to determine the demographic characteristics of respondents. By studying tendencies to respond, the firms can better target future mailings to those segments of the population most likely to purchase their products.

Suppose a distributor of mail-order tools is analyzing the results of a recent mailing. The probability of response is believed to be related to income and age. The percentages of the total number of respondents to the mailing are given by income and age classification in Table 3.4. This table is called a **two-way table** because responses are classified according to two variables, income (columns) and age (rows).

Define the following events:

A: {A respondent's income is more than $50,000.}

B: {A respondents age is 30 or more.}

a. Find $P(A)$ and $P(B)$.

b. Find $P(A \cup B)$.

c. Find $P(A \cap B)$.

Table 3.4	Two-Way Table with Percentage of Respondents in Age-Income Classes		
	Income		
Age	<$25,000	$25,000–$50,000	>$50,000
<30 yrs	5%	12%	10%
30–50 yrs	14%	22%	16%
>50 yrs	Ⓑ 8%	10%	3% Ⓐ

Solution Following the steps for calculating probabilities of events, we first note that the objective is to characterize the income and age distribution of respondents to the mailing. To accomplish this, we define the experiment to consist of selecting a respondent from the collection of all respondents and observing which income and age class he or she occupies. The sample points are the nine different age-income classifications:

E_1: {< 30 yrs, < $25,000} E_4: {< 30 yrs, $25,000–$50,000} E_7: {< 30 yrs, > $50,000}

E_2: {30–50 yrs, < $25,000} E_5: {30–50 yrs, $25,000–$50,000} E_8: {30–50 yrs, > $50,000}

E_3: {> 50 yrs, < $25,000} E_6: {> 50 yrs, $25,000–$50,000} E_9: {> 50 yrs, > $50,000}

Next, we assign probabilities to the sample points. If we blindly select one of the respondents, the probability that he or she will occupy a particular age-income classification is the proportion, or relative frequency, of respondents in the classification. These proportions are given (as percentages) in Table 3.4. Thus,

$$P(E_1) = \text{Relative frequency of respondents in age-income class}$$
$$\{< 30 \text{ yrs}, < \$25,000\} = .05$$
$$P(E_2) = .14$$
$$P(E_3) = .08$$
$$P(E_4) = .12$$
$$P(E_5) = .22$$
$$P(E_6) = .10$$

$$P(E_7) = .10$$
$$P(E_8) = .16$$
$$P(E_9) = .03$$

You may verify that the sample points probabilities add to 1.

a. To find $P(A)$, we first determine the collection of sample points contained in event A. Because A is defined as $\{> \$50,000\}$, we see from Table 3.4 that A contains the three sample points represented by the last column of the table (see shaded area). In other words, the event A consists of the income classification $\{> \$50,000\}$ in all three age classifications. The probability of A is the sum of the probabilities of the sample points in A:

$$P(A) = P(E_7) + P(E_8) + P(E_9) = .10 + .16 + .03 = .29$$

Similarly, $B = \{\geq 30 \text{ yrs}\}$ consists of the six sample points in the second and third rows of Table 3.4 (see shaded area):

$$P(B) = P(E_2) + P(E_3) + P(E_5) + P(E_6) + P(E_8) + P(E_9)$$
$$= .14 + .08 + .22 + .10 + .16 + .03 = .73$$

b. The union of events A and B, $A \cup B$, consists of all the sample points in *either A or B or both*—that is, the union of A and B consists of all respondents whose income exceeds \$50,000 *or* whose age is 30 or more. In Table 3.4 this is any sample point found in the third column *or* the last two rows. Thus,

$$P(A \cup B) = .10 + .14 + .22 + .16 + .08 + .10 + .03 = .83$$

c. The intersection of events A and B, $A \cap B$, consists of all sample points in *both A and B*—that is, the intersection of A and B consists of all respondents whose income exceeds \$50,000 *and* whose age is 30 or more. In Table 3.4 this is any sample point found in the third column *and* the last two rows. Thus,

$$P(A \cap B) = .16 + .03 = .19$$

Look Back As with previous problems, the key to finding the probabilities of parts **b** and **c** is to identify the sample points that comprise the event of interest. In a two-way table like Table 3.4, the number of sample points will be equal to the number of rows times the number of columns.

■ **Now Work Exercise 3.33f–g**

3.3 Complementary Events

A very useful concept in the calculation of event probabilities is the notion of **complementary events:**

> The **complement** of an event A is the event that A does *not* occur—that is, the event consisting of all sample points that are not in event A. We denote the complement of A by A^c.

An event A is a collection of sample points, and the sample points included in A^c are those not in A. Figure 3.9 demonstrates this idea. Note from the figure that all sample points in S are included in *either A or A^c* and that *no* sample point is in both A and A^c. This leads us to conclude that the probabilities of an event and its complement *must sum to 1:*

Figure 3.9
Venn diagram of complementary events

> **Rule of Complements**
>
> The sum of the probabilities of complementary events equals 1:
> $$P(A) + P(A^c) = 1.$$

In many probability problems, calculating the probability of the complement of the event of interest is easier than calculating the event itself. Then, because

$$P(A) + P(A^c) = 1$$

we can calculate $P(A)$ by using the relationship

$$P(A) = 1 - P(A^c)$$

Example 3.11

Probability of a Complementary Event—Coin-Toss Experiment

Problem Consider the experiment of tossing fair coins. Define the following event: A: {Observing at least one head}.

a. Find $P(A)$ if 2 coins are tossed.

b. Find $P(A)$ if 10 coins are tossed.

Solution

a. When 2 coins are tossed, we know that the event A: {Observe at least one head.} consists of the sample points

$$A: \{HH, HT, TH\}$$

The complement of A is defined as the event that occurs when A does not occur. Therefore,

$$A^c: \{\text{Observe no heads.}\} = \{TT\}$$

This complementary relationship is shown in Figure 3.10. Since the coins are balanced, we have

$$P(A^c) = P(TT) = \tfrac{1}{4}$$

and

$$P(A) = 1 - P(A^c) = 1 - \tfrac{1}{4} = \tfrac{3}{4}$$

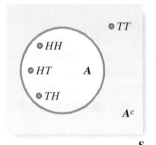

Figure 3.10
Complementary events in the toss of two coins

b. We solve this problem by following the five steps for calculating probabilities of events. (See Section 3.1.)

Step 1: Define the experiment. The experiment is to record the results of the 10 tosses of the coin.

Step 2: List the sample points. A sample point consists of a particular sequence of 10 heads and tails. Thus, one sample point is *HHTTTHTHTT*, which denotes head on first toss, head on second toss, tail on third toss, etc. Others are *HTHHHTTTTT* and *THHTHTHTTH*. Obviously, the number of sample points is very large—too many to list. It can be shown that there are $2^{10} = 1,024$ sample points for this experiment.

Step 3: Assign probabilities. Since the coin is fair, each sequence of heads and tails has the same chance of occurring; therefore, all the sample points are equally likely. Then

$$P(\text{Each sample point}) = \frac{1}{1,024}$$

Step 4: Determine the sample points in event A. A sample point is in A if at least one H appears in the sequence of 10 tosses. However, if we consider the complement of A, we find that

$$A^c = \{\text{No heads are observed in 10 tosses.}\}$$

Thus, A^c contains only one sample point:

$$A^c: \{TTTTTTTTTT\}$$

and $P(A^c) = \dfrac{1}{1{,}024}$

Step 5: Now we use the relationship of complementary events to find $P(A)$:

$$P(A) = 1 - P(A^c) = 1 - \frac{1}{1{,}024} = \frac{1{,}023}{1{,}024} = .999$$

Look Back In part **a,** we can find $P(A)$ by summing the probabilities of the sample points *HH, HT,* and *TH* in A. Many times, however, it is easier to find $P(A^c)$ by using the rule of complements.

Look Forward Since $P(A) = .999$ in part **b,** we are virtually certain of observing at least one head in 10 tosses of the coin.

━━ ■ **Now Work Exercise 3.31e–f**

3.4 The Additive Rule and Mutually Exclusive Events

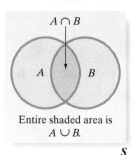

$A \cap B$

A B

Entire shaded area is
$A \cup B.$

S

Figure 3.11
Venn diagram of union

In Section 3.2 we saw how to determine which sample points are contained in a union and how to calculate the probability of the union by adding the probabilities of the sample points in the union. It is also possible to obtain the probability of the union of two events by using the **additive rule of probability.**

The union of two events will often contain many sample points because the union occurs if either one or both of the events occur. By studying the Venn diagram in Figure 3.11, you can see that the probability of the union of two events, A and B, can be obtained by summing $P(A)$ and $P(B)$ and subtracting the probability corresponding to $A \cap B$. We must subtract $P(A \cap B)$ because the sample point probabilities in $A \cap B$ have been included twice—once in $P(A)$ and once in $P(B)$. The formula for calculating the probability of the union of two events is given in the next box.

> **Additive Rule of Probability**
>
> The probability of the union of events A and B is the sum of the probabilities of events A and B minus the probability of the intersection of events A and B—that is,
>
> $$P(A \cup B) = P(A) + P(B) - P(A \cap B)$$

Example 3.12

Applying the Additive Rule—Hospital Admission Study

Problem Hospital records show that 12% of all patients are admitted for surgical treatment, 16% are admitted for obstetrics, and 2% receive both obstetrics and surgical treatment. If a new patient is admitted to the hospital, what is the probability that the patient will be admitted either for surgery, obstetrics, or both?

Solution Consider the following events:

$A:$ {A patient admitted to the hospital receives surgical treatment.}

$B:$ {A patient admitted to the hospital receives obstetrics treatment.}

Then, from the given information,

$$P(A) = .12$$
$$P(B) = .16$$

and the probability of the event that a patient receives both obstetrics and surgical treatment is

$$P(A \cap B) = .02$$

The event that a patient admitted to the hospital receives either surgical treatment, obstetrics treatment, or both is the union $A \cup B$. The probability of $A \cup B$ is given by the additive rule of probability:

$$P(A \cup B) = P(A) + P(B) - P(A \cap B) = .12 + .16 - .02 = .26$$

Thus, 26% of all patients admitted to the hospital receive either surgical treatment, obstetrics treatment, or both.

Look Back From the information given, it is not possible to list and assign probabilities to all the sample points. Consequently, we cannot proceed through the five-step process for finding the probability of an event and must use the additive rule.

◼ **Now Work Exercise 3.28c**

A very special relationship exists between events A and B when $A \cap B$ contains no sample points. In this case we call the events A and B *mutually exclusive events*.

Figure 3.12
Venn diagram of mutually exclusive events

> Events A and B are **mutually exclusive** if $A \cap B$ contains no sample points—that is, if A and B have no sample points in common.

Figure 3.12 shows a Venn diagram of two mutually exclusive events. The events A and B have no sample points in common–that is, A and B cannot occur simultaneously, and $P(A \cap B) = 0$. Thus, we have the important relationship given in the box.

> **Probability of Union of Two Mutually Exclusive Events**
>
> If two events A and B are *mutually exclusive*, the probability of the union of A and B equals the sum of the probabilities of A and B; that is, $P(A \cup B) = P(A) + P(B)$.

> ⚠ **CAUTION** The formula just shown is *false* if the events are *not* mutually exclusive. For two nonmutually exclusive events, you must apply the general additive rule of probability.

Example 3.13

The Union of Two Mutually Exclusive Events—Coin-Tossing Experiment

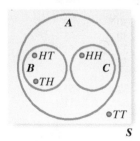

Figure 3.13
Venn diagram for coin-toss experiment

Problem Consider the experiment of tossing two balanced coins. Find the probability of observing *at least* one head.

Solution Define the events

$$A: \{\text{Observe at least one head}\}$$
$$B: \{\text{Observe exactly one head}\}$$
$$C: \{\text{Observe exactly two heads}\}$$

Note that

$$A = B \cup C$$

and that $B \cap C$ contains no sample points (see Figure 3.13). Thus, B and C are mutually exclusive, so that

$$P(A) = P(B \cup C) = P(B) + P(C) = \tfrac{1}{2} + \tfrac{1}{4} = \tfrac{3}{4}$$

Look Back Although this example is very simple, it shows us that writing events with verbal descriptions that include the phrases *at least* or *at most* as unions of mutually exclusive events is very useful. This practice enables us to find the probability of the event by adding the probabilities of the mutually exclusive events.

◼ **Now Work Exercise 3.37**

The Probability of Winning a Wheeling System

Refer to Florida's Pick-6 Lotto game in which you select six numbers of your choice from a field of numbers ranging from 1 to 53. In Section 3.1, we learned that the probability of winning Lotto on a single ticket is only 1 in approximately 23 million. The "experts" at *Lottery Buster* recommend many strategies for increasing the odds of winning the lottery. One strategy is to employ a wheeling system. In a complete wheeling system, you select more than six numbers, say, seven, and play every combination of six of those seven numbers.

Suppose you choose to "wheel" the following seven numbers: 2, 7, 18, 23, 30, 32, and 51. Every combination of six of these seven numbers is listed in Table SIA3.1 You can see that there are seven different possibilities. (Use the Combinations Rule with $N = 7$ and $n = 6$ to verify this.) Thus, we would purchase seven tickets (at a cost of $7) corresponding to these different combinations in a complete wheeling system.

To determine if this strategy does, in fact, increase our odds of winning, we need to find the probability that one of these seven combinations occurs during the $\frac{6}{53}$ Lotto draw—that is, we need to find the probability that either Ticket 1 or Ticket 2 or Ticket 3 or Ticket 4 or Ticket 5 or Ticket 6 or Ticket 7 is the winning combination. Note that this probability is stated using the word *or*, implying a union of seven events. Letting T1 represent the event that Ticket 1 wins, and defining T2, T3,..., T7 in a similar fashion, we want to find

$$P(\text{T1 or T2 or T3 or T4 or T5 or T6 or T7})$$

Recall (Section 3.1, p. 138) that the 22,957,480 possible combinations in Pick-6 Lotto are mutually exclusive and equally likely to occur. Consequently, the probability of the union of the seven events is simply the sum of the probabilities of the individual events, where each event has probability of 1/(22,957,480):

$$P(\text{win Lotto with 7 wheeled numbers})$$

$$= P(\text{T1 or T2 or T3 or T4 or T5 or T6 or T7})$$

$$= 7/(22,957,480) = .0000003$$

In terms of odds, we now have 3 chances in 10 million of winning the Lotto with the complete wheeling system. The "experts" are correct—our odds of winning Lotto have increased (from 1 in 23 million). However, the probability of winning is so close to 0 we question whether the $7 spent on lottery tickets is worth the negligible increase in odds. In fact, it can be shown that to increase your chance of winning the $\frac{6}{53}$ Lotto to 1 chance in 100 (i.e., .01) using a complete wheeling system, you would have to wheel 26 of your favorite numbers—a total of 230,230 combinations at a cost of $230,230!

Table SIA3.1	Wheeling the Seven Numbers 2, 7, 18, 23, 30, 32, and 51					
Ticket 1:	2	7	18	23	30	32
Ticket 2:	2	7	18	23	30	51
Ticket 3:	2	7	18	23	32	51
Ticket 4:	2	7	18	30	32	51
Ticket 5:	2	7	23	30	32	51
Ticket 6:	2	18	23	30	32	51
Ticket 7:	7	18	23	30	32	51

Exercises 3.28–3.48

Learning the Mechanics

3.28 Suppose $P(A) = .4$, $P(B) = .7$, and $P(A \cap B) = .3$. Find the following probabilities:
a. $P(B^c)$
b. $P(A^c)$
c. $P(A \cup B)$

3.29 A fair coin is tossed three times, and the events A and B are defined as follows:

NW

> $A:$ {At least one head is observed.}
> $B:$ {The number of heads observed is odd.}

a. Identify the sample points in the events A, B, $A \cup B$, A^c, and $A \cap B$.
b. Find $P(A)$, $P(B)$, $P(A \cup B)$, $P(A^c)$, and $P(A \cap B)$ by summing the probabilities of the appropriate sample points.
c. Find $P(A \cup B)$ using the additive rule. Compare your answer to the one you obtained in part **b.**
d. Are the events A and B mutually exclusive? Why?

3.30 A pair of fair dice is tossed. Define the following events:

> $A:$ {You will roll a 7.} (i.e., The sum of the dots on the up faces of the two dice is equal to 7.)
> $B:$ {At least one of the two dice shows a 4.}

a. Identify the sample points in the events A, B, $A \cap B$, $A \cup B$ and A^c.
b. Find $P(A)$, $P(B)$, $P(A \cap B)$, $P(A \cup B)$, and $P(A^c)$ by summing the probabilities of the appropriate sample points.
c. Find $P(A \cup B)$ using the additive rule. Compare your answer to that for the same event in part **b.**
d. Are A and B mutually exclusive? Why?

3.31 Consider the Venn diagram below, where

NW

$$P(E_1) = P(E_2) = P(E_3) = \tfrac{1}{5}, P(E_4) = P(E_5) = \tfrac{1}{20},$$
$$P(E_6) = \tfrac{1}{10}, \text{ and } P(E_7) = \tfrac{1}{5}.$$

Find each of the following probabilities:

a. $P(A)$ **e.** $P(A^c)$
b. $P(B)$ **f.** $P(B^c)$
c. $P(A \cup B)$ **g.** $P(A \cup A^c)$
d. $P(A \cap B)$ **h.** $P(A^c \cap B)$

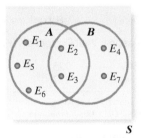

S

3.32 Consider the Venn diagram in the next column, where

$$P(E_1) = .10, P(E_2) = .05, P(E_3) = P(E_4) = .2,$$
$$P(E_5) = .06, P(E_6) = .3, P(E_7) = .06, \text{ and}$$
$$P(E_8) = .03.$$

Find the following probabilities:
a. $P(A^c)$
b. $P(B^c)$
c. $P(A^c \cap B)$
d. $P(A \cup B)$
e. $P(A \cap B)$
f. $P(A^c \cap B^c)$
g. Are events A and B mutually exclusive? Why?

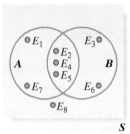

S

3.33 The outcomes of two variables are (Low, Medium, High) and (On, Off), respectively. An experiment is conducted in which the outcomes of each of the two variables are observed. The probabilities associated with each of the six possible outcome pairs are given in the accompanying two-way table.

	Low	Medium	High
On	.50	.10	.05
Off	.25	.07	.03

Consider the following events:

> $A:$ {On}
> $B:$ {Medium or On}
> $C:$ {Off and Low}
> $D:$ {High}

a. Find $P(A)$.
b. Find $P(B)$.
c. Find $P(C)$.
d. Find $P(D)$.
e. Find $P(A^c)$.
NW **f.** Find $P(A \cup B)$.
NW **g.** Find $P(A \cap C)$.
h. Consider each pair of events (A and B, A and C, A and D, B and C, B and D, C and D). List the pairs of events that are mutually exclusive. Justify your choices.

3.34 Refer to Exercise 3.33. Use the same event definitions to do the following exercises.
a. Write the event that the outcome is "On" and "High" as an intersection of two events.
b. Write the event that the outcome is "Low" or "Medium" as the complement of an event.

⚙ Applet Exercise 3.3

Use the applets *Simulating the Probability of Rolling a 6* and *Simulating the Probability of Rolling a 3 or 4* to explore the additive rule for probability.
a. Explain why the applet *Simulating the Probability of Rolling a 6* can also be used to simulate the probability

of rolling a 3. Then use the applet with $n = 1,000$ to simulate the probability of rolling a 3. Record the cumulative proportion. Repeat the process to simulate the probability of rolling a 4.

b. Use the applet *Simulating the Probability of Rolling a 3 or 4* with $n = 1,000$ to simulate the probability of rolling a 3 or 4. Record the cumulative proportion.

c. Add the two cumulative proportions from part **a**. How does this sum compare to the cumulative proportion in part **b**? How does this illustrate the additive rule for probability?

☺ Applet Exercise 3.4

Use the applets *Simulating the Probability of Rolling a 6* and *Simulating the Probability of Rolling a 3 or 4* to simulate the probability of the complement of an event.

a. Explain how the applet *Simulating the Probability of Rolling a 6* can also be used to simulate the probability of the event *rolling a 1, 2, 3, 4, or 5*. Then use the applet with $n = 1,000$ to simulate this probability.

b. Explain how the applet *Simulating the Probability of Rolling a 3 or 4* can also be used to simulate the probability of the event *rolling a 1, 2, 5, or 6*. Then use the applet with $n = 1,000$ to simulate this probability.

c. Which applet could be used to simulate the probability of the event *rolling a 1, 2, 3, or 4*? Explain.

Applying the Concepts—Basic

3.35 **Study of analysts' forecasts.** The *Journal of Accounting Research* (March 2008) published a study on relationship incentives and degree of optimism among analysts' forecasts. Participants were analysts at either a large or small brokerage firm who made their forecasts either early or late in the quarter. Also, some analysts were only concerned with making an accurate forecast, while others were also interested in their relationship with management. Suppose one of these analysts is randomly selected. Consider the following events:

A = {The analyst is concerned only with making an accurate forecast.}
B = {The analyst makes the forecast early in the quarter.}
C = {The analyst is from a small brokerage firm.}

Describe each of the following events in terms of unions, intersections, and complements (e.g., $A \cup B$, $A \cap B$, A^c, etc.).

a. The analyst makes an early forecast and is concerned only with accuracy.

b. The analyst is not concerned only with accuracy.

c. The analyst is from a small brokerage firm or makes an early forecast.

d. The analyst makes a late forecast and is not concerned only with accuracy.

3.36 **Problems at major companies.** The *Organization Development Journal* (Summer 2006) reported on the results of a survey of human resource officers (HROs) at major employers located in a southeastern city. The focus of the study was employee behavior, namely absenteeism, promptness to work, and turnover. The study found that 55% of the HROs had problems with employee absenteeism; also, 41% had problems with turnover. Suppose that 22% of the HROs had problems with both absenteeism and turnover. Use this information to find the probability that an HRO selected from the group surveyed had problems with either employee absenteeism or employee turnover.

3.37 **Do social robots walk or roll?** Refer to the *International Conference on Social Robotics* (Vol. 6414, 2010) study of the trend in the design of social robots, Exercise 2.3 (p. 48). Recall that in a random sample of 106 social (or service) robots designed to entertain, educate, and care for human users, 63 were built with legs only, 20 with wheels only, 8 with both legs and wheels, and 15 with neither legs nor wheels. One of the 106 social robots is randomly selected and the design (e.g., wheels only) is noted.

a. List the sample points for this study.

b. Assign reasonable probabilities to the sample points.

c. What is the probability that the selected robot is designed with wheels?

d. What is the probability that the selected robot is designed with legs?

e. Use the rule of complements to find the probability that the selected robot is designed with either legs or wheels.

3.38 **Scanning errors at Wal-Mart.** The National Institute for Standards and Technology (NIST) mandates that for every 100 items scanned through the electronic checkout scanner at a retail store, no more than 2 should have an inaccurate price. A study of the accuracy of checkout scanners at Wal-Mart stores in California was conducted (*Tampa Tribune*, Nov. 22, 2005). Of the 60 Wal-Mart stores investigated, 52 violated the NIST scanner accuracy standard. If one of the 60 Wal-Mart stores is randomly selected, what is the probability that the store does not violate the NIST scanner accuracy standard?

3.39 **Inactive oil and gas structures.** U.S. federal regulations require that operating companies clear all inactive offshore oil and gas structures within 1 year after production ceases. Researchers at the Louisiana State University Center for Energy Studies gathered data on both active and inactive oil and gas structures in the Gulf of Mexico (*Oil & Gas Journal*, Jan. 3, 2005). They discovered that the Gulf of Mexico has 2,175 active and 1,225 idle (inactive) structures. The following table breaks down these structures by type (caisson, well protector, or fixed platform). Consider the structure type and active status of one of these oil/gas structures.

	Structure Type			
	Caisson	Well Protector	Fixed Platform	Totals
Active	503	225	1,447	2,175
Inactive	598	177	450	1,225

Source: Data from Kaiser, M., and Mesyanzhinov, D. "Study tabulates idle Gulf of Mexico structures," *Oil & Gas Journal*, Vol. 103, No. 1, Jan. 3, 2005 (Table 2).

a. List the simple events for this experiment.

b. Assign reasonable probabilities to the simple events.

c. Find the probability that the structure is active.

d. Find the probability that the structure is a well protector.

e. Find the probability that the structure is an inactive caisson.

f. Find the probability that the structure is either inactive or a fixed platform.

g. Find the probability that the structure is not a caisson.

3.40 **Social networking Web sites in the United Kingdom.** In the United States, MySpace and Facebook are considered the two most popular social networking Web sites. In the United Kingdom (UK), the competition for social networking is between MySpace and Bebo. According to Nielsen/NetRatings (April 2006), 4% of UK citizens visit MySpace, 3% visit Bebo, and 1% visit both MySpace and Bebo.

a. Draw a Venn diagram to illustrate the use of social networking sites in the United Kingdom.

b. Find the probability that a UK citizen visits either the MySpace or Bebo social networking site.

c. Use your answer to part **b** to find the probability that a UK citizen does not visit either social networking site.

Applying the Concepts—Intermediate

3.41 **Study of why EMS workers leave the job.** An investigation into why emergency medical service (EMS) workers leave the profession was published in the *Journal of Allied Health* (Fall 2011). The researchers surveyed a sample of 244 former EMS workers, of which 127 were fully compensated while on the job, 45 were partially compensated, and 72 had noncompensated volunteer positions. The numbers of EMS workers who left because of retirement were 7 for fully compensated workers, 11 for partially compensated workers, and 10 for noncompensated volunteers. One of the 244 former EMS workers is selected at random.

a. Find the probability that the former EMS worker was fully compensated while on the job.

b. Find the probability that the former EMS worker was fully compensated while on the job and left due to retirement.

c. Find the probability that the former EMS worker was not fully compensated while on the job.

d. Find the probability that the former EMS worker was either fully compensated while on the job or left due to retirement.

3.42 **Stock market participation and IQ.** *The Journal of Finance* (December 2011) published a study of whether the decision to invest in the stock market is dependent on IQ. Information on a sample of 158,044 adults living in Finland formed the database for the study. An IQ score (from a low score of 1 to a high score of 9) was determined for each Finnish citizen as well as whether or not the citizen invested in the stock market. The next table gives the number of Finnish citizens in each IQ score/investment category. Suppose one of the 158,044 citizens is selected at random.

a. What is the probability that the Finnish citizen invests in the stock market?

b. What is the probability that the Finnish citizen has an IQ score of 6 or higher?

c. What is the probability that the Finnish citizen invests in the stock market and has an IQ score of 6 or higher?

d. What is the probability that the Finnish citizen invests in the stock market or has an IQ score of 6 or higher?

IQ Score	Invest in Market	No Investment	Totals
1	893	4,659	5,552
2	1,340	9,409	10,749
3	2,009	9,993	12,002
4	5,358	19,682	25,040
5	8,484	24,640	33,124
6	10,270	21,673	31,943
7	6,698	11,260	17,958
8	5,135	7,010	12,145
9	4,464	5,067	9,531
Totals	44,651	113,393	158,044

Source: Based on Grinblatt, M., Keloharju, M., & Linnainaa, J. "IQ and Stock Market Participation," *The Journal of Finance*, Vol. 66, No. 6, December 2011 (adapted from Table 1 and Figure 1).

e. What is the probability that the Finnish citizen does not invest in the stock market?

f. Are the events {Invest in the stock market} and {IQ score of 1} mutually exclusive?

3.43 **Characteristics of a new product.** The long-run success of a business depends on its ability to market products with superior characteristics that maximize consumer satisfaction and that give the firm a competitive advantage (Kotler & Keller, *Marketing Management*, 2006). Ten new products have been developed by a food-products firm. Market research has indicated that the 10 products have the characteristics described by the following Venn diagram:

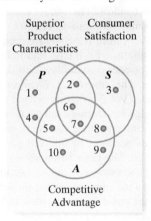

a. Write the event that a product possesses all the desired characteristics as an intersection of the events defined in the Venn diagram. Which products are contained in this intersection?

b. If one of the 10 products were selected at random to be marketed, what is the probability that it would possess all the desired characteristics?

c. Write the event that the randomly selected product would give the firm a competitive advantage or would satisfy consumers as a union of the events defined in the Venn diagram. Find the probability of this union.

d. Write the event that the randomly selected product would possess superior product characteristics and satisfy consumers. Find the probability of this intersection.

3.44 **Guilt in decision making.** The effect of guilt emotion on how a decision maker focuses on a problem was investigated in the Jan. 2007 issue of the *Journal of Behavioral*

Decision Making (see Exercise 1.30, p. 27). A total of 171 volunteer students participated in the experiment, where each was randomly assigned to one of three emotional states (guilt, anger, or neutral) through a reading/writing task. Immediately after the task, students were presented with a decision problem where the stated option had predominantly negative features (e.g., spending money on repairing a very old car). The results (number responding in each category) are summarized in the accompanying table. Suppose one of the 171 participants is selected at random.

Emotional State	Choose Stated Option	Do Not Choose Stated Option	Totals
Guilt	45	12	57
Anger	8	50	58
Neutral	7	49	56
Totals	60	111	171

Source: Based on Gangemi, A., & Mancini, F. "Guilt and focusing in decision-making," *Journal of Behavioral Decision Making*, Vol. 20, Jan. 2007 (Table 2).

a. Find the probability that the respondent is assigned to the guilty state.
b. Find the probability that the respondent chooses the stated option (repair the car).
c. Find the probability that the respondent is assigned to the guilty state and chooses the stated option.
d. Find the probability that the respondent is assigned to the guilty state or chooses the stated option.

3.45 **Cell phone handoff behavior.** A "handoff" is a term used in wireless communications to describe the process of a cell phone moving from the coverage area of one base station to that of another. Each base station has multiple channels (called color codes) that allow it to communicate with the cell phone. The *Journal of Engineering, Computing and Architecture* (Vol. 3., 2009) published a study of cell phone handoff behavior. During a sample driving trip that involved crossing from one base station to another, the different color codes accessed by the cell phone were monitored and recorded. The table below shows the number of times each color code was accessed for two identical driving trips, each using a different cell phone model. (*Note:* The table is similar to the one published in the article.) Suppose you randomly select one point during the combined driving trips.

	Color Code				
	0	5	b	c	Total
Model 1	20	35	40	0	85
Model 2	15	50	6	4	75
Total	35	85	46	4	160

a. What is the probability that the cell phone was using color code 5?
b. What is the probability that the cell phone was using color code 5 or color code 0?
c. What is the probability that the cell phone used was Model 2 and the color code was 0?

3.46 **Likelihood of a tax return audit.** At the beginning of each year, the Internal Revenue Service (IRS) releases information on the likelihood of a tax return being audited.

In 2010, the IRS audited 1,581,394 individual tax returns from the total of 142,823,105 filed returns; also, the IRS audited 29,803 returns from the total of 2,143,808 corporation returns filed (*IRS 2010 Data Book*).

a. Suppose an individual tax return from 2010 is randomly selected. What is the probability that the return was audited by the IRS?
b. Refer to part **a.** Determine the probability that an individual return was not audited by the IRS.
c. Suppose a corporation tax return from 2010 is randomly selected. What is the probability that the return was audited by the IRS?
d. Refer to part **c.** Determine the probability that a corporation return was not audited by the IRS.

3.47 **Reliability of gas station air guages.** Tire and automobile manufacturers and consumer safety experts all recommend that drivers maintain proper tire pressure in their cars. Consequently, many gas stations now provide air pumps and air gauges for their customers. In a *Research Note* (Nov. 2001), the National Highway Traffic Safety Administration studied the reliability of gas station air guages. The next table gives the percentage of gas stations that provide air gauges that overreport the pressure level in the tire.

Station Gauge Pressure	Overreport by 4 psi or More (%)	Overreport by 6 psi or More (%)	Overreport by 8 psi or More (%)
25 psi	16	2	0
35 psi	19	9	0
45 psi	19	14	5
55 psi	20	15	9

a. If the gas station air pressure gauge reads 35 psi, what is the probability that the pressure is overreported by 6 psi or more?
b. If the gas station air pressure gauge reads 55 psi, what is the probability that the pressure is overreported by 8 psi or more?
c. If the gas station air pressure gauge reads 25 psi, what is the probability that the pressure is not overreported by 4 psi or more?
d. Are the events A = {overreport by 4 psi or more} and B = {overreport by 6 psi or more} mutually exclusive? Explain.
e. Based on your answer to part **d,** why do the probabilities in the table not sum to 1?

Applying the Concepts—Advanced

3.48 **Galileo's Passedix game.** Passedix is a game of chance played with three fair dice. Players bet whether the sum of the faces shown on the dice will be above or below 10. During the late sixteenth century, the astronomer and mathematician Galileo Galilei was asked by the Grand Duke of Tuscany to explain why "the chance of throwing a total of 9 with three fair dice was less than that of throwing a total of 10" (*Interstat*, Jan. 2004). The grand duke believed that the chance should be the same because "there are an equal number of partitions of the numbers 9 and 10." Find the flaw in the grand duke's reasoning and answer the question posed to Galileo.

3.5 Conditional Probability

The event probabilities we've been discussing give the relative frequencies of the occurrences of the events when the experiment is repeated a very large number of times. Such probabilities are often called **unconditional probabilities** because no special conditions are assumed, other than those that define the experiment.

Often, however, we have additional knowledge that might affect the likelihood of the outcome of an experiment, so we need to alter the probability of an event of interest. A probability that reflects such additional knowledge is called the **conditional probability** of the event. For example, we've seen that the probability of observing an even number (event A) on a toss of a fair die is $\frac{1}{2}$. But suppose we're given the information that on a particular throw of the die, the result was a number less than or equal to 3 (event B). Would the probability of observing an even number on that throw of the die still be equal to $\frac{1}{2}$? It can't be because making the assumption that B has occurred reduces the sample space from six sample points to three sample points (namely, those contained in event B). This reduced sample space is as shown in Figure 3.14.

Because the sample points for the die-toss experiment are equally likely, each of the three sample points in the reduced sample space is assigned an equal *conditional probability* of $\frac{1}{3}$. Because the only even number of the three in the reduced sample space B is the number 2 and the die is fair, we conclude that the probability that A occurs *given that B occurs* is $\frac{1}{3}$. We use the symbol $P(A|B)$ to represent the probability of event A given that event B occurs. For the die-toss example, $P(A|B) = \frac{1}{3}$.

To get the probability of event A given that event B occurs, we proceed as follows: We divide the probability of the part of A that falls within the reduced sample space B, namely $P(A \cap B)$, by the total probability of the reduced sample space, namely $P(B)$. Thus, for the die-toss example with event A: {Observe an even number} and event B: {Observe a number less than or equal to 3}, we find

$$P(A|B) = \frac{P(A \cap B)}{P(B)} = \frac{P(2)}{P(1) + P(2) + P(3)} = \frac{\frac{1}{6}}{\frac{3}{6}} = \frac{1}{3}$$

The formula for $P(A|B)$ is true in general:

Figure 3.14

Reduced sample space for the die-toss experiment given that event B has occurred

---

Conditional Probability Formula

To find the *conditional probability that event A occurs given that event B occurs*, divide the probability that *both A* and *B* occur by the probability that *B* occurs—that is,

$$P(A|B) = \frac{P(A \cap B)}{P(B)} \quad \text{[We assume that } P(B) \neq 0.]$$

This formula adjusts the probability of $A \cap B$ from its original value in the complete sample space S to a conditional probability in the reduced sample space B. If the sample points in the complete sample space are equally likely, then the formula will assign equal probabilities to the sample points in the reduced sample space, as in the die-toss experiment. If, on the other hand, the sample points have unequal probabilities, the formula will assign conditional probabilities proportional to the probabilities in the complete sample space. This is illustrated by the following practical examples.

Example 3.14

The Conditional Probability Formula— Executives Who Cheat at Golf

Problem To develop programs for business travelers staying at convention hotels, a major hotel chain commissioned a study of executives who play golf. The study revealed that 55% of the executives admitted they had cheated at golf. Also, 20% of the executives admitted they had cheated at golf and had lied in business. Given an executive who had cheated at golf, what is the probability that the executive also had lied in business?

Solution Let's define events A and B as follows:

$$A = \{\text{Executive who had cheated at golf}\}$$

$$B = \{\text{Executive who had lied in business}\}$$

From the study, we know that 55% of executives had cheated at golf, so $P(A) = .55$. Now, executives who both cheat at golf (event A) *and* lie in business (event B) represent the compound event $A \cap B$. From the study, $P(A \cap B) = .20$. We want to know the probability that an executive lied in business (event B), given that he or she cheated at golf (event A)—that is, we want to know the conditional probability $P(A|B)$. Applying the preceding conditional probability formula, we have

$$P(B|A) = \frac{P(A \cap B)}{P(A)} = \frac{.20}{.55} = .364$$

Thus, given an executive who had cheated at golf, the probability that the executive also had lied in business is .364.

Look Back One of the keys to correctly applying the formula is to write the information in the study in the form of probability statements involving the events of interest. The word *and* in the statement "cheat at golf *and* lie in business" implies an intersection of the two events, A and B. The word *given* in the phrase "*given* an executive who cheats at golf" implies that event A is the given event.

■ **Now Work Exercise 3.58b**

Example 3.15

Applying the Conditional Probability Formula to a Two-Way Table— Customer Desire to Buy

Figure 3.15

Sample space for contacting a sales prospect

Problem Suppose you are interested in the probability of the sale of a large piece of earthmoving equipment. A single prospect is contacted. Let F be the event that the buyer has sufficient money (or credit) to buy the product and let F^c denote the complement of F (the event that the prospect does not have the financial capability to buy the product). Similarly, let B be the event that the buyer wishes to buy the product and let B^c be the complement of that event. Then the four sample points associated with the experiment are shown in Figure 3.15, and their probabilities are given in Table 3.5. Use the sample point probabilities to find the probability that a single prospect will buy, given that the prospect is able to finance the purchase.

Table 3.5	Probabilities of Customer Desire to Buy and Ability to Finance		
		Desire	
		To Buy, B	Not to Buy, B^c
Able to Finance	Yes, F	.2	.1
	No, F^c	.4	.3

Solution Suppose you consider the large collection of prospects for the sale of your product and randomly select one person from this collection. What is the probability that the person selected will buy the product? In order to buy the product, the customer must be financially able *and* have the desire to buy, so this probability would correspond to the entry in Table 3.5 {To buy, B} and next to {Yes, F}, or $P(B \cap F) = .2$. This is the unconditional probability of the event $B \cap F$.

In contrast, suppose you know that the prospect selected has the financial capability for purchasing the product. Now you are seeking the probability that the customer will buy given (the condition) that the customer has the financial ability to pay. This probability, the conditional probability of B given that F has occurred and denoted by the symbol $P(B|F)$, would be determined by considering only the sample points in the reduced sample space containing the sample points $B \cap F$ and $B^c \cap F$—that is, sample points that imply the prospect is financially able to buy. (This reduced sample space is shaded in Figure 3.16.) From our definition of conditional probability,

$$P(B|F) = \frac{P(B \cap F)}{P(F)}$$

where $P(F)$ is the sum of the probabilities of the two sample points corresponding to $B \cap F$ and $B^c \cap F$ (given in Table 3.5). Then

$$P(F) = P(B \cap F) + P(B^c \cap F) = .2 + .1 = .3$$

and the conditional probability that a prospect buys, given that the prospect is financially able, is

$$P(B|F) = \frac{P(B \cap F)}{P(F)} = \frac{.2}{.3} = .667$$

As we would expect, the probability that the prospect will buy, given that he or she is financially able, is higher than the unconditional probability of selecting a prospect who will buy.

Look Back Note that the conditional probability formula assigns a probability to the event $(B \cap F)$ in the reduced sample space that is proportional to the probability of the event in the complete sample space. To see this, note that the two sample points in the reduced sample space, $(B \cap F)$ and $(B^c \cap F)$, have probabilities of .2 and .1, respectively, in the complete sample space S. The formula assigns conditional probabilities $\frac{2}{3}$ and $\frac{1}{3}$ (use the formula to check the second one) to these sample points in the reduced sample space F so that the conditional probabilities retain the 2-to-1 proportionality of the original sample point probabilities.

■ **Now Work Exercise 3.49a–b**

$B \cap F$	$B^c \cap F$
(Buy, finance)	(No buy, finance)
$B \cap F^c$	$B^c \cap F^c$
(Buy, no finance)	(No buy, no finance)

S

Figure 3.16

Reduced sample space (shaded) containing sample points implying a financially able prospect

---

| Example | 3.16 |

Applying the Conditional Probability Formula to a Two-Way Table— Customer Complaints

Problem The investigation of consumer product complaints by the Federal Trade Commission (FTC) has generated much interest by manufacturers in the quality of their products. A manufacturer of an electromechanical kitchen utensil conducted an analysis of a large number of consumer complaints and found that they fell into the six categories shown in Table 3.6. If a consumer complaint is received, what is the probability that the cause of the complaint was product appearance given that the complaint originated during the guarantee period?

Table 3.6	Distribution of Product Complaints			
	Reason for Complaint			
Complaint Origin	Electrical	Mechanical	Appearance	Totals
During Guarantee Period	18%	13%	32%	63%
After Guarantee Period	12%	22%	3%	37%
Totals	30%	35%	35%	100%

Solution Let A represent the event that the cause of a particular complaint is product appearance and let B represent the event that the complaint occurred during the guarantee period. Checking Table 3.6, you can see that $(18 + 13 + 32)\% = 63\%$ of the complaints occur during the guarantee period. Hence, $P(B) = .63$. The percentage of complaints that were caused by appearance and occurred during the guarantee period (the event $A \cap B$) is 32%. Therefore, $P(A \cap B) = .32$

Using these probability values, we can calculate the conditional probability $P(A|B)$ that the cause of a complaint is appearance, given that the complaint occurred during the guarantee time:

$$P(A|B) = \frac{P(A \cap B)}{P(B)} = \frac{.32}{.63} = .51$$

Consequently, we can see that slightly more than half the complaints that occurred during the guarantee period were due to scratches, dents, or other imperfections in the surface of the kitchen devices.

Look Back Note that the answer, $\frac{.32}{.63}$, is the proportion for the event of interest A (.32) divided by the row total proportion for the given event B (.63)—that is, it is the proportion of the time A occurs within the given event B.

■ Now Work Exercise 3.60

3.6 The Multiplicative Rule and Independent Events

The probability of an intersection of two events can be calculated using the multiplicative rule, which employs the conditional probabilities we defined in the previous section. Actually, we have already developed the formula in another context (Section 3.5). You will recall that the formula for calculating the conditional probability of A given B is

$$P(A|B) = \frac{P(A \cap B)}{P(B)}$$

Multiplying both sides of this equation by $P(B)$, we obtain a formula for the probability of the intersection of events A and B. This is often called the **multiplicative rule of probability.**

> **Multiplicative Rule of Probability**
>
> $P(A \cap B) = P(A)P(B|A)$ or, equivalently, $P(A \cap B) = P(B)P(A|B)$

Example 3.17

Applying the Multiplicative Rule—Wheat Futures

Problem An investor in wheat futures is concerned with the following events:

B: {U.S. production of wheat will be profitable next year.}

A: {A serious drought will occure next year.}

Based on available information, the investor believes that the probability is .01 that production of wheat will be profitable *assuming* a serious drought will occur in the same year and that the probability is .05 that a serious drought will occur—that is,

$$P(B|A) = .01 \text{ and } P(A) = .05$$

Based on the information provided, what is the probability that a serious drought will occur and that a profit will be made? That is, find $P(A \cap B)$, the probability of the intersection of events A and B.

Solution We want to calculate $P(A \cap B)$. Using the formula for the multiplicative rule, we obtain

$$P(A \cap B) = P(A)P(B|A) = (.05)(.01) = .0005$$

The probability that a serious drought occurs and the production of wheat is profitable is only .0005. As we might expect, this intersection is a very rare event.

Look Back The multiplicative rule can be expressed in two ways: $P(A \cap B) = P(A) \cdot P(B|A)$ or $P(A \cap B) = P(B) \cdot P(A|B)$. Select the formula that involves a given event for which you know the probability (e.g., event B in the example).

■ Now Work Exercise 3.61

Intersections often contain only a few sample points. In this case, the probability of an intersection is easy to calculate by summing the appropriate sample point probabilities. However, the formula for calculating intersection probabilities is invaluable when the intersection contains numerous sample points, as the next example illustrates.

| **Example 3.18** | **Problem** A county welfare agency employs 10 welfare workers who interview prospective food stamp recipients. Periodically the supervisor selects, at random, the forms completed by 2 workers to audit for illegal deductions. Unknown to the supervisor, 3 of the workers have regularly been giving illegal deductions to applicants. What is the probability that both of the 2 workers chosen have been giving illegal deductions? |

Applying the Multiplicative Rule—Study of Welfare Workers

Solution Define the following two events:

$$A: \{\text{First worker selected gives illegal deductions}\}$$
$$B: \{\text{Second worker selected gives illegal deductions}\}$$

We want to find the probability of the event that both selected workers have been giving illegal deductions. This event can be restated as {First worker gives illegal deductions *and* second worker gives illegal deductions}. Thus, we want to find the probability of the intersection, $A \cap B$. Applying the multiplicative rule, we have

$$P(A \cap B) = P(A)P(B|A)$$

Figure 3.17
Venn diagram for finding $P(A)$

To find $P(A)$, it is helpful to consider the experiment as selecting 1 worker from the 10. Then the sample space for the experiment contains 10 sample points (representing the 10 welfare workers), where the 3 workers giving illegal deductions are denoted by the symbol I (I_1, I_2, I_3), and the 7 workers not giving illegal deductions are denoted by the symbol N ($N_1, \ldots, N_7$). The resulting Venn diagram is illustrated in Figure 3.17.

Because the first worker is selected at random from the 10, it is reasonable to assign equal probabilities to the 10 sample points. Thus, each sample point has a probability of $\frac{1}{10}$. The sample points in event A are $\{I_1, I_2, I_3,\}$—the 3 workers who are giving illegal deductions. Thus,

$$P(A) = P(I_1) + P(I_2) + P(I_3) = \tfrac{1}{10} + \tfrac{1}{10} + \tfrac{1}{10} = \tfrac{3}{10}$$

Figure 3.18
Venn diagram for finding $P(B|A)$

To find the conditional probability, $P(B|A)$, we need to alter the sample space S. Because we know A has occurred [the first worker selected is giving illegal deductions (say I_3)], only 2 of the 9 remaining workers in the sample space are giving illegal deductions. The Venn diagram for this new sample space (S') is shown in Figure 3.18. Each of these nine sample points are equally likely, so each is assigned a probability of $\frac{1}{9}$. Because the event $(B|A)$ contains the sample points $\{I_1, I_2\}$, we have

$$P(B|A) = P(I_1) + P(I_2) = \tfrac{1}{9} + \tfrac{1}{9} = \tfrac{2}{9}$$

Substituting $P(A) = \frac{3}{10}$ and $P(B|A) = \frac{2}{9}$ into the formula for the multiplicative rule, we find

$$P(A \cap B) = P(A)P(B|A) = \left(\tfrac{3}{10}\right)\left(\tfrac{2}{90}\right) = \tfrac{6}{90} = \tfrac{1}{15}$$

Thus, there is a 1 in 15 chance that both workers chosen by the supervisor have been giving illegal deductions to food stamp recipients.

Look Back The key words *both* and *and* in the statement "both A and B occur" imply an intersection of two events, which in turn implies that we should *multiply* probabilities to obtain the probability of interest.

◼ **Now Work Exercise 3.53c**

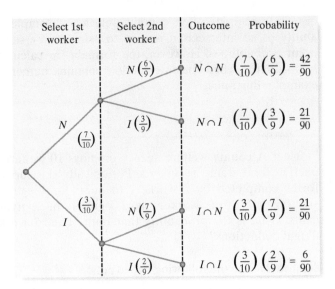

Figure 3.19

Tree diagram for Example 3.18

The sample space approach is only one way to solve the problem posed in Example 3.18. An alternative method employs the tree diagram (introduced in Example 3.1). Tree diagrams are helpful for calculating the probability of an intersection.

To illustrate, a tree diagram for Example 3.18 is displayed in Figure 3.19. The tree begins at the far left with two branches. These branches represent the two possible outcomes N (no illegal deductions) and I (illegal deductions) for the first worker selected. The unconditional probability of each outcome is given (in parentheses) on the appropriate branch—that is, for the first worker selected, $P(N) = \frac{7}{10}$ and $P(I) = \frac{3}{10}$. (These can be obtained by summing sample point probabilities as in Example 3.18.)

The next level of the tree diagram (moving to the right) represents the outcomes for the second worker selected. The probabilities shown here are conditional probabilities because the outcome for the first worker is assumed to be known. For example, if the first worker is giving illegal deductions *(I)*, the probability that the second worker is also giving illegal deductions *(I)* is $\frac{2}{10}$ because of the 9 workers left to be selected, only 2 remain who are giving illegal deductions. This conditional probability, $\frac{2}{9}$, is shown in parentheses on the bottom branch of Figure 3.19.

Finally, the four possible outcomes of the experiment are shown at the end of each of the four tree branches. These events are intersections of two events (outcome of first worker and outcome of second worker). Consequently, the multiplicative rule is applied to calculate each probability, as shown in Figure 3.19. You can see that the intersection $\{I \cap I\}$ (i.e., the event that both workers selected are giving illegal deductions) has probability $\frac{6}{90} = \frac{1}{15}$—the same value obtained in Example 3.18.

In Section 3.5 we showed that the probability of an event A may be substantially altered by the knowledge that an event B has occurred. However, this will not always be the case. In some instances, the assumption that event B has occurred will *not* alter the probability of event A at all. When this is true, we say that the two events A and B are *independent events.*

Events A and B are **independent events** if the occurrence of B does not alter the probability that A has occurred; that is, events A and B are independent if

$$P(A|B) = P(A)$$

When events A and B are independent, it is also true that

$$P(B|A) = P(B)$$

Events that are not independent are said to be **dependent.**

Example 3.19	**Problem** Consider the experiment of tossing a fair die and let

Checking for Independence — Die-Tossing Experiment

$$A: \{\text{Observe an even number.}\}$$
$$B: \{\text{Observe a number less than or equal to 4.}\}$$

Are events A and B independent?

Solution The Venn diagram for this experiment is shown in Figure 3.20. We first calculate

$$P(A) = P(2) + P(4) + P(6) = \tfrac{1}{2}$$
$$P(B) = P(1) + P(2) + P(3) + P(4) = \tfrac{2}{3}$$
$$P(A \cap B) = P(2) + P(4) = \tfrac{1}{3}$$

Now assuming B has occurred, the conditional probability of A given B is

$$P(A|B) = \frac{P(A \cap B)}{P(B)} = \frac{\tfrac{1}{3}}{\tfrac{2}{3}} = \frac{1}{2} = P(A)$$

Thus, assuming that event B occurring does not alter the probability of observing an even number, $P(A)$ remains $\tfrac{1}{2}$. Therefore, the events A and B are independent.

Look Back Note that if we calculate the conditional probability of B given A, our conclusion is the same:

$$P(B|A) = \frac{P(A \cap B)}{P(A)} = \frac{\tfrac{1}{3}}{\tfrac{1}{2}} = \frac{2}{3} = P(B)$$

■ **Now Work Exercise 3.58c**

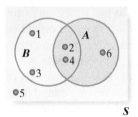

Figure 3.20
Venn diagram for die-toss experiment

Example 3.20	**Problem** Refer to the consumer product complaint study in Example 3.16. The percentages of complaints of various types during and after the guarantee period are shown in Table 3.6. Define the following events:

Checking for Independence — Consumer Product Complaint Study

$$A: \{\text{Cause of complaint is product appearance.}\}$$
$$B: \{\text{Complaint occurred during the guarantee term.}\}$$

Are A and B independent events?

Solution Events A and B are independent if $P(A|B) = P(A)$. We calculated $P(A|B)$ in Example 3.16 to be .51, and from Table 3.6 we see that

$$P(A) = .32 + .03 = .35$$

Therefore, $P(A|B)$ is not equal to $P(A)$, and A and B are dependent events.

■ **Now Work Exercise 3.49c**

To gain an intuitive understanding of independence, think of situations in which the occurrence of one event does not alter the probability that a second event will occur. For example, suppose two small companies are being monitored by a financier for possible investment. If the businesses are in different industries and they are otherwise unrelated, then the success or failure of one company may be *independent* of the success or failure of the other—that is, the event that company A fails may not alter the probability that company B will fail.

As a second example, consider an election poll in which 1,000 registered voters are asked their preference between two candidates. Pollsters try to use procedures for selecting a sample of voters so that the responses are independent—that is, the objective of the pollster is to select the sample so the event that one polled voter prefers candidate A does not alter the probability that a second polled voter prefers candidate A.

We will make three final points about independence. The first is that the property of independence, unlike the mutually exclusive property, cannot be shown on or gleaned from a Venn diagram. This means *you can't trust your intuition.* In general, the only way to check for independence is by performing the calculations of the probabilities in the definition.

The second point concerns the relationship between the mutually exclusive and independence properties. Suppose that events A and B are mutually exclusive, as shown in Figure 3.21, and both events have nonzero probabilities. Are these events independent or dependent? That is, does the assumption that B occurs alter the probability of the occurrence of A? It certainly does, because if we assume that B has occurred, it is impossible for A to have occurred simultaneously—that is, $P(A|B) = 0$. Thus, *mutually exclusive events are dependent events* because $P(A) \neq P(A|B)$.

The third point is that the probability of the intersection of independent events is very easy to calculate. Referring to the formula for calculating the probability of an intersection, we find

$$P(A \cap B) = P(A)P(B|A)$$

Thus, because $P(B|A) = P(B)$ when A and B are independent, we have the following useful rule:

Figure 3.21

Mutually exclusive events are dependent events

Probability of Intersection of Two Independent Events

If events A and B are independent, the probability of the intersection of A and B equals the product of the probabilities of A and B; that is,

$$P(A \cap B) = P(A)P(B)$$

The converse is also true: If $P(A \cap B) = P(A)P(B)$, then events A and B are independent.

In the die-toss experiment, we showed in Example 3.19 that the events *A:* {Observe an even number} and *B:* {Observe a number less than or equal to 4} are independent if the die is fair. Thus,

$$P(A \cap B) = P(A)P(B) = \left(\tfrac{1}{2}\right)\left(\tfrac{2}{3}\right) = \tfrac{1}{3}$$

This agrees with the result that we obtained in the example:

$$P(A \cap B) = P(2) + P(4) = \tfrac{2}{6} = \tfrac{1}{3}$$

Example 3.21

Probability of Independent Events Occurring Simultaneously—Diversity Training Study

Problem Refer to Example 3.5 (pp. 135–136). Recall that *USA Today* found that of all U.S. firms that use diversity training, 38% state that their primary reason for using it is to stay competitive..

a. What is the probability that in a sample of two firms that use diversity training, both primarily use it to stay competitive?

b. What is the probability that in a sample of 10 firms that use diversity training, all 10 primarily use it to stay competitive?

Solution

a. Let C_1 represent the event that firm 1 gives "stay competitive" as the primary reason for using diversity training. Define C_2 similarly for firm 2. The event that *both* firms give "stay competitive" as their primary reason is the intersection of the two events, $C_1 \cap C_2$. Based on the survey that found that 38% of U.S. firms use diversity training to stay competitive, we could reasonably conclude that $P(C_1) = .38$ and $P(C_2) = .38$. However, in order to compute the probability of $C_1 \cap C_2$ from the multiplicative rule, we must make the assumption that the two events are independent. Because the classification of any firm using diversity training is not likely to affect the classification of another firm, this assumption is reasonable. Assuming independence, we have

$$P(C_1 \cap C_2) = P(C_1)P(C_2) = (.38)(.38) = .1444$$

b. To see how to compute the probability that 10 of 10 firms will give "stay competitive" as their primary reason, first consider the event that 3 of 3 firms give "stay competitive" as the primary reason. Using the notation defined earlier, we want to compute the probability of the intersection $C_1 \cap C_2 \cap C_3$. Again assuming independence of the classifications, we have

$$P(C_1 \cap C_2 \cap C_3) = P(C_1)P(C_2)P(C_3) = (.38)(.38)(.38) = .054872$$

Similar reasoning leads us to the conclusion that the intersection of 10 such events can be calculated as follows:

$$P(C_1 \cap C_2 \cap C_3 \cap \ \dots \ \cap C_{10}) = P(C_1)P(C_2) \dots P(C_{10}) = (.38)^{10} = .0000628$$

Thus, the probability that 10 of 10 firms all give "stay competitive" as their primary reason for using diversity training is about 63 in 1 million, assuming the events (stated reasons for using diversity training) are independent.

Look Back The very small probability in part **b** makes it extremely unlikely that 10 of 10 firms would give "stay competitive" as their primary reason for diversity training. If this event should actually occur, we would need to reassess our estimate of the probability of .38 used in the calculation. If all 10 firms' reason is staying competitive, then the probability that any one firm gives staying competitive as their reason is much higher than .38. (This conclusion is another application of the rare event approach to statistical inference.)

──────────────── ◾ **Now Work Exercise 3.72a**

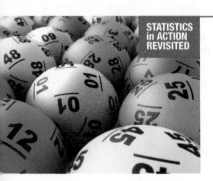

STATISTICS in ACTION REVISITED

The Probability of Winning Cash 3 or Play 4

In addition to biweekly Lotto 6/53, the Florida Lottery runs several other games. Two popular daily games are "Cash 3" and "Play 4." In Cash 3, players pay $1 to select three numbers in sequential order, where each number ranges from 0 to 9. If the three numbers selected (e.g., 2-8-4) match exactly the order of the three numbers drawn, the player wins $500. Play 4 is similar to Cash 3, but players must match four numbers (each number ranging from 0 to 9). For a $1 Play 4 ticket (e.g., 3-8-3-0), the player will win $5,000 if the numbers match the order of the four numbers drawn.

During the official drawing for Cash 3, 10 Ping-Pong balls numbered 0, 1, 2, 3, 4, 5, 6, 7, 8, and 9 are placed into each of three chambers. The balls in the first chamber are colored pink, the balls in the second chamber are blue, and the balls in the third chamber are yellow. One ball of each color is randomly drawn, with the official order as pink-blue-yellow. In Play 4, a fourth chamber with orange balls is added, and the official order is pink-blue-yellow-orange. Because the draws of the colored balls are random and independent, we can apply an extension of the Probability Rule for the Intersection

STATISTICS in ACTION REVISITED CONTINUED

of Two Independent Events to find the odds of winning Cash 3 and Play 4. The probability of matching a numbered ball being drawn from a chamber is $\frac{1}{10}$; therefore,

$P(\text{Win Cash 3}) = P(\text{match pink}) \text{ AND (match blue) AND (match yellow)}$

$= P(\text{match pink}) \times P(\text{match blue}) \times P(\text{match yellow})$

$= \left(\frac{1}{10}\right)\left(\frac{1}{10}\right)\left(\frac{1}{10}\right) = \frac{1}{1000} = .001$

$P(\text{Win Play 4}) = P(\text{match pink AND match blue}$
$\qquad\qquad\qquad \text{AND match yellow AND match orange})$

$= P(\text{match pink}) \times P(\text{match blue}) \times$
$\qquad P(\text{match yellow}) \times P(\text{match orange})$

$= \left(\frac{1}{10}\right)\left(\frac{1}{10}\right)\left(\frac{1}{10}\right)\left(\frac{1}{10}\right)$

$= \frac{1}{10,000} = .0001$

Although the odds of winning one of these daily games is much better than the odds of winning Lotto $\frac{6}{53}$, there is still only a 1 in 1,000 chance (for Cash 3) or a 1 in 10,000 chance (for Play 4) of winning the daily game. And the payoffs ($500 or $5,000) are much smaller. In fact, it can be shown that you will lose an average of 50¢ every time you play either Cash 3 or Play 4!

Exercises 3.49–3.76

Learning the Mechanics

3.49 For two events, A and B, $P(A) = .4$, $P(B) = .2$, and
[NW] $P(A \cap B) = .1$:
   a. Find $P(A|B)$.
   b. Find $P(B|A)$.
   c. Are A and B independent events?

3.50 For two events, A and B, $P(A) = .4$, $P(B) = .2$, and $P(A|B) = .6$:
   a. Find $P(A \cap B)$.
   b. Find $P(B|A)$.

3.51 For two independent events, A and B, $P(A) = .4$ and $P(B) = .2$:
   a. Find $P(A \cap B)$
   b. Find $P(A|B)$.
   c. Find $P(A \cup B)$

3.52 An experiment results in one of three mutually exclusive events, A, B, or C. It is known that $P(A) = .30$, $P(B) = .55$, and $P(C) = .15$. Find each of the following probabilities:
   a. $P(A \cup B)$
   b. $P(A \cap C)$
   c. $P(A|B)$
   d. $P(B \cup C)$
   e. Are B and C independent events? Explain.

3.53 Consider the experiment depicted by the Venn diagram, with the sample space S containing five sample points. The sample points are assigned the following probabilities: $P(E_1) = .20$, $P(E_2) = .30, P(E_3) = .30, P(E_4) = .10, P(E_5) = .10$.

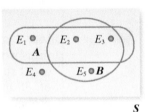

a. Calculate $P(A), P(B),$ and $P(A \cap B)$
b. Suppose we know that event A has occurred, so that the reduced sample space consists of the three sample points in A—namely, E_1, E_2, and E_3. Use the formula for conditional probability to adjust the probabilities of these three sample points for the knowledge that A has occurred [i.e., $P(E_i|A)$]. Verify that the conditional probabilities are in the same proportion to one another as the original sample point probabilities.
[NW] **c.** Calculate the conditional probability $P(B|A)$ in two ways: (1) Add the adjusted (conditional) probabilities of the sample points in the intersection $A \cap B$, as these represent the event that B occurs given that A has occurred; (2) use the formula for conditional probability:

$$P(B|A) = \frac{P(A \cap B)}{P(A)}$$

Verify that the two methods yield the same result.
d. Are events A and B independent? Why or why not?

3.54 Two fair coins are tossed, and the following events are defined:

A: {Observe at least one head}
B: {Observe exactly one head}

a. Draw a Venn diagram for the experiment, showing events *A* and *B.* Assign probabilities to the sample points.
b. Find $P(A)$, $P(B)$, and $P(A \cap B)$
c. Use the formula for conditional probability to find $P(A|B)$ and $P(B|A)$. Verify your answer by inspecting the Venn diagram and using the concept of reduced sample spaces.

3.55 An experiment results in one of five sample points with the following probabilities: $P(E_1) = .22$, $P(E_2) = .31$, $P(E_3) = .15$, $P(E_4) = .22$, and $P(E_5) = .1$. The following events have been defined:

A: {E_1, E_3}
B: {E_2, E_3, E_4}
C: {E_1, E_5}

Find each of the following probabilities:
a. $P(A)$
b. $P(B)$
c. $P(A \cap B)$
d. $P(A|B)$
e. $P(B \cap C)$
f. $P(C|B)$
g. Consider each pair of events: *A* and *B, A* and *C,* and *B* and *C.* Are any of the pairs of events independent? Why?

3.56 Two fair dice are tossed, and the following events are defined:

A: {Sum of the numbers showing is odd}
B: {Sum of the numbers showing is 9, 11, or 12}

Are events *A* and *B* independent? Why?

3.57 A sample space contains six sample points and events *A, B,* and *C* as shown in the Venn diagram. The probabilities of the sample points are

$P(1) = .20, P(2) = .05, P(3) = .30, P(4) = .10,$
$P(5) = .10, P(6) = .25.$

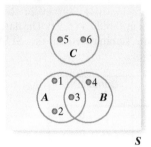

S

a. Which pairs of events, if any, are mutually exclusive? Why?
b. Which pairs of events, if any, are independent? Why?
c. Find $P(A \cup B)$ by adding the probabilities of the sample points and then by using the additive rule. Verify that the answers agree. Repeat for $P(A \cup C)$

● **Applet Exercise 3.5**

Use the applet *Simulating the Probability of Rolling a 6* to simulate conditional probabilities. Begin by running the applet twice with $n = 10$ without resetting between runs. The data on your screen represent 20 rolls of a die. The diagram above the *Roll* button shows the frequency of each of the six possible outcomes. Use this information to find each of the probabilities.

a. The probability of 6 given the outcome is 5 or 6
b. The probability of 6 given the outcome is even
c. The probability of 4 or 6 given the outcome is even
d. The probability of 4 or 6 given the outcome is odd

Applying the Concepts—Basic

3.58 **On-the-job arrogance and task performance.** *Human Performance* (Vol. 23, 2010) published the results of a study that found that arrogant workers are more likely to have poor performance ratings. Suppose that 15% of all full-time workers exhibit arrogant behaviors on the job and that 10% of all full-time workers will receive a poor performance rating. Also, assume that 5% of all full-time workers exhibit arrogant behaviors and receive a poor performance rating. Let *A* be the event that a full-time worker exhibits arrogant behavior on the job. Let *B* be the event that a full-time worker will receive a poor performance rating.
a. Are the events *A* and *B* mutually exclusive? Explain.
b. Find $P(B|A)$.
c. Are the events *A* and *B* independent? Explain.

3.59 **World's largest public companies.** *Forbes* (Apr. 20 , 2011) conducted a survey of the 20 largest public companies in the world. Of these 20 companies, 4 were banking or investment companies based in the United States. A total of 9 U.S. companies were on the top 20 list. Suppose we select one of these 20 companies at random. Given that the company is based in the United States, what is the probability that it is a banking or investment company?

3.60 **Guilt in decision making.** Refer to the *Journal of Behavioral Decision Making* (Jan. 2007) study of the effect of guilt emotion on how a decision maker focuses on a problem, Exercise 3.44 (p. 153). The results (number responding in each category) for the 171 study participants are reproduced in the table below. Suppose one of the 171 participants is selected at random.

Emotional State	Choose Stated Option	Do Not Choose Stated Option	Totals
Guilt	45	12	57
Anger	8	50	58
Neutral	7	49	56
Totals	60	111	171

Source: Based on Gangemi, A., & Mancini, F. "Guilt and focusing in decision-making," *Journal of Behavioral Decision Making,* Vol. 20, Jan. 2007 (Table 2).

a. Given that the respondent is assigned to the guilty state, what is the probability that the respondent chooses the stated option?
b. If the respondent does not choose to repair the car, what is the probability that the respondent is in the anger state?
c. Are the events {repair the car} and {guilty state} independent?

3.61 **Twitter and wireless Internet.** According to the *Pew Internet & American Life Project* (Oct. 2009), 54% of Internet users have a wireless connection to the Internet via a laptop, cell phone, game console, or other mobile device. Of these wireless users, 25% use Twitter to share updates about themselves. What is the probability that an Internet user has a wireless connection and uses Twitter?

3.62 **Identity theft victims.** According to *The National Crime Victimization Survey* (December 2010), published by the U.S. Department of Justice, about 11.7 million people were victims of identity theft over the past 2 years. This number represents 5% of all persons age 16 or older in the United States. Of these victims, 53% reported that the identity theft occurred from the unauthorized use of a credit card. Consider a randomly selected person of age 16 or older in the United States.

  a. What is the probability that this person was a victim of identity theft?

  b. What is the probability that this person was a victim of identity theft that occurred from the unauthorized use of a credit card?

3.63 **Study of why EMS workers leave the job.** Refer to the *Journal of Allied Health* (Fall 2011) study of why emergency medical service (EMS) workers leave the profession, Exercise 3.41 (p. 153). Recall that in a sample of 244 former EMS workers, 127 were fully compensated while on the job, 45 were partially compensated, and 72 had noncompensated volunteer positions. Also, the numbers of EMS workers who left because of retirement were 7 for fully compensated workers, 11 for partially compensated workers, and 10 for noncompensated volunteers.

  a. Given that the former EMS worker was fully compensated while on the job, estimate the probability that the worker left the EMS profession due to retirement.

  b. Given that the former EMS worker had a noncompensated volunteer position, estimate the probability that the worker left the EMS profession due to retirement.

  c. Are the events {a former EMS worker was fully compensated on the job} and {a former EMS worker left the job due to retirement} independent? Explain.

Applying the Concepts–Intermediate

3.64 **Working on summer vacation.** Refer to the *Adweek/Harris* (July 2011) poll of whether U.S. adults work during their summer vacation, Exercise 3.14 (p. 141). Recall that the poll found that 46% of the respondents work during their summer vacation, 35% do not work at all while on vacation,

and 19% were unemployed. Also, 35% of those who work while on vacation do so by monitoring their business e-mails.

  a. Given that a randomly selected poll respondent will work while on summer vacation, what is the probability that the respondent will monitor business e-mails?

  b. What is the probability that a randomly selected poll respondent will work while on summer vacation and will monitor business e-mails?

  c. What is the probability that a randomly selected poll respondent will not work while on summer vacation and will monitor business e-mails?

3.65 **Stock market participation and IQ.** Refer to *The Journal of Finance* (December 2011) study of whether the decision to invest in the stock market is dependent on IQ, Exercise 3.42 (p. 153). The summary table giving the number of the 158,044 Finnish citizens in each IQ score/investment category is reproduced below. Again, suppose one of the citizens is selected at random.

IQ Score	Invest in Market	No Investment	Totals
1	893	4,659	5,552
2	1,340	9,409	10,749
3	2,009	9,993	12,002
4	5,358	19,682	25,040
5	8,484	24,640	33,124
6	10,270	21,673	31,943
7	6,698	11,260	17,958
8	5,135	7,010	12,145
9	4,464	5,067	9,531
Totals	44,651	113,393	158,044

Source: Based on Grinblatt, M., Keloharju, M., & Linnainaa, J. "IQ and Stock Market Participation," *The Journal of Finance*, Vol. 66, No. 6, December 2011 (data from Table 1 and Figure 1).

  a. Given that the Finnish citizen has an IQ score of 6 or higher, what is the probability that he/she invests in the stock market?

  b. Given that the Finnish citizen has an IQ score of 5 or lower, what is the probability that he/she invests in the stock market?

  c. Based on the results, parts **a** and **b**, does it appear that investing in the stock market is dependent on IQ? Explain.

3.66 **Degrees of best-paid CEOs.** Refer to the results of the *Forbes* (April 13, 2011) survey of the top 40 best-paid CEOs shown in Table 2.1 (p. 39). The data on highest degree obtained are summarized in the SPSS printout below.

DEGREE

		Frequency	Percent	Valid Percent	Cumulative Percent
Valid	Bachelors	13	32.5	32.5	32.5
	Law	1	2.5	2.5	35.0
	Masters	5	12.5	12.5	47.5
	MBA	15	37.5	37.5	85.0
	None	4	10.0	10.0	95.0
	PhD	2	5.0	5.0	100.0
	Total	40	100.0	100.0	

SPSS output for Exercise 3.66

Suppose you randomly select five of the CEOs (without replacement) and record the highest degree obtained by each.

a. What is the probability that the highest degree obtained by the first CEO you select is a bachelor's degree?

b. Suppose the highest degree obtained by each of the first four CEOs you select is a bachelor's degree. What is the probability that the highest degree obtained by the fifth CEO you select is a bachelor's degree?

3.67 Ambulance response time. *Geographical Analysis* (Jan. 2010) presented a study of emergency medical service (EMS) ability to meet the demand for an ambulance. In one example, the researchers presented the following scenario. An ambulance station has one vehicle and two demand locations, A and B. The probability that the ambulance can travel to a location in under 8 minutes is .58 for location A and .42 for location B. The probability that the ambulance is busy at any point in time is .3.

a. Find the probability that EMS can meet the demand for an ambulance at location A.

b. Find the probability that EMS can meet the demand for an ambulance at location B.

3.68 Working mothers with children. The U.S. Census Bureau reports a decline in the percentage of mothers in the workforce who have infant children. The following table gives a breakdown of the marital status and working status of the 1.8 million mothers with infant children in the year 2010. (The numbers in the table are reported in thousands.) Consider the following events: A = {Mom with infant works}, B = {Mom with infant is married and living with husband}. Are A and B independent events?

	Working	Not Working
Married/living with husband	1,174	89
All other arrangements	416	121

Source: Data from U.S. Census Bureau, Bureau of Labor Statistics, 2010.

3.69 Intrusion detection systems. A computer intrusion detection system (IDS) is designed to provide an alarm whenever an intrusion (e.g., unauthorized access) is being attempted into a computer system. A probabilistic evaluation of a system with two independently operating intrusion detection systems (a double IDS) was published in the *Journal of Research of the National Institute of Standards and Technology* (November/December 2003). Consider a double IDS with system A and system B. If there is an intruder, system A sounds an alarm with probability .9, and system B sounds an alarm with probability .95. If there is no intruder, the probability that system A sounds an alarm (i.e., a false alarm) is .2, and the probability that system B sounds an alarm is .1. Assume that under a given condition (intruder or not), systems A and B operate independently.

a. Using symbols, express the four probabilities given in the example.

b. If there is an intruder, what is the probability that both systems sound an alarm?

c. If there is no intruder, what is the probability that both systems sound an alarm?

d. Given an intruder, what is the probability that at least one of the systems sounds an alarm?

3.70 Wine quality and soil. The *Journal of Wine Research* (Vol. 21, 2010) published a study of the effects of soil and climate on the quality of wine produced in Spain. The soil at two vineyards—Llarga and Solar—was the focus of the analysis. Wine produced from grapes grown in each of the two vineyards was evaluated for each of three different years (growing seasons) by a wine-tasting panel. Based on the taste tests, the panel (as a group) selected the wine with the highest quality.

a. How many different wines were evaluated by the panel, where one wine was produced for each vineyard/growing season combination?

b. If the wines were all of equal quality, what is the probability that the panel selected a Llarga wine as the wine with the highest quality?

c. If the wines were all of equal quality, what is the probability that the panel selected a wine produced in year 3 as the wine with the highest quality?

d. The panel consisted of four different wine tasters who performed the evaluations independently of each other. If the wines were all of equal quality, what is the probability that all four tasters selected a Llarga wine as the wine with the highest quality?

3.71 Are you really being served red snapper? Red snapper is a rare and expensive reef fish served at upscale restaurants. Federal law prohibits restaurants from serving a cheaper, look-alike variety of fish (e.g., vermillion snapper or lane snapper) to customers who order red snapper. Researchers at the University of North Carolina used DNA analysis to examine fish specimens labeled "red snapper" that were purchased from vendors across the country (*Nature*, July 15, 2004). The DNA tests revealed that 77% of the specimens were not red snapper but the cheaper, look-alike variety of fish.

a. Assuming the results of the DNA analysis are valid, what is the probability that you are actually served red snapper the next time you order it at a restaurant?

b. If there are five customers at a restaurant, all who have ordered red snapper, what is the probability that at least one customer is actually served red snapper?

3.72 Lie detector test. The software for a lie detector based on voice stress levels—called the computerized voice stress analyzer (CVSA)—is available for about $10,000. The manufacturer claims that the CVSA is 98% accurate, and, unlike a polygraph machine, will not be thrown off by drugs and medical factors. However, laboratory studies by the U.S. Defense Department found that the CVSA had an accuracy rate of 49.8%—slightly less than pure chance. Suppose the CVSA is used to test the veracity of four suspects. Assume the suspects' responses are independent.

a. If the manufacturer's claim is true, what is the probability that the CVSA will correctly determine the veracity of all four suspects?

b. If the manufacturer's claim is true, what is the probability that the CVSA will yield an incorrect result for at least one of the four suspects?

c. Suppose that in a laboratory experiment conducted by the U.S. Defense Department on four suspects, the CVSA yielded incorrect results for two of the suspects. Use this result to make an inference about the true accuracy rate of the lie detector.

Applying the Concepts—Advanced

3.73 Patient medical instruction sheets. Physicians and pharmacists sometimes fail to inform patients adequately about the proper application of prescription drugs and about the precautions to take in order to avoid potential side effects. One method of increasing patients' awareness of the problem is for physicians to provide patient medication instruction (PMI) sheets. The American Medical Association, however, has found that only 20% of the doctors who prescribe drugs frequently distribute PMI sheets to their patients. Assume that 20% of all patients receive the PMI sheet with their prescriptions and that 12% receive the PMI sheet and are hospitalized because of a drug-related problem. What is the probability that a person will be hospitalized for a drug-related problem given that the person received the PMI sheet?

3.74 Risk of a natural gas pipeline accident. *Process Safety Progress* (Dec. 2004) published a risk analysis for a natural gas pipeline between Bolivia and Brazil. The most likely scenario for an accident would be natural gas leakage from a hole in the pipeline. The probability that the leak ignites immediately (causing a jet fire) is .01. If the leak does not immediately ignite, it may result in a delayed ignition of a gas cloud. Given no immediate ignition, the probability of delayed ignition (causing a flash fire) is .01. If there is no delayed ignition, the gas cloud will harmlessly disperse. Suppose a leak occurs in the natural gas pipeline. Find the probability that either a jet fire or a flash fire will occur. Illustrate with a tree diagram.

3.75 Most likely coin-tossing sequence. In *Parade Magazine*'s (Nov. 26, 2000) column "Ask Marilyn," the following question was posed: "I have just tossed a [balanced] coin 10 times, and I ask you to guess which of the following three sequences was the result. One (and only one) of the sequences is genuine."

> (1) H H H H H H H H H H
>
> (2) H H T T H T T H H H
>
> (3) T T T T T T T T T T

a. Demonstrate that prior to actually tossing the coins, the three sequences are equally likely to occur.

b. Find the probability that the 10 coin tosses result in all heads or all tails.

c. Find the probability that the 10 coin tosses result in a mix of heads and tails.

d. Marilyn's answer to the question posed was "Though the chances of the three specific sequences occurring randomly are equal . . . it's reasonable for us to choose sequence (2) as the most likely genuine result." If you know that only one of the three sequences actually occurred, explain why Marilyn's answer is correct. [*Hint:* Compare the probabilities in parts **b** and **c**.]

3.76 Software defects in NASA spacecraft instrument code. Portions of computer software code that may contain undetected defects are called *blind spots*. The issue of blind spots in software code evaluation was addressed at the *8th IEEE International Symposium on High Assurance Software Engineering* (March 2004). The researchers developed guidelines for assessing methods of predicting software defects using data on 498 modules of software code written in "C" language for a NASA spacecraft instrument. One simple prediction algorithm is to count the lines of code in the module; any module with more than 50 lines of code is predicted to have a defect. The accompanying file contains the predicted and actual defect status of all 498 modules. A standard approach to evaluating a software defect prediction algorithm is to form a two-way summary table similar to the one shown here. In the table, *a, b, c,* and *d* represent the number of modules in each cell. Software engineers use these table entries to compute several probability measures, called *accuracy, detection rate, false alarm rate,* and *precision*.

		Module Has Defects	
		False	True
Algorithm	No	*a*	*b*
Predicts Defects	Yes	*c*	*d*

a. *Accuracy* is defined as the probability that the prediction algorithm is correct. Write a formula for *accuracy* as a function of the table values *a, b, c,* and *d*.

b. The *detection rate* is defined as the probability that the algorithm predicts a defect, given that the module actually is a defect. Write a formula for *detection rate* as a function of the table values *a, b, c,* and *d*.

c. The *false alarm rate* is defined as the probability that the algorithm predicts a defect, given that the module actually has no defect. Write a formula for *false alarm rate* as a function of the table values *a, b, c,* and *d*.

d. *Precision* is defined as the probability that the module has a defect, given that the algorithm predicts a defect. Write a formula for *precision* as a function of the table values *a, b, c,* and *d*.

e. Access the accompanying file and compute the values of accuracy, detection rate, false alarm rate, and precision. Interpret the results.

3.7 Bayes's Rule

An early attempt to employ probability in making inferences is the basis for a branch of statistical methodology known as **Bayesian statistical methods.** The logic employed by the English philosopher Thomas Bayes in the mid-1700s involves converting an unknown conditional probability, say $P(B|A)$, to one involving a known conditional probability, say $P(A|B)$. The method is illustrated in the next example.

Example 3.22

Applying Bayes's Logic—Intruder Detection System

Problem An unmanned monitoring system uses high-tech video equipment and microprocessors to detect intruders. A prototype system has been developed and is in use outdoors at a weapons munitions plant. The system is designed to detect intruders with a probability of .90. However, the design engineers expect this probability to vary with weather conditions. The system automatically records the weather condition each time an intruder is detected. Based on a series of controlled tests, in which an intruder was released at the plant under various weather conditions, the following information is available: Given the intruder was, in fact, detected by the system, the weather was clear 75% of the time, cloudy 20% of the time, and raining 5% of the time. When the system failed to detect the intruder, 60% of the days were clear, 30% cloudy, and 10% rainy. Use this information to find the probability of detecting an intruder, given rainy weather conditions. (Assume that an intruder has been released at the plant.)

Solution Define D to be the event that the intruder is detected by the system. Then D^c is the event that the system fails to detect the intruder. Our goal is to calculate the conditional probability, $P(D|\text{Rainy})$. From the statement of the problem, the following information is available:

$$P(D) = .90 \qquad P(D^c) = .10$$
$$P(\text{Clear}|D) = .75 \qquad P(\text{Clear}|D^c) = .60$$
$$P(\text{Cloudy}|D) = .20 \qquad P(\text{Cloudy}|D^c) = .30$$
$$P(\text{Rainy}|D) = .05 \qquad P(\text{Rainy}|D^c) = .10$$

Note that $P(D|\text{Rainy})$ is not one of the conditional probabilities that is known. However, we can find

$$P(\text{Rainy} \cap D) = P(D)P(\text{Rainly}|D) = (.90)(.05) = .045$$

and

$$P(\text{Rainy} \cap D^c) = P(D^c)P(\text{Rainy}|D^c) = (.10)(.10) = .01$$

using the multiplicative rule of probability. These two probabilities are highlighted on the tree diagram for the problem in Figure 3.22.

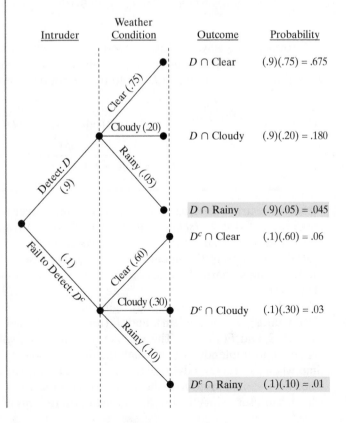

Figure 3.22

Tree diagram for Example 3.22

Now the event Rainy is the union of two mutually exclusive events, (Rainy $\cap D$) and (Rainy $\cap D^c$). Thus, applying the additive rule of probability, we have

$$P(\text{Rainy}) = P(\text{Rainy} \cap D) + P(\text{Rainy} \cap D^c) = .045 + .01 = .055$$

We now apply the formula for conditional probability to obtain

$$P(D|\text{Rainy}) = \frac{P(\text{Rainy} \cap D)}{P(\text{Rainy})} = \frac{P(\text{Rainy} \cap D)}{P(\text{Rainy} \cap D) + P(\text{Rainy} \cap D^c)}$$
$$= \frac{.045}{.055} = .818$$

Therefore, under rainy weather conditions, the prototype system can detect the intruder with a probability of .818—a value lower than the designed probability of .90.

Look Back One key to solving a problem of this type is recognizing that the conditional probability of interest, $P(D|\text{Rainy})$, is not the same as the conditional probability given, $P(\text{Rainy}|D)$.

■ **Now Work Exercise 3.77**

BIOGRAPHY

THOMAS BAYES (1702–1761)
The Inverse Probabilist

The Reverend Thomas Bayes was an ordained English Presbyterian minister who became a Fellow of the Royal Statistical Society without benefit of any formal training in mathematics or any published papers in science during his lifetime. His manipulation of the formula for conditional probability in 1761 is now known as Bayes's Theorem. At the time and for 200 years afterward, use of Bayes's Theorem (or inverse probability, as it was called) was controversial and, to some, considered an inappropriate practice. It was not until the 1960s that the power of the Bayesian approach to decision making began to be tapped.

The technique utilized in Example 3.22, called **Bayes's Rule,** can be applied when an observed event A occurs with any one of several mutually exclusive and exhaustive events, $B_1, B_2, \ldots, B_k$. The formula for finding the appropriate conditional probabilities is given in the box.

Bayes's Rule

Given k mutually exclusive and exhaustive events, $B_1, B_2, \ldots, B_k$, such that $P(B_1) + P(B_2) + \cdots + P(B_k) = 1$, and an observed event A, then

$$P(B_i|A) = \frac{P(B_i \cap A)}{P(A)}$$

$$= \frac{P(B_i)P(A|B_i)}{P(B_1)P(A|B_1) + P(B_2)P(A|B_2) + \cdots + P(B_k)P(A|B_k)}$$

In applying Bayes's Rule to Example 3.22, the observed event $A = \{\text{Rainy}\}$ and the $k = 2$ mutually exclusive and exhaustive events are the complementary events $D = \{\text{intruder detected}\}$ and $D^c = \{\text{intruder not detected}\}$. Hence, the formula

$$P(D|\text{Rainy}) = \frac{P(D)P(\text{Rainy}|D)}{P(D)P(\text{Rainy}|D) + P(D^c)P(\text{Rainy}|D^c)}$$

$$= \frac{(.90)(.05)}{(.90)(.05) + (.10)(.10)} = .818$$

Example   3.23

Bayes's Rule Application—Wheelchair Control

Problem Electric wheelchairs are difficult to maneuver for many disabled people. In a paper presented at the *1st International Workshop on Advances in Service Robotics* (March 2003), researchers applied Bayes's Rule to evaluate an "intelligent" robotic controller that aims to capture the intent of the wheelchair user and aid in navigation. Consider the following scenario. From a certain location in a room, a wheelchair user will either (1) turn sharply to the left and navigate through a door, (2) proceed straight to the other side of the room, or (3) turn slightly right and stop at a table. Denote these three events as D (for door), S (for straight), and T (for table). Based on previous trips, $P(D) = .5$, $P(S) = .2$, and $P(T) = .3$. The wheelchair is installed with a robot-controlled joystick. When the user intends to go through the door, he points the joystick straight 30% of the time; when the user intends to go straight, he points the joystick straight 40% of the time; and when the user intends to go to the table, he points the joystick straight 5% of the time. If the wheelchair user points the joystick straight, where is his most likely destination?

Solution Let $J = \{$joystick is pointed straight$\}$. The user intention percentages can be restated as the following conditional probabilities: $P(J|D) = .3$, $P(J|S) = .4$, and $P(J|T) = .05$. Since the user has pointed the joystick straight, we want to find the following probabilities: $P(D|J)$, $P(S|J)$, and $P(T|J)$. Now, the three events, D, S, and T, represent mutually exclusive and exhaustive events, where $P(D) = .5$, $P(S) = .2$, and $P(T) = .3$. Consequently, we can apply Bayes's Rule as follows:

$$P(D|J) = P(J|D) \cdot P(D) / [P(J|D) \cdot P(D) + P(J|S) \cdot P(S) + P(J|T) \cdot P(T)]$$
$$= (.3)(.5)/[(.3)(.5) + (.4)(.2) + (.05)(.3)] = .15/.245 = .612$$
$$P(S|J) = P(J|S) \cdot P(S) / [P(J|D) \cdot P(D) + P(J|S) \cdot P(S) + P(J|T) \cdot P(T)]$$
$$= (.4)(.2)/[(.3)(.5) + (.4)(.2) + (.05)(.3)] = .08/.245 = .327$$
$$P(T|J) = P(J|T) \cdot P(T) / [P(J|D) \cdot P(D) + P(J|S) \cdot P(S) + P(J|T) \cdot P(T)]$$
$$= (.05)(.3)/[(.3)(.5) + (.4)(.2) + (.05)(.3)] = .015/.245 = .061$$

Note that the largest conditional probability is $P(D|J) = 612$. Thus, if the joystick is pointed straight, the wheelchair user is most likely headed through the door.

■ **Now Work Exercise 3.82**

Exercises 3.77–3.89

Learning the Mechanics

3.77 Suppose the events B_1 and B_2 are mutually exclusive and complementary events, such that $P(B_1) = .75$ and $P(B_2) = .25$. Consider another event A such that $P(A|B_1) = .3$ and $P(A|B_2) = .5$.
  a. Find $P(B_1 \cap A)$.
  b. Find $P(B_2 \cap A)$.
  c. Find $P(A)$ using the results in parts **a** and **b**.
  d. Find $P(B_1|A)$.
  e. Find $P(B_2|A)$.

3.78 Suppose the events B_1, B_2, and B_3 are mutually exclusive and complementary events, such that $P(B_1) = .2$, $P(B_2) = .15$, and $P(B_3) = .65$. Consider another event A such that $P(A|B_1) = .4$, $P(A|B_2) = .25$, and $P(A|B_3) = .6$. Use Bayes's Rule to find
  a. $P(B_1|A)$
  b. $P(B_2|A)$
  c. $P(B_3|A)$

3.79 Suppose the events B_1, B_2, and B_3 are mutually exclusive and complementary events, such that $P(B_1) = .2$, $P(B_2) = .15$, and $P(B_3) = .65$. Consider another event A such that $P(A) = .4$. If A is independent of B_1, B_2, and B_3, use Bayes's Rule to show that $P(B_1|A) = P(B_1) = .2$.

Applying the Concepts—Basic

3.80 **Tests for Down syndrome.** Currently, there are three diagnostic tests available for chromosome abnormalities in a developing fetus: triple serum marker screening, ultrasound, and amniocentesis. The safest (to both the mother and fetus) and least expensive of the three is the ultrasound test. Two San Diego State University statisticians investigated the accuracy of using ultrasound to test for Down syndrome (*Chance*, Summer 2007). Let D denote that the fetus has a genetic marker for Down syndrome and N denote that the ultrasound test is normal (i.e., no indication of chromosome abnormalities). Then,

the statisticians desired the probability $P(D/N)$. Use Bayes's Rule and the following probabilities (provided in the article) to find the desired probability: $P(D) = \frac{1}{180}$, $P(D^c) = \frac{79}{80}$, $P(N|D) = \frac{1}{2}$, $P(N^c|D) = \frac{1}{2}$, $P(N|D^c) = 1$, and $P(N^c|D^c) = 0$.

3.81 **Fingerprint expertise.** Contrary to what is presented on TV shows like *CSI*, fingerprint identification is not fully automated. Expert examiners are required to identify the person who left the fingerprint. A study published in *Psychological Science* (August 2011) tested the accuracy of experts and novices in identifying fingerprints. Participants were presented pairs of fingerprints and asked to judge whether the prints in each pair matched. The pairs were presented under three different conditions: prints from the same individual (*match condition*), nonmatching but similar prints (*similar distracter condition*), and nonmatching and very dissimilar prints (*nonsimilar distracter condition*). The percentages of correct decisions made by the two groups under each of the three conditions are listed in the table.

Condition	Fingerprint Experts	Novices
Match	92.12%	74.55%
Similar Distracter	99.32%	44.82%
Nonsimilar Distracter	100%	77.03%

Source: Based on Tangen, J. M., Thompson, M. B., & McCarthy, D. J. "Identifying fingerprint expertise," *Psychological Science*, Vol. 22, No. 8, August 2011 (Figure 1).

  a. Given a pair of matched prints, what is the probability that an expert failed to identify the match?
  b. Given a pair of matched prints, what is the probability that a novice failed to identify the match?
  c. Assume the study included 10 participants, 5 experts and 5 novices. Suppose that a pair of matched prints was presented to a randomly selected study participant and the participant failed to identify the match. Is the participant more likely to be an expert or a novice?

3.82 Errors in estimating job costs. A construction company employs three sales engineers. Engineers 1, 2, and 3 estimate the costs of 30%, 20%, and 50%, respectively, of all jobs bid by the company. For $i = 1, 2, 3$, define E_i to be the event that a job is estimated by engineer i. The following probabilities describe the rates at which the engineers make serious errors in estimating costs:

$$P(\text{error}|E_1) = .01, \ P(\text{error}|E_2) = .03, \text{ and}$$
$$P(\text{error}|E_3) = .02$$

a. If a particular bid results in a serious error in estimating job cost, what is the probability that the error was made by engineer 1?

b. If a particular bid results in a serious error in estimating job cost, what is the probability that the error was made by engineer 2?

c. If a particular bid results in a serious error in estimating job cost, what is the probability that the error was made by engineer 3?

d. Based on the probabilities, parts **a–c**, which engineer is most likely responsible for making the serious error?

3.83 Fish contaminated by a plant's toxic discharge. Refer to the U.S. Army Corps of Engineers' study on the DDT contamination of fish in the Tennessee River (Alabama), Example 1.5 (p. 13). Part of the investigation focused on how far upstream the contaminated fish have migrated. (A fish is considered to be contaminated if its measured DDT concentration is greater than 5.0 parts per million.)

a. Considering only the contaminated fish captured from the Tennessee River, the data reveal that 52% of the fish are found between 275 and 300 miles upstream, 39% are found 305 to 325 miles upstream, and 9% are found 330 to 350 miles upstream. Use these percentages to determine the probabilities, $P(275-300)$, $P(305-325)$, and $P(330-350)$.

b. Given that a contaminated fish is found a certain distance upstream, the probability that it is a channel catfish (CC) is determined from the data as $P(CC|275-300) = .775$, $P(CC|305-325) = .77$, and $P(CC|330-350) = .86$. If a contaminated channel catfish is captured from the Tennessee River, what is the probability that it was captured 275–300 miles upstream?

3.84 Drug testing in athletes. Due to inaccuracies in drug-testing procedures (e.g., false positives and false negatives) in the medical field, the results of a drug test represent only one factor in a physician's diagnosis. Yet, when Olympic athletes are tested for illegal drug use (i.e., doping), the results of a single positive test are used to ban the athlete from competition. In *Chance* (Spring 2004), University of Texas biostatisticians D. A. Berry and L. Chastain demonstrated the application of Bayes's Rule for making inferences about testosterone abuse among Olympic athletes. They used the following example: In a population of 1,000 athletes, suppose 100 are illegally using testosterone. Of the users, suppose 50 would test positive for testosterone. Of the nonusers, suppose 9 would test positive.

a. Given that the athlete is a user, find the probability that a drug test for testosterone will yield a positive result. (This probability represents the *sensitivity* of the drug test.)

b. Given the athlete is a nonuser, find the probability that a drug test for testosterone will yield a negative result. (This probability represents the *specificity* of the drug test.)

c. If an athlete tests positive for testosterone, use Bayes's Rule to find the probability that the athlete is really doping. (This probability represents the *positive predictive value* of the drug test.)

Applying the Concepts—Intermediate

3.85 Mining for dolomite. Dolomite is a valuable mineral that is found in sedimentary rock. During mining operations, dolomite is often confused with shale. The radioactivity features of rock can aid miners in distinguishing between dolomite and shale rock zones. For example, if the Gamma ray reading of a rock zone exceeds 60 API units, the area is considered to be mostly shale (and is not mined); if the Gamma ray reading of a rock zone is less than 60 API units, the area is considered to be abundant in dolomite (and is mined). Data on 771 core samples in a rock quarry collected by the Kansas Geological Survey revealed the following: 476 of the samples are dolomite and 295 of the samples are shale. Of the 476 dolomite core samples, 34 had a Gamma ray reading greater than 60. Of the 295 shale core samples, 280 had a Gamma ray reading greater than 60. Suppose you obtain a Gamma ray reading greater than 60 at a certain depth of the rock quarry. Should this area be mined?

3.86 Nondestructive evaluation. Nondestructive evaluation (NDE) describes methods that quantitatively characterize materials, tissues, and structures by noninvasive means, such as X-ray computed tomography, ultrasonics, and acoustic emission. Recently, NDE was used to detect defects in steel castings (*JOM*, May 2005). Assume that the probability that NDE detects a "hit" (i.e., predicts a defect in a steel casting) when, in fact, a defect exists is .97. (This is often called the *probability of detection.*) Also assume that the probability that NDE detects a hit when, in fact, no defect exists is .005. (This is called the *probability of a false call.*) Past experience has shown a defect occurs once in every 100 steel castings. If NDE detects a hit for a particular steel casting, what is the probability that an actual defect exists?

3.87 Purchasing microchips. An important component of your desktop or laptop personal computer (PC) is a microchip. The table gives the proportions of microchips that a certain PC manufacturer purchases from seven suppliers.

Supplier	Proportion
S_1	.15
S_2	.05
S_3	.10
S_4	.20
S_5	.12
S_6	.20
S_7	.18

a. It is known that the proportions of defective microchips produced by the seven suppliers are .001, .0003, .0007, .006, .0002, .0002, and .001, respectively. If a single PC microchip failure is observed, which supplier is most likely responsible?

b. Suppose the seven suppliers produce defective microchips at the same rate, .0005. If a single PC microchip failure is observed, which supplier is most likely responsible?

3.88 Intrusion detection systems. Refer to the *Journal of Research of the National Institute of Standards and Technology* (Nov.–Dec. 2003) study of a double intrusion detection system with independent systems, Exercise 3.69 (p. 167). Recall that if there is an intruder, system A sounds an alarm with probability .9, and system B sounds an alarm with probability .95. If there is no intruder, system A sounds an alarm with probability .2, and system B sounds an alarm with probability .1. Now assume that the probability of an intruder is .4. Also assume that under a given condition (intruder or not), systems A and B operate independently. If both systems sound an alarm, what is the probability that an intruder is detected?

Applying the Concepts—Advanced

3.89 Forensic analysis of JFK assassination bullets. Following the assassination of President John F. Kennedy (JFK) in 1963, the House Select Committee on Assassinations

(HSCA) conducted an official government investigation. The HSCA concluded that although there was a probable conspiracy involving at least one shooter in addition to Lee Harvey Oswald, the additional shooter missed all limousine occupants. A recent analysis of assassination bullet fragments, reported in the *Annals of Applied Statistics* (Vol. 1, 2007), contradicted these findings, concluding that the evidence used by the HSCA to rule out a second assassin is fundamentally flawed. It is well documented that at least two different bullets were the source of bullet fragments found after the assassination. Let E = {bullet evidence used by the HSCA}, T = {two bullets used in the aassassination}, and T^c = {more than two bullets used in the assassination}. Given the evidence (E), which is more likely to have occurred—two bullets used (T) or more than two bullets used (T^c)?

a. The researchers demonstrated that the ratio, $P(T|E)/P(T^c|E)$, is less than 1. Explain why this result supports the theory of more than two bullets used in the assassination of JFK.

b. To obtain the result, part **a**, the researchers first showed that

$$P(T|E)/P(T^c|E) = [P(E|T) \cdot P(T)]/[P(E|T^c) \cdot P(T^c)]$$

Demonstrate this equality using Bayes's Rule.

◻ Chapter Notes

Key Terms

Key Symbols

S	**sample space** (collection of all sample points)
$A: \{1,2\}$	set of **sample points in event** A
$P(A)$	**probability** of event A
$A \cup B$	**union** of events A and B (either A or B can occur)
$A \cap B$	**intersection** of events A and B (both A and B occur)
A^c	**complement** of A (event A does not occur)
$A\|B$	event A occurs, **given** event B occurs
$\binom{N}{n}$	number of **combinations** of N elements taken n at a time
$N!$	N **factorial** $= N(N-1)(N-2)\cdots(2)(1)$

Key Ideas

Probability Rules for k Sample Points, $S_1, S_2, S_3, \ldots, S_k$

1. $0 \le P(S_i) \le 1$
2. $\sum P(S_i) = 1$

Combinations Rule

Counting number of samples of n elements selected from N elements

$$\binom{N}{n} = \frac{N!}{n!(N-n)!} = \frac{N(N-1)(N-2)\cdots(N-n+1)}{n(n-1)(n-2)\cdots(2)(1)}$$

Bayes's Rule

For mutually exclusive events $B_1, B_2, \ldots, B_k$, such that $P(B_1) + P(B_2) + \cdots + P(B_k) = 1$,

$$P(B_i|A) = \frac{P(B_i)P(A|B_i)}{P(B_1)P(A|B_1) + P(B_2)P(A|B_2) + \cdots + P(B_k)P(A|B_k)}$$

Guide to Selecting Probability Rules

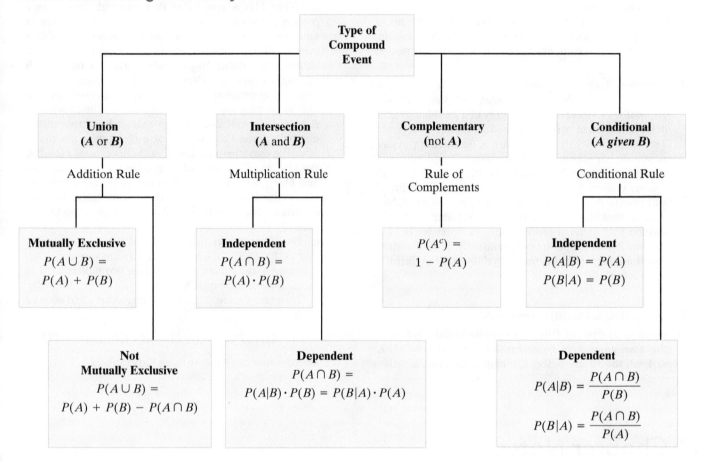

Supplementary Exercises 3.90–3.130

Learning the Mechanics

3.90 Which of the following pairs of events are mutually exclusive? Justify your response.
   a. {The Dow Jones Industrial Average increases on Monday.}, {A large New York bank decreases its prime interest rate on Monday.}
   b. {The next sale by a PC retailer is a notebook computer.}, {The next sale by a PC retailer is a desktop computer.}
   c. {You reinvest all your dividend income in a limited partnership.}, {You reinvest all your dividend income in a money market fund.}

3.91 A sample space consists of four sample points, where $P(S_1) = .2$, $P(S_2) = .1$, $P(S_3) = .3$, and $P(S_4) = .4$.
   a. Show that the sample points obey the two probability rules for a sample space.
   b. If an event $A = \{S_1, S_4\}$, find $P(A)$.

3.92 For two events A and B, suppose $P(A) = .7$, $P(B) = .5$, and $P(A \cap B) = .4$. Find $P(A \cup B)$.

3.93 A and B are mutually exclusive events, with $P(A) = .2$ and $P(B) = .3$.
   a. Find $P(A|B)$.
   b. Are A and B independent events?

3.94 Two events, A and B, are independent, with $P(A) = .3$ and $P(B) = .1$.
   a. Are A and B mutually exclusive? Why?
   b. Find $P(A|B)$ and $P(B|A)$.
   c. Find $P(A \cup B)$.

3.95 Given that $P(A \cap B) = .4$ and $P(A|B) = .8$, find $P(B)$.

3.96 A random sample of $n = 5$ is to be selected from $N = 50$. In how many different ways can the sample be drawn?

3.97 The Venn diagram below illustrates a sample space containing six sample points and three events, A, B, and C. The probabilities of the sample points are $P(1) = .3$, $P(2) = .2$, $P(3) = .1$, $P(4) = .1$, $P(5) = .1$, and $P(6) = .2$.

a. Find $P(A \cap B)$, $P(B \cap C)$, $P(A \cup C)$, $P(A \cup B \cup C)$, $P(B^c)$, $P(A^c \cap B)$, $P(B|C)$, and $P(B|A)$.

b. Are A and B independent? Mutually exclusive? Why?

c. Are B and C independent? Mutually exclusive? Why?

3.98 Find the numerical value of

a. $6!$ **b.** $\binom{10}{9}$ **c.** $\binom{10}{1}$ **d.** $\binom{6}{3}$ **e.** $0!$

⚽ Applet Exercise 3.6

Use the applet entitled *Random Numbers* to generate a list of 50 numbers between 1 and 100, inclusive. Use this list to find each of the probabilities.

a. The probability that a number chosen from the list is less than or equal to 50

b. The probability that a number chosen from the list is even

c. The probability that a number chosen from the list is less than or equal to 50 and even

d. The probability that a number chosen from the list is less than or equal to 50 given that the number is even

e. Do your results from parts **a–d** support the conclusion that the events *less than or equal to 50* and *even* are independent? Explain.

Applying the Concepts—Basic

3.99 Management system failures. Refer to the *Process Safety Progress* (Dec. 2004) study of 83 industrial accidents caused by management system failures, Exercise 2.146 (p. 115). A summary of the root causes of these 83 incidents is reproduced in the following table. One of the 83 incidents is randomly selected and the root cause is determined.

Management System Cause Category	Number of Incidents
Engineering and Design	27
Procedures and Practices	24
Management and Oversight	22
Training and Communication	10
Total	83

Source: Based on *Blair*, A. S. "Management system failures identified in incidents investigated by the U.S. Chemical Safety and Hazard Investigation Board," *Process Safety Progress*, Vol. 23, No. 4, Dec. 2004, pp. 232–236 (Table 1).

a. List the sample points for this problem and assign reasonable probabilities to them.

b. Find and interpret the probability that an industrial accident is caused by faulty engineering and design.

c. Find and interpret the probability that an industrial accident is caused by something other than faulty procedures and practices.

3.100 Annual compensation and benefits report. Each year, Hudson Institute conducts a survey of 10,000 U.S. workers about their total compensation packages. One question in Hudson's *Compensation and Benefits Report* focused on employees who received raises in the past year. Of these employees, 35% reported that their raise was based on job performance, 50% reported that it was based on a standard cost of living, and the remainder (15%) were unsure how their raises were determined. Suppose we select (at random) one of the U.S. workers surveyed who received a raise last year and inquire about how that worker's raise was determined.

a. List the sample points for this experiment.

b. Assign reasonable probabilities to the sample points.

c. Find the probability that the raise was based either on job performance or a standard cost of living.

3.101 Ownership of small businesses. According to the *Journal of Business Venturing* (Vol. 17, 2002), 27% of all small businesses owned by non-Hispanic whites nationwide are women-owned firms. If we select, at random, a small business owned by a non-Hispanic white, what is the probability that it is a male-owned firm?

3.102 Condition of public school facilities. The National Center for Education Statistics (NCES) conducted a survey on the condition of America's public school facilities. The survey revealed the following information. The probability that a public school building has inadequate plumbing is .25. Of the buildings with inadequate plumbing, the probability that the school has plans for repairing the building is .38. Find the probability that a public school building has inadequate plumbing and will be repaired.

3.103 New car crash tests. Refer to the National Highway Traffic Safety Administration (NHTSA) crash tests of new car models, Exercise 2.149 (p. 116). Recall that the NHTSA has developed a "star" scoring system, with results ranging from one star (*) to five stars (*****). The more stars in the rating, the better the level of crash protection in a head-on collision. A summary of the driver-side star ratings for 98 cars is reproduced in the accompanying Minitab printout. Assume that one of the 98 cars is selected at random. State whether each of the following is true or false.

a. The probability that the car has a rating of two stars is 4.

b. The probability that the car has a rating of four or five stars is .7857.

c. The probability that the car has a rating of one star is 0.

d. The car has a better chance of having a two-star rating than of having a five-star rating.

Tally for Discrete Variables: DRIVSTAR

DRIVSTAR	Count	Percent
2	4	4.08
3	17	17.35
4	59	60.20
5	18	18.37
N=	98	

3.104 Speeding linked to fatal car crashes. According to the National Highway Traffic and Safety Administration's National Center for Statistics and Analysis (NCSA), "Speeding is one of the most prevalent factors contributing to fatal traffic crashes" (*NHTSA Technical Report*, Aug. 2005). The probability that speeding is a cause of a fatal crash is .3. Furthermore, the probability that speeding and missing a curve are causes of a fatal crash is .12. Given speeding is a cause of a fatal crash, what is the probability that the crash occurred on a curve?

3.105 Survey on energy conservation. A state energy agency mailed questionnaires on energy conservation to 1,000 homeowners in the state capital. Five hundred questionnaires were returned. Suppose an experiment consists of randomly selecting and reviewing one of the returned questionnaires. Consider the events:

> A: {The home is constructed of brick.}
>
> B: {The home is more than 30 years old.}
>
> C: {The home is heated with oil.}

Describe each of the following events in terms of unions, intersections, and complements (i.e., $A \cup B$, $A \cap B$, A^c, etc.):

a. The home is more than 30 years old and is heated with oil.
b. The home is not constructed of brick.
c. The home is heated with oil or is more than 30 years old.
d. The home is constructed of brick and is not heated with oil.

3.106 Identifying urban counties. *Urban* and *rural* describe geographic areas for which land zoning regulations, school district policy, and public service policy are often set. However, the characteristics of urban/rural areas are not clearly defined. Researchers at the University of Nevada (Reno) asked a sample of county commissioners to give their perception of the single most important factor in identifying urban counties (*Professional Geographer*, Feb. 2000). In all, five factors were mentioned by the commissioners: total population, agricultural change, presence of industry, growth, and population concentration. The survey results are displayed in the pie chart below. Suppose one of the commissioners is selected at random and the most important factor specified by the commissioner is recorded.

a. List the sample points for this experiment.
b. Assign reasonable probabilities to the sample points.
c. Find the probability that the most important factor specified by the commissioner is population related.

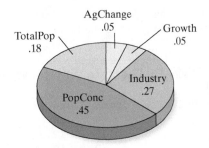

3.107 Use of country club facilities. A local country club has a membership of 600 and operates facilities that include an 18-hole championship golf course and 12 tennis courts. Before deciding whether to accept new members, the club president would like to know how many members regularly use each facility. A survey of the membership indicates that 70% regularly use the golf course, 50% regularly use the tennis courts, and 5% use neither of these facilities regularly.

a. Construct a Venn diagram to describe the results of the survey.
b. If one club member is chosen at random, what is the probability that the member uses either the golf course or the tennis courts or both?

c. If one member is chosen at random, what is the probability that the member uses both the golf and the tennis facilities?
d. A member is chosen at random from among those known to use the tennis courts regularly. What is the probability that the member also uses the golf course regularly?

3.108 Monitoring quality of power equipment. *Mechanical Engineering* (Feb. 2005) reported on the need for wireless networks to monitor the quality of industrial equipment. For example, consider Eaton Corp., a company that develops distribution products. Eaton estimates that 90% of the electrical switching devices it sells can monitor the quality of the power running through the device. Eaton further estimates that of the buyers of electrical switching devices capable of monitoring quality, 90% do not wire the equipment up for that purpose. Use this information to estimate the probability that an Eaton electrical switching device is capable of monitoring power quality and is wired up for that purpose.

Applying the Concepts—Intermediate

3.109 Appeals of federal civil trials. The *Journal of the American Law and Economics Association* (Vol. 3, 2001) published the results of a study of appeals of federal civil trials. The following table, extracted from the article, gives a breakdown of 2,143 civil cases that were appealed by either the plaintiff or the defendant. The outcome of the appeal, as well as the type of trial (judge or jury), was determined for each civil case. Suppose one of the 2,143 cases is selected at random and both the outcome of the appeal and type of trial are observed.

	Jury	Judge	Totals
Plaintiff trial win—reversed	194	71	265
Plaintiff trial win—affirmed/dismissed	429	240	669
Defendant trial win—reversed	111	68	179
Defendant trial win—affirmed/dismissed	731	299	1,030
Totals	1,465	678	2,143

a. Find $P(A)$, where $A = $ {jury trial}.
b. Find $P(B)$, where $B = $ {plaintiff trial win is reversed}.
c. Are A and B mutually exclusive events?
d. Find $P(A^c)$.
e. Find $P(A \cup B)$.
f. Find $P(A \cap B)$.

3.110 Assembling a panel of energy experts. The state legislature has appropriated $1 million to be distributed in the form of grants to individuals and organizations engaged in the research and development of alternative energy sources. You have been hired by the state's energy agency to assemble a panel of five energy experts whose task it will be to determine which individuals and organizations should receive the grant money. You have identified 11 equally qualified individuals who are willing to serve on the panel. How many different panels of five experts could be formed from these 11 individuals?

3.111 Testing a watch manufacturer's claim. A manufacturer of electronic digital watches claims that the probability of its watch running more than 1 minute slow or 1 minute fast after 1 year of use is .05. A consumer protection agency has purchased four of the manufacturer's watches with the intention of testing the claim.

    a. Assuming that the manufacturer's claim is correct, what is the probability that none of the watches are as accurate as claimed?

    b. Assuming that the manufacturer's claim is correct, what is the probability that exactly two of the four watches are as accurate as claimed?

    c. Suppose that only one of the four tested watches is as accurate as claimed. What inference can be made about the manufacturer's claim? Explain.

    d. Suppose that none of the watches tested are as accurate as claimed. Is it necessarily true that the manufacturer's claim is false? Explain.

3.112 Ranking razor blades. The corporations in the highly competitive razor blade industry do a tremendous amount of advertising each year. Corporation G gave a supply of three top-name brands, G, S, and W, to a consumer and asked her to use them and rank them in order of preference. The corporation was, of course, hoping the consumer would prefer its brand and rank it first, thereby giving them some material for a consumer interview advertising campaign. If the consumer did not prefer one blade over any other but was still required to rank the blades, what is the probability that

    a. The consumer ranked brand G first?

    b. The consumer ranked brand G last?

    c. The consumer ranked brand G last and brand W second?

    d. The consumer ranked brand W first, brand G second, and brand S third?

3.113 Link between cigar smoking and cancer. The *Journal of the National Cancer Institute* (Feb. 16, 2000) published the results of a study that investigated the association between cigar smoking and death from tobacco-related cancers. Data were obtained for a national sample of 137,243 American men. The results are summarized in the table. Each male in the study was classified according to his cigar-smoking status and whether or not he died from a tobacco-related cancer.

	Died from Cancer	Did Not Die from Cancer	Totals
Never Smoked Cigars	782	120,747	121,529
Former Cigar Smoker	91	7,757	7,848
Current Cigar Smoker	141	7,725	7,866
Totals	1,014	136,229	137,243

Source: Based on Shapiro, J. A., Jacobs, E. J., & Thun, M. J. "Cigar smoking in men and risk of death from tobacco-related cancers," *Journal of the National Cancer Institute*, Vol. 92, No. 4, Feb. 16, 2000. pp. 333–337 (Table 2).

    a. Find the probability that a man who never smoked cigars died from cancer.

    b. Find the probability that a former cigar smoker died from cancer.

    c. Find the probability that a current cigar smoker died from cancer.

3.114 Which events are independent? Use your intuitive understanding of independence to form an opinion about whether each of the following scenarios represents independent events.

    a. The results of consecutive tosses of a coin

    b. The opinions of randomly selected individuals in a preelection poll

    c. A Major League Baseball player's results in two consecutive at-bats

    d. The amount of gain or loss associated with investments in different stocks if these stocks are bought on the same day and sold on the same day 1 month later

    e. The amount of gain or loss associated with investments in different stocks that are bought and sold in different time periods, 5 years apart

    f. The prices bid by two different development firms in response to a building construction proposal

3.115 Home modifications for wheelchair users. The *American Journal of Public Health* (Jan. 2002) reported on a study of elderly wheelchair users who live at home. A sample of 306 wheelchair users, age 65 or older, were surveyed about whether they had an injurious fall during the year and whether their home features any one of five structural modifications: bathroom modifications, widened doorways/hallways, kitchen modifications, installed railings, and easy-open doors. The responses are summarized in the accompanying table. Suppose we select, at random, one of the 306 surveyed wheelchair users.

Home Features	Injurious Fall(s)	No Falls	Totals
All 5	2	7	9
At least 1 but not all	26	162	188
None	20	89	109
Totals	48	258	306

Source: Based on Berg, K., Hines, M., & Allen, S. "Wheelchair users at home: Few home modifications and many injurious falls," *American Journal of Public Health,* Vol. 92, No. 1, Jan. 2002 (Table 1).

    a. Find the probability that the wheelchair user had an injurious fall.

    b. Find the probability that the wheelchair user had all five features installed in the home.

    c. Find the probability that the wheelchair user had no falls and none of the features installed in the home.

    d. Given the wheelchair user had all five features installed, what is the probability that the user had an injurious fall?

    e. Given the wheelchair user had none of the features installed, what is the probability that the user had an injurious fall?

3.116 World Cup soccer match draws. Every 4 years the world's 32 best national soccer teams compete for the World Cup. Run by FIFA (Fédération Internationale de Football Association), national teams are placed into eight groups of four teams, with the group winners advancing to play for the World Cup. *Chance* (Spring 2007) investigated the fairness of the 2006 World Cup draw. Each of the top 8 seeded teams (teams ranked 1–8, called pot 1) were placed into one of the eight groups (named Group A, B, C, D, E, F, G, and H). The remaining 24 teams were assigned to 3 pots of 8 teams each to achieve the best possible geographical distribution between the groups. The teams in pot 2 were assigned to groups as follows: the first team drawn was placed into Group A, the second team drawn was placed in to Group B, etc. Teams in pots 3 and 4 were assigned to the groups in similar fashion. Because teams in pots 2–4 are not necessarily placed there based on their world ranking, this typically leads to a "group of death," i.e., a group involving at least two highly seeded teams where only one can advance.

a. In 2006, Germany (as the host country) was assigned as the top seed in Group A. What is the probability that Paraguay (with the highest ranking in pot 2) was assigned to Group A?

b. Many soccer experts viewed the South American teams (Ecuador and Paraguay) as the most dangerous teams in pot 2. What is the probability one of the South American teams was assigned to Group A?

c. In 2006, Group B was considered the "group of death," with England (world rank 2), Paraguay (highest rank in pot 2), Sweden (2nd highest rank in pot 3), and Trinidad and Tobago. What is the probability that Group B included the team with the highest rank in pot 2 and the team with one of the top two ranks in pot 3?

d. In drawing teams from pot 2, there was a notable exception in 2006. If a South American team (either Ecuador or Paraguay) was drawn into a group with another South American team, it was automatically moved to the next group. This rule impacted Group C (Argentina as the top seed) and Group F (Brazil as the top seed), because they already had South American teams, and groups that followed these groups in the draw. Now Group D included the eventual champion Italy as its top seed. What is the probability that Group D was not assigned one of the dangerous South American teams in pot 2?

3.117 Chance of an Avon sale. The probability that an Avon salesperson sells beauty products to a prospective customer on the first visit to the customer is .4. If the salesperson fails to make the sale on the first visit, the probability that the sale will be made on the second visit is .65. The salesperson never visits a prospective customer more than twice. What is the probability that the salesperson will make a sale to a particular customer?

3.118 Repairing a computer network. The local area network (LAN) for the College of Business computing system at a large university is temporarily shut down for repairs. Previous shutdowns have been due to hardware failure, software failure, or power failure. Maintenance engineers have determined that the probabilities of hardware, software, and power problems are .01, .05, and .02, respectively. They have also determined that if the system experiences hardware problems, it shuts down 73% of the time. Similarly, if software problems occur, the system shuts down 12% of the time; and if power failure occurs, the system shuts down 88% of the time. What is the probability that the current shutdown of the LAN is due to hardware failure? Software failure? Power failure?

3.119 Profile of a sustainable farmer. *Sustainable development or sustainable farming* means finding ways to live and work the Earth without jeopardizing the future. Studies were conducted in five Midwestern states to develop a profile of a sustainable farmer. The results revealed that farmers can be classified along a sustainability scale, depending on whether they are likely (L) or unlikely (U) to engage in the following practices: (1) Raise a broad mix of crops; (2) raise livestock; (3) use chemicals sparingly; and (4) use techniques for regenerating the soil, such as crop rotation.

a. List the different sets of classifications that are possible for the four practices (e.g., LUUL).

b. Suppose you are planning to interview farmers across the country to determine the frequency with which they fall into the classification sets you listed for part **a.** Because no information is yet available, assume initially that there is an equal chance of a farmer falling into any single classification set. Using that assumption, what is the probability that a farmer will be classified as unlikely on all four criteria (i.e., classified as a nonsustainable farmer)?

c. Using the same assumption as in part b, what is the probability that a farmer will be classified as likely on at least three of the criteria (i.e., classified as a near-sustainable farmer)?

3.120 Evaluating the performance of quality inspectors. The performance of quality inspectors affects both the quality of outgoing products and the cost of the products. A product that passes inspection is assumed to meet quality standards; a product that fails inspection may be reworked, scrapped, or reinspected. Quality engineers at an electric company evaluated performances of inspectors in judging the quality of solder joints by comparing each inspector's classifications of a set of 153 joints with the consensus evaluation of a panel of experts. The results for a particular inspector are shown in the table. One of the 153 solder joints was selected at random.

| | Inspector's Judgment | |
Committee's Judgment	Joint Acceptable	Joint Rejectable
Joint acceptable	101	10
Joint rejectable	23	19

a. What is the probability that the inspector judged the joint to be acceptable? That the committee judged the joint to be acceptable?

b. What is the probability that both the inspector and the committee judged the joint to be acceptable? That neither judged the joint to be acceptable?

c. What is the probability that the inspector and the committee disagreed? Agreed?

3.121 System components operating in series and parallel. Consider the two systems shown in the schematic at the top of the next page. System A operates properly only if all three components operate properly. (The three components are said to operate *in series*.) The probability of failure for system A components 1, 2, and 3 are .12, .09, and .11, respectively. Assume the components operate independently of each other. System B comprises two subsystems said to operate *in parallel*. Each subsystem has two components that operate in series. System B will operate properly as long as at least one of the subsystems functions properly. The probability of failure for each component in the system is .1. Assume the components operate independently of each other.

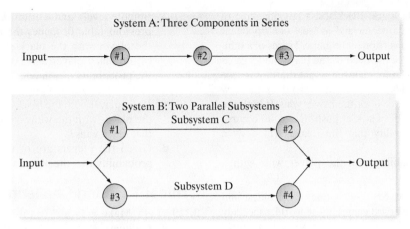

Figures for Exercise 3.121

a. Find the probability that system A operates properly.

b. What is the probability that at least one of the components in system A will fail and therefore that the system will fail?

c. Find the probability that system B operates properly.

d. Find the probability that exactly one subsystem in system B fails.

e. Find the probability that system B fails to operate properly.

f. How many parallel subsystems like the two shown here would be required to guarantee that the system operates properly at least 99% of the time?

3.122 Probability of winning a war. Before a country enters into a war, a prudent government will assess the cost, utility, and probability of a victory. University of Georgia professor P. L. Sullivan has developed a statistical model for determining the probability of winning a war based on a government's capabilities and resources (*Journal of Conflict Resolution,* Vol. 51, 2007). Now consider the recently ended U.S.-Iraq conflict. One researcher used the model to estimate that the probability of a successful regime change in Iraq was .70 prior to the start of the war. Of course, we now know that the successful regime change was achieved. However, the model also estimates that given the mission was extended to support a weak Iraqi government, the probability of ultimate success was only .26. Assume these probabilities are accurate.

a. Prior to the start of the U.S.-Iraq war, what was the probability that a successful regime change would not be achieved?

b. Given that the mission was extended to support a weak Iraqi government, what was the probability that a successful regime change would ultimately be achieved?

c. Suppose the probability of the United States extending the mission to support a weak Iraqi government had been .55. Find the probability that the mission would be extended and would result in a successful regime change.

3.123 Detecting traces of TNT. University of Florida researchers in the Department of Materials Science and Engineering have invented a technique to rapidly detect traces of TNT (*Today,* Spring 2005). The method, which involves shining a laser light on a potentially contaminated object, provides instantaneous results and gives no false positives. In this application, a false positive would occur if the laser light detects traces of TNT when, in fact, no TNT is actually present on the object. Let A be the event that the laser light detects traces of TNT. Let B be the event that the object contains no traces of TNT. The probability of a false positive is 0. Write this probability in terms of A and B using symbols such as $\cup$, $\cap$, and $|$.

Applying the Concepts—Advanced

3.124 Malfunctioning production lines. A manufacturing operation utilizes two production lines to assemble electronic fuses. Both lines produce fuses at the same rate and generally produce 2.5% defective fuses. However, production line 1 recently suffered mechanical difficulty and produced 6.0% defectives during a 3-week period. This situation was not known until several lots of electronic fuses produced in this period were shipped to customers. If one of the two fuses tested by a customer was found to be defective, what is the probability that the lot from which it came was produced on malfunctioning line 1? (Assume all the fuses in the lot were produced on the same line.)

3.125 Scrap rate of machine parts. A press produces parts used in the manufacture of large-screen plasma televisions. If the press is correctly adjusted, it produces parts with a scrap rate of 5%. If it is not adjusted correctly, it produces scrap at a 50% rate. From past company records, the machine is known to be correctly adjusted 90% of the time. A quality-control inspector randomly selects one part from those recently produced by the press and discovers it is defective. What is the probability that the machine is incorrectly adjusted?

3.126 Chance of winning at "craps." A version of the dice game "craps" is played in the following manner. A player starts by rolling two balanced dice. If the roll (the sum of the two numbers showing on the dice) results in a 7 or 11, the player wins. If the roll results in a 2 or a 3 (called *craps*), the player loses. For any other roll outcome, the player continues to throw the dice until the original roll outcome recurs (in which case the player wins) or until a 7 occurs (in which case the player loses).

a. What is the probability that a player wins the game on the first roll of the dice?

b. What is the probability that a player loses the game on the first roll of the dice?

c. If the player throws a total of 4 on the first roll, what is the probability that the game ends (win or lose) on the next roll?

3.127 Chance of winning blackjack. Blackjack, a favorite game of gamblers, is played by a dealer and at least one opponent (called a *player*). In one version of the game, 2 cards of a standard 52-card bridge deck are dealt to the player and 2 cards to the dealer. For this exercise, assume that drawing an ace and a face card is called *blackjack*. If the dealer does not draw a blackjack and the player does, the player wins. If both the dealer and player draw blackjack, a "push" (i.e., a tie) occurs.

a. What is the probability that the dealer will draw a blackjack?

b. What is the probability that the player wins with a blackjack?

3.128 Strategy in the game "Go." "Go" is one of the oldest and most popular strategic board games in the world, especially in Japan and Korea. The University of Virginia requires MBA students to learn Go to understand how the Japanese conduct business. This two-player game is played on a flat surface marked with 19 vertical and 19 horizontal lines. The objective is to control territory by placing pieces, called *stones,* on vacant points on the board. Players alternate placing their stones. The player using black stones goes first, followed by the player using white stones. *Chance* (Summer 1995) published an article that investigated the advantage of playing first (i.e., using the black stones) in Go. The results of 577 games recently played by professional Go players were analyzed.

a. In the 577 games, the player with the black stones won 319 times, and the player with the white stones won 258 times. Use this information to assess the probability of winning when you play first in Go.

b. Professional Go players are classified by level. Group C includes the top-level players, followed by Group B

(middle-level) and Group A (low-level) players. The previous table describes the number of games won by the player with the black stones, categorized by level of the black player and level of the opponent. Assess the probability of winning when you play first in Go for each combination of player and opponent level.

c. If the player with the black stones is ranked higher than the player with the white stones, what is the probability that black wins?

d. Given the players are of the same level, what is the probability that the player with the black stones wins?

Critical Thinking Challenges

3.129 "Let's Make a Deal." Marilyn vos Savant, who is listed in *Guinness Book of World Records Hall of Fame* for "Highest IQ," writes a weekly column in the Sunday newspaper supplement *Parade Magazine*. Her column, "Ask Marilyn," is devoted to games of skill, puzzles, and mind-bending riddles. In one issue (*Parade Magazine*, Feb. 24, 1991), vos Savant posed the following question:

Suppose you're on a game show, and you're given a choice of three doors. Behind one door is a car; behind the others, goats. You pick a door—say, #1—and the host, who knows what's behind the doors, opens another door—say #3—which has a goat. He then says to you, "Do you want to pick door #2?" Is it to your advantage to switch your choice?

Marilyn's answer: "Yes, you should switch. The first door has a $\frac{1}{3}$ chance of winning [the car], but the second has a $\frac{2}{3}$ chance [of winning the car]." Predictably, vos Savant's surprising answer elicited thousands of critical letters, many of them from PhD mathematicians, who disagreed with her. Who is correct, the PhDs or Marilyn?

3.130 Flawed Pentium computer chip. In October 1994, a flaw was discovered in the Pentium microchip installed in personal computers. The chip produced an incorrect result when dividing two numbers. Intel, the manufacturer of the Pentium chip, initially announced that such an error would occur once in 9 billion divisions, or "once in every 27,000 years" for a typical user; consequently, it did not immediately offer to replace the chip.

Depending on the procedure, statistical software packages (e.g., Minitab) may perform an extremely large number of divisions to produce the required output. For heavy users of the software, 1 billion divisions over a short time frame is not unusual. Will the flawed chip be a problem for a heavy Minitab user? [*Note:* Two months after the flaw was discovered, Intel agreed to replace all Pentium chips free of charge.]

Black Player Level	Opponent Level	Number of Wins	Number of Games
C	A	34	34
C	B	69	79
C	C	66	118
B	A	40	54
B	B	52	95
B	C	27	79
A	A	15	28
A	B	11	51
A	C	5	39
Totals		319	577

Source: Kim, J., & Kim, H. J. "The advantage of playing first in Go," *Chance,* Vol. 8, No. 3, Summer 1995, p. 26 (Table 3). Copyright © 1995 by the American Statistical Association. Reprinted with permission.

Activity 3.1 *Exit Polls:* Conditional Probability

Exit polls are conducted in selected locations as voters leave their polling places after voting. In addition to being used to predict the outcome of elections before the votes are counted, these polls are used to gauge tendencies among voters. The results are usually stated in terms of conditional probabilities.

The table on the next page shows the results of exit polling that suggest men were almost evenly spit on voting for John McCain or Barack Obama, while women were more likely to vote for Obama in the 2008 presidential election. In addition, the table also suggests that more women than men voted in the election. The six percentages in the last three columns represent conditional probabilities where the given event is gender.

2008 Presidential Election, Vote by Gender

	Obama	McCain	Other
Male (47%)	49%	48%	3%
Female (53%)	56%	43%	1%

Source: Data from CNN (www.cnn.com).

1. Find similar exit poll results where the voters are categorized by race, income, education, or some other criterion for a recent national, state, or local election. Choose two different examples and interpret the percentages given as probabilities, or conditional probabilities where appropriate.

2. Use the multiplicative rule of probability to find the probabilities related to the percentages given. [For example, in the table on the left find P(Obama and Male) using the multiplicative rule.] Then interpret each of these probabilities and use them to determine the total percentage of the electorate who voted for each candidate.

3. Describe a situation where a business might use a form of exit polling to gauge customer reaction to a new product or service. Identify the type of business, the product or service, the criterion used to categorize customers, and how the customers' reactions will be determined. Then describe how the results will be summarized as conditional probabilities. How might the results of the poll benefit the business?

Activity 3.2 *Keep the Change:* Independent Events

Once again we return to the Bank of America *Keep the Change* savings program, Activity 1.1 (p. 29). This time we look at whether certain events involving purchase totals and amounts transferred to savings are independent. Throughout this activity, the experiment consists of randomly selecting one purchase from a large group of purchases.

1. Define events A and B as follows:

   A: {Purchase total ends in $0.25.}
   B: {Amount transferred is less that $0.50.}

   Explain why events A and B are not independent. Are events A and B mutually exclusive? Use this example to explain the difference between independent events and mutually exclusive events.

2. Now define events A and B in this manner:

   A: {Purchase total is greater than $10.}
   B: {Amount transferred is less than $0.50.}

   Do you believe that these events are independent? Explain your reasoning.

3. To investigate numerically whether the events in Question 2 are independent, we will use the data collected in Activity 1.1, page 29. Pool your data with the data from other students or the entire class so that the combined data set represents at least 100 purchases. Complete the table by counting the number of purchases in each category.

Distribution of Purchases

	Purchase	Total	
Transfer Amount	≤ $10	> $10	Totals
$0.00–$0.49 $0.99–$0.99			
Totals			

Compute appropriate probabilities based on your completed table to test whether the events of Question 2 are independent. If you conclude that the events are not independent, can you explain your conclusion in terms of the original data?

References

Bennett, D. J. *Randomness.* Cambridge, Mass.: Harvard University Press, 1998.

Epstein, R. A. *The Theory of Gambling and Statistical Logic,* rev. ed. New York: Academic Press, 1977.

Feller, W. *An Introduction to Probability Theory and Its Applications,* 3rd ed., Vol. 1. New York: Wiley, 1968.

Lindley, D. V. *Making Decisions,* 2nd ed. London: Wiley, 1985.

Parzen, E. *Modern Probability Theory and Its Applications.* New York: Wiley, 1960.

Wackerly, D., Mendenhall, W., and Scheaffer, R. L. *Mathematical Statistics with Applications,* 7th ed. Boston: Duxbury, 2008.

Williams, B. *A Sampler on Sampling.* New York: Wiley, 1978.

Winkler, R. L. *An Introduction to Bayesian Inference and Decision.* New York: Holt, Rinehart and Winston, 1972.

Wright, G., & Ayton, P., eds. *Subjective Probability.* New York: Wiley, 1994.

USING TECHNOLOGY Technology images shown here are taken from SPSS Statistics Professional 20.0, Minitab 16, XLSTAT for Pearson, and Excel 2010.

Note: Automated commands for generating combinations and permutations are not available in SPSS.

Minitab: Combinations and Permutations

Combinations—Choosing *n* Elements from *N* Elements

Step 1 Click "Calc" from the main menu bar, and then select "Calculator."

Step 2 On the resulting dialog box, specify the column you want to store the result in, and then enter "COMBINATIONS(N,n)" in the "Expression" box. (See Figure 3.M.1.)

Figure 3.M.1 Minitab calculator dialog box entries for combinations

Step 3 Specify the values of *N* and *n,* as shown in Figure 3.M.1.

Step 4 Click "OK" and the result will appear in the specified column in the Minitab worksheet.

Permutations—Choosing *n* Elements from *N* Elements (See Appendix A for an application.)

Step 1 Click "Calc" from the main menu bar, and then select "Calculator."

Step 2 On the resulting dialog box, specify the column you want to store the result in, and then enter "PERMUTATIONS(N, n)" in the "Expression" box. (See Figure 3.M.2.)

Step 3 Specify the values of *N* and *n,* as shown in Figure 3.M.2.

Step 4 Click "OK" and the result will appear in the specified column in the Minitab worksheet.

Excel: Combinations and Permutations

Combinations—Choosing *n* Elements from *N* Elements

Step 1 Click on the cell in the Excel worksheet where you want the result to appear.

Step 2 In the formula bar, enter "=" followed by "COMBIN(N,n)."

Figure 3.M.2 Minitab calculator dialog box entries for permutations

Step 3 Specify the values of *N* and *n,* as shown in Figure 3.E.1.

Step 4 Click "Enter" and the result will appear in the selected cell (see Figure 3.E.1).

Figure 3.E.1 Excel formula for combinations

Permutations—Choosing *n* Elements from *N* Elements (See Appendix A for an application.)

Step 1 Click on the cell in the Excel worksheet where you want the result to appear.

Step 2 In the formula bar, enter "=" followed by "PERMUT(N,n)."

Step 3 Specify the values of *N* and *n,* as shown in Figure 3.E.2.

Step 4 Click "Enter" and the result will appear in the selected cell (see Figure 3.E.2).

Figure 3.E.2 Excel formula for permutations

TI-84 Graphing Calculator: Combinations and Permutations

Combinations — Choosing *n* Elements from *N* Elements

Step 1 Enter the value of *N*.

Step 2 Press **MATH,** and then select **PRB.**

```
MATH NUM CPX PRB
1:rand
2:nPr
3:nCr
4:!
5:randInt(
6:randNorm(
7↓randBin(
```

Step 3 Press **nCr** for combinations.

Step 4 Enter the value of *n*; press **ENTER.**

Permutations — Choosing *n* Elements from *N* Elements (See Appendix A for an application.)

Step 1 Enter the value of *N*.

Step 2 Press **MATH,** and then select **PRB.**

Step 3 Press **nPr** for permutations.

Step 4 Enter the value of *n*; press **ENTER.**

4

CONTENTS

Where We've Been

- Used probability to make an inference about a population from data in an observed sample
- Used probability to measure the reliability of the inference

Where We're Going

- Develop the notion of a random variable (4.1)
- Learn that numerical data are observed values of either discrete or continuous random variables (4.2, 4.5)
- Study two important types of random variables and their probability models: the binomial and normal models (4.3, 4.6, 4.7)
- Present some additional discrete and continuous random variables (4.4, 4.8)

◻ Random Variables and Probability Distributions

STATISTICS in ACTION

Probability in a Reverse Cocaine Sting: Was Cocaine Really Sold?

The American Statistician *described an interesting application of a discrete probability distribution in a case involving illegal drugs. It all started with a "bust" in a midsized Florida city. During the bust, police seized approximately 500 foil packets of a white, powdery substance, presumably cocaine. Since it is not a crime to buy or sell nonnarcotic cocaine look-alikes (e.g., inert powders), detectives had to prove that the packets actually contained cocaine in order to convict their suspects of drug trafficking. When the police laboratory randomly selected and chemically tested 4 of the packets, all 4 tested positive for cocaine. This finding led to the conviction of the traffickers.*

After the conviction, the police decided to use the remaining foil packets (i.e., those not tested) in reverse sting operations. Two of these packets were randomly selected and sold by undercover officers to a buyer. Between the sale and the arrest, however, the buyer disposed of the evidence. The key question is, Beyond a reasonable doubt, did the defendant really purchase cocaine?

In court, the defendant's attorney argued that his client should not be convicted, because the police could not prove that the missing foil packets contained cocaine. The police contended, however, that since 4 of the original packets tested positive for cocaine, the 2 packets sold in the reverse sting were also highly likely to contain cocaine. In this chapter, two Statistics in Action Revisited examples demonstrate how to use probability models to solve the dilemma posed by the police's reverse sting. (The case represented Florida's first cocaine-possession conviction without the actual physical evidence.) (*The American Statistician*, May 1991.)

STATISTICS in ACTION REVISITED

▫ Using the Binomial Model to Solve the Cocaine Sting Case **(p. 208)**

▫ Using the Hypergeometric Model to Solve the Cocaine Sting Case **(p. 214)**

You may have noticed that many of the examples of experiments in Chapter 3 generated quantitative (numerical) observations. The Consumer Price Index, the unemployment rate, the number of sales made in a week, and the yearly profit of a company are all examples of numerical measurements of some phenomenon. Thus, most experiments have sample points that correspond to values of some numerical variable.

To illustrate, consider the coin-tossing experiment of Chapter 3. Figure 4.1 is a Venn diagram showing the sample points when two coins are tossed and the up faces (heads or tails) of the coins are observed. One possible numerical outcome is the total number of heads observed. These values (0, 1, or 2) are shown in parentheses on the Venn diagram, one numerical value associated with each sample point. In the jargon of probability, the variable "total number of heads observed when two coins are tossed" is called a *random variable*.

HH ● (2)	HT ● (1)
TT ● (0)	TH ● (1)

S

Figure 4.1

Venn diagram for coin-tossing experiment

A **random variable** is a variable that assumes numerical values associated with the random outcomes of an experiment, where one (and only one) numerical value is assigned to each sample point.

The term *random variable* is more meaningful than the term *variable* because the adjective *random* indicates that the coin-tossing experiment may result in one of the several possible values of the variable—0, 1, or 2—according to the *random* outcome of the experiment, *HH, HT, TH,* and *TT.* Similarly, if the experiment is to count the number of customers who use the drive-up window of a bank each day, the random variable (the number of customers) will vary from day to day, partly because of random phenomena that influence whether customers use the drive-up window. Thus, the possible values of this random variable range from 0 to the maximum number of customers the window could possibly serve in a day.

We define two different types of random variables, *discrete* and *continuous,* in Section 4.1. Then we spend the remainder of this chapter discussing specific types of both discrete and continuous random variables and the aspects that make them important in business applications.

4.1 Two Types of Random Variables

Recall that the sample point probabilities corresponding to an experiment must sum to 1. Dividing one unit of probability among the sample points in a sample space and consequently assigning probabilities to the values of a random variable is not always as easy as the examples in Chapter 3 might lead you to believe. If the number of sample points can be completely listed, the job is straightforward. But if the experiment results in an infinite number of numerical sample points that are impossible to list, the task of assigning probabilities to the sample points is impossible without the aid of a probability model. The next three examples demonstrate the need for different probability models depending on the number of values that a random variable can assume.

Example 4.1

Values of a Discrete Random Variable—Wine Ratings

Problem A panel of 10 experts for the *Wine Spectator* (a national publication) is asked to taste a new white wine and assign a rating of 0, 1, 2, or 3. A score is then obtained by adding together the ratings of the 10 experts. How many values can this random variable assume?

Solution A sample point is a sequence of 10 numbers associated with the rating of each expert. For example, one sample point is

$$\{1, 0, 0, 1, 2, 0, 0, 3, 1, 0\}$$

The random variable assigns a score to each one of these sample points by adding the 10 numbers together. Thus, the smallest score is 0 (if all 10 ratings are 0), and the largest score is 30 (if all 10 ratings are 3). Because every integer between 0 and 30 is a possible score, the random variable denoted by the symbol x can assume 31 values. Note that the value of the random variable for the sample point above is $x = 8$.*

Look Back This is an example of a *discrete random variable* because there is a finite number of distinct possible values. Whenever all the possible values a random variable can assume can be listed (or counted), the random variable is discrete.

Example 4.2

Values of a Discrete Random Variable—EPA Application

Problem Suppose the Environmental Protection Agency (EPA) takes readings once a month on the amount of pesticide in the discharge water of a chemical company. If the amount of pesticide exceeds the maximum level set by the EPA, the company is forced to take corrective action and may be subject to penalty. Consider the random variable, x, the number of months before the company's discharge exceeds the EPA's maximum level. What values can x assume?

Solution The company's discharge of pesticide may exceed the maximum allowable level on the first month of testing, the second month of testing, and so on. It is possible that the company's discharge will *never* exceed the maximum level. Thus, the set of possible values for the number of months until the level is first exceeded is the set of all positive integers

$$1, 2, 3, 4, \ldots$$

Look Back If we can list the values of a random variable x, even though the list is never ending, we call the list **countable** and the corresponding random variable *discrete*. Thus, the number of months until the company's discharge first exceeds the limit is a *discrete random variable*.

■ **Now Work Exercise 4.4**

Example 4.3

Values of a Continuous Random Variable—Another EPA Application

Problem Refer to Example 4.2. A second random variable of interest is the amount x of pesticide (in milligrams per liter) found in the monthly sample of discharge waters from the chemical company. What values can this random variable assume?

Solution Unlike the *number* of months before the company's discharge exceeds the EPA's maximum level, the set of all possible values for the *amount* of discharge *cannot* be listed—that is, it is not countable. The possible values for the amounts of pesticide would correspond to the points on the interval between 0 and the largest possible value the amount of the discharge could attain, the maximum number of milligrams that could occupy 1 liter of volume. (Practically, the interval would be much smaller, say, between 0 and 500 milligrams per liter.)

Look Ahead When the values of a random variable are not countable but instead correspond to the points on some interval, we call it a *continuous random variable*. Thus, the *amount* of pesticide in the chemical plant's discharge waters is a *continuous random variable*.

■ **Now Work Exercise 4.5**

---

*The standard mathematical convention is to use a capital letter (e.g., X) to denote the theoretical random variable. The possible values (or realizations) of the random variable are typically denoted with a lowercase letter (e.g., x). Thus, in Example 4.1, the random variable X can take on the values $x = 0, 1, 2, \ldots, 30$. Because this notation can be confusing for introductory statistics students, we simplify the notation by using the lowercase x to represent the random variable throughout.

> Random variables that can assume a *countable* number (finite or infinite) of values are called **discrete.**

> Random variables that can assume values corresponding to any of the points contained in one or more intervals (i.e., values that are infinite and *uncountable*) are called **continuous.**

Several more examples of discrete random variables follow:

1. The number of sales made by a salesperson in a given week: $x = 0, 1, 2, \ldots$
2. The number of consumers in a sample of 500 who favor a particular product over all competitors: $x = 0, 1, 2, \ldots, 500$
3. The number of bids received in a bond offering: $x = 0, 1, 2, \ldots$
4. The number of errors on a page of an accountant's ledger: $x = 0, 1, 2, \ldots$
5. The number of customers waiting to be served in a restaurant at a particular time: $x = 0, 1, 2, \ldots$

Note that each of the examples of discrete random variables begins with the words "The number of...." This wording is very common because the discrete random variables most frequently observed are counts.

We conclude this section with some more examples of continuous random variables:

1. The length of time between arrivals at a hospital clinic: $0 \le x < \infty$ (infinity)
2. For a new apartment complex, the length of time from completion until a specified number of apartments are rented: $0 \le x < \infty$
3. The amount of carbonated beverage loaded into a 12-ounce can in a can-filling operation: $0 \le x \le 12$
4. The depth at which a successful oil-drilling venture first strikes oil: $0 \le x \le c$, where c is the maximum depth obtainable
5. The weight of a food item bought in a supermarket: $0 \le x \le 500$ [*Note*: Theoretically, there is no upper limit on x, but it is unlikely that it would exceed 500 pounds.]

Discrete random variables and their probability distributions are discussed in Part I—Sections 4.2–4.4. Continuous random variables and their probability distributions are the topic of Part II—Sections 4.5–4.8.

Exercises 4.1–4.10

Applying the Concepts—Basic

4.1 Types of random variables. Which of the following describe continuous random variables? Which describe discrete random variables?
  a. The number of newspapers sold by the *New York Times* each month
  b. The amount of ink used in printing a Sunday edition of the *New York Times*
  c. The actual number of ounces in a 1-gallon bottle of laundry detergent
  d. The number of defective parts in a shipment of nuts and bolts
  e. The number of people collecting unemployment insurance each month

4.2 Types of finance random variables. Security analysts are professionals who devote full-time efforts to evaluating the investment worth of a narrow list of stocks. The following variables are of interest to security analysts. Which are discrete and which are continuous random variables?
  a. The closing price of a particular stock on the New York Stock Exchange
  b. The number of shares of a particular stock that are traded each business day
  c. The quarterly earnings of a particular firm
  d. The percentage change in yearly earnings between 2011 and 2012 for a particular firm
  e. The number of new products introduced per year by a firm

f. The time until a pharmaceutical company gains approval from the U.S. Food and Drug Administration to market a new drug

4.3 **NHTSA crash tests.** Refer to the National Highway Traffic Safety Administration (NHTSA) crash tests of new car models, Exercise 2.149 (p. 116). Recall that the NHTSA developed a driver-side "star" scoring system, with results ranging from one star (*) to five stars (*****). The more stars in the rating, the better the level of crash protection in a head-on collision. Suppose that a car is selected from the data and its driver-side star rating is determined. Let x equal the number of stars in the rating. Is x a discrete or continuous random variable?

4.4 **Customers in line at a Subway shop.** The number of customers, x, waiting in line to order sandwiches at a Subway shop at noon is of interest to the store manager. What values can x assume? Is x a discrete or continuous random variable?

4.5 **Executive Compensation Scoreboard.** Refer to *Forbes'* 2011 "Executive Compensation Scoreboard" (Table 1.1, p. 4). One variable saved in the file is the CEO's compensation (in $ millions) in 2011. Is x a discrete or continuous random variable?

Applying the Concepts—Intermediate

4.6 **Banking.** Give an example of a discrete random variable that would be of interest to a banker.

4.7 **Economics.** Give an example of a continuous random variable that would be of interest to an economist.

4.8 **Hotel management.** Give an example of a discrete random variable that would be of interest to the manager of a hotel.

4.9 **Retailing.** Give two examples of discrete random variables that would be of interest to the manager of a clothing store.

4.10 **Stock market.** Give an example of a continuous random variable that would be of interest to a stockbroker.

PART I: DISCRETE RANDOM VARIABLES

4.2 Probability Distributions for Discrete Random Variables

A complete description of a discrete random variable requires that we *specify the possible values the random variable can assume and the probability associated with each value.* To illustrate, consider Example 4.4.

Example	4.4

Finding a Probability Distribution— Coin-Tossing Experiment

HH	HT
•	•
$x = 2$	$x = 1$
TH	TT
•	•
$x = 1$	$x = 0$

S

Figure 4.2

Venn diagram for the two-coin-toss experiment

Table 4.1

Probability Distribution for Coin-Toss Experiment: Tabular Form

x	$p(x)$
0	$\frac{1}{4}$
1	$\frac{1}{2}$
2	$\frac{1}{4}$

Problem Recall the experiment of tossing two coins (Section 4.1) and let x be the number of heads observed. Find the probability associated with each value of the random variable x, assuming the two coins are fair. Display these values in a table or graph.

Solution The sample space and sample points for this experiment are reproduced in Figure 4.2. Note that the random variable x can assume values 0, 1, and 2. Recall (from Chapter 3) that the probability associated with each of the four sample points is $\frac{1}{4}$. Then, identifying the probabilities of the sample points associated with each of these values of x, we have

$$P(x = 0) = P(TT) = \tfrac{1}{4}$$
$$P(x = 1) = P(TH) + P(HT) = \tfrac{1}{4} + \tfrac{1}{4} = \tfrac{1}{2}$$
$$P(x = 2) = P(HH) = \tfrac{1}{4}$$

Thus, we now know the values the random variable can assume (0, 1, 2) and how the probability is *distributed over* these values $(\tfrac{1}{4}, \tfrac{1}{2}, \tfrac{1}{4})$. This completely describes the random variable and is referred to as the *probability distribution,* denoted by the symbol $p(x)$.* The probability distribution for the coin-toss example is shown in tabular form in Table 4.1 and in graphical form in Figure 4.3. Because the probability distribution for a discrete random variable is concentrated at specific points (values of x), the graph in Figure 4.3a represents the probabilities as the heights of vertical lines over the corresponding values of x. Although the representation of the probability distribution as a histogram, as in Figure 4.3b, is less precise (because the probability is spread over a unit interval), the histogram representation will prove useful when we approximate probabilities of certain discrete random variables in Section 4.4.

---

*In standard mathematical notation, the probability that a random variable X takes on a value x is denoted $P(X = x) = p(x)$. Thus, $P(X = 0) = p(0)$, $P(X = 1) = p(1)$, etc. In this introductory text, we adopt the simpler $p(x)$ notation.

a. Point representation of $p(x)$ b. Histogram representation of $p(x)$

Figure 4.3

Probability distribution for coin-toss experiment: graphical form

Look Ahead We could also present the probability distribution for x as a formula, but this would unnecessarily complicate a very simple example. We give the formulas for the probability distributions of some common discrete random variables later in this chapter.

——■ **Now Work Exercise 4.16**

> The **probability distribution** of a **discrete random variable** is a graph, table, or formula that specifies the probability associated with each possible value the random variable can assume.

Two requirements must be satisfied by all probability distributions for discrete random variables.

> **Requirements for the Probability Distribution of a Discrete Random Variable, x**
>
> **1.** $p(x) \geq 0$ for all values of x
>
> **2.** $\Sigma p(x) = 1$
>
> where the summation of $p(x)$ is over all possible values of x.*

Example	**4.5**

Probability Distribution from a Graph—Playing Craps

Problem Craps is a popular casino game in which a player throws two dice and bets on the outcome (the sum total of the dots showing on the upper faces of the two dice). Consider a $5 wager. On the first toss (called the *come-out* roll), if the total is 7 or 11 the roller wins $5. If the outcome is a 2, 3, or 12, the roller loses $5 (i.e., the roller wins −$5). For any other outcome (4, 5, 6, 8, 9, or 10), a *point* is established and no money is lost or won on that roll (i.e., the roller wins $0). In a computer simulation of repeated tosses of two dice, the outcome x of the come-out roll wager (−$5, $0, or +$5) was recorded. A relative frequency histogram summarizing the results is shown in Figure 4.4. Use the histogram to find the approximate probability distribution of x.

Solution The histogram shows that the relative frequencies of the outcomes $x = -\$5$, $x = \$0$, and $x = \$5$ are .1, .65, and .25, respectively. For example, in repeated tosses of

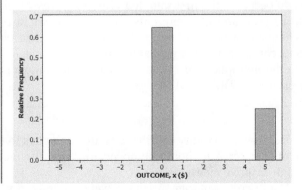

Figure 4.4

Histogram for $5 wager on come-out roll in craps

*Unless otherwise indicated, summations will always be over all possible values of x.

two dice, 25% of the outcomes resulted in a sum of 7 or 11 (a $5 win for the roller). Based on our long-run definition of probability given in Chapter 3, these relative frequencies estimate the probabilities of the three outcomes. Consequently, the approximate probability distribution of x, the outcome of the come-out wager in craps, is $p(-\$5) = .1$, $p(\$0) = .65$, and $p(\$5) = .25$. Note that these probabilities sum to 1.

Look Back When two dice are tossed, there are a total of 36 possible outcomes. (Can you list these outcomes, or sample points?) Of these, 4 result in a sum of 2, 3, or 12; 24 result in a sum of 4, 5, 6, 8, 9, or 10; and 8 result in a sum of 7 or 11. Using the rules of probability established in Chapter 3, you can show that the actual probability distribution for x is $p(-\$5) = 4/36 = .1111$, $p(\$0) = 24/36 = .6667$, and $p(\$5) = 8/36 = .2222$.

━■ **Now Work Exercise 4.11**

Examples 4.4 and 4.5 illustrate how the probability distribution for a discrete random variable can be derived, but for many practical situations, the task is much more difficult. Fortunately, many experiments and associated discrete random variables observed in business possess identical characteristics. Thus, you might observe a random variable in a marketing experiment that possesses the same characteristics as a random variable observed in accounting, economics, or management. We classify random variables according to type of experiment, derive the probability distribution for each of the different types, and then use the appropriate probability distribution when a particular type of random variable is observed in a practical situation. The probability distributions for most commonly occurring discrete random variables have already been derived. This fact simplifies the problem of finding the appropriate probability distributions for the business analyst, as the next example illustrates.

Example **4.6**

Probability Distribution Using a Formula—Texas Droughts

Problem A drought is a period of abnormal dry weather that causes serious problems in the farming industry of the region. University of Arizona researchers used historical annual data to study the severity of droughts in Texas. The researchers showed that the distribution of x, the number of consecutive years that must be sampled until a dry (drought) year is observed, can be modeled using the formula

$$p(x) = (.3)(.7)^{x-1}, x = 1, 2, 3, \ldots$$

Find the probability that exactly 3 years must be sampled before a drought year occurs.

Solution We want to find the probability that $x = 3$. Using the formula, we have

$$p(3) = (.3)(.7)^{3-1} = (.3)(.7)^2 = (.3)(.49) = .147$$

Thus, there is about a 15% chance that exactly 3 years must be sampled before a drought year occurs in Texas.

Look Back The probability of interest can also be derived using the principles of probability developed in Chapter 3. The event of interest is $N_1N_2D_3$, where N_1 represents no drought occurs in the first sampled year, N_2 represents no drought occurs in the second sampled year, and D_3 represents a drought occurs in the third sampled year. The researchers discovered that the probability of a drought occurring in any sampled year is .3 (and, consequently, the probability of no drought occurring in any sampled year is .7). Using the multiplicative rule of probability for independent events, the probability of interest is $(.7)(.7)(.3) = .147$.

━■ **Now Work Exercise 4.29**

Because probability distributions are analogous to the relative frequency distributions of Chapter 2, it should be no surprise that the mean and standard deviation are useful descriptive measures.

If a discrete random variable x were observed a very large number of times, and the data generated were arranged in a relative frequency distribution, the relative

Figure 4.5

Probability distribution for a two-coin toss

frequency distribution would be indistinguishable from the probability distribution for the random variable. Thus, the probability distribution for a random variable is a theoretical model for the relative frequency distribution of a population. To the extent that the two distributions are equivalent (and we will assume they are), the probability distribution for x possesses a mean μ and a variance σ^2 that are identical to the corresponding descriptive measures for the population. How can you find the mean value for a random variable? We illustrate the procedure with an example.

Examine the probability distribution for x (the number of heads observed in the toss of two fair coins) in Figure 4.5. Try to locate the mean of the distribution intuitively. We may reason that the mean μ of this distribution is equal to 1 as follows: In a large number of experiments—say, 100,000—$\frac{1}{4}$ (or 25,000) should result in $x = 0$, $\frac{1}{2}$ (or 50,000) in $x = 1$, and $\frac{1}{4}$ (or 25,000) in $x = 2$ heads. Therefore, the average number of heads is

$$\mu = \frac{0(25,000) + 1(50,000) + 2(25,000)}{100,000} = 0\left(\tfrac{1}{4}\right) + 1\left(\tfrac{1}{2}\right) + 2\left(\tfrac{1}{4}\right) = 0 + \tfrac{1}{2} + \tfrac{1}{2} = 1$$

Note that to get the population mean of the random variable x, we multiply each possible value of x by its probability $p(x)$ and then sum this product over all possible values of x. The *mean of x* is also referred to as the *expected value of x,* denoted $E(x)$.

The **mean**, or **expected value,** of a discrete random variable x is

$$\mu = E(x) = \sum x p(x)$$

Expected is a mathematical term and should not be interpreted as it is typically used. Specifically, a random variable might never be equal to its "expected value." Rather, the expected value is the mean of the probability distribution or a measure of its central tendency. You can think of μ as the mean value of x in a *very large* (actually, *infinite*) number of repetitions of the experiment, where the values of x occur in proportions equivalent to the probabilities of x.

Example 4.7

Finding an Expected Value—An Insurance Application

Problem Suppose you work for an insurance company, and you sell a $10,000 one-year term insurance policy at an annual premium of $290. Actuarial tables show that the probability of death during the next year for a person of your customer's age, sex, health, etc., is .001. What is the expected gain (amount of money made by the company) for a policy of this type?

Solution The experiment is to observe whether the customer survives the upcoming year. The probabilities associated with the two sample points, Live and Die, are .999 and .001, respectively. The random variable you are interested in is the gain x, which can assume the values shown in the following table.

Gain, x	Sample Point	Probability
$290	Customer lives	.999
−$9,710	Customer dies	.001

If the customer lives, the company gains the $290 premium as profit. If the customer dies, the gain is negative because the company must pay $10,000, for a net "gain" of $(290 - 10,000) = -\$9,710$. The expected gain is therefore

$$\mu = E(x) = \sum x p(x)$$
$$= (290)(.999) + (-9,710)(.001) = \$280$$

In other words, if the company were to sell a very large number of one-year $10,000 policies to customers possessing the characteristics previously described, it would (on the average) net $280 per sale in the next year.

Look Back Note that $E(x)$ need not equal a possible value of x—that is, the expected value is $280, but x will equal either $290 or $-$9,710$ each time the experiment is performed (a policy is sold and a year elapses). The expected value is a measure of central tendency—and in this case represents the average over a very large number of one-year policies—but is not a possible value of x.

◼ Now Work Exercise 4.32a

We learned in Chapter 2 that the mean and other measures of central tendency tell only part of the story about a set of data. The same is true about probability distributions. We need to measure variability as well. Because a probability distribution can be viewed as a representation of a population, we will use the population variance to measure its variability.

The *population variance* σ^2 is defined as the average of the squared distance of x from the population mean μ. Because x is a random variable, the squared distance, $(x - \mu)^2$, is also a random variable. Using the same logic used to find the mean value of x, we find the mean value of $(x - \mu)^2$ by multiplying all possible values of $(x - \mu)^2$ by $p(x)$ and then summing over all possible x values.* This quantity,

$$E[(x - \mu)^2] = \sum (x - \mu)^2 p(x)$$

is also called the *expected value of the squared distance from the mean;* that is, $\sigma^2 = E[(x - \mu)^2]$. The standard deviation of x is defined as the square root of the variance σ^2.

The **variance** of a **discrete random variable** x is

$$\sigma^2 = E[(x - \mu)^2] = \sum (x - \mu)^2 p(x)$$

The **standard deviation** of a **discrete random variable** is equal to the square root of the variance, i.e., $\sigma = \sqrt{\sigma^2} = \sqrt{\Sigma(x - \mu)^2 \, p(x)}$.

Knowing the mean μ and standard deviation σ of the probability distribution of x, in conjunction with Chebyshev's Rule (Table 2.6, p. 80) and the Empirical Rule (Table 2.7, p. 80), we can make statements about the likelihood that values of x will fall within the intervals $\mu \pm \sigma$, $\mu \pm 2\sigma$, and $\mu \pm 3\sigma$. These probabilities are given in the box.

Probability Rules for a Discrete Random Variable

Let x be a discrete random variable with probability distribution $p(x)$, mean μ, and standard deviation σ. Then, depending on the shape of $p(x)$, the following probability statements can be made:

	Chebyshev's Rule	Empirical Rule
	Applies to any probability distribution (see Figure 4.6a)	Applies to probability distributions that are mound-shaped and symmetric (see Figure 4.6b)
$P(\mu - \sigma < x < \mu + \sigma)$	≥ 0	$\approx .68$
$P(\mu - 2\sigma < x < \mu + 2\sigma)$	$\geq \frac{3}{4}$	$\approx .95$
$P(\mu - 3\sigma < x < \mu + 3\sigma)$	$\geq \frac{8}{9}$	≈ 1.00

---

*It can be shown that $E[(x - \mu^2)] = E(x^2) - \mu^2$, where $E(x^2) = \Sigma x^2 p(x)$. Note the similarity between this expression and the shortcut formula $\Sigma(x - \bar{x})^2 = \Sigma x^2 - \frac{(\Sigma x)^2}{n}$ given in Chapter 2.

Figure 4.6

Shapes of two probability distributions for a discrete random variable x

a. Skewed distribution

b. Mound-shaped, symmetric

Example	4.8

Finding μ and σ—Internet Business Venture

Problem Suppose you invest a fixed sum of money in each of five Internet business ventures. Assume you know that 70% of such ventures are successful, the outcomes of the ventures are independent of one another, and the probability distribution for the number, x, of successful ventures out of five is

x	0	1	2	3	4	5
$p(x)$	.002	.029	.132	.309	.360	.168

a. Find $\mu = E(x)$. Interpret the result.

b. Find $\sigma = \sqrt{E[(x - \mu)^2]}$. Interpret the result.

c. Graph $p(x)$. Locate μ and the interval $\mu \pm 2\sigma$ on the graph. Use either Chebyshev's Rule or the Empirical Rule to approximate the probability that x falls in this interval. Compare this result with the actual probability.

d. Would you expect to observe fewer than two successful ventures out of five?

Solution

a. Applying the formula,

$$\mu = E(x) = \sum xp(x) = 0(.002) + 1(.029) + 2(.132) + 3(.309)$$
$$+ 4(.360) + 5(.168) = 3.50$$

On average, the number of successful ventures out of five will equal 3.5. Remember that this expected value has meaning only when the experiment—investing in five Internet business ventures—is repeated a large number of times.

b. Now we calculate the variance of x:

$$\sigma^2 = E[(x - \mu)^2] = \sum (x - \mu)^2 p(x)$$
$$= (0 - 3.5)^2(.002) + (1 - 3.5)^2(.029) + (2 - 3.5)^2(.132)$$
$$+ (3 - 3.5)^2(.309) + (4 - 3.5)^2(.360) + (5 - 3.5)^2(.168)$$
$$= 1.05$$

Thus, the standard deviation is

$$\sigma = \sqrt{\sigma^2} = \sqrt{1.05} = 1.02$$

This value measures the spread of the probability distribution of x, the number of successful ventures out of five. A more useful interpretation is obtained by answering parts **c** and **d.**

Figure 4.7

Graph of $p(x)$ for Example 4.8

c. The graph of $p(x)$ in histogram form is shown in Figure 4.7 with the mean μ and the interval $\mu \pm 2\sigma = 3.50 \pm 2(1.02) = 3.50 \pm 2.04 = (1.46, 5.54)$ shown on the graph. Note particularly that $\mu = 3.5$ locates the center of the probability distribution. Because this distribution is a theoretical relative frequency distribution that is moderately mound-shaped (see Figure 4.7), we expect (from Chebyshev's Rule) at least 75% and, more likely (from the Empirical Rule), approximately 95% of observed x values to fall in the interval $\mu \pm 2\sigma$—that is, between 1.46 and 5.54. You can see from Figure 4.7 that the actual probability that x falls in the interval $\mu \pm 2\sigma$ includes the sum of $p(x)$ for the values $x = 2$, $x = 3$, $x = 4$, and $x = 5$. This probability is $p(2) + p(3) + p(4) + p(5) = .132 + .309 + .360 + .168 = .969$. Therefore, 96.9% of the probability distribution lies within 2 standard deviations of the mean. This percentage is consistent with both Chebyshev's Rule and the Empirical Rule.

d. Fewer than two successful ventures out of five implies that $x = 0$ or $x = 1$. Because both these values of x lie outside the interval $\mu \pm 2\sigma$, we know from the Empirical Rule that such a result is unlikely (approximate probability of .05). The exact probability, $P(x \le 1)$, is $p(0) + p(1) = .002 + .029 = .031$. Consequently, in a single experiment where we invest in five Internet business ventures, we would not expect to observe fewer than two successful ones.

■ **Now Work Exercise 4.17**

Exercises 4.11–4.39

Learning the Mechanics

4.11 A discrete random variable x can assume five possible values: 20, 21, 22, 23, and 24. The following Minitab histogram shows the likelihood of each value.
  a. What is $p(22)$?
  b. What is the probability that x equals 20 or 24?
  c. What is $P(x \le 23)$?

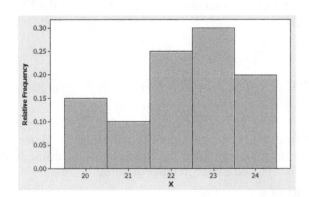

4.12 The random variable x has the following discrete probability distribution:

x	1	3	5	7	9
$p(x)$	.1	.2	.4	.2	.1

  a. List the values x may assume.
  b. What value of x is most probable?
  c. Display the probability distribution as a graph.
  d. Find $P(x = 7)$.
  e. Find $P(x \ge 5)$.
  f. Find $P(x > 2)$.
  g. Find $E(x)$.

4.13 A discrete random variable x can assume five possible values: 2, 3, 5, 8, and 10. Its probability distribution is shown here:

x	2	3	5	8	10
$p(x)$	.15	.10	–	.25	.25

  a. What is $p(5)$?
  b. What is the probability that x equals 2 or 10?
  c. What is $P(x \le 8)$?

4.14 Explain why each of the following is or is not a valid probability distribution for a discrete random variable x:

  a.
x	0	1	2	3
$p(x)$	.1	.3	.3	.2

  b.
x	−2	−1	0
$p(x)$	.25	.50	.25

  c.
x	4	9	20
$p(x)$	−.3	.4	.3

  d.
x	2	3	5	6
$p(x)$	.15	.15	.45	.35

4.15 A die is tossed. Let x be the number of spots observed on the upturned face of the die.
  a. Find the probability distribution of x and display it in tabular form.
  b. Display the probability distribution of x in graphical form.

4.16 Toss three fair coins and let x equal the number of heads observed.
  a. Identify the sample points associated with this experiment and assign a value of x to each sample point.

b. Calculate $p(x)$ for each value of x.
c. Construct a graph for $p(x)$.
d. What is $P(x = 2$ or $x = 3)$?

● Applet Exercise 4.1

Use the applet *Random Numbers* to generate a list of 25 numbers between 1 and 3, inclusive. Let x represent a number chosen from this list.

a. What are the possible values of x?
b. Write a probability distribution for x in table form.
c. Use the probability distribution in part **b** to find the expected value of x.
d. Let y be a number randomly chosen from the set $\{1, 2, 3\}$. Write a probability distribution for y in table form and use it to find the expected value of y.
e. Compare the expected values of x and y in parts **c** and **d**. Why should these two numbers be approximately the same?

● Applet Exercise 4.2

Run the applet *Simulating the Probability of a Head with a Fair Coin* 10 times with $n = 2$, resetting between runs, to simulate flipping two coins 10 times. Count and record the number of heads each time. Let x represent the number of heads on a single flip of the two coins.

a. What are the possible values of x?
b. Use the results of the simulation to write a probability distribution for x in table form and then use it to find the expected value of x.
c. Explain why the expected value in part **b** should be close to 1.

4.17 Consider the probability distribution shown here:
NW

x	-4	-3	-2	-1	0	1	2	3	4
$p(x)$	.02	.07	.10	.15	.30	.18	.10	.06	.02

a. Calculate μ, σ^2, and σ.
b. Graph $p(x)$. Locate μ, $\mu - 2\sigma$, and $\mu + 2\sigma$ on the graph.
c. What is the probability that x is in the interval $\mu \pm 2\sigma$?

4.18 Consider the probability distribution for the random variable x shown here:

x	10	20	30	40	50	60
$p(x)$	.05	.20	.30	.25	.10	.10

a. Find μ, σ^2, and σ.
b. Graph $p(x)$.
c. Locate μ and the interval $\mu \pm 2\sigma$ on your graph. What is the probability that x will fall within the interval $\mu \pm 2\sigma$?

4.19 Consider the probability distributions shown here:

x	0	1	2	y	0	1	2
$p(x)$	.3	.4	.3	$p(y)$	.1	.8	.1

a. Use your intuition to find the mean for each distribution. How did you arrive at your choice?

b. Which distribution appears to be more variable? Why?
c. Calculate μ and σ^2 for each distribution. Compare these answers to your answers in parts **a** and **b**.

Applying the Concepts—Basic

4.20 **Size of TV households.** According to Nielsen's *Television Audience Report, 2010 & 2011*, 26% of all U.S. TV households have a size of 1 person, 32% have a household size of 2, 17% have a household size of 3, and 25% have a household size of 4 or more. Let x represent the size (number of people) in a randomly selected TV household.

a. List the possible values of the discrete random variable x.
b. What is the probability that $x = 1$?
c. What is the probability that $x \geq 4$?
d. Explain why you cannot compute $E(x)$.

4.21 **NHTSA crash tests.** Refer to the NHTSA crash tests of new car models, Exercise 4.3 (p. 188). A summary of the driver-side star ratings for the 98 cars in the file is reproduced in the accompanying Minitab printout. Assume that one of the 98 cars is selected at random and let x equal the number of stars in the car's driver-side star rating.

Tally for Discrete Variables: DRIVSTAR

DRIVSTAR	Count	Percent
2	4	4.08
3	17	17.35
4	59	60.20
5	18	18.37
N=	98	

a. Use the information in the printout to find the probability distribution for x.
b. Find $P(x = 5)$.
c. Find $P(x \leq 2)$.
d. Find $\mu = E(x)$ and practically interpret the result.

4.22 **Ages of "dot-com" employees.** The age distribution for the employees of a highly successful "dot-com" company headquartered in Atlanta is shown in the next table. An employee is to be randomly selected from this population.

Age	20	21	22	23	24	25	26	27	28	29	30	31	32	33
Proportion	.02	.04	.05	.07	.04	.02	.07	.02	.11	.07	.09	.13	.15	.12

Source: Data provided by P. George Benson, University of Charleston.

a. Can the relative frequency distribution in the table be interpreted as a probability distribution? Explain.
b. Graph the probability distribution.
c. What is the probability that the randomly selected employee is over 30 years of age? Over 40 years of age? Under 30 years of age?
d. What is the probability that the randomly selected employee will be 25 or 26 years old?

4.23 **Downloading "apps" to your cell phone.** According to an August 2011 survey by the Pew Internet & American Life Project, nearly 40% of adult cell phone owners have downloaded an application ("app") to their cell phone. The next table gives the probability distribution for x, the number of "apps" used at least once a week by cell phone owners who have downloaded an "app" to their phone. (The probabilities in the table are based on information from the Pew Internet & American Life Project survey.)

Number of "Apps" Used, x	p(x)
0	.17
1	.10
2	.11
3	.11
4	.10
5	.10
6	.07
7	.05
8	.03
9	.02
10	.02
11	.02
12	.02
13	.02
14	.01
15	.01
16	.01
17	.01
18	.01
19	.005
20	.005

a. Show that the properties of a probability distribution for a discrete random variable are satisfied.
b. Find $P(x \geq 10)$.
c. Find the mean and variance of x.
d. Give an interval that will contain the value of x with a probability of at least .75.

4.24 **Choosing portable grill displays.** Refer to the *Journal of Consumer Research* (Mar. 2003) marketing study of influencing consumer choices by offering undesirable alternatives, Exercise 3.23 (p. 142). Recall that each of 124 college students selected showroom displays for portable grills. Five different displays (representing five different-sized grills) were available, but the students were instructed to select only three displays in order to maximize purchases of Grill #2 (a smaller-sized grill). The table shows the grill display combinations and the number of times each was selected by the 124 students. Suppose one of the 124 students is selected at random. Let x represent the sum of the grill numbers selected by this student. (This value is an indicator of the size of the grills selected.)
a. Find the probability distribution for x.
b. What is the probability that x exceeds 10?

Grill Display Combination	Number of Students
1-2-3	35
1-2-4	8
1-2-5	42
2-3-4	4
2-3-5	1
2-4-5	34

Source: Based on Hamilton, R. W. "Why do people suggest what they do not want? Using context effects to influence others' choices," *Journal of Consumer Research*, Vol. 29, Mar. 2003 (Table 1).

4.25 **Do social robots walk or roll?** Refer to the *International Conference on Social Robotics* (Vol. 6414, 2010) study of the trend in the design of social robots, Exercise 2.3 (p. 48).

Recall that in a random sample of 106 social (or service) robots designed to entertain, educate, and care for human users, 63 were built with legs only, 20 with wheels only, 8 with both legs and wheels, and 15 with neither legs nor wheels. Assume the following: Of the 63 robots with legs only, 50 have two legs, 5 have three legs, and 8 have four legs; of the 8 robots with both legs and wheels, all 8 have two legs. Suppose one of the 106 social robots is randomly selected. Let x equal the number of legs on the robot.
a. List the possible values of x.
b. Find the probability distribution of x.
c. Find $E(x)$ and give a practical interpretation of its value.

4.26 **Predicting when a Florida hurricane occurs.** Refer to the *Southeastern Geographer* (Summer 2009) comprehensive analysis of damages caused by Florida hurricanes, Exercise 3.12 (p. 140). In an effort to minimize the monetary losses that result from a devastating Florida hurricane, part of the researchers' analysis included a graphic showing the sequence number of tropical storms within a season that are most likely to develop into a hurricane. Data for 67 hurricanes are summarized in the table. Let x represent the sequence number of a Florida tropical storm within a season that develops into a hurricane.

Sequence of Storm	Number That Develop into Hurricanes
1	4
2	10
3	5
4	6
5	11
6	5
7	5
8	5
9	4
10	2
11	5
12	1
13	1
14	1
15	1
22	1

Source: Based on Malmstadt, J., Scheitlin, K., & Elsner, J. "Florida Hurricanes and Damage Costs," *Southeastern Geographer*, Vol. 49, No. 2, Summer 2009 (adapted from Figure 3).

a. Explain why x represents a discrete random variable.
b. Specify the probability distribution for x.
c. Find $P(x = 5)$.
d. Find $P(x < 5)$.
e. Find $E(x)$ and interpret the result.
f. Is it likely to observe a hurricane after the 15th tropical storm of the season? Explain.

Applying the Concepts—Intermediate

4.27 **Solar energy cells.** According to *Wired* (June 2008), 35% of the world's solar energy cells are manufactured in China. Consider a random sample of five solar energy cells and let x represent the number in the sample that are manufactured in China. In the next section, we show that the probability distribution for x is given by the formula,

$$p(x) = \frac{(5!)(.35)^x(.65)^{5-x}}{(x!)(5-x)!}, \text{ where}$$

$$n! = (n)(n-1)(n-2)\cdots(2)(1)$$

a. Explain why x is a discrete random variable.
b. Find $p(x)$ for $x = 0, 1, 2, 3, 4,$ and 5.
c. Show that the properties for a discrete probability distribution are satisfied.
d. Find the probability that at least four of the five solar energy cells in the sample are manufactured in China.

4.28 USDA chicken inspection. In Exercise 3.17 (p. 141) you learned that one in every 100 slaughtered chickens passes USDA inspection with fecal contamination. Consider a random sample of three slaughtered chickens that all pass USDA inspection. Let x equal the number of chickens in the sample that have fecal contamination.
a. Find $p(x)$ for $x = 0, 1, 2, 3$.
b. Graph $p(x)$.
c. Find $P(x \le 1)$.

4.29 Contaminated gun cartridges. A weapons manufacturer uses a liquid propellant to produce gun cartridges. During the manufacturing process, the propellant can get mixed with another liquid to produce a contaminated cartridge. A University of South Florida statistician, hired by the company to investigate the level of contamination in the stored cartridges, found that 23% of the cartridges in a particular lot were contaminated. Suppose you randomly sample (without replacement) gun cartridges from this lot until you find a contaminated one. Let x be the number of cartridges sampled until a contaminated one is found. It is known that the probability distribution for x is given by the formula

$$p(x) = (.23)(.77)^{x-1}, x = 1, 2, 3, \ldots$$

a. Find $p(1)$. Interpret this result.
b. Find $p(5)$. Interpret this result.
c. Find $P(x \ge 2)$. Interpret this result.

4.30 The "last name" effect in purchasing. The *Journal of Consumer Research* (August 2011) published a study demonstrating the "last name" effect—i.e., the tendency for consumers with last names that begin with a later letter of the alphabet to purchase an item before consumers with last names that begin with earlier letters. To facilitate the analysis, the researchers assigned a number, x, to each consumer based on the first letter of the consumer's last name. For example, last names beginning with "A" were assigned $x = 1$; last names beginning with "B" were assigned $x = 2$; and last names beginning with "Z" were assigned $x = 26$.
a. If the first letters of consumers' last names are equally likely, find the probability distribution for x.
b. Find $E(x)$ using the probability distribution, part **a**. If possible, give a practical interpretation of this value.
c. Do you believe the probability distribution, part **a**, is realistic? Explain. How might you go about estimating the true probability distribution for x?

4.31 Mailrooms contaminated with anthrax. During autumn 2001, there was a highly publicized outbreak of anthrax cases among U.S. Postal Service workers. In *Chance* (Spring 2002), research statisticians discussed the problem of sampling mailrooms for the presence of anthrax spores. Let x equal the number of mailrooms contaminated with anthrax spores in a random sample of n mailrooms

selected from a population of N mailrooms. The researchers showed that the probability distribution for x is given by the formula

$$p(x) = \frac{\binom{k}{x}\binom{N-k}{n-x}}{\binom{N}{n}}$$

where k is the number of contaminated mailrooms in the population. (In section 4.4 we identify this probability distribution as the *hypergeometric distribution*.) Suppose $N = 100$, $n = 3$, and $k = 20$.
a. Find $p(0)$. **b.** Find $p(1)$.
c. Find $p(2)$. **d.** Find $p(3)$.

4.32 Investment risk analysis. The risk of a portfolio of financial assets is sometimes called *investment risk*. In general, investment risk is typically measured by computing the variance or standard deviation of the probability distribution that describes the decision maker's potential outcomes (gains or losses). The greater the variation in potential outcomes, the greater the uncertainty faced by the decision maker; the smaller the variation in potential outcomes, the more predictable the decision maker's gains or losses. The two discrete probability distributions given in the next table were developed from historical data. They describe the potential total physical damage losses next year to the fleets of delivery trucks of two different firms.

Firm A		Firm B	
Loss Next Year	Probability	Loss Next Year	Probability
$ 0	.01	$ 0	.00
500	.01	200	.01
1,000	.01	700	.02
1,500	.02	1,200	.02
2,000	.35	1,700	.15
2,500	.30	2,200	.30
3,000	.25	2,700	.30
3,500	.02	3,200	.15
4,000	.01	3,700	.02
4,500	.01	4,200	.02
5,000	.01	4,700	.01

a. Verify that both firms have the same expected total physical damage loss.
b. Compute the standard deviation of each probability distribution and determine which firm faces the greater risk of physical damage to its fleet next year.

4.33 Ryder Cup miracle in golf. The Ryder Cup is a 3-day golf tournament played between a team of golf professionals from the United States and a team from Europe. A total of 28 matches are played between the teams; one point is awarded to the team winning a match and half a point is awarded to each team if the match ends in a tie (draw). The team with the most points wins the tournament. In 1999, the United States was losing 10 points to 6 when it miraculously won 8.5 of a possible 12 points on the last day of the tournament to seal the win. On the last day, 12 single matches are played. A total of 8.5 points can be won in a variety of ways, as shown in the next table. Given one team scores at least 8.5 points on the last day of the tournament, *Chance* (Fall 2009) determined the probabilities of each of these outcomes assuming each team is equally likely to win a match. Let x be the points scored by the winning team on the last day of the tournament when the team scores at least 8.5 points. Find the probability distribution of x.

Wins	Ties	Points	Probability
5	7	8.5	.000123
6	5	8.5	.008823
6	6	9.0	.000456
7	3	8.5	.128030
7	4	9.0	.020086
7	5	9.5	.001257
8	1	8.5	.325213
8	2	9.0	.153044
8	3	9.5	.032014
8	4	10.0	.002514
9	0	9.0	.115178
9	1	9.5	.108400
9	2	10.0	.032901
9	3	10.5	.003561
10	0	10.0	.034552
10	1	10.5	.021675
10	2	11.0	.003401
11	0	11.0	.006284
11	1	11.0	.001972
12	0	12.0	.000518

4.34 **Stock market participation and IQ.** Refer to *The Journal of Finance* (December 2011) study of whether the decision to invest in the stock market is dependent on IQ, Exercise 3.42 (p. 153). Recall that an IQ score (from a low score of 1 to a high score of 9) was determined for each in a sample of 158,044 Finnish citizens. Also recorded was whether or not the citizen invested in the stock market. The accompanying table gives the number of Finnish citizens in each IQ score/ investment category. Which group of Finnish citizens (market investors or noninvestors) has the highest average IQ score?

IQ Score	Invest in Market	No Investment	Totals
1	893	4,659	5,552
2	1,340	9,409	10,749
3	2,009	9,993	12,002
4	5,358	19,682	25,040
5	8,484	24,640	33,124
6	10,270	21,673	31,943
7	6,698	11,260	17,958
8	5,135	7,010	12,145
9	4,464	5,067	9,531
Totals	44,651	113,393	158,044

Source: Based on Grinblatt, M., Keloharju, M., & Linnainaa, J. "IQ and Stock Market Participation," *The Journal of Finance*, Vol. 66, No. 6, December 2011 (data from Table 1 and Figure 1).

4.35 **Expected loss due to flood damage.** The National Weather Service issues precipitation forecasts that indicate the likelihood of measurable precipitation ($\geq .01$ inch) at a specific point (the official rain gauge) during a given time period. Suppose that if a measurable amount of rain falls during the next 24 hours, a river will reach flood stage and a business will incur damages of $300,000.

The National Weather Service has indicated that there is a 30% chance of a measurable amount of rain during the next 24 hours.
a. Construct the probability distribution that describes the potential flood damages.
b. Find the firm's expected loss due to flood damage.

4.36 **Expected Lotto winnings.** Most states offer weekly lotteries to generate revenue for the state. Despite the long odds of winning, residents continue to gamble on the lottery each week. In SIA, Chapter 3 (p. 128), you learned that the chance of winning Florida's Pick-6 Lotto game is 1 in approximately 23 million. Suppose you buy a $1 Lotto ticket in anticipation of winning the $7 million grand prize. Calculate your expected net winnings. Interpret the result.

4.37 **The showcase showdown.** On the popular television game show *The Price Is Right*, contestants can play "The Showcase Showdown." The game involves a large wheel with 20 nickel values, 5, 10, 15, 20,...,95, 100, marked on it. Contestants spin the wheel once or twice, with the objective of obtaining the highest total score *without going over a dollar* (*100*). [According to the *American Statistician* (Aug. 1995), the optimal strategy for the first spinner in a three-player game is to spin a second time only if the value of the initial spin is 65 or less.] Let x represent the total score for a single contestant playing "The Showcase Showdown." Assume a "fair" wheel (i.e., a wheel with equally likely outcomes). If the total of the player's spins exceeds 100, the total score is set to 0.
a. If the player is permitted only one spin of the wheel, find the probability distribution for x.
b. Refer to part **a.** Find $E(x)$ and interpret this value.
c. Refer to part **a.** Give a range of values within which x is likely to fall.
d. Suppose the player will spin the wheel twice, no matter what the outcome of the first spin. Find the probability distribution for x.
e. What assumption did you make to obtain the probability distribution, part **d**? Is it a reasonable assumption?
f. Find μ and σ for the probability distribution, part **d,** and interpret the results.
g. Refer to part **d.** What is the probability that in two spins the player's total score exceeds a dollar (i.e., is set to 0)?
h. Suppose the player obtains a 20 on the first spin and decides to spin again. Find the probability distribution for x.
i. Refer to part **h.** What is the probability that the player's total score exceeds a dollar?
j. Given the player obtains a 65 on the first spin and decides to spin again, find the probability that the player's total score exceeds a dollar.
k. Repeat part **j** for different first-spin outcomes. Use this information to suggest a strategy for the one-player game.

Applying the Concepts—Advanced

4.38 **Robot-sensor system configuration.** Engineers at Broadcom Corp. and Simon Fraser University collaborated on research involving a robot-sensor system in an unknown environment (*International Journal of Robotics Research*, Dec. 2004). As an example, the engineers presented the three-point, single-link robotic system shown in the accompanying figure. Each point (A, B, or C) in the physical space of the system has either an "obstacle" status or a "free" status. There are two single links in the system: A ↔ B and B ↔ C. A link has a "free" status if and only if both points in the link are "free." Otherwise, the link has an "obstacle" status. Of interest is the random variable Y, the total number of links in the system that are "free."

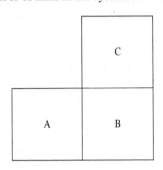

a. List the possible values of Y for the system.
b. The researchers stated that the probability of any point in the system having a "free" status is .5. Assuming the three points in the system operate independently, find the probability distribution for Y.

4.39 Parlay card betting. Odds makers try to predict which professional and college football teams will win and by how much (the *spread*). If the odds makers do this accurately, adding the spread to the underdog's score should make the final score a tie. Suppose a bookie will give you $6 for every $1 you risk if you pick the winners in three games (adjusted by the spread) on a "parlay" card. Thus, for every $1 bet, you will either lose $1 or gain $5. What is the bookie's expected earnings per dollar wagered?

4.3 The Binomial Distribution

Many experiments result in *dichotomous* responses—that is, responses for which there exist two possible alternatives, such as Yes-No, Pass-Fail, Defective-Nondefective, or Male-Female. A simple example of such an experiment is the coin-toss experiment. A coin is tossed a number of times, say 10. Each toss results in one of two outcomes, Head or Tail. Ultimately, we are interested in the probability distribution of x, the number of heads observed. Many other experiments are equivalent to tossing a coin (either balanced or unbalanced) a fixed number n of times and observing the number x of times that one of the two possible outcomes occurs. Random variables that possess these characteristics are called **binomial random variables.**

Public opinion and consumer preference polls (e.g., the CNN, Gallup, and Harris polls) frequently yield observations on binomial random variables. For example, suppose a sample of 100 current customers is selected from a firm's database and each person is asked whether he or she prefers the firm's product (a Head) or prefers a competitor's product (a Tail). Suppose we are interested in x, the number of customers in the sample who prefer the firm's product. Sampling 100 customers is analogous to tossing the coin 100 times. Thus, you can see that consumer preference polls like the one described here are real-life equivalents of coin-toss experiments. We have been describing a **binomial experiment;** it is identified by the following characteristics.

Characteristics of a Binomial Experiment

1. The experiment consists of n identical trials.
2. There are only two possible outcomes on each trial. We will denote one outcome by S (for success) and the other by F (for failure).
3. The probability of S remains the same from trial to trial. This probability is denoted by p, and the probability of F is denoted by q. Note that $q = 1 - p$.
4. The trials are independent.
5. The binomial random variable x is the number of S's in n trials.

Example	4.9

**Assessing Whether *x*
Is Binomial—Business
Problems**

Problem For the following examples, decide whether *x* is a binomial random variable.

a. You randomly select 3 bonds out of a possible 10 for an investment portfolio. Unknown to you, 8 of the 10 will maintain their present value, and the other 2 will lose value due to a change in their ratings. Let *x* be the number of the 3 bonds you select that lose value.

b. Before marketing a new product on a large scale, many companies will conduct a consumer preference survey to determine whether the product is likely to be successful. Suppose a company develops a new diet soda and then conducts a taste preference survey in which 100 randomly chosen consumers state their preferences among the new soda and the two leading sellers. Let *x* be the number of the 100 who choose the new brand over the two others.

c. Some surveys are conducted by using a method of sampling other than simple random sampling (defined in Chapter 3). For example, suppose a television cable company plans to conduct a survey to determine the fraction of households in the city that would use the cable television service. The sampling method is to choose a city block at random and then survey every household on that block. This sampling technique is called *cluster sampling*. Suppose 10 blocks are so sampled, producing a total of 124 household responses. Let *x* be the number of the 124 households that would use the television cable service.

BIOGRAPHY

**JACOB BERNOULLI
(1654–1705)**

The Bernoulli Distribution

Son of a magistrate and spice maker in Basel, Switzerland, Jacob Bernoulli completed a degree in theology at the University of Basel. While at the university, however, he studied mathematics secretly and against the will of his father. Jacob taught mathematics to his younger brother Johan, and they both went on to become distinguished European mathematicians. At first the brothers collaborated on the problems of the time (e.g., calculus); unfortunately, they later became bitter mathematical rivals. Jacob applied his philosophical training and mathematical intuition to probability and the theory of games of chance, where he developed the Law of Large Numbers. In his book *Ars Conjectandi,* published in 1713 (eight years after his death), the binomial distribution was first proposed. Jacob showed that the binomial distribution is a sum of independent 0–1 variables, now known as "Bernoulli" random variables.

Solution

a. In checking the binomial characteristics in the box, a problem arises with both characteristic 3 (probabilities remaining the same from trial to trial) and characteristic 4 (independence). The probability that the first bond you pick loses value is clearly $\frac{2}{10}$. Now suppose the first bond you picked was 1 of the 2 that will lose value. This reduces the chance that the second bond you pick will lose value to $\frac{1}{9}$ because now only 1 of the 9 remaining bonds are in that category. Thus, the choices you make are dependent, and therefore *x*, the number of 3 bonds you select that lose value, is *not* a binomial random variable.

b. Surveys that produce dichotomous responses and use random sampling techniques are classic examples of binomial experiments. In our example, each randomly selected consumer either states a preference for the new diet soda or does not. The sample of 100 consumers is a very small proportion of the totality of potential consumers, so the response of one would be, for all practical purposes, independent of another.* Thus, *x* is a binomial random variable.

c. This example is a survey with dichotomous responses (Yes or No to the cable service), but the sampling method is not simple random sampling. Again, the binomial characteristic of independent trials would probably not be satisfied. The responses of households within a particular block would be dependent because the households within a block tend to be similar with respect to income, level of education, and general interests. Thus, the binomial model would not be satisfactory for *x* if the cluster sampling technique were employed.

Look Back Nonbinomial random variables with two outcomes on every trial typically occur because they do not satisfy characteristics 3 or 4 of a binomial distribution.

■ **Now Work Exercise 4.49a**

*In most real-life applications of the binomial distribution, the population of interest has a finite number of elements (trials), denoted *N*. When *N* is large and the sample size *n* is small relative to *N*, say $n/N \leq .05$, the sampling procedure, for all practical purposes, satisfies the conditions of a binomial experiment.

Example   4.10

Deriving the Binomial Probability Distribution in a PC Purchase Application

Problem A computer retailer sells both desktop and laptop personal computers (PCs) online. Assume that 80% of the PCs that the retailer sells online are desktops and 20% are laptops.

a. Use the steps given in Chapter 3 (box on p. 135) to find the probability that all of the next four online PC purchases are laptops.

b. Find the probability that three of the next four online PC purchases are laptops.

c. Let x represent the number of the next four online PC purchases that are laptops. Explain why x is a binomial random variable.

d. Use the answers to parts **a** and **b** to derive a formula for $p(x)$, the probability distribution of the binomial random variable x.

Solution

a. **1.** The first step is to define the experiment. Here we are interested in observing the type of PC purchased online by each of the next four (buying) customers: desktop (D) or laptop (L).

  2. Next, we list the sample points associated with the experiment. Each sample point consists of the purchase decisions made by the four online customers. For example, $DDDD$ represents the sample point that all four purchase desktop PCs, while $LDDD$ represents the sample point that customer 1 purchases a laptop, while customers 2, 3, and 4 purchase desktops. The tree diagram, Figure 4.8, shows that there are 16 sample points. These 16 sample points are also listed in Table 4.2.

  3. We now assign probabilities to the sample points. Note that each sample point can be viewed as the intersection of four customers' decisions and, assuming the

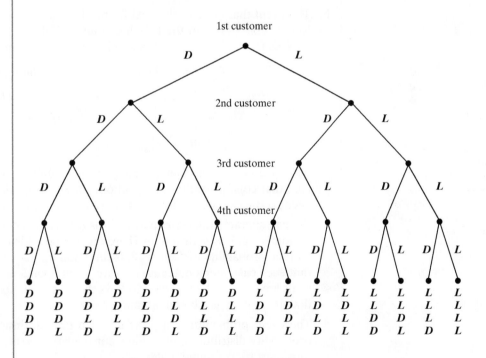

Figure 4.8

Tree diagram showing outcomes for PC purchases

Table 4.2	Sample Points for PC Experiment of Example 4.9			
$DDDD$	$LDDD$	$LLDD$	$DLLL$	LLLL
	$DLDD$	$LDLD$	$LDLL$	
	$DDLD$	$LDDL$	$LLDL$	
	$DDDL$	$DLLD$	$LLLD$	
		$DLDL$		
		$DDLL$		

decisions are made independently, the probability of each sample point can be obtained using the multiplicative rule, as follows:

$$P(DDDD) = P[(\text{customer 1 chooses desktop}) \cap (\text{customer 2 chooses desktop})$$
$$\cap (\text{customer 3 chooses desktop}) \cap (\text{customer 4 chooses desktop})]$$

$$= P(\text{customer 1 chooses desktop}) \times P(\text{customer 2 chooses}$$
$$\text{desktop}) \times P(\text{customer 3 chooses desktop})$$
$$\times P(\text{customer 4 chooses desktop})$$

$$= (.8)(.8)(.8)(.8) = (.8)^4 = .4096$$

All other sample point probabilities are calculated using similar reasoning. For example,

$$P(LDDD) = (.2)(.8)(.8)(.8) = (.2)(.8)^3 = .1024$$

You can check that this reasoning results in sample point probabilities that add to 1 over the 16 points in the sample space.

4. Finally, we add the appropriate sample point probabilities to obtain the desired event probability. The event of interest is that all four online customers purchase laptops. In Table 4.2 we find only one sample point, *LLLL*, contained in this event. All other sample points imply that at least one desktop is purchased. Thus,

$$P(\text{All four purchase laptops}) = P(LLLL) = (.2)^4 = .0016$$

That is, the probability is only 16 in 10,000 that all four customers purchase laptop PCs.

b. The event that three of the next four online buyers purchase laptops consists of the four sample points in the fourth column of Table 4.2: *DLLL, LDLL, LLDL,* and *LLLD.* To obtain the event probability, we add the sample point probabilities:

$$P(3 \text{ of next 4 customers purchase laptops})$$
$$= P(DLLL) + P(LDLL) + P(LLDL) + P(LLLD)$$
$$= (.2)^3(.8) + (.2)^3(.8) + (.2)^3(.8) + (.2)^3(.8)$$
$$= 4(.2)^3(.8) = .0256$$

Note that each of the four sample point probabilities is the same because each sample point consists of three *L*'s and one *D;* the order does not affect the probability because the customers' decisions are (assumed) independent.

c. We can characterize the experiment as consisting of four identical trials—the four customers' purchase decisions. There are two possible outcomes to each trial, *D* or *L,* and the probability of *L, p* = .2, is the same for each trial. Finally, we are assuming that each customer's purchase decision is independent of all others, so that the four trials are independent. Then it follows that *x,* the number of the next four purchases that are laptops, is a binomial random variable.

d. The event probabilities in parts **a** and **b** provide insight into the formula for the probability distribution $p(x)$. First, consider the event that three purchases are laptops (part **b**). We found that

$$P(x = 3) = (\text{Number of sample points for which } x = 3)$$
$$\times (.2)^{\text{Number of laptops purchased}} \times (.8)^{\text{Number of desktops purchased}}$$
$$= 4(.2)^3(.8)^1$$

In general, we can use combinatorial mathematics to count the number of sample points. For example,

Number of sample points for which $x = 3$

$= $ Number of different ways of selecting 3 of the 4 trials for L purchases

$$= \binom{4}{3} = \frac{4!}{3!(4-3)!} = \frac{4 \cdot 3 \cdot 2 \cdot 1}{(3 \cdot 2 \cdot 1) \cdot 1} = 4$$

The formula that works for any value of x can be deduced as follows. Because

$$P(x = 3) = \binom{4}{3}(.2)^3(.8)^1,$$

then $p(x) = \binom{4}{x}(.2)^x(.8)^{4-x}$

The component $\binom{4}{x}$ counts the number of sample points with x laptops and the component $(.2)^x(.8)^{4-x}$ is the probability associated with each sample point having x laptops. For the general binomial experiment, with n trials and probability of success p on each trial, the probability of x successes is

$$p(x) = \binom{n}{x} \cdot \underbrace{p^x(1-p)^{n-x}}$$

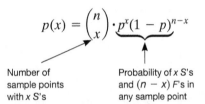

Number of
sample points
with x S's

Probability of x S's
and $(n - x)$ F's in
any sample point

Look Ahead In theory, you could always resort to the principles developed in this example to calculate binomial probabilities; list the sample points and sum their probabilities. However, as the number of trials (n) increases, the number of sample points grows very rapidly (the number of sample points is 2^n). Thus, we prefer the formula for calculating binomial probabilities because its use avoids listing sample points.

The binomial distribution* is summarized in the box.

The Binomial Probability Distribution

$$p(x) = \binom{n}{x}p^x q^{n-x} \quad (x = 0, 1, 2, \ldots , n)$$

where

$p = $ Probability of a success on a single trial

$q = 1 - p$

$n = $ Number of trials

$x = $ Number of successes in n trials

$n - x = $ Number of failures in n trials

$$\binom{n}{x} = \frac{n!}{x!(n-x)!}$$

As noted in Chapter 3, the symbol 5! means $5 \cdot 4 \cdot 3 \cdot 2 \cdot 1 = 120$. Similarly, $n! = n(n-1)(n-2)\ldots 3 \cdot 2 \cdot 1$; remember, $0! = 1$.

---

*The binomial distribution is so named because the probabilities, $p(x), x = 0, 1, \ldots , n$, are terms of the binomial expansion $(q + p)^n$.

| **Example** **4.11** | **Problem** A machine that produces stampings for automobile engines is malfunctioning and producing 10% defectives. The defective and nondefective stampings proceed from the machine in a random manner. If the next five stampings are tested, find the probability that three of them are defective. |

Applying the Binomial Distribution—Manufacture of Automobiles

Solution Let x equal the number of defectives in $n = 5$ trials. Then x is a binomial random variable with p, the probability that a single stamping will be defective, equal to .1, and $q = 1 - p = 1 - .1 = .9$. The probability distribution for x is given by the expression

$$p(x) = \binom{n}{x} p^x q^{n-x} = \binom{5}{x}(.1)^x(.9)^{5-x}$$

$$= \frac{5!}{x!(5-x)!}(.1)^x(.9)^{5-x} \qquad (x = 0, 1, 2, 3, 4, 5)$$

To find the probability of observing $x = 3$ defectives in a sample of $n = 5$, substitute $x = 3$ into the formula for $p(x)$ to obtain

$$p(3) = \frac{5!}{3!(5-3)!}(.1)^3(.9)^{5-3} = \frac{5!}{3!2!}(.1)^3(.9)^2$$

$$= \frac{5 \cdot 4 \cdot 3 \cdot 2 \cdot 1}{(3 \cdot 2 \cdot 1)(2 \cdot 1)}(.1)^3(.9)^2 = 10(.1)^3(.9)^2$$

$$= .0081$$

Look Back Note that the binomial formula tells us that there are 10 sample points having 3 defectives (check this by listing them), each with probability $(.1)^3(.9)^2$.

———————————— ■ **Now Work Exercise 4.47c**

The mean, variance, and standard deviation for the binomial random variable x are shown in the box.

Mean, Variance, and Standard Deviation for a Binomial Random Variable

Mean: $\mu = np$

Variance: $\sigma^2 = npq$

Standard deviation: $\sigma = \sqrt{npq}$

As we demonstrated in Chapter 2, the mean and standard deviation provide measures of the central tendency and variability, respectively, of a distribution. Thus, we can use μ and σ to obtain a rough visualization of the probability distribution for x when the calculation of the probabilities is too tedious. The next example illustrates this idea.

| **Example** **4.12** | **Problem** Refer to Example 4.11 and find the values of $p(0), p(1), p(2), p(4)$ and $p(5)$. Graph $p(x)$. Calculate the mean μ and standard deviation σ. Locate μ and the interval $\mu - 2\sigma$ to $\mu + 2\sigma$ on the graph. If the experiment were to be repeated many times, what proportion of the x observations would fall within the interval $\mu - 2\sigma$ to $\mu + 2\sigma$? |

Finding μ and σ—Automobile Manufacturing Application

Solution Again, $n = 5$, $p = .1$, and $q = .9$. Then, substituting into the formula for $p(x)$:

$$p(0) = \frac{5!}{0!(5-0)!}(.1)^0(.9)^{5-0} = \frac{5 \cdot 4 \cdot 3 \cdot 2 \cdot 1}{(1)(5 \cdot 4 \cdot 3 \cdot 2 \cdot 1)}(1)(.9)^5 = .59049$$

$$p(1) = \frac{5!}{1!(5-1)!}(.1)^1(.9)^{5-1} = 5(.1)(.9)^4 = .32805$$

$$p(2) = \frac{5!}{2!(5-2)!}(.1)^2(.9)^{5-2} = (10)(.1)^2(.9)^3 = .07290$$

$$p(3) = .0081 \text{ (from Example 4.11)}$$

$$p(4) = \frac{5!}{4!(5-4)!}(.1)^4(.9)^{5-4} = (5)(.1)^4(.9) = .00045$$

$$p(5) = \frac{5!}{5!(5-5)!}(.1)^5(.9)^{5-5} = (.1)^5 = .00001$$

The graph of $p(x)$ is shown as a probability histogram in Figure 4.9.

To calculate the values of μ and σ, substitute $n = 5$ and $p = .1$ into the following formulas:

$$\mu = np = (5)(.1) = .5$$
$$\sigma = \sqrt{npq} = \sqrt{(5)(.1)(.9)} = \sqrt{.45} = .67$$

To find the interval $\mu - 2\sigma$ to $\mu + 2\sigma$, we calculate

$$\mu - 2\sigma = .5 - 2(.67) = -.84$$
$$\mu + 2\sigma = .5 + 2(.67) = 1.84$$

Figure 4.9

The binomial distribution: $n = 5$, $p = .1$

If the experiment was repeated a large number of times, what proportion of the x observations would fall within the interval $\mu - 2\sigma$ to $\mu + 2\sigma$? You can see from Figure 4.9 that all observations equal to 0 or 1 will fall within the interval. The probabilities corresponding to these values are .5905 and .3280, respectively. Consequently, you would expect $.5905 + .3280 = .9185$, or approximately 91.9%, of the observations to fall within the interval $\mu - 2\sigma$ to $\mu + 2\sigma$.

Look Back This result again emphasizes that for most probability distributions, observations rarely fall more than 2 standard deviations from μ.

──────── ▪ Now Work Exercise 4.57

Using Tables and Software to Find Binomial Probabilities

Calculating binomial probabilities becomes tedious when n is large. For some values of n and p, the binomial probabilities have been tabulated in Table I in Appendix D. Part of Table I is shown in Table 4.3; a graph of the binomial probability distribution for $n = 10$ and $p = .10$ is shown in Figure 4.10. Table I actually contains a total of nine tables, labeled (a) through (i), each one corresponding to $n = 5, 6, 7, 8, 9, 10, 15, 20,$ and 25. In each of these tables, the columns correspond to values of p, and the rows correspond to values (k) of the random variable x. The entries in the table represent

Table 4.3	Reproduction of Part of Table I in Appendix D: Binomial Probabilities for $n = 10$												
k	p .01	.05	.10	.20	.30	.40	.50	.60	.70	.80	.90	.95	.99
0	.904	.599	.349	.107	.028	.006	.001	.000	.000	.000	.000	.000	.000
1	.996	.914	.736	.376	.149	.046	.011	.002	.000	.000	.000	.000	.000
2	1.000	.988	.930	.678	.383	.167	.055	.012	.002	.000	.000	.000	.000
3	1.000	.999	.987	.879	.650	.382	.172	.055	.011	.001	.000	.000	.000
4	1.000	1.000	.998	.967	.850	.633	.377	.166	.047	.006	.000	.000	.000
5	1.000	1.000	1.000	.994	.953	.834	.623	.367	.150	.033	.002	.000	.000
6	1.000	1.000	1.000	.999	.989	.945	.828	.618	.350	.121	.013	.001	.000
7	1.000	1.000	1.000	1.000	.998	.988	.945	.833	.617	.322	.070	.012	.000
8	1.000	1.000	1.000	1.000	1.000	.998	.989	.954	.851	.624	.264	.086	.004
9	1.000	1.000	1.000	1.000	1.000	1.000	.999	.994	.972	.893	.651	.401	.096

cumulative binomial probabilities, $p(x \le k)$. Thus, for example, the entry in the column corresponding to $p = .10$ and the row corresponding to $k = 2$ is .930 (shaded), and its interpretation is

$$P(x \le 2) = P(x = 0) + P(x = 1) + P(x = 2) = .930$$

This probability is also shaded in the graphical representation of the binomial distribution with $n = 10$ and $p = .10$ in Figure 4.10.

You can also use Table I to find the probability that x equals a specific value. For example, suppose you want to find the probability that $x = 2$ in the binomial distribution with $n = 10$ and $p = .10$. This is found by subtraction as follows:

$$P(x = 2) = [P(x = 0) + P(x = 1) + P(x = 2)] - [P(x = 0) + P(x = 1)]$$
$$= P(x \le 2) - P(x \le 1) = .930 - .736 = .194$$

The probability that a binomial random variable exceeds a specified value can be found using Table I and the notion of complementary events. For example, to find the probability that x exceeds 2 when $n = 10$ and $p = .10$, we use

$$P(x > 2) = 1 - P(x \le 2) = 1 - .930 = .070$$

Note that this probability is represented by the unshaded portion of the graph in Figure 4.10.

All probabilities in Table I are rounded to three decimal places. Thus, although none of the binomial probabilities in the table is exactly zero, some are small enough (less than .0005) to round to .000. For example, using the formula to find $P(x = 0)$ when $n = 10$ and $p = .6$, we obtain

$$P(x = 0) = \binom{10}{0}(.6)^0(.4)^{10-0} = .4^{10} = .00010486$$

but this is rounded to .000 in Table I in Appendix D (see Table 4.3).

Similarly, none of the table entries is exactly 1.0, but when the cumulative probabilities exceed .9995, they are rounded to 1.000. The row corresponding to the largest possible value for x, $x = n$, is omitted because all the cumulative probabilities in that row are equal to 1.0 (exactly). For example, in Table 4.3, with $n = 10$, $P(x \le 10) = 1.0$, no matter what the value of p.

Of course, you can also use a statisitical software package to find binomial probabilities. The following example further illustrates the use of Table I and statistical software.

$p(x)$

Figure 4.10

Binomial probability distribution for $n = 10$ and $p = .10$; $P(x \le 2)$ shaded

---

Example	**4.13**

Using the Binomial Table and Computer Software— Worker Unionization Problem

Problem Suppose a poll of 20 employees is taken in a large company. The purpose is to determine x, the number who favor unionization. Suppose that 60% of all the company's employees favor unionization.

a. Find the mean and standard deviation of x.

b. Use Table I in Appendix D to find the probability that $x \le 10$. Verify this probability using Minitab.

c. Use Table I to find the probability that $x > 12$.

d. Use Table I to find the probability that $x = 11$. Verify this probability using Minitab.

e. Graph the probability distribution of x and locate the interval $\mu \pm 2\sigma$ on the graph.

Solution

a. The number of employees polled is presumably small compared with the total number of employees in this company. Thus, we may treat x, the number of the 20 who favor unionization, as a binomial random variable. The value of p is the fraction of the total employees who favor unionization; that is, $p = .6$. Therefore, we calculate the mean and variance:

$$\mu = np = 20(.6) = 12$$
$$\sigma^2 = npq = 20(.6)(.4) = 4.8$$
$$\sigma = \sqrt{4.8} = 2.19$$

b. Looking in the $k = 10$ row and the $p = .6$ column of Table I (Appendix D) for $n = 20$, we find the value of .245. Thus,

$$P(x \leq 10) = .245$$

This value agrees (to three decimal places) with the cumulative probability shaded at the top of the Minitab printont shown in Figure 4.11.

Cumulative Distribution Function

```
Binomial with n = 20 and p = 0.6

  x   P( X <= x )
 10     0.244663
```

Probability Density Function

```
Binomial with n = 20 and p = 0.6

  x   P( X = x )
 11     0.159738
```

Figure 4.11

Minitab output for Example 4.13

c. To find the probability

$$P(x > 12) = \sum_{x=13}^{20} p(x)$$

we use the fact that for all probability distributions, $\sum_{\text{All } x} p(x) = 1$. Therefore,

$$P(x > 12) = 1 - P(x \leq 12) = 1 - \sum_{x=0}^{12} p(x)$$

Consulting Table I, we find the entry in row $k = 12$, column $p = .6$ to be .584. Thus,

$$P(x > 12) = 1 - .584 = .416$$

d. To find the probability that exactly 11 employees favor unionization, recall that the entries in Table I are cumulative probabilities and use the relationship

$$P(x = 11) = [p(0) + p(1) + \cdots + p(11)] - [p(0) + p(1) + \cdots + p(10)]$$
$$= P(x \leq 11) - P(x \leq 10)$$

Then

$$P(x = 11) = .404 - .245 = .159$$

Again, this value agrees (to three decimal places) with the probability shaded at the bottom of the Minitab printont, Figure 4.11.

e. The probability distribution for x in this example is shown in Figure 4.12. Note that

$$\mu - 2\sigma = 12 - 2(2.2) = 7.6$$
$$\mu + 2\sigma = 12 + 2(2.2) = 16.4$$

Figure 4.12

The binomial probability distribution for x in Example 4.13: $n = 20, p = .6$

The interval (7.6, 16.4) is also shown in Figure 4.12. The probability that x falls in this interval is $P(x = 8, 9, 10, \ldots, 16) = P(x \le 16) - P(x \le 7) = .984 - .021 = .963$. This probability is very close to the .95 given by the Empirical Rule. Thus, we expect the number of employees in the sample of 20 who favor unionization to be between 8 and 16.

◼ Now Work Exercise 4.51

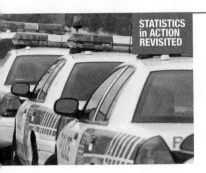

STATISTICS
in ACTION
REVISITED

Using the Binomial Model to Solve the Cocaine Sting Case

Refer to the reverse cocaine sting case described on page 184. During a drug bust, police seized 496 foil packets of a white, powdery substance that appeared to be cocaine. The police laboratory randomly selected 4 packets and found that all 4 tested positive for cocaine. This finding led to the conviction of the drug traffickers. Following the conviction, the police used 2 of the remaining 492 foil packets (i.e., those not tested) in a reverse sting operation. The 2 randomly selected packets were sold by undercover officers to a buyer, who disposed of the evidence before being arrested. Is there evidence beyond a reasonable doubt that the 2 packets contained cocaine?

To solve the dilemma, we will assume that, of the 496 original packets confiscated, 331 contained cocaine and 165 contained an inert (legal) powder. (A statistician hired as an expert witness on the case showed that the chance of the defendant being found not guilty is maximized when 331 packets contain cocaine and 165 do not.) First, we'll find the probability that 4 packets randomly selected from the original 496 will test positive for cocaine. Then we'll find the probability that the 2 packets sold in the reverse sting did not contain cocaine. Finally, we'll find the probability that both events occur (i.e., that the first 4 packets selected test positive for cocaine, but that the next 2 packets selected do not). In each of these probability calculations, we will apply the binomial probability distribution to approximate the probabilities.

Let x be the number of packets that contain cocaine in a sample of n selected from the 496 packets. Here, we are defining a success as a packet that contains cocaine. If n is small, say, $n = 2$ or $n = 4$, then x has an approximate binomial distribution with probability of success $p = 331/496 \approx .67$.

The probability that the first 4 packets selected contain cocaine [i.e., $P(x = 4)$] is obtained from the binomial formula with $n = 4$ and $p = .67$:

$$P(x = 4) = p(4) = \binom{4}{4}p^4(1 - p)^0 = \frac{4!(.67)^4(.33)^0}{4!0!}$$
$$= (.67)^4 = .202$$

Thus, there is about a 20% chance that all 4 of the randomly selected packets contain cocaine.

Given that 4 of the original packets tested positive for cocaine, the probability that the 2 packets randomly selected and sold in the reverse sting *do not* contain cocaine is approximated by a binomial distribution with $n = 2$ and $p = .67$. Since a success is a packet with cocaine, we find $P(x = 0)$:

$$P(x = 0) = p(0) = \binom{2}{0}p^0(1 - p)^2 = \frac{2!(.67)^0(.33)^2}{0!2!}$$
$$= (.33)^2 = .109$$

Finally, to compute the probability that, of the original 496 foil packets, the first 4 selected (at random) test positive for cocaine and the next 2 selected (at random) test negative, we employ the multiplicative law of probability. Let A be the event that the first 4 packets test positive. Let B be the event that the next 2 packets test negative. We want to find the probability of both events occurring [i.e., $P(A \text{ and } B) = P(A \cap B) = P(B|A)P(A)$]. Note that this probability is the product of the two previously calculated probabilities:

$$P(A \text{ and } B) = (.109)(.201) = .022$$

Consequently, there is only a .022 probability (i.e., about 2 chances in a hundred) that the first 4 packets will test positive for cocaine and the next 2 packets will test negative for cocaine. A reasonable jury would likely believe that an event with such a small probability is unlikely to occur and conclude that the 2 "lost" packets contained cocaine. In other words, most of us would infer that the defendant in the reverse cocaine sting was guilty of drug trafficking.

[*Epilogue:* Several of the defendant's lawyers believed that the .022 probability was too high for jurors to conclude guilt "beyond a reasonable doubt." The argument was made moot, however, when, to the surprise of the defense, the prosecution revealed that the remaining 490 packets had not been used in any other reverse sting operations and offered to test a sample of them. On the advice of the statistician, the defense requested that an additional 20 packets be tested. All 20 tested positive for cocaine! As a consequence of this new evidence, the defendant was convicted by the jury.]

Exercises 4.40–4.60

Learning the Mechanics

4.40 Compute the following:

a. $\dfrac{6!}{2!(6-2)!}$ b. $\dbinom{5}{2}$ c. $\dbinom{7}{0}$ d. $\dbinom{6}{6}$ e. $\dbinom{4}{3}$

4.41 Consider the following probability distribution:

$$p(x) = \binom{5}{x}(.7)^x(.3)^{5-x} \quad (x = 0, 1, 2, \ldots, 5)$$

a. Is x a discrete or a continuous random variable?
b. What is the name of this probability distribution?
c. Graph the probability distribution.
d. Find the mean and standard deviation of x.
e. Show the mean and the 2-standard-deviation interval on each side of the mean on the graph you drew in part **c**.

4.42 Suppose x is a binomial random variable with $n = 3$ and $p = .3$.
a. Calculate the value of $p(x)$, $x = 0, 1, 2, 3$, using the formula for a binomial probability distribution.
b. Using your answers to part **a**, give the probability distribution for x in tabular form.

4.43 If x is a binomial random variable, compute $p(x)$ for each of the following cases:
a. $n = 5, x = 1, p = .2$
b. $n = 4, x = 2, q = .4$
c. $n = 3, x = 0, p = .7$
d. $n = 5, x = 3, p = .1$
e. $n = 4, x = 2, q = .6$
f. $n = 3, x = 1, p = .9$

4.44 If x is a binomial random variable, use Table I in Appendix D to find the following probabilities:
a. $P(x = 2)$ for $n = 10, p = .4$
b. $P(x \le 5)$ for $n = 15, p = .6$
c. $P(x > 1)$ for $n = 5, p = .1$
d. $P(x < 10)$ for $n = 25, p = .7$
e. $P(x \ge 10)$ for $n = 15, p = .9$
f. $P(x = 2)$ for $n = 20, p = .2$

4.45 If x is a binomial random variable, calculate μ, σ^2, and σ for each of the following:
a. $n = 25, p = .5$
b. $n = 80, p = .2$

c. $n = 100, p = .6$
d. $n = 70, p = .9$
e. $n = 60, p = .8$
f. $n = 1,000, p = .04$

4.46 The binomial probability distribution is a family of probability distributions with each single distribution depending on the values of n and p. Assume that x is a binomial random variable with $n = 4$.
a. Determine a value of p such that the probability distribution of x is symmetric.
b. Determine a value of p such that the probability distribution of x is skewed to the right.
c. Determine a value of p such that the probability distribution of x is skewed to the left.
d. Graph each of the binomial distributions you obtained in parts **a**, **b**, and **c**. Locate the mean for each distribution on its graph.
e. In general, for what values of p will a binomial distribution be symmetric? Skewed to the right? Skewed to the left?

⚙ Applet Exercise 4.3

Use the applets *Simulating the Probability of a Head with an Unfair Coin (P(H) = .2)*, and *Simulating the Probability of a Head with an Unfair Coin (P(H) = .8)* to study the mean μ of a binomial distribution.
a. Run each applet mentioned above once with $n = 1,000$ and record the cumulative proportions. How does the cumulative proportion for each applet compare to the value of $P(H)$ given for the applet?
b. Using the cumulative proportion from each applet as p, compute $\mu = np$ for each applet where $n = 1,000$. What does the value of μ represent in terms of the results from running each applet in part **a**?
c. In your own words, describe what the mean μ of a binomial distribution represents.

⚙ Applet Exercise 4.4

Open the applet *Sample from a Population*. On the pull-down menu to the right of the top graph, select *Binary*. Set $n = 10$ as the sample size and repeatedly choose samples from the population. For each sample, record the number of 1s in the sample. Let x be the number of 1s in a sample of size 10. Explain why x is a binomial random variable.

⊙ Applet Exercise 4.5

Use the applet *Simulating the Stock Market* to estimate the probability that the stock market will go up each of the next two days. Repeatedly run the applet for $n = 2$, recording the number of up's each time. Use the proportion of 2s among your results as the estimate of the probability. Compare to the binomial probability where $x = 2, n = 2$, and $p = 0.5$.

Applying the Concepts—Basic

4.47 **Working on summer vacation.** Recall (Exercise 3.14, p. 141) that an *Adweek/Harris* (July 2011) poll found that 35% of U.S. adults do not work at all while on summer vacation. In a random sample of 10 U.S. adults, let x represent the number who do not work during summer vacation.

   a. For this experiment, define the event that represents a "success."

   b. Explain why x is (approximately) a binomial random variable.

   c. Give the value of p for this binomial experiment.

   NW **d.** Find $P(x = 3)$.

   e. Find the probability that 2 or fewer of the 10 U.S. adults do not work during summer vacation.

4.48 **Hotel guest satisfaction.** Each year, J.D. Power and Associates publishes the results of its North American Hotel Guest Satisfaction Index Study. For 2009, the study revealed that 66% of hotel guests were aware of the hotel's "green" conservation program. Among these guests, 72% actually participated in the program by reusing towels and bed linens. In a random sample of 15 hotel guests, consider the number (x) of guests who were aware of and participated in the hotel's conservation efforts.

   a. Explain why x is (approximately) a binomial random variable.

   b. Use the rules of probability to determine the value of p for this binomial experiment.

   c. Assume $p = .45$. Find the probability that at least 10 of the 15 hotel guests were aware of and participated in the hotel's conservation efforts.

4.49 **Paying for music downloads.** A *Pew Internet & American Life Project Survey* (October 2010) revealed that half of all U.S. adults use the Internet and have paid to download music. In a random sample of 250 U.S. adults, let x be the number who use the Internet and pay to download music.

   NW **a.** Explain why x is a binomial random variable (to a reasonable degree of approximation).

   b. What is the value of p? Interpret this value.

   c. What is the expected value of x? Interpret this value.

4.50 **Physicians' opinions on a career in medicine.** Many primary care doctors feel overworked and burdened by potential lawsuits. In fact, the Physicians' Foundation reported that 60% of all general practice physicians in the United States do not recommend medicine as a career (*Reuters*, Nov. 18, 2008). Let x represent the number of sampled general practice physicians who do not recommend medicine as a career.

   a. Explain why x is approximately a binomial random variable.

   b. Use the Physicians' Foundation report to estimate p for the binomial random variable.

   c. Consider a random sample of 25 general practice physicians. Use p from part **b** to find the mean and standard deviation of x, the number who do not recommend medicine as a career.

   d. For the sample of part **c**, find the probability that at least one general practice physician does not recommend medicine as a career.

4.51 **Job satisfaction of law librarians.** According to the *Canadian Journal of Information and Library Science* (Vol. 33, 2009), nearly 90% of workers in law libraries are satisfied with their job. Assume the true proportion of law librarians in Canada who are satisfied with their job is .9. In a random sample of 20 law librarians in Canada, what is the probability that at most 2 are unsatisfied with their job?

Applying the Concepts—Intermediate

4.52 **Immediate feedback to incorrect exam answers.** Researchers from the Educational Testing Service (ETS) found that providing immediate feedback to students answering open-ended questions can dramatically improve students' future performance on exams (*Educational and Psychological Measurement*, Feb. 2010). The ETS researchers used questions from the Graduate Record Examination (GRE) in the experiment. After obtaining feedback, students could revise their answers. Consider one of these questions. Initially, 50% of the students answered the question correctly. After providing immediate feedback to students who had answered incorrectly, 70% answered correctly. Consider a bank of 100 open-ended questions similar to those on the GRE.

   a. In a random sample of 20 students, what is the probability that more than half initially answered the question correctly?

   b. Refer to part **a**. After receiving immediate feedback, what is the probability that more than half of the students answered the question correctly?

4.53 **Fingerprint expertise.** Refer to the *Psychological Science* (August 2011) study of fingerprint identification, Exercise 3.81 (p. 171). The study found that when presented with prints from the same individual, a fingerprint expert will correctly identify the match 92% of the time. In contrast, a novice will correctly identify the match 75% of the time. Consider a sample of five different pairs of fingerprints, where each pair is a match.

   a. What is the probability that an expert will correctly identify the match in all five pairs of fingerprints?

   b. What is the probability that a novice will correctly identify the match in all five pairs of fingerprints?

4.54 **Making your vote count.** Refer to the *Chance* (Fall 2007) study on making your vote count, Exercise 3.27 (p. 143). Recall the scenario where you are one of five county commissioners voting on an issue, and each commissioner is equally likely to vote for or against.

   a. Your vote counts (i.e., is the decisive vote) only if the other four voters split, two in favor and two against. Use the binomial distribution to find the probability that your vote counts.

   b. If you convince two other commissioners to "vote in bloc" (i.e., you all agree to vote among yourselves first, and whatever the majority decides is the way all three will vote, guaranteeing that the issue is decided by the bloc), your vote counts only if these two commissioners split their bloc votes, one in favor and one against. Again, use the binomial distribution to find the probability that your vote counts.

4.55 Bridge inspection ratings. According to the National Bridge Inspection Standard (NBIS), public bridges over 20 feet in length must be inspected and rated every 2 years. The NBIS rating scale ranges from 0 (poorest rating) to 9 (highest rating). University of Colorado engineers used a probabilistic model to forecast the inspection ratings of all major bridges in Denver (*Journal of Performance of Constructed Facilities*, Feb. 2005). For the year 2020, the engineers forecast that 9% of all major Denver bridges will have ratings of 4 or below.

a. Use the forecast to find the probability that in a random sample of 10 major Denver bridges, at least 3 will have an inspection rating of 4 or below in 2020.

b. Suppose that you actually observe 3 or more of the sample of 10 bridges with inspection ratings of 4 or below in 2020. What inference can you make? Why?

4.56 Tax returns audited by the IRS. According to the Internal Revenue Service (IRS), the chances of your tax return being audited are about 1 in 100 if your income is less than $1 million and 9 in 100 if your income is $1 million or more (*IRS Enforcement and Services Statistics*).

a. What is the probability that a taxpayer with income less than $1 million will be audited by the IRS? With income $1 million or more?

b. If five taxpayers with incomes under $1 million are randomly selected, what is the probability that exactly one will be audited? That more than one will be audited?

c. Repeat part **b** assuming that five taxpayers with incomes of $1 million or more are randomly selected.

d. If two taxpayers with incomes under $1 million are randomly selected and two with incomes more than $1 million are randomly selected, what is the probability that none of these taxpayers will be audited by the IRS?

e. What assumptions did you have to make in order to answer these questions using the methodology presented in this section?

4.57 FDA report on pesticides in food. Every quarter, the Food and Drug Administration (FDA) produces a report called the *Total Diet Study*. The FDA's report covers a variety of food items, each of which is analyzed for potentially harmful chemical compounds. A *Total Diet Study* reported that no pesticides at all were found in 65% of the domestically produced food samples (*FDA Pesticide Program: Residue Monitoring*, 2008). Consider a random sample of 800 food items analyzed for the presence of pesticides.

a. Compute μ and σ for the random variable x, the number of food items found that showed no trace of pesticide.

b. Based on a sample of 800 food items, is it likely you would observe less than half without any traces of pesticide? Explain.

Applying the Concepts—Advanced

4.58 Purchasing decision. Suppose you are a purchasing officer for a large company. You have purchased 5 million electrical switches, and your supplier has guaranteed that the shipment will contain no more than .1% defectives. To check the shipment, you randomly sample 500 switches, test them, and find that four are defective. Based on this evidence, do you think the supplier has complied with the guarantee? Explain.

4.59 USGA golf ball specifications. According to the U.S. Golf Association (USGA), "The weight of the [golf] ball shall not be greater than 1.620 ounces avoirdupois (45.93 grams). ... The diameter of the ball shall not be less than 1.680 inches. ... The velocity of the ball shall not be greater than 250 feet per second" (USGA, 2002). The USGA periodically checks the specifications of golf balls sold in the United States by randomly sampling balls from pro shops around the country. Two dozen of each kind are sampled, and if more than three do not meet size and/or velocity requirements, that kind of ball is removed from the USGA's approved-ball list.

a. What assumptions must be made and what information must be known in order to use the binomial probability distribution to calculate the probability that the USGA will remove a particular kind of golf ball from its approved-ball list?

b. Suppose 10% of all balls produced by a particular manufacturer are less than 1.680 inches in diameter, and assume that the number of such balls, x, in a sample of two dozen balls can be adequately characterized by a binomial probability distribution. Find the mean and standard deviation of the binomial distribution.

c. Refer to part **b.** If x has a binomial distribution, then so does the number, y, of balls in the sample that meet the USGA's minimum diameter. [*Note:* $x + y = 24$.] Describe the distribution of y. In particular, what are p, q, and n? Also, find $E(y)$ and the standard deviation of y.

4.60 Reliability of a "one-shot" device. A "one-shot" device can be used only once; after use, the device (e.g., a nuclear weapon, space shuttle, automobile air bag) is either destroyed or must be rebuilt. The destructive nature of a one-shot device makes repeated testing either impractical or too costly. Hence, the reliability of such a device must be determined with minimal testing. Consider a one-shot device that has some probability, p, of failure. Of course, the true value of p is unknown, so designers will specify a value of p that is the largest defective rate they are willing to accept. Designers will conduct n tests of the device and determine the success or failure of each test. If the number of observed failures, x, is less than or equal to some specified value, K, then the device is considered to have the desired failure rate. Consequently, the designers want to know the minimum sample size n needed so that observing K or fewer defectives in the sample will demonstrate that the true probability of failure for the one-shot device is no greater than p.

a. Suppose the desired failure rate for a one-shot device is $p = .10$. Also, suppose designers will conduct $n = 20$ tests of the device and conclude that the device is performing to specifications if $K = 1$ (i.e., if 1 or no failures are observed in the sample). Find $P(x \le 1)$.

b. In reliability analysis, $1 - P(x \le K)$ is often called the *level of confidence* for concluding that the true failure rate is less than or equal to p. Find the level of confidence for the one-shot device described in part **a.** In your opinion, is this an acceptable level? Explain.

c. Demonstrate that the confidence level can be increased by either (1) increasing the sample size n or (2) decreasing the number K of failures allowed in the sample.

d. Typically, designers want a confidence level of .90, .95, or .99. Find the values of n and K to use so that the designers can conclude (with at least 95% confidence)

that the failure rate for the one-shot device of part **a** is no greater than $p = .10$.

[*Note:* The U.S. Department of Defense Reliability Analysis Center (DoD RAC) provides designers with free access to tables and toolboxes that give the minimum sample size n required to obtain a desired confidence level for a specified number of observed failures in the sample.]

4.4 Other Discrete Distributions: Poisson and Hypergeometric

Poisson Random Variable

A type of discrete probability distribution that is often useful in describing the number of rare events that will occur in a specific period of time or in a specific area or volume is the **Poisson distribution** (named after the eighteenth-century physicist and mathematician Siméon Poisson). Typical examples of random variables for which the Poisson probability distribution provides a good model are as follows:

1. The number of industrial accidents per month at a manufacturing plant

2. The number of noticeable surface defects (scratches, dents, etc.) found by quality inspectors on a new automobile

3. The parts per million of some toxin found in the water or air emission from a manufacturing plant

4. The number of customer arrivals per unit of time at a supermarket checkout counter

5. The number of death claims received per day by an insurance company

6. The number of errors per 100 invoices in the accounting records of a company

SIMÉON D. POISSON (1781–1840)
A Lifetime Mathematician

Growing up in France during the French Revolution, Siméon Denis Poisson was sent away by his father to become an apprentice surgeon, but he lacked the manual dexterity to perform the delicate procedures required and returned home. He eventually enrolled in Ecole Polytechnique University to study mathematics. In his final year of study, Poisson wrote a paper on the theory of equations that was of such quality that he was allowed to graduate without taking the final examination. Two years later, Poisson was named a professor at the university. During his illustrious career, Poisson published between 300 and 400 mathematics papers. He is most known for his 1837 paper where the distribution of a rare event—the Poisson distribution—first appears. (In fact, the distribution was actually described years earlier by one of the Bernoulli brothers.) Poisson dedicated his life to mathematics, once stating that "life is good for only two things: to study mathematics and to teach it."

Characteristics of a Poisson Random Variable

1. The experiment consists of counting the number of times a certain event occurs during a given unit of time or in a given area or volume (or weight, distance, or any other unit of measurement).

2. The probability that an event occurs in a given unit of time, area, or volume is the same for all the units.

3. The number of events that occur in one unit of time, area, or volume is independent of the number that occur in any other mutually exclusive unit.

4. The mean (or expected) number of events in each unit is denoted by the Greek letter lambda, λ.

The characteristics of the Poisson random variable are usually difficult to verify for practical examples. The examples given satisfy them well enough that the Poisson distribution provides a good model in many instances. As with all probability models, the real test of the adequacy of the Poisson model is in whether it provides a reasonable approximation to reality–that is, whether empirical data support it.

The probability distribution, mean, and variance for a Poisson random variable are shown in the next box.

Probability Distribution, Mean, and Variance for a Poisson Random Variable*

$$p(x) = \frac{\lambda^x e^{-\lambda}}{x!} \quad (x = 0, 1, 2, \ldots)$$

$$\mu = \lambda$$

$$\sigma^2 = \lambda$$

---

*The Poisson probability distribution also provides a good approximation to a binomial distribution with mean $\lambda = np$ when n is large and p is small (say, $np \leq 7$).

where
λ = Mean number of events during given unit of time, area, volume, etc.
$e = 2.71828\cdots$

The calculation of Poisson probabilities is made easier by the use of statistical software, as illustrated in Example 4.14.

Example 4.14

Finding Poisson Probabilities—Worker Absenteeism

Problem Suppose the number, x, of a company's employees who are absent on Mondays has (approximately) a Poisson probability distribution. Furthermore, assume that the average number of Monday absentees is 2.6.

a. Find the mean and standard deviation of x, the number of employees absent on Monday.

b. Use Minitab to find the probability that exactly five employees are absent on a given Monday.

c. Use Minitab to find the probability that fewer than two employees are absent on a given Monday.

d. Use Minitab to find the probability that more than five employees are absent on a given Monday.

Solution

a. The mean and variance of a Poisson random variable are both equal to λ. Thus, for this example,

$$\mu = \lambda = 2.6$$
$$\sigma^2 = \lambda = 2.6$$

Then the standard deviation of x is

$$\sigma = \sqrt{2.6} = 1.61$$

Remember that the mean measures the central tendency of the distribution and does not necessarily equal a possible value of x. In this example, the mean is 2.6 absences, and although there cannot be 2.6 absences on a given Monday, the average number of Monday absences is 2.6. Similarly, the standard deviation of 1.61 measures the variability of the number of absences per week. Perhaps a more helpful measure is the interval $\mu \pm 2\sigma$, which in this case stretches from $-.62$ to 5.82. We expect the number of absences to fall in this interval most of the time–with at least 75% relative frequency (according to Chebyshev's Rule) and probably with approximately 95% relative frequency (the Empirical Rule). The mean and the 2-standard-deviation interval around it are shown in Figure 4.13.

b. Since x represents the number of employees absent on a given Monday, we want to find $P(x = 5)$. Like for binomial probabilities, tables and computer software give Poisson probabilities of the form $P(x = k)$ or cumulative probabilities of the form $P(x \leq k)$. Setting $\lambda = 2.6$ as an option in Minitab and specifying the value "5" for a Poisson probability, we obtain the value (shaded) shown at the top of the Minitab printout, Figure 4.14:

$$P(x = 5) = .0735$$

c. Here, we want to find $P(x < 2)$. Since x is a discrete whole number, we know that

$$P(x < 2) = P(x \leq 1)$$

This probability is now in the form of a cumulative probability and can be found using statistical software. Setting $\lambda = 2.6$ as an option in Minitab and specifying the value "1" for a cumulative Poisson probability, we obtain the value (shaded) shown in the middle of the Minitab printout, Figure 4.14:

$$P(x < 2) = P(x \leq 1) = .2674$$

Figure 4.13

Probability distribution for number of Monday absences

Probability Density Function

```
Poisson with mean = 2.6

x    P( X = x )
5    0.0735394
```

Cumulative Distribution Function

```
Poisson with mean = 2.6

x    P( X <= x )
1    0.267385
```

Cumulative Distribution Function

```
Poisson with mean = 2.6

x    P( X <= x )
5    0.950963
```

Figure 4.14

Minitab output for Example 4.14

d. To find the probability that more than five employees are absent on a given Monday, we consider the complementary event

$$P(x > 5) = 1 - P(x \le 5)$$

Again, we select $\lambda = 2.6$ as an option in Minitab and now specify the value "5" for a cumulative Poisson probability. This yields the probability, .951, shaded at the bottom of the Minitab printout, Figure 4.14. Now, we compute:

$$P(x > 5) = 1 - P(x \le 5) = 1 - .951 = .049$$

Look Back Note from Figure 4.13 that the probability of part **d** is in the area in the interval $\mu \pm 2\sigma$, or $2.6 \pm 2(1.61) = (-.62, 5.82)$. Then, the number of absences should exceed 5—or, equivalently, should be more than 2 standard deviations from the mean—during only about 4.9% of all Mondays. This percentage agrees remarkably well with that given by the Empirical Rule for mound-shaped distributions, which informs us to expect about 5% of the measurements (values of the random variable x) to lie farther than 2 standard deviations from the mean.

■ **Now Work Exercise 4.71**

Hypergeometric Random Variable

The **hypergeometric probability distribution** provides a realistic model for some types of enumerative (countable) data. The characteristics of the hypergeometric distribution are listed in the following box:

Characteristics of a Hypergeometric Random Variable

1. The experiment consists of randomly drawing n elements without replacement from a set of N elements, r of which are S's (for success) and $(N - r)$ of which are F's (for failure).

2. The hypergeometric random variable x is the number of S's in the draw of n elements.

Note that both the hypergeometric and binomial characteristics stipulate that each draw, or trial, results in one of two outcomes. The basic difference between these random variables is that the hypergeometric trials are dependent, while the binomial trials are independent. The draws are dependent because the probability of drawing an S (or an F) is dependent on what occurred on preceding draws.

To illustrate the dependence between trials, we note that the probability of drawing an S on the first draw is r/N. Then the probability of drawing an S on the second draw depends on the outcome of the first. It will be either $(r - 1)/(N - 1)$ or $r/(N - 1)$, depending on whether the first draw was an S or an F. Consequently, the results of the draws represent dependent events.

For example, suppose we define x as the number of women hired in a random selection of three applicants from a total of six men and four women. This random variable satisfies the characteristics of a **hypergeometric random variable** with $N = 10$ and $n = 3$. The possible outcomes on each trial are either the selection of a female (S) or the selection of a male (F). Another example of a hypergeometric random variable is the number x of defective large-screen plasma televisions in a random selection of $n = 4$ from a shipment of $N = 8$. Finally, as a third example, suppose $n = 5$ stocks are randomly selected from a list of $N = 15$ stocks. Then the number x of the five companies selected that pay regular dividends to stockholders is a hypergeometric random variable.

The hypergeometric probability distribution is summarized in the following box:

Probability Distribution, Mean, and Variance of the Hypergeometric Random Variable

$$p(x) = \frac{\binom{r}{x}\binom{N-r}{n-x}}{\binom{N}{n}} \quad [x = \text{Maximum}\,[0, n-(N-r)], \ldots, \text{Minimum}(r, n)]$$

$$\mu = \frac{nr}{N} \qquad \sigma^2 = \frac{r(N-r)n(N-n)}{N^2(N-1)}$$

where

$\quad N = $ Total number of elements

$\quad r = $ Number of S's in the N elements

$\quad n = $ Number of elements drawn

$\quad x = $ Number of S's drawn in the n elements

Example 4.15

Applying the Hypergeometric Distribution—Selecting Teaching Assistants

Problem Suppose a marketing professor randomly selects three new teaching assistants from a total of ten applicants—six male and four female students. Let x be the number of females who are hired.

a. Find the mean and standard deviation of x.

b. Find the probability that no females are hired.

Solution

a. Because x is a hypergeometric random variable with $N = 10$, $n = 3$, and $r = 4$, the mean and variance are

$$\mu = \frac{nr}{N} = \frac{(3)(4)}{10} = 1.2$$

$$\sigma^2 = \frac{r(N-r)n(N-n)}{N^2(N-1)} = \frac{4(10-4)3(10-3)}{(10)^2(10-1)}$$

$$= \frac{(4)(6)(3)(7)}{(100)(9)} = .56$$

The standard deviation is

$$\sigma = \sqrt{.56} = .75$$

b. The probability that no female students are hired by the professor, assuming that the selection is truly random, is

$$P(x = 0) = p(0) = \frac{\binom{4}{0}\binom{10-4}{3-0}}{\binom{10}{3}}$$

$$= \frac{\dfrac{4!}{0!(4-0)!}\dfrac{6!}{3!(6-3)!}}{\dfrac{10!}{3!(10-3)!}} = \frac{(1)(20)}{120} = \frac{1}{6} = .1667$$

Figure 4.16

Probability distribution for x in Example 4.15

We verified this calculation using statistical software. The probability, .166667, shaded on the Minitab printont, Figure 4.15, agrees with our answer.

Probability Density Function

Hypergeometric with N = 10, M = 4, and n = 3

Figure 4.15

Minitab output for Example 4.15

```
x   P( X = x )
0    0.166667
```

Look Back The entire probability distribution for x is shown in Figure 4.16. The mean $\mu = 1.2$ and the interval $\mu \pm 2\sigma = (-.3, 2.7)$ are indicated. You can see that if this random variable were to be observed over and over again a large number of times, most of the values of x would fall within the interval $\mu \pm 2\sigma$.

■ **Now Work Exercise 4.75**

STATISTICS in ACTION REVISITED

Using the Hypergeometric Model to Solve the Cocaine Sting Case

The reverse cocaine sting case solved in Section 4.3 can also be solved by applying the hypergeometric distribution. In fact, the probabilities obtained with the hypergeometric distribution are *exact* probabilities, compared with the approximate probabilities obtained with the binomial distribution.

Our objective, you will recall, is to find the probability that 4 packets (randomly selected from 496 packets confiscated in a drug bust) will contain cocaine and 2 packets (randomly selected from the remaining 492) will not contain cocaine. We assumed that, of the 496 original packets, 331 contained cocaine and 165 contained an inert (legal) powder. Since we are sampling *without replacement* from the 496 packets, the probability of a success (i.e., the probability of a packet containing cocaine) does not remain *exactly* the same from trial to trial. For example, for the first randomly selected packet, the probability of a success is $\frac{331}{496} = .66734$. If we find that the first 3 packets selected contain cocaine, the probability of success for the fourth packet selected is now $\frac{328}{493} = .66531$. You can see that these probabilities are not exactly the same. Hence, the binomial distribution will only approximate the distribution of x, the number of packets that contain cocaine in a sample of size n.

To find the probability that 4 packets randomly selected from the original 496 will test positive for cocaine under the hypergeometric distribution, we first identify the parameters of the distribution:

$N = 496$ is the total number of packets in the population

$S = 331$ is the number of successes (cocaine packets) in the population

$n = 4$ is the sample size

$x = 4$ is the number of successes (cocaine packets) in the sample

Substituting into the formula for $p(x)$ (above), we obtain

$$P(x = 4) = p(4) = \frac{\binom{331}{4}\binom{165}{0}}{\binom{496}{4}} = \frac{\left(\frac{331!}{4!327!}\right)\left(\frac{165!}{0!165!}\right)}{\left(\frac{496!}{4!492!}\right)}$$

$$= .197$$

To find the probability that 2 packets randomly selected from the remaining 492 will test negative for cocaine, *assuming that the first 4 packets tested positive,* we identify the parameters of the relevant hypergeometric distribution:

$N = 492$ is the total number of packets in the population

$S = 327$ is the number of successes (cocaine packets) in the population

$n = 2$ is the sample size

$x = 0$ is the number of successes (cocaine packets) in the sample

Again, we substitute into the formula for $p(x)$ to obtain

$$P(x = 0) = p(0) = \frac{\binom{327}{0}\binom{165}{2}}{\binom{492}{2}} = \frac{\left(\frac{327!}{0!327!}\right)\left(\frac{165!}{2!163!}\right)}{\left(\frac{492!}{2!490!}\right)}$$

$$= .112$$

By the multiplicative law of probability, the probability that the first 4 packets test positive for cocaine and the next 2 packets test negative is the product of the two probabilities just given:

$$P \text{ (first 4 positive and next 2 negative)} = (.197)(.112)$$

$$= .0221$$

Note that this exact probability is almost identical to the approximate probability computed with the binomial distribution in Section 4.3.

Exercises 4.61–4.83

Learning the Mechanics

4.61 Consider the probability distribution shown here:

$$p(x) = \frac{3^x e^{-3}}{x!} \quad (x = 0, 1, 2, \ldots)$$

a. Is x a discrete or continuous random variable? Explain.
b. What is the name of this probability distribution?
c. Graph the probability distribution.
d. Find the mean and standard deviation of x.

4.62 Assume that x is a random variable having a Poisson probability distribution with a mean of 1.5. Use statistical software to find the following probabilities:
a. $P(x \le 3)$ b. $P(x \ge 3)$
c. $P(x = 3)$ d. $P(x = 0)$
e. $P(x > 0)$ f. $P(x > 6)$

4.63 Given that x is a hypergeometric random variable, compute $p(x)$ for each of the following cases:
a. $N = 5, n = 3, r = 3, x = 1$
b. $N = 9, n = 5, r = 3, x = 3$
c. $N = 4, n = 2, r = 2, x = 2$
d. $N = 4, n = 2, r = 2, x = 0$

4.64 Given that x is a hypergeometric random variable with $N = 8, n = 3$, and $r = 5$, compute the following:
a. $P(x = 1)$ b. $P(x = 0)$
c. $P(x = 3)$ d. $P(x \ge 4)$

4.65 Given that x is a random variable for which a Poisson probability distribution provides a good approximation, use statistical software to find the following:

a. $P(x \le 2)$ when $\lambda = 1$
b. $P(x \le 2)$ when $\lambda = 2$
c. $P(x \le 2)$ when $\lambda = 3$
d. What happens to the probability of the event $\{x \le 2\}$ as λ increases from 1 to 3? Is this intuitively reasonable?

4.66 Suppose x is a random variable for which a Poisson probability distribution with $\lambda = 5$ provides a good characterization.
a. Graph $p(x)$ for $x = 0, 1, 2, \ldots, 15$.
b. Find μ and σ for x and locate μ and the interval $\mu \pm 2\sigma$ on the graph.
c. What is the probability that x will fall within the interval $\mu \pm 2\sigma$?

4.67 Suppose you plan to sample 10 items from a population of 100 items and would like to determine the probability of observing 4 defective items in the sample. Which probability distribution should you use to compute this probability under the conditions listed here? Justify your answers.
a. The sample is drawn without replacement.
b. The sample is drawn with replacement.

4.68 Given that x is a hypergeometric random variable with $N = 10, n = 5$, and $r = 7$:
a. Display the probability distribution for x in tabular form.
b. Compute the mean and variance of x.
c. Graph $p(x)$ and locate μ and the interval $\mu \pm 2\sigma$ on the graph.
d. What is the probability that x will fall within the interval $\mu \pm 2\sigma$?

Applying the Concepts—Basic

4.69 **Do social robots walk or roll?** Refer to the *International Conference on Social Robotics* (Vol. 6414, 2010) study of the trend in the design of social robots, Exercise 4.25 (p.196). The study found that of 106 social robots, 63 were built with legs only, 20 with wheels only, 8 with both legs and wheels, and 15 with neither legs nor wheels. Suppose you randomly select 10 of the 106 social robots and count the number, x, with neither legs nor wheels.

   a. Demonstrate why the probability distribution for x should not be approximated by the binomial distribution.

   b. Show that the properties of the hypergeometric probability distribution are satisfied for this experiment.

   c. Find μ and σ for the probability distribution for x.

   d. Calculate the probability that $x = 2$.

4.70 **FDIC bank failures.** The Federal Deposit Insurance Corporation (FDIC) normally insures deposits of up to $100,000 in banks that are members of the Federal Reserve System against losses due to bank failure or theft. Over the last 10 years, the average number of bank failures per year among insured banks was 45 (*FDIC Failed Bank List,* Dec. 2011). Assume that x, the number of bank failures per year among insured banks, can be adequately characterized by a Poisson probability distribution with mean 45.

   a. Find the expected value and standard deviation of x.

   b. In 2011, 360 banks failed. How far (in standard deviations) does $x = 360$ lie above the mean of the Poisson distribution? That is, find the z-score for $x = 360$.

   c. In 2010, 65 banks failed. Find $P(x \le 65)$

4.71 **Airline fatalities.** U.S. airlines average about 4.5 fatalities per month (*Statistical Abstract of the United States: 2012*). Assume the probability distribution for x, the number of fatalities per month, can be approximated by a Poisson probability distribution.

   a. What is the probability that no fatalities will occur during any given month?

   b. What is the probability that one fatality will occur during a month?

   c. Find $E(x)$ and the standard deviation of x.

4.72 **Male nannies.** According to the International Nanny Association (INA), 4,176 nannies were placed in a job during a recent year (www.nanny.org). Of these, only 24 were men. In Exercise 3.11 (p. 140) you found the probability that a randomly selected nanny who was placed during a recent year is a man. Now use the hypergeometric distribution to find the probability that in a random sample of 10 nannies who were placed during a recent year, at least 1 is a man.

4.73 **Contaminated gun cartridges.** Refer to the investigation of contaminated gun cartridges at a weapons manufacturer, presented in Exercise 4.29 (p. 197). In a sample of 158 cartridges from a certain lot, 36 were found to be contaminated and 122 were "clean." If you randomly select 5 of these 158 cartridges, what is the probability that all 5 will be "clean"?

4.74 **NASA and rare planet transits.** A "planet transit" is a rare celestial event in which a planet appears to cross in front of its star as seen from Earth. The planet transit causes a noticeable dip in the star's brightness, allowing scientists to detect a new planet even though it is not directly visible.

The National Aeronautics and Space Administration (NASA) recently launched its Kepler mission, designed to discover new planets in the Milky Way by detecting extrasolar planet transits. After 1 year of the mission in which 3,000 stars were monitored, NASA announced that five planet transits had been detected (NASA, American Astronomical Society, Jan. 4, 2010). Assume that the number of planet transits discovered for every 3,000 stars follows a Poisson distribution with $\lambda = 5$. What is the probability that, in the next 3,000 stars monitored by the Kepler mission, more than 10 planet transits will be seen?

Applying the Concepts—Intermediate

4.75 **Museum management.** Refer to the *Museum Management and Curatorship* (June 2010) study of the criteria used to evaluate museum performance, Exercise 3.16 (p. 141). Recall that the managers of 30 leading museums of contemporary art were asked to provide the performance measure used most often. Of these 30 museums, 8 specified "total visitors" as the performance measure. Consider a random sample of 5 museums selected from the 30. How likely is it that none of the museums in the sample specified "total visitors" as the performance measure?

4.76 **Traffic fatalities and sporting events.** The relationship between close sporting events and game-day traffic fatalities was investigated in the *Journal of Consumer Research* (December 2011). The researchers found that closer football and basketball games are associated with more traffic fatalities. The methodology used by the researchers involved modeling the traffic fatality count for a particular game as a Poisson random variable. For games played at the winner's location (home court or home field), the mean number of traffic fatalities was .5. Use this information to find the probability that at least three game-day traffic fatalities will occur at the winning team's location.

4.77 **Cell phone handoff behavior.** Refer to the *Journal of Engineering, Computing and Architecture* (Vol. 3., 2009) study of cell phone handoff behavior, Exercise 3.45 (p. 154). Recall that a "handoff" describes the process of a cell phone moving from one base channel (identified by a color code) to another. During a particular driving trip, a cell phone changed channels (color codes) 85 times. Color code "b" was accessed 40 times on the trip. You randomly select 7 of the 85 handoffs. How likely is it that the cell phone accessed color code "b" only twice for these 7 handoffs?

4.78 **Guilt in decision making.** The *Journal of Behavioral Decision Making* (Jan. 2007) published a study of how guilty feelings impact on-the-job decisions. In one experiment, 57 participants were assigned to a guilty state through a reading/writing task. Immediately after the task, the participants were presented with a decision problem where the stated option had predominantly negative features (e.g., spending money on repairing a very old car). Of these 57 participants, 45 chose the stated option. Suppose 10 of the 57 guilty-state participants are selected at random. Define x as the number in the sample of 10 who chose the stated option.

   a. Find $P(x = 5)$.

   b. Find $P(x = 8)$.

   c. What is the expected value (mean) of x?

4.79 **Flaws in plastic-coated wire.** The British Columbia Institute of Technology provides on its Web site (www.math.bcit.ca) practical applications of statistics at mechanical engineering firms. The following is a Poisson application. A roll of plastic-coated wire has an average of .8 flaws per 4-meter length of wire. Suppose a quality-control engineer will sample a 4-meter length of wire from a roll of wire 220 meters in length. If no flaws are found in the sample, the engineer will accept the entire roll of wire. What is the probability that the roll will be rejected? What assumption did you make to find this probability?

4.80 **Noise in laser imaging.** Penumbrol imaging is a technique used by scanning companies for imaging objects (e.g., X-rays and lasers) that emit high-energy photons. In *IEICE Transactions on Information & Systems* (Apr. 2005), researchers demonstrated that penumbrol images are always degraded by noise, where the number x of noise events occurring in a unit of time follows a Poisson process with mean λ. Suppose that $\lambda = 9$ for a particular image.
a. Find and interpret the mean of x.
b. Find the standard deviation of x.
c. The signal-to-noise ratio (SNR) for a penumbrol image is defined as SNR $= \mu/\sigma$, where μ and σ are the mean and standard deviation, respectively, of the noise process. Find the SNR for x.

4.81 **Making high-stakes insurance decisions.** The *Journal of Economic Psychology* (Sep. 2008) published the results of a high-stakes experiment where subjects were asked how much they would pay for insuring a valuable painting. The painting was threatened by fire and theft, hence, the need for insurance. To make the risk realistic, the subjects were informed that if it rained on exactly 24 days in July, the painting was considered to be stolen; if it rained on exactly 23 days in August, the painting was considered to be destroyed by fire. Although the probability of these two events, "fire" and "theft," was ambiguous for the subjects, the researchers estimated their probabilities of occurrence at .0001. Rain frequencies for the months of July and August were shown to follow a Poisson distribution with a mean of 10 days per month.
a. Find the probability that it will rain on exactly 24 days in July.
b. Find the probability that it will rain on exactly 23 days in August.
c. Are the probabilities, parts **a** and **b**, good approximations to the probabilities of "fire" and "theft"?

Applying the Concepts—Advanced

4.82 **Waiting for a car wash.** An automatic car wash takes exactly 5 minutes to wash a car. On average, 10 cars per hour arrive at the car wash. Suppose that 30 minutes before closing time, 5 cars are in line. If the car wash is in continuous use until closing time, is it likely anyone will be in line at closing time?

4.83 **Gender discrimination suit.** The *Journal of Business & Economic Statistics* (July 2000) presented a case in which a charge of gender discrimination was filed against the U.S. Postal Service. At the time, there were 302 U.S. Postal Service employees (229 men and 73 women) who applied for promotion. Of the 72 employees who were awarded promotion, 5 were female. Make an inference about whether or not females at the U.S. Postal Service were promoted fairly.

PART II: CONTINUOUS RANDOM VARIABLES

4.5 Probability Distributions for Continuous Random Variables

The graphical form of the probability distribution for a **continuous random variable** x is a smooth curve that might appear as shown in Figure 4.17. This curve, a function of x, is denoted by the symbol $f(x)$ and is variously called a **probability density function (pdf),** a **frequency function,** or a **probability distribution.**

The areas under a probability distribution correspond to probabilities for x. For example, the area A beneath the curve between the two points a and b, as shown in Figure 4.17, is the probability that x assumes a value between a and b ($a < x < b$). Because there is no area over a point, say $x = a$, it follows that (according to our model) the probability associated with a particular value of x is equal to 0; that is, $P(x = a) = 0$ and hence $P(a < x < b) = P(a \le x \le b)$. In other words, the probability is the same whether or not you include the endpoints of the interval. Also, because areas over intervals represent probabilities, it follows that the total area under a probability distribution, the probability assigned to all values of x, should equal 1. Note that probability distributions for continuous random variables possess different shapes depending on the relative frequency distributions of real data that the probability distributions are supposed to model.

Figure 4.17

A probability distribution $f(x)$ for a continuous random variable x

> The **probability distribution for a continuous random variable, x,** can be represented by a smooth curve—a function of x, denoted $f(x)$. The curve is called a **density function** or **frequency function.** The probability that x falls between two values, a and b, i.e., $P(a < x < b)$, is the area under the curve between a and b.

The areas under most probability distributions are obtained by using calculus or numerical methods.* Because these methods often involve difficult procedures, we will give the areas for one of the most common probability distributions in tabular form in Appendix D. Then, to find the area between two values of x, say $x = a$ and $x = b$, you simply have to consult the appropriate table. Of course, you can always use statistical software to find this area.

For each of the continuous random variables presented in this chapter, we will give the formula for the probability distribution along with its mean μ and standard deviation σ. These two numbers will enable you to make some approximate probability statements about a random variable even when you do not have access to a table of areas under the probability distribution.

4.6 The Normal Distribution

One of the most commonly observed continuous random variables has a **bell-shaped** probability distribution (or **bell curve**), as shown in Figure 4.18. It is known as a **normal random variable,** and its probability distribution is called a **normal distribution**.

The normal distribution plays a very important role in the science of statistical inference. Moreover, many business phenomena generate random variables with probability distributions that are very well approximated by a normal distribution. For example, the monthly rate of return for a particular stock is approximately a normal random variable, and the probability distribution for the weekly sales of a corporation might be approximated by a normal probability distribution. The normal distribution might also provide an accurate model for the distribution of scores on an employment aptitude test. You can determine the adequacy of the normal approximation to an existing population by comparing the relative frequency distribution of a large sample of the data to the normal probability distribution. Methods to detect disagreement between a set of data and the assumption of normality are presented in Section 4.7.

The normal distribution is perfectly symmetric about its mean μ, as can be seen in the examples in Figure 4.19. Its spread is determined by the value of its standard deviation σ. The formula for the normal probability distribution is shown in the next box. When plotted, this formula yields a curve like that shown in Figure 4.18.

Note that the mean μ and standard deviation σ appear in this formula, so no separate formulas for μ and σ are necessary. To graph the normal curve, we have to know the numerical values of μ and σ. Computing the area over intervals under the normal

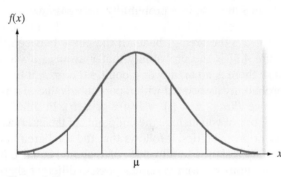

Figure 4.18

A normal probability distribution

Figure 4.19

Several normal distributions with different means and standard deviations

---

*Students with knowledge of calculus should note that the probability that x assumes a value in the interval $a < x < b$ is $P(a < x < b) = \int_a^b f(x)dx$, assuming the integral exists. Similar to the requirement for a discrete probability distribution, we require $f(x) \geq 0$ and $\int_{-\infty}^{\infty} f(x)dx = 1$.

**THE GAUSSIAN
DISTRIBUTION (1777–1855)**
Carl F. Gauss

The normal distribution began
in the eighteenth century as a
theoretical distribution for errors
in disciplines where fluctuations
in nature were believed to behave
randomly. Although he may not
have been the first to discover the
formula, the normal distribution
was named the Gaussian distribution after Carl Friedrich Gauss. A
well-known and respected German
mathematician, physicist, and
astronomer, Gauss applied the
normal distribution while studying
the motion of planets and stars.
Gauss's prowess as a mathematician was exemplified by one of
his most important discoveries.
At the young age of 22, Gauss
constructed a regular 17-gon by
ruler and compasses—a feat that
was the most major advance in
mathematics since the time of
the ancient Greeks. In addition to
publishing close to 200 scientific
papers, Gauss invented the
heliograph as well as a primitive
telegraph device.

Probability Distribution for a Normal Random Variable x

Probability density function: $f(x) = \dfrac{1}{\sigma\sqrt{2\pi}} e^{-\left(\frac{1}{2}\right)[(x-\mu)/\sigma]^2}$

where

μ = Mean of the normal random variable x

σ = Standard deviation

π = 3.1415 . . .

e = 2.71828 . . .

$P(x < a)$ is obtained from a table of normal probabilities or using statistical
software.

---

probability distribution is a difficult task.* Consequently, we will use the computed
areas listed in Table II in Appendix D. Although there are an infinitely large number of
normal curves–one for each pair of values for μ and σ—we have formed a single table
that will apply to any normal curve.

Table II is based on a normal distribution with mean $\mu = 0$ and standard deviation $\sigma = 1$, called a *standard normal distribution*. A random variable with a standard
normal distribution is typically denoted by the symbol z. The formula for the probability
distribution of z is given by

$$f(z) = \frac{1}{\sqrt{2\pi}} e^{-\left(\frac{1}{2}\right)z^2}$$

Figure 4.20 shows the graph of a standard normal distribution.

The **standard normal distribution** is a normal distribution with $\mu = 0$ and $\sigma = 1$.
A random variable with a standard normal distribution, denoted by the symbol z, is
called a *standard normal random variable*.

Because we will ultimately convert all normal random variables to standard nor-
mal in order to use Table II to find probabilities, it is important that you learn to use
Table II well. A partial reproduction of Table II is shown in Table 4.4. Note that the
values of the standard normal random variable z are listed in the left-hand column.
The entries in the body of the table give the area (probability) between 0 and z.
Examples 4.16–4.19 illustrate the use of the table.

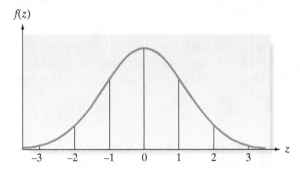

Figure 4.20

Standard normal distribution:
$\mu = 0, \sigma = 1$

---

*The student with knowledge of calculus should note that there is not a closed-form expression for
$P(a < x < b) = \displaystyle\int_a^b f(x)\, dx$ for the normal probability distribution. The value of this definite integral can be
obtained to any desired degree of accuracy by numerical approximation procedures. For this reason, it is tabulated for the user.

Table 4.4	Reproduction of Part of Table II in Appendix D

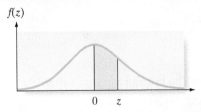

$f(z)$

z	.00	.01	.02	.03	.04	.05	.06	.07	.08	.09
.0	.0000	.0040	.0080	.0120	.0160	.0199	.0239	.0279	.0319	.0359
.1	.0398	.0438	.0478	.0517	.0557	.0596	.0636	.0675	.0714	.0753
.2	.0793	.0832	.0871	.0910	.0948	.0987	.1026	.1064	.1103	.1141
.3	.1179	.1217	.1255	.1293	.1331	.1368	.1406	.1443	.1480	.1517
.4	.1554	.1591	.1628	.1664	.1700	.1736	.1772	.1808	.1844	.1879
.5	.1915	.1950	.1985	.2019	.2054	.2088	.2123	.2157	.2190	.2224
.6	.2257	.2291	.2324	.2357	.2389	.2422	.2454	.2486	.2517	.2549
.7	.2580	.2611	.2642	.2673	.2704	.2734	.2764	.2794	.2823	.2852
.8	.2881	.2910	.2939	.2967	.2995	.3023	.3051	.3078	.3106	.3133
.9	.3159	.3186	.3212	.3238	.3264	.3289	.3315	.3340	.3365	.3389
1.0	.3413	.3438	.3461	.3485	.3508	.3531	.3554	.3577	.3599	.3621
1.1	.3643	.3665	.3686	.3708	.3729	.3749	.3770	.3790	.3810	.3830
1.2	.3849	.3869	.3888	.3907	.3925	.3944	.3962	.3980	.3997	.4015
1.3	.4032	.4049	.4066	.4082	.4099	.4115	.4131	.4147	.4162	.4177
1.4	.4192	.4207	.4222	.4236	.4251	.4265	.4279	.4292	.4306	.4319
1.5	.4332	.4345	.4357	.4370	.4382	.4394	.4406	.4418	.4429	.4441

Example	4.16

Using the Standard Normal Table to Find $P(-z_0 < z < z_0)$

Problem Find the probability that the standard normal random variable z falls between -1.33 and 1.33.

Solution The standard normal distribution is shown again in Figure 4.21. Because all probabilities associated with standard normal random variables can be depicted as areas under the standard normal curve, you should always draw the curve and then equate the desired probability to an area.

In this example, we want to find the probability that z falls between -1.33 and 1.33, which is equivalent to the area between -1.33 and 1.33, shown shaded in Figure 4.21. Table II provides the area between $z = 0$ and any positive value of z, so that if we look up $z = 1.33$ (the value in the 1.3 row and .03 column, as shown in Table 4.4), we find that the area between $z = 0$ and $z = 1.33$ is .4082. This is the area labeled A_1 in Figure 4.21. To find the area A_2 located between $z = 0$ and $z = -1.33$, we note that the symmetry of the normal distribution implies that the area between $z = 0$ and any point to the left is equal to the area between $z = 0$ and the point equidistant to the right. Thus, in this example, the area between $z = 0$ and $z = -1.33$ is equal to the area between $z = 0$ and $z = 1.33$. That is,

$$A_1 = A_2 = .4082$$

The probability that z falls between -1.33 and 1.33 is the sum of the areas of A_1 and A_2. We summarize in probabilistic notation:

$$P(-1.33 < z < 1.33) = P(-1.33 < z < 0) + P(0 < z < 1.33)$$

$$= A_1 + A_2 = .4082 + .4082 = .8164$$

Figure 4.21

Areas under the standard normal curve for Example 4.16

Look Back Remember that "<" and "≤" are equivalent in events involving z because the inclusion (or exclusion) of a single point does not alter the probability of an event involving a continuous random variable.

■ Now Work Exercise 4.87

Example 4.17

Using the Standard Normal Table to Find $P(z > z_0)$

Problem Find the probability that a standard normal random variable exceeds 1.64; that is, find $P(z > 1.64)$.

Solution The area under the standard normal distribution to the right of 1.64 is the shaded area labeled A_1 in Figure 4.22. This area represents the desired probability that z exceeds 1.64. However, when we look up $z = 1.64$ in Table II, we must remember that the probability given in the table corresponds to the area between $z = 0$ and $z = 1.64$ (the area labeled A_2 in Figure 4.22). From Table II, we find that $A_2 = .4495$. To find the area A_1 to the right of 1.64, we make use of two facts:

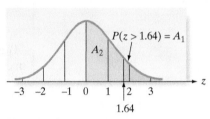

Figure 4.22

Areas under the standard normal curve for Example 4.17

1. The standard normal distribution is symmetric about its mean, $z = 0$.
2. The total area under the standard normal probability distribution equals 1.

Taken together, these two facts imply that the areas on either side of the mean $z = 0$ equal .5; thus, the area to the right of $z = 0$ in Figure 4.22 is $A_1 + A_2 = .5$. Then

$$P(z > 1.64) = A_1 = .5 - A_2 = .5 - .4495 = .0505$$

Look Back To attach some practical significance to this probability, note that the implication is that the chance of a standard normal random variable exceeding 1.64 is approximately .05.

■ Now Work Exercise 4.85a

Example 4.18

Using the Standard Normal Table to Find $P(z < z_0)$

Problem Find the probability that a standard normal random variable lies to the left of .67.

Solution The event is shown as the highlighted area in Figure 4.23. We want to find $P(z < .67)$. We divide the highlighted area into two parts: the area A_1 between $z = 0$ and $z = .67$ and the area A_2 to the left of $z = 0$. We must always make such a division when the desired area lies on both sides of the mean ($z = 0$) because Table II contains areas between $z = 0$ and the point you look up. We look up $z = .67$ in Table II to find that $A_1 = .2486$. The symmetry of the standard normal distribution also implies that half the distribution lies on each side of the mean, so the area A_2 to the left of $z = 0$ is .5. Then

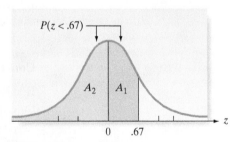

Figure 4.23

Areas under the standard normal curve for Example 4.18

$$P(z < .67) = A_1 + A_2 = .2486 + .5 = .7486$$

Look Back Note that this probability is approximately .75. Thus, about 75% of the time the standard normal random variable z will fall below .67. This implies that $z = .67$ represents the approximate 75th percentile for the distribution.

■ Now Work Exercise 4.86f

Example 4.19

Using the Standard Normal Table to Find $P(|z| > z_0)$

Problem Find the probability that a standard normal random variable exceeds 1.96 in absolute value.

Solution We want to find

$$P(|z| > 1.96) = P(z < -1.96 \text{ or } z > 1.96)$$

This probability is the shaded area in Figure 4.24. Note that the total shaded area is the sum of two areas, A_1 and A_2—areas that are equal because of the symmetry of the normal distribution.

Figure 4.24

Areas under the standard normal curve for Example 4.19

We look up $z = 1.96$ and find the area between $z = 0$ and $z = 1.96$ to be .4750. Then the area to the right of 1.96, A_2, is $.5 - .4750 = .0250$, so that

$$P(|z| > 1.96) = A_1 + A_2 = .0250 + .0250 = .05$$

Look Back We emphasize, again, the importance of drawing the standard normal curve when finding normal probabilities.

To apply Table II to a normal random variable x with any mean μ and any standard deviation σ, we must first convert the value of x to a z-score. The population z-score for a measurement was defined (in Section 2.7) as the *distance* between the measurement and the population mean, divided by the population standard deviation. Thus, the z-score gives the distance between a measurement and the mean in units equal to the standard deviation. In symbolic form, the z-score for the measurement x is

$$z = \frac{x - \mu}{\sigma}$$

Note that when $x = \mu$, we obtain $z = 0$.

An important property of the normal distribution is that if x is normally distributed with any mean and any standard deviation, z is always normally distributed with mean 0 and standard deviation 1. That is, z is a standard normal random variable.

Converting a Normal Distribution to a Standard Normal Distribution

If x is a normal random variable with mean μ and standard deviation σ, then the random variable z, defined by the formula

$$z = \frac{x - \mu}{\sigma}$$

has a standard normal distribution. The value z describes the number of standard deviations between x and μ.

Recall from Example 4.19 that $P(|z| > 1.96) = .05$. This probability coupled with our interpretation of z implies that any normal random variable lies more than 1.96 standard deviations from its mean only 5% of the time. Compare this to the Empirical Rule (Chapter 2), which tells us that about 5% of the measurements in mound-shaped distributions will lie beyond 2 standard deviations from the mean. The normal distribution actually provides the model on which the Empirical Rule is based, along with much "empirical" experience with real data that often approximately obey the rule, whether drawn from a normal distribution or not.

Example   4.20

Finding the Probability of a Normal Random Variable—Cell Phone Application

Problem Assume that the length of time, x, between charges of a cellular phone is normally distributed with a mean of 10 hours and a standard deviation of 1.5 hours. Find the probability that the cell phone will last between 8 and 12 hours between charges.

Figure 4.25

Areas under the normal curve for Example 4.20

Solution The normal distribution with mean $\mu = 10$ and $\sigma = 1.5$ is shown in Figure 4.25. The desired probability that the charge lasts between 8 and 12 hours is shaded. In order to find the probability, we must first convert the distribution to standard normal, which we do by calculating the z-score:

$$z = \frac{x - \mu}{\sigma}$$

The z-scores corresponding to the important values of x are shown beneath the x values on the horizontal axis in Figure 4.25. Note that $z = 0$ corresponds to the mean of $\mu = 10$ hours, whereas the x values 8 and 12 yield z-scores of -1.33 and 1.33, respectively. Thus, the event that the cell phone charge lasts between 8 and 12 hours is equivalent to the event that a standard normal random variable lies between -1.33 and 1.33. We found this probability in Example 4.16 (see Figure 4.21) by doubling the area corresponding to $z = 1.33$ in Table II. That is,

$$P(8 \le x \le 12) = P(-1.33 \le z \le 1.33) = 2(.4082) = .8164$$

▪ Now Work Exercise 4.100a–c

Table II in Appendix D provides good approximations to probabilities under the normal curve. However, if you do not have access to a normal table, you can always rely on statistical software to compute the desired probability. With most statistical software, you will need to specify the mean and standard deviation of the normal distribution, as well as the key values of the variable for which you desire probabilities. In Example 4.20, we desire $P(8 \le x \le 12)$, where $\mu = 10$ and $\sigma = 1.5$. To find this probability using Minitab's normal probability function, we enter 10 for the mean and 1.5 for the standard deviation, and then find two cumulative probabilities: $P(x \le 12)$ and $P(x < 8)$. These two probabilities are shown (shaded) on the Minitab printout, Figure 4.26. The difference between the two probabilities yields the desired result:

$$P(8 \le x \le 12) = P(x \le 12) - P(x < 8) = .908789 - .0912112 = .8175778$$

Note that this probability agrees with the value computed using Table II to two decimal places. The difference is due to rounding of the probabilities given in Table II.

The steps to follow when calculating a probability corresponding to a normal random variable are shown in the box on the next page.

Cumulative Distribution Function

Normal with mean = 10 and standard deviation = 1.5

```
 x   P( X <= x )
12      0.908789
```

Cumulative Distribution Function

Normal with mean = 10 and standard deviation = 1.5

Figure 4.26

Minitab output with cumulative normal probabilities

```
 x   P( X <= x )
 8      0.0912112
```

Steps for Finding a Probability Corresponding to a Normal Random Variable

1. Sketch the normal distribution and indicate the mean of the random variable x. Then shade the area corresponding to the probability you want to find.
2. Convert the boundaries of the shaded area from x values to standard normal random variable z values using the formula

$$z = \frac{x - \mu}{\sigma}$$

   Show the z values under the corresponding x values on your sketch.
3. Use Table II in Appendix D or statistical software to find the areas corresponding to the z values. If necessary, use the symmetry of the normal distribution to find areas corresponding to negative z values and the fact that the total area on each side of the mean equals .5 to convert the areas to the probabilities of the event you have shaded.

Example 4.21

Using Normal Probabilities to Make an Inference—Advertised Gas Mileage

Problem Suppose an automobile manufacturer introduces a new model that has an advertised mean in-city mileage of 27 miles per gallon. Although such advertisements seldom report any measure of variability, suppose you write the manufacturer for the details of the tests, and you find that the standard deviation is 3 miles per gallon. This information leads you to formulate a probability model for the random variable x, the in-city mileage for this car model. You believe that the probability distribution of x can be approximated by a normal distribution with a mean of 27 and a standard deviation of 3.

Figure 4.27

Areas under the normal curve for Example 4.21

a. If you were to buy this model of automobile, what is the probability that you would purchase one that averages less than 20 miles per gallon for in-city driving? In other words, find $P(x < 20)$.

b. Suppose you purchase one of these new models and it does get less than 20 miles per gallon for in-city driving. Should you conclude that your probability model is incorrect?

Solution

a. The probability model proposed for x, the in-city mileage, is shown in Figure 4.27. We are interested in finding the area A to the left of 20 because this area corresponds to the probability that a measurement chosen from this distribution falls below 20. In other words, if this model is correct, the area A represents the fraction of cars that can be expected to get less than 20 miles per gallon for in-city driving. To find A, we first calculate the z-value corresponding to $x = 20$. That is,

$$z = \frac{x - \mu}{\sigma} = \frac{20 - 27}{3} = -\frac{7}{3} = -2.33$$

Then

$$P(x < 20) = P(z < -2.33)$$

as indicated by the shaded area in Figure 4.27. Because Table II gives areas only to the right of the mean (and because the normal distribution is symmetric about its mean), we look up 2.33 in Table II and find that the corresponding area is .4901. This is equal to the area between $z = 0$ and $z = -2.33$, so we find

$$P(x < 20) = A = .5 - .4901 = .0099 \approx .01$$

According to this probability model, you should have only about a 1% chance of purchasing a car of this make with an in-city mileage under 20 miles per gallon.

b. Now you are asked to make an inference based on a sample—the car you purchased. You are getting less than 20 miles per gallon for in-city driving. What do you infer? We think you will agree that one of two possibilities is true:

1. The probability model is correct. You simply were unfortunate to have purchased one of the cars in the 1% that get less than 20 miles per gallon in the city.

2. The probability model is incorrect. Perhaps the assumption of a normal distribution is unwarranted or the mean of 27 is an overestimate, or the standard deviation of 3 is an underestimate, or some combination of these errors was made. At any rate, the form of the actual probability model certainly merits further investigation.

You have no way of knowing with certainty which possibility is correct, but the evidence points to the second one. We are again relying on the rare-event approach to statistical inference that we introduced earlier. The sample (one measurement in this case) was so unlikely to have been drawn from the proposed probability model that it casts serious doubt on the model. We would be inclined to believe that the model is somehow in error.

Look Back When applying the rare-event approach, the calculated probability must be small (say, less than or equal to .05) in order to infer that the observed event is, indeed, unlikely.

—■ **Now Work Exercise 4.100d**

Occasionally you will be given a probability and will want to find the values of the normal random variable that correspond to the probability. For example, suppose the scores on a college entrance examination are known to be normally distributed, and a certain prestigious university will consider for admission only those applicants whose scores exceed the 90th percentile of the test score distribution. To determine the minimum score for admission consideration, you will need to be able to use Table II or statistical software in reverse, as demonstrated in the following example.

Example 4.22	

Finding a z-value Associated with a Normal Probability

Problem Find the value of z, call it z_0, in the standard normal distribution that will be exceeded only 10% of the time—that is, find z_0 such that $P(z \geq z_0) = .10$.

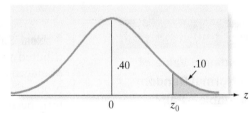

Figure 4.28
Area under the standard normal curve for Example 4.22

Solution In this case we are given a probability, or an area, and asked to find the value of the standard normal random variable that corresponds to the area. Specifically, we want to find the value z_0 such that only 10% of the standard normal distribution exceeds z_0 (see Figure 4.28).

We know that the total area to the right of the mean $z = 0$ is .5, which implies that z_0 must lie to the right of (above) 0. To pinpoint the value, we use the fact that the area to the right of z_0 is .10, which implies that the area between $z = 0$ and z_0 is $.5 - .1 = .4$. But areas between $z = 0$ and some other z-value are exactly the types given in Table II. Therefore, we look up the area .4000 in the body of Table II and find that the corresponding z-value is (to the closest approximation) $z_0 = 1.28$. The implication is that the point 1.28 standard deviations above the mean is the 90th percentile of a normal distribution.

We can also arrive at this answer using statistical software. In Minitab, we use the inverse cumulative distribution function for a normal random variable and specify the cumulative probability,

$$P(z \leq z_0) = .9$$

Figure 4.29
Minitab output for Example 4.22

Inverse Cumulative Distribution Function

Normal with mean = 0 and standard deviation = 1

```
P( X <= x )       x
         0.9  1.28155
```

The value of z_0 is shown (shaded) on the Minitab printout, Figure 4.29. You can see that this value agrees with our solution using the normal table.

Look Back As with earlier problems, it is critical to draw correctly the normal probability of interest on the normal curve. Placement of z_0 to the left or right of 0 is the key. Be sure to shade the probability (area) involving z_0. If it does not agree with the probability of interest (i.e., the shaded area is greater than .5 and the probability of interest is smaller than .5), then you need to place z_0 on the opposite side of 0.

■ **Now Work Exercise 4.89**

Example 4.23

Finding a z-Value Associated with a Normal Probability

Problem Find the value of z_0 such that 95% of the standard normal z values lie between $-z_0$ and z_0; that is, $P(-z_0 \le z \le z_0) = .95$.

Solution Here we wish to move an equal distance z_0 in the positive and negative directions from the mean $z = 0$ until 95% of the standard normal distribution is enclosed. This means that the area on each side of the mean will be equal to $\frac{1}{2}(.95) = .475$, as shown in Figure 4.30. Because the area between $z = 0$ and z_0 is .475, we look up .475 in the body of Table II to find the value $z_0 = 1.96$. Thus, as we found in the reverse order in Example 4.22, 95% of a normal distribution lies between -1.96 and 1.96 standard deviations of the mean.

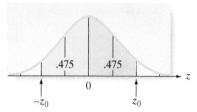

Figure 4.30
Areas under the standard normal curve for Example 4.23

■ **Now Work Exercise 4.92**

Now that you have learned how to find a standard normal z-value that corresponds to a specified probability, we demonstrate a practical application in Example 4.24.

Example 4.24

Finding a Value of a Normal Random Variable — Paint Manufacturing Application

Problem Suppose a paint manufacturer has a daily production, x, that is normally distributed with a mean of 100,000 gallons and a standard deviation of 10,000 gallons. Management wants to create an incentive bonus for the production crew when the daily production exceeds the 90th percentile of the distribution, in hopes that the crew will, in turn, become more productive. At what level of production should management pay the incentive bonus?

Solution In this example, we want to find a production level, x_0, such that 90% of the daily levels (x values) in the distribution fall below x_0 and only 10% fall above x_0—that is,

$$P(x \le x_0) = .90$$

Converting x to a standard normal random variable, where $\mu = 100,000$ and $\sigma = 10,000$, we have

$$P(x \le x_0) = P\left(z \le \frac{x_0 - \mu}{\sigma}\right)$$

$$= P\left(z \le \frac{x_0 - 100,000}{10,000}\right) = .90$$

In Example 4.22 (see Figure 4.28) we found the 90th percentile of the standard normal distribution to be $z_0 = 1.28$—that is, we found $P(z \le 1.28) = .90$. Consequently, we know the production level x_0 at which the incentive bonus is paid corresponds to a z-score of 1.28; that is,

$$\frac{x_0 - 100{,}000}{10{,}000} = 1.28$$

If we solve this equation for x_0, we find

$$x_0 = 100{,}000 + 1.28(10{,}000) = 100{,}000 + 12{,}800 = 112{,}800$$

This x value is shown in Figure 4.31. Thus, the 90th percentile of the production distribution is 112,800 gallons. Management should pay an incentive bonus when a day's production exceeds this level if its objective is to pay only when production is in the top 10% of the current daily production distribution.

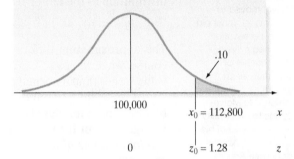

Figure 4.31

Area under the normal curve
for Example 4.24

Look Back As this example shows, in practical applications of the normal table in reverse, first find the value of z_0, then convert the value to the units of x using the z-score formula in reverse.

■ Now Work Exercise 4.97a

We close this section with one final application of the normal distribution. When n is large, a normal probability distribution may be used to provide a good approximation to the probability distribution of the discrete binomial random variable (Section 4.3). To show how this approximation works, we refer to Example 4.13, in which we used the binomial distribution to model the number x of 20 employees who favor unionization. We assumed that 60% of the company's employees favored unionization. The mean and standard deviation of x were found to be $\mu = 12$ and $\sigma = 2.2$. The binomial distribution for $n = 20$ and $p = .6$ is shown in Figure 4.32 and the approximating normal distribution with mean $\mu = 12$ and standard deviation $\sigma = 2.2$ is superimposed.

As part of Example 4.13, we used Table I to find the probability that $x \le 10$. This probability, which is equal to the sum of the areas contained in the rectangles (shown in Figure 4.32) that correspond to $p(0), p(1), p(2), \ldots, p(10)$, was found to equal .245. The portion of the approximating normal curve that would be used to approximate the

Figure 4.32

Binomial distribution for $n = 20$,
$p = .6$, and normal distribution
with $\mu = 12, \sigma = 2.2$

area $p(0) + p(1) + p(2) + \cdots + p(10)$ is shaded in Figure 4.32. Note that this shaded area lies to the left of 10.5 (not 10), so we may include all of the probability in the rectangle corresponding to $p(10)$. Because we are approximating a discrete distribution (the binomial) with a continuous distribution (the normal), we call the use of 10.5 (instead of 10 or 11) a **correction for continuity,** that is, we are correcting the discrete distribution so that it can be approximated by the continuous one. The use of the correction for continuity leads to the calculation of the following standard normal z-value:

$$z = \frac{x - \mu}{\sigma} = \frac{10.5 - 12}{2.2} = -.68$$

Using Table II, we find the area between $z = 0$ and $z = .68$ to be .2517. Then the probability that x is less than or equal to 10 is approximated by the area under the normal distribution to the left of 10.5, shown shaded in Figure 4.32—that is,

$$P(x \le 10) \approx P(z \le -.68) = .5 - P(-.68 < z \le 0) = .5 - .2517 = .2483$$

The approximation differs only slightly from the exact binomial probability, .245. Of course, when tables of exact binomial probabilities are available, we will use the exact value rather than a normal approximation.

Use of the normal distribution will not always provide a good approximation for binomial probabilities. The following is a useful rule of thumb to determine when n is large enough for the approximation to be effective: *The interval $\mu \pm 3\sigma$ should lie within the range of the binomial random variable x (i.e., 0 to n) in order for the normal approximation to be adequate.* The rule works well because almost all of the normal distribution falls within 3 standard deviations of the mean, so if this interval is contained within the range of x values, there is "room" for the normal approximation to work.

As shown in Figure 4.33a for the preceding example with $n = 20$ and $p = .6$, the interval $\mu \pm 3\sigma = 12 \pm 3(2.2) = (5.4, 18.6)$ lies within the range 0 to 20. However, if we were to try to use the normal approximation with $n = 10$ and $p = .1$, the interval $\mu \pm 3\sigma$ is $1 \pm 3(.95)$, or $(-1.85, 3.85)$. As shown in Figure 4.33b, this interval is

a. $n = 20, p = .6$: Normal approximation is good

Figure 4.33

Rule of thumb for normal approximation to binomial probabilities

b. $n = 10, p = .1$: Normal approximation is poor

not contained within the range of x because $x = 0$ is the lower bound for a binomial random variable. Note in Figure 4.33b that the normal distribution will not "fit" in the range of x, and therefore it will not provide a good approximation to the binomial probabilities.

Example 4.25

Applying the Normal Approximation to a Binomial Probability—Lot Acceptance Sampling

Problem One problem with any product (e.g., a graphing calculator) that is mass produced is quality control. The process must somehow be monitored or audited to be sure the output of the process conforms to requirements. One method of dealing with this problem is *lot acceptance sampling,* in which items being produced are sampled at various stages of the production process and are carefully inspected. The lot of items from which the sample is drawn is then accepted or rejected, based on the number of defectives in the sample. Lots that are accepted may be sent forward for further processing or may be shipped to customers; lots that are rejected may be reworked or scrapped. For example, suppose a manufacturer of calculators chooses 200 stamped circuits from the day's production and determines x, the number of defective circuits in the sample. Suppose that up to a 6% rate of defectives is considered acceptable for the process.

a. Find the mean and standard deviation of x, assuming the defective rate is 6%.

b. Use the normal approximation to determine the probability that 20 or more defectives are observed in the sample of 200 circuits (i.e., find the approximate probability that $x \geq 20$).

Solution

a. The random variable x is binomial with $n = 200$ and the fraction defective $p = .06$. Thus,

$$\mu = np = 200(.06) = 12$$
$$\sigma = \sqrt{npq} = \sqrt{200(.06)(.94)} = \sqrt{11.28} = 3.36$$

We first note that

$$\mu \pm 3\sigma = 12 \pm 3(3.36) = 12 \pm 10.08 = (1.92, 22.08)$$

lies completely within the range from 0 to 200. Therefore, a normal probability distribution should provide an adequate approximation to this binomial distribution.

b. Using the rule of complements, $P(x \geq 20) = 1 - P(x \leq 19)$. To find the approximating area corresponding to $x \leq 19$, refer to Figure 4.34. Note that we want to include all the binomial probability histogram from 0 to 19, inclusive. Because the event is of the form $x \leq a$, the proper correction for continuity is $a + .5 = 19 + .5 = 19.5$. Thus, the z-value of interest is

$$z = \frac{(a + .5) - \mu}{\sigma} = \frac{19.5 - 12}{3.36} = \frac{7.5}{3.36} = 2.23$$

Figure 4.34

Normal approximation to the binomial distribution with $n = 200, p = .06$

Figure 4.35

Standard normal distribution

Referring to Table II in Appendix D, we find that the area to the right of the mean 0 corresponding to $z = 2.23$ (see Figure 4.35) is .4871. So the area $A = P(z \leq 2.23)$ is

$$A = .5 + .4871 = .9871$$

Thus, the normal approximation to the binomial probability we seek is

$$P(x \geq 20) = 1 - P(x \leq 19) \approx 1 - .9871 = .0129$$

In other words, the probability is extremely small that 20 or more defectives will be observed in a sample of 200 circuits—*if in fact the true fraction of defectives is .06.*

Look Back If the manufacturer observes $x \geq 20$, the likely reason is that the process is producing more than the acceptable 6% defectives. The lot acceptance sampling procedure is another example of using the rare-event approach to make inferences.

◼ **Now Work Exercise 4.95**

The steps for approximating a binomial probability by a normal probability are given in the next box.

Using a Normal Distribution to Approximate Binomial Probabilities

1. After you have determined n and p for the binomial distribution, calculate the interval

$$\mu \pm 3\sigma = np \pm 3\sqrt{npq}$$

If the interval lies in the range 0 to n, the normal distribution will provide a reasonable approximation to the probabilities of most binomial events.

2. Express the binomial probability to be approximated in the form $P(x \leq a)$ or $P(x \leq b) - P(x \leq a)$. For example,

$$P(x < 3) = P(x \leq 2)$$
$$P(x \geq 5) = 1 - P(x \leq 4)$$
$$P(7 \leq x \leq 10) = P(x \leq 10) - P(x \leq 6)$$

3. For each value of interest a, the correction for continuity is $(a + .5)$, and the corresponding standard normal z-value is

$$z = \frac{(a + .5) - \mu}{\sigma} \quad \text{(See Figure 4.36)}$$

4. Sketch the approximating normal distribution and shade the area corresponding to the probability of the event of interest, as in Figure 4.36. Verify that the rectangles you have included in the shaded area correspond to the event probability you wish to approximate. Using Table II and the z-value(s) you calculated in step 3, find the shaded area. This is the approximate probability of the binomial event.

Figure 4.36

Approximating binomial probabilities by normal probabilities

Exercises 4.84–4.116

Learning the Mechanics

4.84 Find the area under the standard normal probability distribution between the following pairs of z-scores:
  a. $z = 0$ and $z = 2.00$ **b.** $z = 0$ and $z = 3$
  c. $z = 0$ and $z = 1.5$ **d.** $z = 0$ and $z = .80$

4.85 Find the following probabilities for the standard normal
NW random variable z:
  a. $P(z > 1.46)$ **b.** $P(z < -1.56)$
  c. $P(.67 \leq z < 2.41)$ **d.** $P(-1.96 \leq z < -.33)$
  e. $P(z \geq 0)$ **f.** $P(-2.33 < z < 1.50)$

4.86 Find the following probabilities for the standard normal random variable z:
  a. $P(-1 < z < 1)$ **b.** $P(-2 < z < 2)$
  c. $P(-2.16 \leq z \leq .55)$ **d.** $P(-.42 < z < 1.96)$
  e. $P(z \geq -2.33)$ NW **f.** $P(z < 2.33)$

4.87 Find each of the following probabilities for the standard
NW normal random variable z:
  a. $P(-1 \leq z \leq 1)$ **b.** $P(-1.96 \leq z \leq 1.96)$
  c. $P(-1.645 \leq z \leq 1.645)$ **d.** $P(-2 \leq z \leq 2)$

4.88 Find a value of the standard normal random variable z, call it z_0, such that
  a. $P(z \geq z_0) = .05$ **b.** $P(z \geq z_0) = .025$
  c. $P(z \leq z_0) = .025$ **d.** $P(z \geq z_0) = .10$
  e. $P(z > z_0) = .10$

4.89 Find a value of the standard normal random variable z, call
NW it z_0, such that
  a. $P(z \leq z_0) = .2090$
  b. $P(z \leq z_0) = .7090$
  c. $P(-z_0 \leq z < z_0) = .8472$
  d. $P(-z_0 \leq z < z_0) = .1664$
  e. $P(z_0 \leq z \leq 0) = .4798$
  f. $P(-1 < z < z_0)$

4.90 Give the z-score for a measurement from a normal distribution for the following:
  a. 1 standard deviation above the mean
  b. 1 standard deviation below the mean
  c. Equal to the mean
  d. 2.5 standard deviations below the mean
  e. 3 standard deviations above the mean

4.91 Suppose the random variable x is best described by a normal distribution with $\mu = 30$ and $\sigma = 4$. Find the z-score that corresponds to each of the following x values:
  a. $x = 20$ **b.** $x = 30$
  c. $x = 2.75$ **d.** $x = 15$
  e. $x = 35$ **f.** $x = 25$

4.92 The random variable x has a normal distribution with
NW $\mu = 1,000$ and $\sigma = 10$.
  a. Find the probability that x assumes a value more than 2 standard deviations from its mean. More than 3 standard deviations from μ.
  b. Find the probability that x assumes a value within 1 standard deviation of its mean. Within 2 standard deviations of μ.
  c. Find the value of x that represents the 80th percentile of this distribution. The 10th percentile.

4.93 Suppose x is a normally distributed random variable with $\mu = 11$ and $\sigma = 2$. Find each of the following:
  a. $P(10 \leq x \leq 12)$ **b.** $P(6 \leq x \leq 10)$
  c. $P(13 \leq x \leq 16)$ **d.** $P(7.8 \leq x \leq 12.6)$
  e. $P(x \geq 13.24)$ **f.** $P(x \geq 7.62)$

4.94 Suppose x is a normally distributed random variable with $\mu = 50$ and $\sigma = 3$. Find a value of the random variable, call it x_0, such that
  a. $P(x \leq x_0) = .8413$
  b. $P(x > x_0) = .025$
  c. $P(x > x_0) = .95$
  d. $P(41 \leq x < x_0) = .8630$
  e. 10% of the values of x are less than x_0.
  f. 1% of the values of x are greater than x_0.

4.95 Suppose x is a binomial random variable with $p = .4$ and
NW $n = 25$.
  a. Would it be appropriate to approximate the probability distribution of x with a normal distribution? Explain.
  b. Assuming that a normal distribution provides an adequate approximation to the distribution of x, what are the mean and variance of the approximating normal distribution?
  c. Use Table I in Appendix D to find the exact value of $P(x \geq 9)$.
  d. Use the normal approximation to find $P(x \geq 9)$.

4.96 Assume that x is a binomial random variable with $n = 1,000$ and $p = .50$. Use a normal approximation to find each of the following probabilities:
  a. $P(x > 500)$
  b. $P(490 \leq x < 500)$
  c. $P(x > 550)$

⊙ Applet Exercise 4.6

Open the applet *Sample from a Population*. On the pull-down menu to the right of the top graph, select *Bell shaped*. The box to the left of the top graph displays the population mean, median, and standard deviation.
  a. Run the applet for each available value of n on the pull-down menu for the sample size. Go from the smallest to the largest value of n. For each value of n, observe the shape of the graph of the sample data and record the mean, median, and standard deviation of the sample.
  b. Describe what happens to the shape of the graph and the mean, median, and standard deviation of the sample as the sample size increases.

Applying the Concepts—Basic

4.97 **Tomato as a taste modifier.** Miraculin—a protein naturally produced in a rare tropical fruit—can convert a sour taste into a sweet taste. Consequently, miraculin has the potential to be an alternative low-calorie sweetener. In *Plant Science* (May 2010), a group of Japanese environmental scientists investigated the ability of a hybrid tomato plant to produce miraculin. For a particular generation of the tomato plant, the amount x of miraculin produced (measured in micrograms per gram of fresh weight) had a mean of 105.3 and a standard deviation of 8.0. Assume that x is normally distributed.

a. Find $P(x > 120)$.

b. Find $P(100 < x < 110)$.

NW **c.** Find the value a for which $P(x < a) = .25$.

4.98 Corporate sustainability of CPA firms. Refer to the *Business and Society* (March 2011) study on the sustainability behaviors of CPA corporations, Exercise 2.23 (p. 59).
CORSUS Recall that the level of support for corporate sustainability (measured on a quantitative scale ranging from 0 to 160 points) was obtained for each of 992 senior managers at CPA firms. The accompanying Minitab printout gives the mean and standard deviation for the level of support variable. It can be shown that level of support is approximately normally distributed.

a. Find the probability that the level of support for corporate sustainability of a randomly selected senior manager is less than 40 points.

b. Find the probability that the level of support for corporate sustainability of a randomly selected senior manager is between 40 and 120 points.

c. Find the probability that the level of support for corporate sustainability of a randomly selected senior manager is greater than 120 points.

d. One-fourth of the 992 senior managers indicated a level of support for corporate sustainability below what value?

Descriptive Statistics: Support

Variable	N	Mean	StDev	Variance	Minimum	Maximum	Range
Support	992	67.755	26.871	722.036	0.000	155.000	155.000

4.99 Shopping vehicle and judgment. Refer to the *Journal of Marketing Research* (Dec. 2011) study of whether you are more likely to choose a vice product (e.g., a candy bar) when your arm is flexed (as when carrying a shopping basket) than when your arm is extended (as when pushing a shopping cart), Exercise 2.85 (p. 85). The study measured choice scores (on a scale of 0 to 100, where higher scores indicate a greater preference for vice options) for consumers shopping under each of the two conditions. Recall that the average choice score for consumers with a flexed arm was 59, while the average for consumers with an extended arm was 43. For both conditions, assume that the standard deviation of the choice scores is 5. Also assume that both distributions are approximately normally distributed.

a. In the flexed arm condition, what is the probability that a consumer has a choice score of 60 or greater?

b. In the extended arm condition, what is the probability that a consumer has a choice score of 60 or greater?

4.100 The business of casino gaming. Casino gaming yields over
NW $35 billion in revenue each year in the United States. In *Chance* (Spring 2005), University of Denver statistician R. C. Hannum discussed the business of casino gaming and its reliance on the laws of probability. Casino games of pure chance (e.g., craps, roulette, baccarat, and keno) always yield a "house advantage." For example, in the game of double-zero roulette, the expected casino win percentage is 5.26% on bets made on whether the outcome will be either black or red. (This implies that for every $5 bet on black or red, the casino will earn a net of about 25¢.)

It can be shown that in 100 roulette plays on black/red, the average casino win percentage is normally distributed with mean 5.26% and standard deviation 10%. Let x represent the average casino win percentage after 100 bets on black/red in double-zero roulette.

a. Find $P(x > 0)$. (This is the probability that the casino wins money.)

b. Find $P(5 < x < 15)$.

c. Find $P(x < 1)$.

d. If you observed an average casino win percentage of -25% after 100 roulette bets on black/red, what would you conclude?

4.101 Buy-side vs. sell-side analysts' earnings forecasts. Financial analysts who make forecasts of stock prices are categorized as either "buy-side" analysts or "sell-side" analysts. Refer to the *Financial Analysts Journal* (Jul./Aug. 2008) comparison of earnings forecasts of buy-side and sell-side analysts, Exercise 2.86 (p. 86). The mean and standard deviation of forecast errors for both types of analysts are reproduced in the table. Assume that the distribution of forecast errors are approximately normally distributed.

a. Find the probability that a buy-side analyst has a forecast error of $+2.00$ or higher.

b. Find the probability that a sell-side analyst has a forecast error of $+2.00$ or higher.

	Buy-Side Analysts	Sell-Side Analysts
Mean	0.85	−0.05
Standard Deviation	1.93	0.85

Source: Based on Groysberg, B., Healy, P., & Chapman, C. *Financial Analysis Journal*, Vol. 64, No. 4, Jul./Aug. 2008.

4.102 NHTSA crash safety tests. Refer to Exercise 4.21 (p. 195)
CRASH and the NHTSA crash test data for new cars. One of the variables saved in the accompanying file is the severity of a driver's head injury when the car is in a head-on collision with a fixed barrier while traveling at 35 miles per hour. The more points assigned to the head-injury rating, the more severe the injury. The head-injury ratings can be shown to be approximately normally distributed with a mean of 605 points and a standard deviation of 185 points. One of the crash-tested cars is randomly selected from the data, and the driver's head-injury rating is observed.

a. Find the probability that the rating will fall between 500 and 700 points.

b. Find the probability that the rating will fall between 400 and 500 points.

c. Find the probability that the rating will be less than 850 points.

d. Find the probability that the rating will exceed 1,000 points.

4.103 Paying for music downloads. In Exercise 4.49 (p. 210) you learned that half of all U.S. adults use the Internet and have paid to download music (*Pew Internet & American Life Project Survey,* October 2010). In a random sample of 250 U.S. adults, let x be the number who use the Internet and pay to download music.

a. Find the mean of x. (This value should agree with your answer to Exercise 4.49c.)

b. Find the standard deviation of x.

c. Find the z-score for the value $x = 200$.

d. Find the approximate probability that the number of the 250 adults who use the Internet and pay to download music is less than or equal to 200.

4.104 LASIK surgery complications. According to studies, 1% of all patients who undergo laser surgery (i.e., LASIK) to correct their vision have serious postlaser vision problems (*All About Vision*, 2012). In a sample of 100,000 patients, what is the approximate probability that fewer than 950 will experience serious postlaser vision problems?

Applying the Concepts—Intermediate

4.105 Optimal goal target in soccer. When attempting to score a goal in soccer, where should you aim your shot? Should you aim for a goalpost (as some soccer coaches teach), the middle of the goal, or some other target? To answer these questions, *Chance* (Fall 2009) utilized the normal probability distribution. Suppose the accuracy x of a professional soccer player's shots follows a normal distribution with a mean of 0 feet and a standard deviation of 3 feet. (For example, if the player hits his target, $x = 0$; if he misses his target 2 feet to the right, $x = 2$; and if he misses 1 foot to the left, $x = -1$.) Now, a regulation soccer goal is 24 feet wide. Assume that a goalkeeper will stop (save) all shots within 9 feet of where he is standing; all other shots on goal will score. Consider a goalkeeper who stands in the middle of the goal.

a. If the player aims for the right goalpost, what is the probability that he will score?

b. If the player aims for the center of the goal, what is the probability that he will score?

c. If the player aims for halfway between the right goalpost and the outer limit of the goalkeeper's reach, what is the probability that he will score?

4.106 Mean shifts on a production line. *Six Sigma* is a comprehensive approach to quality goal setting that involves statistics. An article in *Aircraft Engineering and Aerospace Technology* (Vol. 76, No. 6, 2004) demonstrated the use of the normal distribution in Six Sigma goal setting at Motorola Corporation. Motorola discovered that the average defect rate for parts produced on an assembly line varies from run to run and is approximately normally distributed with a mean equal to 3 defects per million. Assume that the goal at Motorola is for the average defect rate to vary no more than 1.5 standard deviations above or below the mean of 3. How likely is it that the goal will be met?

4.107 Rating employee performance. Almost all companies utilize some type of year-end performance review for their employees. Human Resources (HR) at the University of Texas Health Science Center provides guidelines for supervisors rating their subordinates. For example, raters are advised to examine their ratings for a tendency to be either too lenient or too harsh. According to HR, "If you have this tendency, consider using a normal distribution—10% of employees (rated) exemplary, 20% distinguished, 40% competent, 20% marginal, and 10% unacceptable." Suppose you are rating an employee's performance on a scale of 1 (lowest) to 100 (highest). Also, assume the ratings follow a normal distribution with a mean of 50 and a standard deviation of 15.

a. What is the lowest rating you should give to an "exemplary" employee if you follow the University of Texas HR guidelines?

b. What is the lowest rating you should give to a "competent" employee if you follow the University of Texas HR guidelines?

4.108 Ambulance response time. Ambulance response time is measured as the time (in minutes) between the initial call to emergency medical services (EMS) and when the patient is reached by ambulance. *Geographical Analysis* (Vol. 41, 2009) investigated the characteristics of ambulance response time for EMS calls in Edmonton, Alberta. For a particular EMS station (call it Station A), ambulance response time is known to be normally distributed with $\mu = 7.5$ minutes and $\sigma = 2.5$ minutes.

a. Regulations require that 90% of all emergency calls be reached in 9 minutes or less. Are the regulations met at EMS Station A? Explain.

b. A randomly selected EMS call in Edmonton has an ambulance response time of 2 minutes. Is it likely that this call was serviced by Station A? Explain.

4.109 Personnel dexterity tests. Personnel tests are designed to test a job applicant's cognitive and/or physical abilities. The Wonderlic IQ test is an example of the former; the Purdue Pegboard speed test involving the arrangement of pegs on a peg board is an example of the latter. A particular dexterity test is administered nationwide by a private testing service. It is known that for all tests administered last year, the distribution of scores was approximately normal with mean 75 and standard deviation 7.5.

a. A particular employer requires job candidates to score at least 80 on the dexterity test. Approximately what percentage of the test scores during the past year exceeded 80?

b. The testing service reported to a particular employer that one of its job candidate's scores fell at the 98th percentile of the distribution (i.e., approximately 98% of the scores were lower than the candidate's, and only 2% were higher). What was the candidate's score?

4.110 Manufacturing hourly pay rate. Government data indicate that the mean hourly wage for manufacturing workers in the United States is $18.50 (*Statistical Abstract of the United States: 2012*). Suppose the distribution of manufacturing wage rates nationwide can be approximated by a normal distribution with standard deviation $1.25 per hour. The first manufacturing firm contacted by a particular worker seeking a new job pays $19.80 per hour.

a. If the worker were to undertake a nationwide job search, approximately what proportion of the wage rates would be greater than $19.80 per hour?

b. If the worker were to randomly select a U.S. manufacturing firm, what is the probability the firm would pay more than $19.80 per hour?

c. The population median, call it η, of a continuous random variable x is the value such that $P(x \geq \eta) = P(x \leq \eta) = .5$—that is, the median is the value η such that half the area under the probability distribution lies above η and half lies below it. Find the median of the random variable corresponding to the wage rate and compare it to the mean wage rate.

4.111 California's electoral college votes. During a presidential election, each state is allotted a different number of votes in the Electoral College depending on population. For example, California is allotted 55 votes (the most) while several states (including the District of Columbia) are allotted 3 votes each (the least). When a presidential candidate wins the popular vote in a state, the candidate wins all the Electoral College votes in that state. To become president, a candidate must win 270 of the total of 538 votes in the Electoral College. *Chance* (Winter 2010) demonstrated the impact on the presidential election of winning California. Assuming a candidate wins California's 55 votes, the number of additional Electoral College votes the candidate will win can be approximated by a normal distribution with $\mu = 241.5$ votes and $\sigma = 49.8$ votes. If a presidential candidate wins the popular vote in California, what are the chances that he or she becomes the next U.S. president?

4.112 Hotel guest satisfaction. Refer to the North American Hotel Guest Satisfaction Index Study, Exercise 4.48 (p. 210). You determined that the probability of a hotel guest participating in the hotel's "green" conservation program by reusing towels and bed linens is .45. Suppose a large hotel chain randomly samples 200 of its guests. The chain's national director claims that more than 110 of these guests participated in the conservation program. Do you believe this claim? Explain.

4.113 Credit card market shares. The following table reports the U.S. credit card industry's market share data for 2011. A random sample of 100 credit card users is to be questioned regarding their satisfaction with their credit card company. For simplification, assume that each credit card user carries just one credit card and that the market share percentages are the percentages of all credit card customers that carry each brand.

Credit Card	Market Share %
Visa	50
MasterCard	33
Discover	9
American Express	8

Source: Based on *Nilson Report* data, May 2008.

a. Propose a procedure for randomly selecting the 100 credit card users.

b. For random samples of 100 credit card users, what is the expected number of customers who carry Visa? Discover?

c. What is the probability that half or more of the sample of credit card users carry Visa? American Express?

d. Justify the use of the normal approximation to the binomial in answering the question in part **c.**

Applying the Concepts—Advanced

4.114 Industrial filling process. The characteristics of an industrial filling process in which an expensive liquid is injected into a container were investigated in the *Journal of Quality Technology* (July 1999). The quantity injected per container is approximately normally distributed with

mean 10 units and standard deviation .2 units. Each unit of fill costs $20 per unit. If a container contains less than 10 units (i.e., is underfilled), it must be reprocessed at a cost of $10. A properly filled container sells for $230.

a. Find the probability that a container is underfilled. Not underfilled.

b. A container is initially underfilled and must be reprocessed. Upon refilling, it contains 10.60 units. How much profit will the company make on this container?

c. The operations manager adjusts the mean of the filling process upward to 10.10 units in order to make the probability of underfilling approximately zero. Under these conditions, what is the expected profit per container?

4.115 Executive coaching and meeting effectiveness. Poor executive leadership during business meetings can result in counterproductive outcomes (e.g., negative employee attitudes, ambiguous objectives). Can executive coaching help improve business meeting effectiveness? This was the question of interest in an article published in *Consulting Psychology Journal: Practice and Research* (Vol. 61, 2009). Certain behaviors by leaders during meetings were categorized as content behaviors (e.g., seeking information, disagreeing/attacking) or process behaviors (e.g., asking clarifying questions, summarizing). The goal of executive coaching is to reduce content behaviors in favor of process behaviors. The study reported that prior to receiving executive coaching, the percentage of observed process behaviors of leaders had a mean of 75% with a standard deviation of 8.5%. In contrast, after receiving executive coaching, the percentage of observed process behaviors of leaders had a mean of 52% with a standard deviation of 7.5%. Assume that the percentage of observed process behaviors is approximately normally distributed for both leaders with and without executive coaching. Suppose you observe 70% process behaviors by the leader of a business meeting. Give your opinion on whether or not the leader has received executive coaching.

4.116 Box plots and the standard normal distribution. What relationship exists between the standard normal distribution and the box-plot methodology (Section 2.8) for describing distributions of data using quartiles? The answer depends on the true underlying probability distribution of the data. Assume for the remainder of this exercise that the distribution is normal.

a. Calculate the values of the standard normal random variable z, call them z_L and z_U, that correspond to the hinges of the box plot—that is, the lower and upper quartiles, Q_L and Q_U—of the probability distribution.

b. Calculate the z values that correspond to the inner fences of the box plot for a normal probability distribution.

c. Calculate the z values that correspond to the outerfences of the box plot for a normal probability distribution.

d. What is the probability that an observation lies beyond the inner fences of a normal probability distribution? The outer fences?

e. Can you better understand why the inner and outer fences of a box plot are used to detect outliers in a distribution? Explain.

4.7 Descriptive Methods for Assessing Normality

In the chapters that follow, we learn how to make inferences about the population based on information in the sample. Several of these techniques are based on the assumption that the population is approximately normally distributed. Consequently, it will be important to determine whether the sample data come from a normal population before we can properly apply these techniques.

Several descriptive methods can be used to check for normality. In this section, we consider the four methods summarized in the box.

Determining Whether the Data Are from an Approximately Normal Distribution

1. Construct either a histogram or stem-and-leaf display for the data and note the shape of the graph. If the data are approximately normal, the shape of the histogram or stem-and-leaf display will be similar to the normal curve, Figure 4.18 (i.e., mound-shaped and symmetric about the mean).

2. Compute the intervals $\bar{x} \pm s$, $\bar{x} \pm 2s$, and $\bar{x} \pm 3s$, and determine the percentage of measurements falling in each. If the data are approximately normal, the percentages will be approximately equal to 68%, 95%, and 100%, respectively.

3. Find the interquartile range, IQR, and standard deviation, s, for the sample, then calculate the ratio IQR/s. If the data are approximately normal, then IQR/s $\approx$ 1.3.

4. Examine a *normal probability plot* for the data. If the data are approximately normal, the points will fall (approximately) on a straight line.

The first two methods come directly from the properties of a normal distribution established in Section 4.6. Method 3 is based on the fact that for normal distributions, the z values corresponding to the 25th and 75th percentiles are $-.67$ and $.67$, respectively (see Example 4.18). Because $\sigma = 1$ for a standard normal distribution,

$$\frac{\text{IQR}}{\sigma} = \frac{Q_{\text{U}} - Q_{\text{L}}}{\sigma} = \frac{.67 - (-.67)}{1} = 1.34$$

The final descriptive method for checking normality is based on a *normal probability plot*. In such a plot, the observations in a data set are ordered from smallest to largest and then plotted against the expected z-scores of observations calculated under the assumption that the data come from a normal distribution. When the data are, in fact, normally distributed, a linear (straight-line) trend will result. A nonlinear trend in the plot suggests that the data are nonnormal.

A **normal probability plot** for a data set is a scatterplot with the ranked data values on one axis and their corresponding expected z-scores from a standard normal distribution on the other axis. [*Note:* Computation of the expected standard normal z-scores is beyond the scope of this text. Therefore, we will rely on available statistical software packages to generate a normal probability plot.]

Example 4.26

Checking for Normal Data—EPA Estimated Gas Mileages

Problem The Environmental Protection Agency (EPA) performs extensive tests on all new car models to determine their mileage ratings. The results of 100 EPA tests on a certain new car model are displayed in Table 4.5. Numerical and graphical descriptive measures for the data are shown on the Minitab and SPSS printouts, Figures 4.37a–c. Determine whether the EPA mileage ratings are from an approximate normal distribution.

Table 4.5		EPA Gas Mileage Ratings for 100 Cars (miles per gallon)							
36.3	41.0	36.9	37.1	44.9	36.8	30.0	37.2	42.1	36.7
32.7	37.3	41.2	36.6	32.9	36.5	33.2	37.4	37.5	33.6
40.5	36.5	37.6	33.9	40.2	36.4	37.7	37.7	40.0	34.2
36.2	37.9	36.0	37.9	35.9	38.2	38.3	35.7	35.6	35.1
38.5	39.0	35.5	34.8	38.6	39.4	35.3	34.4	38.8	39.7
36.3	36.8	32.5	36.4	40.5	36.6	36.1	38.2	38.4	39.3
41.0	31.8	37.3	33.1	37.0	37.6	37.0	38.7	39.0	35.8
37.0	37.2	40.7	37.4	37.1	37.8	35.9	35.6	36.7	34.5
37.1	40.3	36.7	37.0	33.9	40.1	38.0	35.2	34.8	39.5
39.9	36.9	32.9	33.8	39.8	34.0	36.8	35.0	38.1	36.9

 Data Set: EPAGAS

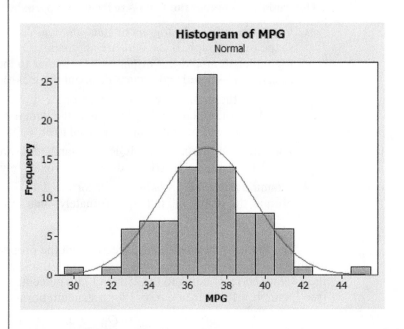

Figure 4.37a

Minitab histogram for gas mileage data

Descriptive Statistics: MPG

Variable	N	Mean	StDev	Minimum	Q1	Median	Q3	Maximum
MPG	100	36.994	2.418	30.000	35.625	37.000	38.375	44.900

Figure 4.37b

Minitab descriptive statistics for gas mileage data

Figure 4.37c

SPSS normal probability plot for gas mileage data

Table 4.6	
Describing the 100 EPA Mileage Ratings	
Interval	Percentage in Interval
$\bar{x} \pm s = (34.6, 39.4)$	68
$\bar{x} \pm 2s = (32.2, 41.8)$	96
$\bar{x} \pm 3s = (29.8, 44.2)$	99

Solution As a first check, we examine the Minitab histogram of the data shown in Figure 4.37a. Clearly, the mileages fall in an approximately mound-shaped, symmetric distribution centered around the mean of approximately 37 mpg. Note that a normal curve is superimposed on the figure. Therefore, using check #1 in the box, the data appear to be approximately normal.

To apply check #2, we obtain $\bar{x} = 37$ and $s = 2.4$ from the Minitab printout, Figure 4.37b. The intervals $\bar{x} \pm s$, $\bar{x} \pm 2s$ and $\bar{x} \pm 3s$ are shown in Table 4.6, as well as the percentage of mileage ratings that fall in each interval. These percentages agree almost exactly with those from a normal distribution.

Check #3 in the box requires that we find the ratio IQR/s. From Figure 4.37b, the 25th percentile (called Q_1 by Minitab) is $Q_L = 35.625$, and the 75th percentile (labeled Q_3 by Minitab) is $Q_U = 38.375$. Then, IQR $= Q_U - Q_L = 2.75$, and the ratio is

$$\frac{\text{IQR}}{s} = \frac{2.75}{2.4} = 1.15$$

Because this value is approximately equal to 1.3, we have further confirmation that the data are approximately normal.

A fourth descriptive method is to interpret a normal probability plot. An SPSS normal probability plot for the mileage data is shown in Figure 4.37c. Notice that the ordered mileage values (shown on the horizontal axis) fall reasonably close to a straight line when plotted against the expected z-scores from a normal distribution. Thus, check #4 also suggests that the EPA mileage data are likely to be approximately normally distributed.

Look Back The checks for normality given in the box are simple, yet powerful, techniques to apply, but they are only descriptive in nature. It is possible (although unlikely) that the data are nonnormal even when the checks are reasonably satisfied. Thus, we should be careful not to claim that the 100 EPA mileage ratings of Example 4.26 are, in fact, normally distributed. We can only state that it is reasonable to believe that the data are from a normal distribution.*

■ **Now Work Exercise 4.120**

As we will learn in Chapter 6, several inferential methods of analysis require the data to be approximately normal. If the data are clearly nonnormal, inferences derived from the method may be invalid. Therefore, it is advisable to check the normality of the data prior to conducting the analysis.

Exercises 4.117–4.131

Learning the Mechanics

4.117 If a population data set is normally distributed, what is the proportion of measurements you would expect to fall within the following intervals?
   a. $\mu \pm \sigma$
   b. $\mu \pm 2\sigma$
   c. $\mu \pm 3\sigma$

4.118 Consider a sample data set with the following summary statistics: $s = 95$, $Q_L = 72$, $Q_U = 195$.
   a. Calculate IQR.
   b. Calculate IQR/s.
   c. Is the value of IQR/s approximately equal to 1.3? What does this imply?

4.119 Normal probability plots for three data sets are shown on the next page. Which plot indicates that the data are approximately normally distributed?

4.120 Examine the sample data in the accompanying table.

NW

L04120

5.9	5.3	1.6	7.4	8.6	1.2	2.1
4.0	7.3	8.4	8.9	6.7	4.5	6.3
7.6	9.7	3.5	1.1	4.3	3.3	8.4
1.6	8.2	6.5	1.1	5.0	9.4	6.4

   a. Construct a stem-and-leaf plot to assess whether the data are from an approximately normal distribution.
   b. Compute s for the sample data.

*Statistical tests of normality that provide a measure of reliability for the inference are available. However, these tests tend to be very sensitive to slight departures from normality (i.e., they tend to reject the hypothesis of normality for any distribution that is not perfectly symmetrical and mound-shaped). Consult the references (see Ramsey & Ramsey, 1990) if you want to learn more about these tests.

Normal probability plots for Exercise 4.119

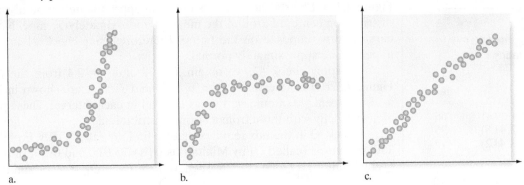

a.   b.   c.

c. Find the values of Q_L and Q_U and the value of s from part **b** to assess whether the data come from an approximately normal distribution.

d. Generate a normal probability plot for the data and use it to assess whether the data are approximately normal.

Applying the Concepts—Basic

4.121 Corporate sustainability of CPA firms. Refer to the *Business and Society* (March 2011) study on the sustainability behaviors of CPA corporations, Exercise 4.98 (p. 234). Data on the level of support for corporate sustainability (measured on a quantitative scale ranging from 0 to 160 points) for each of 992 senior managers at CPA firms are saved in the accompanying file. In Exercise 4.98 you assumed that the level of support variable was approximately normally distributed.

a. Construct a histogram for the data and use it to evaluate the validity of the normality assumption.

b. Obtain the mean and standard deviation for the data and use these statistics to evaluate the validity of the normality assumption.

c. Obtain the interquartile range (IQR) for the data and use it to evaluate the validity of the normality assumption.

d. Construct a normal probability plot for the data and use it to evaluate the validity of the normality assumption.

4.122 Shear strength of rock fractures. Understanding the characteristics of rock masses, especially the nature of the fractures, is essential when building dams and power plants. The shear strength of rock fractures was investigated in *Engineering Geology* (May 12, 2010). The Joint Roughness Coefficient (JRC) was used to measure shear strength. Civil engineers collected JRC data for over 750 rock fractures. The results (simulated from information provided in the article) are summarized in the accompanying SPSS histogram. Should the engineers use the normal probability distribution to model the behavior of shear strength for rock fractures? Explain.

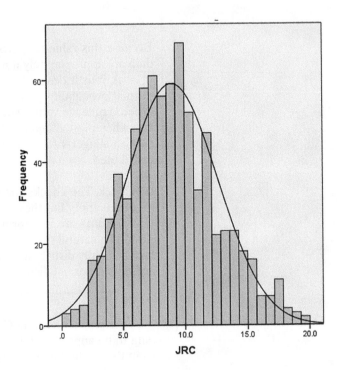

4.123 Drug content assessment. Scientists at GlaxoSmithKline Medicines Research Center used high-performance liquid chromatography (HPLC) to determine the amount of drug in a tablet produced by the company (*Analytical Chemistry*, Dec. 15, 2009). Drug concentrations (measured as a percentage) for 50 randomly selected tablets are listed in the table below and saved in the accompanying file.

a. Descriptive statistics for the drug concentrations are shown at the top of the XLSTAT printout on the next page. Use this information to assess whether the data are approximately normal.

b. An XLSTAT normal probability plot follows. Use this information to assess whether the data are approximately normal.

91.28	92.83	89.35	91.90	82.85	94.83	89.83	89.00	84.62
86.96	88.32	91.17	83.86	89.74	92.24	92.59	84.21	89.36
90.96	92.85	89.39	89.82	89.91	92.16	88.67	89.35	86.51
89.04	91.82	93.02	88.32	88.76	89.26	90.36	87.16	91.74
86.12	92.10	83.33	87.61	88.20	92.78	86.35	93.84	91.20
93.44	86.77	83.77	93.19	81.79				

Source: Based on Borman, P. J., Marion, J. C., Damjanov, I., & Jackson, P. "Design and analysis of method equivalence studies," *Analytical Chemistry,* Vol. 81, No. 24, December 15, 2009 (Table 3).

Descriptive statistics (Quantitative data):	
Statistic	**Content**
No. of observations	50
Minimum	81.7900
Maximum	94.8300
Range	13.0400
1st Quartile	87.2725
Median	89.3750
3rd Quartile	91.8800
Mean	89.2906
Variance (n-1)	10.1343
Standard deviation (n-1)	3.1834

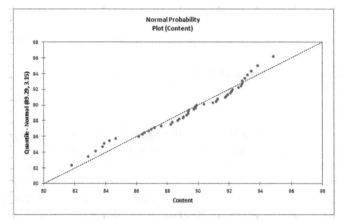

XLSTAT output for Exercise 4.123

4.124 Ranking PhD programs in economics. Refer to the *Southern Economic Journal* (Apr. 2008) rankings of PhD programs in economics at 129 colleges and universities, Exercise 2.103 (p. 90). Recall that the number of publications published by faculty teaching in the PhD program and the quality of the publications were used to calculate an overall productivity score for each program. The mean and standard deviation of these 129 productivity scores were then used to compute a z-score for each economics program. The data (z-scores) for all 129 economic programs are saved in the accompanying file. A Minitab normal probability plot for the z-scores is shown below. Use the graph to assess whether the data are approximately normal.

4.125 Software file updates. Software configuration management was used to monitor a software engineering team's performance at Motorola, Inc. (*Software Quality Professional,* Nov. 2004). One of the variables of interest was the number of updates to a file that was changed because of a problem report. Summary statistics for $n = 421$ files yielded the following results: $\bar{x} = 4.71$, $s = 6.09$, $Q_L = 1$, and $Q_U = 6$. Are these data approximately normally distributed? Explain.

Applying the Concepts—Intermediate

4.126 Wear-out of used display panels. Wear-out failure time of electronic components is often assumed to have a normal distribution. Can the normal distribution be applied to the wear-out of used manufactured products, such as colored display panels? A lot of 50 used display panels was purchased by an outlet store. Each panel displays 12 to 18 color characters. Prior to acquisition, the panels had been used for about one-third of their expected lifetimes. The data in the accompanying table (saved in the file) give the failure times (in years) of the 50 used panels. Use the techniques of this section to determine whether the used panel wear-out times are approximately normally distributed.

0.01	1.21	1.71	2.30	2.96	0.19	1.22	1.75	2.30	2.98	0.51
1.24	1.77	2.41	3.19	0.57	1.48	1.79	2.44	3.25	0.70	1.54
1.88	2.57	3.31	0.73	1.59	1.90	2.61	1.19	0.75	1.61	1.93
2.62	3.50	0.75	1.61	2.01	2.72	3.50	1.11	1.62	2.16	2.76
3.50	1.16	1.62	2.18	2.84	3.50					

Source: Based on Irony, T. Z., Lauretto, M., Pereira, C., & Stern, J. M. "A Weibull wearout test: Full Bayesian approach," paper presented at *Mathematical Sciences Colloquium,* Binghamton University, Bringhamton, UK, December 2001.

4.127 NHTSA crash tests. Refer to the NHTSA crash test data for new cars. In Exercise 4.102 (p. 234), you assumed that the driver's head-injury rating is approximately normally distributed. Apply the methods of this chapter to the data saved in the accompanying file to support this assumption.

4.128 Sanitation inspection of cruise ships. Refer to the data on the Dec. 2008 sanitation scores for 186 cruise ships, first presented in Exercise 2.24 (p. 59). The data are saved in the accompanying file. Assess whether the sanitation scores are approximately normally distributed.

4.129 Ranking driving performance of professional golfers. Refer to *The Sport Journal* (Winter 2007) article on a new method for ranking the driving performance of PGA golfers, Exercise 2.50 (p. 72). Recall that the method incorporates a golfer's average driving distance (yards) and driving accuracy (percent of drives that land in the fairway) into a driving performance index. Data on these three variables for the top 40 PGA golfers are saved in the accompanying file. Determine which of these variables—driving distance, driving accuracy, and driving performance index—are approximately normally distributed.

4.130 Department of Defense START sheets. The DoD RAC publishes START sheets for government and industry. These START sheets are designed to improve the reliability, maintainability, supportability, and quality of manufactured components and systems. In Volume 11 (2004), the DoD analyzed the following data set on tensile strength measurements taken at two different temperatures. (The data are saved in the accompanying file.) In the START

Temperature	Strength
75	328.2
75	334.7
75	347.8
75	346.3
75	338.7
75	340.8
−67	343.6
−67	334.2
−67	348.7
−67	356.3
−67	344.1

sheet, the DoD demonstrated that the data for the 11 tensile strength measurements were sampled from an approximately normal distribution. Do you agree?

Applying the Concepts—Advanced

4.131 Semester hours taken by CPA candidates. Refer to the *Journal of Accounting and Public Policy* (Spring 2002) study of first-time candidates for the CPA exam, Exercise 2.51 (p. 72). The variable of interest is the total semester hours of college credit for each candidate. Recall that the mean and median for the data set were 141.31 and 140 hours, respectively, and the standard deviation was 17.77 hours. Demonstrate why the probability distribution for the variable, total semester hours, is unlikely to be normally distributed.

4.8 Other Continuous Distributions: Uniform and Exponential

Uniform Random Variable

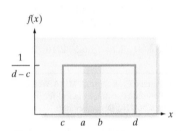

Figure 4.38

The uniform probability distribution

Continuous random variables that appear to have equally likely outcomes over their range of possible values possess a **uniform probability distribution.** For example, if a short exists in a 5-meter stretch of electrical wire, it may have an equal probability of being in any particular 1-centimeter segment along the line. Or if a safety inspector plans to choose a time at random during the four afternoon work hours to pay a surprise visit to a certain area of a plant, then each 1-minute time interval in this 4-work-hour period will have an equally likely chance of being selected for the visit.

Suppose the random variable x can assume values only in an interval $c \le x \le d$. Then the **uniform frequency function** has a rectangular shape, as shown in Figure 4.38. Note that the possible values of x consist of all points in the interval between point c and point d. The height of $f(x)$ is constant in that interval and equals $1/(d - c)$. Therefore, the total area under $f(x)$ is given by

$$\text{Total area of rectangle} = (\text{Base})(\text{Height}) = (d - c)\left(\frac{1}{d - c}\right) = 1$$

The uniform probability distribution provides a model for continuous random variables that are *evenly distributed* over a certain interval—that is, a uniform random variable is one that is just as likely to assume a value in one interval as it is to assume a value in any other interval of equal size. There is no clustering of values around any value; instead, there is an even spread over the entire region of possible values.

The uniform distribution is sometimes referred to as the **randomness distribution** because one way of generating a uniform random variable is to perform an experiment in which a point is *randomly selected* on the horizontal axis between the points c and d. If we were to repeat this experiment infinitely often, we would create a uniform probability distribution like that shown in Figure 4.38. The random selection of points in an interval can also be used to generate random numbers such as those in Table I in Appendix B. Recall that random numbers are selected in such a way that every number would have an equal probability of selection. Therefore, random numbers are realizations of a uniform random variable. (Random numbers were used to draw random samples in Section 3.7.) The formulas for the uniform probability distribution, its mean, and its standard deviation are shown in the next box.

Suppose the interval $a < x < b$ lies within the domain of x; that is, it falls within the larger interval $c \le x \le d$. Then the probability that x assumes a value within the

> **Probability Distribution for a Uniform Random Variable x**
>
> Probability density function: $f(x) = \dfrac{1}{d - c} \quad c \leq x \leq d$
>
> Mean: $\mu = \dfrac{c + d}{2}$ Standard deviation: $\sigma = \dfrac{d - c}{\sqrt{12}}$
>
> $P(a < x < b) = (b - a)/(d - c), c \leq a < b \leq d$

interval $a < x < b$ is equal to the area of the rectangle over the interval, namely, $(b - a)/(d - c)$.* (See the shaded area in Figure 4.38.)

Example 4.27

Applying the Uniform Distribution—Steel Manufacturing

Problem Suppose the research department of a steel manufacturer believes that one of the company's rolling machines is producing sheets of steel of varying thickness. The thickness is a uniform random variable with values between 150 and 200 millimeters. Any sheets less than 160 millimeters must be scrapped because they are unacceptable to buyers.

a. Calculate and interpret the mean and standard deviation of x, the thickness of the sheets produced by this machine.

b. Graph the probability distribution of x, and show the mean on the horizontal axis. Also show 1- and 2-standard-deviation intervals around the mean.

c. Calculate the fraction of steel sheets produced by this machine that have to be scrapped.

Solution

a. To calculate the mean and standard deviation for x, we substitute 150 and 200 millimeters for c and d, respectively, in the formulas for uniform random variables. Thus,

$$\mu = \frac{c + d}{2} = \frac{150 + 200}{2} = 175 \text{ millimeters}$$

and

$$\sigma = \frac{d - c}{\sqrt{12}} = \frac{200 - 150}{\sqrt{12}} = \frac{50}{3.464} = 14.43 \text{ millimeters}$$

Our interpretations follow:

The average thickness of all manufactured steel sheets is $\mu = 175$ millimeters. From Chebyshev's Rule (Table 2.6, p. 80), we know that at least 75% of the thickness values, x, in the distribution will fall in the interval

$$\mu \pm 2\sigma = 175 \pm 2(14.43)$$
$$= 175 \pm 28.86$$

or between 146.14 and 203.86 millimeters. (This demonstrates, once again, the conservativeness of Chebyshev's Rule because we know that all values of x fall between 150 and 200 millimeters.)

b. The uniform probability distribution is

$$f(x) = \frac{1}{d - c} = \frac{1}{200 - 150} = \frac{1}{50} \, (150 \leq x \leq 200)$$

The graph of this function is shown in Figure 4.39. The mean and 1- and 2-standard-deviation intervals around the mean are shown on the horizontal axis.

*The student with knowledge of calculus should note that

$$P(a < x < b) = \int_{a}^{b} f(x)d(x) = \int_{a}^{b} 1/(d - c)dx = (b - a)/(d - c)$$

Figure 4.39

Distribution for x in Example 4.27

c. To find the fraction of steel sheets produced by the machine that have to be scrapped, we must find the probability that x, the thickness, is less than 160 millimeters. As indicated in Figure 4.40, we need to calculate the area under the frequency function $f(x)$ between the points $x = 150$ and $x = 160$. Therefore, in this case, $a = 150$ and $b = 160$. Applying the formula in the box, we have

$$P(x < 160) = P(150 < x < 160)$$
$$= \frac{b - a}{d - c} = \frac{160 - 150}{200 - 150} = \frac{10}{50} = \frac{1}{5} = .2$$

That is, 20% of all the sheets made by this machine must be scrapped.

Figure 4.40

Probability that sheet thickness, x, is between 150 and 160 millimeters

Look Back The calculated probability in part **c** is the area of a rectangle with base $160 - 150 = 10$ and height $\frac{1}{50}$. Alternatively, we can find the fraction that has to be scrapped as

$$P(x < 160) = (\text{Base})(\text{Height}) = (10)\left(\frac{1}{50}\right) = \frac{1}{5} = .2$$

Or, we can use statistical software to find the probability, as shown on the Minitab printout, Figure 4.41.

Cumulative Distribution Function

```
Continuous uniform on 150 to 200

  x   P( X <= x )
160        0.2
```

Figure 4.41

Minitab output for Example 4.27

■ **Now Work Exercise 4.142**

Exponential Random Variable

The length of time between emergency arrivals at a hospital, the length of time between breakdowns of manufacturing equipment, and the length of time between catastrophic events (e.g., a stock market crash), are all continuous random phenomena that we might want to describe probabilistically. The length of time or the distance between occurrences of random events like these can often be described by the **exponential probability distribution.** For this reason, the exponential distribution is sometimes called the **waiting-time distribution.** The formula for the exponential probability distribution is shown in the following box, along with its mean and standard deviation.

Unlike the normal distribution, which has a shape and location determined by the values of the two quantities μ and σ, the shape of the exponential distribution is governed by a single quantity: θ. Further, it is a probability distribution with the property that its mean equals its standard deviation. Exponential distributions corresponding to $\theta = .5, 1,$ and 2 are shown in Figure 4.42.

Figure 4.42

Exponential distributions

Probability Distribution for an Exponential Random Variable x

Probability density function: $f(x) = \dfrac{1}{\theta} e^{-x/\theta}$ $(x > 0)$

Mean: $\mu = \theta$

Standard deviation: $\sigma = \theta$

To calculate probabilities of **exponential random variables,** we need to be able to find areas under the exponential probability distribution. Suppose we want to find the area A to the right of some number a, as shown in Figure 4.43. This area can be calculated by means of the formula shown in the box that follows or by using statistical software.

Finding the Area A to the Right of a Number a for an Exponential Distribution*

$$A = P(x \geq a) = e^{-a/\theta}$$

Figure 4.43

The area A to the right of a number a for an exponential distribution

---

Example 4.28

Finding an Exponential Probability—Hospital Emergency Arrivals

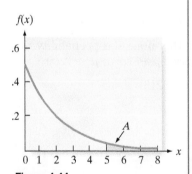

Figure 4.44

Area to the right of $a = 5$ for Example 4.28

Problem Suppose the length of time (in hours) between emergency arrivals at a certain hospital is modeled as an exponential distribution with $\theta = 2$. What is the probability that more than 5 hours pass without an emergency arrival?

Solution The probability we want is the area A to the right of $a = 5$ in Figure 4.44. To find this probability, we use the area formula:

$$A = e^{-a/\theta} = e^{-(5/2)} = e^{-2.5}$$

Using a calculator with an exponential function, we find that

$$A = e^{-2.5} = .082085$$

Our exponential model indicates that the probability that more than 5 hours pass between emergency arrivals is about .08 for this hospital.

Look Back The desired probability can also be found with a statistical software package. We accessed the exponential probability function of Minitab, specified a mean of 2, and requested the cumulative probability, $P(x \leq 5)$. This probability is shaded in Figure 4.45. Using the rule of complements, the desired probability is

Cumulative Distribution Function

Exponential with mean = 2

```
x   P( X <= x )
5      0.917915
```

Figure 4.45

Minitab output for Example 4.28

$$P(x > 5) = 1 - P(x \leq 5) = 1 - .917915 = .082085$$

■ **Now Work Exercise 4.135**

---

*For students with a knowledge of calculus, the shaded area in Figure 4.43 corresponds to the integral

$$\int_a^b \frac{1}{\theta} e^{-x/\theta} dx = -e^{-x/\theta} \Big|_a^\infty = e^{-a/\theta}.$$

<table>
<tr><td>

Example 4.29

The Mean and Variance of an Exponential Random Variable—Length of Life of a Microwave Oven

</td><td>

Problem A manufacturer of microwave ovens is trying to determine the length of warranty period it should attach to its magnetron tube, the most critical component in the oven. Preliminary testing has shown that the length of life (in years), x, of a magnetron tube has an exponential probability distribution with $\theta = 6.25$.

a. Find the mean and standard deviation of x.

b. Suppose a warranty period of 5 years is attached to the magnetron tube. What fraction of tubes must the manufacturer plan to replace, assuming that the exponential model with $\theta = 6.25$ is correct?

c. Find the probability that the length of life of a magnetron tube will fall within the interval $\mu - 2\sigma$ to $\mu + 2\sigma$.

Solution

a. Because $\theta = \mu = \sigma$, both μ and σ equal 6.25.

b. To find the fraction of tubes that will have to be replaced before the 5-year warranty period expires, we need to find the area between 0 and 5 under the distribution. This area, A, is shown in Figure 4.46. To find the required probability, we recall the formula

$$P(x > a) = e^{-a/\theta}$$

Using this formula, we find that

$$P(x > 5) = e^{-a/\theta} = e^{-5/6.25} = e^{-.80} = .449329$$

To find the area A, we use the complementary relationship:

$$P(x \leq 5) = 1 - P(x > 5) = 1 - .449329 = .550671$$

So approximately 55% of the magnetron tubes will have to be replaced during the 5-year warranty period.

c. We would expect the probability that the life of a magnetron tube, x, falls within the interval $\mu - 2\sigma$ to $\mu + 2\sigma$ to be quite large. A graph of the exponential distribution showing the interval from $\mu - 2\sigma$ to $\mu + 2\sigma$ is given in Figure 4.47. Because the point $\mu - 2\sigma$ lies below $x = 0$, we need to find only the area between $x = 0$ and $x = \mu + 2\sigma = 6.25 + 2(6.25) = 18.75$.

This area, P, which is shaded in Figure 4.47, is

$$P = 1 - P(x > 18.75) = 1 - e^{-18.75/\theta} = 1 - e^{-18.75/6.25} = 1 - e^{-3}$$

Using a calculator, we find that $e^{-3} = .049787$. Therefore, the probability that the life x of a magnetron tube will fall within the interval $\mu - 2\sigma$ to $\mu + 2\sigma$ is

$$P = 1 - e^{-3} = 1 - .049787 = .950213$$

</td></tr>
</table>

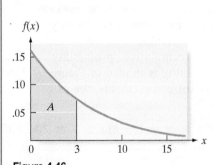

Figure 4.46
Area to the left of $a = 5$ for Example 4.29

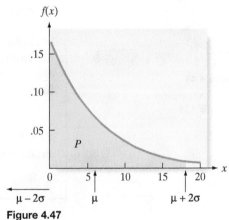

Figure 4.47
Area in the interval $\mu \pm 2\sigma$ for Example 4.29

> **Look Back** You can see that this probability agrees well with the interpretation of a standard deviation given by the Empirical Rule (Table 2.7, p. 80), even though the probability distribution that we were given is not mound-shaped. (It is strongly skewed to the right.)

Exercises 4.132–4.155

Learning the Mechanics

4.132 Suppose x is a random variable best described by a uniform probability distribution with $c = 3$ and $d = 7$.
   a. Find $f(x)$.
   b. Find the mean and standard deviation of x.
   c. Find $P(\mu - \sigma \le x \le \mu + \sigma)$.

4.133 Suppose x is a random variable best described by a uniform probability distribution with $c = 20$ and $d = 45$.
   a. Find $f(x)$.
   b. Find the mean and standard deviation of x.
   c. Graph $f(x)$ and locate μ and the interval $\mu \pm 2\sigma$ on the graph. Note that the probability that x assumes a value within the interval $\mu \pm 2\sigma$ is equal to 1.

4.134 Refer to Exercise 4.133. Find the following probabilities:
   a. $P(20 \le x \le 30)$ **b.** $P(20 < x \le 30)$
   c. $P(x \ge 30)$ **d.** $P(x \ge 45)$
   e. $P(x \le 40)$ **f.** $P(x < 40)$
   g. $P(15 \le x \le 35)$ **h.** $P(21.5 \le x \le 31.5)$

4.135 Suppose x has an exponential distribution with $\theta = 1$. Find the following probabilities:
   a. $P(x > 1)$ **b.** $P(x \le 3)$
   c. $P(x > 1.5)$ **d.** $P(x \le 5)$

4.136 Suppose x has an exponential distribution with $\theta = 2.5$. Find the following probabilities:
   a. $P(x \le 4)$ **b.** $P(x > 5)$
   c. $P(x \le 2)$ **d.** $P(x > 3)$

4.137 The random variable x is best described by a uniform probability distribution with $c = 100$ and $d = 200$. Find the probability that x assumes a value
   a. More than 2 standard deviations from μ.
   b. Less than 3 standard deviations from μ.
   c. Within 2 standard deviations of μ.

4.138 The random variable x can be adequately approximated by an exponential probability distribution with $\theta = 2$. Find the probability that x assumes a value
   a. More than 3 standard deviations from μ.
   b. Less than 2 standard deviations from μ.
   c. Within half a standard deviation of μ.

⊙ Applet Exercise 4.7

Open the applet *Sample from a Population*. On the pull-down menu to the right of the top graph, select *Uniform*. The box to the left of the top graph displays the population mean, median, and standard deviation.
   a. Run the applet for each available value of n on the pull-down menu for the sample size. Go from the smallest to the largest value of n. For each value of n, observe the shape of the graph of the sample data and record the mean, median, and standard deviation of the sample.
   b. Describe what happens to the shape of the graph and the mean, median, and standard deviation of the sample as the sample size increases.

⊙ Applet Exercise 4.8

Suppose we set the *Random Numbers* applet to generate one number between 1 and 100, inclusive. We let the value of the random variable x be the number generated when the *Sample* button is clicked. Explain why the distribution of x is approximately uniform even though x is a discrete rather than continuous random variable.

Applying the Concepts—Basic

4.139 **Requests to a Web server.** According to Brighton Webs LTD, a British company that specializes in data analysis, the arrival time of requests to a Web server within each hour can be modeled by a uniform distribution (www. brighton-webs.co.uk). Specifically, the number of seconds x from the start of the hour that the request is made is uniformly distributed between 0 and 3,600 seconds. Find the probability that a request is made to a Web server sometime during the last 15 minutes of the hour.

4.140 **Preventative maintenance tests.** The optimal scheduling of preventative maintenance tests of some (but not all) of n independently operating components was developed in *Reliability Engineering and System Safety* (Jan. 2006). The time (in hours) between failures of a component was approximated by an exponential distribution with mean θ.
   a. Suppose $\theta = 1,000$ hours. Find the probability that the time between component failures ranges between 1,200 and 1,500 hours.
   b. Again, assume $\theta = 1,000$ hours. Find the probability that the time between component failures is at least 1,200 hours.
   c. Given that the time between failures is at least 1,200 hours, what is the probability that the time between failures is less than 1,500 hours?

4.141 **Maintaining pipe wall temperature.** Maintaining a constant pipe wall temperature in some hot-process applications is critical. A technique that utilizes bolt-on trace elements to maintain temperature was presented in the *Journal of Heat Transfer* (Nov. 2000). Without bolt-on trace elements, the pipe wall temperature of a switch condenser used to produce plastic has a uniform distribution ranging from 260° to 290°F. When several bolt-on trace elements are attached to the piping, the wall temperature is uniform from 278° to 285°F.

a. Ideally, the pipe wall temperature should range between 280° and 284°F. What is the probability that the temperature will fall in this ideal range when no bolt-on trace elements are used? When bolt-on trace elements are attached to the pipe?

b. When the temperature is 268°F or lower, the hot liquid plastic hardens (or plates), causing a buildup in the piping. What is the probability of plastic plating when no bolt-on trace elements are used? When bolt-on trace elements are attached to the pipe?

4.142 New method for detecting anthrax. Researchers at the University of South Florida Center for Biological Defense have developed a safe method for rapidly detecting anthrax spores in powders and on surfaces (*USF Magazine*, Summer 2002). The method has been found to work well even when there are very few anthrax spores in a powder specimen. Consider a powder specimen that has exactly 10 anthrax spores. Suppose that the number of anthrax spores in the sample detected by the new method follows an approximate uniform distribution between 0 and 10.

a. Find the probability that 8 or fewer anthrax spores are detected in the powder specimen.

b. Find the probability that between 2 and 5 anthrax spores are detected in the powder specimen.

4.143 Lead in metal shredder residue. On the basis of data collected from metal shredders across the nation, the amount x of extractable lead in metal shredder residue has an approximate exponential distribution with mean $\theta = 2.5$ milligrams per liter (Florida Shredder's Association).

a. Find the probability that x is greater than 2 milligrams per liter.

b. Find the probability that x is less than 5 milligrams per liter.

4.144 Critical-part failures in NASCAR vehicles. In NASCAR races such as the Daytona 500, 43 drivers start the race; however, about 10% of the cars do not finish due to the failure of critical parts. University of Portland professors conducted a study of critical-part failures from 36 NASCAR races (*The Sport Journal*, Winter 2007). The researchers discovered that the time (in hours) until the first critical-part failure is exponentially distributed with a mean of .10 hour.

a. Find the probability that the time until the first critical-part failure is 1 hour or more.

b. Find the probability that the time until the first critical-part failure is less than 30 minutes.

Applying the Concepts—Intermediate

4.145 Social network densities. Social networking sites for business professionals are used to promote one's business. Each social network involves interactions (connections) between members of the network. Researchers define network density as the ratio of actual network connections to the number of possible one-to-one connections. For example, a network with 10 members has $\binom{10}{2} = 45$ total possible connections. If that network has only 5 connections, the network density is $\frac{5}{45} = .111$. Sociologists at the

University of Michigan assumed that the density x of a social network would follow a uniform distribution between 0 and 1 (*Social Networks*, 2010).

a. On average, what is the density of a randomly selected social network?

b. What is the probability that the randomly selected network has a density higher than .7?

c. Consider a social network with only 2 members. Explain why the uniform model would not be a good approximation for the distribution of network density.

4.146 Marine losses for an oil company. The frequency distribution shown in the next table depicts the property and marine losses incurred by a large oil company over the last 2 years. This distribution can be used by the company to predict future losses and to help determine an appropriate level of insurance coverage. In analyzing the losses within an interval of the distribution, for simplification, analysts may treat the interval as a uniform probability distribution (*Research Review*, Summer 1998). In the insurance business, intervals like these are often called *layers*.

Layer	Property and Marine Losses (millions of $)	Frequency
1	0.00–0.01	668
2	0.01–0.05	38
3	0.05–0.10	7
4	0.10–0.25	4
5	0.25–0.50	2
6	0.50–1.00	1
7	1.00–2.50	0

Source: Based on Cozzolino, J. M., & Mikolaj, P. J. "Applications of the piecewise constant pareto distribution," *Research Review*, Summer 1998, pp. 39–59.

a. Use a uniform distribution to model the loss amount in layer 2. Graph the distribution. Calculate and interpret its mean and variance.

b. Repeat part **a** for layer 6.

c. If a loss occurs in layer 2, what is the probability that it exceeds $10,000? That it is under $25,000?

d. If a layer-6 loss occurs, what is the probability that it is between $750,000 and $1,000,000? That it exceeds $900,000? That it is exactly $900,000?

4.147 Soft-drink dispenser. The manager of a local soft-drink bottling company believes that when a new beverage-dispensing machine is set to dispense 7 ounces, it in fact dispenses an amount x at random anywhere between 6.5 and 7.5 ounces inclusive. Suppose x has a uniform probability distribution.

a. Is the amount dispensed by the beverage machine a discrete or a continuous random variable? Explain.

b. Graph the frequency function for x, the amount of beverage the manager believes is dispensed by the new machine when it is set to dispense 7 ounces.

c. Find the mean and standard deviation for the distribution graphed in part **b** and locate the mean and the interval $\mu \pm 2\sigma$ on the graph.

d. Find $P(x \geq 7)$.

e. Find $P(x < 6)$.

f. Find $P(6.5 \leq x \leq 7.25)$.

g. What is the probability that each of the next six bottles filled by the new machine will contain more than

7.25 ounces of beverage? Assume that the amount of beverage dispensed in one bottle is independent of the amount dispensed in another bottle.

4.148 Phishing attacks to e-mail accounts. Refer to the *Chance* (Summer 2007) article on phishing attacks at a company, Exercise 2.33 (p. 62). Recall that *phishing* describes an attempt to extract personal/financial information through fraudulent e-mail. The company set up a publicized e-mail account—called a "fraud box"—that enabled employees to notify them if they suspected an e-mail phishing attack. If there is minimal or no collaboration or collusion from within the company, the interarrival times (i.e., the time between successive e-mail notifications, in seconds) have an approximate exponential distribution with a mean of 95 seconds.

a. What is the probability of observing an interarrival time of at least 2 minutes?

b. Data for a sample of 267 interarrival times are saved in the accompanying file. Do the data appear to follow an exponential distribution with $\theta = 95$?

4.149 Product failure behavior. An article in *Hotwire* (Dec. 2002) discussed the length of time till failure of a product produced at Hewlett-Packard. At the end of the product's lifetime, the time till failure is modeled using an exponential distribution with mean 500 thousand hours. In reliability jargon this is known as the "wear-out" distribution for the product. During its normal (useful) life, assume the product's time till failure is uniformly distributed over the range 100 thousand to 1 million hours.

a. At the end of the product's lifetime, find the probability that the product fails before 700 thousand hours.

b. During its normal (useful) life, find the probability that the product fails before 700 thousand hours.

c. Show that the probability of the product failing before 830 thousand hours is approximately the same for both the normal (useful) life distribution and the wear-out distribution.

4.150 Cycle availability of a system. In the jargon of system maintenance, *cycle availability* is defined as the probability that the system is functioning at any point in time. The DoD developed a series of performance measures for assessing system cycle availability (START, Vol. 11, 2004). Under certain assumptions about the failure time and maintenance time of a system, cycle availability is shown to be uniformly distributed between 0 and 1. Find the following parameters for cycle availability: mean, standard deviation, 10th percentile, lower quartile, and upper quartile. Interpret the results.

4.151 Gouges on a spindle. A tool-and-die machine shop produces extremely high-tolerance spindles. The spindles are 18-inch slender rods used in a variety of military equipment. A piece of equipment used in the manufacture of the spindles malfunctions on occasion and places a single gouge somewhere on the spindle. However, if the spindle can be cut so that it has 14 consecutive inches without a gouge, then the spindle can be salvaged for other purposes. Assuming that the location of the gouge along the spindle is random, what is the probability that a defective spindle can be salvaged?

4.152 Reliability of CD-ROMs. In *Reliability Ques* (March 2004), the exponential distribution was used to model the lengths of life of CD-ROM drives in a two-drive system. The two CD-ROM drives operate independently, and at least one drive must be operating for the system to operate successfully. Both drives have a mean length of life of 25,000 hours.

a. The reliability $R(t)$ of a single CD-ROM drive is the probability that the life of the drive exceeds t hours. Give a formula for $R(t)$.

b. Use the result from part **a** to find the probability that the life of the single CD-ROM drive exceeds 8,760 hours (the number of hours of operation in a year).

c. The reliability $S(t)$ of the two-drive/CD-ROM system is the probability that the life of at least one drive exceeds t hours. Give a formula for $S(t)$. [*Hint*: Use the rule of complements and the fact that the two drives operate independently.]

d. Use the result from part **c** to find the probability that the two-drive CD-ROM system has a life whose length exceeds 8,760 hours.

e. Compare the probabilities you found in parts **b** and **d**.

Applying the Concepts—Advanced

4.153 Acceptance sampling of a product. An essential tool in the monitoring of the quality of a manufactured product is *acceptance sampling*. An acceptance sampling plan involves knowing the distribution of the life length of the item produced and determining how many items to inspect from the manufacturing process. The *Journal of Applied Statistics* (Apr. 2010) demonstrated the use of the exponential distribution as a model for the life length x of an item (e.g., a bullet). The article also discussed the importance of using the median of the lifetime distribution as a measure of product quality, since half of the items in a manufactured lot will have life lengths exceeding the median. For an exponential distribution with mean θ, give an expression for the median of the distribution. (*Hint:* Your answer will be a function of θ.)

4.154 Reliability of a robotic device. The *reliability* of a piece of equipment is frequently defined to be the probability, p, that the equipment performs its intended function successfully for a given period of time under specific conditions (Render and Heizer, *Principles of Operations Management*, 1995). Because p varies from one point in time to another, some reliability analysts treat p as if it were a random variable. Suppose an analyst characterizes the uncertainty about the reliability of a particular robotic device used in an automobile assembly line using the following distribution:

$$f(p) = \begin{cases} 1 & 0 \le p \le 1 \\ 0 & \text{otherwise} \end{cases}$$

a. Graph the analyst's probability distribution for p.

b. Find the mean and variance of p.

c. According to the analyst's probability distribution for p, what is the probability that p is greater than .95? Less than .95?

d. Suppose the analyst receives the additional information that p is definitely between .90 and .95, but that there is complete uncertainty about where it lies between these values. Describe the probability distribution the analyst should now use to describe p.

4.155 Length of life of a halogen bulb. For a certain type of halogen light bulb, an old bulb that has been in use for a while tends to have a longer life than a new bulb. Let x represent the life (in hours) of a new halogen light bulb and assume that x has an exponential distribution with mean $\theta = 250$ hours. According to *Microelectronics and Reliability* (Jan. 1986), the "life" distribution of x is considered *new better than used* (NBU) if

$$P(x > a + b) \leq P(x > a)P(x > b)$$

Alternatively, a "life" distribution is considered *new worse than used* (NWU) if

$$P(x > a + b) \geq P(x > a)P(x > b)$$

a. Show that when $a = 300$ and $b = 200$, the exponential distribution is both NBU and NWU.

b. Choose any two positive numbers a and b and repeat part **a**.

c. Show that, in general, for any positive a and b, the exponential distribution with mean θ is both NBU and NWU. Such a "life" distribution is said to be *new same as used*, or *memoryless*. Explain why.

□ Chapter Notes

Key Terms

Bell curve 220
Bell-shaped distribution 220
Binomial experiment 199
Binomial probability distribution 203
Binomial random variable 199
Continuous random variable 219
Correction for continuity 230
Countable 186
Cumulative binomial probabilities 206
Discrete random variable 189
Expected value 191
Exponential probability distribution 244
Exponential random variable 245
Frequency function 219
Hypergeometric probability distribution 214
Hypergeometric random variable 214
Mean of a binomial random variable 204
Mean of a discrete random variable 191
Mean of a hypergeometric random variable 215
Mean of a Poisson random variable 212
Normal distribution 220
Normal probability plot 237
Normal random variable 220
Poisson distribution 212
Poisson random variable 212
Probability density function 219

Probability distribution 189
Probability distribution of a discrete random variable 189
Probability distribution of an exponential random variable 245
Probability distribution of a hypergeometric random variable 215
Probability distribution of a normal random variable 221
Probability distribution of a Poisson random variable 212
Probability distribution for a uniform random variable 243
Random variable 185
Randomness distribution 242
Standard deviation of a binomial random variable 204
Standard deviation of a discrete random variable 192
Standard normal distribution 221
Uniform frequency function 242
Uniform probability distribution 242
Uniform random variable 242
Variance of a binomial random variable 204
Variance of a discrete random variable 192
Variance of a hypergeometric random variable 215
Variance of a Poisson random variable 212
Waiting-time distribution 244

Key Symbols

$p(x)$ Probability distribution for discrete random variable, x
$f(x)$ Probability distribution for continuous random variable, x
S Outcome of binomial trial denoted "success"
F Outcome of binomial trial denoted "failure"
p $P(S)$ in binomial trial
q $P(F)$ in binomial trial = $1 - p$

e Constant used in normal and Poisson probability distributions, $e = 2.71828\ldots$
π Constant used in normal probability distributions, $\pi = 3.1415\ldots$

Key Ideas

Properties of Probability Distributions

Discrete Distributions
  1. $p(x) \geq 0$
  2. $\sum_{\text{all } x} p(x) = 1$

Continuous Distributions
  1. $P(x = a) = 0$
  2. $P(a < x < b)$ is area under curve between a and b

Normal Approximation to Binomial

x is binomial (n, p)
$P(x \leq a) \approx P\{z < (a + .5) - \mu\}$

Methods for Assessing Normality

1. *Histogram*

2. *Stem-and-leaf display*

```
1 | 7
2 | 3389
3 | 245677
4 | 19
5 | 2
```

3. $(IQR)/S \approx 1.3$
4. *Normal probability plot*

Key Formulas

Random Variable	Probability Distribution	Mean	Variance
General Discrete:	Table, formula, or graph for $p(x)$	$\displaystyle\sum_{\text{all } x} x \cdot p(x)$	$\displaystyle\sum_{\text{all } x} (x - \mu)^2 \cdot p(x)$
Binomial:	$p(x) = \dbinom{n}{x} p^x q^{n-x}$ $x = 0, 1, 2, \cdots, n$	np	npq
Poisson:	$p(x) = \dfrac{\lambda^x e^{-\lambda}}{x!}$ $x = 0, 1, 2, \cdots$	λ	λ
Hypergeometric	$p(x) = \dfrac{\dbinom{r}{x}\dbinom{N-r}{n-x}}{\dbinom{N}{n}}$	$\dfrac{nr}{N}$	$\dfrac{r(N-r)n(N-n)}{N^2(N-1)}$
Uniform:	$f(x) = 1/(d-c)$ $(c \le x \le d)$	$(c+d)/2$	$(d-c)^2/12$
Normal:	$f(x) = \dfrac{1}{\sigma\sqrt{2\pi}}\, e^{-\frac{1}{2}[(x-\mu)/\sigma]^2}$	μ	σ^2
Exponential	$f(x) = \dfrac{1}{\theta}\, e^{-x/\theta}$	θ	θ
Standard Normal:	$f(z) = \dfrac{1}{\sqrt{2\pi}}\, e^{-\frac{1}{2}(z)^2}$ $z = (x-\mu)/\sigma$	$\mu = 0$	$\sigma^2 = 1$

Guide to Selecting a Probability Distribution

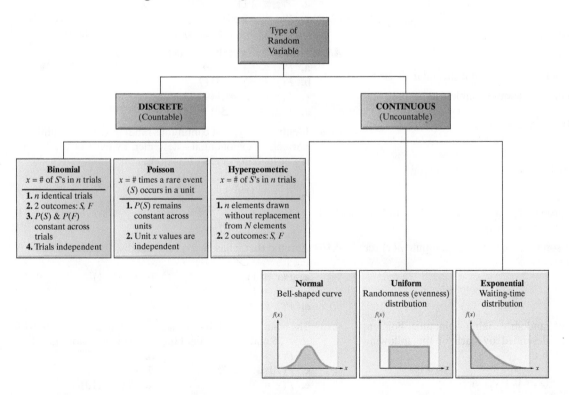

Supplementary Exercises 4.156–4.206

Learning the Mechanics

4.156 For each of the following examples, decide whether x is a binomial random variable and explain your decision:

   a. A manufacturer of computer chips randomly selects 100 chips from each hour's production in order to estimate the proportion defective. Let x represent the number of defectives in the 100 sampled chips.

   b. Of five applicants for a job, two will be selected. Although all applicants appear to be equally qualified, only three have the ability to fulfill the expectations of the company. Suppose that the two selections are made at random from the five applicants and let x be the number of qualified applicants selected.

   c. A software developer establishes a support hotline for customers to call in with questions regarding use of the software. Let x represent the number of calls received on the support hotline during a specified workday.

   d. Florida is one of a minority of states with no state income tax. A poll of 1,000 registered voters is conducted to determine how many would favor a state income tax in light of the state's current fiscal condition. Let x be the number in the sample who would favor the tax.

4.157 Given that x is a binomial random variable, compute $p(x)$ for each of the following cases:

   a. $n = 7, x = 3, p = .5$

   b. $n = 4, x = 3, p = .8$

   c. $n = 15, x = 1, p = .1$

4.158 Consider the discrete probability distribution shown here.

x	10	12	18	20
$p(x)$	.2	.3	.1	.4

   a. Calculate μ, σ^2, and σ.

   b. What is $P(x < 15)$?

   c. Calculate $\mu \pm 2\sigma$.

   d. What is the probability that x is in the interval $\mu \pm 2\sigma$?

4.159 Suppose x is a binomial random variable with $n = 20$ and $p = .7$.

   a. Find $P(x = 14)$.

   b. Find $P(x \le 12)$.

   c. Find $P(x > 12)$.

   d. Find $P(9 \le x \le 18)$.

   e. Find $P(8 < x < 18)$.

   f. Find μ, σ^2, and σ.

   g. What is the probability that x is in the interval $\mu \pm 2\sigma$?

4.160 Suppose x is a Poisson random variable. Compute $p(x)$ for each of the following cases:

   a. $\lambda = 2, x = 3$

   b. $\lambda = 1, x = 4$

   c. $\lambda = .5, x = 2$

4.161 Identify the type of random variable—binomial, Poisson, or hypergeometric—described by each of the following probability distributions:

   a. $p(x) = \dfrac{.5^x e^{-5}}{x!}$ $(x = 0, 1, 2, \ldots)$

   b. $p(x) = \dbinom{6}{x}(.2)^x(.8)^{6-x}$ $(x = 0, 1, 2, \ldots, 6)$

   c. $p(x) = \dfrac{10!}{x!(10 - x)!}(.9)^x(.1)^{10-x}$

   d. $(x = 0, 1, 2, \ldots, 10)$

4.162 Given that x is a hypergeometric random variable, compute $p(x)$ for each of the following cases:

   a. $N = 8, n = 5, r = 3, x = 2$

   b. $N = 6, n = 2, r = 2, x = 2$

   c. $N = 5, n = 4, r = 4, x = 3$

4.163 Which of the following describe discrete random variables, and which describe continuous random variables?

   a. The number of damaged inventory items

   b. The average monthly sales revenue generated by a salesperson over the past year

   c. Square feet of warehouse space a company rents

   d. The length of time a firm must wait before its copying machine is fixed

4.164 Assume that x is a random variable best described by a uniform distribution with $c = 10$ and $d = 90$.

   a. Find $f(x)$.

   b. Find the mean and standard deviation of x.

   c. Graph the probability distribution for x and locate its mean and the interval $\mu \pm 2\sigma$ on the graph.

   d. Find $P(x \le 60)$.

   e. Find $P(x \ge 90)$.

   f. Find $P(x \le 80)$.

   g. Find $P(\mu - \sigma \le x \le \mu + \sigma)$.

   h. Find $P(x > 75)$.

4.165 Find the following probabilities for the standard normal random variable z:

   a. $P(z \le 2.1)$ **b.** $P(z \ge 2.1)$

   c. $P(z \ge -1.65)$ **d.** $P(-2.13 \le z \le -.41)$

   e. $P(-1.45 \le z \le 2.15)$ **f.** $P(z \le -1.43)$

4.166 Find a z-score, call it z_0, such that

   a. $P(z \le z_0) = .5080$

   b. $P(z \ge z_0) = .5517$

   c. $P(z \ge z_0) = .1492$

   d. $P(z_0 \le z \le .59) = .4773$

4.167 Identify the type of continuous random variable—uniform, normal, or exponential—described by each of the following probability density functions:

   a. $f(x) = (e^{-x/7})/7, x > 0$

   b. $f(x) = 1/20, 5 < x < 25$

   c. $f(x) = \dfrac{e^{-.5[(x-10)/5]^2}}{5\sqrt{2\pi}}$

4.168 Assume that x has an exponential distribution with $\theta = 3$. Find

   a. $P(x \le 1)$ **b.** $P(x > 1)$

   c. $P(x = 1)$ **d.** $P(x \le 6)$

   e. $P(2 \le x \le 10)$

4.169 The random variable x has a normal distribution with $\mu = 75$ and $\sigma = 10$. Find the following probabilities:

   a. $P(x \le 80)$ **b.** $P(x \ge 85)$

   c. $P(70 \le x \le 75)$ **d.** $P(x > 80)$

   e. $P(x = 78)$ **f.** $P(x \le 110)$

4.170 Assume that x is a binomial random variable with $n = 100$ and $p = .5$. Use the normal probability distribution to approximate the following probabilities:
a. $P(x \leq 48)$ **b.** $P(50 \leq x \leq 65)$
c. $P(x \geq 70)$ **d.** $P(55 \leq x \leq 58)$
e. $P(x = 62)$ **f.** $P(x \leq 49 \text{ or } x \geq 72)$

4.171 The random variable x has a normal distribution with $\mu = 40$ and $\sigma^2 = 36$. Find a value of x, call it x_0, such that
a. $P(x \geq x_0) = .10$ **b.** $P(\mu \leq x < x_0) = .40$
c. $P(x < x_0) = .05$ **d.** $P(x \geq x_0) = .40$
e. $P(x_0 \leq x < \mu) = .45$

Applying the Concepts—Basic

4.172 Analysis of bottled water. Is the bottled water you're drinking really purified water? A 4-year study of bottled water brands conducted by the Natural Resources Defense Council found that 25% of bottled water is just tap water packaged in a bottle (*Scientific American*, July 2003). Consider a sample of five bottled water brands and let x equal the number of these brands that use tap water.
a. Explain why x is (approximately) a binomial random variable.
b. Give the probability distribution for x as a formula.
c. Find $P(x = 2)$.
d. Find $P(x \leq 1)$.
e. In a random sample of 65 bottled water brands, is it likely that 20 or more brands will contain tap water? Explain.

4.173 Dentists' use of laughing gas. According to the American Dental Association, 60% of all dentists use nitrous oxide in their practice. If x equals the number of dentists in a random sample of five dentists who use laughing gas in practice, then the probability distribution of x is

x	0	1	2	3	4	5
$p(x)$	.0102	.0768	.2304	.3456	.2592	.0778

a. Verify that the probabilities for x sum to 1.
b. Find $P(x = 4)$.
c. Find $P(x < 2)$.
d. Find $P(x \geq 3)$.
e. Find $\mu = E(x)$ and practically interpret this value.

4.174 Transmission delays in wireless technology. Resource reservation protocol (RSVP) was originally designed to establish signaling links for stationary networks. In *Mobile Networks and Applications* (Dec. 2003), RSVP was applied to mobile wireless technology (e.g., a PC notebook with wireless LAN card for Internet access). A simulation study revealed that the transmission delay (measured in milliseconds) of an RSVP linked wireless device has an approximate normal distribution with mean $\mu = 48.5$ milliseconds and $\sigma = 8.5$ milliseconds.
a. What is the probability that the transmission delay is less than 57 milliseconds?
b. What is the probability that the transmission delay is between 40 and 60 milliseconds?

4.175 Trajectory of an electrical circuit. Researchers at the University of California–Berkeley have designed, built, and tested a switched-capacitor circuit for generating random signals (*International Journal of Circuit Theory and Applications*, May–June 1990). The circuit's

trajectory was shown to be uniformly distributed on the interval $(0, 1)$.
a. Give the mean and variance of the circuit's trajectory.
b. Compute the probability that the trajectory falls between .2 and .4.
c. Would you expect to observe a trajectory that exceeds .995? Explain.

4.176 Spare line replacement units. The DoD RAC publishes Selected Topics in Assurance Related Technologies (START) sheets to help improve the quality of manufactured components and systems. One START sheet, titled "Application of the Poisson Distribution" (Vol. 9, No. 1, 2002), focuses on a spare line replacement unit (LRU). Failures of LRUs are assumed to follow a Poisson distribution with a mean failure rate of 1.2 failures per 10,000 hours.
a. Find the probability that there are no LRU failures during the next 10,000 hours of operation.
b. Find the probability that there are at least two LRU failures during the next 10,000 hours of operation.

4.177 Hospital patient interarrival times. The length of time between arrivals at a hospital clinic has an approximately exponential probability distribution. Suppose the mean time between arrivals for patients at a clinic is 4 minutes.
a. What is the probability that a particular interarrival time (the time between the arrival of two patients) is less than 1 minute?
b. What is the probability that the next four interarrival times are all less than 1 minute?
c. What is the probability that an interarrival time will exceed 10 minutes?

4.178 Dutch elm disease. A nursery advertises that it has 10 elm trees for sale. Unknown to the nursery, 3 of the trees have already been infected with Dutch elm disease and will die within a year.
a. If a buyer purchases 2 trees, what is the probability that both trees will be healthy?
b. Refer to part **a.** What is the probability that at least 1 of the trees is infected?

4.179 Tracking missiles with satellite imagery. The U.S. government has devoted considerable funding to missile defense research over the past 20 years. The latest development is the Space-Based Infrared System (SBIRS), which uses satellite imagery to detect and track missiles (*Chance*, Summer 2005). The probability that an intruding object (e.g., a missile) will be detected on a flight track by SBIRS is .8. Consider a sample of 20 simulated tracks, each with an intruding object. Let x equal the number of these tracks where SBIRS detects the object.
a. Demonstrate that x is (approximately) a binomial random variable.
b. Give the values of p and n for the binomial distribution.
c. Find $P(x = 15)$, the probability that SBIRS will detect the object on exactly 15 tracks.
d. Find $P(x \geq 15)$, the probability that SBIRS will detect the object on at least 15 tracks.
e. Find $E(x)$ and interpret the result.

4.180 Estimating demand for white bread. A bakery has determined that the number of loaves of its white bread demanded daily has a normal distribution with mean 7,200 loaves and standard deviation 300 loaves. Based on cost considerations, the company has decided that its best strategy is to produce a sufficient number of loaves so that it will fully supply demand on 94% of all days.

a. How many loaves of bread should the company produce?

b. Based on the production in part **a**, on what percentage of days will the company be left with more than 500 loaves of unsold bread?

4.181 Machine repair times. An article in *IEEE Transactions* (Mar. 1990) gave an example of a flexible manufacturing system with four machines operating independently. The repair rates for the machines (i.e., the time, in hours, it takes to repair a failed machine) are exponentially distributed with means $\mu_1 = 1$, $\mu_2 = 2$, $\mu_3 = .5$, and $\mu_4 = .5$, respectively.

a. Find the probability that the repair time for machine 1 exceeds 1 hour.

b. Repeat part **a** for machine 2.

c. Repeat part **a** for machines 3 and 4.

d. If all four machines fail simultaneously, find the probability that the repair time for the entire system exceeds 1 hour.

4.182 Public transit deaths. Millions of suburban commuters use the public transit system (e.g., subway trains) as an alternative to the automobile. While generally perceived as a safe mode of transportation, the average number of deaths per week due to public transit accidents is a surprisingly high 16 (Bureau of Transportation Statistics, 2010).

a. Construct arguments both for and against the use of the Poisson distribution to characterize the number of deaths per week due to public transit accidents.

b. For the remainder of this exercise, assume the Poisson distribution is an adequate approximation for x, the number of deaths per week due to public transit accidents. Find $E(x)$ and the standard deviation of x.

c. Based strictly on your answers to part **b**, is it likely that only four or fewer deaths occur next week? Explain.

d. Find $P(x \leq 4)$. Is this probability consistent with your answer to part **c**? Explain.

4.183 On-site treatment of hazardous waste. The Resource Conservation and Recovery Act mandates the tracking and disposal of hazardous waste produced at U.S. facilities. *Professional Geographer* (Feb. 2000) reported the hazardous-waste generation and disposal characteristics of 209 facilities. Only 8 of these facilities treated hazardous waste on-site. Use the hypergeometric distribution to answer the following:

a. In a random sample of 10 of the 209 facilities, what is the expected number in the sample that treat hazardous waste on-site? Interpret this result.

b. Find the probability that 4 of the 10 selected facilities treat hazardous waste on-site.

4.184 Random numbers. The data set listed in the table (next column) was created using the Minitab random number generator. Construct a relative frequency histogram for the data. Except for the expected variation in relative frequencies among the class intervals, does your histogram suggest that the data are observations on a uniform random variable with $c = 0$ and $d = 100$? Explain.

38.8759	98.0716	64.5788	60.8422	.8413
88.3734	31.8792	32.9847	.7434	93.3017
12.4337	11.7828	87.4506	94.1727	23.0892
47.0121	43.3629	50.7119	88.2612	69.2875
62.6626	55.6267	78.3936	28.6777	71.6829
44.0466	57.8870	71.8318	28.9622	23.0278
35.6438	38.6584	46.7404	11.2159	96.1009
95.3660	21.5478	87.7819	12.0605	75.1015

4.185 Time in bankruptcy. Refer to the *Financial Management* (Spring 1995) study of 49 companies that filed for a pre-packaged bankruptcy, Exercise 2.32 (p. 62). The time in bankruptcy (measured in months) for each company is saved in the accompanying file. Determine whether the bankruptcy times are approximately normally distributed.

4.186 Environmental failures of Arkansas companies. Refer to the study of 38 Arkansas corporations that were penalized for violating one or more environmental laws, Exercise 2.155 (p. 117). The financial penalties assessed to the companies are saved in the accompanying file. Determine whether the financial penalties are approximately normally distributed.

Applying the Concepts—Intermediate

4.187 Errors in measuring truck weights. To help highway planners anticipate the need for road repairs and design future construction projects, data are collected on the estimated volume and weight of truck traffic on specific roadways (*Transportation Planning Handbook,* 2008) using specialized "weigh-in-motion" equipment. In an experiment performed by the Minnesota Department of Transportation involving repeated weighing of a 27,907-pound truck, it was found that the weights recorded by the weigh-in-motion equipment were approximately normally distributed with a mean of 27,315 and a standard deviation of 628 pounds (Minnesota Department of Transportation). It follows that the difference between the actual weight and recorded weight, the error of measurement, is normally distributed with a mean of 592 pounds and a standard deviation of 628 pounds.

a. What is the probability that the weigh-in-motion equipment understates the actual weight of the truck?

b. If a 27,907-pound truck was driven over the weigh-in-motion equipment 100 times, approximately how many times would the equipment overstate the truck's weight?

c. What is the probability that the error in the weight recorded by the weigh-in-motion equipment for a 27,907-pound truck exceeds 400 pounds?

d. It is possible to adjust (or *calibrate*) the weigh-in-motion equipment to control the mean error of measurement. At what level should the mean error be set so the equipment will understate the weight of a 27,907-pound truck 50% of the time? Only 40% of the time?

4.188 Detecting a computer virus attack. *Chance* (Winter 2004) presented basic methods for detecting virus attacks (e.g., Trojan programs or worms) on a network computer that are sent from a remote host. These viruses reach the network through requests for communication (e.g., e-mail, Web chat, or remote log-in) that are identified as "packets." For example, the "SYN flood" virus ties up the network computer by "flooding" the network with multiple packets. Cybersecurity experts can detect this type of virus attack if at least one packet is observed by a network sensor. Assume that the probability of observing a single packet sent from a new virus is only .001. If the virus actually sends 150 packets to a network computer, what is the probability that the virus is detected by the sensor?

4.189 Whistle-blowing among federal employees. *Whistle-blowing* refers to an employee's reporting of wrongdoing by coworkers. A survey found that about 5% of employees contacted had reported wrongdoing during the past 12 months. Assume that a sample of 25 employees in one agency are contacted and let x be the number who have observed and reported wrongdoing in the last 12 months. Assume that the probability of whistle-blowing is .05 for any federal employee over the past 12 months.
   a. Find the mean and standard deviation of x. Can x be equal to its expected value? Explain.
   b. Write the event that at least 5 of the employees are whistle-blowers in terms of x. Find the probability of the event.
   c. If 5 of the 25 contacted have been whistle-blowers over the past 12 months, what would you conclude about the applicability of the 5% assumption to this agency? Use your answer to part **b** to justify your conclusion.

4.190 Cotton crop yield study. The crop yield for a particular farm in a particular year is typically measured as the amount of the crop produced per acre. For example, cotton is measured in pounds per acre. It has been demonstrated that the normal distribution can be used to characterize crop yields over time (*American Journal of Agricultural Economics*, May 1999). Historical data indicate that next summer's cotton yield for a particular Georgia farmer can be characterized by a normal distribution with mean 1,500 pounds per acre and standard deviation 250. The farm in question will be profitable if it produces at least 1,600 pounds per acre.
   a. What is the probability that the farm will lose money next summer?
   b. Assume the same normal distribution is appropriate for describing cotton yield in each of the next two summers. Also assume that the two yields are statistically independent. What is the probability that the farm will lose money for two straight years?
   c. What is the probability that the cotton yield falls within 2 standard deviations of 1,500 pounds per acre next summer?

4.191 Awarding of home improvement grants. A curious event was described in the *Minneapolis Star and Tribune*. The Minneapolis Community Development Agency (MCDA) makes home improvement grants each year to homeowners in depressed city neighborhoods. Of the $708,000 granted one year, $233,000 was awarded by the city council via a "random selection" of 140 homeowners' applications from among a total of 743 applications: 601 from the north side, and 142 from the south side, of Minneapolis. Oddly, all 140 grants awarded were from the north side—clearly a highly improbable outcome if, in fact, the 140 winners were randomly selected from among the 743 applicants.
   a. Suppose the 140 winning applications were randomly selected from among the total of 743 and let x equal the number in the sample from the north side. Find the mean and standard deviation of x.

   b. Use the results of part **a** to support a contention that the grant winners were not randomly selected.

4.192 Time delays at a bus stop. A bus is scheduled to stop at a certain bus stop every half hour on the hour and the half hour. At the end of the day, buses still stop after every 30 minutes, but because delays often occur earlier in the day, the bus is never early and is likely to be late. The director of the bus line claims that the length of time a bus is late is uniformly distributed, and the maximum time that a bus is late is 20 minutes.
   a. If the director's claim is true, what is the expected number of minutes a bus will be late?
   b. If the director's claim is true, what is the probability that the last bus on a given day will be more than 19 minutes late?
   c. If you arrive at the bus stop at the end of a day at exactly half past the hour and must wait more than 19 minutes for the bus, what would you conclude about the director's claim? Why?

4.193 Reliability of a flow network. The journal *Networks* periodically publishes studies on the reliability of flow networks. For example, *Networks* (Sep. 2007) provided applications in mobile ad hoc and sensor networks. Consider a similar network with four activities, called *arcs*. The probability distribution of the capacity x for each of the four arcs is provided in the following table.

Arc 1	x	0	1	2	3
	$p(x)$	.05	.10	.25	.60

Arc 2	x	0	1	2	3
	$p(x)$	.10	.30	.60	0

Arc 3	x	0	1	2	3
	$p(x)$	.05	.25	.70	0

Arc 4	x	0	1	2	3
	$p(x)$	.90	.10	0	0

Source: Adapted from Lin, J. "On Reliability Evaluation of Capacitated-Flow Network in Terms of Minimal Pathsets." *Networks,* Vol. 25, No. 3, May 1995 (Table 1).

   a. Verify that the properties of discrete probability distributions are satisfied for each arc capacity distribution.
   b. Find the probability that the capacity for Arc 1 will exceed 1.
   c. Repeat part **b** for each of the remaining three arcs.
   d. Compute μ for each arc and interpret the results.
   e. Compute σ for each arc and interpret the results.

4.194 Doctors and ethics. Refer to the *Journal of Medical Ethics* (Vol. 32, 2006) study of the extent to which doctors refuse ethics consultation, Exercise 2.11 (p. 49). Consider a random sample of 10 doctors, each of whom is confronted with an ethical dilemma (e.g., an end-of-life issue or treatment of a patient without insurance). What is the probability that at least two of the doctors refuse ethics consultation? Use your answer to 2.11b to estimate p, the probability that a doctor will refuse to use ethics consultation.

4.195 LAN video conferencing. A network administrator is installing a video conferencing module to a local area network (LAN) computer system. Of interest is the capacity of the

LAN to handle users who attempt to call in for video conferencing during peak hours. Calls are blocked if the user finds all LAN lines are "busy." The capacity is directly related to the rate at which calls are blocked ("Traffic Engineering Model for LAN Video Conferencing," Intel, 2005). Let x equal the number of calls blocked during the peak hour (busy) video conferencing call time. The network administrator believes that x has a Poisson distribution with mean $\lambda = 5$.

a. Find the probability that fewer than three calls are blocked during the peak hour.

b. Find $E(x)$ and interpret its value.

4.196 Testing for spoiled wine. Suppose that you are purchasing cases of wine (12 bottles per case) and that, periodically, you select a test case to determine the adequacy of the bottles' seals. To do this, you randomly select and test 3 bottles in the case. If a case contains 1 spoiled bottle of wine, what is the probability that this bottle will turn up in your sample?

4.197 Testing a manufacturer's claim. A manufacturer of CD-ROMs claims that 99.4% of its CDs are defect-free. A large software company that buys and uses a large number of the CDs wants to verify this claim, so it selects 1,600 CDs to be tested. The tests reveal 12 CDs to be defective. Assuming that the manufacturer's claim is correct, what is the probability of finding 12 or more defective CDs in a sample of 1,600? Does your answer cast doubt on the manufacturer's claim? Explain.

4.198 Checkout lanes at a supermarket. A team of consultants working for a large national supermarket chain based in the New York metropolitan area developed a statistical model for predicting the annual sales of potential new store locations. Part of their analysis involved identifying variables that influence store sales, such as the size of the store (in square feet), the size of the surrounding population, and the number of checkout lanes. They surveyed 52 supermarkets in a particular region of the country and constructed the relative frequency distribution shown below to describe the number of checkout lanes per store, x.

x	1	2	3	4	5	6	7	8	9	10
Relative Frequency	.01	.04	.04	.08	.10	.15	.25	.20	.08	.05

Source: Based on Chow, W., et.al. "A model for predicting a supermarket's annual sales per square foot." Graduate School of Management, Rutgers University, 1994.

a. Why do the relative frequencies in the table represent the approximate probabilities of a randomly selected supermarket having x number of checkout lanes?

b. Find $E(x)$ and interpret its value in the context of the problem.

c. Find the standard deviation of x.

d. According to Chebyshev's Rule (Chapter 2, p. 80), what percentage of supermarkets would be expected to fall within $\mu \pm \sigma$? Within $\mu \pm 2\sigma$?

e. What is the actual number of supermarkets that fall within $\mu \pm \sigma$? $\mu \pm 2\sigma$? Compare your answers to those of part **d**. Are the answers consistent?

4.199 Model for long-term construction cost. Before negotiating a long-term construction contract, building contractors must carefully estimate the total cost of completing the project. Benzion Barlev of New York University proposed a model for total cost of a long-term contract based on the normal distribution (*Journal of Business Finance and Accounting*, July 1995). For one particular construction contract, Barlev assumed total cost, x, to be normally distributed with mean $850,000 and standard deviation $170,000. The revenue, R, promised to the contractor is $1,000,000.

a. The contract will be profitable if revenue exceeds total cost. What is the probability that the contract will be profitable for the contractor?

b. What is the probability that the project will result in a loss for the contractor?

c. Suppose the contractor has the opportunity to renegotiate the contract. What value of R should the contractor strive for in order to have a .99 probability of making a profit?

4.200 Ship-to-shore transfer times. Lack of port facilities or shallow water may require cargo on a large ship to be transferred to a pier in smaller craft. The smaller craft may have to cycle back and forth from ship to shore many times. Researchers G. Horne (Center for Naval Analysis) and T. Irony (George Washington University) developed models of this transfer process that provide estimates of ship-to-shore transfer times (*Naval Research Logistics*, Vol. 41, 1994). They used an exponential distribution to model the time between arrivals of the smaller craft at the pier.

a. Assume that the mean time between arrivals at the pier is 17 minutes. Give the value of θ for this exponential distribution. Graph the distribution.

b. Suppose there is only one unloading zone at the pier available for the small craft to use. If the first craft docks at 10:00 A.M. and doesn't finish unloading until 10:15 A.M., what is the probability that the second craft will arrive at the unloading zone and have to wait before docking?

Applying the Concepts—Advanced

4.201 How many questionnaires to mail? The probability that a consumer responds to a marketing department's mailed questionnaire is .4. How many questionnaires should be mailed if you want to be reasonably certain that at least 100 will be returned?

4.202 Establishing tolerance limits. The *tolerance limits* for a particular quality characteristic (e.g., length, weight, or strength) of a product are the minimum and/or maximum values at which the product will operate properly. Tolerance limits are set by the engineering design function of the manufacturing operation (*Total Quality Management*, Vol. 11, 2000). The tensile strength of a particular metal part can be characterized as being normally distributed with a mean of 25 pounds and a standard deviation of 2 pounds. The upper and lower tolerance limits for the part are 30 pounds and 21 pounds, respectively. A part that falls within the tolerance limits results in a profit of $10. A part that falls below the lower tolerance limit costs the company $2; a part that falls above the upper tolerance limit costs the company $1. Find the company's expected profit per metal part produced.

4.203 Load on frame structures. In the *Journal of the International Association for Shell and Spatial Structures* (Apr. 2004), Japanese environmental researchers studied the performance of truss and frame structures subjected to uncertain loads. The load was assumed to have a normal distribution with a mean of 20,000 pounds. Also, the probability that the load is between 10,000 and 30,000 pounds is .95. Based on this information, find the standard deviation of the load distribution.

4.204 Luggage inspection at Newark airport. *New Jersey Business* reports that Newark Liberty International Airport's new terminal handles an average of 3,000 international passengers an hour but is capable of handling twice that number. Also, after scanning all luggage, 20% of arriving international passengers are detained for intrusive luggage inspection. The inspection facility can handle 600 passengers an hour without unreasonable delays for the travelers.

a. When international passengers arrive at the rate of 1,500 per hour, what is the expected number of passengers who will be detained for luggage inspection?

b. In the future, it is expected that as many as 4,000 international passengers will arrive per hour. When that occurs, what is the expected number of passengers who will be detained for luggage inspection?

c. Refer to part **b**. Find the approximate probability that more than 600 international passengers will be detained for luggage inspection. (This is also the probability that travelers will experience unreasonable luggage inspection delays.)

Critical Thinking Challenges

4.205 Super weapons development. The U.S. Army is working with a major defense contractor (not named here for both confidentiality and security reasons) to develop a "super" weapon. The weapon is designed to fire a large number of sharp tungsten bullets—called flechettes—with a single shot that will destroy a large number of enemy soldiers. (Flechettes are about the size of an average nail, with small fins at one end to stabilize them in flight.) The defense contractor has developed a prototype gun that fires 1,100 flechettes with a single round. In range tests, three 2-feet-wide targets were set up at a distance of 500 meters (approximately 1500 feet) from the weapon. Using a number line as a reference, the centers of the three targets were at 0, 5, and 10 feet, respectively, as shown in the accompanying figure. The prototype gun was aimed at the middle target (center at 5 feet) and fired once. The point x where each of the 1,100 flechettes landed at the 500-meter distance was measured using a horizontal grid. For example, a flechette with a horizontal value of $x = 5.5$ (shown in the figure) hit the middle target, but a flechette with a horizontal value of $x = 2.0$ (also shown in the figure) did not hit any of the three targets. The 1,100 measurements on the random variable x are saved in the accompanying file. (The data are simulated for confidentiality reasons.)

The defense contractor is interested in the likelihood of any one of the targets being hit by a flechette, and in

particular, wants to set the gun specifications to maximize the number of target hits. The weapon is designed to have a mean horizontal value, $E(x)$, equal to the aim point (e.g., $\mu = 5$ feet when aimed at the center target). By changing specifications, the contractor can vary the standard deviation, σ. The data file contains flechette measurements for three different range tests—one with a standard deviation of $\sigma = 1$ foot, one with $\sigma = 2$ feet, and one with $\sigma = 4$ feet. Let $x_1, x_2,$ and x_4 represent the random variables for horizontal measurements with $\sigma = 1$, $\sigma = 2$, and $\sigma = 4$, respectively. From past experience, the defense contractor has found that the distribution of the horizontal flechette measurements is closely approximated by a normal distribution.

a. For each of the three values of σ, use the normal distribution to find the approximate probability that a single flechette shot from the weapon will hit any one of the three targets. [*Hint:* Note that the three targets range from -1 to 1, 4 to 6, and 9 to 11 feet on the horizontal grid.]

b. The actual results of the three range tests are saved in the data file. Use this information to calculate the proportion of the 1,100 flechettes that actually hit each target—called the hit ratio—for each value of σ. How do these actual hit ratios compare to the estimated probabilities of a hit using the normal distribution?

c. If the U.S. Army wants to maximize the chance of hitting the target that the prototype gun is aimed at, what setting should be used for σ? If the Army wants to hit multiple targets with a single shot of the weapon, what setting should be used for σ?

Targets: 2 feet wide

Left   Middle   Right

4.206 Space shuttle disaster. On January 28, 1986, the space shuttle *Challenger* exploded, killing all seven astronauts aboard. An investigation concluded that the explosion was caused by the failure of the O ring seal in the joint between the two lower segments of the right solid rocket booster. In a report made 1 year prior to the catastrophe, the National Aeronautics and Space Administration (NASA) claimed that the probability of such a failure was about $\frac{1}{60,000}$, or about once in every 60,000 flights. But a risk-assessment study conducted for the Air Force at about the same time assessed the probability to be $\frac{1}{35}$, or about once in every 35 missions. (*Note:* The shuttle had flown 24 successful missions prior to the disaster.) Given the events of January 28, 1986, which risk assessment—NASA's or the Air Force's—appears to be more appropriate?

Activity 4.1   *Warehouse Club Memberships:* **Exploring a Binomial Random Variable**

Warehouse clubs are retailers that offer lower prices than traditional retailers, but they sell only to customers who have purchased memberships and often merchandise must be purchased in large quantities. A warehouse club may offer more than one type of membership, such as a regular

membership R for a low annual fee and an upgraded membership U for a higher annual fee. The upgraded membership has additional benefits that might include extended shopping hours, additional discounts on certain products, or cash back on purchases.

(Continued)

A local warehouse club has determined that 20% of its customer base has the upgraded membership.

1. What is the probability $P(U)$ that a randomly chosen customer entering the store has an upgraded membership? What is the probability $P(R)$ that a randomly chosen customer entering the store has a regular (not upgraded) membership?

    In an effort to sell more upgraded memberships, sales associates are placed at the entrance to the store to explain the benefits of the upgraded membership to customers as they enter. Suppose that in a given time period five customers enter the store.

2. Given that 20% of the store's customers have an upgraded membership, how many of the five customers would you expect to have an upgraded membership?

3. Because there are five customers and each customer either has an upgraded membership (U) or does not (R), there are $2^5 = 32$ different possible combinations of membership types among the five customers. List these 32 possibilities.

4. Find the probability of each of the 32 outcomes. Assume that each of the five customers' membership type is independent of each of the other customers' membership type

and use your probabilities $P(U)$ and $P(R)$ with the multiplicative rule. For example, $P(RRUUR) = P(R)P(R)P(U)P(U)P(R)$.

5. Notice that $P(URRRR) = P(RURRR) = P(RRURR) = P(RRRUR) = P(RRRRU) = P(U)^1 P(R)^4$ so that P(exactly one U) = $P(URRRR) + P(RURRR) + P(RRURR) + P(RRRUR) + P(RRRRU) = 5P(U)^1 P(R)^4$ where 5 is the number of ways that exactly one U can occur. Find P(exactly one U). Use similar reasoning to establish that P(no U's) = $1P(U)^0 P(R)^5$, P(exactly two U's) = $10P(U)^2 (R)^3$, P(exactly three U's) = $10P(U)^3 P(R)^2$, P(exactly four U's) = $5P(U)^4 P(R)^1$, and P(five U's) = $1P(U)^5 P(R)^0$.

6. Let x be the number of upgraded memberships U in a sample of five customers. Use the results of Part **5** to write a probability distribution for the random variable x in table form. Find the mean and standard deviation of the distribution using the formulas in Section 4.2.

7. Calculate np and $\sqrt{npq}$ where $n = 5$, $p = P(U)$, and $q = P(R)$. How do these numbers compare to the mean and standard deviation of the random variable x in Part **6** and to the expected number of customers with upgraded memberships in Part **1**?

8. Explain how the characteristics of a binomial random variable are illustrated in this activity.

<table>
<tr><td>**Activity**</td><td>**4.2**</td><td>**Identifying the Type of Probability Distribution**</td></tr>
</table>

Collect data for at least 50 observations on a variable of interest to you (e.g., scores on a statistics exam, monthly sales of a pre-owned auto dealership, time spent preparing for the GMAT, number of bank failures per year). Be sure to identify the experimental unit prior to beginning your data search.

1. Before you actually collect the data, identify the probability distribution that you believe will be the best model

for the variable you selected. (Be sure to check the properties of the different random variables presented in this chapter.)

2. Enter the data into a statistical software package and graph the distribution. Does the graph match the probability distribution you identified?

References

Deming, W. E. *Out of the Crisis*. Cambridge, Mass.: MIT Center for Advanced Engineering Study, 1986.

Hogg, R. V., McKean, J. W., and Craig, A. T. *Introduction to Mathematical Statistics*, 6th ed. Upper Saddle River, N.J.: Prentice Hall, 2005.

Larsen, R. J., & Marx, M. L. *An Introduction to Mathematical Statistics and Its Applications*, 4th ed. Upper Saddle River, N.J.: Prentice Hall, 2005.

Lindgren, B. W. *Statistical Theory*, 4th ed. New York: Chapman & Hall, 1993.

Ramsey, P. P., & Ramsey, P. H. "Simple tests of normality in small samples," *Journal of Quality Technology*, Vol. 22, 1990.

Wackerly, D., Mendenhall, W., and Scheaffer, R. *Mathematical Statistics with Applications*, 7th ed. North Scituate, Mass.: Duxbury, 2008.

USING TECHNOLOGY Technology images shown here are taken from SPSS Statistics Professional 20.0, Minitab 16, XLSTAT for Pearson, and Excel 2010.

SPSS: Discrete Probabilities, Continuous Probabilities, and Normal Probability Plots

Discrete and Continuous Probabilities

Step 1 Select "Transform" on the SPSS menu bar and then click on "Compute Variable," as shown in Figure 4.S.1. The resulting dialog box appears as shown in Figure 4.S.2.

Figure 4.S.1 SPSS menu options for obtaining discrete and continuous probabilities

Figure 4.S.2 SPSS compute cumulative binomial probabilities dialog box

Step 2 Specify a name for the "Target Variable."

Step 3 Select either "CDF" (for cumulative probabilities) or "PDF" (for exact probabilities) in the "Function group" box.

Step 4 Select the appropriate probability distribution in the "Functions and Special Variables" box. (For example, for cumulative probabilities of the binomial, use the function CDF.BINOM. For exact binomial probabilities, use the PDF.BINOM function.)

Step 5 Enter the parameters of the distribution in the "Numeric Expression" box. For example, Figure 4.S.2 shows the cumulative binomial function with parameters of $x = 3$ (the first number in the function), $n = 10$ (the second number), and $p = .2$ (the third number).

Step 6 Click "OK"; SPSS will compute the requested probability (in this example, the cumulative binomial probability that x is less than or equal to 3) and display it on the SPSS spreadsheet. Similarly, for example, Figure 4.S.3 shows the cumulative normal function with parameters of $x = 3.7$ (the first number in the function), $\mu = 5$ (the second number), and $\sigma = 2$ (the third number). When you click "OK," SPSS will compute the requested probability (in this example, the cumulative normal probability that x is less than 3.7) and display it on the SPSS spreadsheet.

Figure 4.S.3 SPSS compute cumulative normal probabilities dialog box

Normal Probability Plot

Step 1 Select "Analyze" on the SPSS menu bar, and then select "Descriptive Statistics" and "Q-Q Plots," as shown in Figure 4.S.4. The resulting dialog box appears as shown in Figure 4.S.5.

Step 2 Specify the variable of interest in the "Variables" box and select "Normal" in the "Test Distribution" box.

Figure 4.S.4 SPSS options for a normal probability plot

Figure 4.S.5 SPSS normal probability plot dialog box

Step 3 Click "OK" to generate the normal probability plot.

Minitab: Discrete Probabilities, Continuous Probabilities, and Normal Probability Plots

Discrete and Continuous Probabilities

Step 1 Select the "Calc" button on the Minitab menu bar, click on "Probability Distributions," and then finally select the distribution of your choice (e.g., "Binomial"), as shown in Figure 4.M.1.

Figure 4.M.1 Minitab menu options for obtaining discrete and continuous probabilities

Step 2 Select either "Probability" or "Cumulative probability" on the resulting dialog box.

Step 3 Specify the parameters of the distribution (e.g., sample size n, probability of success p, μ or σ.)

Step 4 Specify the value of x of interest in the "Input constant" box.

Step 5 Click "OK." The probability for the value of x will appear on the Minitab session window.

[*Note:* Figure 4.M.2 gives the specifications for finding $P(x = 1)$ in a binomial distribution with $n = 5$ and $p = .2$. Figure 4.M.3 gives the specifications for finding $P(x \leq 20)$ in a normal distribution with $\mu = 24.5$ and $\sigma = 3.1$.]

Figure 4.M.2 Minitab binomial distribution dialog box

Figure 4.M.3 Minitab normal distribution dialog box

Normal Probability Plot

Step 1 Select "Graph" on the Minitab menu bar and then click on "Probability Plot," as shown in Figure 4.M.4.

Figure 4.M.4 Minitab options for a normal probability plot

Step 2 Select "Single" (for one variable) on the next box, and the dialog box will appear as shown in Figure 4.M.5.

Figure 4.M.5 Minitab normal probability plot dialog box

Step 3 Specify the variable of interest in the "Graph variables" box and then click the "Distribution" button and select the "Normal" option. Click "OK" to return to the Probability Plot dialog box.

Step 4 Click "OK" to generate the normal probability plot.

Excel/XLSTAT: Discrete Probabilities, Continuous Probabilities, and Normal Probability Plots

Discrete and Continuous Probabilities

Step 1 Click on the cell in the Excel worksheet where you want the probability to appear.

Step 2 In the formula bar, enter "=" followed by the appropriate probability function. A list of different probability functions is shown in Figure 4.E.1.

Type of Probability	Excel Function
Binomial Probability, $P(x = a)$	= BINOMDIST (a, n, p, FALSE)
Cumulative Binomial Probability, $P(X \leq a)$	= BINOMDIST (a, n, p, TRUE)
Poisson Probability, $P(X = a)$	= POISSON $(a, \lambda, \text{FALSE})$
Cumulative Poisson Probability, $P(x \leq a)$	= POISSON $(a, \lambda, \text{TRUE})$
Hypergeometric Probability, $P(x = a)$	= HYPERGEOMDIST (a, n, r, N)
Cumulative Normal Probability, $P(X \leq a)$	= NORMDIST $(a, \mu, \sigma, \text{TRUE})$
Value of Normal Variable, given Probability p	= NORMINV (p, μ, σ)
Cumulative Exponential Probability, $P(X \leq a)$	= EXPONDIST (a, σ, TRUE)

Note: Probabilities from the uniform distribution function are not available in Excel.

Figure 4.E.1 List of probability functions in Excel

Step 3 Specify the parameters (e.g., *n*, *p*, μ, and σ) of the probability distribution as well as a specific value of the random variable (denoted "a") in the probability function on the formula bar, as shown in Figure 4.E.2.

Step 4 Click "Enter" and the probability will appear in the selected cell (see Figure 4.E.2).

Figure 4.E.2 Normal probability function in Excel

Normal Probability Plot

Step 1 Click the "XLSTAT" button on the Excel main menu bar and then click "Describing Data."

Step 2 From the resulting menu, select "Normality tests" (see Figure 4.E.3).

Figure 4.E.3 XLSTAT menu options for describing data

Step 3 When the resulting dialog box appears, highlight the data column(s) you want to graph so that the column information appears in the "Data" entry (see Figure 4.E.4).

Figure 4.E.4 XLSTAT normality tests dialog box

Step 4 Click the "Charts" tab, and then select "Normal Q-Q plots" on the resulting menu.

Step 5 Click "OK" and then "Continue" to display the normal probability plot.

TI-84 Graphing Calculator: Discrete and Continuous Random Variables Normal Probability Plots

Calculating the Mean and Standard Deviation of a Discrete Random Variable

Step 1 *Enter the data*

- Press **STAT** and select **1:Edit**

Note: If the lists already contain data, clear the old data. Use the up **ARROW** to highlight **L1**

- Press **CLEAR ENTER**
- Use the up **ARROW** to highlight **L2**
- Press **CLEAR ENTER**
- Use the **ARROW** and **ENTER** keys to enter the *x*-values of the variable into **L1**
- Use the **ARROW** and **ENTER** keys to enter the probabilities, *P(x)*, into **L2**

Step 2 *Access the Calc Menu*

- Press **STAT**
- Arrow right to **CALC**
- Select **1-Var Stats**
- Press **ENTER**
- Press **2nd 1** for **L1**
- Press **COMMA**
- Select **2nd 2** for **L2**
- Press **ENTER**

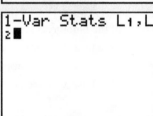

The mean and standard deviation will be displayed on the screen, as well as the quartiles, min, and max.

Calculating Binomial Probabilities
I. *P(x = k)*

To compute the probability of *k* successes in *n* trials, where *p* is the probability of success for each trial, use the **binompdf(** command. *Binompdf* stands for "binomial probability density function." This command is under the **DISTR**ibution menu and has the format **binompdf(*n, p, k*).**

Example Compute the probability of 5 successes in 8 trials, where the probability of success for a single trial is 40%. In this example, *n* = 8, *p* = .4, and *k* = 5.

Step 1 *Enter the binomial parameters*

- Press **2nd VARS** for **DISTR**
- Press the down **ARROW** key until **binompdf** is highlighted
- Press **ENTER**

- After **binompdf(**, type
  8, .4, 5) (*Note:* Be sure to use
  the **COMMA** key between
  each parameter)
- Press **ENTER**
- You should see

Thus, $P(x = 5)$ is about 12.4%.

```
binompdf(8,.4,5)
         .12386304
```

II. $P(x \leq k)$

To compute the probability of k or fewer successes in n trials,
where p is the probability of success for each trial, use
the **binomcdf(** command. *Binomcdf* stands for "binomial *cumulative* probability density function." This command is under the
DISTRibution menu and has the format **binomcdf(n, p, k)**.

Example Compute the probability of 5 or fewer successes in
8 trials, where the probability of success for a single trial is 40%.
In this example, $n = 8$, $p = .4$, and $k = 5$.

Step 2 *Enter the binomial parameters*

- Press **2nd VARS** for **DISTR**
- Press down the **ARROW** key
  until **binomcdf** is highlighted
- Press **ENTER**
- After **binomcdf(**, type
  8, .4, 5)
- Press **ENTER**
- You should see

Thus, $P(x \leq k)$ is about 95%.

```
binomcdf(8,.4,5)
         .95019264
```

III. $P(x < k), (x > k), (x \geq k)$

To find the probability of fewer than k successes $P(x < k)$, more
than k successes $P(x > k)$, or at least k successes $P(x \geq k)$, variations of the **binomcdf(** command must be used as shown below.

- $P(x < k)$ use **binomcdf(n, p, k − 1)**
- $P(x > k)$ use **1 − binomcdf(n, p, k)**
- $P(x \geq k)$ use **1 − binomcdf(n, p, k − 1)**

Calculating Poisson Probabilities
I. $P(x = k)$

To compute $P(x = k)$, the probability of exactly k successes in
a specified interval where λ is the mean number of successes
in the interval, use the **poissonpdf(** command. *Poissonpdf*
stands for "Poisson probability density function." This command is under the **DISTR**ibution menu and has the format
poissonpdf( ).

Example Suppose that the number, x, of reported sightings per
week of blue whales is recorded. Assume that x has approximately a Poisson probability distribution and that the average
number of weekly sightings is 2.6. Compute the probability that
exactly five sightings are made during a given week. In this
example, $\lambda = 2.6$ and $k = 5$.

Step 1 *Enter the Poisson parameters*

- Press **2nd VARS** for **DISTR**
- Press the down **ARROW** key until **poissonpdf**
  is highlighted
- Press **ENTER**

- After **poissonpdf(**, type **2.6,
  5)** (*Note:* Be sure to use the
  COMMA key between each
  parameter)
- Press **ENTER**
- You should see

Thus, the $P(x = 5)$ is about 7.4%.

```
poissonpdf(2.6,5
)
       .0735393591
```

II. $P(x \leq k)$

To compute the probability of k or fewer successes in a
specified interval, where λ is the mean number of successes in
the interval, use the **poissoncdf(** command. *Poissoncdf* stands
for "Poisson *cumulative* probability density function." This
command is under the **DISTR**ibution menu and has the
format **poissoncdf(.**

Example In the preceding example, compute the probability
that five or fewer sightings are made during a given week.
In this example, $\lambda = 2.6$ and $k = 5$.

Step 2 *Enter the Poisson parameters*

- Press **2nd VARS** for **DISTR**
- Press the down **ARROW**
  key until **poissoncdf** is
  highlighted
- Press **ENTER**
- After **poissoncdf(**, type **2.6, 5)**
- Press **ENTER**
- You should see

Thus, the $P(x = 5)$ is about 95.1%.

```
poissoncdf(2.6,5
)
       .9509628481
```

III. $P(x < k), (x > k), (x \geq k)$

To find the probability of fewer than k successes, more than k
successes, or at least k successes, variations of the **poissoncdf(**
command must be used as shown below.

- $P(x < k)$ use **poissoncdf(λ, k − 1)**
- $P(x > k)$ use **1 − poissoncdf(λ, k)**
- $P(x \geq k)$ use **1 − poissoncd(λ, k − 1)**

Graphing the Area under the Standard Normal Curve

Step 1 *Turn off all plots*

- Press **2nd PRGM** and select **1:ClrDraw**
- Press **ENTER** and "Done" will appear on the screen
- Press **2nd Y=** and select **4:PlotsOff**
- Press **ENTER** and "Done" will appear on the screen

Step 2 *Set the viewing window (Recall that almost all of the area
under the standard normal curve falls between −5 and 5. A height
of 0.5 is a good choice for Ymax.)*

Note: When entering a negative number, be sure to use the negative sign (−), not the minus sign.

- Set **Xmin = −5**
- **Xmax = 5**
- **Xscl = 1**
- **Ymin = 0**
- **Ymax = .5**
- **Yscl = 0**
- **Xres = 1**

Step 3 *View graph*

- Press **2nd VARS**
- Arrow right to **DRAW**
- Press **ENTER** to select **1:ShadeNorm(**
- Enter your lower limit (e.g., −5)
- Press **COMMA**
- Enter your upper limit (e.g., 1.5)
- Press **)**
- Press **ENTER**

The graph will be displayed along with the area, lower limit, and upper limit.

Thus, $P(z < 1.5) = .9332$.

Nonstandard Normal Probabilities
I. Finding Normal Probabilities without a Graph

To compute probabilities for a normal distribution, use the **normalcdf(** command. *Normalcdf* stands for "normal cumulative density function." This command is under the **DISTR**ibution menu and has the format **normalcdf(*lower limit, upper limit, mean, standard deviation*)**.

Step 1 *Find probability*

- Press **2nd VARS** for **DISTR** and select **Normalcdf(**
- After **Normalcdf(,** type in the lower limit
- Press **COMMA**
- Enter the upper limit
- Press **COMMA**
- Enter the mean
- Press **COMMA**
- Enter the standard deviation
- Press **)**
- Press **ENTER**

The probability will be displayed on the screen.

Example What is $P(x < 115)$ for a normal distribution with $\mu = 100$ and $\sigma = 10$?

In this example, the lower limit is $-\infty$, the upper limit is 115, the mean is 100, and the standard deviation is 10. To represent $-\infty$ on the calculator, enter **(−) 1**, press **2nd** and press the **COMMA** key for **EE**, and then press **99**. The screen appears as follows:

Thus, $P(x < 115)$ is .9332.

II. Finding Normal Probabilities with a Graph

Step 1 *Turn off all plots*

- Press **Y=** and **CLEAR** all functions from the Y registers
- Press **2nd   Y =**   and select **4:PlotsOff**
- Press **ENTER ENTER**, and 'Done' will appear on the screen

Step 2 *Set the viewing window (These values depend on the mean and standard deviation of the data.) Note:* When entering a negative number, be sure to use the negative sign (−), not the minus sign.

- Press **WINDOW**
- Set **Xmin** $= \mu - 5\sigma$
- **Xmax** $= \mu + 5\sigma$
- **Xscl** $= \sigma$
- **Ymin** $= -.125/gs$
- **Ymax** $= .5/\sigma$
- **Yscl** $= 1$
- **Xres** $= 1$

Step 3 *View graph*

- Press **2nd VARS**
- **ARROW** right to **DRAW**
- Press **ENTER** to select **1:ShadeNorm(**
- Enter the lower limit
- Press **COMMA**
- Enter the upper limit
- Press **COMMA**
- Enter the mean
- Press **COMMA**
- Enter the standard deviation
- Press **)**
- Press **ENTER**

The graph will be displayed along with the area, lower limit, and upper limit.

Example What is $P(x < 115)$ for a normal distribution with $\mu = 100$ and $\sigma = 10$? In this example, the lower limit is $-\infty$, the upper limit is 115, the mean is 100, and the standard deviation is 10. To represent $-\infty$ on the calculator, enter $(-)$**1**, press **2nd** and press the **COMMA** key for **EE**, and then press **99**. The screens appear as follows:

Graphing a Normal Probability Plot

Step 1 *Enter the data*

- Press **STAT** and select **1:Edit**

Note: If the list already contains data, clear the old data. Use the up **ARROW** to highlight **L1**.

- Press **CLEAR ENTER**
- Use the **ARROW** and **ENTER** keys to enter the data set into **L1**

Step 2 *Set up the normal probability plot*

- Press **Y=** and **CLEAR** all functions from the Y registers
- Press **2nd** and press **Y=** for **STAT PLOT**
- Press **1** for **Plot 1**
- Set the cursor so that **ON** is flashing
- For **Type**, use the **ARROW** and **ENTER** keys to highlight and select the last graph in the bottom row
- For **Data List**, choose the column containing the data (in most cases, L1) (*Note:* Press **2nd 1** for **L1**)
- For **Data Axis**, choose **X** and press **ENTER**

Step 3 *View plot*

- Press **ZOOM 9**

Your data will be displayed against the expected *z*-scores from a normal distribution. If you see a "generally" linear relationship, your data set is approximately normal.

5

Where We've Been

- Learned that the objective of most statistical investigations is inference—that is, making decisions about a population on the basis of information about a sample

- Discovered that sample statistics such as the sample mean and sample variance can be used to make decisions

- Found that probability distributions for random variables are used to construct theoretical models of populations

Where We're Going

- Establish that a sample statistic is a random variable with a probability distribution (5.1)

- Define a *sampling distribution* as the probability distribution of a sample statistic (5.1)

- Give two important properties of sampling distributions (5.2)

- Learn that the sampling distribution of both the sample mean and sample proportion tends to be approximately normal (5.3, 5.4)

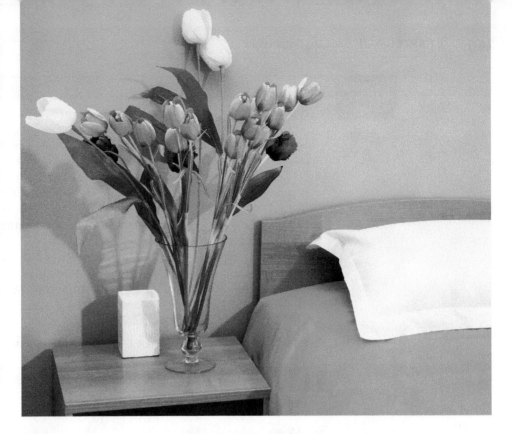

☐ Sampling Distributions

STATISTICS in ACTION   The Insomnia Pill: Is It Effective?

More than 15 years ago, neuroscientists at the Massachusetts Institute of Technology (MIT) began experimenting with melatonin—a hormone secreted by the pineal gland in the brain—as a sleep-inducing hormone. Their original study, published in the Proceedings of the National Academy of Sciences *(March 1994), brought encouraging news to insomniacs and travelers who suffer from jet lag: Melatonin was discovered to be effective in reducing sleep onset latency (the amount of time between a person lying down to sleep and the actual onset of stage one sleep). Furthermore, since the hormone is naturally produced, it is nonaddictive.*

Since then, pharmaceutical companies that produce melatonin pills for treating insomnia have received negative reports on the efficacy of the drug. Many people don't think the melatonin pills work. Consequently, the MIT researchers undertook a follow-up study and published their results in *Sleep Medicine Reviews* (Feb. 2005). They reported that commercially available melatonin pills contain too high a dosage of the drug. When the melatonin receptors in the brain are exposed to too much of the hormone, they become unresponsive. The researchers' analysis of all previous studies on melatonin as a sleep inducer confirmed that, taken in small doses, melatonin is effective in reducing sleep onset latency.

In this Statistics in Action, our focus is on the original MIT study. Young male volunteers were given various doses of melatonin or a placebo (a dummy medication containing no melatonin). Then they were placed in a dark room at midday and told to close their eyes for 30 minutes. The variable of interest was sleep onset latency (in minutes).

According to the lead investigator, Professor Richard Wurtman, "Our volunteers fall asleep in 5 or 6 minutes on melatonin, while those on placebo take about 15 minutes." Wurtman warned, however, that uncontrolled doses of melatonin could cause mood-altering side effects.

Now, consider a random sample of 40 young males, each of whom is given a dosage of the sleep-inducing hormone melatonin. The times taken (in minutes) to fall asleep for these 40 males are listed in Table SIA5.1 and saved in the **SLEEP** file. The researchers know that with the placebo (i.e., no hormone), the mean sleep onset latency is $\mu = 15$ minutes and the standard deviation is $\sigma = 10$ minutes. They want to use the data to make an inference about the true value of μ for those taking the melatonin. Specifically, the researchers want to know whether melatonin is an effective drug against insomnia.

In this chapter, a Statistics in Action Revisited example demonstrates how we can use one of the topics discussed in the chapter—the Central Limit Theorem—to make an inference about the effectiveness of melatonin as a sleep-inducing hormone.

STATISTICS in ACTION REVISITED

□ Making an Inference about the Mean Sleep Onset Latency for Insomnia Pill Takers **(p. 282)**

Table SIA5.1	Times Taken (in Minutes) for 40 Male Volunteers to Fall Asleep								
7.6	2.1	1.4	1.5	3.6	17.0	14.9	4.4	4.7	20.1
7.7	2.4	8.1	1.5	10.3	1.3	3.7	2.5	3.4	10.7
2.9	1.5	15.9	3.0	1.9	8.5	6.1	4.5	2.2	2.6
7.0	6.4	2.8	2.8	22.8	1.5	4.6	2.0	6.3	3.2

[Note: These data are simulated sleep times based on summary information provided in the MIT study.]

Data Set: SLEEP

In Chapter 4, we assumed that we knew the probability distribution of a random variable, and using this knowledge, we were able to compute the mean, variance, and probabilities associated with the random variable. However, in most practical applications, this information is not available. To illustrate, in Example 4.13 (p. 206), we calculated the probability that the binomial random variable x, the number of 20 employees who favor unionization, assumed specific values. To do this, it was necessary to assume some value for p, the proportion of all employees who favor unionization. Thus, for the purposes of illustration, we assumed that $p = .6$ when, in all likelihood, the exact value of p would be unknown. In fact, the probable purpose of taking the poll is to estimate p. Similarly, when we modeled the in-city gas mileage of a certain automobile model in Example 4.21 (p. 226), we used the normal probability distribution with an *assumed* mean and standard deviation of 27 and 3 miles per gallon, respectively. In most situations, the true mean and standard deviation are unknown quantities that have to be estimated. Numerical quantities that describe probability distributions are called *parameters*. Thus, p, the probability of a success in a binomial experiment, and μ and σ, the mean and standard deviation, respectively, of a normal distribution, are examples of parameters.

> A **parameter** is a numerical descriptive measure of a population. Because it is based on the observations in the population, its value is almost always unknown.

We have also discussed the sample mean $\bar{x}$ sample variance s^2, sample standard deviation s, and the like, which are numerical descriptive measures calculated from the sample. (See Table 5.1 for a list of the statistics covered so far in this text.) We will often use the information contained in these *sample statistics* to make inferences about the parameters of a population.

> A **sample statistic** is a numerical descriptive measure of a sample. It is calculated from the observations in the sample.

Table 5.1	List of Population Parameters and Corresponding Sample Statistics	
	Population Parameter	Sample Statistic
Mean:	μ	$\bar{x}$
Median:	η	m
Variance:	σ^2	s^2
Standard deviation:	σ	s
Binomial proportion:	p	$\hat{p}$

Note that the term *statistic* refers to a *sample* quantity and the term *parameter* refers to a *population* quantity.

Before we can show you how to use sample statistics to make inferences about population parameters, we need to be able to evaluate their properties. Does one sample statistic contain more information than another about a population parameter? On what basis should we choose the "best" statistic for making inferences about a parameter? The purpose of this chapter is to answer these questions.

5.1 The Concept of a Sampling Distribution

If we want to estimate a parameter of a population—say, the population mean μ—we can use a number of sample statistics for our estimate. Two possibilities are the sample mean $\bar{x}$ and the sample median m. Which of these do you think will provide a better estimate of μ?

Before answering this question, consider the following example: Toss a fair die, and let x equal the number of dots showing on the up face. Suppose the die is tossed three times, producing the sample measurements 2, 2, 6. The sample mean is then $\bar{x} = 3.33$, and the sample median is $m = 2$. Since the population mean of x is $\mu = 3.5$, you can see that, for this sample of three measurements, the sample mean $\bar{x}$ provides an estimate that falls closer to μ than does the sample median (see Figure 5.1a). Now suppose we toss the die three more times and obtain the sample measurements 3, 4, 6. Then the mean and median of this sample are $\bar{x} = 4.33$ and $m = 4$, respectively. This time m is closer to μ. (See Figure 5.1b.)

This simple example illustrates an important point: Neither the sample mean nor the sample median will *always* fall closer to the population mean. Consequently, we cannot compare these two sample statistics, or, in general, any two sample statistics, on the basis of their performance for a single sample. Instead, we need to recognize that sample statistics are themselves random variables because different samples can lead to different values for the sample statistics. As random variables, sample statistics must be judged and compared on the basis of their probability distributions (i.e., the *collection* of values and associated probabilities of each statistic that would be obtained if the sampling experiment was repeated a *very large number of times*). We will illustrate this concept with another example.

Suppose it is known that the connector module manufactured for a certain brand of pacemaker has a mean length of $\mu = .3$ inch and a standard deviation of .005 inch. Consider an experiment consisting of randomly selecting 25 recently manufactured connector modules, measuring the length of each, and calculating the sample mean length $\bar{x}$. If this experiment was repeated a very large number of times, the value of $\bar{x}$ would vary from sample to sample. For example, the first sample of 25 length measurements might have a mean $\bar{x} = .301$, the second sample a mean $\bar{x} = .298$, the third sample a mean

Figure 5.1

Comparing the sample mean ($\bar{x}$) and sample median (m) as estimators of the population mean (μ)

a. Sample 1: $\bar{x}$ is closer than m to μ

b. Sample 2: m is closer than $\bar{x}$ to μ

Figure 5.2

Sampling distribution for $\bar{x}$ based on a sample of $n = 25$ length measurements

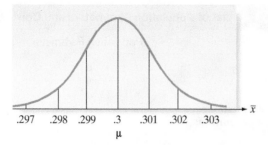

$\bar{x} = .303$, etc. If the sampling experiment were repeated a very large number of times, the resulting histogram of sample means would be approximately the probability distribution of $\bar{x}$. If $\bar{x}$ is a good estimator of μ, we would expect the values of $\bar{x}$ to cluster around μ, as shown in Figure 5.2. This probability distribution is called a *sampling distribution* because it is generated by repeating a sampling experiment a very large number of times.

The **sampling distribution** of a sample statistic calculated from a sample of n measurements is the probability distribution of the statistic.

In actual practice, the sampling distribution of a statistic is obtained mathematically or (at least approximately) by simulating the sample on a computer using a procedure similar to that just described.

If $\bar{x}$ has been calculated from a sample of $n = 25$ measurements selected from a population with mean $\mu = .3$ and standard deviation $\sigma = .005$, the sampling distribution (Figure 5.2) provides information about the behavior of $\bar{x}$ in repeated sampling. For example, the probability that you will draw a sample of 25 length measurements and obtain a value of $\bar{x}$ in the interval $.299 \leq \bar{x} \leq .3$ will be the area under the sampling distribution over that interval.

Because the properties of a statistic are typified by its sampling distribution, it follows that to compare two sample statistics, you compare their sampling distributions. For example, if you have two statistics, A and B, for estimating the same parameter (for purposes of illustration, suppose the parameter is the population variance σ^2) and if their sampling distributions are as shown in Figure 5.3, you would choose statistic A in preference to statistic B. You would make this choice because the sampling distribution for statistic A centers over σ^2 and has less spread (variation) than the sampling distribution for statistic B. When you draw a single sample in a practical sampling situation, the probability is higher that statistic A will fall nearer σ^2.

Remember that in practice we will not know the numerical value of the unknown parameter σ^2, so we will not know whether statistic A or statistic B is closer to σ^2 for a sample. We have to rely on our knowledge of the theoretical sampling distributions to choose the best sample statistic and then use it sample after sample. The procedure for finding the sampling distribution for a statistic is demonstrated in Example 5.1.

Figure 5.3

Two sampling distributions for estimating the population variance, σ^2

Sampling distribution for statistic B

Sampling distribution for statistic A

σ^2

Example   5.1

Finding a Sampling Distribution—Come-Out Roll in Craps

Problem Consider the popular casino game of craps, in which a player throws two dice and bets on the outcome (the sum total of the dots showing on the upper faces of the two dice). In Example 4.5 (p. 189), we looked at the possible outcomes of a $5 wager on the first toss (called the *come-out* roll). Recall that if the sum total of the dice is 7 or 11, the roller wins $5; if the total is a 2, 3, or 12, the roller loses $5 (i.e., the roller "wins" −$5); and, for any other total (4, 5, 6, 8, 9, or 10) no money is lost or won on that roll (i.e., the roller wins $0). Let x represent the result of the come-out roll wager ($-\$5$, $\$0$, or $+\$5$). We showed in Example 4.5 that the actual probability distribution of x is:

Outcome of wager, x	-5	0	5
$p(x)$	1/9	6/9	2/9

Now, consider a random sample of $n = 3$ come-out rolls.

a. Find the sampling distribution of the sample mean, $\bar{x}$.

b. Find the sampling distribution of the sample median, m.

Solution The outcomes for every possible sample of $n = 3$ come-out rolls are listed in Table 5.2, along with the sample mean and median. The probability of each sample is obtained using the multiplicative rule. For example, the probability of the sample $(0, 0, 5)$ is $p(0) \cdot p(0) \cdot p(5) = \left(\frac{6}{9}\right)\left(\frac{6}{9}\right)\left(\frac{2}{9}\right) = \frac{72}{729} = .099$. The probability for each sample is also listed in Table 5.2. Note that the sum of these probabilities is equal to 1.

a. From Table 5.2, you can see that $\bar{x}$ can assume the values -5, -3.33, -1.67, 0, 1.67, 3.33, and 5. Because $\bar{x} = -5$ occurs only in one sample, $P(\bar{x} = -5) = \frac{1}{729}$. Similarly, $\bar{x} = -3.33$ occurs in three samples, $(-5, -5, 0)$, $(-5, 0, -5)$, and $(0, -5, -5)$. Therefore, $P(\bar{x} = -3.33) = \frac{6}{729} + \frac{6}{729} + \frac{6}{729} = \frac{18}{729}$. Calculating the probabilities of the remaining values of $\bar{x}$ and arranging them in a table, we obtain the following probability distribution:

$\bar{x}$	-5	-3.33	-1.67	0	1.67	3.33	5
$p(\bar{x})$	1/729 = .0014	18/729 = .0247	114/729 = .1564	288/729 = .3951	288/729 = .3127	72/729 = .0988	8/729 = .0110

Table 5.2 **All Possible Samples of $n = 3$ Come-Out Rolls in Craps**

Possible Samples	$\bar{x}$	m	Probability
$-5, -5, -5$	-5	-5	$(1/9)(1/9)(1/9) = 1/729$
$-5, -5, 0$	-3.33	-5	$(1/9)(1/9)(6/9) = 6/729$
$-5, -5, 5$	-1.67	-5	$(1/9)(1/9)(2/9) = 2/729$
$-5, \ \ 0, -5$	-3.33	-5	$(1/9)(6/9)(1/9) = 6/729$
$-5, \ \ 0, 0$	-1.67	0	$(1/9)(6/9)(6/9) = 36/729$
$-5, \ \ 0, 5$	0	0	$(1/9)(6/9)(2/9) = 12/729$
$-5, \ \ 5, -5$	-1.67	-5	$(1/9)(2/9)(1/9) = 2/729$
$-5, \ \ 5, 0$	0	0	$(1/9)(2/9)(6/9) = 12/729$
$-5, \ \ 5, 5$	1.67	5	$(1/9)(2/9)(2/9) = 4/729$
$0, -5, -5$	-3.33	-5	$(6/9)(1/9)(1/9) = 6/729$
$0, -5, 0$	-1.67	0	$(6/9)(1/9)(6/9) = 36/729$
$0, -5, 5$	0	0	$(6/9)(1/9)(2/9) = 12/729$
$0, \ \ 0, -5$	-1.67	0	$(6/9)(6/9)(1/9) = 36/729$
$0, \ \ 0, 0$	0	0	$(6/9)(6/9)(6/9) = 216/729$
$0, \ \ 0, 5$	1.67	0	$(6/9)(6/9)(2/9) = 72/729$
$0, \ \ 5, -5$	0	0	$(6/9)(2/9)(1/9) = 12/729$
$0, \ \ 5, 0$	1.67	0	$(6/9)(2/9)(6/9) = 72/729$
$0, \ \ 5, 5$	3.33	5	$(6/9)(2/9)(2/9) = 24/729$
$5, -5, -5$	-1.67	-5	$(2/9)(1/9)(1/9) = 2/729$
$5, -5, 0$	0	0	$(2/9)(1/9)(6/9) = 12/729$
$5, -5, 5$	1.67	5	$(2/9)(1/9)(2/9) = 4/729$
$5, \ \ 0, -5$	0	0	$(2/9)(6/9)(1/9) = 12/729$
$5, \ \ 0, 0$	1.67	0	$(2/9)(6/9)(6/9) = 72/729$
$5, \ \ 0, 5$	3.33	5	$(2/9)(6/9)(2/9) = 24/729$
$5, \ \ 5, -5$	1.67	5	$(2/9)(2/9)(1/9) = 4/729$
$5, \ \ 5, 0$	3.33	5	$(2/9)(2/9)(6/9) = 24/729$
$5, \ \ 5, 5$	5	5	$(2/9)(2/9)(2/9) = 8/729$

Sum = 729/729 = 1

This is the sampling distribution for $\bar{x}$ because it specifies the probability associated with each possible value of $\bar{x}$. You can see that the most likely mean outcome after 3 randomly selected come-out rolls is $\bar{x} = \$0$; this result occurs with probability $\frac{288}{729} = .3951$.

b. In Table 5.2, you can see that the median m can assume one of three values: $-5, 0$, or 5. The value $m = -5$ occurs in 7 different samples. Therefore, $P(m = -5)$ is the sum of the probabilities associated with these 7 samples; that is, $P(m = -5) = \frac{1}{729} + \frac{6}{729} + \frac{2}{729} + \frac{6}{729} + \frac{2}{729} + \frac{6}{729} + \frac{2}{729} = \frac{25}{729}$. Similarly, $m = 0$ occurs in 13 samples and $m = 5$ occurs in 7 samples. These probabilities are obtained by summing the probabilities of their respective sample points. After performing these calculations, we obtain the following probability distribution for the median m:

m	-5	0	5
$p(m)$	25/729 = .0343	612/729 = .8395	92/729 = .1262

Once again, the most likely median outcome after 3 randomly selected come-out rolls is $\bar{x} = \$0$—a result that occurs with probability $\frac{612}{729} = .8395$.

Look Back The sampling distributions of parts **a** and **b** are found by first listing all possible distinct values of the statistic and then calculating the probability of each value. Note that if the values of x were equally likely, the 27 sample points in Table 5.2 would all have the same probability of occurring, namely, $\frac{1}{27}$.

◼ **Now Work Exercise 5.1**

Example 5.1 demonstrates the procedure for finding the exact sampling distribution of a statistic when the number of different samples that could be selected from the population is relatively small. In the real world, populations often consist of a large number of different values, making samples difficult (or impossible) to enumerate. When this situation occurs, we may choose to obtain the approximate sampling distribution for a statistic by simulating the sampling over and over again and recording the proportion of times different values of the statistic occur. Example 5.2 illustrates this procedure.

Example   5.2

Simulating a Sampling Distribution—Thickness of Steel Sheets

Figure 5.4

Uniform distribution for thickness of steel sheets

Problem Refer to Example 4.27 (p. 243). Recall that the thickness of a steel sheet follows a uniform distribution with values between 150 and 200 millimeters. Suppose we perform the following experiment over and over again: Randomly sample 11 steel sheets from the production line and record the thickness, x, of each. Calculate the two sample statistics

$$\bar{x} = \text{Sample mean} = \frac{\Sigma x}{11}$$

$$m = \text{Median} = \text{Sixth sample measurement when the 11 thicknesses}$$
$$\text{are arranged in ascending order}$$

Obtain approximations to the sampling distributions of $\bar{x}$ and m.

Solution Recall from Section 4.8 that the population of thicknesses follows the uniform distribution shown in Figure 5.4. We used Minitab to generate 1,000 samples from this population, each with $n = 11$ observations. Then we compute $\bar{x}$ and m for each sample. Our goal is to obtain approximations to the sampling distributions of $\bar{x}$ and m to find out which sample statistic ($\bar{x}$ or m) contains more information about μ. [*Note:* In this particular example, we *know* the population mean is $\mu = 175$ mm. (See Section 4.8.)]

Table 5.3	First 10 Samples of $n = 11$ Thickness Measurements from Uniform Distribution												
Sample	Thickness Measurements											Mean	Median
1	173	171	187	151	188	181	182	157	162	169	193	174.00	173
2	181	190	182	171	187	177	162	172	188	200	193	182.09	182
3	192	195	187	187	172	164	164	189	179	182	173	180.36	182
4	173	157	150	154	168	174	171	182	200	181	187	172.45	173
5	169	160	167	170	197	159	174	174	161	173	160	169.46	169
6	179	170	167	174	173	178	173	170	173	198	187	176.55	173
7	166	177	162	171	154	177	154	179	175	185	193	172.09	175
8	164	199	152	153	163	156	184	151	198	167	180	169.73	164
9	181	193	151	166	180	199	180	184	182	181	175	179.27	181
10	155	199	199	171	172	157	173	187	190	185	150	176.18	173

Data Set: SIMUNI

The first 10 of the 1,000 samples generated are presented in Table 5.3. For instance, the first computer-generated sample from the uniform distribution (arranged in ascending order) contain the following thickness measurements: 151, 157, 162, 169, 171, 173, 181, 182, 187, 188, and 193 millimeters. The sample mean $\bar{x}$ and median m computed for this sample are

$$\bar{x} = \frac{151 + 157 + \cdots + 193}{11} = 174.0$$

$$m = \text{Sixth ordered measurement} = 173$$

The Minitab relative frequency histograms for $\bar{x}$ and m for the 1,000 samples of size $n = 11$ are shown in Figure 5.5. These histograms represent approximations to the true sampling distributions of $\bar{x}$ and m.

Look Back You can see that the values of $\bar{x}$ tend to cluster around μ to a greater extent than do the values of m. Thus, on the basis of the observed sampling distributions, we conclude that $\bar{x}$ contains more information about μ than m does—at least for samples of $n = 11$ measurements from the uniform distribution.

Figure 5.5

Minitab histograms for sample mean and sample median, Example 5.2

■ **Now Work Exercise 5.6**

As noted earlier, many sampling distributions can be derived mathematically, but the theory necessary to do this is beyond the scope of this text. Consequently, when we need to know the properties of a statistic, we will present its sampling distribution and simply describe its properties. Several of the important properties we look for in sampling distributions are discussed in the next section.

Exercises 5.1–5.7

Learning the Mechanics

5.1 The probability distribution shown here describes a population of measurements that can assume values of 0, 2, 4, and 6, each of which occurs with the same relative frequency:

x	0	2	4	6
$p(x)$	$\frac{1}{4}$	$\frac{1}{4}$	$\frac{1}{4}$	$\frac{1}{4}$

a. List all the different samples of $n = 2$ measurements that can be selected from this population.

b. Calculate the mean of each different sample listed in part **a**.

c. If a sample of $n = 2$ measurements is randomly selected from the population, what is the probability that a specific sample will be selected?

d. Assume that a random sample of $n = 2$ measurements is selected from the population. List the different values of $\bar{x}$ found in part **b** and find the probability of each. Then give the sampling distribution of the sample mean $\bar{x}$ in tabular form.

e. Construct a probability histogram for the sampling distribution of $\bar{x}$.

5.2 Simulate sampling from the population described in Exercise 5.1 by marking the values of x, one on each of four identical coins (or poker chips, etc.). Place the coins (marked 0, 2, 4, and 6) into a bag, randomly select one, and observe its value. Replace this coin, draw a second coin, and observe its value. Finally, calculate the mean $\bar{x}$ for this sample of $n = 2$ observations randomly selected from the population (Exercise 5.1, part **b**). Replace the coins, mix, and using the same procedure, select a sample of $n = 2$ observations from the population. Record the numbers and calculate $\bar{x}$ for this sample. Repeat this sampling process until you acquire 100 values of $\bar{x}$. Construct a relative frequency distribution for these 100 sample means. Compare this distribution to the exact sampling distribution of $\bar{x}$ found in part **e** of Exercise 5.1. [*Note:* The distribution obtained in this exercise is an approximation to the exact sampling distribution. But, if you were to repeat the sampling procedure, drawing two coins not 100 times but 10,000 times, the relative frequency distribution for the 10,000 sample means would be almost identical to the sampling distribution of $\bar{x}$ found in Exercise 5.1, part **e**.]

5.3 Consider the population described by the probability distribution shown below.

x	1	2	3	4	5
$p(x)$	.2	.3	.2	.2	.1

The random variable x is observed twice. If these observations are independent, verify that the different samples of size 2 and their probabilities are as shown in the next column.

Sample	Probability	Sample	Probability
1, 1	.04	3, 4	.04
1, 2	.06	3, 5	.02
1, 3	.04	4, 1	.04
1, 4	.04	4, 2	.06
1, 5	.02	4, 3	.04
2, 1	.06	4, 4	.04
2, 2	.09	4, 5	.02
2, 3	.06	5, 1	.02
2, 4	.06	5, 2	.03
2, 5	.03	5, 3	.02
3, 1	.04	5, 4	.02
3, 2	.06	5, 5	.01
3, 3	.04		

a. Find the sampling distribution of the sample mean $\bar{x}$.

b. Construct a probability histogram for the sampling distribution of $\bar{x}$.

c. What is the probability that $\bar{x}$ is 4.5 or larger?

d. Would you expect to observe a value of $\bar{x}$ equal to 4.5 or larger? Explain.

5.4 Refer to Exercise 5.3 and find $E(x) = \mu$. Then use the sampling distribution of $\bar{x}$ found in Exercise 5.3 to find the expected value of $\bar{x}$. Note that $E(\bar{x}) = \mu$.

5.5 Refer to Exercise 5.3. Assume that a random sample of $n = 2$ measurements is randomly selected from the population.

a. List the different values that the sample median m may assume and find the probability of each. Then give the sampling distribution of the sample median.

b. Construct a probability histogram for the sampling distribution of the sample median and compare it with the probability histogram for the sample mean (Exercise 5.3, part **b**).

5.6 In Example 5.2 we used a computer to generate 1,000 samples, each containing $n = 11$ observations, from a uniform distribution over the interval from 150 to 200. For this exercise, use a computer to generate 500 samples, each containing $n = 15$ observations, from this population.

a. Calculate the sample mean for each sample. To approximate the sampling distribution of $\bar{x}$, construct a relative frequency histogram for the 500 values of $\bar{x}$.

b. Repeat part **a** for the sample median. Compare this approximate sampling distribution with the approximate sampling distribution of $\bar{x}$ found in part **a**.

5.7 Consider a population that contains values of x equal to 00, 01, 02, 03,..., 96, 97, 98, 99. Assume that these values of x occur with equal probability. Use a computer to generate 500 samples, each containing $n = 25$ measurements, from this population. Calculate the sample mean $\bar{x}$ and sample variance s^2 for each of the 500 samples.

a. To approximate the sampling distribution of $\bar{x}$, construct a relative frequency histogram for the 500 values of $\bar{x}$.

b. Repeat part **a** for the 500 values of s^2.

5.2 Properties of Sampling Distributions: Unbiasedness and Minimum Variance

The simplest type of statistic used to make inferences about a population parameter is a *point estimator*—a rule or formula that tells us how to use the sample data to calculate a single number that is intended to estimate the value of some population parameter. For example, the sample mean $\bar{x}$ is a point estimator of the population mean μ. Similarly, the sample variance s^2 is a point estimator of the population variance σ^2.

> A **point estimator** of a population parameter is a rule or formula that tells us how to use the sample data to calculate a single number that can be used as an *estimate* of the population parameter.

Often, many different point estimators can be found to estimate the same parameter. Each will have a sampling distribution that provides information about the point estimator. By examining the sampling distribution, we can determine how large the difference between an estimate and the true value of the parameter (called the **error of estimation**) is likely to be. We can also tell whether an estimator is more likely to overestimate or to underestimate a parameter.

Example 5.3

Comparing Two Statistics

Problem Suppose two statistics, A and B, exist to estimate the same population parameter θ (theta). (Note that θ could be any parameter: μ, σ^2, σ, etc.) Suppose the two statistics have sampling distributions as shown in Figure 5.6. On the basis of these sampling distributions, which statistic is more attractive as an estimator of θ?

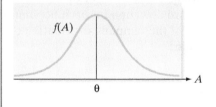

a. Unbiased sample statistic for the parameter θ

Mean of sampling distribution

b. Biased sample statistic for the parameter θ

Figure 5.6

Sampling distributions of unbiased and biased estimators

Solution As a first consideration, we would like the sampling distribution to center over the value of the parameter we wish to estimate. One way to characterize this property is in terms of the mean of the sampling distribution. Consequently, we say that a statistic is *unbiased* if the mean of the sampling distribution is equal to the parameter it is intended to estimate. This situation is shown in Figure 5.6a, where the mean μ_A of statistic A is equal to θ. If the mean of a sampling distribution is *not* equal to the parameter it is intended to estimate, the statistic is said to be *biased*. The sampling distribution for a biased statistic is shown in Figure 5.6b. The mean μ_B of the sampling distribution for statistic B is not equal to θ; in fact, it is shifted to the right of θ.

Look Back You can see that biased statistics tend either to overestimate or to underestimate a parameter. Consequently, when other properties of statistics tend to be equivalent, we will choose an unbiased statistic to estimate a parameter of interest.*

▪ Now Work Exercise 5.8

---

*Unbiased statistics do not exist for all parameters of interest, but they do exist for all the parameters considered in this text.

The standard deviation of a sampling distribution measures another important property of statistics: the spread of these estimates generated by repeated sampling. Suppose two statistics, A and B, are both unbiased estimators of the population parameter. Since the means of the two sampling distributions are the same, we turn to their standard deviations in order to decide which will provide estimates that fall closer to the unknown population parameter we are estimating. Naturally, we will choose the sample statistic that has the smaller standard deviation. Figure 5.7 depicts sampling distributions for A and B. Note that the standard deviation of the distribution for A is smaller than the standard deviation of the distribution for B, indicating that, over a large number of samples, the values of A cluster more closely around the unknown population parameter than do the values of B. Stated differently, the probability that A is close to the parameter value is higher than the probability that B is close to the parameter value.

Figure 5.7
Sampling distributions for two unbiased estimators

In sum, to make an inference about a population parameter, we use the sample statistic with a sampling distribution that is unbiased and has a small standard deviation (usually smaller than the standard deviation of other unbiased sample statistics). The derivation of this sample statistic will not concern us, because the "best" statistic for estimating specific parameters is a matter of record. We will simply present an unbiased estimator with its standard deviation for each population parameter we consider. [*Note:* The standard deviation of the sampling distribution of a statistic is also called the **standard error of the statistic.**]

<table>
<tr><td>

Example 5.4

Biased and Unbiased Estimators—Craps Application

</td><td>

Problem Refer to Example 5.1 and the outcome x of a $5 wager in craps. We found the sampling distributions of the sample mean $\bar{x}$ and the sample median m for random samples of $n = 3$ dice rolls from a population defined by the following probability distribution:

</td></tr>
</table>

x	−5	0	5
$p(x)$	$\frac{1}{9}$	$\frac{6}{9}$	$\frac{2}{9}$

The sampling distributions of $\bar{x}$ and m were found to be as follows:

x	−5	−3.33	−1.67	0	1.67	3.33	5
$p(\bar{x})$	$\frac{1}{729}$	$\frac{18}{729}$	$\frac{114}{729}$	$\frac{288}{729}$	$\frac{228}{729}$	$\frac{72}{729}$	$\frac{8}{729}$

m	−5	0	5
$p(m)$	$\frac{25}{729}$	$\frac{612}{729}$	$\frac{92}{729}$

a. Show that $\bar{x}$ is an unbiased estimator of μ in this situation.

b. Show that m is a biased estimator of μ in this situation.

Solution

a. The expected value of a discrete random variable x (see Section 4.3) is defined as $E(x) = \Sigma x p(x)$, where the summation is over all values of x. Then

$$E(x) = \mu = \Sigma x p(x) = (-5)\left(\tfrac{1}{9}\right) + (0)\left(\tfrac{6}{9}\right) + (5)\left(\tfrac{2}{9}\right) = \frac{5}{9} = .556$$

The expected value of the discrete random variable $\bar{x}$ is

$$E(\bar{x}) = \Sigma(\bar{x})p(\bar{x})$$

summed over all values of $\bar{x}$, or

$$E(\bar{x}) = (-5)\left(\tfrac{1}{729}\right) + (-3.33)\left(\tfrac{18}{729}\right) + (-1.67)\left(\tfrac{114}{729}\right) + \cdots + (5)\left(\tfrac{8}{729}\right) = .556$$

Since $E(\bar{x}) = \mu$, $\bar{x}$ is an unbiased estimator of μ.

b. The expected value of the sample median m is

$$E(m) = \Sigma m p(m) = (-5)\left(\tfrac{25}{729}\right) + (0)\left(\tfrac{612}{729}\right) + (5)\left(\tfrac{92}{729}\right) = \frac{335}{729} = .460$$

Since the expected value of m is not equal to $\mu(\mu = .556)$, the sample median m is a biased estimator of μ.

■ **Now Work Exercise 5.10 a, b, c, d**

Example 5.5

Variance of Estimators—Craps Application

Problem Refer to Example 5.4 and find the standard deviations of the sampling distributions of $\bar{x}$ and m. Which statistic would appear to be a better estimator of μ?

Solution The variance of the sampling distribution of $\bar{x}$ (we denote it by the symbol $\sigma_{\bar{x}}^2$) is found to be

$$\sigma_{\bar{x}}^2 = E\{[\bar{x} - E(\bar{x})]^2\} = \Sigma(\bar{x} - \mu)^2 p(\bar{x})$$

where, from Example 5.4,

$$E(\bar{x}) = \mu = .556$$

Then

$$\sigma_{\bar{x}}^2 = (-5 - .556)^2\left(\tfrac{1}{729}\right) + (-3.33 - .556)^2\left(\tfrac{18}{729}\right) + \cdots (5 - .556)^2\left(\tfrac{8}{729}\right)$$

$$= 2.675$$

and

$$\sigma_{\bar{x}} = \sqrt{2.675} = 1.64$$

Similarly, the variance of the sampling distribution of m (we denote it by σ_m^2) is

$$\sigma_m^2 = E\{[m - E(m)]^2\}$$

where, from Example 5.4, the expected value of m is $E(m) = .460$. Then

$$\sigma_m^2 = E\{[m - E(m)]^2\} = \Sigma[m - E(m)]^2 p(m)$$

$$= (-5 - .460)\left(\tfrac{25}{729}\right) + (0 - .460)\left(\tfrac{612}{729}\right) + (5 - .460)\left(\tfrac{92}{729}\right) = 3.801$$

and

$$\sigma_m = \sqrt{3.801} = 1.95$$

Which statistic appears to be the better estimator for the population mean μ, the sample mean $\bar{x}$ or the median m? To answer this question, we compare the sampling distributions of the two statistics. The sampling distribution of the sample median m is biased (i.e., it is located to the left of the mean μ), and its standard deviation $\sigma_m = 1.95$ is larger than the standard deviation of the sampling distribution of $\bar{x}$, $\sigma_{\bar{x}} = 1.64$. Consequently, for the population in question, the sample mean $\bar{x}$ would be a better estimator of the population mean μ than the sample median m would be.

Look Back Ideally, we desire an estimator that is unbiased *and* has the smallest variance among all unbiased estimators. We call this statistic the **minimum-variance unbiased estimator (MVUE).**

■ **Now Work Exercise 5.10 e, f**

Exercises 5.8–5.14

Learning the Mechanics

5.8 Consider the following probability distribution:

x	0	1	4
$p(x)$	$\frac{1}{3}$	$\frac{1}{3}$	$\frac{1}{3}$

a. Find μ and σ^2.
b. Find the sampling distribution of the sample mean $\bar{x}$ for a random sample of $n = 2$ measurements from this distribution.
c. Show that $\bar{x}$ is an unbiased estimator of μ. [*Hint:* Show that $E(\bar{x}) = \Sigma\bar{x}p(\bar{x}) = \mu$.]
d. Find the sampling distribution of the sample variance s^2 for a random sample of $n = 2$ measurements from this distribution.
e. Show that s^2 is an unbiased estimator for σ^2.

5.9 Consider the following probability distribution:

x	2	4	9
$p(x)$	$\frac{1}{3}$	$\frac{1}{3}$	$\frac{1}{3}$

a. Calculate μ for this distribution.
b. Find the sampling distribution of the sample mean $\bar{x}$ for a random sample of $n = 3$ measurements from this distribution, and show that $\bar{x}$ is an unbiased estimator of μ.
c. Find the sampling distribution of the sample median m for a random sample of $n = 3$ measurements from this distribution, and show that the median is a biased estimator of μ.
d. If you wanted to use a sample of three measurements from this population to estimate μ, which estimator would you use? Why?

5.10 Consider the following probability distribution:

x	0	1	2
$p(x)$	$\frac{1}{3}$	$\frac{1}{3}$	$\frac{1}{3}$

a. Find μ.
b. For a random sample of $n = 3$ observations from this distribution, find the sampling distribution of the sample mean.
c. Find the sampling distribution of the median of a sample of $n = 3$ observations from this population.
d. Refer to parts **b** and **c**, and show that both the mean and median are unbiased estimators of μ for this population.
e. Find the variances of the sampling distributions of the sample mean and the sample median.
f. Which estimator would you use to estimate μ? Why?

5.11 Use the computer to generate 500 samples, each containing $n = 25$ measurements, from a population that contains values of x equal to 1, 2, ..., 48, 49, 50. Assume that these values of x are equally likely. Calculate the sample mean $\bar{x}$ and median m for each sample. Construct relative frequency histograms for the 500 values of $\bar{x}$ and the 500 values of m. Use these approximations to the sampling distributions of $\bar{x}$ and m to answer the following questions:
a. Does it appear that $\bar{x}$ and m are unbiased estimators of the population mean? [*Note:* $\mu = 25.5$.]
b. Which sampling distribution displays greater variation?

5.12 Refer to Exercise 5.3.
a. Show that $\bar{x}$ is an unbiased estimator of μ.
b. Find $\sigma_{\bar{x}}^2$.
c. Find the probability that $\bar{x}$ will fall within $2\sigma_{\bar{x}}$ of μ.

5.13 Refer to Exercise 5.3.
a. Find the sampling distribution of s^2.
b. Find the population variance σ^2.
c. Show that s^2 is an unbiased estimator of σ^2.
d. Find the sampling distribution of the sample standard deviation s.
e. Show that s is a biased estimator of σ.

5.14 Refer to Exercise 5.5, in which we found the sampling distribution of the sample median. Is the median an unbiased estimator of the population mean μ?

5.3 # The Sampling Distribution of the Sample Mean and the Central Limit Theorem

Estimating the mean useful life of automobiles, the mean monthly sales for all iPhone dealers in a large city, and the mean breaking strength of new plastic are practical problems with something in common. In each case, we are interested in making an inference about the mean μ of some population. As we mentioned in Chapter 2, the sample mean $\bar{x}$ is, in general, a good estimator of μ. We now develop pertinent information about the sampling distribution for this useful statistic. We will show that $\bar{x}$ is the minimum-variance unbiased estimator (MVUE) of μ.

Example 5.6

Describing the Sampling Distribution of $\bar{x}$

Problem Suppose a population has the uniform probability distribution given in Figure 5.8. The mean and standard deviation of this probability distribution are $\mu = 175$ and $\sigma = 14.43$. (See Section 4.8 for the formulas for μ and σ.) Now suppose a sample of 11 measurements is selected from this population. Describe the sampling distribution of the sample mean $\bar{x}$ based on the 1,000 sampling experiments discussed in Example 5.2.

Figure 5.8
Sampled uniform population

Solution You will recall that in Example 5.2 we generated 1,000 samples of $n = 11$ measurements each. The Minitab histogram for the 1,000 sample means is shown in Figure 5.9 with a normal probability distribution superimposed. You can see that this normal probability distribution approximates the computer-generated sampling distribution very well.

To fully describe a normal probability distribution, it is necessary to know its mean and standard deviation. Minitab gives these statistics for the 1,000 $\bar{x}$'s in the upper right corner of the histogram, Figure 5.9. You can see that the mean is 175.2, and the standard deviation is 4.383.

To summarize our findings based on 1,000 samples, each consisting of 11 measurements from a uniform population, the sampling distribution of $\bar{x}$ appears to be approximately normal with a mean of about 175 and a standard deviation of about 4.38.

Figure 5.9
Minitab histogram for sample mean in 1,000 samples

Look Back Note that the simulated value $\mu_{\bar{x}} = 175.2$ is very close to $\mu = 175$ for the uniform distribution—that is, the simulated sampling distribution of $\bar{x}$ appears to provide an accurate estimate of μ.

The true sampling distribution of $\bar{x}$ has the properties given in the next box, assuming only that a random sample of n observations has been selected from *any* population.

Properties of the Sampling Distribution of $\bar{x}$

1. Mean of sampling distribution equals mean of sampled population, that is, $\mu_{\bar{x}} = E(\bar{x}) = \mu$.

2. Standard deviation of sampling distribution equals

$$\frac{\text{Standard deviation of sampled population}}{\text{Square root of sample size}}$$

That is, $\sigma_{\bar{x}} = \sigma/\sqrt{n}$.*

The standard deviation $\sigma_{\bar{x}}$ is often referred to as the **standard error of the mean.**

You can see that our approximation to $\mu_{\bar{x}}$ in Example 5.6 was precise because property 1 assures us that the mean is the same as that of the sampled population: 175. Property 2 tells us how to calculate the standard deviation of the sampling distribution of $\bar{x}$. Substituting $\sigma = 14.43$, the standard deviation of the sampled uniform distribution, and the sample size $n = 11$ into the formula for $\sigma_{\bar{x}}$, we find

$$\sigma_{\bar{x}} = \frac{\sigma}{\sqrt{n}} = \frac{14.43}{\sqrt{11}} = 4.35$$

Thus, the approximation we obtained in Example 5.6, $\sigma_{\bar{x}} = 4.38$, is very close to the exact value, $\sigma_{\bar{x}} = 4.35$. It can be shown (proof omitted) that the value of $\sigma_{\bar{x}}^2$ is the smallest variance among all unbiased estimators of μ; thus, $\bar{x}$ is the MVUE for μ.

What about the shape of the sampling distribution of $\bar{x}$? Two important theorems provide this information. One is applicable whenever the original population data are normally distributed. The other, applicable when the sample size n is large, represents one of the most important theoretical results in statistics: the **Central Limit Theorem.**

Theorem 5.1

If a random sample of n observations is selected from a population with a normal distribution, the sampling distribution of $\bar{x}$ will be a normal distribution.

Theorem 5.2 (Central Limit Theorem)

Consider a random sample of n observations selected from a population (*any* probability distribution) with mean μ and standard deviation σ. Then, when n is sufficiently large, the sampling distribution of $\bar{x}$ will be approximately a normal distribution with mean $\mu_{\bar{x}} = \mu$ and standard deviation $\sigma_{\bar{x}} = \sigma/\sqrt{n}$. The larger the sample size, the better will be the normal approximation to the sampling distribution of $\bar{x}$.[†]

Thus, for sufficiently large samples, the sampling distribution of $\bar{x}$ is approximately normal. How large must the sample size n be so that the normal distribution provides a good approximation for the sampling distribution of $\bar{x}$? The answer depends on the shape of the distribution of the sampled population, as shown by Figure 5.10. Generally speaking, the greater the skewness of the sampled population distribution, the larger the

*If the sample size, n, is large relative to the number, N, of elements in the population (e.g., 5% or more), $\sigma/\sqrt{n}$ must be multiplied by a finite population correction factor, $\sqrt{(N - n)/(N - 1)}$. For most sampling situations, this correction factor will be close to 1 and can be ignored.

†Moreover, because of the Central Limit Theorem, the sum of a random sample on n observations, Σx, will possess a sampling distribution that is approximately normal for large samples. This distribution will have a mean equal to $n\mu$ and a variance equal to $n\sigma^2$. Proof of the Central Limit Theorem is beyond the scope of this book, but it can be found in many mathematical statistics texts.

Figure 5.10

Sampling distributions of $\bar{x}$ for different populations and different sample sizes (*Note*: Distributions not drawn to scale. All areas under the curves are equal to 1.)

sample size must be before the normal distribution is an adequate approximation for the sampling distribution of $\bar{x}$. For most sampled populations, sample sizes of $n \geq 30$ will suffice for the normal approximation to be reasonable.

| Example | 5.7 |

Using the Central Limit Theorem to Find a Probability

Problem Suppose we have selected a random sample of $n = 36$ observations from a population with mean equal to 80 and standard deviation equal to 6. It is known that the population is not extremely skewed.

a. Sketch the relative frequency distributions for the population and for the sampling distribution of the sample mean, $\bar{x}$.

b. Find the probability that $\bar{x}$ will be larger than 82.

Solution

a. We do not know the exact shape of the population relative frequency distribution, but we do know that it should be centered about $\mu = 80$, its spread should be measured by $\sigma = 6$, and it is not highly skewed. One possibility is shown in Figure 5.11a. From the Central Limit Theorem, we know that the sampling distribution of $\bar{x}$ will be approximately normal because the sampled population distribution is not extremely skewed. We also know that the sampling distribution will have mean and standard deviation

$$\mu_{\bar{x}} = \mu = 80 \quad \text{and} \quad \sigma_{\bar{x}} = \frac{\sigma}{\sqrt{n}} = \frac{6}{\sqrt{36}} = 1$$

The sampling distribution of $\bar{x}$ is shown in Figure 5.11b.

b. The probability that $\bar{x}$ will exceed 82 is equal to the darker shaded area in Figure 5.12. To find this area, we need to find the z-value corresponding to $\bar{x} = 82$. Recall that the standard normal random variable z is the difference between any normally distributed random variable and its mean, expressed in units of its standard deviation. Because $\bar{x}$ is approximately a normally distributed random variable with mean

a. Population relative frequency distribution

Figure 5.11

A population relative frequency distribution and the sampling distribution for $\bar{x}$

b. Sampling distribution of $\bar{x}$

$\mu_{\bar{x}} = \mu$ and $\sigma_{\bar{x}} = \sigma/\sqrt{n}$, it follows that the standard normal z-value corresponding to the sample mean, $\bar{x}$, is

$$z = \frac{(\text{Normal random variable}) - (\text{Mean})}{\text{Standard deviation}} = \frac{\bar{x} - \mu_{\bar{x}}}{\sigma_{\bar{x}}}$$

Therefore, for $\bar{x} = 82$, we have

$$z = \frac{\bar{x} - \mu_{\bar{x}}}{\sigma_{\bar{x}}} = \frac{82 - 80}{1} = 2$$

Figure 5.12

The sampling distribution of $\bar{x}$

The area A in Figure 5.12 corresponding to $z = 2$ is given in the table of areas under the normal curve (see Table II in Appendix D) as .4772. Therefore, the tail area corresponding to the probability that $\bar{x}$ exceeds 82 is

$$P(\bar{x} > 82) = P(z > 2) = .5 - .4772 = .0228$$

Look Back The key to finding the probability, part **b,** is to recognize that the distribution of $\bar{x}$ is normal with mean $\mu_{\bar{x}} = \mu$ and $\sigma_{\bar{x}} = \sigma/\sqrt{n}$.

■ Now Work Exercises 5.18–5.19

Example 5.8

Application of the Central Limit Theorem—Testing a Manufacturer's Claim

Problem A manufacturer of automobile batteries claims that the distribution of the lengths of life of its best battery has a mean of 54 months and a standard deviation of 6 months. Recently, the manufacturer has received a rash of complaints from unsatisfied customers whose batteries have died earlier than expected. Suppose a consumer group decides to check the manufacturer's claim by purchasing a sample of 50 of these batteries and subjecting them to tests that determine battery life.

a. Assuming that the manufacturer's claim is true, describe the sampling distribution of the mean lifetime of a sample of 50 batteries.

b. Assuming that the manufacturer's claim is true, what is the probability that the consumer group's sample has a mean life of 52 or fewer months?

Solution

a. Even though we have no information about the shape of the probability distribution of the lives of the batteries, we can use the Central Limit Theorem to deduce that the sampling distribution for a sample mean lifetime of 50 batteries is approximately normally distributed. Furthermore, the mean of this sampling distribution is the same as the mean of the sampled population, which is $\mu = 54$ months according to the manufacturer's claim. Finally, the standard deviation of the sampling distribution is given by

$$\sigma_{\bar{x}} = \frac{\sigma}{\sqrt{n}} = \frac{6}{\sqrt{50}} = .85 \text{ month}$$

Note that we used the claimed standard deviation of the sampled population, $\sigma = 6$ months. Thus, if we assume that the claim is true, the sampling distribution for the mean life of the 50 batteries sampled is as shown in Figure 5.13.

b. If the manufacturer's claim is true, the probability that the consumer group observes a mean battery life of 52 or fewer months for their sample of 50 batteries, $P(\bar{x} \leq 52)$, is equivalent to the darker shaded area in Figure 5.13. Because the sampling distribution is approximately normal, we can find this area by computing the standard normal z-value:

$$z = \frac{\bar{x} - \mu_{\bar{x}}}{\sigma_{\bar{x}}} = \frac{52 - 54}{.85} = -2.35$$

where $\mu_{\bar{x}}$, the mean of the sampling distribution of $\bar{x}$, is equal to μ, the mean of the lives of the sampled population, and $\sigma_{\bar{x}}$ is the standard deviation of the sampling distribution of $\bar{x}$. Note that z is the familiar standardized distance (z-score) of Section 2.7 and because $\bar{x}$ is approximately normally distributed, it will possess (approximately) the standard normal distribution of Section 4.6.

Figure 5.13

Sampling distribution of $\bar{x}$ in Example 5.8 for $n = 50$

The area A shown in Figure 5.13 between $\bar{x} = 52$ and $\bar{x} = 54$ (corresponding to $z = -2.35$) is found in Table II in Appendix D to be .4906. Therefore, the area to the left of $\bar{x} = 52$ is

$$P(\bar{x} \leq 52) = .5 - A = .5 - .4906 = .0094$$

Thus, the probability that the consumer group will observe a sample mean of 52 or less is only .0094 if the manufacturer's claim is true.

Look Back If the 50 tested batteries do exhibit a mean of 52 or fewer months, the consumer group will have strong evidence that the manufacturer's claim is untrue because such an event is very unlikely to occur if the claim is true. (This is still another application of the *rare-event approach to statistical inference.*)

■ **Now Work Exercise 5.24**

We conclude this section with two final comments on the sampling distribution of $\bar{x}$. First, from the formula $\sigma_{\bar{x}} = \sigma/\sqrt{n}$, we see that the standard deviation of the sampling distribution of $\bar{x}$ gets smaller as the sample size n gets larger. For example, we computed $\sigma_{\bar{x}} = .85$ when $n = 50$ in Example 5.8. However, for $n = 100$, we obtain $\sigma_{\bar{x}} = \sigma/\sqrt{n} = 6/\sqrt{100} = .60$. This relationship will hold true for most of the sample statistics encountered in this text–that is, *the standard deviation of the sampling distribution decreases as the sample size increases.* Consequently, the larger the sample size, the more accurate the sample statistic (e.g., $\bar{x}$) is in estimating a population parameter (e.g., μ). We will use this result in Chapter 6 to help us determine the sample size needed to obtain a specified accuracy of estimation.

Our second comment concerns the Central Limit Theorem. In addition to providing a very useful approximation for the sampling distribution of a sample mean, the Central Limit Theorem offers an explanation for the fact that many relative frequency distributions of data possess mound-shaped distributions. Many of the measurements we take in business are really means or sums of a large number of small phenomena. For example, a company's sales for 1 year are the total of the many individual sales the company made during the year. Similarly, we can view the length of time a construction company takes to build a house as the total of the times taken to complete a multitude of distinct jobs, and we can regard the monthly demand for blood at a hospital as the total of the many individual patients' needs. Whether or not the observations entering into these sums satisfy the assumptions basic to the Central Limit Theorem is open to question. However, it is a fact that many distributions of data in nature are mound-shaped and possess the appearance of normal distributions.

STATISTICS in ACTION REVISITED

Making an Inference about the Mean Sleep Onset Latency for Insomnia Pill Takers

In a Massachusetts Institute of Technology (MIT) study, each member of a sample of 40 young male volunteers was given a dosage of the sleep-inducing hormone melatonin or a placebo, was placed in a dark room at midday, and was told to close his eyes for 30 minutes. The researchers measured the time (in minutes) elapsed before each volunteer fell asleep—called sleep onset latency. Recall that the data (shown in Table SIA5.1) are saved in the **SLEEP** file.

Previous research established that with the placebo (i.e., no hormone), the mean sleep onset latency is $\mu = 15$ minutes and the standard deviation is $\sigma = 10$ minutes. If the true value of μ for those taking the melatonin is $\mu < 15$ (i.e., if, on average, the volunteers fall asleep faster with the drug than with the placebo), then the researchers can infer that melatonin is an effective drug against insomnia.

Descriptive statistics for the 40 sleep times are displayed in the SPSS printout shown in Figure SIA5.1. You can see that the mean for the sample is $\bar{x} = 5.935$ minutes. If the drug is not effective in reducing sleep times, then the distribution of sleep times will be no different from the distribution with the placebo. That is, if the drug is not effective, the mean and standard deviation of the population of sleep times are $\mu = 15$ and $\sigma = 10$. If this is true, how likely is it to observe a sample mean that is below 6 minutes?

To answer this question, we desire the probability $P(\bar{x} < 6)$. To find this probability, we invoke the Central Limit Theorem. According to the theorem, the sampling distribution of $\bar{x}$ has the following mean and standard deviation:

$$\mu_{\bar{x}} = \mu = 15$$

$$\sigma_{\bar{x}} = \sigma/\sqrt{n} = 10/\sqrt{40} = 1.58$$

Descriptive Statistics

	N	Minimum	Maximum	Mean	Std. Deviation
SLEEPTIME	40	1.3	22.8	5.935	5.3917
Valid N (listwise)	40				

Figure SIA5.1

SPSS descriptive statistics for sleep time data

The theorem also states that $\bar{x}$ is approximately normally distributed. Therefore, we find the desired probability (using the standard normal table) as follows:

$$P(\bar{x} < 6) = P\left(z < \frac{6 - \mu_{\bar{x}}}{\sigma_{\bar{x}}}\right)$$

$$= P\left(z < \frac{6 - 15}{1.58}\right) = P(z < -5.70) \approx 0$$

In other words, the probability that we observe a sample mean below $\bar{x} = 6$ minutes *if the mean and standard deviation of the sleep times are,* respectively, $\mu = 15$ and $\sigma = 10$ *(i.e., if the drug is not effective),* is almost 0. Therefore, either the drug is not effective and the researchers have observed an extremely rare event (one with almost no chance of happening), or the true value of μ for those taking the melatonin pill is much less than 15 minutes. The rare-event approach to making statistical inferences, of course, would favor the second conclusion. Melatonin appears to be an effective insomnia pill, one that lowers the average time it takes the volunteers to fall asleep.

Data Set: SLEEP

Exercises 5.15–5.35

Learning the Mechanics

5.15 Will the sampling distribution of $\bar{x}$ always be approximately normally distributed? Explain.

5.16 Suppose a random sample of $n = 25$ measurements is selected from a population with mean μ and standard deviation σ. For each of the following values of μ and σ, give the values of $\mu_{\bar{x}}$ and $\sigma_{\bar{x}}$.
  a. $\mu = 10, \sigma = 3$
  b. $\mu = 100, \sigma = 25$
  c. $\mu = 20, \sigma = 40$
  d. $\mu = 10, \sigma = 100$

5.17 Suppose a random sample of n measurements is selected from a population with mean $\mu = 100$ and variance $\sigma^2 = 100$. For each of the following values of n, give the mean and standard deviation of the sampling distribution of the sample mean $\bar{x}$.
  a. $n = 4$ **b.** $n = 25$
  c. $n = 100$ **d.** $n = 50$
  e. $n = 500$ **f.** $n = 1,000$

5.18 A random sample of $n = 64$ observations is drawn from a
  NW population with a mean equal to 20 and a standard deviation equal to 16.
  a. Give the mean and standard deviation of the (repeated) sampling distribution of $\bar{x}$.
  b. Describe the shape of the sampling distribution of $\bar{x}$. Does your answer depend on the sample size?
  c. Calculate the standard normal z-score corresponding to a value of $\bar{x} = 15.5$.
  d. Calculate the standard normal z-score corresponding to $\bar{x} = 23$.

5.19 Refer to Exercise 5.18. Find the probability that
  NW **a.** $\bar{x}$ is less than 16.
  b. $\bar{x}$ is greater than 23.

  c. $\bar{x}$ is greater than 25.
  d. $\bar{x}$ falls between 16 and 22.
  e. $\bar{x}$ is less than 14.

5.20 A random sample of $n = 900$ observations is selected from a population with $\mu = 100$ and $\sigma = 10$.
  a. What are the largest and smallest values of $\bar{x}$ that you would expect to see?
  b. How far, at the most, would you expect $\bar{x}$ to deviate from μ?
  c. Did you have to know μ to answer part **b**? Explain.

5.21 A random sample of $n = 100$ observations is selected from a population with $\mu = 30$ and $\sigma = 16$. Approximate the following probabilities:
  a. $P(\bar{x} \geq 28)$
  b. $P(22.1 \leq \bar{x} \leq 26.8)$
  c. $P(\bar{x} \leq 28.2)$
  d. $P(\bar{x} \geq 27.0)$

5.22 Consider a population that contains values of x equal to 0, 1, 2, ..., 97, 98, 99. Assume that the values of x are equally likely. For each of the following values of n, use a computer to generate 500 random samples and calculate $\bar{x}$ for each sample. For each sample size, construct a relative frequency histogram of the 500 values of $\bar{x}$. What changes occur in the histograms as the value of n increases? What similarities exist? Use $n = 2, n = 5, n = 10, n = 30,$ and $n = 50$.

◉ Applet Exercise 5.1

Open the applet *Sampling Distributions*. On the pull-down menu to the right of the top graph, select *Binary*.
  a. Run the applet for the sample size $n = 10$ and the number of samples $N = 1,000$. Observe the shape of the graph of the sample proportions and record the mean, median, and standard deviation of the sample proportions.

b. How does the mean of the sample proportions compare to the mean $\mu = 0.5$ of the original distribution?

c. Compute the standard deviation of the original distribution using the formula $\sigma = \sqrt{np(1 - p)}$ where $n = 1$ and $p = 0.5$. Divide the result by $\sqrt{10}$, the square root of the sample size used in the sampling distribution. How does this result compare to the standard deviation of the sample proportions?

d. Explain how the graph of the distribution of sample proportions suggests that the distribution may be approximately normal.

e. Explain how the results of parts **b–d** illustrate the Central Limit Theorem.

● Applet Exercise 5.2

Open the applet *Sampling Distributions*. On the pull-down menu to the right of the top graph, select *Uniform*. The box to the left of the top graph displays the population mean, median, and standard deviation of the original distribution.

a. Run the applet for the sample size $n = 30$ and the number of samples $N = 1,000$. Observe the shape of the graph of the sample means and record the mean, median, and standard deviation of the sample means.

b. How does the mean of the sample means compare to the mean of the original distribution?

c. Divide the standard deviation of the original distribution by $\sqrt{30}$, the square root of the sample size used in the sampling distribution. How does this result compare to the standard deviation of the sample proportions?

d. Explain how the graph of the distribution of sample means suggests that the distribution may be approximately normal.

e. Explain how the results of parts **b–d** illustrate the Central Limit Theorem.

Applying the Concepts—Basic

5.23 **Phishing attacks to e-mail accounts.** In Exercise 2.33 (p. 62), you learned that *phishing* describes an attempt to extract personal/financial information from unsuspecting people through fraudulent e-mail. Data from an actual phishing attack against an organization were presented in *Chance* (Summer 2007). The interarrival times, i.e., the time differences (in seconds), for 267 fraud box e-mail notifications, were recorded and are saved in the accompanying file. For this exercise, consider these interarrival times to represent the population of interest.

a. In Exercise 2.33 you constructed a histogram for the interarrival times. Describe the shape of the population of interarrival times.

b. Find the mean and standard deviation of the population of interarrival times.

c. Now consider a random sample of $n = 40$ interarrival times selected from the population. Describe the shape of the sampling distribution of $\bar{x}$, the sample mean. Theoretically, what are $\mu_{\bar{x}}$ and $\sigma_{\bar{x}}$?

d. Find $P(\bar{x} < 90)$.

e. Use a random number generator to select a random sample of $n = 40$ interarrival times from the population, and calculate the value of $\bar{x}$. (Every student in the class should do this.)

f. Refer to part **e.** Obtain the values of $\bar{x}$ computed by the students and combine them into a single data set. Form a histogram for these values of $\bar{x}$. Is the shape approximately normal?

g. Refer to part **f.** Find the mean and standard deviation of the $\bar{x}$-values. Do these values approximate $\mu_{\bar{x}}$ and $\sigma_{\bar{x}}$, respectively?

5.24 **Salary of a travel management professional.** According to a National Business Travel Association (NBTA) 2010 survey, the average salary of a travel management professional is \$96,850. Assume that the standard deviation of such salaries is \$30,000. Consider a random sample of 50 travel management professionals and let $\bar{x}$ represent the mean salary for the sample.

a. What is $\mu_{\bar{x}}$?

b. What is $\sigma_{\bar{x}}$?

c. Describe the shape of the sampling distribution of $\bar{x}$.

d. Find the z-score for the value $\bar{x} = 89,500$.

e. Find $P(\bar{x} > 89,500)$.

5.25 **Corporate sustainability of CPA firms.** Refer to the *Business and Society* (March 2011) study on the sustainability behaviors of CPA corporations, Exercise 1.26 (p. 27). *Corporate sustainability*, recall, refers to business practices designed around social and environmental considerations. The level of support senior managers have for corporate sustainability was measured quantitatively on a scale ranging from 0 to 160 points, where higher point values indicate a higher level of support for sustainability. The study provided the following information on the distribution of levels of support for sustainability: $\mu = 68$, $\sigma = 27$. Now consider a random sample of 45 senior managers and let $\bar{x}$ represent the sample mean level of support.

a. Give the value of $\mu_{\bar{x}}$, the mean of the sampling distribution of $\bar{x}$, and interpret the result.

b. Give the value of $\sigma_{\bar{x}}$, the standard deviation of the sampling distribution of $\bar{x}$, and interpret the result.

c. What does the Central Limit Theorem say about the shape of the sampling distribution of $\bar{x}$?

d. Find $P(\bar{x} > 65)$.

5.26 **Critical-part failures in NASCAR vehicles.** Refer to *The Sport Journal* (Winter 2007) analysis of critical-part failures at NASCAR races, Exercise 4.144 (p. 248). Recall that researchers found that the time x (in hours) until the first critical-part failure is exponentially distributed with $\mu = .10$ and $\sigma = .10$. Now consider a random sample of $n = 50$ NASCAR races and let $\bar{x}$ represent the sample mean time until the first critical-part failure.

a. Find $E(\bar{x})$ and $\text{Var}(\bar{x})$.

b. Although x has an exponential distribution, the sampling distribution of $\bar{x}$ is approximately normal. Why?

c. Find the probability that the sample mean time until the first critical-part failure exceeds .13 hour.

5.27 **Tomato as a taste modifier.** Miraculin is a protein naturally produced in a rare tropical fruit that can convert a sour taste into a sweet taste. Refer to the *Plant Science* (May 2010) investigation of the ability of a hybrid tomato plant to produce miraculin, Exercise 4.97 (p. 233). Recall that the amount x of miraculin produced in the plant had a mean of 105.3 micrograms per gram of fresh weight with a standard deviation of 8.0. Consider a random sample of $n = 64$

hybrid tomato plants and let $\bar{x}$ represent the sample mean amount of miraculin produced. Would you expect to observe a value of $\bar{x}$ less than 103 micrograms per gram of fresh weight? Explain.

Applying the Concepts—Intermediate

5.28 Requests to a Web server. In Exercise 4.139 (p. 247) you learned that Brighton Webs LTD modeled the arrival time of requests to a Web server within each hour using a uniform distribution. Specifically, the number of seconds x from the start of the hour that the request is made is uniformly distributed between 0 and 3,600 seconds. In a random sample of $n = 60$ Web server requests, let $\bar{x}$ represent the sample mean number of seconds from the start of the hour that the request is made.
a. Find $E(\bar{x})$ and interpret its value.
b. Find $\text{Var}(\bar{x})$.
c. Describe the shape of the sampling distribution of $\bar{x}$.
d. Find the probability that $\bar{x}$ is between 1,700 and 1,900 seconds.
e. Find the probability that $\bar{x}$ exceeds 2,000 seconds.

5.29 Levelness of concrete slabs. Geotechnical engineers use water-level "manometer" surveys to assess the levelness of newly constructed concrete slabs. Elevations are typically measured at eight points on the slab; of interest is the maximum differential between elevations. The *Journal of Performance of Constructed Facilities* (Feb. 2005) published an article on the levelness of slabs in California residential developments. Elevation data collected for over 1,300 concrete slabs *before tensioning* revealed that maximum differential, x, has a mean of $\mu = .53$ inch and a standard deviation of $\sigma = .193$ inch. Consider a sample of $n = 50$ slabs selected from those surveyed and let $\bar{x}$ represent the mean of the sample.
a. Fully describe the sampling distribution of $\bar{x}$.
b. Find $P(\bar{x} > .58)$.
c. The study also revealed that the mean maximum differential of concrete slabs measured *after tensioning and loading* is $\mu = .58$ inch. Suppose the sample data yield $\bar{x} = .59$ inch. Comment on whether the sample measurements were obtained before tensioning or after tensioning and loading.

5.30 Surface roughness of pipe. Refer to the *Anti-Corrosion Methods and Materials* (Vol. 50, 2003) study of the surface roughness of oil field pipes, Exercise 2.44 (p. 70). Recall that a scanning probe instrument was used to measure the surface roughness x (in micrometers) of 20 sampled sections of coated interior pipe. Consider the sample mean, $\bar{x}$.
a. Assume that the surface roughness distribution has a mean of $\mu = 1.8$ micrometers and a standard deviation of $\sigma = .5$ micrometer. Use this information to find the probability that $\bar{x}$ exceeds 1.85 micrometers.
b. The sample data are reproduced in the following table. Compute $\bar{x}$.
c. Based on the result, part **b,** comment on the validity of the assumptions made in part **a.**

1.72	2.50	2.16	2.13	1.06	2.24	2.31	2.03	1.09	1.40
2.57	2.64	1.26	2.05	1.19	2.13	1.27	1.51	2.41	1.95

Source: Based on Farshad, F., & Pesacreta, T. "Coated pipe interior surface roughness as measured by three scanning probe instruments," *Anti-Corrosion Methods and Materials,* Vol. 50, No. 1, 2003 (Table III).

5.31 Is exposure to a chemical in Teflon-coated cookware hazardous? Perfluorooctanoic acid (PFOA) is a chemical used in Teflon-coated cookware to prevent food from sticking. The EPA is investigating the potential risk of PFOA as a cancer-causing agent (*Science News Online,* August 27, 2005). It is known that the blood concentration of PFOA in people in the general population has a mean of $\mu = 6$ parts per billion (ppb) and a standard deviation of $\sigma = 10$ ppb. *Science News Online* reported on tests for PFOA exposure conducted on a sample of 326 people who live near DuPont's Teflon-making Washington (West Virginia) Works facility.
a. What is the probability that the average blood concentration of PFOA in the sample is greater than 7.5 ppb?
b. The actual study resulted in $\bar{x} = 300$ ppb. Use this information to make an inference about the true mean μ PFOA concentration for the population of people who live near DuPont's Teflon facility.

5.32 Rental car fleet evaluation. National Car Rental Systems, Inc., commissioned the U.S. Automobile Club (USAC) to conduct a survey of the general condition of the cars rented to the public by Hertz, Avis, National, and Budget Rent-a-Car.* USAC officials evaluate each company's cars using a demerit point system. Each car starts with a perfect score of 0 points and incurs demerit points for each discrepancy noted by the inspectors. One measure of the overall condition of a company's cars is the mean of all scores received by the company (i.e., the company's *fleet mean score*). To estimate the fleet mean score of each rental car company, 10 major airports were randomly selected, and 10 cars from each company were randomly rented for inspection from each airport by USAC officials (i.e., a sample of size $n = 100$ cars from each company's fleet was drawn and inspected).
a. Describe the sampling distribution of $\bar{x}$, the mean score of a sample of $n = 100$ rental cars.
b. Interpret the mean of $\bar{x}$ in the context of this problem.
c. Assume $\mu = 30$ and $\sigma = 60$ for one rental company. For this company, find $P(\bar{x} \geq 45)$.
d. Refer to part **c.** The company claims that their true fleet mean score "couldn't possibly be as high as 30." The sample mean score tabulated by USAC for this company was 45. Does this result tend to support or refute the claim? Explain.

5.33 Motivation of drug dealers. Refer to the *Applied Psychology in Criminal Justice* (Sep. 2009) investigation of the personality characteristics of drug dealers, Exercise 2.80 (p. 85). Convicted drug dealers were scored on the Wanting Recognition (WR) Scale—a scale that provides a quantitative measure of a person's level of need for approval and sensitivity to social situations. (Higher scores indicate a greater need for approval.) Based on the study results, we can assume that the WR scores for the population of convicted drug dealers has a mean of 40 and a standard deviation of 5. Suppose that in a sample of 100 people, the mean WR scale score is $\bar{x} = 42$. Is this sample likely to have been selected from the population of convicted drug dealers? Explain.

*Information by personal communication with Rajiv Tandon, corporate vice president and general manager of the Car Rental Division, National Car Rental Systems, Inc., Minneapolis, Minnesota.

Applying the Concepts—Advanced

5.34 Plastic fill process. University of Louisville researchers J. Usher, S. Alexander, and D. Duggins examined the process of filling plastic pouches of dry blended biscuit mix (*Quality Engineering*, Vol. 91, 1996). The current fill mean of the process is set at $\mu = 406$ grams, and the process fill standard deviation is $\sigma = 10.1$ grams. (According to the researchers, "The high level of variation is due to the fact that the product has poor flow properties and is, therefore, difficult to fill consistently from pouch to pouch.") Operators monitor the process by randomly sampling 36 pouches each day and measuring the amount of biscuit mix in each. Consider $\bar{x}$, the mean fill amount of the sample of 36 products. Suppose that on one particular day, the operators observe $\bar{x} = 400.8$. One of the operators believes that this indicates that the true process fill mean μ for that day is less than 406 grams. Another operator argues that $\mu = 406$, and the small value of $\bar{x}$ observed is due to random variation in the fill process. Which operator do you agree with? Why?

5.35 Handwashing vs. handrubbing. The *British Medical Journal* (Aug. 17, 2002) published the results of a study to compare the effectiveness of handwashing with soap and handrubbing with alcohol. Health care workers who used handrubbing had a mean bacterial count of 35 per hand with a standard deviation of 59. Health care workers who used handwashing had a mean bacterial count of 69 per hand with a standard deviation of 106. In a random sample of 50 health care workers, all using the same method of cleaning their hands, the mean bacterial count per hand, $\bar{x}$, is less than 30. Give your opinion on whether this sample of workers used handrubbing with alcohol or handwashing with soap.

5.4 The Sampling Distribution of the Sample Proportion

Suppose you want to estimate the proportion of voters in favor of a bill to legalize gambling in your state, or the percentage of store customers who use a store credit card to make a purchase, or the fraction of company CEOs who defer their annual pay. In each case, the data of interest are categorical in nature with two outcomes (e.g., favor or do not favor); consequently, we want to make an inference about a binomial proportion, p.

Just as the sample mean is a good estimator of the population mean, the sample proportion—denoted $\hat{p}$— is a good estimator of the population proportion p. How good the estimator $\hat{p}$ is will depend on the sampling distribution of the statistic. This sampling distribution has properties similar to those of the sampling distribution of $\bar{x}$, as shown in the following example.

Example	5.9

Simulating the Sampling Distribution of $\hat{p}$—Worker Unionization

Problem Refer to Example 4.13 (p. 206) and the problem of sampling workers to determine whether they are in favor of unionization. We assumed that 60% of all workers at a large plant were, in fact, in favor of unionization. Suppose we will randomly sample 100 plant workers and ask each if he or she is or is not in favor of unionization. Use a computer and statistical software to simulate the sampling distribution of $\hat{p}$, the sample proportion of workers in favor of unionization. What properties do you observe?

Solution Consider a single random sample of 100 workers. If we define a "success" as a worker in favor of unionization, and if 58 of the 100 are in favor of unionization, then our estimate of the binomial proportion p is $\hat{p} = 58/100 = .58$. By repeatedly taking samples in this manner and calculating $\hat{p}$ each time, we can simulate the sampling distribution.

We used SPSS to generate 1,000 samples of size $n = 100$ from a binomial population with probability of success $p = .6$. For each sample, we calculated $\hat{p} = x/n$, where x is the number of successes in the sample. The estimated proportions for the first 20 samples are shown in Table 5.4. An SPSS histogram for all 1,000 estimated proportions is shown in Figure 5.14. This histogram approximates the sampling distribution of $\hat{p}$.

First, note that the sampling distribution appears to be normally distributed. Thus, the sampling distribution of $\hat{p}$ has the same property as the sampling distribution of $\bar{x}$—normally distributed for large n. Second, you can see that the sampling distribution is centered around the value $p = .6$. That is, it appears that the mean of the sampling distribution is equal to p, the proportion being estimated.

Look Back The normal distribution property identified with computer simulation becomes obvious once you recognize that the sample proportion $\hat{p}$ can be written as an average of 0s and 1s, where 1 represents a "success" (a worker in favor of unionization)

Table 5.4	Results for First 20 Samples of $n = 100$ Workers	
Sample	Number of Success, x	Sample Proportion, $\hat{p}$
1	60	.60
2	58	.58
3	56	.56
4	61	.61
5	54	.54
6	67	.67
7	54	.54
8	55	.55
9	56	.56
10	69	.69
11	59	.59
12	64	.64
13	53	.53
14	65	.65
15	66	.66
16	61	.61
17	60	.60
18	55	.55
19	57	.57
20	61	.61

Descriptive Statistics

	N	Minimum	Maximum	Mean	Std. Deviation
phat	1000	.44	.74	.5988	.04823
Valid N (listwise)	1000				

Figure 5.14

SPSS histogram of 1,000 values of $\hat{p}$, Example 5.9

and 0 represents a "failure" (a worker not in favor of unionization). In the first sample shown in Table 5.4, there were 60 successes and 40 failures; thus

$$\hat{p} = \frac{(60)(1) + (40)(0)}{100} = 60/100 = .60$$

Since $\hat{p}$ is a mean, the Central Limit Theorem can be applied when the sample size n is large.

The true sampling distribution of $\hat{p}$ has the properties listed in the next box.

> **Sampling Distribution of $\hat{p}$**
>
> 1. Mean of the sampling distribution is equal to the true binomial proportion, p; that is, $E(\hat{p}) = p$. Consequently, $\hat{p}$ is an unbiased estimator of p.
> 2. Standard deviation of the sampling distribution is equal to $\sqrt{p(1-p)/n}$; that is, $\sigma_{\hat{p}} = \sqrt{p(1-p)/n}$.
> 3. For large samples, the sampling distribution is approximately normal. (A sample is considered large if $n\hat{p} \geq 15$ and $n(1-\hat{p}) \geq 15$.)

In Example 5.9, $p = .6$. Thus, the true mean of the sampling distribution of $\hat{p}$ is equal to .6. Also, the true standard deviation of the sampling distribution of $\hat{p}$ is

$$\sigma_{\hat{p}} = \sqrt{p(1 - p)/n} = \sqrt{(.6)(.4)/100} = .049$$

Note that our estimates of the mean and standard deviation using simulation—.599 and .048, respectively—closely approximate the true values.

Example 5.10

Finding a Probability Involving $\hat{p}$—Workers in Favor of Unionization

Problem Refer to Example 5.9 (p. 286). Again, assume that 60% of all workers at a large plant are in favor of unionization. In a random sample of 100 plant workers, what is the probability that fewer than half are in favor of unionization?

Solution We want to find the probability that the sample proportion is less than .5, i.e., $P(\hat{p} < .5)$. From previous work, we know that the sampling distribution of $\hat{p}$ is normally distributed (since n is large), with mean $p = .6$ and standard deviation $\sigma_{\hat{p}} = .049$. Consequently,

$$P(\hat{p} < .5) = P\{(\hat{p} - p)/\sigma_{\hat{p}} < (.5 - p)/\sigma_{\hat{p}}\} = P\{z < (.5 - .6)/.049\} = P(z < -2.04)$$

Using Minitab software (see Figure 5.15), we find $P(\hat{p} < .5) = P(z < -2.04) = .021$.

Cumulative Distribution Function

Figure 5.15

Minitab output for a normal probability, Example 5.10

```
Normal with mean = 0 and standard deviation = 1

    x   P( X <= x )
-2.04    0.0206752
```

■ **Now Work Exercise 5.39**

In the next two chapters, we utilize the sampling distributions of both $\bar{x}$ and $\hat{p}$ to make inferences about population means and proportions.

Exercises 5.36–5.49

Learning the Mechanics

5.36 Suppose a random sample of n measurements is selected from a binomial population with probability of success $p = .2$. For each of the following values of n, give the mean and standard deviation of the sampling distribution of the sample proportion, $\hat{p}$.
  a. $n = 50$
  b. $n = 1,000$
  c. $n = 400$

5.37 Suppose a random sample of $n = 500$ measurements is selected from a binomial population with probability of success p. For each of the following values of p, give the mean and standard deviation of the sampling distribution of the sample proportion, $\hat{p}$.
  a. $p = .1$
  b. $p = .5$
  c. $p = .7$

5.38 A random sample of $n = 80$ measurements is drawn from a binomial population with probability of success .3.
  a. Give the mean and standard deviation of the sampling distribution of the sample proportion, $\hat{p}$.
  b. Describe the shape of the sampling distribution of $\hat{p}$.
  c. Calculate the standard normal z-score corresponding to a value of $\hat{p} = .35$.
  d. Find $P(\hat{p} > .35)$.

5.39 A random sample of $n = 250$ measurements is drawn from a binomial population with probability of success .85.
  a. Find $E(\hat{p})$ and $\sigma_{\hat{p}}$.
  b. Describe the shape of the sampling distribution of $\hat{p}$.
  c. Find $P(\hat{p} < .9)$.

5.40 A random sample of $n = 1,500$ measurements is drawn from a binomial population with probability of success .4. What are the smallest and largest values of $\hat{p}$ you would expect to see?

5.41 Consider a population with values of x equal to 0 or 1. Assume that the values of x are equally likely. For each of the following values of n, use a computer to generate 500 random samples and calculate the sample proportion of 1s observed for each sample. Then construct a histogram of the 500 sample proportions for each sample.
  a. $n = 10$
  b. $n = 25$
  c. $n = 100$
  d. Refer to the histograms, parts **a–c**. What changes occur as the value of n increases? What similarities exist?

Applying the Concepts—Basic

5.42 **Do social robots walk or roll?** Refer to the *International Conference on Social Robotics* (Vol. 6414, 2010) study of the trend in the design of social robots, Exercise 2.3 (p. 48).

The researchers obtained a random sample of 106 social robots through a Web search and determined the number that were designed with legs, but no wheels. Let $\hat{p}$ represent the sample proportion of social robots designed with legs, but no wheels. Assume that in the population of all social robots, 40% are designed with legs, but no wheels.

a. Give the mean and standard deviation of the sampling distribution of $\hat{p}$.

b. Describe the shape of the sampling distribution of $\hat{p}$.

c. Find $P(\hat{p} > .59)$.

d. Recall that the researchers found that 63 of the 106 robots were built with legs only. Does this result cast doubt on the assumption that 40% of all social robots are designed with legs, but no wheels? Explain.

5.43 Paying for music downloads. According to a recent *Pew Internet & American Life Project Survey* (October 2010), 67% of adults who use the Internet have paid to download music. (See Exercise 2.4, p. 48.) In a random sample of $n = 1,000$ adults who use the Internet, let $\hat{p}$ represent the proportion who have paid to download music.

a. Find the mean of the sampling distribution of $\hat{p}$.

b. Find the standard deviation of the sampling distribution of $\hat{p}$.

c. What does the Central Limit Theorem say about the shape of the sampling distribution of $\hat{p}$?

d. Compute the probability that $\hat{p}$ is less than .75.

e. Compute the probability that $\hat{p}$ is greater than .50.

5.44 Working on summer vacation. According to an *Adweek/ Harris* (July 2011) poll of U.S. adults, about 45% work during their summer vacation. (See Exercise 3.14, p. 141.) Assume that the true proportion of all U.S. adults that work during summer vacation is $p = .45$. Now consider a random sample of 500 U.S. adults.

a. What is the probability that between 40% and 50% of the sampled adults work during summer vacation?

b. What is the probability that over 60% of the sampled adults work during summer vacation?

5.45 Study of why EMS workers leave the job. A study of full-time emergency medical service (EMS) workers published in the *Journal of Allied Health* (Fall 2011) found that only about 3% leave their job in order to retire. (See Exercise 3.41, p. 153.) Assume that the true proportion of all full-time EMS workers who leave their job in order to retire is $p = .03$. In a random sample of 1,000 full-time EMS workers, let $\hat{p}$ represent the proportion who leave their job in order to retire.

a. Describe the properties of the sampling distribution of $\hat{p}$.

b. Compute $P(\hat{p} < .05)$. Interpret this result.

c. Compute $P(\hat{p} > .025)$. Interpret this result.

Applying the Concepts—Intermediate

5.46 Stock market participation and IQ. Refer to *The Journal of Finance* (December 2011) study of whether the decision to invest in the stock market is dependent on IQ, Exercise 3.42 (p. 153). The researchers found that the probability of a Finnish citizen investing in the stock market differed depending on IQ score. For those with a high IQ score, the probability is .44; for those with an average IQ score, the probability is .26; and for those with a low IQ score, the probability is .14.

a. In a random sample of 500 Finnish citizens with high IQ scores, what is the probability that more than 150 invest in the stock market?

b. In a random sample of 500 Finnish citizens with average IQ scores, what is the probability that more than 150 invest in the stock market?

c. In a random sample of 500 Finnish citizens with low IQ scores, what is the probability that more than 150 invest in the stock market?

5.47 Downloading "apps" to your cell phone. Refer to Exercise 4.23 (p. 195) and the August 2011 survey by the Pew Internet & American Life Project. The study found that 40% of adult cell phone owners have downloaded an application ("app") to their cell phone. Assume this percentage applies to the population of all adult cell phone owners.

a. In a random sample of 50 adult cell phone owners, how likely is it to find that more than 60% have downloaded an "app" to their cell phone?

b. Refer to part **a.** Suppose you observe a sample proportion of .62. What inference can you make about the true proportion of adult cell phone owners who have downloaded an "app"?

c. Suppose the sample of 50 cell phone owners is obtained at a convention for the International Association for the Wireless Telecommunications Industry. How will your answer to part **b** change, if at all?

5.48 Hotel guest satisfaction. Refer to the results of the 2009 North American Hotel Guest Satisfaction Index Study referenced in Exercise 4.48 (p. 210). Recall that 66% of hotel guests were aware of the hotel's "green" conservation program; of these guests, 72% actually participated in the program by reusing towels and bed linens. In a random sample of 100 hotel guests, find the probability that fewer than 42 were aware of and participated in the hotel's conservation efforts.

5.49 Fingerprint expertise. Refer to the *Psychological Science* (August 2011) study of fingerprint identification, Exercise 4.53 (p. 210). Recall that when presented with prints from the same individual, a fingerprint expert will correctly identify the match 92% of the time. Consider a forensic database of 1,000 different pairs of fingerprints, where each pair is a match.

a. What proportion of the 1,000 pairs would you expect an expert to correctly identify as a match?

b. What is the probability that an expert will correctly identify fewer than 900 of the fingerprint matches?

◻ Chapter Notes

Key Terms

Biased estimate 274
Central Limit Theorem 278
Error of estimation 273
Minimum-variance unbiased
  estimator (MVUE) 276
Parameter 266

Point estimator 273
Sample statistic 266
Sampling distribution 268
Standard error of the mean 278
Standard error of the statistic 274
Unbiased estimate 274

Key Formulas

	Mean	Standard Deviation	z-score
Sampling distribution of $\bar{x}$:	$\mu_{\bar{x}} = \mu$	$\sigma_{\bar{x}} = \dfrac{\sigma}{\sqrt{n}}$	$z = \dfrac{\bar{x} - \mu_{\bar{x}}}{\sigma_{\bar{x}}}$ $= \dfrac{\bar{x} - \mu}{\sigma/\sqrt{n}}$
Sampling distribution of $\hat{p}$:	p	$\sigma_{\hat{p}} = \sqrt{p(1-p)/n}$	$z = \dfrac{\hat{p} - p}{\sqrt{p(1-p)/n}}$

Key Ideas

Sampling distribution of a statistic—the theoretical probability distribution of the statistic in repeated sampling
Unbiased estimator—a statistic with a sampling distribution mean equal to the population parameter being estimated
Central Limit Theorem—the sampling distribution of the sample mean, $\bar{x}$, or the sample proportion, $\hat{p}$, is approximately normal for large n
$\bar{x}$ is the **minimum-variance unbiased estimator (MVUE)** of μ
$\hat{p}$ is the MVUE of p

Key Symbols

θ	Population parameter (general)
$\mu_{\bar{x}}$	True mean of sampling distribution of $\bar{x}$
$\sigma_{\bar{x}}$	True standard deviation of sampling distribution of $\bar{x}$
p	True mean of sampling distribution of $\hat{p}$
$\sigma_{\hat{p}}$	True standard deviation of sampling distribution of $\hat{p}$

Generating the Sampling Distribution of $\bar{x}$

Select sample size n (large) from target population

Calculate $\bar{x}$

$\bar{x}_1$
$\bar{x}_2$
$\bar{x}_3$

Population:
  Mean = μ
  Std. Dev. = σ
  Unknown shape

Repeat this process an infinite number of times

Sampling distribution of $\bar{x}$ (i.e., theoretical population of x's)
  Mean = $\mu_{\bar{x}} = \mu$
  Std. Dev. = $\sigma_{\bar{x}} = \sigma/\sqrt{n}$
  Normal distribution (Central Limit Theorem)

Supplementary Exercises 5.50–5.75

Learning the Mechanics

5.50 The standard deviation (or, as it is usually called, the *standard error*) of the sampling distribution for the sample mean, $\bar{x}$, is equal to the standard deviation of the population from which the sample was selected, divided by the square root of the sample size. That is,

$$\sigma_{\bar{x}} = \frac{\sigma}{\sqrt{n}}$$

  a. As the sample size is increased, what happens to the standard error of $\bar{x}$? Why is this property considered important?

  b. Suppose a sample statistic has a standard error that is not a function of the sample size. In other words, the standard error remains constant as n changes. What would this imply about the statistic as an estimator of a population parameter?

  c. Suppose another unbiased estimator (call it A) of the population mean is a sample statistic with a standard error equal to

$$\sigma_A = \frac{\sigma}{\sqrt[3]{n}}$$

  Which of the sample statistics, $\bar{x}$ or A, is preferable as an estimator of the population mean? Why?

d. Suppose that the population standard deviation σ is equal to 10 and that the sample size is 64. Calculate the standard errors of $\bar{x}$ and A. Assuming that the sampling distribution of A is approximately normal, interpret the standard errors. Why is the assumption of (approximate) normality unnecessary for the sampling distribution of $\bar{x}$?

5.51 Consider a sample statistic A. As with all sample statistics, A is computed by utilizing a specified function (formula) of the sample measurements. (For example, if A were the sample mean, the specified formula would sum the measurements and divide by the number of measurements.)

a. Describe what we mean by the phrase "the sampling distribution of the sample statistic A."

b. Suppose A is to be used to estimate a population parameter θ. What is meant by the assertion that A is an unbiased estimator of θ?

c. Consider another sample statistic, B. Assume that B is also an unbiased estimator of the population parameter α. How can we use the sampling distributions of A and B to decide which is the better estimator of θ?

d. If the sample sizes on which A and B are based are large, can we apply the Central Limit Theorem and assert that the sampling distributions of A and B are approximately normal? Why or why not?

5.52 A random sample of 40 observations is to be drawn from a large population of measurements. It is known that 30% of the measurements in the population are 1s, 20% are 2s, 20% are 3s, and 30% are 4s.

a. Give the mean and standard deviation of the (repeated) sampling distribution of $\bar{x}$, the sample mean of the 40 observations.

b. Describe the shape of the sampling distribution of $\bar{x}$. Does your answer depend on the sample size?

5.53 A random sample of $n = 68$ observations is selected from a population with $\mu = 19.6$ and $\sigma = 3.2$. Approximate each of the following probabilities:

a. $P(\bar{x} \leq 19.6)$
b. $P(\bar{x} \leq 19)$
c. $P(\bar{x} \geq 20.1)$
d. $P(19.2 \leq \bar{x} \leq 20.6)$

5.54 A random sample of $n = 500$ observations is selected from a binomial population with $p = .35$.

a. Give the mean and standard deviation of the (repeated) sampling distribution of $\hat{p}$, the sample proportion of successes for the 500 observations.

b. Describe the shape of the sampling distribution of $\hat{p}$. Does your answer depend on the sample size?

5.55 A random sample of $n = 300$ observations is selected from a binomial population with $p = .8$. Approximate each of the following probabilities:

a. $P(\hat{p} < .83)$
b. $P(\hat{p} > .75)$
c. $P(.79 < \hat{p} < .81)$

5.56 Use a statistical software package to generate 100 random samples of size $n = 2$ from a population characterized by a normal probability distribution with a mean of 100 and a standard deviation of 10. Compute $\bar{x}$ for each sample, and plot a frequency distribution for the 100 values of $\bar{x}$. Repeat this process for $n = 5, 10, 30$, and 50. How does the fact that the sampled population is normal affect the sampling distribution of $\bar{x}$?

5.57 Use a statistical software package to generate 100 random samples of size $n = 2$ from a population characterized by a uniform probability distribution with $c = 0$ and $d = 10$. Compute $\bar{x}$ for each sample, and plot a frequency distribution for the 100 $\bar{x}$ values. Repeat this process for $n = 5,10,30$, and 50. Explain how your plots illustrate the Central Limit Theorem.

5.58 Suppose x equals the number of heads observed when a single coin is tossed; that is, $x = 0$ or $x = 1$ The population corresponding to x is the set of 0s and 1s generated when the coin is tossed repeatedly a large number of times. Suppose we select $n = 2$ observations from this population. (That is, we toss the coin twice and observe two values of x.)

a. List the three different samples (combinations of 0s and 1s) that could be obtained.

b. Calculate the value of $\bar{x}$ for each of the samples.

c. Show that the sample proportion of 1s, $\hat{p}$, is equal to $\bar{x}$.

d. List the values that $\hat{p}$ can assume, and find the probabilities of observing these values.

e. Construct a graph of the sampling distribution of $\hat{p}$.

5.59 A random sample of size n is to be drawn from a large population with mean 100 and standard deviation 10, and the sample mean $\bar{x}$ is to be calculated. To see the effect of different sample sizes on the standard deviation of the sampling distribution of $\bar{x}$, plot $\sigma/\sqrt{n}$ against n for $n = 1, 5, 10, 20, 30, 40$, and 50.

Applying the Concepts—Basic

5.60 **Semester hours taken by CPA candidates.** Refer to the *Journal of Accounting and Public Policy* (Spring 2002) study of first-time candidates for the CPA exam, Exercise 2.51 (p. 72). The number of semester hours of college credit taken by candidates has a distribution with a mean of 141 hours and a standard deviation of 18 hours. Consider a random sample of 100 first-time candidates for the CPA exam and let $\bar{x}$ represent the mean number of hours of college credit taken for the sample.

a. What is $\mu_{\bar{x}}$?
b. What is $\sigma_{\bar{x}}$?
c. Describe the shape of the sampling distribution of $\bar{x}$.
d. Find the z-score for the value $\bar{x} = 142$ hours.
e. Find $P(\bar{x} > 142)$.

5.61 **Improving SAT scores.** Refer to the *Chance* (Winter 2001) examination of Scholastic Assessment Test (SAT) scores of students who pay a private tutor to help them improve their results, Exercise 2.88 (p. 86). On the SAT—Mathematics test, these students had a mean score change of +19 points, with a standard deviation of 65 points. In a random sample of 100 students who pay a private tutor to help them improve their results, what is the likelihood that the sample mean score change is less than 10 points?

5.62 **Back injuries at work.** A poll by the Gallup Organization sponsored by Philadelphia-based CIGNA Integrated Care found that about 40% of employees have missed work due to a musculoskeletal (back) injury of some kind (*National Underwriter*, Apr. 5, 1999). Let *x* be the number of sampled workers who have missed work due to a back injury.

a. Explain why *x* is approximately a binomial random variable.

b. Use the Gallup poll data to estimate *p* for the binomial random variable of part **a.**

c. A random sample of 100 workers is to be drawn from a particular manufacturing plant. Use the *p* from part **b** to find the mean and standard deviation of $\hat{p}$ the proportion of workers who missed work due to back injuries in the sample.

d. Refer to part **c.** Find the probability that the sample proportion is less than .38.

5.63 **Dentists' use of laughing gas.** According to the American Dental Association, 60% of all dentists use nitrous oxide in their practice. In a random sample of 75 dentists, let $\hat{p}$ represent the proportion who use laughing gas in practice.

a. Find $E(\hat{p})$.

b. Find $\sigma_{\hat{p}}$.

c. Describe the shape of the sampling distribution of $\hat{p}$.

d. Find $P(\hat{p} > .70)$.

5.64 **Ocean quahog harvesting.** The ocean quahog is a type of clam found in the coastal waters of New England and the mid-Atlantic states. A federal survey of offshore ocean quahog harvesting in New Jersey, conducted from 1980 to 1992, revealed an average catch per unit effort (CPUE) of 89.34 clams. The CPUE standard deviation was 7.74 (*Journal of Shellfish Research*, June 1995). Let $\bar{x}$ represent the mean CPUE for a sample of 35 attempts to catch ocean quahogs off the New Jersey shore.

a. Compute $\mu_{\bar{x}}$ and $\sigma_{\bar{x}}$. Interpret their values.

b. Sketch the sampling distribution of $\bar{x}$.

c. Find $P(\bar{x} > 88)$.

d. Find $P(\bar{x} < 87)$.

Applying the Concepts—Intermediate

5.65 **Analysis of supplier lead time.** In determining when to place orders to replenish depleted product inventories, a retailer should take into consideration the lead times for the products. *Lead time* is the time between placing the order and having the product available to satisfy customer demand. It includes time for placing the order, receiving the shipment from the supplier, inspecting the units received, and placing them in inventory (Clauss, *Applied Management Science and Spreadsheet Modeling*, 1996). Interested in average lead time, μ, for a particular supplier of men's apparel, the purchasing department of a national department store chain randomly sampled 50 of the supplier's lead times and found $\bar{x} = 44$ days.

a. Describe the shape of the sampling distribution of $\bar{x}$.

b. If μ and σ are really 40 and 12, respectively, what is the probability that a second random sample of size 50 would yield $\bar{x}$ greater than or equal to 44?

c. Using the values for μ and σ in part **b,** what is the probability that a sample of size 50 would yield a sample mean within the interval $\mu \pm 2\sigma/\sqrt{n}$?

5.66 **Producing machine bearings.** To determine whether a metal lathe that produces machine bearings is properly adjusted, a random sample of 25 bearings is collected and the diameter of each is measured.

a. If the standard deviation of the diameters of the bearings measured over a long period of time is .001 inch, what is the approximate probability that the mean diameter $\bar{x}$ of the sample of 25 bearings will lie within .0001 inch of the population mean diameter of the bearings?

b. If the population of diameters has an extremely skewed distribution, how will your approximation in part **a** be affected?

5.67 **Quality control.** Refer to Exercise 5.66. The mean diameter of the bearings produced by the machine is supposed to be .5 inch. The company decides to use the sample mean from Exercise 5.66 to decide whether the process is in control (i.e., whether it is producing bearings with a mean diameter of .5 inch). The machine will be considered out of control if the mean of the sample of $n = 25$ diameters is less than .4994 inch or larger than .5006 inch. If the true mean diameter of the bearings produced by the machine is .501 inch, what is the approximate probability that the test will imply that the process is out of control?

5.68 **Length of job tenure.** Researchers at the Terry College of Business at the University of Georgia sampled 344 business students and asked them this question: "Over the course of your lifetime, what is the maximum number of years you expect to work for any one employer?" The sample resulted in $\bar{x} = 19.1$ years. Assume that the sample of students was randomly selected from the 6,000 undergraduate students at the Terry College and that $\sigma = 6$ years.

a. Describe the sampling distribution of $\bar{x}$

b. If the mean for the 6,000 undergraduate students is $\mu = 18.5$ years, find $P(\bar{x} > 19.1)$

c. If the mean for the 6,000 undergraduate students is $\mu = 19.5$ years, find $P(\bar{x} > 19.1)$

d. If $P(\bar{x} > 19.1) = .5$, what is μ?

e. If $P(\bar{x} > 19.1) = .2$, is μ greater than or less than 19.1 years? Explain.

5.69 **Switching banks after a merger.** Banks that merge with others to form "mega-banks" sometimes leave customers dissatisfied with the impersonal service. A poll by the Gallup Organization found 20% of retail customers switched banks after their banks merged with another. One year after the acquisition of First Fidelity by First Union, a random sample of 250 retail customers who had banked with First Fidelity were questioned. Let $\hat{p}$ be the proportion of those customers who switched their business from First Union to a different bank.

a. Find the mean and the standard deviation of $\hat{p}$.

b. Calculate the interval $E(\hat{p}) \pm 2\sigma_{\hat{p}}$.

c. If samples of size 250 were drawn repeatedly a large number of times and $\hat{p}$ determined for each sample, what proportion of the $\hat{p}$ values would fall within the interval you calculated in part **c**?

5.70 **Piercing rating of fencing safety jackets.** A manufacturer produces safety jackets for competitive fencers. These jackets are rated by the minimum force, in newtons, that will allow a weapon to pierce the jacket. When this process is operating correctly, it produces jackets that have ratings with an average of 840 newtons and a standard deviation of 15 newtons. FIE, the international governing body for fencing, requires jackets to be rated at a minimum of 800 newtons. To check whether the process is operating correctly, a manager takes a sample of 50 jackets from the process, rates them, and calculates $\bar{x}$, the mean rating for jackets in the sample. She assumes that the standard deviation of the process is fixed but is worried that the mean rating of the process may have changed.

a. What is the sampling distribution of $\bar{x}$ if the process is still operating correctly?

b. Suppose the manager's sample has a mean rating of 830 newtons. What is the probability of getting an $\bar{x}$ of 830 newtons or lower if the process is operating correctly?

c. Given the manager's assumption that the standard deviation of the process is fixed, what does your answer to part **b** suggest about the current state of the process (i.e., does it appear that the mean jacket rating is still 840 newtons)?

d. Now suppose that the mean of the process has not changed, but the standard deviation of the process has increased from 15 newtons to 45 newtons. What is the sampling distribution of $\bar{x}$ in this case? What is the probability of getting an $\bar{x}$ of 830 newtons or lower when $\bar{x}$ has this distribution?

5.71 Errors in filling prescriptions A large number of preventable errors (e.g., overdoses, botched operations, misdiagnoses) are being made by doctors and nurses in U.S. hospitals. A study of a major metropolitan hospital revealed that of every 100 medications prescribed or dispensed, 1 was in error, but only 1 in 500 resulted in an error that caused significant problems for the patient. It is known that the hospital prescribes and dispenses 60,000 medications per year.

a. What is the expected proportion of errors per year at this hospital? The expected proportion of significant errors per year?

b. Within what limits would you expect the proportion significant errors per year to fall?

5.72 Purchasing decision. A building contractor has decided to purchase a load of factory-reject aluminum siding as long as the average number of flaws per piece of siding in a sample of size 35 from the factory's reject pile is 2.1 or less. If it is known that the number of flaws per piece of siding in the factory's reject pile has a Poisson probability distribution with a mean of 2.5, find the approximate probability that the contractor will not purchase a load of siding.

Applying the Concepts—Advanced

5.73 Machine repair time. An article in *Industrial Engineering* (August 1990) discussed the importance of modeling machine downtime correctly in simulation studies. As an illustration, the researcher considered a single-machine-tool system with repair times (in minutes) that can be modeled by an exponential distribution with $\theta = 60$. Of interest is the mean repair time $\bar{x}$ of a sample of 100 machine breakdowns.

a. Find $E(\bar{x})$ and the variance of $\bar{x}$.

b. What probability distribution provides the best model of the sampling distribution of $\bar{x}$? Why?

c. Calculate the probability that the mean repair time $\bar{x}$ is no longer than 30 minutes.

Critical Thinking Challenges

5.74 Soft-drink bottles. A soft-drink bottler purchases glass bottles from a vendor. The bottles are required to have an internal pressure of at least 150 pounds per square inch (psi). A prospective bottle vendor claims that its production process yields bottles with a mean internal pressure of 157 psi and a standard deviation of 3 psi. The bottler strikes an agreement with the vendor that permits the bottler to sample from the vendor's production process to verify the vendor's claim. The bottler randomly selects 40 bottles from the last 10,000 produced, measures the internal pressure of each, and finds the mean pressure for the sample to be 1.3 psi below the process mean cited by the vendor.

a. Assuming the vendor's claim to be true, what is the probability of obtaining a sample mean this far or farther below the process mean? What does your answer suggest about the validity of the vendor's claim?

b. If the process standard deviation were 3 psi as claimed by the vendor, but the mean were 156 psi, would the observed sample result be more or less likely than in part **a**? What if the mean were 158 psi?

c. If the process mean were 157 psi as claimed, but the process standard deviation were 2 psi, would the sample result be more or less likely than in part **a**? What if instead the standard deviation were 6 psi?

5.75 Fecal pollution at Huntington Beach. The state of California mandates fecal indicator bacteria monitoring at all public beaches. When the concentration of fecal bacteria in the water exceeds a certain limit (400 colony-forming units of fecal coliform per 100 milliliters), local health officials must post a sign (called surf zone posting) warning beachgoers of potential health risks upon entering the water. For fecal bacteria, the state uses a single-sample standard; that is, if the fecal limit is exceeded in a single sample of water, surf zone posting is mandatory. This single-sample standard policy has led to a recent rash of beach closures in California.

Joon Ha Kim and Stanley B. Grant, engineers at the University of California at Irvine, conducted a study of the surf water quality at Huntington Beach in California and reported the results in *Environmental Science & Technology* (September 2004). The researchers found that beach closings were occurring despite low pollution levels in some instances, while in others, signs were not posted when the fecal limit was exceeded. They attributed these "surf zone posting errors" to the variable nature of water quality in the surf zone (for example, fecal bacteria concentration tends to be higher during ebb tide and at night) and the inherent time delay between when a water sample is collected and when a sign is posted or removed. In order to prevent posting errors, the researchers recommend using an averaging method, rather than a single sample, to determine unsafe water quality. (For example, one simple averaging method is to take a random sample of multiple water specimens and compare the average fecal bacteria level of the sample with the limit of 400 cfu/100 mL in order to determine whether the water is safe.)

Discuss the pros and cons of using the single-sample standard versus the averaging method. Part of your discussion should address the probability of posting a sign when in fact the water is safe and the probability of posting a sign when in fact the water is unsafe. (Assume that the fecal bacteria concentrations of water specimens at Huntington Beach follow an approximately normal distribution.)

Activity 5.1   Simulating a Sampling Distribution—Cell Phone Usage

[*Note:* This activity is designed for small groups or the entire class.] Consider the length of time a student spends making a cell phone call, sending/retrieving a text message, or accessing e-mail on his/her cell phone. Let x represent the length of time, in seconds, for a single cell phone activity (call, text, or e-mail). Here, we are interested in the sampling distribution of $\bar{x}$, the mean length of time for a sample of size n cell phone activities.

1. Keep track of the time lengths for all cell phone activities you engage in over the next week.

2. Pool your time length data with data from other class members or the entire class so that the pooled data set has at least 100 observations. Designate someone in the group to calculate the mean and standard deviation of the pooled data set.

3. Devise a convenient way to choose random samples from the pooled data set. (For example, you could assign each observation a number beginning with "1" and use a random number generator to select a sample.)

4. Choose a random sample of size $n = 30$ from the pooled data, and find the mean of the sample. Group members should repeat the process of choosing a sample of size $n = 30$ from the pooled data and finding the sample mean until the group has accumulated at least 25 sample means. (Call this data set *Sample Means*.)

5. Find the mean and standard deviation of the *Sample Means* data set. Also, form a histogram for the *Sample Means* data set. Explain how the Central Limit Theorem is illustrated in this activity.

References

Hogg, R. V., McKean, J. W., and Craig, A. T. *Introduction to Mathematical Statistics,* 6th ed. Upper Saddle River, N.J.: Prentice Hall, 2005.

Larsen, R. J., & Marx, M. L. *An Introduction to Mathematical Statistics and Its Applications,* 4th ed. Upper Saddle River, N.J.: Prentice Hall, 2005.

Lindgren, B. W. *Statistical Theory,* 3rd ed. New York: Macmillan, 1976.

Wackerly, D., Mendenhall, W., & Scheaffer, R. L. *Mathematical Statistics with Applications,* 7th ed. North Scituate, Mass.: Duxbury, 2008.

USING TECHNOLOGY   Technology images shown here are taken from SPSS Statistics Professional 20.0, Minitab 16, XLSTAT for Pearson, and Excel 2010.

SPSS: Simulating a Sampling Distribution

Generating a sampling distribution with SPSS is not a simple process. Consult the SPSS user's guide for help with this feature.

Minitab: Simulating a Sampling Distribution

Step 1 Select "Calc" on the Minitab menu bar, and then click on "Random Data" (see Figure 5.M.1).

Step 2 On the resulting menu list, click on the distribution of your choice (e.g., "Uniform"). A dialog box similar to the one (the Uniform Distribution) shown in Figure 5.M.2 will appear.

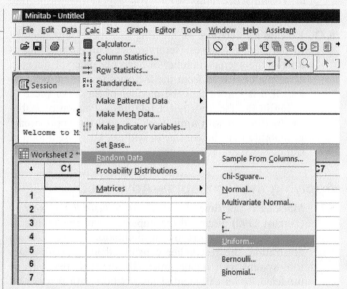

Figure 5.M.1 Minitab options for generating random data

Figure 5.M.2 Minitab dialog box for simulating the uniform distribution

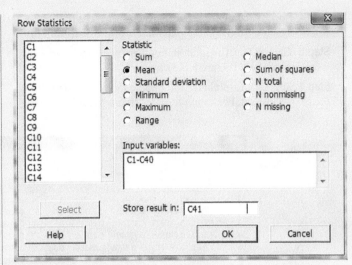

Figure 5.M.4 Minitab row statistics dialog box

Step 3 Specify the number of samples (e.g., 1,000) to generate in the "Number of rows of data to generate" box and the columns where the data will be stored in the "Store in columns" box. (The number of columns will be equal to the sample size, e.g., 40.) Finally, specify the parameters of the distribution (e.g., the lower and upper range of the uniform distribution). When you click "OK," the simulated data will appear on the Minitab worksheet.

Step 4 Calculate the value of the sample statistic of interest for each sample. To do this, click on the "Calc" button on the Minitab menu bar, and then click on "Row Statistics," as shown in Figure 5.M.3. The resulting dialog box appears in Figure 5.M.4.

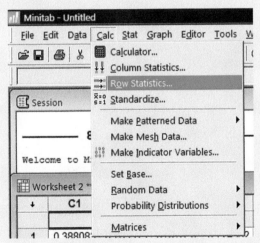

Figure 5.M.3 Minitab selections for generating sample statistics for the simulated data

Step 5 Check the sample statistic (e.g., the mean) you want to calculate, specify the "Input variables" (or columns), and the column where you want the value of the sample statistic to be saved. Click "OK" and the value of the statistic for each sample will appear on the Minitab worksheet.

[Note: Use the Minitab menu choices provided in the Using Technology section in Chapter 2, p. 122, to generate a histogram of the sampling distribution of the statistic or to find the mean and variance of the sampling distribution.]

Excel: Simulating a Sampling Distribution

Step 1 Select "Data" on the main menu bar and then click on "Data Analysis." The resulting menu is shown in Figure 5.E.1.

Figure 5.E.1 Excel data analysis menu options

Step 2 Select "Random Number Generation" from the Data Analysis menu and then click "OK." The dialog box in Figure 5.E.2 will appear.

Figure 5.E.2 Excel dialog box for generating uniform random numbers

Step 3 Specify the number of samples (e.g., 10) to generate in the "Number of Variables" box and the sample size of each (e.g., 100) in the "Number of Random Numbers" box.

Step 4 Specify the distribution (e.g., uniform) that the samples will be selected from and the parameters of the distribution.

Step 5 Click "OK"; the random numbers will appear on a new Excel spreadsheet (Figure 5.E.3).

Step 6 Specify a formula for the sample mean on the resulting Excel spreadsheet. For example, the formula "=AVERAGE

(A2:J2)" in column "L" computes the mean of the 10 random numbers in each row of the spreadsheet shown in Figure 5.E.3.

Step 7 Once the means of the random samples are computed, you can generate a histogram or summary statistics for the mean by following the steps outlined in Using Technology, Chapter 2.

	A	B	C	D	E	F	G	H	I	J	K	L
1	x1	x2	x3	x4	x4	x6	x7	x8	x9	x10		xbar
2	0.969176	0.277139	0.916257	0.403027	0.950652	0.123386	0.140416	0.037599	0.338603	0.445662		0.460192
3	0.63094	0.445875	0.718406	0.760155	0.523515	0.668569	0.124577	0.992676	0.451064	0.074862		0.539064
4	0.145299	0.791559	0.730979	0.426191	0.856349	0.349895	0.022736	0.527482	0.991668	0.518906		0.536106
5	0.11301	0.497971	0.2566	0.493667	0.983428	0.192145	0.189734	0.852351	0.817957	0.802454		0.519932
6	0.479904	0.230049	0.106357	0.174749	0.144536	0.408826	0.499008	0.868191	0.475753	0.104892		0.349226
7	0.570299	0.490005	0.159734	0.234474	0.146428	0.337565	0.477035	0.939207	0.353862	0.877773		0.458638

Figure 5.E.3 Excel formula for computing sample means from random numbers

The Furniture Fire Case

A wholesale furniture retailer stores in-stock items at a large warehouse located in Tampa, Florida. Early in the year, a fire destroyed the warehouse and all the furniture in it. After determining the fire was an accident, the retailer sought to recover costs by submitting a claim to its insurance company.

As is typical in a fire insurance policy of this type, the furniture retailer must provide the insurance company with an estimate of "lost" profit for the destroyed items. Retailers calculate profit margin in percentage form using the Gross Profit Factor (GPF). By definition, the GPF for a single sold item is the ratio of the profit to the item's selling price measured as a percentage, that is,

Item GPF = (Profit/Sales price) × 100%

Of interest to both the retailer and the insurance company is the average GPF for all of the items in the warehouse. Because these furniture pieces were all destroyed, their eventual selling prices and profit values are obviously unknown. Consequently, the average GPF for all the warehouse items is unknown.

One way to estimate the mean GPF of the destroyed items is to use the mean GPF of similar, recently sold items. The retailer sold 3,005 furniture items in the year prior to the fire and kept paper invoices on all sales. Rather than calculate the mean GPF for all 3,005 items (the data were not computerized), the retailer sampled a total of 253 of the invoices and computed the mean GPF for these items. The 253 items were obtained by first selecting a sample of 134 items and then augmenting this sample with a second sample of 119 items. The mean GPFs for the two subsamples were calculated to be 50.6% and 51.0%, respectively, yielding an overall average GPF of 50.8%. This average GPF can be applied to the costs of the furniture items destroyed in the fire to obtain an estimate of the "lost" profit.

According to experienced claims adjusters at the insurance company, the GPF for sale items of the type destroyed in the fire rarely exceeds 48%. Consequently, the estimate of 50.8% appeared to be unusually high. (A 1% increase in GPF for items of this type equates to, approximately, an additional $16,000 in profit.) When the insurance company questioned the retailer on this issue, the retailer responded, "Our estimate was based on selecting two independent, random samples from the population of 3,005 invoices. Because the samples were selected randomly and the total sample size is large, the mean GPF estimate of 50.8% is valid."

A dispute arose between the furniture retailer and the insurance company, and a lawsuit was filed. In one portion of the suit, the insurance company accused the retailer of fraudulently representing their sampling methodology. Rather than selecting the samples randomly, the retailer was accused of selecting an unusual number of "high-profit" items from the population in order to increase the average GPF of the overall sample.

To support their claim of fraud, the insurance company hired a CPA firm to independently assess the retailer's Gross Profit Factor. Through the discovery process, the CPA firm legally obtained the paper invoices for the entire population of 3,005 items sold and input the information into a computer. The selling price, profit, profit margin, and month sold for these 3,005 furniture items are stored in the **FIRE** file, described below.

Your objective in this case is to use these data to determine the likelihood of fraud. Is it likely that a random sample of 253 items selected from the population of 3,005 items would yield a mean GPF of at least 50.8%? Or, is it likely that two independent, random samples of sizes 134 and 119 would yield mean GPFs of at least 50.6% and 51.0%, respectively? (These were the questions posed to a statistician retained by the CPA firm.) Use the ideas of probability and sampling distributions to guide your analysis.

Prepare a professional document that presents the results of your analysis and gives your opinion regarding fraud. Be sure to describe the assumptions and methodology used to arrive at your findings.

Variable	Type	Description
MONTH	QL	Month in which item was sold in 1991
INVOICE	QN	Invoice number
SALES	QN	Sales price of item in dollars
PROFIT	QN	Profit amount of item in dollars
MARGIN	QN	Profit margin of item = (Profit/Sales) × 100%

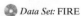 *Data Set:* FIRE

6

Where We've Been

- Learned that populations are characterized by numerical descriptive measures called *parameters*

- Found that decisions about population parameters are based on *statistics* computed from the sample

- Discovered that *inferences* about parameters are subject to uncertainty and that this uncertainty is reflected in the *sampling distribution* of a statistic

Where We're Going

- Estimate a population parameter (means, proportion, or variance) based on a large sample selected from the population (6.1)

- Use the sampling distribution of a statistic to form a confidence interval for the population parameter (6.2–6.4, 6.6, 6.7)

- Show how to select the proper sample size for estimating a population parameter (6.5)

☐ Inferences Based on a Single Sample *Estimation with Confidence Intervals*

STATISTICS in ACTION **Medicare Fraud Investigations**

United States Department of Justice (USDOJ) press release (Feb. 17, 2011): *The Medicare Fraud Strike Force today charged 111 defendants in nine cities, including doctors, nurses, health care company owners and executives, and others, for their alleged participation in Medicare fraud schemes involving more than $225 million in false billing.*

The joint Department of Justice (DOJ) and Health and Human Services (HHS) Medicare Fraud Strike Force is a multi-agency team of federal, state, and local investigators designed to combat Medicare fraud through the use of Medicare data analysis techniques and an increased focus on community policing. More than 700 law enforcement agents from the FBI, HHS-Office of Inspector General (HHS-OIG), multiple Medicaid Fraud Control Units, and other state and local law enforcement agencies participated in today's operation. In addition to making arrests, agents also executed 16 search warrants across the country in connection with ongoing strike force investigations.

In Miami, 32 defendants . . . were charged for their participation in various fraud schemes involving a total of $55 million in false billings for home health care, durable medical equipment and prescription drugs.

Twenty-one defendants . . . were charged in Detroit for schemes to defraud Medicare of more than $23 million. [These] cases involve false claims for home health care, nerve conduction tests, psychotherapy, physical therapy and podiatry.

In Brooklyn, N.Y., 10 individuals . . . were charged with fraud schemes involving $90 million in false billings for physical therapy, proctology services and nerve conduction tests.

Ten defendants were charged in Tampa for participating in schemes involving more than $5 million related to false claims for physical therapy, durable medical equipment and pharmaceuticals.

Nine individuals were charged in Houston for schemes involving $8 million in fraudulent Medicare claims for physical therapy, durable medical equipment, home health care and chiropractor services.

In Dallas, seven defendants were indicted for conspiring to submit $2.8 million in false billing to Medicare related to durable medical equipment and home health care.

Five defendants were charged in Los Angeles for their roles in schemes to defraud Medicare of more than $28 million. [These] cases involve false claims for durable medical equipment and home health care.

In Baton Rouge, La., six individuals were charged for a durable medical equipment fraud scheme involving more than $9 million in false claims.

In Chicago, charges were filed against 11 individuals associated with businesses that have billed Medicare more than $6 million for home health [care], diagnostic testing and prescription drugs.

As the above press release implies, the U.S. Department of Justice (USDOJ) and its Medicare Fraud Strike Force conduct investigations into suspected fraud and abuse of the Medicare system by health care providers. According to published reports, the Strike Force is responsible for 25% of the Medicare fraud charges brought nationwide.

One way in which Medicare fraud occurs is through the use of "upcoding," which refers to the practice of providers coding Medicare claims at a higher level of care than was actually provided to the patient. For example, suppose a particular kind of claim can be coded at three levels, where Level 1 is a routine office visit, Level 2 is a thorough examination involving advanced diagnostic tests, and Level 3 involves performing minor surgery. The amount of Medicare payment is higher for each increased level of claim. Thus, upcoding would occur if Level 1 services were billed at Level 2 or Level 3 payments, or if Level 2 services were billed at Level 3 payment.

The USDOJ relies on sound statistical methods to help identify Medicare fraud. Once the USDOJ has determined that possible upcoding has occurred, it next seeks to further investigate whether it is the result of legitimate practice (perhaps the provider is a specialist giving higher levels of care) or the result of fraudulent action on the part of the provider. To further its investigation, the USDOJ will next ask a statistician to select a sample of the provider's claims. For example, the statistician might determine that a random sample of 52 claims from the 1,000 claims in question will provide a sufficient sample to estimate the overcharge reliably. The USDOJ then asks a health care expert to audit each of the medical files corresponding to the sampled claims and determine whether the level of care matches the level billed by the provider, and, if not, to determine what level should have been billed. Once the audit has been completed, the USDOJ will calculate the overcharge.

In this chapter, we present a recent Medicare fraud case investigated by the USDOJ. Results for the audit of 52 sampled claims, with the amount paid for each claim, the amount disallowed by the auditor, and the amount that should have been paid for each claim, are saved in the **MFRAUD** file.* Knowing that a total of $103,500 was paid for the 1,000 claims, the USDOJ wants to use the sample results to extrapolate the overpayment amount to the entire population of 1,000 claims.

STATISTICS in ACTION REVISITED

▫ Estimating the Mean Overpayment **(p. 316)**

▫ Estimating the Coding Error Rate **(p. 324)**

▫ Determining Sample Size **(p. 331)**

Data Set: MFRAUD ▫

*Data provided (with permission) from Info Tech, Inc., Gainesville, Florida.

6.1 Identifying and Estimating the Target Parameter

In this chapter, our goal is to estimate the value of an unknown population parameter, such as a population mean or a proportion from a binomial population. For example, we might want to know the mean gas mileage for a new car model, the average expected life of a flat-screen computer monitor, or the proportion of dot-com companies that fail within a year of start-up.

You'll see that different techniques are used for estimating a mean or proportion, depending on whether a sample contains a large or small number of measurements. Nevertheless, our objectives remain the same. We want to use the sample information to estimate the population parameter of interest (called the **target parameter**) and assess the reliability of the estimate.

> The unknown population parameter (e.g., mean or proportion) that we are interested in estimating is called the **target parameter.**

Often, there are one or more key words in the statement of the problem that indicate the appropriate target parameter. Some key words associated with the two parameters covered in this section are listed in the following box.

Determining the Target Parameter		
Parameter	Key Words or Phrases	Type of Data
μ	Mean; average	Quantitative
p	Proportion; percentage; fraction; rate	Qualitative
σ^2 (optional)	Variance; variability; spread	Quantitative

For the examples given above, the words *mean* in *mean gas mileage* and *average* in *average life expectancy* imply that the target parameter is the population mean, μ. The word *proportion* in *proportion of dot-com companies that fail within one year of start-up* indicates that the target parameter is the binomial proportion, p.

In addition to key words and phrases, the type of data (quantitative or qualitative) collected is indicative of the target parameter. With quantitative data, you are likely to be estimating the mean or variance of the data. With qualitative data with two outcomes (success or failure), the binomial proportion of successes is likely to be the parameter of interest.

A single number calculated from the sample that estimates a target population parameter is called a **point estimator.** For example, we'll use the sample mean, $\bar{x}$, to estimate the population mean μ. Consequently, $\bar{x}$ is a point estimator. Similarly, we'll learn that the sample proportion of successes, denoted $\hat{p}$, is a point estimator for the binomial proportion p and that the sample variance s^2 is a point estimator for the population variance σ^2. Also, we will attach a measure of reliability to our estimate by obtaining an **interval estimator**—a range of numbers that contain the target parameter with a high degree of confidence. For this reason the interval estimate is also called a **confidence interval.**

> A **point estimator** of a population parameter is a rule or formula that tells us how to use the sample data to calculate a *single* number that can be used as an *estimate* of the target parameter.

> An **interval estimator** (or **confidence interval**) is a formula that tells us how to use the sample data to calculate an *interval* that *estimates* the target parameter.

We consider confidence intervals for estimating a population mean in Sections 6.2 and Section 6.3. Confidence intervals for a population proportion are presented in Section 6.4. In Section 6.5, we show how to determine the sample sizes necessary for reliable estimates of the target parameters based on simple random sampling. Optional Section 6.6 presents a method to apply when the sample size is large relative to the population size. Finally, in Section 6.7 we discuss estimation of a population variance.

6.2 Confidence Interval for a Population Mean: Normal (z) Statistic

Suppose a large bank wants to estimate the average amount of money owed by its delinquent debtors (i.e., debtors who are more than 2 months behind in payment). To accomplish this objective, the bank plans to randomly sample 100 of its delinquent accounts and use the sample mean, $\bar{x}$, of the amounts overdue to estimate μ, the mean for *all* delinquent accounts. Because the sample mean $\bar{x}$ represents a single number estimator, it is the *point estimator* of the target parameter μ. How can we assess the accuracy of this point estimator?

According to the Central Limit Theorem, the sampling distribution of the sample mean is approximately normal for large samples, as shown in Figure 6.1. Let us calculate the interval estimator:

$$\bar{x} \pm 1.96\sigma_{\bar{x}} = \bar{x} \pm \frac{1.96\sigma}{\sqrt{n}}$$

Figure 6.1

Sampling distribution of $\bar{x}$

That is, we form an interval from 1.96 standard deviations below the sample mean to 1.96 standard deviations above the mean. *Prior to drawing the sample*, what are the chances that this interval will enclose μ, the population mean?

To answer this question, refer to Figure 6.1. If the 100 measurements yield a value of $\bar{x}$ that falls between the two lines on either side of μ (i.e., within 1.96 standard deviations of μ), then the interval $\bar{x} \pm 1.96\sigma_{\bar{x}}$ will contain μ; if $\bar{x}$ falls outside these boundaries, the interval $\bar{x} \pm 1.96\sigma_{\bar{x}}$ will not contain μ. From Section 5.3, we know that the area under the normal curve (the sampling distribution of $\bar{x}$) between these boundaries is exactly .95. Thus, the probability that a randomly selected interval, $\bar{x} \pm 1.96\sigma_{\bar{x}}$, will contain μ is equal to .95.

Example 6.1

Estimating the Mean, σ Known—Delinquent Debtors

Problem Consider the large bank that wants to estimate the average amount of money owed by its delinquent debtors, μ. The bank randomly samples $n = 100$ of its delinquent accounts and finds that the sample mean amount owed is $\bar{x} = \$230$. Also, suppose it is known that the standard deviation of the amount owed for all delinquent accounts is $\sigma = \$90$. Use the interval estimator $\bar{x} \pm 1.96\sigma_{\bar{x}}$ to calculate a confidence interval for the target parameter, μ.

Solution Substituting $\bar{x} = 230$ and $\sigma = 90$ into the interval estimator formula, we obtain:

$$\bar{x} \pm 1.96\sigma_{\bar{x}} = \bar{x} \pm (1.96)\sigma/\sqrt{n} = 230 \pm (1.96)(90/\sqrt{100}) = 230 \pm 17.64$$

Or, (212.36, 247.64). We can also obtain this confidence interval using statistical software, as shown (highlighted) on the Minitab printout, Figure 6.2.

One-Sample Z

The assumed standard deviation = 90

Figure 6.2

Minitab output showing 95% confidence interval for μ, σ known

N	Mean	SE Mean	95% CI
100	230.00	9.00	(212.36, 247.64)

Look Back Because we know the probability that the interval $\bar{x} \pm 1.96\sigma_{\bar{x}}$ will contain μ is .95, we call the interval estimator a *95% confidence interval* for μ.

━ **Now Work Exercise 6.3a**

The interval $\bar{x} \pm 1.96\sigma_{\bar{x}}$ in Example 6.1 is called a *large-sample* 95% confidence interval for the population mean μ. The term *large-sample* refers to the sample being of sufficiently large size that we can apply the Central Limit Theorem and the normal (z) statistic to determine the form of the sampling distribution of $\bar{x}$. Empirical research suggests that a sample size n exceeding a value between 20 and 30 will usually yield a sampling distribution of $\bar{x}$ that is approximately normal. This result led many practitioners to adopt the rule of thumb that a sample size of $n \geq 30$ is required to use large-sample confidence interval procedures. Keep in mind, though, that 30 is not a magical number and, in fact, is quite arbitrary.

Also, *note that the large-sample interval estimator requires knowing the value of the population standard deviation, σ.* In most (if not nearly all) practical business applications, however, the value of σ will be unknown. For large samples, the fact that σ is unknown poses only a minor problem because the sample standard deviation s provides a very good approximation to σ*. The next example illustrates the more realistic large-sample confidence interval procedure.

Example 6.2

Estimating the Mean, σ Unknown—Delinquent Debtors

Problem Refer to Example 6.1 and the problem of estimating μ, the average amount of money owed by a bank's delinquent debtors. The overdue amounts for the $n = 100$ delinquent accounts are shown in Table 6.1. Use the data to find a 95% confidence interval for μ and interpret the result.

Table 6.1 Overdue Amounts (in Dollars) for 100 Delinquent Accounts

195	243	132	133	209	400	142	312	221	289
221	162	134	275	355	293	242	458	378	148
278	222	236	178	202	222	334	208	194	135
363	221	449	265	146	215	113	229	221	243
512	193	134	138	209	207	206	310	293	310
237	135	252	365	371	238	232	271	121	134
203	178	180	148	162	160	86	234	244	266
119	259	108	289	328	331	330	227	162	354
304	141	158	240	82	17	357	187	364	268
368	274	278	190	344	157	219	77	171	280

🔵 *Data Set:* OVRDUE

	A	B
1	*AMOUNT*	
2		
3	Mean	233.28
4	Standard Error	9.033988347
5	Median	222
6	Mode	221
7	Standard Deviation	90.33988347
8	Sample Variance	8161.294545
9	Kurtosis	0.254810234
10	Skewness	0.476799829
11	Range	495
12	Minimum	17
13	Maximum	512
14	Sum	23328
15	Count	100

Figure 6.3a

Excel summary statistics for overdue amounts

Solution The large bank almost surely does not know the true standard deviation, σ, of the population of overdue amounts. However, because the sample size is large, we will use the sample standard deviation, s, as an estimate for σ in the confidence interval formula. An Excel printout of summary statistics for the sample of 100 overdue amounts is shown in Figure 6.3a. From the shaded portion of the printout, we

---

*In the terminology of Chapter 5, it can be shown that s is an *unbiased* estimator of σ.

find $\bar{x} = 233.28$ and $s = 90.34$. Substituting these values into the interval estimator formula, we obtain:

$$\bar{x} \pm (1.96)\sigma/\sqrt{n} \approx \bar{x} \pm (1.96)s/\sqrt{n} = 233.28 \pm (1.96)(90.34)/\sqrt{100} = 233.28 \pm 17.71$$

Or, $(215.57, 250.99)$. That is, we estimate the mean amount of delinquency for all accounts to fall within the interval \$215.57 to \$250.99.

Look Back The confidence interval is also shown (highlighted) at the bottom of the Excel/XLSTAT printout, Figure 6.3b. Note that the endpoints of the interval vary slightly from those computed in the example. This is due to the fact that when σ is unknown and n is large, the sampling distribution of $\bar{x}$ will deviate slightly from the normal (z) distribution. In practice, these differences can be ignored.

Figure 6.3b

XLSTAT output showing 95% confidence interval for μ, σ unknown

Statistic	AMOUNT
No. of observations	100
Minimum	17.0000
Maximum	512.0000
Mean	233.2800
Standard deviation (n-1)	90.3399
Lower bound on mean (95%)	215.3546
Upper bound on mean (95%)	251.2054

■ **Now Work Exercise 6.14**

Can we be sure that μ, the true mean, is in the interval $(215.57, 250.99)$ in Example 6.2? We cannot be certain, but we can be reasonably confident that it is. This confidence is derived from the knowledge that if we were to draw repeated random samples of 100 measurements from this population and form the interval $\bar{x} \pm 1.96\sigma_{\bar{x}}$ each time, 95% of the intervals would contain μ. We have no way of knowing (without looking at all the delinquent accounts) whether our sample interval is one of the 95% that contains μ or one of the 5% that does not, but the odds certainly favor its containing μ. The probability, .95, that measures the confidence we can place in the interval estimate is called a *confidence coefficient*. The percentage, 95%, is called the *confidence level* for the interval estimate.

> The **confidence coefficient** is the probability that a randomly selected confidence interval encloses the population parameter—that is, the relative frequency with which similarly constructed intervals enclose the population parameter when the estimator is used repeatedly a very large number of times. The **confidence level** is the confidence coefficient expressed as a percentage.

Figure 6.4

Confidence intervals for μ: 10 samples

Now we have seen how an interval can be used to estimate a population mean. When we use an interval estimator, we can usually calculate the probability that the estimation *process* will result in an interval that contains the true value of the population mean—that is, the probability that the interval contains the parameter in repeated usage is usually known. Figure 6.4 shows what happens when 10 different samples are drawn from a population, and a confidence interval for μ is calculated from each. The location of μ is indicated by the vertical line in the figure. Ten confidence intervals, each based on one of 10 samples, are shown as horizontal line segments. Note that the confidence intervals move from sample to sample—sometimes containing μ and other times missing μ. *If our confidence level is 95%, then in the long run, 95% of our confidence intervals will contain μ and 5% will not.*

Suppose you wish to choose a confidence coefficient other than .95. Notice in Figure 6.1 that the confidence coefficient .95 is equal to the total area under the sampling distribution, less .05 of the area, which is divided equally between the two tails. Using this idea, we can construct a confidence interval with any desired confidence coefficient by increasing or decreasing the area (call it α) assigned to the tails of the sampling distribution (see Figure 6.5). For example, if we place area $\frac{\alpha}{2}$ in each tail and if $z_{\alpha/2}$ is the z-value such that the area $\frac{\alpha}{2}$ lies to its right, then the confidence interval with confidence coefficient $(1 - \alpha)$ is

$$\bar{x} \pm (z_{\alpha/2})\sigma_{\bar{x}}$$

Figure 6.5

Locating $z_{\alpha/2}$ on the standard normal curve

BIOGRAPHY

JERZEY NEYMAN (1894–1981)

Speaking Statistics with a Polish Accent

Polish-born Jerzey Neyman was educated at the University of Kharkov (Russia) in elementary mathematics but taught himself graduate mathematics by studying journal articles on the subject. After receiving his doctorate in 1924 from the University of Warsaw (Poland), Neyman accepted a position at University College (London). There, he developed a friendship with Egon Pearson; Neyman and Pearson together developed the theory of hypothesis testing (Chapter 7). In 1934, in a talk to the Royal Statistical Society, Neyman first proposed the idea of interval estimation, which he called *confidence intervals*. (It is interesting that Neyman rarely receives credit in textbooks as the originator of the confidence interval procedure.) In 1938, he immigrated to the United States and the University of California at Berkeley. At Berkeley, he built one of the strongest statistics departments in the country. Jerzey Neyman is considered one of the great founders of modern statistics. He was a superb teacher and innovative researcher who loved his students, always sharing his ideas with them. Neyman's influence on those he met is best expressed by a quote from prominent statistician David Salsburg: "We have all learned to speak statistics with a Polish accent."

The value z_α is defined as the value of the standard normal random variable z such that the area α will lie to its right. In other words, $P(z > z_\alpha) = \alpha$.

To illustrate, for a confidence coefficient of .90, we have $(1 - \alpha) = .90$, $\alpha = .10$, and $\frac{\alpha}{2} = .05$; $z_{.05}$ is the z-value that locates area .05 in the upper tail of the sampling distribution. Recall that Table II in Appendix D gives the areas between the mean and a specified z-value. Because the total area to the right of the mean is .5, we find that $z_{.05}$ will be the z-value corresponding to an area of $.5 - .05 = .45$ to the right of the mean (see Figure 6.6). This z-value is $z_{.05} = 1.645$.

Confidence coefficients used in practice usually range from .90 to .99. The most commonly used confidence coefficients with corresponding values of α and $z_{\alpha/2}$ are shown in Table 6.2.

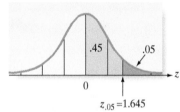

Figure 6.6

The z-value ($z_{.05}$) corresponding to an area equal to .05 in the upper tail of the z-distribution

Large-Sample $100(1 - \alpha)$% Confidence Interval for μ, Based on a Normal (z) Statistic

$$\sigma \text{ known: } \bar{x} \pm (z_{\alpha/2})\sigma_{\bar{x}} = \bar{x} \pm (z_{\alpha/2})(\sigma/\sqrt{n})$$
$$\sigma \text{ unknown: } \bar{x} \pm (z_{\alpha/2})\sigma_{\bar{x}} \approx \bar{x} \pm (z_{\alpha/2})(s/\sqrt{n})$$

where $z_{\alpha/2}$ is the z-value corresponding to an area $\frac{\alpha}{2}$ in the tail of a standard normal distribution (see Figure 6.5), $\sigma_{\bar{x}}$ is the standard deviation of the sampling distribution of $\bar{x}$, σ is the standard deviation of the population, and s is the standard deviation of the sample.

Conditions Required for a Valid Large-Sample Confidence Interval for μ

1. A random sample is selected from the target population.
2. The sample size n is large (i.e., $n \geq 30$). Due to the Central Limit Theorem, this condition guarantees that the sampling distribution of $\bar{x}$ is approximately normal. (Also, for large n, s will be a good estimator of σ.)

Table 6.2	Commonly Used Values of $z_{\alpha/2}$		
Confidence Level			
$100(1 - \alpha)$	α	$\alpha/2$	$z_{\alpha/2}$
90%	.10	.05	1.645
95%	.05	.025	1.960
98%	.02	.01	2.326
99%	.01	.005	2.576

Example 6.3

Large-Sample Confidence Interval for μ—Unoccupied Seats per Flight

Problem Unoccupied seats on flights cause airlines to lose revenue. Suppose a large airline wants to estimate its average number of unoccupied seats per flight over the past year. To accomplish this, the records of 225 flights are randomly selected, and the number of unoccupied seats is noted for each of the sampled flights. (The data are saved in the **NOSHOW** file.) Descriptive statistics for the data are displayed in the Minitab printout, Figure 6.7.

```
Variable    N    Mean   StDev  SE Mean      90% CI
NOSHOWS   225  11.596  4.103   0.274   (11.144, 12.047)
```

Figure 6.7

Minitab confidence interval for mean, Example 6.3

Estimate μ, the mean number of unoccupied seats per flight during the past year, using a 90% confidence interval.

Solution The general form of the 90% confidence interval for a population mean is

$$\bar{x} \pm z_{\alpha/2}\sigma_{\bar{x}} = \bar{x} \pm z_{.05}\sigma_{\bar{x}} = \bar{x} \pm 1.645\left(\frac{\sigma}{\sqrt{n}}\right)$$

From Figure 6.7, we find (after rounding) $\bar{x} = 11.6$. Because we do not know the value of σ (the standard deviation of the number of unoccupied seats per flight for all flights of the year), we use our best approximation—the sample standard deviation s. Then the 90% confidence interval is, approximately,

$$11.6 \pm 1.645\left(\frac{4.1}{\sqrt{225}}\right) = 11.6 \pm .45$$

or from 11.15 to 12.05—that is, at the 90% confidence level, we estimate the mean number of unoccupied seats per flight to be between 11.15 and 12.05 during the sampled year. This result is verified (except for rounding) on the right side of the Minitab printout in Figure 6.7.

Look Back We stress that the confidence level for this example, 90%, refers to the procedure used. If we were to apply this procedure repeatedly to different samples, approximately 90% of the intervals would contain μ. Although we do not know whether this particular interval (11.15, 12.05) is one of the 90% that contain μ or one of the 10% that do not, our knowledge of probability gives us "confidence" that the interval contains μ.

■ **Now Work Exercise 6.12**

The interpretation of confidence intervals for a population mean is summarized in the next box.

> **Interpretation of a Confidence Interval for a Population Mean**
>
> When we form a $100(1 - \alpha)\%$ confidence interval for μ, we usually express our confidence in the interval with a statement such as, "We can be $100(1 - \alpha)\%$ confident that μ lies between the lower and upper bounds of the confidence interval," where for a particular application, we substitute the appropriate numerical values for the confidence and for the lower and upper bounds. *The statement reflects our confidence in the estimation process rather than in the particular interval that is calculated from the sample data.* We know that repeated application of the same procedure will result in different lower and upper bounds on the interval. Furthermore, we know that $100(1 - \alpha)\%$ of the resulting intervals will contain μ. There is (usually) no way to determine whether any particular interval is one of those that contain μ, or one that does not. However, unlike point estimators, confidence intervals have some measure of reliability, the confidence coefficient, associated with them. For that reason they are generally preferred to point estimators.

Sometimes, the estimation procedure yields a confidence interval that is too wide for our purposes. In this case, we will want to reduce the width of the interval to obtain a more precise estimate of μ. One way to accomplish this is to decrease the confidence coefficient, $1 - \alpha$. For example, reconsider the problem of estimating the mean amount owed, μ, for all delinquent accounts. Recall that for a sample of 100 accounts, $\bar{x} = \$233.28$ and $s = \$90.34$. A 90% confidence interval for μ is

$$\bar{x} \pm 1.645\sigma/\sqrt{n} \approx 233.28 \pm (1.645)(90.34/\sqrt{100}) = 233.28 \pm 14.86$$

or ($218.42, $248.14). You can see that this interval is narrower than the previously calculated 95% confidence interval ($215.57, $250.99). Unfortunately, we also have "less confidence" in the 90% confidence interval. An alternative method used to decrease the width of an interval without sacrificing "confidence" is to increase the sample size n. We demonstrate this method in Section 6.5.

Exercises 6.1–6.22

Learning the Mechanics

6.1 Find $z_{\alpha/2}$ for each of the following:
a. $\alpha = .10$
b. $\alpha = .01$
c. $\alpha = .05$
d. $\alpha = .20$

6.2 What is the confidence level of each of the following confidence intervals for μ?

a. $\bar{x} \pm 1.96\left(\dfrac{\sigma}{\sqrt{n}}\right)$

b. $\bar{x} \pm 1.645\left(\dfrac{\sigma}{\sqrt{n}}\right)$

c. $\bar{x} \pm 2.575\left(\dfrac{\sigma}{\sqrt{n}}\right)$

d. $\bar{x} \pm 1.282\left(\dfrac{\sigma}{\sqrt{n}}\right)$

e. $\bar{x} \pm .99\left(\dfrac{\sigma}{\sqrt{n}}\right)$

6.3 A random sample of n measurements was selected from NW a population with unknown mean μ and known standard deviation σ. Calculate a 95% confidence interval for μ for each of the following situations:
a. $n = 75, \bar{x} = 28, \sigma^2 = 12$
b. $n = 200, \bar{x} = 102, \sigma^2 = 22$
c. $n = 100, \bar{x} = 15, \sigma = .3$
d. $n = 100, \bar{x} = 4.05, \sigma = .83$
e. Is the assumption that the underlying population of measurements is normally distributed necessary to ensure the validity of the confidence intervals in parts **a–d**? Explain.

6.4 A random sample of 90 observations produced a mean $\bar{x} = 25.9$ and a standard deviation $s = 2.7$.
a. Find an approximate 95% confidence interval for the population mean μ.
b. Find an approximate 90% confidence interval for μ.
c. Find an approximate 99% confidence interval for μ.

6.5 A random sample of 70 observations from a normally distributed population possesses a sample mean equal to 26.2 and a sample standard deviation equal to 4.1.
a. Find an approximate 95% confidence interval for μ.
b. What do you mean when you say that a confidence coefficient is .95?
c. Find an approximate 99% confidence interval for μ.

d. What happens to the width of a confidence interval as the value of the confidence coefficient is increased while the sample size is held fixed?
e. Would your confidence intervals of parts **a** and **c** be valid if the distribution of the original population was not normal? Explain.

Applet Exercise 6.1

Use the applet *Confidence Intervals for a Mean (the impact of confidence level)* to investigate the situation in Exercise 6.5 further. For this exercise, assume that $\mu = 2.62$ is the population mean and $\sigma = 4.1$ is the population standard deviation.
a. Using $n = 70$ and the normal distribution with the mean and standard deviation above, run the applet one time. How many of the 95% confidence intervals contain the mean? How many would you expect to contain the mean? How many of the 99% confidence intervals contain the mean? How many would you expect to contain the mean?
b. Which confidence level has a greater frequency of intervals that contain the mean? Is this result what you would expect? Explain.
c. Without clearing, run the applet several more times. What happens to the proportion of 95% confidence intervals that contain the mean as you run the applet more and more? What happens to the proportion of 99% confidence intervals that contain the mean as you run the applet more and more? Interpret these results in terms of the meanings of the 95% confidence interval and the 99% confidence interval.
d. Change the distribution to *right skewed*, clear, and run the applet several more times. Do you get the same results as in part **c**? Would you change your answer to part **e** of Exercise 6.5? Explain.

Applet Exercise 6.2

Use the applet *Confidence Intervals for a Mean (the impact of confidence level)* to investigate the effect of the sample size on the proportion of confidence intervals that contain the mean when the underlying distribution is skewed. Set the distribution to *right skewed*, the mean to 10, and the standard deviation to 1.

a. Using $n = 30$, run the applet several times without clearing. What happens to the proportion of 95% confidence intervals that contain the mean as you run the applet more and more? What happens to the proportion of 99% confidence intervals that contain the mean as you run the applet more and more? Do the proportions seem to be approaching the values that you would expect?

b. Clear and run the applet several times using $n = 100$. What happens to the proportions of 95% confidence intervals and 99% confidence intervals that contain the mean this time? How do these results compare to your results in part **a?**

c. Clear and run the applet several times using $n = 1,000$. How do the results compare to your results in parts **a** and **b?**

d. Describe the effect of sample size on the likelihood that a confidence interval contains the mean for a skewed distribution.

6.6 Explain what is meant by the statement, "We are 95% confident that an interval estimate contains μ."

6.7 Explain the difference between an interval estimator and a point estimator for μ.

6.8 The mean and standard deviation of a random sample of n measurements are equal to 33.9 and 3.3, respectively.
a. Find a 95% confidence interval for μ if $n = 100$.
b. Find a 95% confidence interval for μ if $n = 400$.
c. Find the widths of the confidence intervals found in parts **a** and **b**. What is the effect on the width of a confidence interval of quadrupling the sample size while holding the confidence coefficient fixed?

6.9 Will a large-sample confidence interval be valid if the population from which the sample is taken is not normally distributed? Explain.

Applying the Concepts—Basic

6.10 **Bankruptcy effect on U.S. airfares.** Recently, both Delta Airlines and USAir filed for bankruptcy. A study of the impact of bankruptcy on the fares charged by U.S. airlines was published in *Research in Applied Economics* (Vol. 2, 2010). The researchers collected data on Orlando-bound airfares for three airlines in 2005—Southwest (a stable airline), Delta (just entering bankruptcy at the time), and USAir (emerging from bankruptcy). A large sample of nonrefundable ticket prices was obtained for each airline following USAir's emergence from bankruptcy, and then a 95% confidence interval for the true mean airfare was obtained for each. The results for 7-day advanced bookings are shown in the accompanying table.

Airline	95% Confidence Interval
Southwest	($412, $496)
Delta	($468, $500)
USAir	($247, $372)

Source: Based on Sturm, R. R & Winters, D. B. "The Effect of Bankruptcy on U.S. Air Fares," *Research in Applied Economics* Vol. 2, No. 2, © 2010 Macrothink Institute.

a. What confidence coefficient was used to generate the confidence intervals?
b. Give a practical interpretation of each of the 95% confidence intervals. Use the phrase "95% confident" in your answer.

c. When you say you are "95% confident," what do you mean?
d. If you want to reduce the width of each confidence interval, should you use a smaller or larger confidence coefficient? Explain.

6.11 **College dropout study.** Refer to the *American Economic Review* (Dec. 2008) study of college dropouts, Exercise 2.77 (p. 84). Recall that one factor thought to influence the college dropout decision was expected GPA for a student who studied 3 hours per day. In a representative sample of 307 college students who studied 3 hours per day, the mean GPA was $\bar{x} = 3.11$ and the standard deviation was $s = .66$. Of interest is μ, the true mean GPA of all college students who study 3 hours per day.
a. Give a point estimate for μ.
b. Give an interval estimate for μ. Use a confidence coefficient of .98.
c. Comment on the validity of the following statement: "98% of the time, the true mean GPA will fall in the interval computed in part **b**."
d. It is unlikely that the GPA values for college students who study 3 hours per day are normally distributed. In fact, it is likely that the GPA distribution is highly skewed. If so, what impact, if any, does this have on the validity of inferences derived from the confidence interval?

6.12 **Corporate sustainability of CPA firms.** *Corporate sustainability* refers to business practices designed around social and environmental considerations. Refer to the *Business and Society* (March 2011) study on the sustainability behaviors of CPA corporations, Exercise 2.23 (p. 59). Recall that the level of support for corporate sustainability (measured on a quantitative scale ranging from 0 to 160 points) was obtained for each in a sample of 992 senior managers at CPA firms. Higher point values indicate a higher level of support for sustainability. The accompanying Minitab printout gives a 90% confidence interval for the mean level of support for all senior managers at CPA firms.

One-Sample T: Support

```
Variable    N    Mean    StDev   SE Mean      90% CI
Support    992  67.755  26.871    0.853   (66.350, 69.160)
```

a. Locate the 90% confidence interval on the printout.
b. Use the sample mean and standard deviation on the printout to calculate the 90% confidence interval. Does your result agree with the interval shown on the printout?
c. Give a practical interpretation of the 90% confidence interval.
d. Suppose the CEO of a CPA firm claims that the true mean level of support for sustainability is 75 points. Do you believe this claim Explain.

6.13 **Budget lapsing at army hospitals.** Budget lapsing occurs when unspent funds do not carry over from one budgeting period to the next. Refer to the *Journal of Management Accounting Research* (Vol. 19, 2007) study on budget lapsing at U.S. Army hospitals, Exercise 2.111 (p. 99). Because budget lapsing often leads to a spike in expenditures at the end of the fiscal year, the researchers recorded expenses per full-time equivalent employee for each in a sample of 1,751 army hospitals. The sample yielded the following summary statistics: $\bar{x}$ = \$6,563 and s = \$2,484. Estimate the mean expenses per full-time equivalent employee of all U.S. Army hospitals using a 90% confidence interval. Interpret the result.

6.14 **Wear-out of used display panels.** Refer to Exercise 4.126 (p. 241) and the study of the wear-out failure time of used colored display panels purchased by an outlet store. Recall that prior to acquisition, the panels had been used for about one-third of their expected lifetimes. The failure times (in years) for a sample of 50 used panels are reproduced in the table. An SPSS printout of the analysis is shown below.

PANEL
NW

    a. Locate a 95% confidence interval for the true mean failure time of used colored display panels on the printout.

    b. Give a practical interpretation of the interval, part **a.**

    c. In repeated sampling of the population of used colored display panels, where a 95% confidence interval for the mean failure time is computed for each sample, what proportion of all the confidence intervals generated will capture the true mean failure time?

0.01	1.21	1.71	2.30	2.96	0.19	1.22	1.75	2.30	2.98	0.51
1.24	1.77	2.41	3.19	0.57	1.48	1.79	2.44	3.25	0.70	1.54
1.88	2.57	3.31	0.73	1.59	1.90	2.61	1.19	0.75	1.61	1.93
2.62	3.50	0.75	1.61	2.01	2.72	3.50	1.11	1.62	2.16	2.76
3.50	1.16	1.62	2.18	2.84	3.50					

Source: Based on Irony, T. Z., Lauretto, M., Pereira, C., & Stern, J. M. "A Weibull wearout Test: Full Bayesian approach," paper presented at *Mathematical Sciences Colloquium*, Binghamton University, Binghamton, UK, December 2001.

Applying the Concepts—Intermediate

6.15 **Do social robots walk or roll?** Refer to the *International Conference on Social Robotics* (Vol. 6414, 2010) study on the current trend in the design of social robots, Exercise 2.76 (p. 84). Recall that in a random sample of social robots obtained through a Web search, 28 were built with wheels. The number of wheels on each of the 28 robots are reproduced in the next table.

ROBOTS

    a. Estimate μ, the average number of wheels used on all social robots built with wheels, with 99% confidence.

    b. Practically interpret the interval, part **a.**

    c. Refer to part **a.** In repeated sampling, what proportion of all similarly constructed confidence intervals will contain the true mean, μ?

4	4	3	3	3	6	4	2	2	2	1	3	3	3
3	4	4	3	2	8	2	2	3	4	3	3	4	2

Source: Based on Chew, S., et al. "Do social robots walk or roll?," *International Conference on Social Robotics,* Vol. 6414, 2010 (adapted from Figure 2).

6.16 **Shopping on Black Friday.** The day after Thanksgiving—called Black Friday—is one of the largest shopping days in the United States. Winthrop University researchers conducted interviews with a sample of 38 women shopping on Black Friday to gauge their shopping habits and reported the results in the *International Journal of Retail and Distribution Management* (Vol. 39, 2011). One question was "How many hours do you usually spend shopping on Black Friday?" Data for the 38 shoppers are listed in the accompanying table.

BLKFRI

    a. Describe the population of interest to the researchers.

    b. What is the quantitative variable of interest to the researchers?

    c. Use the information in the table to estimate the population mean number of hours spent shopping on Black Friday with a 95% confidence interval.

    d. Give a practical interpretation of the interval.

    e. A retail store advertises that the true mean number of hours spent shopping on Black Friday is 5.5 hours. Can the store be sued for false advertising? Explain.

6	6	4	4	3	16	4	4	5	6	6	5	5	4
6	5	6	4	5	4	4	4	7	12	5	8	6	10
5	8	8	3	3	8	5	6	10	11				

Source: Based on Thomas, J. B., & Peters, C. "An exploratory investigation of Black Friday consumption rituals," *International Journal of Retail and Distribution Management,* Vol. 39, No. 7, 2011 (Table I).

6.17 **Executive Compensation Scoreboard.** Refer to *Forbes'* 2011 "Executive Compensation Scoreboard." Recall that the data file contains the 2011 salaries (in \$ millions) of the 500 CEOs that participated in the *Forbes'* survey. Suppose you are interested in estimating the mean 2011 salary for these 500 CEOs.

CEOPAY

    a. What is the target parameter?

    b. Obtain a random sample of 50 salaries from the data set.

Descriptives

			Statistic	Std. Error
FAILTIME	Mean		1.9350	.13133
	95% Confidence Interval for Mean	Lower Bound	1.6711	
		Upper Bound	2.1989	
	5% Trimmed Mean		1.9454	
	Median		1.8350	
	Variance		.862	
	Std. Deviation		.92865	
	Minimum		.01	
	Maximum		3.50	
	Range		3.49	
	Interquartile Range		1.43	
	Skewness		-.008	.337
	Kurtosis		-.755	.662

SPSS output for Exercise 6.14

c. Find the mean of the 50 salaries, part **b.**

d. Verify that the standard deviation for the population of 500 salaries is $\sigma = \$9.84$ million.

e. Use the information, parts **c** and **d,** to form a 99% confidence interval for the true mean 2011 salary of the 500 CEOs in the *Forbes'* survey.

f. Give a practical interpretation of the interval, part **e.**

g. Find the true mean salary of the 500 CEOs and check to see if this value falls within the 99% confidence interval, part **e.**

6.18 **401(k) Participation rates.** Named for the section of the 1978 Internal Revenue Code that authorized them, 401(k) plans permit employees to shift part of their before-tax salaries into investments such as mutual funds. Employers typically match 50% of the employee's contribution up to about 6% of salary. One company, concerned with what it believed was a low employee participation rate in its 401(k) plan, sampled 30 other companies with similar plans and asked for their 401(k) participation rates. The following rates (in percentages) were obtained.

PR401K

80	76	81	77	82	80	85	60	80	79	82	70
88	85	80	79	83	75	87	78	80	84	72	75
90	84	82	77	75	86						

a. Construct a 90% confidence interval for the mean participation rate for all companies that have 401(k) plans.

b. Interpret the interval in the context of this problem.

c. What assumption is necessary to ensure the validity of this confidence interval?

d. If the company that conducted the sample has a 71% participation rate, can it safely conclude that its rate is below the population mean rate for all companies with 401(k) plans? Explain.

e. If in the data set the 60% had been 80%, how would the center and width of the confidence interval you constructed in part **a** be affected?

6.19 **Accounting and Machiavellianism.** Refer to the *Behavioral Research in Accounting* (Jan. 2008) study of Machiavellian traits in accountants, Exercise 1.31 (p. 27). Recall that *Machiavellian* describes negative character traits that include manipulation, cunning, duplicity, deception, and bad faith. A Machiavellian ("Mach") rating score was determined for each in a sample of accounting alumni of a large southwestern university. Scores range from a low of 40 to a high of 160, with the theoretical neutral Mach rating score of 100. The 122 purchasing managers in the sample had a mean Mach rating score of 99.6, with a standard deviation of 12.6.

a. From the sample, estimate the true mean Mach rating score of all purchasing managers.

b. Form a 95% confidence interval for the estimate, part **b.**

c. Give a practical interpretation of the interval, part **c.**

d. A director of purchasing at a major firm claims that the true mean Mach rating score of all purchasing managers is 85. Is there evidence to dispute this claim?

6.20 **Facial structure of CEOs.** In *Psychological Science* (Vol. 22, 2011), researchers reported that a chief executive officer's facial structure can be used to predict a firm's financial performance. The study involved measuring the facial width-to-height ratio (WHR) for each in a sample of 55 CEOs at publicly traded *Fortune* 500 firms. These WHR values (determined by a computer analyzing a photo of the CEO's face) had a mean of $\bar{x} = 1.96$ and a standard deviation of $s = .15$.

a. Find and interpret a 95% confidence interval for μ, the mean facial WHR for all CEOs at publicly traded *Fortune* 500 firms.

b. The researchers found that CEOs with wider faces (relative to height) tended to be associated with firms that had greater financial performance. They based their inference on an equation that uses facial WHR to predict financial performance. Suppose an analyst wants to predict the financial performance of a *Fortune* 500 firm based on the value of the true mean facial WHR of CEOs. The analyst wants to use the value of $\mu = 2.2$. Do you recommend he use this value?

Applying the Concepts—Advanced

6.21 **Improving SAT scores.** Refer to the *Chance* (Winter 2001) and National Education Longitudinal Survey (NELS) study of 265 students who paid a private tutor to help them improve their SAT scores, Exercise 2.88 (p. 86). The changes in both the SAT–Mathematics and SAT–Verbal scores for these students are reproduced in the table. Suppose the true population mean change in score on one of the SAT tests for all students who paid a private tutor is 15. Which of the two tests, SAT–Mathematics or SAT–Verbal, is most likely to have this mean change? Explain.

	SAT–Math	SAT–Verbal
Mean change in score	19	7
Standard deviation of score changes	65	49

6.22 **The "Raid" test kitchen.** According to scientists, the cockroach has had 300 million years to develop a resistance to destruction. In a study conducted by researchers for S. C. Johnson & Son, Inc. (manufacturers of Raid and Off!), 5,000 roaches (the expected number in a roach-infested house) were released in the Raid test kitchen. One week later, the kitchen was fumigated, and 16,298 dead roaches were counted, a gain of 11,298 roaches for the 1-week period. Assume that none of the original roaches died during the 1-week period and that the standard deviation of x, the number of roaches produced per roach in a 1-week period, is 1.5. Use the number of roaches produced by the sample of 5,000 roaches to find a 95% confidence interval for the mean number of roaches produced per week for each roach in a typical roach-infested house.

Confidence Interval for a Population Mean: Student's *t*-Statistic

Federal legislation requires pharmaceutical companies to perform extensive tests on new drugs before they can be marketed. Initially, a new drug is tested on animals. If the drug is deemed safe after this first phase of testing, the pharmaceutical company is then permitted to begin human testing on a limited basis. During this second phase, inferences must be made about the safety of the drug based on information in very small samples.

Suppose a pharmaceutical company must estimate the average increase in blood pressure of patients who take a certain new drug. Assume that only six patients (randomly selected from the population of all patients) can be used in the initial phase of human testing. The use of a *small sample* in making an inference about μ presents two immediate problems when we attempt to use the standard normal *z* as a test statistic.

BIOGRAPHY

WILLIAM S. GOSSET (1876–1937)
Student's t-Distribution

At the age of 23, William Gosset earned a degree in chemistry and mathematics at prestigious Oxford University. He was immediately hired by the Guinness Brewing Company in Dublin, Ireland, for his expertise in chemistry. However, Gosset's mathematical skills allowed him to solve numerous practical problems associated with brewing beer. For example, Gosset applied the Poisson distribution to model the number of yeast cells per unit volume in the fermentation process. His most important discovery was that of the *t*-distribution in 1908. Because most applied researchers worked with small samples, Gosset was interested in the behavior of the mean in the small sample case. He tediously took numerous small sets of numbers, calculated the mean and standard deviation, obtained their *t*-ratio, and plotted the results on graph paper. The shape of the distribution was always the same—the *t*-distribution. Under company policy, employees were forbidden to publish their research results, so Gosset used the pen name *Student* to publish a paper on the subject. Hence, the distribution has been called Student's *t*-distribution.

Problem 1   The shape of the sampling distribution of the sample mean $\bar{x}$ (and the *z*-statistic) now depends on the shape of the population that is sampled. We can no longer assume that the sampling distribution of $\bar{x}$ is approximately normal because the Central Limit Theorem ensures normality only for samples that are sufficiently large.

Solution to Problem 1   According to Theorem 5.1, the sampling distribution of $\bar{x}$ (and *z*) is exactly normal, even for small samples, if the sampled population is normal. It is approximately normal if the sampled population is approximately normal.

Problem 2   The population standard deviation σ is almost always unknown. Although it is still true that $\sigma_{\bar{x}} = \frac{\sigma}{\sqrt{n}}$, the sample standard deviation *s* may provide a poor approximation for σ when the sample size is small.

Solution to Problem 2   Instead of using the standard normal statistic

$$z = \frac{\bar{x} - \mu}{\sigma_{\bar{x}}} = \frac{\bar{x} - \mu}{\sigma/\sqrt{n}}$$

which requires knowledge of or a good approximation to σ, we define and use the statistic

$$t = \frac{\bar{x} - \mu}{s/\sqrt{n}}$$

in which the sample standard deviation, *s*, replaces the population standard deviation, σ.

If we are sampling from a normal distribution, the **t-statistic** has a sampling distribution very much like that of the **z-statistic:** mound-shaped, symmetric, with mean 0. The primary difference between the sampling distributions of t and z is that the t-statistic is more variable than the z, which follows intuitively when you realize that t contains two random quantities ($\bar{x}$ and s), whereas z contains only one ($\bar{x}$).

The actual amount of variability in the sampling distribution of t depends on the sample size n. A convenient way of expressing this dependence is to say that the t-statistic has $(n-1)$ **degrees of freedom (df).** Recall that the quantity $(n-1)$ is the divisor that appears in the formula for s^2. This number plays a key role in the sampling distribution of s^2 and appears in discussions of other statistics in later chapters. In particular, the smaller the number of degrees of freedom associated with the t-statistic, the more variable will be its sampling distribution.

In Figure 6.8 we show both the sampling distribution of z and the sampling distribution of a t-statistic with 4 and 20 df. Note that the t-distribution is more variable than the z-distribution, and this variability increases as the degrees of freedom decrease. Also, the increased variability of the t-statistic means that the t-value, t_α, that locates an area α in the upper tail of the t-distribution is larger than the corresponding value z_α. For any given value of α, the t-value t_α increases as the df decreases. Values of t that will be used in forming small-sample confidence intervals of μ are given in Table III in Appendix D. A partial reproduction of this table is shown in Table 6.3

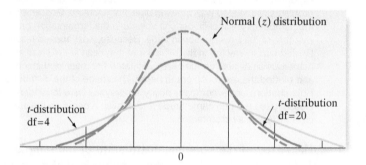

Figure 6.8

Standard normal (z) distribution and t-distributions

| Table 6.3 | Reproduction of Part of Table III in Appendix D |

Degrees of Freedom	$t_{.100}$	$t_{.050}$	$t_{.025}$	$t_{.010}$	$t_{.005}$	$t_{.001}$	$t_{.0005}$
1	3.078	6.314	12.706	31.821	63.657	318.13	636.62
2	1.886	2.920	4.303	6.965	9.925	22.326	21.598
3	1.638	2.353	3.182	4.541	5.841	10.213	12.924
4	1.533	2.132	2.776	3.747	4.604	7.173	8.610
5	1.476	2.015	2.571	3.365	4.032	5.893	6.869
6	1.440	1.943	2.447	3.132	3.707	5.208	5.959
7	1.415	1.895	2.365	2.998	3.499	4.785	5.408
8	1.397	1.860	2.306	2.896	3.355	4.501	5.041
9	1.383	1.833	2.262	2.821	3.250	4.297	4.781
10	1.372	1.812	2.228	2.764	3.169	4.144	4.587
11	1.363	1.796	2.201	2.718	3.106	4.025	4.437
12	1.356	1.782	2.179	2.681	3.055	3.930	4.318
13	1.350	1.771	2.160	2.650	3.012	3.852	4.221
14	1.345	1.761	2.145	2.624	2.977	3.787	4.140
15	1.341	1.753	2.131	2.602	2.947	3.733	4.073
⋮	⋮	⋮	⋮	⋮	⋮	⋮	⋮
∞	1.282	1.645	1.960	2.326	2.576	3.090	3.291

Note that t_α values are listed for various degrees of freedom, where α refers to the tail area under the *t*-distribution to the right of t_α. For example, if we want the *t*-value with an area of .025 to its right and 4 df, we look in the table under the column $t_{.025}$ for the entry in the row corresponding to 4 df. This entry, $t_{.025} = 2.776$, is highlighted in Figure 6.8. Recall that the corresponding standard normal *z*-score is $z_{.025} = 1.96$.

The last row of Table III, where df = ∞ (infinity), contains the standard normal *z*-values. This follows from the fact that as the sample size *n* grows very large, *s* becomes closer to σ and thus *t* becomes closer in distribution to *z*. In fact, when df = 29, there is little difference between corresponding tabulated values of *z* and *t*. Thus, researchers often choose the arbitrary cutoff of *n* = 30 (df = 29) to distinguish between the large-sample and small-sample inferential techniques when σ is unknown.

Example 6.4

A Confidence Interval for μ Using the *t*-statistic — Blood Pressure Drug

Table 6.4

Blood Pressure Increases for *n* = 6 Patients

1.7	3.0	.8	3.4	2.7	2.1

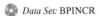 *Data Set:* BPINCR

Problem Consider the pharmaceutical company that desires an estimate of the mean increase in blood pressure of patients who take a new drug. The blood pressure increases (points) for the *n* = 6 patients in the human testing phase are shown in Table 6.4. Use this information to construct a 95% confidence interval for μ, the mean increase in blood pressure associated with the new drug for all patients in the population.

Solution First, note that we are dealing with a sample too small to assume that the sample mean $\bar{x}$ is approximately normally distributed by the Central Limit Theorem — that is, we do not get the normal distribution of $\bar{x}$ "automatically" from the Central Limit Theorem when the sample size is small. Instead, the measured variable, in this case the increase in blood pressure, must be normally distributed in order for the distribution of $\bar{x}$ to be normal.

Second, unless we are fortunate enough to know the population standard deviation σ, which in this case represents the standard deviation of *all* the patients' increases in blood pressure when they take the new drug, we cannot use the standard normal *z*-statistic to form our confidence interval for μ. Instead, we must use the *t*-distribution, with $(n-1)$ degrees of freedom.

In this case, $n - 1 = 5$ df, and the *t*-value is found in Table 6.3 to be $t_{.025} = 2.571$ with 5 df. Recall that the large-sample confidence interval would have been of the form

$$\bar{x} \pm z_{\alpha/2}\sigma_{\bar{x}} = \bar{x} \pm z_{\alpha/2}\frac{\sigma}{\sqrt{n}} = \bar{x} \pm z_{.025}\frac{\sigma}{\sqrt{n}}$$

where 95% is the desired confidence level. To form the interval for a small sample from *a normal distribution, we simply substitute t for z and s for σ in the preceding formula:*

$$\bar{x} \pm t_{\alpha/2}\frac{s}{\sqrt{n}}$$

An SPSS printout showing descriptive statistics for the six blood pressure increases is displayed in Figure 6.9. Note that $\bar{x} = 2.283$ and $s = .950$. Substituting these numerical values into the confidence interval formula, we get

$$2.283 \pm (2.571)\left(\frac{.950}{\sqrt{6}}\right) = 2.283 \pm .997$$

or 1.286 to 3.280 points. Note that this interval agrees (except for rounding) with the confidence interval generated by SPSS in Figure 6.9.

We interpret the interval as follows: We can be 95% confident that the mean increase in blood pressure associated with taking this new drug is between 1.286 and 3.28 points. As with our large-sample interval estimates, our confidence is in the process, not in

Descriptives

			Statistic	Std. Error
BPINCR	Mean		2.283	.3877
	95% Confidence Interval for Mean	Lower Bound	1.287	
		Upper Bound	3.280	
	5% Trimmed Mean		2.304	
	Median		2.400	
	Variance		.902	
	Std. Deviation		.9496	
	Minimum		.8	
	Maximum		3.4	
	Range		2.6	
	Interquartile Range		1.625	
	Skewness		−.573	.845
	Kurtosis		−.389	1.741

Figure 6.9

SPSS confidence interval for mean blood pressure increase

this particular interval. We know that if we were to repeatedly use this estimation procedure, 95% of the confidence intervals produced would contain the true mean μ, *assuming that the probability distribution of changes in blood pressure from which our sample was selected is normal.* The latter assumption is necessary for the small-sample interval to be valid.

Look Back What price did we pay for having to use a small sample to make the inference? First, we had to assume the underlying population was normally distributed, and if the assumption was invalid, our interval might also have been invalid.* Second, we had to form the interval using a t-value of 2.571 rather than a z-value of 1.96, resulting in a wider interval to achieve the same 95% level of confidence. If the interval from 1.286 to 3.28 is too wide to be of use, then we know how to remedy the situation: increase the number of patients sampled to decrease the interval width (on average).

◼ **Now Work Exercise 6.24**

The procedure for forming a small-sample confidence interval is summarized in the accompanying boxes.

Small-Sample Confidence Interval for μ, Student's t-statistic

$$\sigma \text{ unknown: } \bar{x} \pm t_{\alpha/2}\left(\frac{s}{\sqrt{n}}\right)$$

where $t_{\alpha/2}$ is the t-value corresponding to an area $\frac{\alpha}{2}$ in the upper tail of the student's t-distribution based on $(n - 1)$ degrees of freedom.

$$\sigma \text{ known: } \bar{x} \pm z_{\alpha/2}\left(\frac{\sigma}{\sqrt{n}}\right)$$

Conditions Required for a Valid Small-Sample Confidence Interval for μ

1. A random sample is selected from the target population.
2. The population has a relative frequency distribution that is approximately normal.

---

*By *invalid*, we mean that the probability that the procedure will yield an interval that contains μ is not equal to $(1 - \alpha)$. Generally, if the underlying population is approximately normal, then the confidence coefficient will approximate the probability that a randomly selected interval contains μ.

Example 6.5

A Small-Sample Confidence Interval for μ—Destructive Sampling

Table 6.5

Number of Characters (in Millions) for $n = 15$ Printhead Tests

1.13	1.55	1.43	.92	1.25
1.36	1.32	.85	1.07	1.48
1.20	1.33	1.18	1.22	1.29

Data Set: PRHEAD

Problem Some quality-control experiments require *destructive sampling* (i.e., the test to determine whether the item is defective destroys the item) in order to measure some particular characteristic of the product. The cost of destructive sampling often dictates small samples. For example, suppose a manufacturer of printers for personal computers wishes to estimate the mean number of characters printed before the printhead fails. Suppose the printer manufacturer tests $n = 15$ randomly selected printheads and records the number of characters printed until failure for each. These 15 measurements (in millions of characters) are listed in Table 6.5, followed by an XLSTAT summary statistics printout in Figure 6.10.

a. Form a 99% confidence interval for the mean number of characters printed before the printhead fails. Interpret the result.

b. What assumption is required for the interval, part **a**, to be valid? Is it reasonably satisfied?

Solution

a. For this small sample ($n = 15$), we use the *t*-statistic to form the confidence interval. We use a confidence coefficient of .99 and $n - 1 = 14$ degrees of freedom to find $t_{\alpha/2}$ in Table III:

$$t_{\alpha/2} = t_{.005} = 2.977$$

[*Note:* The small sample forces us to extend the interval almost 3 standard deviations (of $\bar{x}$) on each side of the sample mean in order to form the 99% confidence interval.] From the XLSTAT printout, Figure 6.10, we find $\bar{x} = 1.239$ and $s = .193$. Substituting these values into the confidence interval formula, we obtain

Statistic	NUMBER
No. of observations	15
Minimum	0.8500
Maximum	1.5500
Mean	1.2387
Standard deviation (n-1)	0.1932
Lower bound on mean (99%)	1.0902
Upper bound on mean (99%)	1.3871

Figure 6.10

XLSTAT output showing summary statistics and 95% confidence interval for μ, Example 6.5

$$\bar{x} \pm t_{.005}\left(\frac{s}{\sqrt{n}}\right) = 1.239 \pm 2.977\left(\frac{.193}{\sqrt{15}}\right)$$

$$= 1.239 \pm .148 \text{ or } (1.091, 1.387)$$

This interval is shown (shaded) at the bottom of the printout, Figure 6.10.

Our interpretation is as follows: The manufacturer can be 99% confident that the printhead has a mean life of between 1.091 and 1.387 million characters. If the manufacturer were to advertise that the mean life of its printheads is (at least) 1 million characters, the interval would support such a claim. Our confidence is derived from the fact that 99% of the intervals formed in repeated applications of this procedure would contain μ.

b. Because n is small, we must assume that the number of characters printed before printhead failure is a random variable from a normal distribution—that is, we assume that the population from which the sample of 15 measurements is selected is distributed normally. One way to check this assumption is to graph the distribution of data in Table 6.5. If the sample data are approximately normal, then the population from which the sample is selected is very likely to be normal. A Minitab stem-and-leaf plot for the sample data is displayed in Figure 6.11. The distribution is mound-shaped and nearly symmetric. Therefore, the assumption of normality appears to be reasonably satisfied.

Stem-and-Leaf Display: NUMBER

```
Stem-and-leaf of NUMBER   N  = 15
Leaf Unit = 0.010

   1    8    5
   2    9    2
   3   10    7
   5   11    38
  (4)   12    0259
   6   13    236
   3   14    38
   1   15    5
```

Figure 6.11

Minitab stem-and-leaf display of data in Table 6.5

Look Back Other checks for normality, such as a normal probability plot and the ratio IQR/S, may also be used to verify the normality condition.

◼ **Now Work Exercise 6.35**

We have emphasized throughout this section that an assumption that the population is approximately normally distributed is necessary for making small-sample inferences about μ when σ is unknown and when using the t-statistic. Although many phenomena do have approximately normal distributions, it is also true that many random phenomena have distributions that are not normal or even mound-shaped. Empirical evidence acquired over the years has shown that confidence intervals based on the t-distribution are rather insensitive to moderate departures from normality—that is, use of the t-statistic when sampling from slightly or moderately skewed mound-shaped populations generally produces credible results; however, for cases in which the distribution is distinctly nonnormal, we must either take a large sample or use a *nonparametric method* (the topic of Chapter 15).

What Do You Do When the Population Relative Frequency Distribution Departs Greatly from Normality?

Answer: Use the nonparametric statistical methods of Chapter 15 (available on the text resource CD).

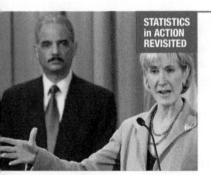

STATISTICS
in ACTION
REVISITED

Estimating the Mean Overpayment

Refer to the Medicare fraud investigation described in the Statistics in Action (pp. 299–300). Recall that the United States Department of Justice (USDOJ) obtained a random sample of 52 claims from a population of 1,000 Medicare claims. For each claim, the amount paid, the amount disallowed (denied) by the auditor, and the amount that should have been paid (allowed) were recorded and saved in the **MFRAUD** file. The USDOJ wants to use these data to calculate an estimate of the overpayment for all 1,000 claims in the population.

One way to do this is to first use the sample data to estimate the mean overpayment per claim for the population, then use the estimated mean to extrapolate the overpayment amount to the population of all 1,000 claims. The difference between the amount paid and the amount allowed by the auditor represents the overpayment for each claim. This value is recorded as the amount denied in the **MFRAUD** file. These overpayment amounts in dollars are listed in the accompanying table.

Minitab software is used to find a 95% confidence interval for μ, the mean overpayment amount. The Minitab printout is displayed in Figure SIA6.1. The 95% confidence interval for μ (highlighted on the printout) is (16.51, 27.13). Thus, the USDOJ can be 95% confident that the mean overpayment amount for the population of 1,000 claims is between $16.51 and $27.13.

Table SIA6.1	Overpayment Amounts (Dollars) for Sample of 52 Claims						
0.00	31.00	0.00	37.20	37.20	0.00	43.40	0.00
37.20	43.40	0.00	37.20	0.00	24.80	0.00	0.00
37.20	0.00	37.20	0.00	37.20	37.20	37.20	0.00
37.20	37.20	0.00	0.00	37.20	0.00	43.40	37.20
0.00	37.20	0.00	37.20	37.20	0.00	37.20	37.20
0.00	37.20	43.40	0.00	37.20	37.20	37.20	0.00
43.40	0.00	43.40	0.00				

Data Set: MFRAUD

Variable	N	Mean	StDev	SE Mean	95% CI
Denied_Amount	52	21.82	19.08	2.65	(16.51, 27.13)

Figure SIA6.1

Minitab confidence interval for mean overpayment

Now, let x_i represent the overpayment amount for the ith claim. If the true mean μ were known, then the total overpayment amount for all 1,000 claims would be equal to

$$\sum_{i=1}^{1,000} x_i = (1,000)\left[\sum_{i=1}^{1,000} x_i\right]/(1,000) = (1,000)\mu$$

Consequently, to estimate the total overpayment amount for the 1,000 claims, the USDOJ will simply multiply the endpoints of the interval by 1,000. This yields the 95% confidence interval ($16,510, $27,130).* Typically, the USDOJ is willing to give the Medicare provider in question the benefit of the doubt by demanding a repayment equal to the lower 95% confidence bound—in this case, $16,510.

Exercises 6.23–6.39

Learning the Mechanics

6.23 Suppose you have selected a random sample of $n = 5$ measurements from a normal distribution. Compare the standard normal *z*-values with the corresponding *t*-values if you were forming the following confidence intervals.
   a. 80% confidence interval
   b. 90% confidence interval
   c. 95% confidence interval
   d. 98% confidence interval
   e. 99% confidence interval
   f. Use the table values you obtained in parts **a–e** to sketch the *z*-and *t*-distributions. What are the similarities and differences?

● Applet Exercise 6.3

Use the applet *Confidence Intervals for a Mean (the impact of not knowing the standard deviation)* to compare proportions of *z*-intervals and *t*-intervals that contain the mean for a population that is normally distributed.
   a. Using $n = 5$ and the normal distribution with mean 50 and standard deviation 10, run the applet several times. How do the proportions of *z*-intervals and *t*-intervals that contain the mean compare?
   b. Repeat part **a** first for $n = 10$ and then for $n = 20$. Compare your results to part **a**.
   c. Describe any patterns you observe between the proportion of *z*-intervals that contain the mean and the proportion of *t*-intervals that contain the mean as the sample size increases.

● Applet Exercise 6.4

Use the applet *Confidence Intervals for a Mean (the impact of not knowing the standard deviation)* to compare proportions of *z*-intervals and *t*-intervals that contain the mean for a population with a skewed distribution.
   a. Using $n = 5$ and the right skewed distribution with mean 50 and standard deviation 10, run the applet several times. How do the proportions of *z*-intervals and *t*-intervals that contain the mean compare?
   b. Repeat part **a** first for $n = 10$ and then for $n = 20$. Compare your results to part **a**.

   c. Describe any patterns you observe between the proportion of *z*-intervals that contain the mean and the proportion of *t*-intervals that contain the mean as the sample size increases.
   d. How does skewedness of the underlying distribution affect the proportions of *z*-intervals and *t*-intervals that contain the mean?

6.24 Explain the differences in the sampling distributions of $\bar{x}$ for large and small samples under the following assumptions.
   a. The variable of interest, x, is normally distributed.
   b. Nothing is known about the distribution of the variable x.

6.25 Let t_0 be a particular value of t. Use Table III in Appendix D to find t_0 values such that the following statements are true.
   a. $P(-t_0 < t < t_0) = .95$ where df $= 10$
   b. $P(t \le -t_0 \text{ or } t \ge t_0)$ where df $= 10$
   c. $P(t \le t_0) = .05$ where df $= 10$
   d. $P(t \le -t_0 \text{ or } t \ge t_0) = .10$ where df $= 20$
   e. $P(t \le -t_0 \text{ or } t \ge t_0) = .01$ where df $= 5$

6.26 *Let t_0 be a specific value of t. Use Table III in Appendix D to find t_0 values such that the following statements are true.*
   a. $P(t \ge t_0) = .025$ where df $= 11$
   b. $P(t \ge t_0) = .01$ where df $= 9$
   c. $P(t \le t_0) = .005$ where df $= 6$
   d. $P(t \le t_0) = .05$ where df $= 18$

6.27 The following random sample was selected from a normal distribution: 4, 6, 3, 5, 9, 3.
   a. Construct a 90% confidence interval for the population mean μ.
   b. Construct a 95% confidence interval for the population mean μ.
   c. Construct a 99% confidence interval for the population mean μ.
   d. Assume that the sample mean $\bar{x}$ and sample standard deviation s remain exactly the same as those you just calculated but are based on a sample of $n = 25$ observations rather than $n = 6$ observations. Repeat parts **a–c**. What is the effect of increasing the sample size on the width of the confidence intervals?

*This interval represents an approximation to the true 95% confidence interval for the total amount of overpayment. The precise interval involves use of a continuity correction for population size (see Section 6.6).

6.28 The following sample of 16 measurements was selected from a population that is approximately normally distributed:

LO6028

91	80	99	110	95	106	78	121	106	100	97	82
100	83	115	104								

a. Construct an 80% confidence interval for the population mean.

b. Construct a 95% confidence interval for the population mean and compare the width of this interval with that of part a.

c. Carefully interpret each of the confidence intervals and explain why the 80% confidence interval is narrower.

Applying the Concepts—Basic

6.29 **Lobster trap placement.** Strategic placement of lobster traps is one of the keys for a successful lobster fisherman. An observational study of teams fishing for the red spiny lobster in Baja California Sur, Mexico, was conducted and the results published in *Bulletin of Marine Science* (April 2010). One of the variables of interest was the average distance separating traps—called *trap spacing*—deployed by the same team of fishermen. Trap-spacing measurements (in meters) for a sample of seven teams of red spiny lobster fishermen are shown in the accompanying table. Of interest is the mean trap spacing for the population of red spiny lobster fishermen fishing in Baja California Sur, Mexico.

TRAPS

93	99	105	94	82	70	86

Source: Based on Shester, G. G. "Explaining catch variation among Baja California lobster fishers through spatial analysis of trap-placement decisions," *Bulletin of Marine Science,* Vol. 86, No. 2, April 2010 (Table 1), pp. 479–498.

a. Identify the target parameter for this study.

b. Compute a point estimate of the target parameter.

c. What is the problem with using the normal (z) statistic to find a confidence interval for the target parameter?

d. Find a 95% confidence interval for the target parameter.

e. Give a practical interpretation of the interval, part d.

f. What conditions must be satisfied for the interval, part d, to be valid?

6.30 **Radon exposure in Egyptian tombs.** Many ancient Egyptian tombs were cut from limestone rock that contained uranium. Since most tombs are not well ventilated, guards, tour guides, and visitors may be exposed to deadly radon gas. In *Radiation Protection Dosimetry* (December 2010), a study of radon exposure in tombs in the Valley of Kings, Luxor, Egypt (recently opened for public tours), was conducted. The radon levels—measured in becquerels per cubic meter (Bq/m^3)—in the inner chambers of a sample of 12 tombs were determined. Summary statistics follow: $\bar{x} = 3,643$ Bq/m^3 and $s = 4,487$ Bq/m^3. Use this information to estimate, with 95% confidence, the true mean level of radon exposure in tombs in the Valley of Kings. Interpret the resulting interval.

TOMBS

6.31 **Assessing the bending strength of a wooden roof.** The white wood material used for the roof of an ancient Japanese temple is imported from Northern Europe. The wooden roof must withstand as much as 100 centimeters of snow in the winter. Architects at Tohoku University (Japan) conducted a study to estimate the mean bending strength of the white wood roof (*Journal of the International Association for Shell and Spatial Structures,* Aug. 2004). A sample of 25 pieces of the imported wood was tested and yielded the following statistics on breaking strength (MPa): $\bar{x} = 75.4$, $s = 10.9$. Estimate the true mean breaking strength of the white wood with a 90% confidence interval. Interpret the result.

6.32 **Hospital length of stay.** Health insurers and the federal government are both putting pressure on hospitals to shorten the average length of stay (LOS) of their patients. The average LOS for men in the United States is 5.4 days, and the average for women is 4.6 days (*Statistical Abstract of the United States: 2012*). A random sample of 20 hospitals in one state had a mean LOS for women of 3.8 days and a standard deviation of 1.2 days.

a. Use a 90% confidence interval to estimate the population mean LOS for women for the state's hospitals.

b. Interpret the interval in terms of this application.

c. What is meant by the phrase "90% confidence interval"?

6.33 **Surface roughness of pipe.** Refer to the *Anti-corrosion Methods and Materials* (Vol. 50, 2003) study of the surface roughness of coated interior pipe used in oil fields, Exercise 2.44 (p. 70). The data (in micrometers) for 20 sampled pipe sections are reproduced in the accompanying table; a Minitab analysis of the data appears below.

RPIPE

1.72	2.50	2.16	2.13	1.06	2.24	2.31	2.03	1.09	1.40
2.57	2.64	1.26	2.05	1.19	2.13	1.27	1.51	2.41	1.95

Source: Data from Farshad, F., & Pesacreta, T. "Coated pipe interior surface roughness as measured by three scanning probe instruments," *Anti-corrosion Methods and Materials,* Vol. 50, No. 1, 2003 (Table III).

a. Locate a 95% confidence interval for the mean surface roughness of coated interior pipe on the accompanying Minitab printout.

b. Would you expect the average surface roughness to be as high as 2.5 micrometers? Explain.

One-Sample T: ROUGH

```
Variable   N    Mean    StDev   SE Mean       95% CI
ROUGH     20  1.88100  0.52391  0.11715  (1.63580, 2.12620)
```

Applying the Concepts—Intermediate

6.34 **Performance of stock screeners.** In Exercise 2.42 (p. 70) you learned that stock screeners are automated tools used by investment companies to help clients select a portfolio of stocks to invest in. The table below lists the annualized percentage return on investment (as compared to the Standard & Poor's 500 Index) for 13 randomly selected stock screeners provided by the American Association of Individual Investors (AAII).

SCREEN

9.0	−.1	−1.6	14.6	16.0	7.7	19.9	9.8	3.2	24.8	17.6	10.7	9.1

a. Find a 90% confidence interval for the average annualized percentage return on investment of all stock screeners provided by AAII. Interpret the result.

b. Recall that a negative annualized return reflects a stock portfolio that performed worse than the S&P 500. On average, do the AAII stock screeners perform worse or better than the S&P 500? Explain.

c. What assumption about the distribution of the annualized percentage returns on investment is required for the inference, part **b,** to be valid? Is this assumption reasonably satisfied?

6.35 **Minimizing tractor skidding distance.** When planning for a new forest road to be used for tree harvesting, planners must select the location to minimize tractor skidding distance. In the *Journal of Forest Engineering* (July 1999), researchers wanted to estimate the true mean skidding distance along a new road in a European forest. The skidding distances (in meters) were measured at 20 randomly selected road sites. These values are given in the accompanying table.

SKID
NW

a. Estimate the true mean skidding distance for the road with a 95% confidence interval.
b. Give a practical interpretation of the interval, part **a.**
c. What conditions are required for the inference, part **b,** to be valid? Are these conditions reasonably satisfied?
d. A logger working on the road claims the mean skidding distance is at least 425 meters. Do you agree?

488	350	457	199	285	409	435	574	439	546
385	295	184	261	273	400	311	312	141	425

Source: Based on Tujek, J., & Pacola, E. "Algorithms for skidding distance modeling on a raster digital terrain model" *Journal of Forest Engineering,* Vol. 10, No. 1, July 1999 (Table 1).

6.36 **Contamination of New Jersey wells.** Methyl *t*-butyl ether (MTBE) is an organic water contaminant that often results from gasoline spills. The level of MTBE (in parts per billion) was measured for a sample of 12 well sites located near a gasoline service station in New Jersey (*Environmental Science & Technology,* Jan. 2005). The data are listed in the accompanying table.

NJGAS

150	367	38	12	11	134
12	251	63	8	13	107

Source: Based on Kuder, T., et al. "Enrichment of stable carbon and hydrogen isotopes during anaerobic biodegradation of MTBE: Microcosm and field evidence," *Environmental Science & Technology,* Vol. 39, No. 1, Jan. 2005, pp. 213–220 (Table 1).

a. Give a point estimate for μ, the true mean MTBE level for all well sites located near the New Jersey gasoline service station.
b. Calculate and interpret a 99% confidence interval for μ.
c. What assumptions are required for the interval, part **b,** to be valid? Are these assumptions reasonably satisfied?

6.37 **Crude oil biodegradation.** Refer to the *Journal of Petroleum Geology* (April 2010) study of the environmental factors associated with biodegradation in crude oil reservoirs, Exercise 2.29 (p. 61). One indicator of biodegradation is the level of dioxide in the water. Recall that 16 water specimens were randomly selected from various locations in a reservoir on the floor of a mine and the amount of dioxide (milligrams/liter) as well as presence of oil were determined for each specimen. These data are reproduced in the next table.

BIODEG

a. Estimate the true mean amount of dioxide present in water specimens that contain oil using a 95% confidence interval. Give a practical interpretation of the interval.
b. Repeat part **a** for water specimens that do not contain oil.
c. Based on the results, parts **a** and **b,** make an inference about biodegradation at the mine reservoir.

Dioxide Amount	Crude Oil Present
3.3	No
0.5	Yes
1.3	Yes
0.4	Yes
0.1	No
4.0	No
0.3	No
0.2	Yes
2.4	No
2.4	No
1.4	No
0.5	Yes
0.2	Yes
4.0	No
4.0	No
4.0	No

Source: Based on Permanyer, A., et al. "Crude oil biodegradation and environmental factors at the Riutort oil shale mine, SE Pyrenees," *Journal of Petroleum Geology,* Vol. 33, No. 2, April 2010 (Table 1).

6.38 **Overbooking policies for major airlines.** Airlines overbook flights in order to reduce the odds of flying with unused seats. An article in *Transportation Research* (Vol. 38, 2002) investigated the optimal overbooking policies for major airlines. One of the variables measured for each airline was the compensation (in dollars) per bumped passenger required to maximize future revenue. Consider the *threshold* levels of compensation for a random sample of 10 major airlines shown in the table. Estimate the true mean threshold compensation level for all major worldwide airlines using a 90% confidence interval. Interpret the result practically.

OVERBK

825	850	1,210	1,370	1,415
1,500	1,560	1,625	2,155	2,220

Source: Data from Suzuki, Y. "An empirical analysis of the optimal overbooking policies for US major airlines." *Transportation Research, Part E,* Vol. 38, 2002, pp. 135–149 (Table 4).

6.39 **Largest private companies.** IPOs—initial public offerings of stock—create billions of dollars of new wealth for owners, managers, and employees of companies that were previously privately owned. Nevertheless, hundreds of large and thousands of small companies remain privately owned. The revenues of a random sample of 15 firms from *Forbes* 212 Largest Private Companies list is given in the table below.

PRIVCO

Company	Revenue (in billions)
Enterprise Rent-A-Car	$14.10
Pilot Flying J	17.77
Tenaska Energy	9.95
Wawa	6.99
Gulf States Toyota	5.10
Brookshire Grocery	2.30
BrightStar	4.61
Bose	2.28
Mary Kay	2.50
Drummoend	3.03
Petco	2.80
SAS	2.43
Forever 21	2.60
Burger King	2.33
Conair	2.01

Source: Data from "America's Largest Private Companies," *Forbes,* Nov. 16, 2011.

a. Describe the population from which the random sample was drawn.

b. Use a 98% confidence interval to estimate the mean revenue of the population of companies in question.

c. Interpret your confidence interval in the context of the problem.

d. What characteristic must the population possess to ensure the appropriateness of the estimation procedure used in part **b?**

e. Suppose *Forbes* reports that the true mean revenue of the 212 companies on the list is $5.0 billion. Is the claim believable?

6.4 Large-Sample Confidence Interval for a Population Proportion

The number of public opinion polls has grown at an astounding rate in recent years. Almost daily, the news media report the results of some poll. Pollsters regularly determine the percentage of people who approve of the president's on-the-job performance, the fraction of voters in favor of a certain candidate, the fraction of customers who prefer a particular product, and the proportion of households that watch a particular TV program. In each case, we are interested in estimating the percentage (or proportion) of some group with a certain characteristic. In this section, we consider methods for making inferences about population proportions when the sample is large.

Example 6.6

Estimating a Population Proportion—Preference for Breakfast Cereal

Problem A food-products company conducted a market study by randomly sampling and interviewing 1,000 consumers to determine which brand of breakfast cereal they prefer. Suppose 313 consumers were found to prefer the company's brand. How would you estimate the true fraction of *all* consumers who prefer the company's cereal brand?

Solution In this study, consumers are asked which brand of breakfast cereal they prefer. Note that "brand" is a qualitative variable and that what we are asking is how you would estimate the probability p of success in a binomial experiment, where p is the probability that a chosen consumer prefers the company's brand. One logical method of estimating p for the population is to use the proportion of successes in the sample—that is, we can estimate p by calculating

$$\hat{p} = \frac{\text{Number of consumers sampled who prefer the company's brand}}{\text{Number of consumers sampled}}$$

where $\hat{p}$ is read "*p* hat." Thus, in this case,

$$\hat{p} = \frac{313}{1{,}000} = .313$$

Look Back To determine the reliability of the estimator $\hat{p}$, we need to know its sampling distribution—that is, if we were to draw samples of 1,000 consumers over and over again, each time calculating a new estimate $\hat{p}$, what would be the frequency distribution of all the $\hat{p}$ values? Recall (Section 5.4) that the answer lies in viewing $\hat{p}$ as the average, or mean, number of successes per trial over the n trials. If each success is assigned a value equal to 1 and a failure is assigned a value of 0, then the sum of all n sample observations is x, the total number of successes, and $\hat{p} = x/n$ is the average, or mean, number of successes per trial in the n trials. The Central Limit Theorem tells us that the *relative frequency distribution of the sample mean for any population is approximately normal for sufficiently large samples.*

■ **Now Work Exercise 6.49a**

The repeated sampling distribution of $\hat{p}$ was the topic of Section 5.4. The characteristics are repeated in the next box and shown in Figure 6.12.

Figure 6.12

Sampling distribution of $\hat{p}$

Properties of the Sampling Distribution of $\hat{p}$

1. The mean of the sampling distribution of $\hat{p}$ is p; that is, $\hat{p}$ is an unbiased estimator of p.
2. The standard deviation of the sampling distribution of $\hat{p}$ is $\sqrt{pq/n}$; that is, $\sigma_{\hat{p}} = \sqrt{pq/n}$, where $q = 1 - p$.
3. For large samples, the sampling distribution of $\hat{p}$ is approximately normal. A sample size is considered large if both $n\hat{p} \geq 15$ and $n\hat{q} \geq 15$.

The fact that $\hat{p}$ is a "sample mean number of successes per trial" allows us to form confidence intervals about p in a manner that is completely analogous to that used for large-sample estimation of μ.

Large-Sample Confidence Interval for $\hat{p}$

$$\hat{p} \pm z_{\alpha/2}\sigma_{\hat{p}} = \hat{p} \pm z_{\alpha/2}\sqrt{\frac{pq}{n}} \approx \hat{p} \pm z_{\alpha/2}\sqrt{\frac{\hat{p}\hat{q}}{n}}$$

where $\hat{p} = \dfrac{x}{n}$ and $\hat{q} = 1 - \hat{p}$

Note: When n is large, $\hat{p}$ can approximate the value of p in the formula for $\sigma_{\hat{p}}$.

Conditions Required for a Valid Large-Sample Confidence Interval for p

1. A random sample is selected from the target population.
2. The sample size n is large. (This condition will be satisfied if both $n\hat{p} \geq 15$ and $n\hat{q} \geq 15$. Note that $n\hat{p}$ and $n\hat{q}$ are simply the number of successes and number of failures, respectively, in the sample.)

Thus, if 313 of 1,000 consumers prefer the company's cereal brand, a 95% confidence interval for the proportion of *all* consumers who prefer the company's brand is

$$\hat{p} \pm z_{\alpha/2}\sigma_{\hat{p}} = .313 \pm 1.96\sqrt{\frac{pq}{1,000}}$$

Table 6.6

Values of pq for Several Different Values of p

p	pq	$\sqrt{pq}$
.5	.25	.50
.6 or .4	.24	.49
.7 or .3	.21	.46
.8 or .2	.16	.40
.9 or .1	.09	.30

where $q = 1 - p$. Just as we needed an approximation for σ in calculating a large-sample confidence interval for μ, we now need an approximation for p. As Table 6.6 shows, the approximation for p does not have to be especially accurate because the value of $\sqrt{pq}$ needed for the confidence interval is relatively insensitive to changes in p. Therefore, we can use $\hat{p}$ to approximate p. Keeping in mind that $\hat{q} = 1 - \hat{p}$, we substitute these values into the formula for the confidence interval:

$$\hat{p} \pm 1.96\sqrt{\frac{pq}{1,000}} \approx \hat{p} \pm 1.96\sqrt{\frac{\hat{p}\hat{q}}{1,000}}$$

$$= .313 \pm 1.96\sqrt{\frac{(.313)(.687)}{1,000}}$$

$$= .313 \pm .029$$

$$= (.284, .342)$$

The company can be 95% confident that the interval from 28.4% to 34.2% contains the true percentage of *all* consumers who prefer its brand—that is, in repeated construction of confidence intervals, approximately 95% of all samples would produce confidence intervals that enclose p. Note that the guidelines for interpreting a confidence interval about μ also apply to interpreting a confidence interval for p because p is the "population fraction of successes" in a binomial experiment.

Example 6.7

Large-Sample Confidence Interval for p—Proportion Optimistic about the Economy

Problem Many public polling agencies conduct surveys to determine the current consumer sentiment concerning the state of the economy. For example, the Bureau of Economic and Business Research (BEBR) at the University of Florida conducts quarterly surveys to gauge consumer sentiment in the Sunshine State. Suppose that the BEBR randomly samples 484 consumers and finds that 157 are optimistic about the state of the economy. Use a 90% confidence interval to estimate the proportion of all consumers in Florida who are optimistic about the state of the economy. Based on the confidence interval, can BEBR infer that a minority of Florida consumers is optimistic about the economy?

Solution The number, x, of the 484 sampled consumers who are optimistic about the Florida economy is a binomial random variable if we can assume that the sample was randomly selected from the population of Florida consumers and that the poll was conducted identically for each sampled consumer.

The point estimate of the proportion of Florida consumers who are optimistic about the economy is

$$\hat{p} = \frac{x}{n} = \frac{157}{484} = .324$$

We first check to be sure that the sample size is sufficiently large that the normal distribution provides a reasonable approximation for the sampling distribution of $\hat{p}$. We require the number of successes in the sample, $n\hat{p}$, and the number of failures, $n\hat{q}$, to both be at least 15. Since the number of successes is $n\hat{p} = 157$ and the number of failures is $n\hat{q} = 327$, we may conclude that the normal approximation is reasonable.

We now proceed to form the 90% confidence interval for p, the true proportion of Florida consumers who are optimistic about the state of the economy:

$$\hat{p} \pm z_{\alpha/2}\sigma_{\hat{p}} = \hat{p} \pm z_{\alpha/2}\sqrt{\frac{pq}{n}} \approx \hat{p} \pm z_{\alpha/2}\sqrt{\frac{\hat{p}\hat{q}}{n}}$$

$$= .324 \pm 1.645\sqrt{\frac{(.324)(.676)}{484}} = .324 \pm .035 = (.289, .359)$$

(This interval is also shown on the Minitab printout, Figure 6.13.) Thus, we can be 90% confident that the proportion of all Florida consumers who are confident about the economy is between .289 and .359. As always, our confidence stems from the fact that 90% of all similarly formed intervals will contain the true proportion p and not from any knowledge about whether this particular interval does.

Test and CI for One Proportion

```
Sample    X    N   Sample p        90% CI
1        157  484  0.324380   (0.289379, 0.359381)

Using the normal approximation.
```

Figure 6.13

Minitab output showing 95% confidence interval for p, Example 6.7

Can we conclude that a minority of Florida consumers is optimistic about the economy based on this interval? If we wished to use this interval to infer that a minority is optimistic, the interval would have to support the inference that p is less than .5—that is, that less than 50% of the Florida consumers are optimistic about the economy. Note that the interval contains only values below .5. Therefore, we can conclude that the true value of p is less than .5 based on this 90% confidence interval.

Look Back If the confidence interval includes .5 (e.g., an interval from .42 to .54), then we could not conclude that the true proportion of consumers who are optimistic is less than .5. (This is because it is possible that p is as high as .54.)

■ Now Work Exercise 6.49

We conclude this section with a warning and an illustrative example.

> ⚠ **CAUTION** Unless n is extremely large, the large-sample procedure presented in this section performs poorly when p is near 0 or near 1.

The problem stated in the above warning can be illustrated as follows. Suppose you want to estimate the proportion of executives who die from a work-related injury using a sample size of $n = 100$. This proportion is likely to be near 0, say $p \approx .001$. If so, then $np \approx 100(.001) = .1$ is less than the recommended value of 15 (see Conditions in the box on p. 321). Consequently, a confidence interval for p based on a sample of $n = 100$ will probably be misleading.

To overcome this potential problem, an *extremely* large sample size is required. Because the value of n required to satisfy "extremely large" is difficult to determine, statisticians (see Agresti & Coull, 1998) have proposed an alternative method, based on the Wilson (1927) point estimator of p. The procedure is outlined in the box below. Researchers have shown that this confidence interval works well for any p, even when the sample size n is very small.

Adjusted $(1 - \alpha)100\%$ Confidence Interval for a Population Proportion, p

$$\tilde{p} \pm z_{\alpha/2}\sqrt{\frac{\tilde{p}(1 - \tilde{p})}{n + 4}}$$

where $\tilde{p} = \frac{x + 2}{n + 4}$ is the adjusted sample proportion of observations with the characteristic of interest, x is the number of successes in the sample, and n is the sample size.

Example 6.8

Adjusted Confidence Interval Procedure for p—Injury Rate at a Jewelry Store

Problem According to the Bureau of Labor Statistics (2012), the probability of injury while working at a jewelry store is less than .01. Suppose that in a random sample of 200 jewelry store workers, 3 were injured on the job. Estimate the true proportion of jewelry store workers who are injured on the job using a 95% confidence interval.

Solution Let p represent the true proportion of all jewelry store workers who are injured on the job. Because p is near 0, an "extremely large" sample is required to estimate its value using the usual large-sample method. Note that the number of "successes," 3, is less than 15. Thus, we doubt whether the sample size of 200 is large enough to apply the large-sample method. Alternatively, we will apply the adjustment outlined in the box.

Because the number of "successes" (i.e., number of injured jewelry store workers) in the sample is $x = 3$, the adjusted sample proportion is

$$\tilde{p} = \frac{x + 2}{n + 4} = \frac{3 + 2}{200 + 4} = \frac{5}{204} = .025$$

Note that this adjusted sample proportion is obtained by adding a total of four observations—two "successes" and two "failures"—to the sample data. Substituting $\tilde{p} = .025$ into the equation for a 95% confidence interval, we obtain

$$\tilde{p} \pm 1.96\sqrt{\frac{\tilde{p}(1 - \tilde{p})}{n + 4}} = .025 \pm 1.96\sqrt{\frac{(.025)(.975)}{204}}$$

$$= .025 \pm .021$$

or $(.004, .046)$. Consequently, we are 95% confident that the true proportion of jewelry store workers who are injured while on the job falls between .004 and .046.

Look Back If we apply the standard large-sample confidence interval formula, where $\hat{p} = \frac{3}{200} = .015$, we obtain

$$\hat{p} \pm 1.96\sqrt{\frac{\hat{p}\hat{q}}{200}} = .015 \pm 1.96\sqrt{\frac{(.015)(.985)}{200}}$$

$$= .015 \pm .017 \text{ or } (-.002, .032)$$

> Note that the interval contains negative (nonsensical) values for the true proportion. Such a result is typical when the large-sample method is misapplied.

■ Now Work Exercise 6.50

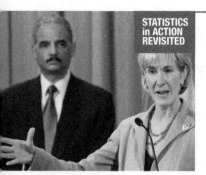

STATISTICS in ACTION REVISITED

Estimating the Coding Error Rate

In the previous Statistics in Action Revisited (p. 316), we showed how to estimate the mean overpayment amount for claims in a Medicare fraud study. In addition to estimating overcharges, the USDOJ also is interested in estimating the *coding error rate* of a Medicare provider. The coding error rate is defined as the proportion of Medicare claims that are coded incorrectly. Thus, for this inference, the USDOJ is interested in estimating a population proportion, p. Typically, the USDOJ finds that about 50% of the claims in a Medicare fraud case are incorrectly coded.

If you examine the sample data in Table SIA6.1, you can verify that of the 52 audited claims, 31 were determined to be coded incorrectly, resulting in an overcharge. These are the claims with a disallowed amount greater than $0. Therefore, an estimate of the coding error rate, p, for this Medicare provider is

$$\hat{p} = 31/52 = .596$$

A 95% confidence interval for p can be obtained with the use of a confidence interval formula or with statistical software.

The **MFRAUD** file includes a qualitative variable (called "Coding Error") at two levels, where "Yes" represents that the claim is coded incorrectly and "No" represents that the claim is coded correctly. Thus, the USDOJ desires an estimate of the proportion of "Yes" values for the "Coding Error" variable. A confidence interval for the proportion of incorrectly coded claims is highlighted on the accompanying Minitab printout, Figure SIA6.2. The interval, (.45, .73), implies that the true coding error rate for the 1,000 claims in the population falls between .45 and .73, with 95% confidence. Note that the value .5—the proportion of incorrectly coded claims expected by the USDOJ—falls within the 95% confidence interval.

```
Event = Yes

Variable        X   N   Sample p        95% CI
Coding_Error   31  52   0.596154   (0.451016, 0.729940)
```

Figure SIA6.2
Minitab confidence interval for coding error rate

Data Set: MFRAUD

Exercises 6.40–6.59

Learning the Mechanics

6.40 Describe the sampling distribution of $\hat{p}$ based on large samples of size n—that is, give the mean, the standard deviation, and the (approximate) shape of the distribution of $\hat{p}$ when large samples of size n are (repeatedly) selected from the binomial distribution with probability of success p.

● Applet Exercise 6.5

Use the applet *Confidence Intervals for a Proportion* to investigate the effect of the value of p on the number of confidence intervals that contain the population proportion p for a fixed sample size. For this exercise, use sample size $n = 10$.

    a. Run the applet several times without clearing for $p = .1$. What proportion of the 95% confidence intervals contain p? What proportion of the 99% confidence intervals contain p? Do the results surprise you? Explain.

    b. Repeat part **a** for each value of p: $p = .2$, $p = .3$, $p = .4$, $p = .5$, $p = .6$, $p = .7$, $p = .8$, and $p = .9$.

    c. Which value of p yields the greatest proportion of each type of interval that contain p?

    d. Based on your results, what values of p will yield more reliable confidence intervals for a fixed sample size n? Explain.

● Applet Exercise 6.6

Use the applet *Confidence Intervals for a Proportion* to investigate the effect of the sample size on the number of confidence intervals that contain the population proportion p for a value of p close to 0 or 1.

    a. Run the applet several times without clearing for $p = .5$ and $n = 50$. Record the proportion of the 99% confidence intervals containing p.

    b. Now set $p = .1$ and run the applet several times without clearing for $n = 50$. How does the proportion of the 99% confidence intervals containing p compare to that in part **a**?

c. Repeat part **b** keeping $p = .1$ and increasing the sample size by 50 until you find a sample size that yields a similar proportion of the 99% confidence intervals containing p as that in part **a.**

d. Based on your results, describe how the value of p affects the sample size needed to guarantee a certain level of confidence.

6.41 For the binomial sample information summarized in each part, indicate whether the sample size is large enough to use the methods of this chapter to construct a confidence interval for p.
a. $n = 400, \hat{p} = .10$ **b.** $n = 50, \hat{p} = .10$
c. $n = 20, \hat{p} = .5$ **d.** $n = 20, \hat{p} = .3$

6.42 A random sample of size $n = 121$ yielded $\hat{p} = .88$.
a. Is the sample size large enough to use the methods of this section to construct a confidence interval for p? Explain.
b. Construct a 90% confidence interval for p.
c. What assumption is necessary to ensure the validity of this confidence interval?

6.43 A random sample of size $n = 225$ yielded $\hat{p} = .46$.
a. Is the sample size large enough to use the methods of this section to construct a confidence interval for p? Explain.
b. Construct a 95% confidence interval for p.
c. Interpret the 95% confidence interval.
d. Explain what is meant by the phrase "95% confidence interval."

6.44 A random sample of 50 consumers taste-tested a new snack food. Their responses were coded (0: do not like; 1: like; 2: indifferent) and recorded as follows:

1	0	0	1	2	0	1	1	0	0
0	1	0	2	0	2	2	0	0	1
1	0	0	0	0	1	0	2	0	0
0	1	0	0	1	0	0	1	0	1
0	2	0	0	1	1	0	0	0	1

a. Use an 80% confidence interval to estimate the proportion of consumers who like the snack food.
b. Provide a statistical interpretation for the confidence interval you constructed in part **a.**

Applying the Concepts—Basic

6.45 **Zillow.com estimates of home values.** Zillow.com is a real estate Web site that provides free estimates of the market value of homes. Refer to *The Appraisal Journal* (Winter 2010) study of the accuracy of Zillow's estimates, Exercise 1.15 (p. 25). Data were collected for a sample of 2,045 single-family residential properties in Arlington, Texas. The researchers determined that Zillow overestimated by more than 10% the market value of 818 of the 2,045 homes. Suppose you want to estimate p, the true proportion of Arlington, Texas, homes with market values that are overestimated by more than 10% by Zillow.
a. Find $\hat{p}$, the point estimate of p.
b. Describe the sampling distribution of $\hat{p}$.
c. Find a 95% confidence interval for p.
d. Give a practical interpretation of the confidence interval, part **c.**

e. Suppose a *Zillow* representative claims that $p = .3$. Is the claim believable? Explain.

6.46 **Paying for music downloads.** If you use the Internet, have you ever paid to access or download music? This was one of the questions of interest in a recent *Pew Internet & American Life Project Survey* (October 2010). Telephone interviews were conducted on a representative sample of 1,003 adults living in the United States. For this sample, 506 adults admitted that they have paid to download music.
a. Use the survey information to find a point estimate for the true proportion of U.S. adults who have paid to download music.
b. Find an interval estimate for the proportion, part **a.** Use a 90% confidence interval.
c. Give a practical interpretation of the interval, part **b.** Your answer should begin with "We are 90% confident…."
d. Explain the meaning of the phrase "90% confident."

6.47 **Is Starbucks coffee overpriced?** The *Minneapolis Star Tribune* (August 12, 2008) reported that 73% of Americans say that Starbucks coffee is overpriced. The source of this information was a national telephone survey of 1,000 American adults conducted by Rasmussen Reports.
a. Identify the population of interest in this study.
b. Identify the sample for the study.
c. Identify the parameter of interest in the study.
d. Find and interpret a 95% confidence interval for the parameter of interest.

6.48 **Do social robots walk or roll?** Refer to the *International Conference on Social Robotics* (Vol. 6414, 2010) study of the trend in the design of social robots, Exercise 5.42 (p. 288). The researchers obtained a random sample of 106 social robots through a Web search and determined that 63 were designed with legs, but no wheels.
a. Find a 99% confidence interval for the proportion of all social robots designed with legs, but no wheels. Interpret the result.
b. In Exercise 5.42, you assumed that 40% of all social robots are designed with legs, but no wheels. Comment on the validity of this assumption.

6.49 **Cell phone use by drivers.** Studies have shown that drivers who use cell phones while operating a motor passenger vehicle increase their risk of an accident. Nevertheless, drivers continue to make cell phone calls while driving. A June 2011 *Harris Poll* of 2,163 adults found that 60% (1,298 adults) use cell phones while driving.
a. Give a point estimate of p, the true driver cell phone use rate (i.e., the proportion of all drivers who are using a cell phone while operating a motor passenger vehicle).
b. Find a 95% confidence interval for p.
c. Give a practical interpretation of the interval, part **b.**

6.50 **Nannies who work for celebrities.** The International Nanny Association reports that in a sample of 528 in-home child care providers (nannies), 20 work for either a nationally known, locally known, or internationally known celebrity (*2011 International Nanny Association Salary and Benefits Survey*). Use Wilson's adjustment to find a 95% confidence interval for the true proportion of all nannies who work for a celebrity. Interpret the resulting interval.

Applying the Concepts—Intermediate

6.51 Annual survey of computer crimes. Refer to the *CSI Computer Crime and Security Survey (2010/2011)*, first presented in Exercise 1.22 (p. 26). Recall that of the 351 organizations that responded to the survey, 144 (or 41%) admitted unauthorized use of computer systems at their firms during the year. Estimate the probability of unauthorized use of computer systems at an organization with a 90% confidence interval. Explain how 90% is used as a measure of reliability for the confidence interval.

6.52 Minority ownership of franchises. According to *Franchised Business Ownership: By Minority and Gender Groups* (2011), a report for IFA Educational Foundation, 20.5% of all franchised businesses in the United States are minority owned. (This information is based on the U.S. Census Bureau's survey of 27 million business owners.) Suppose that you obtain a sample of 100 franchised businesses located in Mississippi and find that 15 are owned by minorities. Does this result lead you to conclude that the percentage of minority-owned franchises in Mississippi is less than the national value of 20.5%? Explain.

6.53 History of corporate acquisitions. Refer to the *Academy of Management Journal* (Aug. 2008) investigation of the performance and timing of corporate acquisitions, Exercise 2.12 (p. 50). Recall that a corporate acquisition occurs when one corporation purchases all the stock shares of another. The investigation discovered that in a sample of 2,778 firms, 748 announced one or more acquisitions during the year 2000. Estimate the true percentage of all firms that announced one or more acquisitions during the year 2000 using a 90% confidence interval. Interpret the result.

6.54 Interviewing candidates for a job. The costs associated with conducting interviews for a job opening have skyrocketed over the years. According to a Harris Interactive survey, 211 of 502 senior human resources executives at U.S. companies believe that their hiring managers are interviewing too many people to find qualified candidates for the job (*Business Wire*, June 8, 2006).
  a. Describe the population of interest in this study.
  b. Identify the population parameter of interest, p.
  c. Is the sample size large enough to provide a reliable estimate of p?
  d. Find and interpret an interval estimate for the true proportion of senior human resources executives who believe that their hiring managers interview too many candidates during a job search. Use a confidence level of 98%.
  e. If you had constructed a 90% confidence interval, would it be wider or narrower?

6.55 Splinting in mountain climbing accidents. The most common injury that occurs among mountain climbers is trauma to the lower extremity (leg). Consequently, rescuers must be proficient in immobilizing and splinting fractures. In *High Altitude Medicine & Biology* (Vol. 10, 2009), researchers provided official recommendations for mountain emergency medicine. As part of the document, the researchers examined the likelihood of mountain climbers needing certain types of splints. A Scottish Mountain Rescue study reported that there was 1 femoral shaft splint needed among 333 live casualties. The researchers will use this study to estimate the proportion of all mountain casualties that require a femoral shaft splint.
  a. Is the sample large enough to apply the large-sample estimation method of this section? Show why or why not.
  b. Use Wilson's adjustment to find a 95% confidence interval for the true proportion of all mountain casualties that require a femoral shaft splint. Interpret the result.

6.56 Diamonds sold on the open market. Refer to the sample of 308 diamond stones that were listed for sale on the open market in Singapore's *Business Times*. Recall that the color of each diamond is classified as D, E, F, G, H, or I, while the clarity of each is classified as VVS1, VVS2, VS1, or VS2.
  a. Find a 99% confidence interval for the proportion of all diamonds for sale on the open market that are classified as "D" color. Interpret the result.
  b. Find a 99% confidence interval for the proportion of all diamonds for sale on the open market that are classified as "VS1" clarity. Interpret the result.

6.57 Are you really being served red snapper? Refer to the *Nature* (July 15, 2004) study of fish specimens labeled "red snapper," Exercise 3.71 (p. 167). Recall that federal law prohibits restaurants from serving a cheaper, look-alike variety of fish (e.g., vermillion snapper or lane snapper) to customers who order red snapper. A team of University of North Carolina (UNC) researchers analyzed the meat from each in a sample of 22 "red snapper" fish fillets purchased from vendors across the United States in an effort to estimate the true proportion of fillets that are really red snapper. DNA tests revealed that 17 of the 22 fillets (or 77%) were not red snapper but the cheaper, look-alike variety of fish.
  a. Identify the parameter of interest to the UNC researchers.
  b. Explain why a large-sample confidence interval is inappropriate to apply in this study.
  c. Construct a 95% confidence interval for the parameter of interest using Wilson's adjustment.
  d. Give a practical interpretation of the confidence interval.

Applying the Concepts—Advanced

6.58 Eye shadow, mascara, and nickel allergies. Pigmented makeup products like mascara and eye shadow may contain metal (e.g., nickel) allergens. Is a nickel allergy more likely to occur in women who report cosmetic dermatitis from using eye shadow or mascara? This was the question of interest in a paper published in the *Journal of the European Academy of Dermatology and Venereology* (June 2010). In a sample of 131 women with cosmetic dermatitis from using eye shadow, 12 were diagnosed with a nickel allergy. In a sample of 250 women with cosmetic dermatitis from using mascara, 25 were diagnosed with a nickel allergy.
  a. Compute a 95% confidence interval for the proportion of women with cosmetic dermatitis from using eye shadow who have a nickel allergy. Interpret the result.

b. Compute a 95% confidence interval for the proportion of women with cosmetic dermatitis from using mascara who have a nickel allergy. Interpret the result.

c. Suppose you are informed that the true proportion with a nickel allergy for one of the two groups (eye shadow or mascara) is .12. Can you determine which group is referenced? Explain.

6.59 **U.S. Postal Service's performance.** The U.S. Postal Service (USPS) reports that 95% of first-class mail within the same city is delivered on time (i.e., within 2 days of the time of mailing). To gauge the USPS performance, Price Waterhouse monitored the delivery of first-class mail items between Dec. 10 and Mar. 3—the most difficult delivery season due to bad weather conditions and holidays. In a sample of 332,000 items, Price Waterhouse determined that 282,200 were delivered on time. Comment on the performance of USPS first-class mail service over this time period.

6.5 Determining the Sample Size

Recall (Section 1.6) that one way to collect the relevant data for a study used to make inferences about the population is to implement a designed (planned) experiment. Perhaps the most important design decision faced by the analyst is to determine the size of the sample. We show in this section that the appropriate sample size for making an inference about a population mean or proportion depends on the desired reliability.

Estimating a Population Mean

Consider Example 6.2 (p. 303), in which we estimated the mean overdue amount for all delinquent accounts in a large credit corporation. A sample of 100 delinquent accounts produced the 95% confidence interval $\bar{x} \pm 1.96\sigma_{\bar{x}} \approx 233.28 \pm 17.71$. Consequently, our estimate $\bar{x}$ was within \$17.71 of the true mean amount due, μ, for all the delinquent accounts at the 95% confidence level—that is, the 95% confidence interval for μ was $2(17.71) = \$35.42$ wide when 100 accounts were sampled. This is illustrated in Figure 6.14a.

Now suppose we want to estimate μ to within \$5 with 95% confidence—that is, we want to narrow the width of the confidence interval from \$35.42 to \$10, as shown in Figure 6.14b. How much will the sample size have to be increased to accomplish this? If we want the estimator $\bar{x}$ to be within \$5 of μ, we must have

$$1.96\sigma_{\bar{x}} = 5 \quad \text{or, equivalently,} \quad 1.96\left(\frac{\sigma}{\sqrt{n}}\right) = 5$$

The necessary sample size is obtained by solving this equation for n. To do this, we need an approximation for σ. We have an approximation from the initial sample of

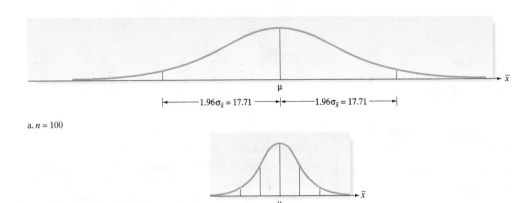

Figure 6.14

Relationship between sample size and width of confidence interval: delinquent debtors example

100 accounts—namely, the sample standard deviation, $s = 90.34$ (see the Solution to Example 6.2). Thus,

$$1.96\left(\frac{\sigma}{\sqrt{n}}\right) \approx 1.96\left(\frac{s}{\sqrt{n}}\right) = 1.96\left(\frac{90.34}{\sqrt{n}}\right) = 5$$

$$\sqrt{n} = \frac{1.96(90.34)}{5} = 35.413$$

$$n = (35.413)^2 = 1,254.1 \approx 1,254$$

Approximately 1,254 accounts will have to be randomly sampled to estimate the mean overdue amount μ to within \$5 with (approximately) 95% confidence. The confidence interval resulting from a sample of this size will be approximately \$10 wide (see Figure 6.14b).

In general, we express the reliability associated with a confidence interval for the population mean μ by specifying the **margin of sampling error,** within which we want to estimate μ with $100(1 - \alpha)\%$ confidence. The margin of error (denoted ME), then, is equal to the half-width of the confidence interval, as shown in Figure 6.15.

Sample Size Determination for $100(1 - \alpha)\%$ Confidence Interval for μ

In order to estimate μ with a margin of error ME and with $100(1 - \alpha)\%$ confidence, the required sample size is found as follows:

$$z_{\alpha/2}\left(\frac{\sigma}{\sqrt{n}}\right) = \text{ME}$$

The solution for n is given by the equation

$$n = \left[\frac{(z_{\alpha/2})\sigma}{\text{ME}}\right]^2$$

Note: The value of σ is usually unknown. It can be estimated by the standard deviation, s, from a prior sample. Alternatively, we may approximate the range R of observations in the population, and (conservatively) estimate $\sigma \approx \frac{R}{4}$. In any case, you should round the value of n obtained *upward* to ensure that the sample size will be sufficient to achieve the specified reliability.

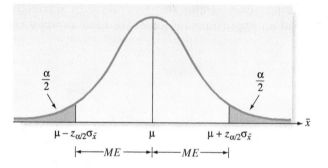

Figure 6.15

Specifying the sampling error as the half-width of a confidence interval

---

Example   6.9

Sample Size for Estimating μ—Mean Inflation Pressure of Footballs

Problem The manufacturer of official NFL footballs uses a machine to inflate its new balls to a pressure of 13.5 pounds. When the machine is properly calibrated, the mean inflation pressure is 13.5 pounds, but uncontrollable factors cause the pressures of individual footballs to vary randomly from about 13.3 to 13.7 pounds. For quality-control purposes, the manufacturer wishes to estimate the mean inflation pressure to within .025 pound of its true value with a 99% confidence interval. What sample size should be used?

Solution We desire a 99% confidence interval that estimates μ with a margin of error of ME = .025 pound. For a 99% confidence interval, we have $z_{\alpha/2} = z_{.005} = 2.576$. No previous estimate of s is available; however, we are given that the range of observations is $R = 13.7 - 13.3 = .4$. A conservative estimate (based on Chebychev's Rule) is $\sigma \approx R/4 = .1$. Now we use the formula derived in the box to find the sample size n:

$$n = \left[\frac{(z_{\alpha/2})\sigma}{\text{ME}} \right]^2 = \left[\frac{(2.576)(.1)}{.025} \right]^2 = 106.17$$

We round this up to $n = 107$. Realizing that σ was approximated by $R/4$, we might even advise that the sample size be specified as $n = 110$ to be more certain of attaining the objective of a 99% confidence interval with a sampling error of .025 pound or less.

Look Back To determine the value of the margin of error ME, look for the value that follows the key words "estimate μ to within...."

■ Now Work Exercise 6.70

Sometimes the formula will yield a small sample size (say, $n < 30$). Unfortunately, this solution is invalid because the procedures and assumptions for small samples differ from those for large samples, as we discovered in Section 6.3. Therefore, if the formulas yield a small sample size, one simple strategy is to select a sample size $n = 30$.

Estimating a Population Proportion

The method outlined above is easily applied to a population proportion p. To illustrate, in Example 6.6 (p. 320), a company used a sample of 1,000 consumers to estimate the proportion of consumers who prefer its cereal brand. As a follow-up, we obtained the 95% confidence interval, $.313 \pm .029$. Suppose the company wishes to estimate its market share more precisely, say to within .015 with a 95% confidence interval.

The company wants a confidence interval with a margin of error for the estimate of p of ME = .015. The sample size required to generate such an interval is found by solving the following equation for n (see Figure 6.16):

$$z_{\alpha/2}\sigma_{\hat{p}} = \text{ME} \qquad \text{or} \qquad z_{\alpha/2}\sqrt{\frac{pq}{n}} = .015$$

Since a 95% confidence interval is desired, the appropriate z-value is $z_{\alpha/2} = z_{.025} = 1.96$. We must approximate the value of the product pq before we can solve the equation for n. As shown in Table 6.6, the closer the values of p and q to .5, the larger the product pq. Thus, to find a conservatively large sample size that will generate a confidence interval with the specified reliability, we generally choose an approximation of p close to .5. In the case of the food-products company, however, we have an initial sample estimate of $\hat{p} = .313$. A conservatively large estimate of pq can therefore be obtained by using, say, $p = .35$. We now substitute into the equation and solve for n:

$$1.96\sqrt{\frac{(.35)(.65)}{n}} = .015$$

$$n = \frac{(1.96)^2(.35)(.65)}{(.015)^2}$$

$$= 3,884.28 \approx 3,885$$

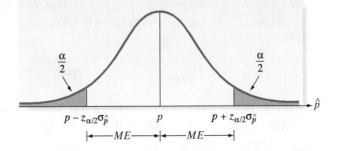

Figure 6.16

Specifying the sampling error of a confidence interval for a population proportion p

The company must sample about 3,885 consumers to estimate the percentage who prefer its brand to within .015 with a 95% confidence interval.

The procedure for finding the sample size necessary to estimate a population proportion p with a specified margin of error ME is given in the box.

Sample Size Determination for $100(1 - \alpha)\%$ Confidence Interval for p

In order to estimate a binomial probability p with margin of error ME and with $100(1 - \alpha)\%$ confidence, the required sample size is found by solving the following equation for n:

$$z_{\alpha/2}\sqrt{\frac{pq}{n}} = ME$$

The solution for n can be written as follows:

$$n = \frac{(z_{\alpha/2})^2(pq)}{(ME)^2}$$

Note: Because the value of the product pq is unknown, it can be estimated by using the sample fraction of successes, $\hat{p}$, from a prior sample. Remember (Table 6.6) that the value of pq is at its maximum when p equals .5, so you can obtain conservatively large values of n by approximating p by .5 or values close to .5. In any case, you should round the value of n obtained *upward* to ensure that the sample size will be sufficient to achieve the specified reliability.

Example 6.10	**Problem** A cellular telephone manufacturer that entered the postregulation market too quickly has an initial problem with excessive customer complaints and consequent

Sample Size for Estimating p—Fraction of Defective Cell Phones

Problem A cellular telephone manufacturer that entered the postregulation market too quickly has an initial problem with excessive customer complaints and consequent returns of the cell phones for repair or replacement. The manufacturer wants to determine the magnitude of the problem in order to estimate its warranty liability. How many cellular telephones should the company randomly sample from its warehouse and check in order to estimate the fraction defective, p, to within .01 with 90% confidence?

Solution In order to estimate p to within .01 of its true value, we set the half-width of the confidence interval equal to ME $= .01$, as shown in Figure 6.17.

Figure 6.17

Specified reliability for estimate of fraction defective in Example 6.10

The equation for the sample size n requires an estimate of the product pq. We could most conservatively estimate $pq = .25$ (i.e., use $p = .5$), but this may be overly conservative when estimating a fraction defective. A value of .1, corresponding to 10% defective, will probably be conservatively large for this application. The solution is therefore

$$n = \frac{(z_{\alpha/2})^2(pq)}{(ME)^2} = \frac{(1.645)^2(.1)(.9)}{(.01)^2} = 2,435.4 \approx 2,436$$

Thus, the manufacturer should sample 2,436 cellular telephones in order to estimate the fraction defective, p, to within .01 with 90% confidence.

Look Back Remember that this answer depends on our approximation for pq, where we used .09. If the fraction defective is closer to .05 than to .10, we can use a sample of 1,286 cell phones (check this) to estimate p to within .01 with 90% confidence.

■ Now Work Exercise 6.71

The cost of sampling will also play an important role in the final determination of the sample size to be selected to estimate either μ or p. Although more complex formulas can be derived to balance the reliability and cost considerations, we will solve for the necessary sample size and note that the sampling budget may be a limiting factor. (Consult the references for a more complete treatment of this problem.) Once the sample size n is determined, be sure to devise a sampling plan that will ensure a representative sample is selected from the target population.

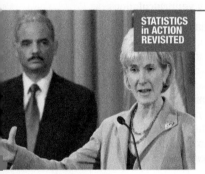

STATISTICS in ACTION REVISITED

Determining Sample Size

In the previous Statistics in Action applications in this chapter, we used confidence intervals (1) to estimate μ, the mean overpayment amount for claims in a Medicare fraud study, and (2) to estimate p, the coding error rate (i.e., proportion of claims that are incorrectly coded) of a Medicare provider. Both of these confidence intervals were based on selecting a random sample of 52 claims from the population of claims handled by the Medicare provider. How does the USDOJ determine how many claims to sample for auditing?

Consider the problem of estimating the coding error rate, p. As stated in a previous Statistics in Action Revisited, the USDOJ typically finds that about 50% of the claims in a Medicare fraud case are incorrectly coded. Suppose the USDOJ wants to estimate the true coding error rate of a Medicare provider to within .1 with 95% confidence. How many claims should be randomly sampled for audit in order to attain the desired estimate?

Here, the USDOJ desires a margin of error of ME = .1, a confidence level of $1 - \alpha = .95$ (for which $z_{\alpha/2} = 1.96$), and uses an estimate $p \approx .50$. Substituting these values into the sample size formula (p. 330), we obtain:

$$n = (z_{\alpha/2})^2(pq)/(\text{ME})^2$$
$$= (1.96)^2(.5)(.5)/(.1)^2$$
$$= 96.04$$

Consequently, the USDOJ should audit about 97 randomly selected claims to attain a 95% confidence interval for p with a sampling error of .10.

[*Note:* You may wonder why the sample actually used in the fraud analysis included only 52 claims. The sampling strategy employed involved more than selecting a simple random sample; rather, it used a more sophisticated sampling scheme, called stratified random sampling. (See Section 1.6.) The 52 claims represented the sample for just one of the strata.]

Exercises 6.60–6.78

Learning the Mechanics

6.60 If you wish to estimate a population mean with a margin of error of ME = .3 using a 95% confidence interval, and you know from prior sampling that σ^2 is approximately equal to 7.2, how many observations would have to be included in your sample?

6.61 Suppose you wish to estimate a population mean correct to within .20 with probability equal to .90. You do not know σ^2, but you know that the observations will range in value between 30 and 34.

a. Find the approximate sample size that will produce the desired accuracy of the estimate. You wish to be conservative to ensure that the sample size will be ample to achieve the desired accuracy of the estimate. [*Hint:* Using your knowledge of data variation from Section 2.6, assume that the range of the observations will equal 4σ.]

b. Calculate the approximate sample size, making the less conservative assumption that the range of the observations is equal to 6σ.

6.62 In each case, find the approximate sample size required to construct a 95% confidence interval for p that has margin of error of ME = .08.

  a. Assume p is near .2.

  b. Assume you have no prior knowledge about p, but you wish to be certain that your sample is large enough to achieve the specified accuracy for the estimate.

6.63 The following is a 90% confidence interval for p: (.26, .54). How large was the sample used to construct this interval?

6.64 It costs you $10 to draw a sample of size $n = 1$ and measure the attribute of interest. You have a budget of $1,500.

  a. Do you have sufficient funds to estimate the population mean for the attribute of interest with a 95% confidence interval 5 units in width? Assume $\sigma = 14$.

  b. If you used a 90% confidence level, would your answer to part **a** change? Explain.

6.65 Suppose you wish to estimate the mean of a normal population using a 95% confidence interval, and you know from prior information that $\sigma^2 \approx 1$.

  a. To see the effect of the sample size on the width of the confidence interval, calculate the width of the confidence interval for $n = 16, 25, 49, 100$, and 400.

  b. Plot the width as a function of sample size n on graph paper. Connect the points by a smooth curve and note how the width decreases as n increases.

6.66 If nothing is known about p, .5 can be substituted for p in the sample size formula for a population proportion. But when this is done, the resulting sample size may be larger than needed. Under what circumstances will using $p = .5$ in the sample size formula yield a sample size larger than needed to construct a confidence interval for p with a specified bound and a specified confidence level?

Applying the Concepts—Basic

6.67 **Lobster trap placement.** Refer to the *Bulletin of Marine Science* (April 2010) study of lobster trap placement, Exercise 6.29 (p. 318). Recall that you used a 95% confidence interval to estimate the mean trap spacing (in meters) for the population of red spiny lobster fishermen fishing in Baja California Sur, Mexico. How many teams of fishermen would need to be sampled in order to reduce the width of the confidence interval to 5 meters? Use the sample standard deviation from Exercise 6.29 in your calculation.

6.68 **Do social robots walk or roll?** Refer to the *International Conference on Social Robotics* (Vol. 6414, 2010) study of the trend in the design of social robots, Exercise 6.48 (p. 325). Recall that you used a 99% confidence interval to estimate the proportion of all social robots designed with legs, but no wheels. How many social robots would need to be sampled in order to estimate the proportion to within .075 of its true value?

6.69 **Assessing the bending strength of a wooden roof.** Refer to the *Journal of the International Association for Shell and Spatial Structures* (Aug. 2004) study to estimate the mean bending strength of imported white wood used on the roof of an ancient Japanese temple, Exercise 6.31 (p. 318). Suppose you want to estimate the true mean breaking strength of the white wood to within 4 MPa using a 90%

confidence interval. How many pieces of the imported wood need to be tested? Recall that the sample standard deviation of the breaking strengths from the study was 10.9 MPa.

6.70 **Accounting and Machiavellianism.** Refer to the *Behavioral Research in Accounting* (Jan. 2008) study of Machiavellian traits in accountants, Exercise 6.19 (p. 310), where a Mach rating score was determined for each in a sample of accounting alumni who work as purchasing managers. Suppose you want to reduce the width of the 95% confidence interval for the true mean Mach rating score of all purchasing managers you obtained in Exercise 6.19b. How many purchasing managers should be included in the sample if you desire a sampling error of only 1.5 Mach rating points? Use $\sigma \approx 12$ in your calculations.

6.71 **Aluminum cans contaminated by fire.** A gigantic warehouse located in Tampa, Florida, stores approximately 60 million empty aluminum beer and soda cans. Recently, a fire occurred at the warehouse. The smoke from the fire contaminated many of the cans with blackspot, rendering them unusable. A University of South Florida statistician was hired by the insurance company to estimate p, the true proportion of cans in the warehouse that were contaminated by the fire. How many aluminum cans should be randomly sampled to estimate p to within .02 with 90% confidence?

Applying the Concepts—Intermediate

6.72 **Shopping on Black Friday.** Refer to the *International Journal of Retail and Distribution Management* (Vol. 39, 2011) survey of Black Friday shoppers, Exercise 6.16 (p. 309). One question was "How many hours do you usually spend shopping on Black Friday?"

  a. How many Black Friday shoppers should be included in a sample designed to estimate the average number of hours spent shopping on Black Friday if you want the estimate to deviate no more than .5 hour from the true mean?

  b. Devise a sampling plan for collecting the data that will likely result in a representative sample.

6.73 **Bacteria in bottled water.** Is the bottled water you drink safe? The Natural Resources Defense Council warns that the bottled water you are drinking may contain more bacteria and other potentially carcinogenic chemicals than allowed by state and federal regulations. Of the more than 1,000 bottles studied, nearly one-third exceeded government levels (www.nrdc.org). Suppose that the Natural Resources Defense Council wants an updated estimate of the population proportion of bottled water that violates at least one government standard. Determine the sample size (number of bottles) needed to estimate this proportion to within ±0.01 with 99% confidence.

6.74 **Eye shadow, mascara and nickel allergies.** Refer to the *Journal of the European Academy of Dermatology and Venereology* (June 2010) study of the link between nickel allergies and use of mascara or eye shadow, Exercise 6.58 (p. 326). Recall that two groups of women were sampled—one group with cosmetic dermatitis from using eye shadow and another group with cosmetic dermatitis from using mascara. In either group, how many women would need to be sampled in order to yield an estimate of the population percentage with a nickel allergy that falls no more than 3% from the true value?

6.75 Monitoring phone calls to a toll-free number. A large food-products company receives about 100,000 phone calls a year from consumers on its toll-free number. A computer monitors and records how many rings it takes for an operator to answer, how much time each caller spends "on hold," and other data. However, the reliability of the monitoring system has been called into question by the operators and their labor union. As a check on the computer system, approximately how many calls should be manually monitored during the next year to estimate the true mean time that callers spend on hold to within 3 seconds with 95% confidence? Answer this question for the following values of the standard deviation of waiting times (in seconds): 10, 20, and 30.

6.76 USGA golf ball tests. The United States Golf Association (USGA) tests all new brands of golf balls to ensure that they meet USGA specifications. One test conducted is intended to measure the average distance traveled when the ball is hit by a machine called "Iron Byron," a name inspired by the swing of the famous golfer Byron Nelson. Suppose the USGA wishes to estimate the mean distance for a new brand to within 1 yard with 90% confidence. Assume that past tests have indicated that the standard deviation of the distances Iron Byron hits golf balls is approximately 10 yards. How many golf balls should be hit by Iron Byron to achieve the desired accuracy in estimating the mean?

Applying the Concepts—Advanced

6.77 Is caffeine addictive? Does the caffeine in coffee, tea, and cola induce an addiction similar to that induced by alcohol, tobacco, heroin, and cocaine? In an attempt to answer this question, researchers at Johns Hopkins University examined 27 caffeine drinkers and found 25 who displayed some type of withdrawal symptoms when abstaining from caffeine. [*Note:* The 27 caffeine drinkers volunteered for the study.] Furthermore, of 11 caffeine drinkers who were diagnosed as caffeine dependent, 8 displayed dramatic withdrawal symptoms (including impairment in normal functioning) when they consumed a caffeine-free diet in a controlled setting. The National Coffee Association claimed, however, that the study group was too small to draw conclusions. Is the sample large enough to estimate the true proportion of caffeine drinkers who are caffeine dependent to within .05 of the true value with 99% confidence? Explain.

6.78 Preventing production of defective items. It costs more to produce defective items—because they must be scrapped or reworked—than it does to produce nondefective items. This simple fact suggests that manufacturers should ensure the quality of their products by perfecting their production processes rather than through inspection of finished products (*Out of the Crisis,* Deming, 1986). In order to better understand a particular metal-stamping process, a manufacturer wishes to estimate the mean length of items produced by the process during the past 24 hours.

a. How many parts should be sampled in order to estimate the population mean to within .1 millimeter (mm) with 90% confidence? Previous studies of this machine have indicated that the standard deviation of lengths produced by the stamping operation is about 2 mm.

b. Time permits the use of a sample size no larger than 100. If a 90% confidence interval for μ is constructed using $n = 100$, will it be wider or narrower than would have been obtained using the sample size determined in part **a**? Explain.

c. If management requires that μ be estimated to within .1 mm and that a sample size of no more than 100 be used, what is (approximately) the maximum confidence level that could be attained for a confidence interval that meets management's specifications?

6.6 Finite Population Correction for Simple Random Sampling*

The large-sample confidence intervals for a population mean μ and a population proportion p presented in the previous sections are based on a simple random sample selected from the target population. Although we did not state it, the procedure also assumes that the number N of measurements (i.e., sampling units) in the population is large relative to the sample size n.

In some sampling situations, the sample size n may represent 5% or perhaps 10% of the total number N of sampling units in the population. When the sample size is large relative to the number of measurements in the population (see the next box), the standard errors of the estimators of μ and p given in Sections 6.2 and 6.4, respectively, should be multiplied by a **finite population correction factor.**

The form of the finite population correction factor depends on how the population variance σ^2 is defined. In order to simplify the formulas of the standard errors, it is common to define σ^2 as division of the sum of squares of deviations by $N - 1$ *rather than by* N (analogous to the way we defined the sample variance). If we adopt this convention, the finite population correction factor becomes $\sqrt{(N - n)/N}$. Then the estimated standard errors of $\bar{x}$ (the estimator of μ) and $\hat{p}$ (the estimator of p) are as shown in the box.*

---

*For most surveys and opinion polls, the finite population correction factor is approximately equal to 1 and, if desired, can be safely ignored. However, if $n/N > .05$, the finite population correction factor should be included in the calculation of the standard error.

Rule of Thumb for Finite Population Correction Factor

Use the finite population correction factor (shown in the next box) when $n/N > .05$.

Simple Random Sampling with Finite Population of Size N
Estimation of the Population Mean

Estimated standard error:

$$\hat{\sigma}_{\bar{x}} = \frac{s}{\sqrt{n}} \sqrt{\frac{N-n}{N}}$$

Approximate 95% confidence interval: $\bar{x} \pm 2\hat{\sigma}_{\bar{x}}$

Estimation of the Population Proportion

Estimated standard error:

$$\hat{\sigma}_{\hat{p}} = \sqrt{\frac{\hat{p}(1-\hat{p})}{n}} \sqrt{\frac{N-n}{N}}$$

Approximate 95% confidence interval: $\hat{p} \pm 2\hat{\sigma}_{\hat{p}}$

Note: The confidence intervals are "approximate" because we are using 2 to approximate the value $z_{.025} = 1.96$.

Example	6.11

Applying the Finite Population Correction Factor—Manufacture of Sheet Aluminum Foil

Problem A specialty manufacturer wants to purchase remnants of sheet aluminum foil. The foil, all of which is the same thickness, is stored on 1,462 rolls, each containing a varying amount of foil. To obtain an estimate of the total number of square feet of foil on all the rolls, the manufacturer randomly sampled 100 rolls and measured the number of square feet on each roll. The sample mean was 47.4, and the sample standard deviation was 12.4.

a. Find an approximate 95% confidence interval for the mean amount of foil on the 1,462 rolls.

b. Estimate the total number of square feet of foil on all the rolls by multiplying the confidence interval, part **a,** by 1,462. Interpret the result.

Solution

a. Each roll of foil is a sampling unit, and there are $N = 1,462$ units in the population, and the sample size is $n = 100$. Because $\frac{n}{N} = \frac{100}{1,462} = .068$ exceeds .05, we need to apply the finite population correction factor. We have $n = 100$, $\bar{x} = 47.4$, and $s = 12.4$. Substituting these quantities, we obtain the approximate 95% confidence interval:

$$\bar{x} \pm 2\frac{s}{\sqrt{n}} \sqrt{\frac{(N-n)}{N}} = (47.4) \pm 2\frac{12.4}{\sqrt{100}} \sqrt{\frac{(1,462 - 100)}{1,462}}$$

$$= 47.4 \pm 2.39$$

or, (45.01, 49.79).

b. For finite populations of size N, the sum of all measurements in the population—called a *population total*—is

$$\sum_{i=1}^{N} x_i = N\mu$$

Because the confidence interval, part **a,** estimates μ, an estimate of the population total is obtained by multiplying the endpoints of the interval by N. For we have

$$\text{Lower Limit} = N(45.01) = 1,462(45.01) = 65,804.6$$
$$\text{Upper Limit} = N(49.79) = 1,462(49.79) = 72,793.0$$

Consequently, the manufacturer estimates the total amount of foil to be in the interval of 65,805 square feet to 72,793 square feet with 95% confidence.

Look Back If the manufacturer wants to adopt a conservative approach, the bid for the foil will be based on the lower confidence limit, 65,805 square feet of foil.

■ **Now Work Exercise 6.86a**

Exercises 6.79–6.91

Learning the Mechanics

6.79 Calculate the percentage of the population sampled and the finite population correction factor for each of the following situations.
  a. $n = 1,000, N = 2,500$
  b. $n = 1,000, N = 5,000$
  c. $n = 1,000, N = 10,000$
  d. $n = 1,000, N = 100,000$

6.80 Suppose the standard deviation of the population is known to be $\sigma = 200$. Calculate the standard error of $\bar{x}$ for each of the situations described in Exercise 6.79.

6.81 Suppose $N = 10,000$, $n = 2,000$, and $s = 50$.
  a. Compute the standard error of $\bar{x}$ using the finite population correction factor.
  b. Repeat part **a** assuming $n = 4,000$.
  c. Repeat part **a** assuming $n = 10,000$.
  d. Compare parts **a, b,** and **c** and describe what happens to the standard error of $\bar{x}$ as n increases.
  e. The answer to part **c** is 0. This indicates that there is no sampling error in this case. Explain.

6.82 Suppose $N = 5,000$, $n = 64$, and $s = 24$.
  a. Compare the size of the standard error of $\bar{x}$ computed with and without the finite population correction factor.
  b. Repeat part **a,** but this time assume $n = 400$.
  c. Theoretically, when sampling from a finite population, the finite population correction factor should always be used in computing the standard error of $\bar{x}$. However, when n is small relative to N, the finite population correction factor is close to 1 and can safely be ignored. Explain how parts **a** and **b** illustrate this point.

6.83 Suppose you want to estimate a population proportion, p, and $\hat{p} = .42$, $N = 6,000$, and $n = 1,600$. Find an approximate 95% confidence interval for p.

6.84 Suppose you want to estimate a population mean, μ, and $\bar{x} = 422$, $s = 14$, $N = 375$, and $n = 40$. Find an approximate 95% confidence interval for μ.

6.85 A random sample of size $n = 30$ was drawn from a population of size $N = 300$. The following measurements were obtained:

L06085

21	33	19	29	22	38	58	29	52	36	37	30
53	37	29	18	35	42	36	41	35	36	33	38
29	38	39	54	42	42						

  a. Estimate μ with an approximate 95% confidence interval.
  b. Estimate p, the proportion of measurements in the population that are greater than 30, with an approximate 95% confidence interval.

Applying the Concepts—Basic

6.86 **Magazine subscriber salaries.** Each year, the trade magazine *Quality Progress* publishes a study of subscribers' salaries. One year, the 223 vice presidents sampled had a mean salary of $116,754 and a standard deviation of $39,185. Suppose the goal of the study is to estimate the true mean salary of all vice presidents who subscribe to *Quality Progress*.
  a. If 2,193 vice presidents subscribe to *Quality Progress,* NW estimate the mean with an approximate 95% confidence interval.
  b. Interpret the result.

6.87 **NFL player survey.** Researchers at the University of Pennsylvania's Wharton Sports Business Initiative collaborated with the National Football League Players Association (NFLPA) to produce the first NFL Player Survey. Of the 1,696 active NFL players, 1,355 (almost 80%) responded to the survey. One of the survey questions asked, "Who is the coach—professional, college, or high school—that has been the most influential in your career?" Of the 1,355 respondents, 759 selected an NFL (professional) coach.
  a. Construct a 95% confidence interval for the true proportion of active NFL players who select a professional coach as the most influential in their careers.
  b. Why is it necessary to use the continuity correction factor in the construction of the interval, part **a?**
  c. Give a practical interpretation of the interval, part **a.**

Applying the Concepts—Intermediate

6.88 **Furniture brand familiarity.** A brand name that consumers recognize is a highly valued commodity in any industry. To assess brand familiarity in the furniture industry, NPD (a market research firm) surveyed 1,333 women who head U.S. households that have incomes of $25,000 or more. The sample was drawn from a database of 25,000 households that match the criteria listed above. Of the 10 furniture brands evaluated, La-Z-Boy was the most recognized brand; 70.8% of the respondents indicated they were "very familiar" with La-Z-Boy.
  a. Describe the population being investigated by NPD.
  b. In constructing a confidence interval to estimate the proportion of households that are very familiar with the La-Z-Boy brand, is it necessary to use the finite population correction factor? Explain.
  c. What estimate of the standard error of $\hat{p}$ should be used in constructing the confidence interval of part **b?**
  d. Construct a 90% confidence interval for the true proportion and interpret it in the context of the problem.

6.89 **Auditing sampling methods.** Traditionally, auditors have relied to a great extent on sampling techniques, rather than 100% audits, to help them test and evaluate the financial records of a client firm. When sampling is used to obtain an estimate of the total dollar value of an account—the account balance—the examination is known as *a substantive test* (*Audit Sampling—AICPA Audit Guide*, 2012). In order to evaluate the reasonableness of a firm's stated total value of its parts inventory, an auditor randomly samples 100 of the total of 500 parts in stock, prices each part, and reports the results shown in the next table.

Part Number	Part Price	Sample Size
002	$ 108	3
101	55	2
832	500	1
077	73	10
688	300	1
910	54	4
839	92	6
121	833	5
271	50	9
399	125	12
761	1,000	2
093	62	8
505	205	7
597	88	11
830	100	19

a. Give a point estimate of the mean value of the parts inventory.

b. Find the estimated standard error of the point estimate of part **a.**

c. Construct an approximate 95% confidence interval for the mean value of the parts inventory.

d. The firm reported a mean parts inventory value of $300. What does your confidence interval of part **c** suggest about the reasonableness of the firm's reported figure? Explain.

6.90 **Invoice errors in a billing system.** In a study of invoice errors in a company's new billing system, an auditor randomly sampled 35 invoices produced by the new system and recorded actual amount (A), invoice amount (I), and the difference (or error), $x = (A - I)$. The results were $\bar{x} = \$1$ and $s = \$124$. At the time that the sample was drawn, the new system had produced 1,500 invoices. Use this information to find an approximate 95% confidence interval for the true mean error per invoice of the new system. Interpret the result.

Applying the Concepts—Advanced

6.91 **Pesticide residue in corn products.** The U.S. Environmental Protection Agency (EPA) bans use of the cancer-causing pesticide ethylene dibromide (EDB) as a fumigant for grain- and flour-milling equipment. EDB was once used to protect against infestation by microscopic roundworms called *nematodes*. The EPA sets maximum safe levels for EDB presence in raw grain, flour, cake mixes, cereals, bread, and other grain products on supermarket shelves and in warehouses. Of the 3,000 corn-related products sold in one state, tests indicated that 15 of a random sample of 175 had EDB residues above the safe level. Will more than 7% of the corn-related products in this state have to be removed from shelves and warehouses? Explain.

6.7 Confidence Interval for a Population Variance*

In the previous sections, we considered interval estimation for population means or proportions. In this optional section, we discuss a confidence interval for a population variance, σ^2.

Recall Example 1.5 (p. 13) and the U.S. Army Corps of Engineers study of contaminated fish in the Tennessee River, Alabama. It is important for the Corps of Engineers to know how stable the weights of the contaminated fish are. That is, how large is the variation in the fish weights? The key word "variation" indicates that the target population parameter is σ^2, the variance of the weights of all contaminated fish inhabiting the Tennessee River. Of course, the exact value of σ^2 will be unknown. Consequently, the Corps of Engineers wants to estimate its value with a high level of confidence.

Intuitively, it seems reasonable to use the sample variance, s^2, to estimate σ^2. However, unlike with sample means and proportions, the sampling distribution of s^2 does not follow a normal (z) distribution or a Student's t-distribution. Rather, when certain assumptions are satisfied (we discuss these later), the sampling distribution of s^2 possesses approximately a **chi-square (χ^2) distribution.** The chi-square probability distribution, like the t-distribution, is characterized by a quantity called the *degrees of freedom* (df) associated with the distribution. Several chi-square distributions with different df values are shown in Figure 6.18. You can see that unlike z- and t-distributions, the chi-square distribution is not symmetric about 0.

The upper-tail areas for this distribution have been tabulated and are given in Table IV in Appendix D, a portion of which is reproduced in Table 6.7. The table gives the values of χ^2, denoted as χ^2_α, that locate an area of α in the upper tail of the chi-square distribution; that is, $P(\chi^2 > \chi^2_\alpha) = \alpha$. As with the t-statistic, the degrees of freedom

$f(\chi^2)$

df = 1

df = 4

df = 6

0 2 4 6 8 10 12 14 16 χ^2

Figure 6.18

Several χ^2 probability distributions

| Table 6.7 | Reproduction of Part of Table IV in Appendix D: Critical Values of Chi Square |

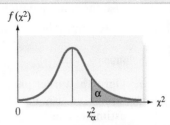

Degrees of Freedom	$\chi^2_{.100}$	$\chi^2_{.050}$	$\chi^2_{.025}$	$\chi^2_{.010}$	$\chi^2_{.005}$
1	2.70554	3.84146	5.02389	6.63490	7.87944
2	4.60517	5.99147	7.37776	9.21034	10.5966
3	6.25139	7.81473	9.34840	11.3449	12.8381
4	7.77944	9.48773	11.1433	13.2767	14.8602
5	9.23635	11.0705	12.8325	15.0863	16.7496
6	10.6446	12.5916	14.4494	16.8119	18.5476
7	12.0170	14.0671	16.0128	18.4753	20.2777
8	13.3616	15.5073	17.5346	20.0902	21.9550
9	14.6837	16.9190	19.0228	21.6660	23.5893
10	15.9871	18.3070	20.4831	23.2093	25.1882
11	17.2750	19.6751	21.9200	24.7250	25.7569
12	18.5494	21.0261	23.3367	26.2170	28.2995
13	19.8119	22.3621	24.7356	27.6883	29.8194
14	21.0642	23.6848	26.1190	29.1413	31.3193
15	22.3072	24.9958	27.4884	30.5779	32.8013
16	23.5418	26.2862	28.8454	31.9999	34.2672
17	24.7690	27.5871	30.1910	33.4087	35.7185
18	25.9894	28.8693	31.5264	34.8053	37.1564
19	27.2036	30.1435	32.8523	36.1908	38.5822

associated with s^2 are $(n - 1)$. Thus, for $n = 10$ and an upper-tail value $\alpha = .05$, you will have $n - 1 = 9$ df and $\chi^2_{.05} = 16.9190$ (highlighted in Table 6.7).

The chi-square distribution is used to find a confidence interval for σ^2, as shown in the box. An illustrative example follows.

A $100(1 - \alpha)$ Confidence Interval for σ^2

$$\frac{(n - 1)s^2}{\chi^2_{\alpha/2}} \leq \sigma^2 \leq \frac{(n - 1)s^2}{\chi^2_{(1 - \alpha/2)}}$$

where $\chi^2_{\alpha/2}$ and $\chi^2_{(1 - \alpha/2)}$ are values corresponding to an area of $\alpha/2$ in the right (upper) and left (lower) tails, respectively, of the chi-square distribution based on $(n - 1)$ degrees of freedom.

Conditions Required for a Valid Confidence Interval for σ^2

1. A random sample is selected from the target population.

2. The population of interest has a relative frequency distribution that is approximately normal.

Example 6.12

Estimating σ^2—Weight Variance of Contaminated Fish

Problem Refer to the U.S. Army Corps of Engineers study of contaminated fish in the Tennessee River. The Corps of Engineers has collected data for a random sample of 144 fish contaminated with DDT. (The engineers made sure to capture contaminated fish in several different randomly selected streams and tributaries of the river.) The fish weights (in grams) are saved in the **DDT** file. The Army Corps of Engineers wants to estimate the true variation in fish weights in order to determine whether the fish are stable enough to allow further testing for DDT contamination.

a. Use the sample data to find a 95% confidence interval for the parameter of interest.

b. Determine whether the confidence interval, part **a,** is valid.

Solution

a. Here, the target parameter is σ^2, the variance of the population of weights of contaminated fish. First we need to find the sample variance, s^2, to compute the interval estimate. The Minitab printout, Figure 6.19 gives descriptive statistics for the sample weights saved in the **DDT** file. You can see that $s = 376.5$ grams. Consequently, $s^2 = (376.5)^2 = 141,752.25$.

Figure 6.19

Minitab descriptive statistics for fish weights, Example 6.12

Descriptive Statistics: WEIGHT

Variable	N	Mean	StDev	Minimum	Median	Maximum
WEIGHT	144	1049.7	376.5	173.0	1000.0	2302.0

Next, we require the critical values $\chi^2_{\alpha/2}$ and $\chi^2_{(1-\alpha/2)}$ for a chi-square distribution. For a 95% confidence interval, $\alpha = .05$, $\alpha/2 = .025$, and $(1 - \alpha/2) = .975$. Therefore, we need $\chi^2_{.025}$ and $\chi^2_{.975}$. Now, for a sample size $n = 144$, the degrees of freedom associated with the distribution is df $= (n - 1) = 143$. Looking in the df $= 150$ row of Table IV, Appendix D (the row with the df value closest to 143), we find $\chi^2_{.025} = 185.800$ and $\chi^2_{.975} = 117.985$.

Substituting the appropriate values into the formula given in the box, we obtain

$$\frac{(144 - 1)(376.5)^2}{185.500} \le \sigma^2 \le \frac{(144 - 1)(376.5)^2}{117.985}$$

Or,

$$109,275 \le \sigma^2 \le 171,806$$

Thus, the Army Corps of Engineers can be 95% confident that the variance in weights of the population of contaminated fish ranges between 109,275 and 171,806.

b. According to the box, two conditions are required for the confidence interval to be valid. First, the sample must be randomly selected from the population. The Army Corps of Engineers did, indeed, collect a random sample of contaminated fish, making sure to sample fish from different location in the Tennessee River. Second, the population data (the fish weights) must be approximately normally distributed. A Minitab histogram for the sampled fish weights (with a normal curve superimposed) is displayed in Figure 6.20. Clearly, the data appear to be approximately normally distributed. Thus, the confidence interval is valid.

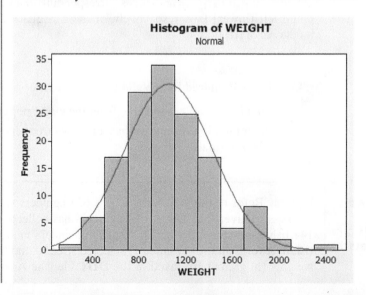

Figure 6.20

Minitab histogram of fish weights, Example 6.12

Look Ahead Will this confidence interval to practically useful in helping the Corps of Engineers decide whether the weights of the fish are stable? Only if it is clear what a weight variance of, say, 150,000 grams^2 implies. Most likely, the Corps of Engineers will want the interval in the same units as the weight measurement—grams. Consequently, a confidence interval for σ, the standard deviation of the population of fish weights, is desired. We demonstrate how to obtain this interval estimate in the next example.

■ **Now Work Exercise 6.98a, b**

Example 6.13

Estimating σ—Weight Standard Deviation of Contaminated Fish

Problem Refer to Example 6.12. Find a 95% confidence interval for σ, the true standard deviation of the contaminated fish weights.

Solution A confidence interval for σ is obtained by taking the square roots of the lower and upper endpoints of a confidence interval for σ^2. Consequently, the 95% confidence interval for σ is:

$$\sqrt{109,275} \le \sigma \le \sqrt{171,806}$$

Or,

$$330.5 \le \sigma \le 414.5$$

Thus, the engineers can be 95% confident that the true standard deviation of fish weights is between 330.5 grams and 414.5 grams.

Look Back Suppose the Corps of Engineers' threshold is $\sigma = 500$ grams. That is, if the standard deviation in fish weights is 500 grams or higher, further DDT contamination tests will be suspended due to the unstableness of the fish weights. Since the 95% confidence interval for σ lies below 500 grams, the engineers will continue the DDT contamination tests on the fish.

■ **Now Work Exercise 6.98c, d, e, f**

⚠ **CAUTION** The procedure for estimating either σ^2 or σ requires an assumption regardless of whether the sample size n is large or small (see the condition in the box). The sampled data must come from a population that has an approximate normal distribution. Unlike small-sample confidence intervals for μ based on the t-distribution, *slight to moderate departures from normality will render the chi-square confidence interval for σ^2 invalid.*

Exercises 6.92–6.104

Learning the Mechanics

6.92 For each of the following combinations of α and degrees of freedom (df), use Table IV in Appendix D to find the values of $\chi^2_{\alpha/2}$ and $\chi^2_{(1-\alpha/2)}$ that would be used to form a confidence interval for σ^2.
  a. $\alpha = .05, df = 7$
  b. $\alpha = .10, df = 16$
  c. $\alpha = .01, df = 20$
  d. $\alpha = .05, df = 20$

6.93 Given the following values of $\bar{x}$, s, and n, form a 90% confidence interval for σ^2.
  a. $\bar{x} = 21, s = 2.5, n = 50$
  b. $\bar{x} = 1.3, s = .02, n = 15$
  c. $\bar{x} = 167, s = 31.6, n = 22$
  d. $\bar{x} = 9.4, s = 1.5, n = 5$

6.94 Refer to Exercise 6.93. For each part, **a–d,** form a 90% confidence interval for σ.

6.95 A random sample of $n = 6$ observations from a normal distribution resulted in the data shown in the table. Compute a 95% confidence interval for σ^2.

L06095

8	2	3	7	11	6

Applying the Concepts—Basics

6.96 **Motivation of drug dealers.** Refer to the *Applied Psychology in Criminal Justice* (Sep. 2009) study of the personality characteristics of convicted drug dealers, Exercise 5.33 (p. 285). A random sample of 100 drug dealers had a mean Wanting Recognition (WR) score of 39 points, with a standard deviation of 6 points. The researchers are interested in σ^2, the variation in WR scores for all convicted drug dealers.

a. Identify the target parameter, in symbols and words.

b. Compute a 99% confidence interval for σ^2.

c. What does it mean to say that the target parameter lies within the interval with "99% confidence"?

d. What assumption about the data must be satisfied in order for the confidence interval to be valid?

e. To obtain a practical interpretation of the interval, part **b,** explain why a confidence interval for the standard deviation, σ, is desired.

f. Use the results, part **b,** to compute a 99% confidence interval for σ. Give a practical interpretation of the interval.

6.97 Facial structure of CEOs. Refer to the *Psychological Science* (Vol. 22, 2011) study of a chief executive officer's facial structure, Exercise 6.20 (p. 310). Recall that the facial width-to-height ratio (WHR) was determined by computer analysis for each in a sample of 55 CEOs at publicly traded *Fortune* 500 firms, with the following results: $\bar{x} = 1.96, s = .15$.

a. Find and interpret a 95% confidence interval for the standard deviation, σ, of the facial WHR values for all CEOs at publicly traded *Fortune* 500 firms. Interpret the result.

b. For the interval, part **a,** to be valid, the population of WHR values should be distributed how? Draw a sketch of the required distribution to support your answer.

6.98 Corporate sustainability of CPA firms. Refer to the *Business and Society* (March 2011) study on the sustainability behaviors of CPA corporations, Exercise 6.12 (p. 308). Recall that the level of support for corporate sustainability (measured on a quantitative scale ranging from 0 to 160 points) was obtained for each in a sample of 992 senior managers at CPA firms. The accompanying Minitab printout gives 90% confidence intervals for both the variance and standard deviation of level of support for all senior managers at CPA firms.

```
Statistics

Variable    N   StDev  Variance
Support    992   26.9      722


90% Confidence Intervals

                       CI for      CI for
Variable  Method       StDev       Variance
Support   Chi-Square  (25.9, 27.9) (672, 779)
```

a. Locate the 90% confidence interval for σ^2 on the printout. Interpret the result.

b. Use the sample variance on the printout to calculate the 90% confidence interval for σ^2. Does your result agree with the interval shown on the printout?

c. Locate the 90% confidence interval for σ on the printout.

d. Use the result, part **a,** to calculate the 90% confidence interval for σ. Does your result agree with the interval shown on the printout?

e. Give a practical interpretation of the 90% confidence interval for σ.

f. What assumption about the distribution of level of support is required for the inference, part **e,** to be valid? Is this assumption reasonably satisfied? (Use your answer to Exercise 4.121, p. 240.)

6.99 Radon exposure in Egyptian tombs. Refer to the *Radiation Protection Dosimetry* (December 2010) study of radon exposure in tombs carved from limestone in the Egyptian Valley of Kings, Exercise 6.30 (p. 318). The radon levels in the inner chambers of a sample of 12 tombs were determined, yielding the following summary statistics: $\bar{x} = 3,643 \text{ Bq/m}^3$ and $s = 4,487 \text{ Bq/m}^3$. Use this information to estimate, with 95% confidence, the true standard deviation of radon levels in tombs in the Valley of Kings. Interpret the resulting interval.

Applying the Concepts—Intermediate

6.100 Jitter in a water power system. *Jitter* is a term used to describe the variation in conduction time of a water power system. Low throughput jitter is critical to successful waterline technology. An investigation of throughput jitter in the opening switch of a prototype system (*Journal of Applied Physics*) yielded the following descriptive statistics on conduction time for $n = 18$ trials: $\bar{x} = 334.8$ nanoseconds, $s = 6.3$ nanoseconds. (Conduction time is defined as the length of time required for the downstream current to equal 10% of the upstream current.)

a. Construct a 95% confidence interval for the true standard deviation of conduction times of the prototype system.

b. Practically interpret the confidence interval, part **a.**

c. A system is considered to have low throughput jitter if the true conduction time standard deviation is less than 7 nanoseconds. Does the prototype system satisfy this requirement? Explain.

6.101 Drug content assessment. Refer to the *Analytical Chemistry* (Dec. 15, 2009) study of a new method used by GlaxoSmithKline Medicines Research Center to determine the amount of drug in a tablet, Exercise 4.123 (p. 240). Drug concentrations (measured as a percentage) for 50 randomly selected tablets are repeated in the accompanying table. For comparisons against a standard method, the scientists at GlaxoSmithKline desire an estimate of the variability in drug concentrations for the new method. Obtain the estimate for the scientists using a 99% confidence interval. Interpret the interval.

91.28	92.83	89.35	91.90	82.85	94.83	89.83	89.00	84.62
86.96	88.32	91.17	83.86	89.74	92.24	92.59	84.21	89.36
90.96	92.85	89.39	89.82	89.91	92.16	88.67	89.35	86.51
89.04	91.82	93.02	88.32	88.76	89.26	90.36	87.16	91.74
86.12	92.10	83.33	87.31	88.20	92.78	86.35	93.84	91.20
93.44	86.77	83.77	93.19	81.79				

Source: Based on Borman, P. J., Marion, J. C., Damjanov, I., & Jackson, P. "Design and analysis of method equivalence studies," *Analytical Chemistry,* Vol. 81, No. 24, December 15, 2009 (Table 3).

6.102 Phishing attacks on e-mail accounts. Refer to the *Chance* (Summer 2007) study of an actual phishing attack against an organization, Exercise 5.23 (p. 284). Recall that *phishing* describes an attempt to extract personal/financial information from unsuspecting people through fraudulent e-mail. The interarrival times (in seconds) for 267 fraud box e-mail notifications are saved in the accompanying file. Like with Exercise 5.23, consider these interarrival times to represent the population of interest.

a. Obtain a random sample of $n = 10$ interarrival times from the population.

b. Use the sample, part **b,** to obtain an interval estimate of the population variance of the interarrival times. What is the measure of reliability for your estimate?

c. Find the true population variance for the data. Does the interval, part **b,** contain the true variance? Give one reason why it may not.

6.103 Lobster trap placement. Refer to the *Bulletin of Marine Science* (April 2010) observational study of teams fishing for the red spiny lobster in Baja California Sur, Mexico, Exercise 6.29 (p. 318). Trap-spacing measurements (in meters) for a sample of seven teams of red spiny lobster fishermen are repeated in the table. The researchers want to know how variable the trap-spacing measurements are for the population of red spiny lobster fishermen fishing in Baja California Sur, Mexico. Provide the researchers with an estimate of the target parameter using a 99% confidence interval.

93	99	105	94	82	70	86

Source: Based on Shester, G. G. "Explaining catch variation among Baja California lobster fishers through spatial analysis of trap-placement decisions," *Bulletin of Marine Science,* Vol. 86, No. 2, April 2010 (Table 1) , pp. 479–498.

6.104 Is honey a cough remedy? Refer to the *Archives of Pediatrics and Adolescent Medicine* (Dec. 2007) study of honey as a remedy for coughing, Exercise 2.30 (p. 61). Recall that the 105 ill children in the sample were randomly divided into groups. One group received a dosage of an over-the-counter cough medicine (DM); another group received a dosage of honey (H). The coughing improvement scores (as determined by the children's parents) for the patients in the two groups are reproduced in the accompanying table. The pediatric researchers desire information on the variation in coughing improvement scores for each of the two groups.

a. Find a 90% confidence interval for the standard deviation in improvement scores for the honey dosage group.

b. Repeat part **a** for the DM dosage group.

c. Based on the results, parts **a** and **b,** what conclusions can the pediatric researchers draw about which group has the smaller variation in improvement scores? (We demonstrate a more statistically valid method for comparing variances in Chapter 8.)

Honey Dosage:	12 11 15 11 10 13 10 4 15 16 9 14 10 6 10 8 11 12 12 8 12 9 11 15 10 15 9 13 8 12 10 8 9 5 12
DM Dosage:	4 6 9 4 7 7 7 9 12 10 11 6 3 4 9 12 7 6 8 12 12 4 12 13 7 10 13 9 4 4 10 15 9

Source: Based on Paul, I. M., et al. "Effect of honey, dextromethorphan, and no treatment on nocturnal cough and sleep quality for coughing children and their parents," *Archives of Pediatrics and Adolescent Medicine,* Vol. 161, No. 12, Dec. 2007 (data simulated).

◼ Chapter Notes

Key Terms

Note: Asterisks (*) denote items from the optional sections of this chapter.

Adjusted $(1 - \alpha)100\%$ confidence interval for a population parameter 323
*Chi-square distribution 336
Confidence coefficient 304
Confidence interval 301
Confidence level 304
Degrees of freedom 312
*Finite population correction factor 333

Interval estimator 301
Large-sample confidence interval for p 321
Margin of sampling error 328
Point estimator 301
Target parameter 301
t-statistic 312
z-statistic 312

Key Symbols

θ	General population parameter (theta)
μ	Population mean
σ^2	Population variance
σ	Population standard deviation
p	Population proportion; $P(\text{Success})$ in binomial trial
q	$1 - p$
$\bar{x}$	Sample mean (estimator of μ)
$\hat{p}$	Sample proportion (estimator of p)
$*s^2$	Sample variance (estimator of σ^2)
$\mu_{\bar{x}}$	Mean of the population sampling distribution of $\bar{x}$
$\sigma_{\bar{x}}$	Standard deviation of the sampling distribution of $\bar{x}$
$\sigma_{\hat{p}}$	Standard deviation of the sampling distribution of $\hat{p}$
ME	Margin of sampling error in estimation
α	$(1 - \alpha)$ represents the confidence coefficient
$z_{\alpha/2}$	z-value used in a $100(1 - \alpha)\%$ large-sample confidence interval for μ or p
$t_{\alpha/2}$	Student's t-value used in a $100(1 - \alpha)\%$ small-sample confidence interval for μ
$*N$	Number of observations in the target population
$*\chi^2_{\alpha/2}$	Chi-square value used in a $100(1 - \alpha)\%$ confidence interval for σ^2

Key Ideas

Population Parameters, Estimators, and Standard Errors

Parameter (θ)	Estimator $(\hat{\theta})$	Standard Error of Estimator $(\sigma_{\hat{\theta}})$	Estimated Std. Error $(\hat{\sigma}_{\hat{\theta}})$
Mean, μ	$\bar{x}$	$\sigma/\sqrt{n}$	$s/\sqrt{n}$
Proportion, p	$\hat{p}$	$\sqrt{pq/n}$	$\sqrt{\hat{p}\hat{q}/n}$
*Variance, σ^2	s^2	—	—

Confidence Interval: An interval that encloses an unknown population parameter with a certain level of confidence $(1 - \alpha)$

Confidence Coefficient: The probability $(1 - \alpha)$ that a randomly selected confidence interval encloses the true value of the population parameter.

Key Words for Identifying the Target Parameter

μ—Mean, Average
p—Proportion, Fraction, Percentage, Rate, Probability
*σ^2—Variance, Variation, Spread

Commonly Used z-Values for a Large-Sample Confidence Interval

90% CI: $\quad (1 - \alpha) = .10 \quad z_{.05} = 1.645$
95% CI: $\quad (1 - \alpha) = .05 \quad z_{.025} = 1.96$
98% CI: $\quad (1 - \alpha) = .02 \quad z_{.01} = 2.326$
99% CI: $\quad (1 - \alpha) = .01 \quad z_{.005} = 2.576$

Determining the Sample Size n

Estimating μ: $n = (z_{\alpha/2})^2(\sigma^2)/(ME)^2$
Estimating p: $n = (z_{\alpha/2})^2(pq)/(ME)^2$

*Finite Population Correction Factor

Required when $n/N > .05$

Illustrating the Notion of "95% Confidence"

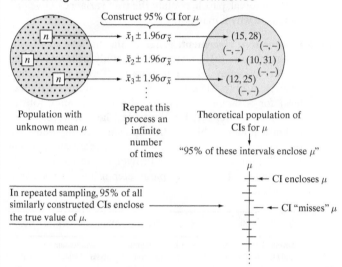

Guide to Forming a Confidence Interval

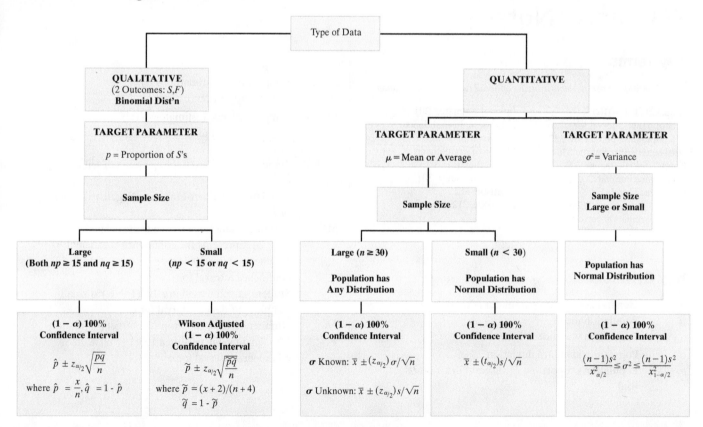

Supplementary Exercises 6.105–6.137

Note: List the assumptions necessary for the valid implementation of the statistical procedures you use in solving all these exercises. Exercises marked with an asterisk (*) are from the optional sections in this chapter.

Learning the Mechanics

6.105 Let t_0 represent a particular value of t from Table III in Appendix D. Find the table values such that the following statements are true.
  a. $P(t \le t_0) = .05$ where df $= 20$
  b. $P(t \ge t_0) = .005$ where df $= 9$
  c. $P(t \le -t_0 \text{ or } t \le t_0) = .10$ where df $= 8$
  d. $P(t \le -t_0 \text{ or } t \ge t_0) = .01$ where df $= 17$

6.106 In each of the following instances, determine whether you would use a z- or t-statistic (or neither) to form a 95% confidence interval and then look up the appropriate z- or t-value.
  a. Random sample of size $n = 23$ from a normal distribution with unknown mean μ and standard deviation σ
  b. Random sample of size $n = 135$ from a normal distribution with unknown mean μ and standard deviation σ
  c. Random sample of size $n = 10$ from a normal distribution with unknown mean μ and standard deviation $s = 5$
  d. Random sample of size $n = 73$ from a distribution about which nothing is known
  e. Random sample of size $n = 12$ from a distribution about which nothing is known

6.107 A random sample of 225 measurements is selected from a population, and the sample mean and standard deviation are $\bar{x} = 32.5$ and $s = 30.0$, respectively.
  a. Use a 99% confidence interval to estimate the mean of the population, μ.
  b. How large a sample would be needed to estimate m to within .5 with 99% confidence?
  *c. Use a 99% confidence interval to estimate the population variance, σ^2.
  d. What is meant by the phrase *99% confidence* as it is used in this exercise?

6.108 In a random sample of 400 measurements, 227 of the measurements possess the characteristic of interest, A.
  a. Use a 95% confidence interval to estimate the true proportion p of measurements in the population with characteristic A.
  b. How large a sample would be needed to estimate p to within .02 with 95% confidence?

*6.109 Find $\chi^2_{\alpha/2}$ and $\chi^2_{(1-\alpha/2)}$ from Table IV, Appendix D, for each of the following:
  a. $n = 10, \alpha = .05$
  b. $n = 20, \alpha = .05$
  c. $n = 50, \alpha = .01$

*6.110 Calculate the finite population correction factor for each of the following situations:
  a. $n = 50, N = 2,000$
  b. $n = 20, N = 100$
  c. $n = 300, N = 1,500$

Applying the Concepts—Basic

6.111 General health survey. The Centers for Disease Control and Prevention (CDCP) in Atlanta, Georgia, conducts an annual survey of the general health of the U.S. population as part of its Behavioral Risk Factor Surveillance System. Using random-digit dialing, the CDCP telephones U.S. citizens over 18 years of age and asks them the following four questions:
  1. Is your health generally excellent, very good, good, fair, or poor?
  2. How many days during the previous 30 days was your physical health not good because of injury or illness?
  3. How many days during the previous 30 days was your mental health not good because of stress, depression, or emotional problems?
  4. How many days during the previous 30 days did your physical or mental health prevent you from performing your usual activities?

Identify the parameter of interest for each question.

6.112 Latex allergy in health care workers. Health care workers who use latex gloves with glove powder on a daily basis are particularly susceptible to developing a latex allergy. Symptoms of a latex allergy include conjunctivitis, hand eczema, nasal congestion, skin rash, and shortness of breath. Each in a sample of 46 hospital employees who were diagnosed with latex allergy based on a skin-prick test reported on their exposure to latex gloves (*Current Allergy & Clinical Immunology,* Mar. 2004). Summary statistics for the number of latex gloves used per week are $\bar{x} = 19.3, s = 11.9$.
  a. Give a point estimate for the average number of latex gloves used per week by all health care workers with a latex allergy.
  b. Form a 95% confidence interval for the average number of latex gloves used per week by all health care workers with a latex allergy.
  c. Give a practical interpretation of the interval, part **b**.
  d. Give the conditions required for the interval, part **b**, to be valid.

6.113 Material safety data sheets. For more than 20 years, the Occupational Safety & Health Administration has required companies that handle hazardous chemicals to complete material safety data sheets (MSDSs). These MSDSs have been criticized for being too hard to understand and complete by workers. Although improvements were implemented in 1990, a more recent study of 150 MSDSs revealed that only 11% were satisfactorily completed (*Chemical & Engineering News,* Feb. 7, 2005).
  a. Give a point estimate of p, the true proportion of MSDSs that are satisfactorily completed.
  b. Find a 95% confidence interval for p.
  c. Give a practical interpretation of the interval, part **b**.

6.114 Products "Made in the USA." Refer to Exercise 2.152 (p. 116) and the *Journal of Global Business* (Spring 2002) survey to determine what "Made in the USA" means to consumers. Recall that 106 shoppers at a shopping mall in Muncie, Indiana, responded to the question, "'Made in the USA' means what percentage of U.S. labor and materials?" Sixty-four shoppers answered, "100%."

a. Define the population of interest in the survey.

b. What is the characteristic of interest in the population?

c. Estimate the true proportion of consumers who believe "Made in the USA" means 100% U.S. labor and materials using a 90% confidence interval.

d. Give a practical interpretation of the interval, part **c.**

e. Explain what the phrase "90% confidence" means for this interval.

f. Compute the sample size necessary to estimate the true proportion to within .05 using a 90% confidence interval.

6.115 Water pollution testing. The EPA wants to test a randomly selected sample of n water specimens and estimate the mean daily rate of pollution produced by a mining operation. If the EPA wants a 95% confidence interval estimate with a sampling error of 1 milligram per liter (mg/L), how many water specimens are required in the sample? Assume prior knowledge indicates that pollution readings in water samples taken during a day are approximately normally distributed with a standard deviation equal to 5 mg/L.

6.116 Lead and copper in drinking water. Periodically, the Hillsborough County (Florida) Water Department tests the drinking water of homeowners for contaminants such as lead and copper. The lead and copper levels in water specimens collected for a sample of 10 residents of the Crystal Lakes Manors subdivision are shown below, followed by a Minitab printout analyzing the data.

PBCU

Lead (µg/L)	Copper (mg/L)
1.32	.508
0	.279
13.1	.320
.919	.904
.657	.221
3.0	.283
1.32	.475
4.09	.130
4.45	.220
0	.743

Source: Data from Hillsborough Country Water Department Environmental Laboratory, Tampa, Florida.

Variable	N	Mean	StDev	SE Mean	90% CI
LEAD	10	2.89	3.92	1.24	(0.61, 5.16)
COPPER	10	0.4083	0.2495	0.0789	(0.2637, 0.5529)

a. Locate a 90% confidence interval for the mean lead level in water specimens from Crystal Lakes Manors on the printout.

b. Locate a 90% confidence interval for the mean copper level in water specimens from Crystal Lakes Manors on the printout.

c. Interpret the intervals, parts **a** and **b,** in the words of the problem.

d. Discuss the meaning of the phrase "90% confident."

***6.117 Employees with substance abuse problems.** According to the New Jersey *Governor's Council for a Drug-Free Workplace Report,* 50 of the 72 sampled businesses that are members of the council admitted that they had employees with substance abuse problems. At the time of the survey, 251 New Jersey businesses were members of the Governor's Council. Use the finite population correction factor to find a 95% confidence interval for the proportion of all New Jersey Governor's Council business members who have employees with substance abuse problems. Interpret the resulting interval.

6.118 Sick leave taken by employees. A company is interested in estimating μ, the mean number of days of sick leave taken by all its employees. The firm's statistician selects at random 100 personnel files and notes the number of sick days taken by each employee. The following sample statistics are computed: $\bar{x} = 12.2$ days, $s = 10$ days.

a. Estimate μ using a 90% confidence interval. Interpret the result.

b. How many personnel files would the statistician have to select in order to estimate μ to within 2 days with a 99% confidence interval?

***c.** Estimate σ using a 90% confidence interval. Interpret the result.

6.119 Blogs for *Fortune* 500 firms. Refer to the *Journal of Relationship Marketing* (Vol. 7, 2008) study of the prevalence of blogs and forums at *Fortune* 500 firms with both English and Chinese Web sites, Exercise 2.78 (p. 84). In a sample of 56 firms that provide blogs and forums as marketing tools, the mean number of blogs/forums per site was 4.25, with a standard deviation of 12.02.

a. Find a 99% confidence interval for the mean number of blogs/forums per site of all *Fortune* 500 firms that provide blogs and forums as marketing tools.

b. Give a practical interpretation of the interval, part **a.**

c. The number of blogs/forums per site is known to have a highly skewed distribution. Does this impact the validity of the inference, part **b?**

Applying the Concepts—Intermediate

6.120 Size of diamonds sold at retail. Refer to Exercise 2.157 (p. 117) and the *Journal of Statistics Education* data on diamonds saved in the accompanying file. Consider the quantitative variable, number of carats, recorded for each of the 308 diamonds for sale on the open market.

DIAMND

a. Select a random sample of 30 diamonds from the 308 diamonds.

b. Find the mean and standard deviation of the number of carats per diamond for the sample.

c. Use the sample information, part **b,** to construct a 95% confidence interval for the mean number of carats in the population of 308 diamonds.

d. Interpret the phrase *95% confidence* when applied to the interval, part **c.**

e. Refer to the mean of all 308 diamonds you calculated in Exercise 2.157. Does the "population" mean fall within the confidence interval of part **c?**

6.121 Fish contaminated by a plant's discharge. Refer (Example 1.5, p. 13) to the U.S. Army Corps of Engineers data on a sample of 144 contaminated fish collected from the river adjacent to a chemical plant. Estimate the proportion of contaminated fish that are of the channel catfish species. Use a 90% confidence interval and interpret the result.

DDT

6.122 Improving the productivity of chickens. Farmers have discovered that the more domestic chickens peck at objects placed in their environment, the healthier and more productive the chickens seem to be. White string has been found to be a particularly attractive pecking stimulus. In one experiment, 72 chickens were exposed to a string stimulus. Instead of white string, blue-colored string was used. The number of pecks each chicken took at the blue string over a specified time interval was recorded. Summary statistics for the 72 chickens were $\bar{x} = 1.13$ pecks, $s = 2.21$ pecks (*Applied Animal Behaviour Science*, Oct. 2000).

a. Estimate the population mean number of pecks made by chickens pecking at blue string using a 99% confidence interval. Interpret the result.

b. Previous research has shown that $\mu = 7.5$ pecks if chickens are exposed to white string. Based on the results, part **a**, is there evidence that chickens are more apt to peck at white string than blue string? Explain.

6.123 Petroleum waste contamination. Accidental spillage and misguided disposal of petroleum wastes have resulted in extensive contamination of soils across the country. A common hazardous compound found in the contaminated soil is benzo(a)pyrene [B(a)p]. An experiment was conducted to determine the effectiveness of a method designed to remove B(a)p from soil (*Journal of Hazardous Materials*, June 1995). Three soil specimens contaminated with a known amount of B(a)p were treated with a toxin that inhibits microbial growth. After 95 days of incubation, the percentage of B(a)p removed from each soil specimen was measured. The experiment produced the following summary statistics: $\bar{x} = 49.3$ and $s = 1.5$.

a. Use a 99% confidence interval to estimate the mean percentage of B(a)p removed from a soil specimen in which the toxin was used.

b. Interpret the interval in terms of this application.

c. What assumption is necessary to ensure the validity of this confidence interval?

d. Comment on whether the true mean percent removed could be as high as 50%.

*e. Find and interpret a 90% confidence interval for the true variance in the percentages of B(a)p removed.

6.124 IRS answers to gift tax questions. According to estimates made by the General Accounting Office, the Internal Revenue Service (IRS) answered 18.3 million telephone inquiries during a recent tax season, and 17% of the IRS offices provided wrong answers. These estimates were based on data collected from sample calls to numerous IRS offices. How many IRS offices should be randomly selected and contacted in order to estimate the proportion of IRS offices that fail to correctly answer questions about gift taxes with a 90% confidence interval of width .06?

6.125 IQ comparison of older vs. younger workers. The Age Discrimination in Employment Act (ADEA) made it illegal to discriminate against workers 40 years of age and older. Opponents of the law argue that there are sound economic reasons why employers would not want to hire and train workers who are very close to retirement. They also argue that people's abilities tend to deteriorate with age. Do 25-year-olds score significantly higher than 60-year-olds on the Wechsler Adult Intelligence Scale, the most popular IQ test? The data in the next table are raw test scores (i.e., not the familiar normalized IQ scores) for a sample of thirty-six 25-year-olds and thirty-six 60-year-olds.

25-Year-Olds					
54	61	80	92	41	63
59	68	66	76	82	80
82	47	81	77	88	94
49	86	55	82	45	51
70	72	63	50	52	67
75	60	58	49	63	68

60-Year-Olds					
42	54	38	22	58	37
60	49	51	60	45	42
73	28	65	65	60	34
34	33	40	28	36	60
45	61	47	30	45	45
45	37	27	40	37	58

a. Estimate the mean raw test score for all 25-year-olds using a 99% confidence interval. Give a practical interpretation of the confidence interval.

b. What assumption(s) must hold for the method of estimation used in part **a** to be appropriate?

c. Find a 95% confidence interval for the mean raw score of all 60-year-olds and interpret your result.

6.126 Air bags pose danger for children. By law, all new cars must be equipped with both driver-side and passenger-side safety air bags. There is concern, however, over whether air bags pose a danger to children sitting on the passenger side. In a National Highway Traffic Safety Administration (NHTSA) study of 55 people killed by the explosive force of air bags, 35 were children seated on the front-passenger side (*www.nhtsa.org*). This study led some car owners with children to disconnect the passenger-side air bag. Consider all fatal automobile accidents in which it is determined that air bags were the cause of death. Let p represent the true proportion of these accidents involving children seated on the front-passenger side.

a. Use the data from the NHTSA study to estimate p.

b. Construct a 99% confidence interval for p.

c. Interpret the interval, part **b**, in the words of the problem.

d. NHTSA investigators determined that 24 of the 35 children killed by the air bags were not wearing seat belts or were improperly restrained. How does this information impact your assessment of the risk of an air bag fatality?

e. How many fatal accidents should the NHTSA sample in order to estimate the proportion to within .1 of its true value using a 99% confidence interval?

6.127 Accuracy of price scanners at Wal-Mart. The National Institute for Standards and Technology (NIST) mandates that for every 100 items scanned through the electronic checkout scanner at a retail store, no more than 2 should have an inaccurate price. A study of the accuracy of checkout scanners at Wal-Mart stores in California was conducted. At each of 60 randomly selected Wal-Mart stores, 100 random items were scanned. The researchers found that 52 of the 60 stores had more than 2 items that were inaccurately priced.

a. Give an estimate of p, the proportion of Wal-Mart stores in California that have more than 2 inaccurately priced items per 100 items scanned.

b. Construct a 95% confidence interval for *p*.

c. Give a practical interpretation of the interval, part **b.**

d. Suppose a Wal-Mart spokesperson claims that 99% of California Wal-Mart stores are in compliance with the NIST mandate on accuracy of price scanners. Comment on the believability of this claim.

e. Are the conditions required for a valid large-sample confidence interval for *p* satisfied in this application? If not, comment on the validity of the inference in part *d.*

f. Determine the number of Wal-Mart stores that must be sampled in order to estimate the true proportion to within .05 with 90% confidence using the large-sample method.

6.128 Performance appraisal process. The relationship between an employee's participation in the performance appraisal process and subsequent subordinate reactions toward the appraisal was investigated in the *Journal of Applied Psychology* (Aug. 1998). In Chapter 11 we will discuss a quantitative measure of the relationship between two variables, called the *coefficient* of *correlation r.* The researchers obtained *r* for a sample of 34 studies that examined the relationship between appraisal participation and a subordinate's satisfaction with the appraisal. These correlations are listed in the table. (Values of *r* near +1 reflect a strong positive relationship between the variables.) Find a 95% confidence interval for the mean of the data and interpret it in the words of the problem.

.50	.58	.71	.46	.63	.66	.31	.35	.51	.06	.35	.19
.40	.63	.43	.16	−.08	.51	.59	.43	.30	.69	.25	.20
.39	.20	.51	.68	.74	.65	.34	.45	.31	.27		

Source: Data from Cawley, B. D., Keeping, L. M., & Levy, P. E. "Participation in the performance appraisal process and employees reactions: A meta-analytic review of field investigations," *Journal of Applied Psychology,* Vol. 83, No. 4, Aug. 1998, pp. 632–633 (Appendix).

6.129 Vacation times at major companies. The primary determinant of the amount of vacation time U.S. employees receive is their length of service. According to data released by Hewitt Associates, more than 8 of 10 employers provide 2 weeks of vacation after the first year. After 5 years, 75% of employers provide 3 weeks, and after 15 years most provide 4-week vacations. To more accurately estimate *p*, the proportion of U.S. employers who provide only 2 weeks of vacation to new hires, a random sample of 24 major U.S. companies was contacted. The following vacation times were reported (in days).

10	12	10	10	10	10
15	10	10	10	10	10
10	10	10	10	10	15
10	10	15	10	10	10

a. Construct a 95% confidence interval for *p*.

b. Is the sample size large enough to ensure that the normal distribution provides a reasonable approximation to the sampling distribution of $\hat{p}$? Justify your answer.

c. How large a sample would be required to estimate *p* to within .02 with 95% confidence?

6.130 Salmonella poisoning from eating an ice cream bar. Recently, a case of salmonella (bacterial) poisoning was traced to a particular brand of ice cream bar, and the manufacturer removed the bars from the market. Despite this response, many consumers refused to purchase *any* brand of ice cream bars for some period of time after the event (McClave, personal consulting). One manufacturer conducted a survey of consumers 6 months after the outbreak. A sample of 244 ice cream bar consumers was contacted, and 23 respondents indicated that they would not purchase ice cream bars because of the potential for food poisoning.

a. What is the point estimate of the true fraction of the entire market who refuse to purchase bars 6 months after the outbreak?

b. Is the sample size large enough to use the normal approximation for the sampling distribution of the estimator of the binomial probability? Justify your response.

c. Construct a 95% confidence interval for the true proportion of the market who still refuses to purchase ice cream bars 6 months after the event.

d. Interpret both the point estimate and confidence interval in terms of this application.

6.131 Salmonella poisoning from eating an ice cream bar (cont'd). Refer to Exercise 6.130. Suppose it is now 1 year after the outbreak of food poisoning was traced to ice cream bars. The manufacturer wishes to estimate the proportion who still will not purchase bars to within .02 using a 95% confidence interval. How many consumers should be sampled?

6.132 Latex allergy in health care workers. Refer to the *Current Allergy & Clinical Immunology* (Mar. 2004) study of health care workers who use latex gloves, Exercise 6.112 (p. 343). In addition to the 46 hospital employees who were diagnosed with a latex allergy based on a skin-prick test, another 37 health care workers were diagnosed with the allergy using a latex-specific serum test. Of these 83 workers with confirmed latex allergy, only 36 suspected that they had the allergy when asked on a questionnaire. Make a statement about the likelihood that a health care worker with latex allergy suspects he or she actually has the allergy. Attach a measure of reliability to your inference.

6.133 Interpreting margin of sampling error. When a poll reports, for example, that 61% of the public supports a program of national health insurance, it usually also reports the sampling error. For example, a poll might report that the estimate is accurate to within plus or minus 3%. A classic essay in *Time* magazine ("How not to read polls," Apr. 28, 1980) points out the following:

> *Readers consistently misinterpret the meaning of this "warning label." ...[The sampling error warning] says nothing about errors that might be caused by a sloppily worded question or a biased one or a single question that evokes complex feelings. Example: "Are you satisfied with your job?" Most important of all, warning labels about sampling error say nothing about whether or not the public is conflict-ridden or has given a subject much thought. This is the most serious source of opinion poll misinterpretation.*

Carefully explain the difference between sampling error and nonsampling error, both in general and in the context of the above quotation.

Applying the Concepts—Advanced

6.134 Accountants' salary survey. Each year, *Management Accounting* reports the results of a salary survey of the members of the Institute of Management Accountants (IMA). One year, the 2,112 members responding had a salary distribution with a 20th percentile of $35,100; a median of $50,000; and an 80th percentile of $73,000.

   a. Use this information to determine the minimum sample size that could be used in next year's survey to estimate the mean salary of IMA members to within $2,000 with 98% confidence. [*Hint*: To estimate *s*, first apply Chebyshev's Theorem to find *k* such that at least 60% of the data fall within *k* standard deviations of μ. Then find $s \approx$ (80th percentile – 20th percentile)/$2k$.]

   b. Explain how you estimated the standard deviation required for the sample size calculation.

   c. List any assumptions you make.

6.135 Internal auditing of invoices. A firm's president, vice presidents, department managers, and others use financial data generated by the firm's accounting system to help them make decisions regarding such things as pricing, budgeting, and plant expansion. To provide reasonable certainty that the system provides reliable data, internal auditors periodically perform various checks of the system (Horngren, Foster, and Datar, *Cost Accounting: A Managerial Emphasis*, 2005). Suppose an internal auditor is interested in determining the proportion of sales invoices in a population of 5,000 sales invoices for which the "total sales" figure is in error. She plans to estimate the true proportion of invoices in error based on a random sample of size 100.

   a. Assume that the population of invoices is numbered from 1 to 5,000 and that every invoice ending with a 0 is in error (i.e., 10% are in error). Use a random number generator to draw a random sample of 100 invoices from the population of 5,000 invoices. For example, random number 456 stands for invoice number 456. List the invoice numbers in your sample and indicate which of your sampled invoices are in error (i.e., those ending in a 0).

   b. Use the results of your sample of part **a** to construct a 90% confidence interval for the true proportion of invoices in error.

   c. Recall that the true population proportion of invoices in error is equal to .1. Compare the true proportion with the estimate of the true proportion you developed in part **b**. Does your confidence interval include the true proportion?

Critical Thinking Challenge

6.136 "Out of control" production process. When companies employ control charts to monitor the quality of their products, a series of small samples is typically used to determine if the process is "in control" during the period of time in which each sample is selected. (We cover quality-control charts in Chapter 13.) Suppose a concrete-block manufacturer samples nine blocks per hour and tests the breaking strength of each. During 1 hour's test, the mean and standard deviation are 985.6 pounds per square inch (psi) and 22.9 psi, respectively. The process is to be considered "out

of control" if the true mean strength differs from 1,000 psi. The manufacturer wants to be reasonably certain that the process is really out of control before shutting down the process and trying to determine the problem. What is your recommendation?

6.137 Scallops, sampling, and the law. *Interfaces* (March–April 1995) presented the case of a ship that fishes for scallops off the coast of New England. In order to protect baby scallops from being harvested, the U.S. Fisheries and Wildlife Service requires that "the average meat per scallop weigh at least $\frac{1}{36}$ of a pound." The ship was accused of violating this weight standard. Author Arnold Barnett lays out the scenario:

> *The vessel arrived at a Massachusetts port with 11,000 bags of scallops, from which the harbormaster randomly selected 18 bags for weighing. From each such bag, his agents took a large scoopful of scallops; then, to estimate the bag's average meat per scallop, they divided the total weight of meat in the scoopful by the number of scallops it contained. Based on the 18 [numbers] thus generated, the harbormaster estimated that each of the ship's scallops possessed an average of $\frac{1}{39}$ of a pound of meat (that is, they were about seven percent lighter than the minimum requirement). Viewing this outcome as conclusive evidence that the weight standard had been violated, federal authorities at once confiscated 95 percent of the catch (which they then sold at auction). The fishing voyage was thus transformed into a financial catastrophe for its participants.*

The actual scallop weight measurements for each of the 18 sampled bags are listed in the table below. For ease of exposition, Barnett expressed each number as a multiple of $\frac{1}{36}$ of a pound, the minimum permissible average weight per scallop. Consequently, numbers below 1 indicate individual bags that do not meet the standard.

The ship's owner filed a lawsuit against the federal government, declaring that his vessel had fully complied with the weight standard. A Boston law firm was hired to represent the owner in legal proceedings, and Barnett was retained by the firm to provide statistical litigation support and, if necessary, expert witness testimony.

| .93 | .88 | .85 | .91 | .91 | .84 | .90 | .98 | .88 |
| .89 | .98 | .87 | .91 | .92 | .99 | 1.14 | 1.06 | .93 |

Source: Based on Barnett, A. "Misapplications review: Jail terms," *Interfaces*, Vol. 25, No. 2, Mar.–Apr. 1995, p. 20.

   a. Recall that the harbormaster sampled only 18 of the ship's 11,000 bags of scallops. One of the questions the lawyers asked Barnett was, "Can a reliable estimate of the mean weight of all the scallops be obtained from a sample of size 18?" Give your opinion on this issue.

   b. As stated in the article, the government's decision rule is to confiscate a catch if the sample mean weight of the scallops is less than $\frac{1}{36}$ of a pound. Do you see any flaws in this rule?

   c. Develop your own procedure for determining whether a ship is in violation of the minimum-weight restriction. Apply your rule to the data. Draw a conclusion about the ship in question.

Activity 6.1   Conducting a Pilot Study

Choose a population parameter pertinent to your major area of interest—a population that has an unknown mean, or if the population is binomial, an unknown probability of success. For example, a marketing major may be interested in the proportion of consumers who prefer a certain brand of diet cola. An economics or finance major might want to estimate the mean annual salary of Internet Web site designers. A management major may wish to estimate the proportion of companies that have mandatory sensitivity training for all employees. A pre-med student might desire an estimate of the average number of patients treated daily in the emergency room. An accounting major may want to find the percentage of audits that result in substantive changes to a company's accounting

system. We could continue with examples, but the point should be clear: Choose something of interest to you.

Define the parameter you want to estimate and conduct a *pilot study* to obtain an initial estimate of the parameter of interest and, more importantly, an estimate of the variability associated with the estimator. A pilot study is a small experiment (perhaps 15 to 20 observations) used to gain information about some phenomenon. The purpose of the study is to help plan more elaborate future experiments. Using the results of your pilot study, determine the sample size necessary to estimate the parameter to within a reasonable bound (of your choice) with a 95% confidence interval. Present the results to your class.

References

Agresti, A., & Coull, B. A. "Approximate is better than 'exact' for interval estimation of binomial proportions," *The American Statistician*, Vol. 52, No. 2, May 1998, pp. 119–126.

Arkin, H. *Sampling Methods for the Auditor*. New York: McGraw-Hill, 1982.

Cochran, W. G. *Sampling Techniques*, 3rd ed. New York: Wiley, 1977.

Freedman, D., Pisani, R., & Purves, R. *Statistics*. New York: Norton, 1978.

Kish, L. *Survey Sampling*. New York: Wiley, 1965.

Mendenhall, W., Beaver, R. J., & Beaver, B. *Introduction to Probability and Statistics*, 13th ed. Belmont, CA: Brooks/Cole, 2009.

Wilson, E. G. "Probable inference, the law of succession, and statistical inference," *Journal of the American Statistical Association*, Vol. 22, 1927, pp. 209–212.

USING TECHNOLOGY   Technology images shown here are taken from SPSS Statistics Professional 20.0, Minitab 16, XLSTAT for Pearson, and Excel 2010.

SPSS: Confidence Intervals

SPSS can be used to obtain one-sample confidence intervals for a population mean and a population proportion, but cannot currently produce confidence intervals for a population variance.

Confidence Interval for a Mean

Step 1 Access the SPSS spreadsheet file that contains the sample data.

Step 2 Click on the "Analyze" button on the SPSS menu bar and then click on "Descriptive Statistics" and "Explore," as shown in Figure 6.S.1.

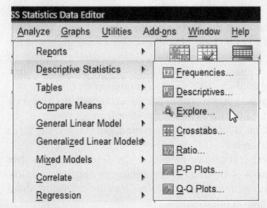

Figure 6.S.1 SPSS menu options—confidence interval for the mean

Step 3 On the resulting dialog box (shown in Figure 6.S.2), specify the quantitative variable of interest in the "Dependent List" and then click on the "Statistics" button.

Figure 6.S.2 SPSS explore dialog box

Step 4 Specify the confidence level in the resulting dialog box, as shown in Figure 6.S.3.

Figure 6.S.3 SPSS explore statistics options

Step 5 Click "Continue" to return to the "Explore" dialog box and then click "OK" to produce the confidence interval.

Confidence Interval for a Proportion

Step 1 Access the SPSS spreadsheet that contains the qualitative variable of interest.

Step 2 Click on the "Analyze" button on the main menu bar, and then click on "Nonparametric Tests" and "1 Sample" (see Figure 6.S.1).

Step 3 Click the "Fields" option, and then on the resulting dialog box (shown in Figure 6.S.4), move the qualitative (categorical) variable to the "Test Fields" box.

Step 4 Click the "Settings" option, and then on the resulting dialog box (shown in Figure 6.S.5), select "Customize Tests" and "Compare observed binary probability to hypothesized (Binomial test)." Then click "Options."

Figure 6.S.4

SPSS field options for binomial confidence interval

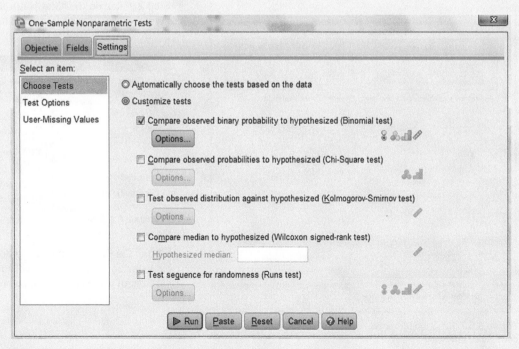

Figure 6.S.5

SPSS settings options for binomial confidence interval

Figure 6.S.6
SPSS binomial options

Step 5 On the resulting dialog box (see Figure 6.S.6), click "Likelihood ratio" in the "Confidence Interval" box, click "OK," and then click "Run."

Step 6 On the resulting output, double click on the "Hypothesis Test Summary" output to display the "Model Viewer" screen, as shown in Figure 6.S.7.

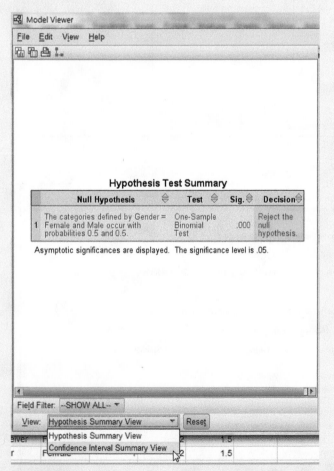

Figure 6.S.7 SPSS model viewer selections for binomial confidence interval

Step 7 At the bottom of the "Model Viewer" screen, select "Confidence Interval Summary View" (as shown in Figure 6.S.7) to view the resulting 95% confidence interval.

Minitab: Confidence Intervals

Minitab can be used to obtain one-sample confidence intervals for a population mean, a population proportion, and a population variance.

Confidence Interval for a Mean

Step 1 Access the Minitab data worksheet that contains the quantitative variable of interest.

Step 2 Click on the "Stat" button on the Minitab menu bar and then click on "Basic Statistics" and "1-Sample t," as shown in Figure 6.M.1.

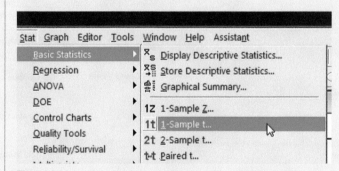

Figure 6.M.1 Minitab menu options—confidence interval for the mean

Step 3 On the resulting dialog box (shown in Figure 6.M.2.), click on "Samples in columns," and then specify the quantitative variable of interest in the open box.

Figure 6.M.2 Minitab 1-sample t dialog box

Step 4 Click on the "Options" button at the bottom of the dialog box and specify the confidence level in the resulting dialog box, as shown in Figure 6.M.3.

Figure 6.M.3 Minitab 1-sample t options

Step 5 Click "OK" to return to the "1-Sample t" dialog box, and then click "OK" again to produce the confidence interval.

Note: If you want to produce a confidence interval for the mean from summary information (e.g., the sample mean, sample standard deviation, and sample size), click on "Summarized data" in the "1-Sample t" dialog box, as shown in Figure 6.M.4. Enter the values of the summary statistics and then click "OK."

Figure 6.M.4 Minitab 1-sample t dialog box with summary statistics options

Important: The Minitab 1-sample t procedure uses the *t*-statistic to generate the confidence interval. When the sample size *n* is small, this is the appropriate method. When the sample size *n* is large, the *t*-value will be approximately equal to the large-sample *z*-value and the resulting interval will still be valid. If you have a large sample and you know the value of the population standard deviation σ (which will rarely be the case), select "1-Sample z" from the "Basic Statistics" menu options (see Figure 6.M.1) and make the appropriate selections.

Confidence Interval for a Proportion

Step 1 Access the Minitab data worksheet that contains the qualitative variable of interest.

Step 2 Click on the "Stat" button on the Minitab menu bar and then click on "Basic Statistics" and "1 Proportion" (see Figure 6.M.1).

Step 3 On the resulting dialog box (shown in Figure 6.M.5), click on "Samples in Columns" and then specify the qualitative variable of interest in the open box.

Figure 6.M.5 Minitab 1-proportion dialog box

Step 4 Click on the "Options" button at the bottom of the dialog box and specify the confidence level in the resulting dialog box, as shown in Figure 6.M.6. Also, check the "Use test and interval based on normal distribution" box at the bottom.

Figure 6.M.6 Minitab 1-proportion dialog box options

Step 5 Click "OK" to return to the "1-Proportion" dialog box and then click "OK" again to produce the confidence interval.

Note: If you want to produce a confidence interval for a proportion from summary information (e.g., the number of successes and the sample size), click on "Summarized data" in the "1-Proportion" dialog box (see Figure 6.M.5). Enter the value for the number of trials (i.e., the sample size) and the number of events (i.e., the number of successes) and then click "OK."

Confidence Interval for a Variance

Step 1 Access the Minitab data worksheet that contains the quantitative variable of interest.

Step 2 Click on the "Stat" button on the main Minitab menu bar, and then click on "Basic Statistics" and "1 Variance" (Figure 6.M.1).

Step 3 On the resulting dialog box (shown in Figure 6.M.7), select "Samples in columns" in the "Data" box, and then specify the quantitative variable of interest in the "Columns" box.

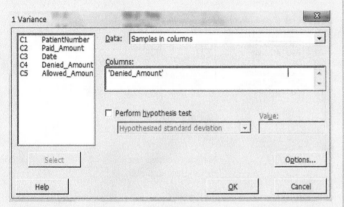

Figure 6.M.7 Minitab 1 Variance dialog box

Step 4 Click the "Options" button at the bottom of the dialog box and specify the confidence level in the resulting menu, as shown in Figure 6.M.8.

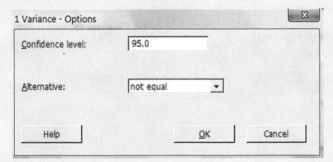

Figure 6.M.8 Minitab 1 Variance options

Step 5 Click "OK" to return to the "1 Variance" dialog box and then click "OK" again to produce the confidence interval.

Note: If you want to produce a confidence interval for a variance from summary information (e.g., the sample variance), select "Sample variance" in the "Data" box of the "1 Variance" dialog box (see Figure 6.M.9). Enter the values of the sample size and sample variance in the appropriate boxes, and then click "OK."

Figure 6.M.9 Minitab 1 Variance dialog box with summary statistics option

Excel/XLSTAT: Confidence Intervals

XLSTAT can produce a confidence interval for a population mean or a population proportion. Currently, confidence intervals for a population variance are not available in XLSTAT.

Confidence Interval for a Mean

Step 1 Click the "XLSTAT" button on the Excel main menu bar, select "Describing data," and then click "Descriptive Statistics," as shown in Figure 6.E.1.

Figure 6.E.1 XLSTAT menu options for descriptive statistics

Step 2 When the resulting dialog box appears, check "Quantitative data" and then highlight the column that contains the values of the quantitative variable you want to analyze so that the column appears in the appropriate entry (see, for example, Figure 6.E.2).

Figure 6.E.2 XLSTAT descriptive statistics dialog box

Step 3 Click the "Options" tab, and then select "Descriptive statistics" and specify the confidence level in the open box, as shown in Figure 6.E.3.

Figure 6.E.3 XLSTAT options for a confidence interval for the mean

Step 4 Click "OK" and then "Continue" to display the confidence interval.

Confidence Interval for a Proportion

[*Note:* To form a confidence interval for a binomial proportion using XLSTAT, you will need summary information on your qualitative data, e.g., the sample size and either the number of successes or the proportion of successes in the sample.]

Step 1 Click the "XLSTAT" button on the Excel main menu bar, select "Parametric tests," and then click "Tests for one proportion," as shown in Figure 6.E.4.

Figure 6.E.4 XLSTAT menu options for a binomial proportion

Step 2 When the resulting dialog box appears, check "Frequency" in the "Data format" area, and then enter the number of successes and the sample size in the "Frequency" and "Sample size" boxes, respectively, as shown in Figure 6.E.5. (Alternatively, you can check "Proportion" in the "Data format" area and enter the sample proportion in the "Test proportion" box.)

Figure 6.E.5 XLSTAT test for one proportion dialog box

Step 3 Click "OK" to display the confidence interval.

TI-84 Graphing Calculator: Confidence Intervals

Confidence Interval for a Population Mean (Known σ or $n \geq 30$)

Step 1 *Enter the data (skip to Step 2 if you have summary statistics, not raw data)*

- Press **STAT** and select **1:Edit**

Note: If the list already contains data, clear the old data. Use the up **ARROW** to highlight "L1."

- Press **CLEAR ENTER**
- Use the **ARROW** and **ENTER** keys to enter the data set into **L1**

Step 2 *Access the Statistical Tests Menu*

- Press **STAT**
- Arrow right to **TESTS**
- Arrow down to **ZInterval**
- Press **ENTER**

Step 3 *Choose "**Data**" or "**Stats**." ("Data" is selected when you have entered the raw data into a List. "Stats" is selected when you are given only the mean, standard deviation, and sample size.)*

- Press **ENTER**

If you selected "Data," enter a value for σ (the best approximation is s, the sample standard deviation)

- Set **List** to **L1**
- Set **Freq** to **1**
- Set **C-Level** to the confidence level
- Arrow down to "**Calculate**"
- Press **ENTER**

If you selected "Stats," enter a value for σ (the best approximation is s, the sample standard deviation)

- Enter the sample mean and sample size
- Set **C-Level** to the confidence level
- Arrow down to "**Calculate**"
- Press **ENTER**

(The bottom screen at right is set up for an example with a standard deviation of 20, a mean of 200, and a sample size of 40.) The confidence interval will be displayed along with the sample mean and the sample size.

Confidence Interval for a Population Mean ($n < 30$)

Step 1 *Enter the data (skip to Step 2 if you have summary statistics, not raw data)*

- Press **STAT** and select **1:Edit**

Note: If the list already contains data, clear the old data. Use the up **ARROW** to highlight "**L1.**"

- Press **CLEAR ENTER**
- Use the **ARROW** and **ENTER** keys to enter the data set into **L1**

Step 2 *Access the Statistical Tests Menu*

- Press **STAT**
- Arrow right to **TESTS**
- Arrow down to **TInterval**
- Press **ENTER**

Step 3 *Choose "**Data**" or "**Stats.**" ("Data" is selected when you have entered the raw data into a List. "Stats" is selected when you are given only the mean, standard deviation, and sample size.)*

- Press **ENTER**
- If you selected "Data," set **List** to **L1**
- Set **Freq** to **1**
- Set **C-Level** to the confidence level

- Arrow down to "**Calculate**"
- Press **ENTER**

If you selected "Stats," enter the mean, standard deviation, and sample size.

- Set **C-Level** to the confidence level
- Arrow down to "**Calculate**"
- Press **ENTER**

(The screen here is set up for an example with a mean of 100 and a standard deviation of 10.)

The confidence interval will be displayed with the mean, standard deviation, and sample size.

Confidence Interval for a Population Proportion (Large Samples)

Step 1 *Access the Statistical Tests Menu*

- Press **STAT**
- Arrow right to **TESTS**
- Arrow down to **1-PropZInt**
- Press **ENTER**

Step 2 *Enter the values for x, n, and C-Level*

- where x = number of successes
- n = sample size
- **C-Level** = level of Confidence
- Arrow down to "**Calculate**"
- Press **ENTER**

(The screens at the right are set up for an example with $x = 532$, $n = 1,100$, and confidence level of .95.)

7

Where We've Been

▫ Used sample information to provide a *point estimate* of a population parameter

▫ Used the sampling distribution of a statistic to assess the reliability of an estimate through a *confidence interval*

Where We're Going

▫ Introduce the concept of a *test of hypothesis* (7.1–7.2)

▫ Provide a measure of reliability for the hypothesis test, called the *significance level* of the test (7.2, 7.3)

▫ Test a specific value of a population parameter (mean, proportion or variance) called a *test of hypothesis* (7.4–7.7)

▫ Show how to estimate the reliability of a test (7.8)

☐ Inferences Based on a Single Sample *Tests of Hypotheses*

STATISTICS in ACTION

Diary of a Kleenex® User—How Many Tissues in a Box?

In 1924, Kimberly-Clark Corporation invented a facial tissue for removing cold cream and began marketing it as Kleenex® brand tissues. Today, Kleenex® is recognized as the top-selling brand of tissue in the world. A wide variety of Kleenex® products are available, ranging from extra-large tissues to tissues with lotion. Over the past 80 years, Kimberly-Clark Corporation has packaged the tissues in boxes of different sizes and shapes and varied the number of tissues packaged in each box. For example, currently a family-size box contains 144 two-ply tissues, a cold-care box contains 70 tissues (coated with lotion), and a convenience pocket pack contains 15 miniature tissues.

How does Kimberly-Clark Corp. decide how many tissues to put in each box? According to the *Wall Street Journal*, marketing experts at the company use the results of a survey of Kleenex® customers to help determine how many tissues should be packed in a box. In the mid-1980s, when Kimberly-Clark Corp. developed the cold-care box designed especially for people who have a cold, the company conducted their initial survey of customers for this purpose. Hundreds of customers were asked to keep count of their Kleenex® use in diaries. According to the *Wall Street Journal* report, the survey results left "little doubt that the company should put 60 tissues in each box." The number 60 was "the average number of times people blow their nose during a cold." In 2000, the company increased the number of tissues packaged in a cold-care box to 70 based on the results of a more recent survey.

From summary information provided in the *Wall Street Journal* article, we constructed a data set that represents the results of a survey similar to the one described above. In the data file named **TISSUE,** we recorded the number of

355

STATISTICS in ACTION CONTINUED tissues used by each of 250 consumers during a period when they had a cold. We apply the hypothesis-testing methodology presented in this chapter to this data set in several Statistics in Action Revisited examples.

STATISTICS in ACTION REVISITED

◻ Key Elements of a Hypothesis Test **(p. 365)**

◻ Testing a Population Mean **(p. 375)**

◻ Testing a Population Proportion **(p. 391)**

◉ *Data Set:* TISSUE ◻

Suppose you wanted to determine whether the mean waiting time in the drive-through line of a fast-food restaurant is less than 5 minutes, or whether the majority of consumers are optimistic about the economy. In both cases you are interested in making an inference about how the value of a parameter relates to a specific numerical value. Is it less than, equal to, or greater than the specified number? This type of inference, called a **test of hypothesis**, is the subject of this chapter.

We introduce the elements of a test of hypothesis in Sections 7.1–7.3. We then show how to conduct a large-sample test of hypothesis about a population mean in Section 7.4. In Section 7.5 we use small samples to conduct tests about means. Large-sample tests about binomial probabilities are the subject of Section 7.6, and a test about a population variance is covered in Section 7.7. Finally, some advanced methods for determining the reliability of a test are covered in Section 7.8.

7.1 The Elements of a Test of Hypothesis

Suppose building specifications in a certain city require that the average breaking strength of residential sewer pipe be more than 2,400 pounds per foot of length (i.e., per linear foot). Each manufacturer who wants to sell pipe in this city must demonstrate that its product meets the specification. Note that we are interested in making an inference about the mean μ of a population. However, in this example we are less interested in estimating the value of μ than we are in testing a **hypothesis** about its value—that is, *we want to decide whether the mean breaking strength of the pipe exceeds 2,400 pounds per linear foot.*

> A statistical **hypothesis** is a statement about the numerical value of a population parameter.

The method used to reach a decision is based on the rare-event concept explained in earlier chapters. We define two hypotheses: (1) The **null hypothesis** is that which represents the status quo to the party performing the sampling experiment—the hypothesis that will be accepted unless the data provide convincing evidence that it is false. (2) The **alternative**, or **research, hypothesis** is that which will be accepted only if the data provide convincing evidence of its truth. From the point of view of the city conducting the tests, the null hypothesis is that the manufacturer's pipe does *not* meet specifications unless the tests provide convincing evidence otherwise. The null and alternative hypotheses are therefore

Null hypothesis (H_0): $\mu \leq 2,400$

(i.e., the manufacturer's pipe does not meet specifications)

Alternative (research) hypothesis (H_a): $\mu > 2,400$

(i.e., the manufacturer's pipe meets specifications)

The **null hypothesis,** denoted H_0, represents the hypothesis that will be accepted unless the data provide convincing evidence that it is false. This usually represents the "status quo" or some claim about the population parameter that the researcher wants to test.

The **alternative (research) hypothesis,** denoted H_a, represents the hypothesis that will be accepted only if the data provide convincing evidence of its truth. This usually represents the values of a population parameter for which the researcher wants to gather evidence to support.

How can the city decide when enough evidence exists to conclude that the manufacturer's pipe meets specifications? Because the hypotheses concern the value of the population mean μ, it is reasonable to use the sample mean $\bar{x}$ to make the inference, just as we did when forming confidence intervals for μ in Sections 6.2 and 6.3. The city will conclude that the pipe meets specifications only when the sample mean $\bar{x}$ convincingly indicates that the population mean exceeds 2,400 pounds per linear foot.

"Convincing" evidence in favor of the alternative hypothesis will exist when the value of $\bar{x}$ exceeds 2,400 by an amount that cannot be readily attributed to sampling variability. To decide, we compute a **test statistic,** i.e., a numerical value computed from the sample. Here, the test statistic is the z-value that measures the distance (in units of the standard deviation) between the value of $\bar{x}$ and the value of μ specified in the null hypothesis. When the null hypothesis contains more than one value of μ, as in this case (H_0: $\mu \leq 2,400$), we use the value of μ closest to the values specified in the alternative hypothesis. The idea is that if the hypothesis that μ *equals* 2,400 can be rejected in favor of $\mu > 2,400$, then μ *less than or equal to* 2,400 can certainly be rejected. Thus, the test statistic is

$$z = \frac{\bar{x} - 2,400}{\sigma_{\bar{x}}} = \frac{\bar{x} - 2,400}{\sigma/\sqrt{n}}$$

Note that a value of $z = 1$ means that $\bar{x}$ is 1 standard deviation above $\mu = 2,400$; a value of $z = 1.5$ means that $\bar{x}$ is 1.5 standard deviations above $\mu = 2,400$; and so on. How large must z be before the city can be convinced that the null hypothesis can be rejected in favor of the alternative and conclude that the pipe meets specifications?

The **test statistic** is a sample statistic, computed from information provided in the sample, that the researcher uses to decide between the null and alternative hypotheses.

If you examine Figure 7.1, you will note that the chance of observing $\bar{x}$ more than 1.645 standard deviations above 2,400 is only .05—*if in fact the true mean μ is 2,400.* Thus, if the sample mean is more than 1.645 standard deviations above 2,400, either H_0 is true and a relatively rare event has occurred (.05 probability), or H_a is true and the

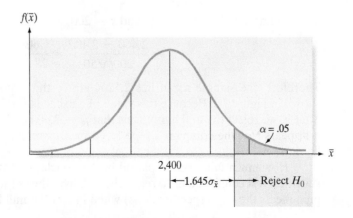

Figure 7.1

The sampling distribution of $\bar{x}$, assuming $\mu = 2,400$

population mean exceeds 2,400. Because we would most likely reject the notion that a rare event has occurred, we would reject the null hypothesis ($\mu \leq 2{,}400$) and conclude that the alternative hypothesis ($\mu > 2{,}400$) is true. What is the probability that this procedure will lead us to an incorrect decision?

Such an incorrect decision—deciding that the null hypothesis is false when in fact it is true—is called a **Type I error.** As indicated in Figure 7.1, the risk of making a Type I error is denoted by the symbol α—that is,

$$\alpha = P(\text{Type I error})$$
$$= P(\text{Rejecting the null hypothesis when in fact the null hypothesis is true})$$

> A **Type I error** occurs if the researcher rejects the null hypothesis in favor of the alternative hypothesis when, in fact, H_0 is true. The probability of committing a Type I error is denoted by α.

In our example,

$$\alpha = P(z > 1.645 \text{ when in fact } \mu = 2{,}400) = .05$$

We now summarize the elements of the test:

$$H_0: \mu \leq 2{,}400 \quad \text{(Pipe does not meet specifications)}$$
$$H_a: \mu > 2{,}400 \quad \text{(Pipe meets specifications)}$$
$$\text{Test statistic: } z = \frac{\bar{x} - 2{,}400}{\sigma_{\bar{x}}}$$
$$\text{Rejection region: } z > 1.645, \text{ which corresponds to } \alpha = .05$$

Note that the **rejection region** refers to the values of the test statistic for which we will *reject the null hypothesis.*

> The **rejection region** of a statistical test is the set of possible values of the test statistic for which the researcher will reject H_0 in favor of H_a.

To illustrate the use of the test, suppose we test 50 sections of sewer pipe and find the mean and standard deviation for these 50 measurements to be

$$\bar{x} = 2{,}460 \text{ pounds per linear foot}$$
$$s = 200 \text{ pounds per linear foot}$$

As in the case of estimation, we can use s to approximate σ when s is calculated from a large set of sample measurements.

The test statistic is

$$z = \frac{\bar{x} - 2{,}400}{\sigma_{\bar{x}}} = \frac{\bar{x} - 2{,}400}{\sigma/\sqrt{n}} \approx \frac{\bar{x} - 2{,}400}{s/\sqrt{n}}$$

Substituting $\bar{x} = 2{,}460$, $n = 50$, and $s = 200$, we have

$$z \approx \frac{2{,}460 - 2{,}400}{200/\sqrt{50}} = \frac{60}{28.28} = 2.12$$

Therefore, the sample mean lies $2.12\sigma_{\bar{x}}$ above the hypothesized value of μ, 2,400, as shown in Figure 7.2. Because this value of z exceeds 1.645, it falls in the rejection region. That is, we reject the null hypothesis that $\mu = 2{,}400$ and conclude that $\mu > 2{,}400$. Thus, it appears that the company's pipe has a mean strength that exceeds 2,400 pounds per linear foot.

How much faith can be placed in this conclusion? What is the probability that our statistical test could lead us to reject the null hypothesis (and conclude that the company's pipe meets the city's specifications) when in fact the null hypothesis is true? The answer

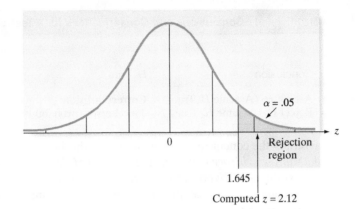

Figure 7.2

Location of the test statistic for a test of the hypothesis $H_0: \mu = 2,400$

EGON S. PEARSON
(1895–1980)
The Neyman-Pearson Lemma

Egon Pearson was the only son of noteworthy British statistician Karl Pearson (see Biography, p. 000). As you might expect, Egon developed an interest in the statistical methods developed by his father and, upon completing graduate school, accepted a position to work for Karl in the Department of Applied Statistics at University College, London. Egon is best known for his collaboration with Jerzey Neyman (see Biography, p. 305) on the development of the theory of hypothesis testing. One of the basic concepts in the Neyman-Pearson approach was that of the "null" and "alternative" hypotheses. Their famous Neyman-Pearson lemma was published in *Biometrika* in 1928. Egon Pearson had numerous other contributions to statistics and was known as an excellent teacher and lecturer. In his last major work, Egon fulfilled a promise made to his father by publishing an annotated version of Karl Pearson's lectures on the early history of statistics.

is $\alpha = .05$—that is, we selected the level of risk, α, of making a Type I error when we constructed the test. Thus, the chance is only 1 in 20 that our test would lead us to conclude the manufacturer's pipe satisfies the city's specifications when in fact the pipe does *not* meet specifications.

Now, suppose the sample mean breaking strength for the 50 sections of sewer pipe turned out to be $\bar{x} = 2,430$ pounds per linear foot. Assuming that the sample standard deviation is still $s = 200$, the test statistic is

$$z = \frac{2,430 - 2,400}{200/\sqrt{50}} = \frac{30}{28.28} = 1.06$$

Therefore, the sample mean $\bar{x} = 2,430$ is only 1.06 standard deviations above the null hypothesized value of $\mu = 2,400$. As shown in Figure 7.3, this value does not fall into the rejection region ($z > 1.645$). Therefore, we know that we cannot reject H_0 using $\alpha = .05$. Even though the sample mean exceeds the city's specification of 2,400 by 30 pounds per linear foot, it does not exceed the specification by enough to provide *convincing* evidence that the *population mean* exceeds 2,400.

Should we accept the null hypothesis $H_0: \mu \leq 2,400$ and conclude that the manufacturer's pipe does not meet specifications? To do so would be to risk a **Type II error**—that of concluding that the null hypothesis is true (the pipe does not meet specifications) when in fact it is false (the pipe does meet specifications). We denote the probability of committing a Type II error by β, and we show in Section 7.8 that β is often difficult to determine precisely. Rather than make a decision (accept H_0) for which the probability of error (β) is unknown, we avoid the potential Type II error by

A **Type II error** occurs if the researcher accepts the null hypothesis when, in fact, H_0 is false. The probability of committing a Type II error is denoted by β.

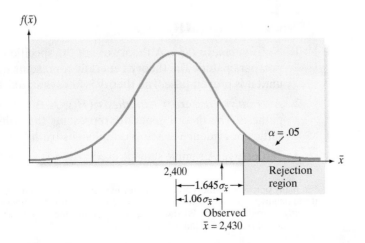

Figure 7.3

Location of test statistic when $\bar{x} = 2,430$

Table 7.1	Conclusions and Consequences for a Test of Hypothesis	
	True State of Nature	
Conclusion	H_0 True	H_a True
Accept H_0 (Assume H_0 True)	Correct decision	Type II error (probability β)
Reject H_0 (Assume H_a True)	Type I error (probability α)	Correct decision

avoiding the conclusion that the null hypothesis is true. Instead, we will simply state that *the sample evidence is insufficient to reject H_0 at $\alpha = .05$.* Because the null hypothesis is the "status-quo" hypothesis, the effect of not rejecting H_0 is to maintain the status quo. In our pipe-testing example, the effect of having insufficient evidence to reject the null hypothesis that the pipe does not meet specifications is probably to prohibit the use of the manufacturer's pipe unless and until there is sufficient evidence that the pipe does meet specifications—that is, until the data indicate convincingly that the null hypothesis is false, we usually maintain the status quo implied by its truth.

Table 7.1 summarizes the four possible outcomes (i.e., **conclusions**) of a test of hypothesis. The "true state of nature" columns in Table 7.1 refer to the fact that either the null hypothesis H_0 is true or the alternative hypothesis H_a is true. Note that the true state of nature is unknown to the researcher conducting the test. The "decision" rows in Table 7.1 refer to the action of the researcher, assuming that he or she will either conclude that H_0 is true or that H_a is true, based on the results of the sampling experiment. Note that a Type I error can be made *only* when the null hypothesis is rejected in favor of the alternative hypothesis, and a Type II error can be made *only* when the null hypothesis is accepted. Our policy will be to make a decision only when we know the probability of making the error that corresponds to that decision. Because α is usually specified by the analyst, we will generally be able to reject H_0 (accept H_a) when the sample evidence supports that decision. However, because β is usually not specified, *we will generally avoid the decision to accept H_0, preferring instead to state that the sample evidence is insufficient to reject H_0 when the test statistic is not in the rejection region.*

 CAUTION Be careful not to "accept H_0" when conducting a test of hypothesis because the measure of reliability, $\beta = P(\text{Type II error})$, is almost always unknown. If the test statistic does not fall into the rejection region, it is better to state the conclusion as "insufficient evidence to reject H_0."*

The elements of a test of hypothesis are summarized in the following box. Note that the first four elements are all specified *before* the sampling experiment is performed. In no case will the results of the sample be used to determine the hypotheses; the data are collected to test the predetermined hypotheses, not to formulate them.

Elements of a Test of Hypothesis

1. *Null hypothesis* (H_0): A theory about the specific values of one or more population parameters. The theory generally represents the status quo, which we adopt until it is proven false. The theory is always stated as H_0: parameter = value.

2. *Alternative (research) hypothesis* (H_a): A theory that contradicts the null hypothesis. The theory generally represents that which we will adopt only when sufficient evidence exists to establish its truth.

3. *Test statistic:* A sample statistic used to decide whether to reject the null hypothesis.

*In many practical business applications of hypothesis testing, nonrejection leads management to behave as if the null hypothesis were accepted. Accordingly, the distinction between acceptance and nonrejection is frequently blurred in practice. We discuss the issues connected with the acceptance of the null hypothesis and the calculation of β in more detail in Section 7.8.

4. *Rejection region:* The numerical values of the test statistic for which the null hypothesis will be rejected. The rejection region is chosen so that the probability is α that it will contain the test statistic when the null hypothesis is true, thereby leading to a Type I error. The value of α is usually chosen to be small (e.g., .01, .05, or .10) and is referred to as the **level of significance** of the test.

5. *Assumptions:* Clear statement(s) of any assumptions made about the population(s) being sampled.

6. *Experiment and calculation of test statistic:* Performance of the sampling experiment and determination of the numerical value of the test statistic.

7. *Conclusion:*
   a. If the numerical value of the test statistic falls in the rejection region, we reject the null hypothesis and conclude that the alternative hypothesis is true. We know that the hypothesis-testing process will lead to this conclusion incorrectly (Type I error) only $100\alpha\%$ of the time when H_0 is true.
   b. If the test statistic does not fall in the rejection region, we do not reject H_0. Thus, we reserve judgment about which hypothesis is true. We do not conclude that the null hypothesis is true because we do not (in general) know the probability β that our test procedure will lead to an incorrect acceptance of H_0 (Type II error).

As with confidence intervals, the methodology for testing hypotheses varies depending on the target population parameter. In this chapter, we develop methods for testing a population mean, a population proportion, and a population variance. Some key words and the type of data associated with these target parameters are listed in the accompanying box.

Determining the Target Parameter

Parameter	Key Words or Phrases	Type of Data
μ	Mean; average	Quantitative
p	Proportion; percentage; fraction; rate	Qualitative
σ^2	Variance; variability; spread	Quantitative

7.2 Formulating Hypotheses and Setting Up the Rejection Region

In Section 7.1 we learned that the null and alternative hypotheses form the basis for inference using a test of hypothesis. The null and alternative hypotheses may take one of several forms. In the sewer pipe example, we tested the null hypothesis that the population mean strength of the pipe is less than or equal to 2,400 pounds per linear foot against the alternative hypothesis that the mean strength exceeds 2,400—that is, we tested

$$H_0: \mu \leq 2{,}400 \quad \text{(Pipe does not meet specifications)}$$
$$H_a: \mu > 2{,}400 \quad \text{(Pipe meets specifications)}$$

This is a **one-tailed** (or **one-sided**) **statistical test** because the alternative hypothesis specifies that the population parameter (the population mean μ in this example) is strictly greater than a specified value (2,400 in this example). If the null hypothesis had been $H_0: \mu \geq 2{,}400$ and the alternative hypothesis had been $H_a: \mu < 2{,}400$, the test would still be one-sided because the parameter is still specified to be on "one side" of the null hypothesis value. Some statistical investigations seek to show that the population parameter is *either larger or smaller* than some specified value. Such an alternative hypothesis is called a **two-tailed** (or **two-sided**) **hypothesis.**

While alternative hypotheses are always specified as strict inequalities, such as $\mu < 2{,}400$, $\mu > 2{,}400$, or $\mu \neq 2{,}400$, null hypotheses are usually specified as equalities, such as $\mu = 2{,}400$. Even when the null hypothesis is an inequality, such as $\mu \leq 2{,}400$, we specify $H_0\colon \mu = 2{,}400$, reasoning that if sufficient evidence exists to show that $H_a\colon \mu > 2{,}400$ is true when tested against $H_0\colon \mu = 2{,}400$, then surely sufficient evidence exists to reject $\mu < 2{,}400$ as well. Therefore, the null hypothesis is specified as the value of μ closest to a one-sided alternative hypothesis and as the only value *not* specified in a two-tailed alternative hypothesis. The steps for selecting the null and alternative hypotheses are summarized in the following box.

Steps for Selecting the Null and Alternative Hypotheses

1. Select the *alternative hypothesis* as that which the sampling experiment is intended to establish. The alternative hypothesis will assume one of three forms:
   a. One-tailed, **upper-tailed**   (e.g., $H_a\colon \mu > 2{,}400$)
   b. One-tailed, **lower-tailed**   (e.g., $H_a\colon \mu < 2{,}400$)
   c. Two-tailed   (e.g., $H_a\colon \mu \neq 2{,}400$)

2. Select the *null hypothesis* as the status quo, that which will be presumed true unless the sampling experiment conclusively establishes the alternative hypothesis. The null hypothesis will be specified as that parameter value closest to the alternative in one-tailed tests and as the complementary (or only unspecified) value in two-tailed tests.

$$\text{(e.g., } H_0\colon \mu = 2{,}400\text{)}$$

A **one-tailed test** of hypothesis is one in which the alternative hypothesis is directional and includes the symbol "<" or ">."

A **two-tailed test** of hypothesis is one in which the alternative hypothesis does not specify departure from H_0 in a particular direction and is written with the symbol "$\neq$."

Example **7.1** **Formulating H_0 and H_a for a Test of a Population Mean—Quality Control**	**Problem** A metal lathe is checked periodically by quality-control inspectors to determine whether it is producing machine bearings with a mean diameter of .5 inch. If the mean diameter of the bearings is larger or smaller than .5 inch, then the process is out of control and must be adjusted. Formulate the null and alternative hypotheses for a test to determine whether the bearing production process is out of control.

Solution The hypotheses must be stated in terms of a population parameter. Here, we define μ as the true mean diameter (in inches) of all bearings produced by the metal lathe. If either $\mu > .5$ or $\mu < .5$, then the lathe's production process is out of control. Because the inspectors want to be able to detect either possibility (indicating that the process is in need of adjustment), these values of μ represent the alternative (or research) hypothesis. Alternatively, because $\mu = .5$ represents an in-control process (the status quo), this represents the null hypothesis. Therefore, we want to conduct the two-tailed test:

$$H_0\colon \mu = .5 \text{ (i.e., the process is in control)}$$
$$H_a\colon \mu \neq .5 \text{ (i.e., the process is out of control)}$$

Look Back Here, the alternative hypothesis is not necessarily the hypothesis that the quality-control inspectors desire to support. However, they will make adjustments to the metal lathe settings only if there is strong evidence to indicate that the process is out of control. Consequently, $\mu \neq .5$ must be stated as the alternative hypothesis.

▪ Now Work Exercise 7.10a

Example 7.2

Formulating H_0 and H_a for a Test of a Population Proportion—Cigarette Advertisements

Problem Cigarette advertisements are required by federal law to carry the following statement: "Warning: The surgeon general has determined that cigarette smoking is dangerous to your health." However, this warning is often located in inconspicuous corners of the advertisements and printed in small type. Suppose the Federal Trade Commission (FTC) claims that 80% of cigarette consumers fail to see the warning. A marketer for a large tobacco firm wants to gather evidence to show that the FTC's claim is too high, i.e., that fewer than 80% of cigarette consumers fail to see the warning. Specify the null and alternative hypotheses for a test of the FTC's claim.

Solution The marketer wants to make an inference about p, the true proportion of all cigarette consumers who fail to see the surgeon general's warning. In particular, the marketer wants to collect data to show that fewer than 80% of cigarette consumers fail to see the warning, i.e., $p < .80$. Consequently, $p < .80$. represents the alternative hypothesis and $p = .80$ (the claim made by the FTC) represents the null hypothesis. That is, the marketer desires the one-tailed (lower-tailed) test:

$$H_0: p = .80 \text{ (i.e., the FTC's claim is true)}$$
$$H_a: p < .80 \text{ (i.e., the FTC's claim is false)}$$

Look Back Whenever a claim is made about the value of a particular population parameter and the researcher wants to test the claim, believing that it is false, the claimed value will represent the null hypothesis.

━━■ **Now Work Exercise 7.11**

The rejection region for a two-tailed test differs from that for a one-tailed test. When we are trying to detect departure from the null hypothesis in *either* direction, we must establish a rejection region in both tails of the sampling distribution of the test statistic. Figures 7.4a and 7.4b show the one-tailed rejection regions for lower- and upper-tailed tests, respectively. The two-tailed rejection region is illustrated in Figure 7.4c. Note that a rejection region is established in each tail of the sampling distribution for a two-tailed test.

The rejection regions corresponding to typical values selected for α are shown in Table 7.2 for one- and two-tailed tests. Note that the smaller the α you select, the more evidence (the larger the z) you will need before you can reject H_0.

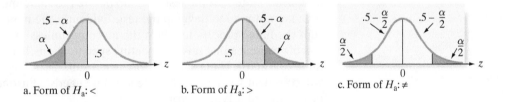

Figure 7.4

Rejection regions corresponding to one- and two-tailed tests

a. Form of H_a: <   b. Form of H_a: >   c. Form of H_a: ≠

Table 7.2	Rejection Regions for Common Values of α		
	Alternative Hypotheses		
	Lower-Tailed	Upper-Tailed	Two-Tailed
$\alpha = .10$	$z < -1.282$	$z > 1.282$	$z < -1.645$ or $z > 1.645$
$\alpha = .05$	$z < -1.645$	$z > 1.645$	$z < -1.96$ or $z > 1.96$
$\alpha = .01$	$z < -2.326$	$z > 2.326$	$z < -2.576$ or $z > 2.576$

Example 7.3

Setting Up a Hypothesis Test for μ—Mean Amount of Cereal in a Box

Problem A manufacturer of cereal wants to test the performance of one of its filling machines. The machine is designed to discharge a mean amount of 12 ounces per box, and the manufacturer wants to detect any departure from this setting. This quality study calls for randomly sampling 100 boxes from today's production run and determining whether the mean fill for the run is 12 ounces per box. Set up a test of hypothesis for this study, using $\alpha = .01$.

Solution The key word *mean* in the statement of the problem implies that the target parameter is μ, the mean amount of cereal discharged into each box. Because the manufacturer wishes to detect a departure from the setting of $\mu = 12$ in either direction, $\mu < 12$ or $\mu > 12$, we conduct a two-tailed statistical test. Following the procedure for selecting the null and alternative hypotheses, we specify as the alternative hypothesis that the mean differs from 12 ounces because detecting the machine's departure from specifications is the purpose of the quality-control study. The null hypothesis is the presumption that the filling machine is operating properly unless the sample data indicate otherwise. Thus,

H_0: $\mu = 12$ (Population mean fill amount is 12 ounces)

H_a: $\mu \neq 12$ (i.e., $\mu < 12$ or $\mu > 12$; machine is under- or overfilling each box)

The test statistic measures the number of standard deviations between the observed value of $\bar{x}$ and the null hypothesized value $\mu = 12$:

$$\text{Test statistic: } z = \frac{\bar{x} - 12}{\sigma_{\bar{x}}}$$

The rejection region must be designated to detect a departure from $\mu = 12$ in *either* direction, so we will reject H_0 for values of z that are either too small (negative) or too large (positive). To determine the precise values of z that comprise the rejection region, we first select α, the probability that the test will lead to incorrect rejection of the null hypothesis. Then we divide α equally between the lower and upper tails of the distribution of z, as shown in Figure 7.5. In this example, $\alpha = .01$, so $\frac{\alpha}{2} = .005$ is placed in each tail. The areas in the tails correspond to $z = -2.576$ and $z = 2.576$, respectively (from Table 7.2):

Rejection region: $z < -2.576$ or $z > 2.576$ (see Figure 7.5)

Assumptions: Because the sample size of the experiment is large enough ($n > 30$), the Central Limit Theorem will apply, and no assumptions need be made about the population of fill measurements. The sampling distribution of the sample mean fill of 100 boxes will be approximately normal regardless of the distribution of the individual boxes' fills.

Look Back Note that the test is set up *before* the sampling experiment is conducted. The data are not used to develop the test. Evidently, the manufacturer does not want to disrupt the filling process to adjust the machine, unless the sample data provide very convincing evidence that it is not meeting specifications, because the value of α has been set quite low at .01. If the sample evidence results in the rejection of H_0, the manufacturer will confidently conclude that the machine needs adjustment because there is only a .01 probability of a Type I error.

Figure 7.5

Two-tailed rejection region: $\alpha = .01$

■ **Now Work Exercise 7.10b, c**

Once the test is set up, the manufacturer is ready to perform the sampling experiment and conduct the test. The test is performed in the next section.

STATISTICS
in ACTION
REVISITED

Key Elements of a Hypothesis Test

In Kimberly-Clark Corp.'s survey of people with colds, each of 250 customers was asked to keep count of his or her use of Kleenex® tissues in diaries. One goal of the company was to determine how many tissues to package in a cold-care box of Kleenex®; consequently, the total number of tissues used was recorded for each person surveyed. Since the number of tissues is a quantitative variable, the parameter of interest is either μ, the mean number of tissues used by all customers with colds, or σ^2, the variance of the number of tissues used.

Recall that in 2000, the company increased from 60 to 70 the number of tissues it packages in a cold-care box of Kleenex® tissues. The decision was based on a claim made by marketing experts that the average number of times a person will blow his or her nose during a cold exceeds the previous mean of 60. The key word *average* implies that the parameter of interest is μ, and the marketers are claiming that $\mu > 60$. In order to test the claim, we set up the following null and alternative hypotheses:

$$H_0: \mu = 60 \qquad H_a: \mu > 60$$

We'll conduct this test in the next Statistics in Action Revisited on page 375.

Exercises 7.1–7.18

Learning the Mechanics

7.1 Which hypothesis, the null or the alternative, is the status-quo hypothesis? Which is the research hypothesis?

7.2 Which element of a test of hypothesis is used to decide whether to reject the null hypothesis in favor of the alternative hypothesis?

7.3 What is the level of significance of a test of hypothesis?

7.4 What is the difference between Type I and Type II errors in hypothesis testing? How do α and β relate to Type I and Type II errors?

7.5 List the four possible results of the combinations of decisions and true states of nature for a test of hypothesis.

7.6 We reject the null hypothesis when the test statistic falls in the rejection region, but we do not accept the null hypothesis when the test statistic does not fall in the rejection region. Why?

7.7 If you test a hypothesis and reject the null hypothesis in favor of the alternative hypothesis, does your test prove that the alternative hypothesis is correct? Explain.

7.8 For each of the following rejection regions, sketch the sampling distribution for z and indicate the location of the rejection region.
  a. $z > 1.96$
  b. $z > 1.645$
  c. $z > 2.576$
  d. $z < -1.282$
  e. $z < -1.645$ or $z > 1.645$
  f. $z < -2.576$ or $z > 2.576$
  g. For each of the rejection regions specified in parts **a–f**, what is the probability that a Type I error will be made?

⊘ Applet Exercise 7.1

Use the applet *Hypothesis Test for a Mean* to investigate the frequency of Type I and Type II errors. For this exercise, use $n = 100$ and the normal distribution with mean 50 and standard deviation 10.
  a. Set the null mean equal to 50 and the alternative to *not equal*. Run the applet one time. How many times was the null hypothesis rejected at level .05? In this case, the null hypothesis is true. Which type of error occurred each time the true null hypothesis was rejected? What is the probability of rejecting a true null hypothesis at level .05? How does the proportion of times the null hypothesis was rejected compare to this probability?
  b. Clear the applet, then set the null mean equal to 47 and keep the alternative at *not equal*. Run the applet one time. How many times was the null hypothesis *not* rejected at level .05? In this case, the null hypothesis is false. Which type of error occurred each time the null hypothesis was *not* rejected? Run the applet several more times without clearing. Based on your results, what can you conclude about the probability of failing to reject the null hypothesis for the given conditions?

Applying the Concepts—Basic

7.9 **Effectiveness of online courses.** The Sloan Survey of Online Learning, "Going the Distance: Online Education in the United States, 2011," reported that 68% of college presidents believe that their online education courses are as good as or superior to courses that use traditional, face-to-face instruction.
  a. Give the null hypothesis for testing the claim made by the Sloan Survey.
  b. Give the rejection region for a two-tailed test conducted at $\alpha = .01$.

7.10 Play Golf America program. The Professional Golf Association (PGA) and *Golf Digest* have developed the Play Golf America program, in which teaching professionals at participating golf clubs provide a free 10-minute lesson to new customers. According to *Golf Digest* (July 2008), golf facilities that participate in the program gain, on average, $2,400 in greens, fees, lessons, or equipment expenditures. A teaching professional at a golf club believes that the average gain in greens fees, lessons, or equipment expenditures for participating golf facilities exceeds $2,400.

  a. In order to support the claim made by the teaching professional, what null and alternative hypotheses should you test?

  b. Suppose you select $\alpha = .05$. Interpret this value in the words of the problem.

  c. For $\alpha = .05$, specify the rejection region of a large-sample test.

7.11 Student loan default rate. The national student loan default rate has fluctuated over the last several years. A few years ago, the Department of Education reported the default rate (i.e., the proportion of college students who default on their loans) at .07. Set up the null and alternative hypotheses if you want to determine if the student loan default rate this year is less than .07.

7.12 Work travel policy. American Express Consulting reported in *USA Today* (June 15, 2001) that 80% of U.S. companies have formal, written travel and entertainment policies for their employees. Give the null hypothesis for testing the claim made by American Express Consulting.

7.13 Calories in school lunches. A University of Florida economist conducted a study of Virginia elementary school lunch menus. During the state-mandated testing period, school lunches averaged 863 calories (National Bureau of Economic Research, Nov. 2002). The economist claims that after the testing period ends, the average caloric content of Virginia school lunches drops significantly. Set up the null and alternative hypotheses to test the economist's claim.

7.14 Libor interest rate. The interest rate at which London banks lend money to one another is called the *London interbank offered rate,* or *Libor.* The British Bankers Association regularly surveys international banks for the Libor rate. One recent report (*Bankrate.com,* Jan. 25, 2012) had the average Libor rate at 1.10% for 1-year loans—a value considered high by many Western banks. Set up the null and alternative hypotheses for testing the reported value.

Applying the Concepts—Intermediate

7.15 FDA certification of new drugs. According to *Chemical Marketing Reporter,* pharmaceutical companies spend $15 billion per year on research and development of new drugs. The pharmaceutical company must subject each new drug to lengthy and involved testing before receiving the necessary permission from the Food and Drug Administration (FDA) to market the drug. The FDA's policy is that the pharmaceutical company must provide substantial evidence that a new drug is safe prior to receiving FDA approval, so that the FDA can confidently certify the safety of the drug to potential consumers.

  a. If the new drug testing were to be placed in a test of hypothesis framework, would the null hypothesis be that the drug is safe or unsafe? The alternative hypothesis?

  b. Given the choice of null and alternative hypotheses in part **a,** describe Type I and Type II errors in terms of this application. Define α and β in terms of this application.

  c. If the FDA wants to be very confident that the drug is safe before permitting it to be marketed, is it more important that α or β be small? Explain.

7.16 Authorizing computer users. At high-technology industries, computer security is achieved by using a *password*—a collection of symbols (usually letters and numbers) that must be supplied by the user before the computer permits access to the account. The problem is that persistent hackers can create programs that enter millions of combinations of symbols into a target system until the correct password is found. The newest systems solve this problem by requiring authorized users to identify themselves by unique body characteristics. For example, a system developed by Palmguard, Inc. tests the hypothesis

  H_0: The proposed user is authorized
  H_a: The proposed user is unauthorized

by checking characteristics of the proposed user's palm against those stored in the authorized users' data bank.

  a. Define a Type I error and Type II error for this test. Which is the more serious error? Why?

  b. Palmguard reports that the Type I error rate for its system is less than 1%, whereas the Type II error rate is .00025%. Interpret these error rates.

  c. Another successful security system, the EyeDentifyer, "spots authorized computer users by reading the one-of-a-kind patterns formed by the network of minute blood vessels across the retina at the back of the eye." The EyeDentifyer reports Type I and II error rates of .01% (1 in 10,000) and .005% (5 in 100,000), respectively. Interpret these rates.

Applying the Concepts—Advanced

7.17 Jury trial outcomes. Sometimes, the outcome of a jury trial defies the "common sense" expectations of the general public (e.g., the O. J. Simpson verdict and the 2011 Casey Anthony verdict). Such a verdict is more acceptable if we understand that the jury trial of an accused murderer is analogous to the statistical hypothesis-testing process. The null hypothesis in a jury trial is that the accused is innocent. (The status-quo hypothesis in the U.S. system of justice is innocence, which is assumed to be true until proven *beyond a reasonable doubt.*) The alternative hypothesis is guilt, which is accepted only when sufficient evidence exists to establish its truth. If the vote of the jury is unanimous in favor of guilt, the null hypothesis of innocence is rejected, and the court concludes that the accused murderer is guilty. Any vote other than a unanimous one for guilt results in a "not guilty" verdict. The court never accepts the null hypothesis; that is, the court never declares the accused "innocent." A "not guilty" verdict (as in the Casey Anthony) implies that the court could not find the defendant guilty *beyond a reasonable doubt.*

  a. Define Type I and Type II errors in a murder trial.

  b. Which of the two errors is the more serious? Explain.

c. The court does not, in general, know the values of α and β; but ideally, both should be small. One of these probabilities is assumed to be smaller than the other in a jury trial. Which one, and why?

d. The court system relies on the belief that the value of α is made very small by requiring a unanimous vote before guilt is concluded. Explain why this is so.

e. For a jury prejudiced against a guilty verdict as the trial begins, will the value of α increase or decrease? Explain.

f. For a jury prejudiced against a guilty verdict as the trial begins, will the value of β increase or decrease? Explain.

7.18 Intrusion detection systems. Refer to the *Journal of Research of the National Institute of Standards and Technology* (Nov.–Dec. 2003) study of a computer intrusion detection system (IDS), Exercise 3.69 (p. 167). Recall that an IDS is designed to provide an alarm whenever unauthorized access (e.g., an intrusion) to a computer system occurs. The probability of the system giving a false alarm (i.e., providing a warning when no intrusion occurs) is defined by the symbol α, while the probability of a missed detection (i.e., no warning given when an intrusion occurs) is defined by the symbol β. These symbols are used to represent Type I and Type II error rates, respectively, in a hypothesis-testing scenario.

a. What is the null hypothesis, H_0?

b. What is the alternative hypothesis, H_a?

c. According to actual data on the EMERALD system collected by the Massachusetts Institute of Technology Lincoln Laboratory, only 1 in 1,000 computer sessions with no intrusions resulted in a false alarm. For the same system, the laboratory found that only 500 of 1,000 intrusions were actually detected. Use this information to estimate the values of α and β.

7.3 Observed Significance Levels: *p*-Values

According to the statistical test procedure described in Section 7.2, the rejection region and, correspondingly, the value of α are selected prior to conducting the test, and the conclusions are stated in terms of rejecting or not rejecting the null hypothesis. A second method of presenting the results of a statistical test is one that reports the extent to which the test statistic disagrees with the null hypothesis and leaves to the reader the task of deciding whether to reject the null hypothesis. This measure of disagreement is called the *observed significance level* (or *p-value*) for the test.

> The **observed significance level,** or *p*-value, for a specific statistical test is the probability (assuming H_0 is true) of observing a value of the test statistic that is at least as contradictory to the null hypothesis, and supportive of the alternative hypothesis, as the actual one computed from the sample data.

Recall testing $H_0: \mu = 2{,}400$ versus $H_a: \mu = 2{,}400$, where μ is the mean breaking strength of sewer pipe (Section 7.1). The value of the test statistic computed for the sample of $n = 50$ sections of sewer pipe was $z = 2.12$. Because the test is one-tailed—that is, the alternative (research) hypothesis of interest is $H_a: \mu > 2{,}400$—values of the test statistic even more contradictory to H_0 than the one observed would be values larger than $z = 2.12$. Therefore, the observed significance level (*p*-value) for this test is

$$p\text{-value} = P(z > 2.12)$$

or, equivalently, the area under the standard normal curve to the right of $z = 2.12$ (see Figure 7.6).

The area A in Figure 7.6 is given in Table II in Appendix D as .4830. Therefore, the upper-tail area corresponding to $z = 2.12$ is

$$p\text{-value} = .5 - .4830 = .0170$$

Figure 7.6

Finding the *p*-value for an upper-tailed test when $z = 2.12$

Consequently, we say that these test results are "very significant" (i.e., they disagree rather strongly with the null hypothesis, H_0: μ = 2,400, and favor H_a: μ > 2,400). The probability of observing a z-value as large as 2.12 is only .0170, if in fact the true value of μ is 2,400.

If you are inclined to select α = .05 for this test, then you would reject the null hypothesis because the p-value for the test, .0170, is less than .05. In contrast, if you choose α = .01, you would not reject the null hypothesis because the p-value for the test is larger than .01. Thus, the use of the observed significance level is identical to the test procedure described in the preceding sections except that the choice of α is left to you.

The steps for calculating the p-value corresponding to a test statistic for a population mean are given in the next box.

Steps for Calculating the p-Value for a Test of Hypothesis

1. Determine the value of the test statistic z corresponding to the result of the sampling experiment.

2. **a.** If the test is one-tailed, the p-value is equal to the tail area beyond z in the same direction as the alternative hypothesis. Thus, if the alternative hypothesis is of the form >, the p-value is the area to the right of, or above, the observed z-value. Conversely, if the alternative is of the form <, the p-value is the area to the left of, or below, the observed z-value. (See Figure 7.7.)
   b. If the test is two-tailed, the p-value is equal to twice the tail area beyond the observed z-value in the direction of the sign of z—that is, if z is positive, the p-value is twice the area to the right of, or above, the observed z-value. Conversely, if z is negative, the p-value is twice the area to the left of, or below, the observed z-value. (See Figure 7.8.)

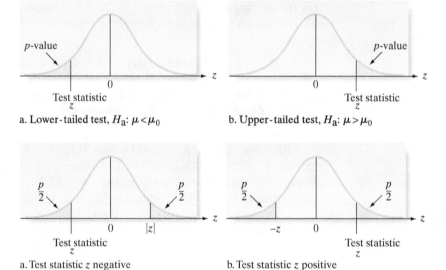

Figure 7.7

Finding the p-value for a one-tailed test

a. Lower-tailed test, H_a: $\mu < \mu_0$ b. Upper-tailed test, H_a: $\mu > \mu_0$

Figure 7.8

Finding the p-value for a two-tailed test: p-value = $2\left(\frac{p}{2}\right)$

a. Test statistic z negative b. Test statistic z positive

Example 7.4

Comparing Rejection Regions to p-Values

Problem Consider the one-tailed test of hypothesis, H_0: μ = 100 versus H_a: μ > 100.

a. Suppose the test statistic is z = 1.44. Find the p-value of the test and the rejection region for the test when α = .05. Then show that the conclusion using the rejection region approach will be identical to the conclusion based on the p-value.

b. Now suppose the test statistic is z = 3.01; find the p-value and rejection region for the test when α = .05. Again, show that the conclusion using the rejection region approach will be identical to the conclusion based on the p-value.

Solution

a. The p-value for the test is the probability of observing a test statistic more contradictory to the null hypothesis (i.e., more supportive of the alternative hypothesis) than the value $z = 1.44$. Since we are conducting an upper-tailed test (H_a: $\mu > 100$), the probability we seek is:

$$p\text{-value} = P(z > 1.44) = 1 - P(z < 1.44)$$

The latter probability in the expression is a cumulative probability that can be obtained from the standard normal table (Table II, Appendix D) or using statistical software. The Minitab printout giving this probability is shown in Figure 7.9.

Cumulative Distribution Function

Normal with mean = 0 and standard deviation = 1

```
     x    P( X <= x )
  1.44     0.925066
```

Figure 7.9

Minitab normal probability for Example 7.4a

Therefore, we compute

$$p\text{-value} = P(z > 1.44) = 1 - P(z < 1.44) = 1 - .925 = .075$$

This *p*-value is shown on Figure 7.10.

Since $\alpha = .05$ and the test is upper-tailed, the rejection region for the test is $z > 1.645$ (see Table 7.2). This rejection region is also shown in Figure 7.10. Observe that the test statistic ($z = 1.44$) falls outside the rejection region, implying that we fail to reject H_0. Also, $\alpha = .05$ is less than *p*-value $= .075$. This result also implies that we should fail to reject H_0. Consequently, both decision rules agree—there is insufficient evidence to reject H_0.

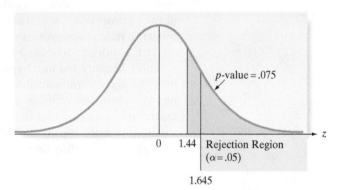

Figure 7.10

Test for Example 7.4a—Fail to reject H_0

b. For $z = 3.01$, the observed significance level of the test is:

$$p\text{-value} = P(z > 3.01) = 1 - P(z < 3.01)$$

A Minitab printout giving the cumulative probability, $P(z < 3.01)$, is shown in Figure 7.11.

Cumulative Distribution Function

Normal with mean = 0 and standard deviation = 1

```
     x    P( X <= x )
  3.01     0.998694
```

Figure 7.11

Minitab normal probability for Example 7.4b

Thus, we have

$$p\text{-value} = P(z > 3.01) = 1 - P(z < 3.01) = 1 - .9987 = .0013.$$

This *p*-value is shown on Figure 7.12.

Again, for $\alpha = .05$ and an upper-tailed test, the rejection region is $z > 1.645$. This rejection region is also shown in Figure 7.12. Now the test statistic ($z = 3.01$) falls within the rejection region, leading us to reject H_0. And, $\alpha = .05$ now exceeds the *p*-value

(.0013), which also implies that we should reject H_0. Once again, both decision rules agree—and they always will if the same value of α is used to make the decision.

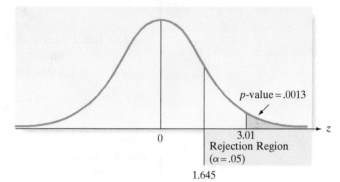

Figure 7.12
Test for Example 7.4b—Reject H_0

Look Ahead Since p-values are easily computed using statistical software, most analysts and researchers utilize the p-value approach to hypothesis testing. In future examples, we will adopt this approach generally, although we'll continue to show the appropriate rejection regions where necessary for illustrative purposes.

■ **Now Work: Exercise 7.19**

When publishing the results of a statistical test of hypothesis in journals, case studies, reports, and so on, many researchers make use of p-values. Instead of selecting α beforehand and then conducting a test, as outlined in this chapter, the researcher computes (usually with the aid of a statistical software package) and reports the value of the appropriate test statistic and its associated p-value. It is left to the reader of the report to judge the significance of the result (i.e., the reader must determine whether to reject the null hypothesis in favor of the alternative hypothesis, based on the reported p-value). Usually, the null hypothesis is rejected if the observed significance level is *less than* the fixed significance level, α, chosen by the reader. The inherent advantage of reporting test results in this manner are twofold: (1) Readers are permitted to select the maximum value of α that they would be willing to tolerate if they actually carried out a standard test of hypothesis in the manner outlined in this chapter, and (2) a measure of the degree of significance of the result (i.e., the p-value) is provided.

ETHICS in STATISTICS

Selecting the value of α *after* computing the observed significance level (p-value) in order to guarantee a preferred conclusion is considered *unethical statistical practice*.

> **Reporting Test Results as p-Values: How to Decide Whether to Reject H_0**
>
> **1.** Choose the maximum value of α that you are willing to tolerate.
>
> **2.** If the observed significance level (p-value) of the test is less than the chosen value of α, reject the null hypothesis. Otherwise, do not reject the null hypothesis.

Note: Some statistical software packages (e.g., SPSS) will conduct only two-tailed tests of hypothesis. For these packages, you obtain the p-value for a one-tailed test as shown in the box:

> **Converting a Two-Tailed p-Value from a Printout to a One-Tailed p-Value**
>
> $$p = \frac{\text{Reported } p\text{-value}}{2} \quad \text{if} \begin{cases} H_a \text{ is of form} > \text{ and } z \text{ is positive} \\ H_a \text{ is of form} < \text{ and } z \text{ is negative} \end{cases}$$
>
> $$p = 1 - \left(\frac{\text{Reported } p\text{-value}}{2}\right) \quad \text{if} \begin{cases} H_a \text{ is of form} > \text{ and } z \text{ is negative} \\ H_a \text{ is of form} < \text{ and } z \text{ is positive} \end{cases}$$

Exercises 7.19–7.27

Learning the Mechanics

7.19 Consider the test of $H_0: \mu = 7$. For each of the following, find the p-value of the test:
a. $H_a: \mu > 7, z = 1.20$
b. $H_a: \mu < 7, z = -1.20$
c. $H_a: \mu \neq 7, z = 1.20$

7.20 If a hypothesis test were conducted using $\alpha = .05$, for which of the following p-values would the null hypothesis be rejected?
a. .06   b. .10
c. .01   d. .001
e. .251   f. .042

7.21 For each α and observed significance level (p-value) pair, indicate whether the null hypothesis would be rejected.
a. $\alpha = .05, p\text{-value} = .10$
b. $\alpha = .10, p\text{-value} = .05$
c. $\alpha = .01, p\text{-value} = .001$
d. $\alpha = .025, p\text{-value} = .05$
e. $\alpha = .10, p\text{-value} = .45$

7.22 In a test of the hypothesis $H_0: \mu = 50$ versus $H_a: \mu > 50$, a sample of $n = 100$ observations possessed mean $\bar{x} = 49.4$ and standard deviation $s = 4.1$. Find and interpret the p-value for this test.

7.23 In a test of $H_0: \mu = 100$ against $H_a: \mu > 100$, the sample data yielded the test statistic $z = 2.17$. Find and interpret the p-value for the test.

7.24 In a test of the hypothesis $H_0: \mu = 10$ versus $H_a: \mu \neq 10$, a sample of $n = 50$ observations possessed mean $\bar{x} = 10.7$ and standard deviation $s = 3.1$. Find and interpret the p-value for this test.

7.25 In a test of $H_0: \mu = 100$ against $H_a: \mu \neq 100$, the sample data yielded the test statistic $z = 2.17$. Find the p-value for the test.

7.26 In a test of $H_0: \mu = 75$ performed using the computer, SPSS reports a two-tailed p-value of .1032. Make the appropriate conclusion for each of the following situations:
a. $H_a: \mu < 75, z = -1.63, \alpha = .05$
b. $H_a: \mu < 75, z = 1.63, \alpha = .10$
c. $H_a: \mu > 75, z = 1.63, \alpha = .10$
d. $H_a: \mu \neq 75, z = -1.63, \alpha = .01$

7.27 An analyst tested the null hypothesis $\mu \geq 20$ against the alternative hypothesis that $\mu < 20$. The analyst reported a p-value of .06. What is the smallest value of α for which the null hypothesis would be rejected?

7.4 Test of Hypothesis about a Population Mean: Normal (z) Statistic

When testing a hypothesis about a population mean μ, the test statistic we use will depend on whether the sample size n is large (say, $n \geq 30$) or small, and whether or not we know the value of the population standard deviation, σ. In this section, we consider the large-sample case.

Because the sample size is large, the Central Limit Theorem guarantees that the sampling distribution of $\bar{x}$ is approximately normal. Consequently, the test statistic for a test based on large samples will be based on the normal z-statistic. Although the z-statistic requires that we know the true population standard deviation σ, we rarely if ever know σ. However, we established in Chapter 6 that when n is large, the sample standard deviation s provides a good approximation to σ, and the z-statistic can be approximated as follows:

$$z = \frac{\bar{x} - \mu_0}{\sigma_{\bar{x}}} = \frac{\bar{x} - \mu_0}{\sigma/\sqrt{n}} \approx \frac{\bar{x} - \mu_0}{s/\sqrt{n}}$$

where μ_0 represents the value of μ specified in the null hypothesis.

The setup of a large-sample test of hypothesis about a population mean is summarized in the following boxes. Both the one- and two-tailed tests are shown.

Conditions Required for a Valid Large-Sample Hypothesis Test for μ

1. A random sample is selected from the target population.
2. The sample size n is large (i.e., $n \geq 30$). (Due to the Central Limit Theorem, this condition guarantees that the test statistic will be approximately normal regardless of the shape of the underlying probability distribution of the population.)

Large-Sample Test of Hypothesis about μ Based on a Normal (z) Statistic

One-Tailed Test	Two-Tailed Test
H_0: $\mu = \mu_0$ H_a: $\mu < \mu_0$ (or H_a: $\mu > \mu_0$)	H_0: $\mu = \mu_0$ H_a: $\mu \neq \mu_0$
Test statistic (σ known): $z = \dfrac{\bar{x} - \mu_0}{\sigma/\sqrt{n}}$	Test statistic (σ known): $z = \dfrac{\bar{x} - \mu_0}{\sigma/\sqrt{n}}$
Test statistic (σ unknown): $z \approx \dfrac{\bar{x} - \mu_0}{\sigma/\sqrt{n}}$	Test statistic (σ unknown): $z \approx \dfrac{\bar{x} - \mu_0}{s\sqrt{n}}$

Rejection region: $z < -z_\alpha$
   (or $z > z_\alpha$ when H_a: $\mu > \mu_0$)
 where z_α is chosen so that
   $P(z > z_\alpha) = \alpha$
	Rejection region: $|z| > z_{\alpha/2}$
	
	 where $z_{\alpha/2}$ is chosen so that
	   $P(|z| > z_{\alpha2}) = \alpha/2$

Note: μ_0 is the symbol for the numerical value assigned to μ under the null hypothesis.

Once the test has been set up, the sampling experiment is performed and the test statistic and corresponding *p*-value are calculated. The next box reviews possible conclusions for a test of hypothesis, depending on the result of the sampling experiment.

Possible Conclusions for a Test of Hypothesis

1. If the calculated test statistic falls in the rejection region (or, $\alpha > p$-value), reject H_0 and conclude that the alternative hypothesis H_a is true. State that you are rejecting H_0 at the α level of significance. Remember that the confidence is in the testing *process*, not in the particular result of a single test.

2. If the test statistic does not fall in the rejection region (or, $\alpha < p$-value), conclude that the sampling experiment does not provide sufficient evidence to reject H_0 at the α level of significance. [Generally, we will not "accept" the null hypothesis unless the probability β of a Type II error has been calculated (see Section 7.8).]

Example 7.5

Carrying Out a Hypothesis Test for μ—Mean Amount of Cereal in a Box

Problem Refer to the quality-control test set up in Example 7.3 (p. 363). Recall that a machine is designed to discharge a mean of 12 ounces of cereal per box. A sample of 100 boxes yielded the fill amounts (in ounces) shown in Table 7.3. Use these data to conduct the following test:

$$H_0: \mu = 12 \quad \text{(Population mean fill amount is 12 ounces)}$$
$$H_a: \mu \neq 12 \quad \text{(Machine is under- or overfilling the box)}$$

Table 7.3	Fill Amounts from Quality-Control Tests								
12.3	12.2	12.9	11.8	12.1	11.7	11.8	11.3	12.0	11.7
11.0	12.7	11.2	11.8	11.4	11.3	11.5	12.1	12.5	11.7
12.3	11.7	11.6	11.6	11.1	12.1	12.4	11.4	11.6	11.4
10.9	11.0	11.5	11.6	11.6	11.4	11.9	11.1	11.7	12.1
12.2	11.7	11.6	11.4	12.4	11.0	11.8	12.9	13.2	11.5
11.5	12.0	11.9	11.8	12.5	11.8	12.4	12.0	12.2	12.4
11.8	12.6	11.8	11.8	11.5	12.0	12.7	11.5	11.0	11.8
11.2	12.6	12.0	12.6	12.0	12.0	12.5	12.0	12.8	11.8
12.6	12.4	10.9	12.0	11.9	11.6	11.3	12.1	11.8	12.2
12.2	11.5	12.7	11.5	11.0	11.7	12.5	11.6	11.3	11.1

Data Set: CEREAL

Descriptive Statistics: FILL

Variable	N	Mean	StDev	Minimum	Q1	Median	Q3	Maximum
FILL	100	11.851	0.512	10.900	11.500	11.800	12.200	13.200

Figure 7.13

Minitab descriptive statistics for fill amounts, Example 7.5

Solution To carry out the test, we need to find the values of $\bar{x}$ and s. These values, $\bar{x} = 11.851$ and $s = .512$, are shown (highlighted) on the Minitab printout, Figure 7.13. Now, we substitute these sample statistics into the test statistic and obtain:

$$z = \frac{\bar{x} - 12}{\sigma_{\bar{x}}} = \frac{\bar{x} - 12}{\sigma/\sqrt{n}} = \frac{11.851 - 12}{\sigma/\sqrt{100}}$$

$$\approx \frac{11.851 - 12}{s/10} = \frac{-.149}{.512/10} = -2.91$$

The implication is that the sample mean, 11.851, is (approximately) 3 standard deviations below the null hypothesized value of 12.0 in the sampling distribution of $\bar{x}$. You can see in Figure 7.5 that this value of z is in the lower-tail rejection region, which consists of all values of $z < -2.576$. These sample data provide sufficient evidence to reject H_0 and conclude, at the $\alpha = .01$ level of significance, that the mean fill differs from the specification of $\mu = 12$ ounces. It appears that the machine is, on average, underfilling the boxes.

Look Back Three points about the test of hypothesis in this example apply to all statistical tests:

1. Because z is less than -2.576, it is tempting to state our conclusion at a significance level lower than $\alpha = .01$. We resist the temptation because the level of α is determined before the sampling experiment is performed. If we decide that we are willing to tolerate a 1% Type I error rate, the result of the sampling experiment should have no effect on that decision. In general, *the same data should not be used both to set up and to conduct the test.*

2. When we state our conclusion at the .01 level of significance, we are referring to the failure rate of the procedure, not the result of this particular test. We know that the test procedure will lead to the rejection of the null hypothesis only 1% of the time when in fact $\mu = 12$. Therefore, *when the test statistic falls in the rejection region, we infer that the alternative $\mu \neq 12$ is true and express our confidence in the procedure by quoting the α level of significance, or the $100(1 - \alpha)\%$ confidence level.*

3. Although a test may lead to a "statistically significant" result (i.e., rejecting H_0 at significance level α, as in the test above), it may not be "practically significant." For example, suppose the quality-control study tested $n = 100,000$ cereal boxes, resulting in $\bar{x} = 11.995$ and $s = .5$. Now, a two-tailed hypothesis test of H_0: $\mu = 12$ results in a test statistic of $z = \dfrac{(11.995 - 12)}{.5/\sqrt{100,000}} = -3.16$.

This result at $\alpha = .01$ leads us to "reject H_0" and conclude that the mean, μ, is "statistically different" from 12. However, for all practical purposes, the sample mean, $\bar{x} = 11.995$, and hypothesized mean, $\mu = 12$, are the same. Because the result is not "practically significant," the company is not likely to spend money fixing a machine that, for all practical purposes, is dispensing an average of 12 ounces of cereal into the boxes. Consequently, *not all "statistically significant" results are "practically significant."*

■ **Now Work Exercise 7.34**

Example 7.6

Using p-Values—Test of Mean Filling Weight

Problem Find the observed significance level (*p*-value) for the test of the mean filling weight in Examples 7.3 and 7.5. Interpret the result.

Solution Again, we are testing $H_0: \mu = 12$ ounces versus $H_a: \mu \neq 12$ ounces. The observed value of the test statistic in Example 7.5 was $z = -2.91$, and any value of z less than -2.91 or greater than 2.91 (because this is a two-tailed test) would be even more contradictory to H_0. Therefore, the observed significance level for the test is

$$p\text{-value} = P(z < -2.91 \text{ or } z > 2.91) = P(|z| > 2.91)$$

Thus, we calculate the area below the observed *z*-value, $z = -2.91$, and double it. Consulting Table II in Appendix D, we find that $P(z < -2.91) = .5 - .4982 = .0018$. Therefore, the *p*-value for this two-tailed test is

$$2P(z < -2.91) = 2(.0018) = .0036$$

This *p*-value can also be obtained using statistical software. The rounded *p*-value is shown (highlighted) on the Minitab printout, Figure 7.14. Since $\alpha = .01$ is greater than *p*-value $= .0036$, our conclusion is identical to that in Example 7.5—reject H_0.

Figure 7.14

Minitab test of mean fill amount, Example 7.6

```
Test of mu = 12 vs not = 12


Variable    N     Mean   StDev  SE Mean        95% CI        T       P
FILL      100  11.8510  0.5118  0.0512  (11.7495, 11.9525)  -2.91  0.004
```

Look Back We can interpret this *p*-value as a strong indication that the machine is not filling the boxes according to specifications because we would observe a test statistic this extreme or more extreme only 36 in 10,000 times if the machine were meeting specifications ($\mu = 12$). The extent to which the mean differs from 12 could be better determined by calculating a confidence interval for μ.

━━ ■ **Now Work Exercise 7.25**

Example 7.7

Using p-Values—Test of Mean Hospital Length of Stay

Problem Knowledge of the amount of time a patient occupies a hospital bed—called *length of stay* (LOS)—is important for allocating resources. At one hospital, the mean LOS was determined to be 5 days. A hospital administrator believes the mean LOS may now be less than 5 days due to a newly adopted managed health care system. To check this, the LOSs (in days) for 100 randomly selected hospital patients were recorded; these data are listed in Table 7.4. Suppose we want to test the hypothesis that the true mean length of stay at the hospital is less than 5 days; that is,

$$H_0: \mu = 5 \text{(Mean LOS after adoption is 5 days)}$$

$$H_a: \mu < 5 \text{(Mean LOS after adoption is less than 5 days)}$$

Assuming that $\sigma = 3.68$, use the data in the table to conduct the test at $\alpha = .05$.

Table 7.4	Lengths of Stay for 100 Hospital Patients								
2	3	8	6	4	4	6	4	2	5
8	10	4	4	4	2	1	3	2	10
1	3	2	3	4	3	5	2	4	1
2	9	1	7	17	9	9	9	4	4
1	1	1	3	1	6	3	3	2	5
1	3	3	14	2	3	9	6	6	3
5	1	4	6	11	22	1	9	6	5
2	2	5	4	3	6	1	5	1	6
17	1	2	4	5	4	4	3	2	3
3	5	2	3	3	2	10	2	4	2

Data Set: LOS

Solution The data were entered into a computer and Minitab was used to conduct the analysis. The Minitab printout for the lower-tailed test is displayed in Figure 7.15. Both the test statistic, $z = -1.28$, and the *p*-value of the test, $p = .101$, are highlighted on the Minitab printout. Since the *p*-value exceeds our selected α value, $\alpha = .05$, we cannot reject the null hypothesis. Hence, there is insufficient evidence (at $\alpha = .05$) to conclude that the true mean LOS at the hospital is less than 5 days.

One-Sample Z: LOS

```
Test of mu = 5 vs < 5
The assumed standard deviation = 3.68
```

Variable	N	Mean	StDev	SE Mean	95% Upper Bound	Z	P
LOS	100	4.530	3.678	0.368	5.135	-1.28	0.101

Figure 7.15

Minitab lower-tailed test of mean LOS, Example 7.7

Look Back A hospital administrator, desirous of a mean length of stay less than 5 days, may be tempted to select an α level that leads to a rejection of the null hypothesis *after* determining *p*-value = .101. There are two reasons one should resist this temptation. First, the administrator would need to select $\alpha > .101$ (say, $\alpha = .15$) in order to conclude that $H_a\colon \mu < 5$ is true. A Type I error rate of 15% is considered too large by most researchers. Second, and more importantly, such a strategy is considered unethical statistical practice. (See marginal note, p. 370.)

■ **Now Work Exercise 7.32**

In the next section, we demonstrate how to conduct a test for μ when the sample size is small.

STATISTICS in ACTION REVISITED

Testing a Population Mean

Refer to Kimberly-Clark Corporation's survey of 250 people who kept a count of their use of Kleenex® tissues in diaries (p. 355). We want to test the claim made by marketing experts that μ, the average number of tissues used by people with colds, is greater than 60 tissues. That is, we want to test

$$H_0\colon \mu = 60 \quad H_a\colon > 60$$

We will select $\alpha = .05$ as the level of significance for the test.

The survey results for the 250 sampled Kleenex® users are stored in the **TISSUE** data file. A Minitab analysis of the data yielded the printout displayed in Figure SIA7.1.

The observed significance level of the test, highlighted on the printout, is *p*-value = 000. Since this *p*-value is less than $\alpha = .05$, we have sufficient evidence to reject H_0; therefore, we conclude that the mean number of tissues used by a person with a cold is greater than 60 tissues. This result supports the company's decision to put 70 tissues in a cold-care box of Kleenex.

```
Test of mu = 60 vs > 60
```

Variable	N	Mean	StDev	SE Mean	95% Lower Bound	T	P
NUMUSED	250	68.68	25.03	1.58	66.06	5.48	0.000

Figure SIA7.1

Minitab test of $\mu = 60$ for Kleenex survey

Data Set: TISSUE

Exercises 7.28–7.46

Learning the Mechanics

7.28 Consider the test $H_0: \mu = 70$ versus $H_a: \mu > 70$ using a large sample of size $n = 400$. Assume $\sigma = 20$.

    a. Describe the sampling distribution of $\bar{x}$.

    b. Find the value of the test statistic if $\bar{x} = 72.5$.

    c. Refer to part **b**. Find the p-value of the test.

    d. Find the rejection region of the test for $\alpha = .01$.

    e. Refer to parts **c** and **d**. Use the p-value approach to make the appropriate conclusion.

    f. Repeat part **e**, but use the rejection region approach.

    g. Do the conclusions, parts **e** and **f**, agree?

7.29 Suppose you are interested in conducting the statistical test of $H_0: \mu = 255$ against $H_a: \mu > 255$, and you have decided to use the following decision rule: Reject H_0 if the sample mean of a random sample of 81 items is more than 270. Assume that the standard deviation of the population is 63.

    a. Express the decision rule in terms of z.

    b. Find α, the probability of making a Type I error, by using this decision rule.

7.30 A random sample of 100 observations from a population with standard deviation 60 yielded a sample mean of 110.

    a. Test the null hypothesis that $\mu = 100$ against the alternative hypothesis that $\mu > 100$ using $\alpha = .05$. Interpret the results of the test.

    b. Test the null hypothesis that $\mu = 100$ against the alternative hypothesis that $\mu \neq 100$ using $\alpha = .05$. Interpret the results of the test.

    c. Compare the results of the two tests you conducted. Explain why the results differ.

7.31 A random sample of 64 observations produced the following summary statistics: $\bar{x} = .323$ and $s^2 = .034$.

    a. Test the null hypothesis that $\mu = .36$ against the alternative hypothesis that $\mu < .36$ using $\alpha = .10$.

    b. Test the null hypothesis that $\mu = .36$ against the alternative hypothesis that $\mu \neq .36$ using $\alpha = .10$. Interpret the result.

⚽ Applet Exercise 7.2

Use the applet *Hypotheses Test for a Mean* to investigate the effect of the underlying distribution on the proportion of Type I errors. For this exercise use $n = 100$, mean = 50, standard deviation = 10, null mean = 50, and alternative <.

    a. Select the normal distribution and run the applet several times without clearing. What happens to the proportion of times the null hypothesis is rejected at the .05 level as the applet is run more and more times?

    b. Clear the applet and then repeat part **a** using the right skewed distribution. Do you get similar results? Explain.

    c. Describe the effect that the underlying distribution has on the probability of making a Type I error.

⚽ Applet Exercise 7.3

Use the applet *Hypotheses Test for a Mean* to investigate the effect of the underlying distribution on the proportion of

Type II errors. For this exercise use $n = 100$, mean = 50, standard deviation = 10, null mean = 52, and alternative <.

    a. Select the normal distribution and run the applet several times without clearing. What happens to the proportion of times the null hypothesis is rejected at the .01 level as the applet is run more and more times? Is this what you would expect? Explain.

    b. Clear the applet and then repeat part **a** using the right skewed distribution. Do you get similar results? Explain.

    c. Describe the effect that the underlying distribution has on the probability of making a Type II error.

⚽ Applet Exercise 7.4

Use the applet *Hypotheses Test for a Mean* to investigate the effect of the null mean on the probability of making a Type II error. For this exercise use $n = 100$, mean = 50, standard deviation = 10, and alternative < with the normal distribution. Set the null mean to 55 and run the applet several times without clearing. Record the proportion of Type II errors that occurred at the .01 level. Clear the applet and repeat for null means of 54, 53, 52, and 51. What can you conclude about the probability of a Type II error as the null mean gets closer to the actual mean? Can you offer a reasonable explanation for this?

Applying the Concepts—Basic

7.32 **Corporate sustainability of CPA firms.** Refer to the *Business and Society* (March 2011) study on the sustainability behaviors of CPA corporations, Exercise 6.12 (p. 308). Recall that the level of support for corporate sustainability (measured on a quantitative scale ranging from 0 to 160 points) was obtained for each in a sample of 992 senior managers at CPA firms. The data (where higher point values indicate a higher level of support for sustainability) are saved in the accompanying file. The CEO of a CPA firm claims that the true mean level of support for sustainability is 75 points.

    a. Specify the null and alternative hypotheses for testing this claim.

    b. For this problem, what is a Type I error? A Type II error?

    c. The XLSTAT printout on the following page gives the results of the test. Locate the test statistic and p-value on the printout.

    d. At $\alpha = .05$, give the appropriate conclusion.

    e. What assumptions, if any, about the distribution of support levels must hold true in order for the inference derived from the test to be valid? Explain.

7.33 **Packaging of a children's health food.** Junk foods (e.g., potato chips) are typically packaged to appeal to children. Can similar packaging of a healthy food product influence children's desire to consume the product? This was the question of interest in an article published in the *Journal of Consumer Behaviour* (Vol. 10, 2011). A fictitious brand of a healthy food product—sliced apples—was packaged to appeal to children (a smiling cartoon apple was on the front of the package). The researchers showed the packaging to a sample of 408 school children and asked each whether he or she was willing to eat the product. Willingness to eat

B	C	D	E	F	G
XLSTAT 2011.4.02 - One-sample t-test and z-test					
Theoretical mean: 75					
Significance level (%): 5					
Summary statistics ▼					
Summary statistics:					
Variable	**Observations**	**Minimum**	**Maximum**	**Mean**	**Std. deviation**
Support	992	0.0000	155.0000	67.7550	26.8707
One-sample z-test / Two-tailed test:					
95% confidence interval on the mean:					
(66.0829, 69.4271)					
Difference	-7.2450				
z (Observed value)	-8.4923				
|z| (Critical value)	1.9600				
p-value (Two-tailed)	< 0.0001				
alpha	0.05				

XLSTAT output for Exercise 7.32

was measured on a 5-point scale, with 1 = "not willing at all" and 5 = "very willing." The data are summarized as follows: $\bar{x} = 3.69$, $s = 2.44$. Suppose the researchers knew that the mean willingness to eat an actual brand of sliced apples (which is not packaged for children) is $\mu = 3$.

a. Conduct a test to determine whether the true mean willingness to eat the brand of sliced apples packaged for children exceeded 3. Use $\alpha = .05$ to make your conclusion.

b. The data (willingness to eat values) are not normally distributed. How does this impact (if at all) the validity of your conclusion in part **a**? Explain.

7.34 Accounting and Machiavellianism. Refer to the *Behavioral Research in Accounting* (Jan. 2008) study of Machiavellian traits in accountants, Exercise 6.19 (p. 310). A Mach rating score was determined for each in a random sample of 122 purchasing managers, with the following results: $\bar{x} = 99.6$, $s = 12.6$. Recall that a director of purchasing at a major firm claims that the true mean Mach rating score of all purchasing managers is 85.

a. Suppose you want to test the director's claim. Specify the null and alternative hypotheses for the test.

b. Give the rejection region for the test using $\alpha = .10$.

c. Find the value of the test statistic.

d. Use the result, part **c**, to make the appropriate conclusion.

7.35 Facial structure of CEOs. Refer to the *Psychological Science* (Vol. 22, 2011) study on using a chief executive officer's facial structure to predict a firm's financial performance, Exercise 6.20 (p. 310). Recall that the facial width-to-height ratio (WHR) for each in a sample of 55 CEOs at publicly traded *Fortune* 500 firms was determined. The sample resulted in $\bar{x} = 1.96$ and $s = .15$. An analyst wants to predict the financial performance of a *Fortune* 500 firm based on the value of the true mean facial WHR of CEOs. The analyst wants to use the value of $\mu = 2.2$. Do you recommend he use this value? Conduct a test of hypothesis for μ to help you answer the question. Specify all the elements of the test: H_0, H_a, test statistic, p-value, α, and your conclusion.

7.36 Trading skills of institutional investors. Managers of stock portfolios make decisions as to what stocks to buy and sell in a given quarter. The trading skills of these institutional investors were quantified and analyzed in *The Journal of Finance* (April 2011). The study focused on "round-trip" trades, i.e., trades in which the same stock was both bought and sold in the same quarter. Consider a random sample of 200 round-trip trades made by institutional investors. Suppose the sample mean rate of return is 2.95% and the sample standard deviation is 8.82%. If the true mean rate of return of round-trip trades is positive, then the population of institutional investors is considered to have performed successfully.

a. Specify the null and alternative hypotheses for determining whether the population of institutional investors performed successfully.

b. Find the rejection region for the test using $\alpha = .05$.

c. Interpret the value of α in the words of the problem.

d. A Minitab printout of the analysis is shown below. Locate the test statistic and p-value on the printout. [*Note:* For large samples, $z \approx t$.]

e. Give the appropriate conclusion in the words of the problem.

```
Test of mu = 0 vs > 0


                                    95% Lower
   N   Mean  StDev  SE Mean         Bound      T      P
 200  2.950  8.820    0.624         1.919   4.73  0.000
```

7.37 **Producer's and consumer's risk.** In quality-control applications of hypothesis testing, the null and alternative hypotheses are frequently specified as

H_0: The production process is performing satisfactorily.

H_a: The process is performing inan unsatisfactory manner.

Accordingly, α is sometimes referred to as the *producer's risk,* while β is called the *consumer's risk* (Stevenson, *Operations Management,* 2008). An injection molder produces plastic golf tees. The process is designed to produce tees with a mean weight of .250 ounce. To investigate whether the injection molder is operating satisfactorily, 40 tees were randomly sampled from the last hour's production. Their weights (in ounces) are listed in the following table.

.247	.251	.254	.253	.253	.248	.253	.255	.256	.252
.253	.252	.253	.256	.254	.256	.252	.251	.253	.251
.253	.253	.248	.251	.253	.256	.254	.250	.254	.255
.249	.250	.254	.251	.251	.255	.251	.253	.252	.253

a. Write H_0 and H_a in terms of the true mean weight of the golf tees, μ.
b. Access the data and find $\bar{x}$ and s.
c. Calculate the test statistic.
d. Find the *p*-value for the test.
e. Locate the rejection region for the test using $\alpha = .01$.
f. Do the data provide sufficient evidence to conclude that the process is not operating satisfactorily?
g. In the context of this problem, explain why it makes sense to call α the producer's risk and β the consumer's risk.

Applying the Concepts—Intermediate

7.38 **Birth order, IQ, and earnings.** Recent research suggests that your annual pay is linked to your birth order—firstborn individuals tend to earn higher salaries than non-firstborn individuals. The evidence on whether IQ is associated with birth order is not as conclusive. An international team of economists investigated the possible link between IQ and birth order in *CESifo Economic Studies* (Vol. 57, 2011). The data source for the research was the Medical Birth Registry of Norway. It is known that the mean IQ (measured in stanines) for all Norway residents is 5.2 points. In the study, a sample of 581 Norway residents who were the sixth-born or later in their families had a mean IQ score of 4.7 points with a standard deviation of 1.8 points. Is this sufficient evidence to conclude that the mean IQ score of all Norway residents who were the sixth-born or later in their families is lower than the country mean of 5.2 points? Use $\alpha = .01$ as a measure of reliability for your inference.

7.39 **Time required to complete a task.** When a person is asked, "How much time will you require to complete this task?"

cognitive theory posits that people (e.g., a business consultant) will typically underestimate the time required. Would the opposite theory hold if the question was phrased in terms of how much work could be completed in a given amount of time? This was the question of interest to researchers writing in *Applied Cognitive Psychology* (Vol. 25, 2011). For one study conducted by the researchers, each in a sample of 40 University of Oslo students was asked how many minutes it would take to read a 32-page report. In a second study, 42 students were asked how many pages of a lengthy report they could read in 48 minutes. (The students in either study did not actually read the report.) Numerical descriptive statistics (based on summary information published in the article) for both studies are provided in the accompanying table.

	Estimated Time (minutes)	Estimated Number of Pages
Sample size, n	40	42
Sample mean, $\bar{x}$	60	28
Sample standard deviation, s	41	14

a. The researchers determined that the actual mean time it takes to read the report is $\mu = 48$ minutes. Is there evidence to support the theory that the students, on average, overestimated the time it would take to read the report? Test using $\alpha = .10$.
b. The researchers also determined that the actual mean number of pages of the report that is read within the allotted time is $\mu = 32$ pages. Is there evidence to support the theory that the students, on average, underestimated the number of report pages that could be read? Test using $\alpha = .10$.
c. The researchers noted that the distribution of both estimated time and estimated number of pages is highly skewed (i.e., not normally distributed). Does this fact impact the inferences derived in parts **a** and **b**? Explain.

7.40 **Cooling method for gas turbines.** During periods of high electricity demand, especially during the hot summer months, the power output from a gas turbine engine can drop dramatically. One way to counter this drop in power is by cooling the inlet air to the gas turbine. An increasingly popular cooling method uses high-pressure inlet fogging. The performance of a sample of 67 gas turbines augmented with high-pressure inlet fogging was investigated in the *Journal of Engineering for Gas Turbines and Power* (Jan. 2005). One measure of performance is heat rate (kilojoules per kilowatt per hour). Heat rates for the 67 gas turbines are listed in the table below. Suppose that a standard gas turbine has, on average, a heat rate of 10,000 kJ/kWh. Conduct a test to determine if the mean heat rate of gas turbines augmented with high-pressure inlet fogging exceeds 10,000 kJ/kWh. Use $\alpha = .05$.

14622	13196	11948	11289	11964	10526	10387	10592	10460	10086
14628	13396	11726	11252	12449	11030	10787	10603	10144	11674
11510	10946	10508	10604	10270	10529	10360	14796	12913	12270
11842	10656	11360	11136	10814	13523	11289	11183	10951	9722
10481	9812	9669	9643	9115	9115	11588	10888	9738	9295
9421	9105	10233	10186	9918	9209	9532	9933	9152	9295
16243	14628	12766	8714	9469	11948	12414			

Data for Exercise 7.40

7.41 Point spreads of NFL games. During the National Football League (NFL) season, Las Vegas odds makers establish a point spread on each game for betting purposes. For example, the New England Patriots were established as 3.5-point favorites over the eventual champion New York Giants in the 2012 Super Bowl. The final scores of NFL games were compared against the final point spreads established by the odds makers in *Chance* (Fall 1998). The difference between the game outcome and point spread (called a *point-spread error*) was calculated for 240 NFL games. The mean and standard deviation of the point-spread errors are $\bar{x} = -1.6$ and $s = 13.3$. Use this information to test the hypothesis that the true mean point-spread error for all NFL games differs from 0. Conduct the test at $\alpha = .01$ and interpret the result.

7.42 Revenue for a full-service funeral. According to the National Funeral Directors Association (NFDA), the nation's 22,000 funeral homes collected an average of $6,500 per full-service funeral in 2009 (www.nfda.org). A random sample of 36 funeral homes reported revenue data for the current year. Among other measures, each reported its average fee for a full-service funeral. These data (in thousands of dollars) are shown in the following table.

7.4	9.4	5.3	8.4	7.5	6.5	6.2	8.3	6.7
11.6	6.3	5.9	6.7	5.8	5.2	6.4	6.0	7.4
7.2	6.6	6.3	5.3	6.6	5.6	8.4	7.2	7.4
5.8	6.3	6.1	7.0	7.2	6.1	5.4	7.4	6.6

a. What are the appropriate null and alternative hypotheses to test whether the average full-service fee of U. S. funeral homes this year exceeds $6,500?

b. Conduct the test at $\alpha = .05$. Do the sample data provide sufficient evidence to conclude that the average fee this year is higher than in 2009?

c. In conducting the test, was it necessary to assume that the population of average full-service fees was normally distributed? Justify your answer.

7.43 Buy-side vs. sell-side analysts' earnings forecasts. Refer to the *Financial Analysts Journal* (Jul./Aug. 2008) study of earnings forecasts of buy-side and sell-side analysts, Exercise 2.86 (p. 86). Buy-side analysts differ from sell-side analysts on a variety of factors, including scope of industry coverage, sources of information used, and target audience. Recall that data were collected on 3,526 forecasts made by buy-side analysts and 58,562 forecasts made by sell-side analysts, and the relative absolute forecast error was determined for each. A positive forecast error indicates that the analyst is overestimating earnings, while a negative forecast error implies that the analyst is underestimating earnings. Summary statistics for the forecast errors in the two samples are reproduced in the table below.

	Buy-Side Analysts	Sell-Side Analysts
Mean	0.85	−0.05
Standard Deviation	1.93	0.85

Source: Based on Groysberg, B., Healy, P., & Chapman, C. "Buy-side vs. sell-side analysts' earnings forecast," *Financial Analysts Journal,* Vol. 64, No. 4, Jul./Aug. 2008.

a. Conduct a test (at $\alpha = .01$) to determine if the true mean forecast error for buy-side analysts is positive.

Use the observed significance level (*p*-value) of the test to make your decision and state your conclusion in the words of the problem.

b. Conduct a test (at $\alpha = .01$) to determine if the true mean forecast error for sell-side analysts is negative. Use the observed significance level (*p*-value) of the test to make your decision and state your conclusion in the words of the problem.

7.44 Solder-joint inspections. Current technology uses high-resolution X-rays and lasers for inspection of solder-joint defects on printed circuit boards (PCBs) (*Global SMT & Packaging,* April 2008). A particular manufacturer of laser-based inspection equipment claims that its product can inspect on average at least 10 solder joints per second when the joints are spaced .1 inch apart. The equipment was tested by a potential buyer on 48 different PCBs. In each case, the equipment was operated for exactly 1 second. The number of solder joints inspected on each run follows:

10	9	10	10	11	9	12	8	8	9	6	10
7	10	11	9	9	13	9	10	11	10	12	8
9	9	9	7	12	6	9	10	10	8	7	9
11	12	10	0	10	11	12	9	7	9	9	10

a. The potential buyer wants to know whether the sample data refute the manufacturer's claim. Specify the null and alternative hypotheses that the buyer should test.

b. In the context of this exercise, what is a Type I error? A Type II error?

c. Conduct the hypothesis test you described in part **a** and interpret the test's results in the context of this exercise. Use $\alpha = .05$.

Applying the Concepts—Advanced

7.45 Why do small firms export? What motivates small firms to export their products? To answer this question, California State University Professor Ralph Pope conducted a survey of 137 exporting firms listed in the *California International Trade Register* (*Journal of Small Business Management,* Vol. 40, 2002). Firm CEOs were asked to respond to the statement "Management believes that the firm can achieve economies of scale by exporting" on a scale of 1 (strongly disagree) to 5 (strongly agree). Summary statistics for the $n = 137$ scale scores were reported as $\bar{x} = 3.85$ and $s = 1.5$. In the journal article, the researcher hypothesized that if the true mean scale score exceeds 3.5, then CEOs at all California small firms generally agree with the statement.

a. Conduct the appropriate test using $\alpha = .05$. State your conclusion in the words of the problem.

b. Explain why the results of the study, although "statistically significant," may not be practically significant.

c. The scale scores for the sample of 137 small firms are unlikely to be normally distributed. Does this invalidate the inference you made in part **a?** Explain.

7.46 Salaries of postgraduates. The *Economics of Education Review* (Vol. 21, 2002) published a paper on the relationship between education level and earnings. The data for the research were obtained from the National Adult Literacy Survey of more than 25,000 respondents. The survey revealed that males with a postgraduate degree have a mean salary of $61,340 (with standard error $s_{\bar{x}} = $2,185$), while females with a postgraduate degree have a mean of $32,227 (with standard error $s_{\bar{x}} = \$932$).

a. The article reports that a 95% confidence interval for μ_M, the population mean salary of all males with postgraduate degrees, is ($57,050, $65,631). Based on this interval, is there evidence to say that μ_M differs from $60,000? Explain.

b. Use the summary information to test the hypothesis that the true mean salary of males with postgraduate degrees differs from $60,000. Use $\alpha = .05$.

c. Explain why the inferences in parts **a** and **b** agree.

d. The article reports that a 95% confidence interval for μ_F, the population mean salary of all females with postgraduate degrees, is ($30,396, $34,058). Based on this interval, is there evidence to say that μ_F differs from $33,000? Explain.

e. Use the summary information to test the hypothesis that the true mean salary of females with postgraduate degrees differs from $33,000. Use $\alpha = .05$.

f. Explain why the inferences in parts **d** and **e** agree.

7.5 Test of Hypothesis about a Population Mean: Student's *t*-Statistic

A manufacturing operation consists of a single-machine-tool system that produces an average of 15.5 transformer parts every hour. After undergoing a complete overhaul, the system was monitored by observing the number of parts produced in each of 17 randomly selected 1-hour periods. The mean and standard deviation for the 17 production runs are

$$\bar{x} = 15.42 \qquad s = .16$$

Does this sample provide sufficient evidence to conclude that the true mean number of parts produced every hour by the overhauled system differs from 15.5?

This inference can be placed in a test of hypothesis framework. We establish the preoverhaul mean as the null hypothesized value and use a two-tailed alternative that the true mean of the overhauled system differs from the preoverhaul mean:

$H_0: \mu = 15.5$ (Mean of overhauled system equals 15.5 parts per hour.)

$H_a: \mu \neq 15.5$ (Mean of overhauled system differs from 15.5 parts per hour.)

Recall from Section 6.3 that when we are faced with making inferences about a population mean using the information in a small sample, two problems emerge:

1. The normality of the sampling distribution for $\bar{x}$ does not follow from the Central Limit Theorem when the sample size is small. We must assume that the distribution of measurements from which the sample was selected is approximately normally distributed in order to ensure the approximate normality of the sampling distribution of $\bar{x}$.

2. If the population standard deviation σ is unknown, as is usually the case, then we cannot assume that s will provide a good approximation for σ when the sample size is small. Instead, we must use the *t*-distribution rather than the standard normal *z*-distribution to make inferences about the population mean μ.

Therefore, as the test statistic of a small-sample test of a population mean, we use the *t*-statistic:

$$\text{Test statistic: } t = \frac{\bar{x} - \mu_0}{s/\sqrt{n}} = \frac{\bar{x} - 15.5}{s/\sqrt{n}}$$

where μ_0 is the null hypothesized value of the population mean μ. In our example, $\mu_0 = 15.5$.

To find the rejection region, we must specify the value of α, the probability that the test will lead to rejection of the null hypothesis when it is true, and then consult either the *t*-table (Table III in Appendix D) or use computer software. Using $\alpha = .05$, the two-tailed rejection region is

$$\text{Rejection region: } t_{\alpha/2} = t_{.025} = 2.120 \text{ with } n - 1 = 16 \text{ df}$$

$$\text{Reject } H_0 \text{ if } t < -2.120 \text{ or } t > 2.120$$

The rejection region is shown in Figure 7.16.

We are now prepared to calculate the test statistic and reach a conclusion:

$$t = \frac{\bar{x} - \mu_0}{s/\sqrt{n}} = \frac{15.42 - 15.50}{.16/\sqrt{n}} = \frac{-.08}{.0388} = -2.06$$

Because the calculated value of *t* does not fall in the rejection region (Figure 7.16), we cannot reject H_0 at the $\alpha = .05$ level of significance. Based on the sample evidence, we should not conclude that the mean number of parts produced per hour by the overhauled system differs from 15.5.

It is interesting to note that the calculated *t*-value, −2.06, is *less than* $-z_{.05} = -1.96$. The implication is that if we had *incorrectly* used a *z*-statistic for this test, we would have rejected the null hypothesis at $\alpha = .05$, concluding that the mean production per hour of the overhauled system differs from 15.5 parts. The important point is that the statistical procedure to be used must always be closely scrutinized, with all the assumptions understood. Many statistical distortions are the result of misapplications of otherwise valid procedures.

Figure 7.16

Two-tailed rejection region for small-sample *t*-test

The technique for conducting a small-sample test of hypothesis about a population mean is summarized in the following box.

Small-Sample Test of Hypothesis about μ Based on Student's *t*-Statistic

One-Tailed Test	Two-Tailed Test
$H_0: \mu = \mu_0$	$H_0: \mu = \mu_0$
$H_a: \mu < \mu_0$ (or $H_a: \mu > \mu_0$)	$H_a: \mu \neq \mu_0$
Test statistic: $t = \dfrac{\bar{x} - \mu_0}{s/\sqrt{n}}$	Test statistic: $t = \dfrac{\bar{x} - \mu_0}{s/\sqrt{n}}$
Rejection region: $t < -t_\alpha$ (or $t > t_\alpha$ when $H_a: \mu > \mu_0$)	Rejection region: $\lvert t \rvert > t_{\alpha/2}$

where t_α and $t_{\alpha/2}$ are based on $(n - 1)$ degrees of freedom

---

Conditions Required for a Valid Small-Sample Hypothesis Test for μ

1. A random sample is selected from the target population.
2. The population from which the sample is selected has a distribution that is approximately normal.

Example 7.8

Small-Sample Test for μ—Does a New Engine Meet Air Pollution Standards?

Problem A major car manufacturer wants to test a new engine to determine whether it meets new air pollution standards. The mean emission μ of all engines of this type must be less than 20 parts per million of carbon. Ten engines are manufactured for testing purposes, and the emission level of each is determined. The data (in parts per million) are listed in Table 7.5.

Do the data supply sufficient evidence to allow the manufacturer to conclude that this type of engine meets the pollution standard? Assume that the production process is stable and the manufacturer is willing to risk a Type I error with probability $\alpha = .01$.

Table 7.5	Emission Levels for Ten Engines								
15.6	16.2	22.5	20.5	16.4	19.4	19.6	17.9	12.7	14.9

Data Set: CARBON

Solution The manufacturer wants to support the research hypothesis that the mean emission level μ for all engines of this type is less than 20 parts per million. The elements of this small-sample one-tailed test are

$$H_0: \mu = 20 \qquad \text{(Mean emission level equals 20 ppm.)}$$

$$H_a: \mu < 20 \qquad \begin{array}{l}\text{(Mean emission level is less than} \\ \text{20 ppm— i.e., engine meets pollution standard.)}\end{array}$$

Test statistic: $t = \dfrac{\bar{x} - 20}{s/\sqrt{n}}$

Rejection region: For $\alpha = .01$ and df $= n - 1 = 9$, the one-tailed rejection region (see Figure 7.17) is $t < -t_{.01} = -2.821$.

Assumption: The relative frequency distribution of the population of emission levels for all engines of this type is approximately normal. Based on the shape of the Minitab stem-and-leaf display of the data shown in Figure 7.18, this assumption appears to be reasonably satisfied.

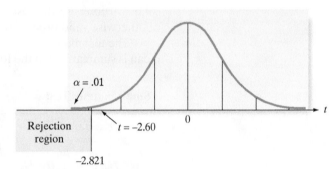

Figure 7.17

A *t*-distribution with 9 df and the rejection region for Example 7.8

To calculate the test statistic, we entered the data into a computer and analyzed it using Minitab. The Minitab printout is shown in Figure 7.18. From the printout, we obtain $\bar{x} = 17.57, s = 2.95$. Substituting these values into the test statistic formula, we get

$$t = \frac{\bar{x} - 20}{s/\sqrt{n}} = \frac{17.57 - 20}{2.95/\sqrt{10}} = -2.60$$

Stem-and-Leaf Display: E-LEVEL

```
Stem-and-leaf of E-LEVEL   N  = 10
Leaf Unit = 1.0


   1    1   2
   3    1   45
  (3)   1   667
   4    1   99
   2    2   0
   1    2   2
```

One-Sample T: E-LEVEL

```
Test of mu = 20 vs < 20
```

Figure 7.18

Minitab analysis of 10 emission levels, Example 7.8

Variable	N	Mean	StDev	SE Mean	95% Upper Bound	T	P
E-LEVEL	10	17.5700	2.9522	0.9336	19.2814	-2.60	0.014

Because the calculated *t* falls outside the rejection region (see Figure 7.17), the manufacturer cannot reject H_0. There is insufficient evidence to conclude that $\mu < 20$ parts per million. Consequently, we cannot conclude that the new engine type meets the pollution standard.

Look Back Are you satisfied with the reliability associated with this inference? The probability is only $\alpha = .01$ that the test would support the research hypothesis if, in fact, it were false.

■ **Now Work Exercise 7.50a, b**

| Example | 7.9 |

The *p*-Value for a Small-Sample Test of μ

Problem Find the observed significance level for the test described in Example 7.8. Interpret the result.

Solution The test of Example 7.8 was a lower-tailed test: H_0: $\mu = 20$ versus H_a: $\mu < 20$. Because the value of *t* computed from the sample data was $t = -2.60$, the observed significance level (or *p*-value) for the test is equal to the probability that *t* would assume a value less than or equal to -2.60 if, in fact, H_0 were true. This is equal to the area in the lower tail of the *t*-distribution (shaded in Figure 7.19).

One way to find this area (i.e., the *p*-value for the test) is to consult the *t*-table (Table III in Appendix D). Unlike the table of areas under the normal curve, Table III gives only the *t*-values corresponding to the areas .100, .050, .025, .010, .005, .001, and .0005. Therefore, we can only approximate the *p*-value for the test. Because the observed *t*-value was based on 9 degrees of freedom, we use the df = 9 row in Table III and move across the row until we reach the *t*-values that are closest to the observed $t = -2.60$. [*Note:* We ignore the minus sign.] The *t*-values cor-

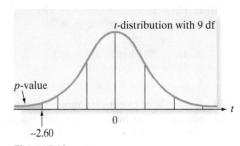

Figure 7.19

The observed significance level for the test of Example 7.8

responding to *p*-values of .010 and .025 are 2.821 and 2.262, respectively. Because the observed *t*-value falls between $t_{.010}$ and $t_{.025}$, the *p*-value for the test lies between .010 and .025. In other words, $.010 < p\text{-value} < .025$. Thus, we would reject the null hypothesis, H_0: $\mu = 20$ parts per million, for any value of α larger than .025 (the upper bound of the *p*-value).

A second, more accurate, way to obtain the *p*-value is to use a statistical software package to conduct the test of hypothesis. The Minitab printout shown in Figure 7.18 gives both the test statistic (-2.60) and *p*-value (.014).

You can see that the actual *p*-value of the test falls within the bounds obtained from Table III. Based on the actual *p*-value, we will reject H_0: $\mu = 20$ in favor of H_a: $\mu < 20$ for any α level larger than .014.

■ **Now Work Exercise 7.50c**

Small-sample inferences typically require more assumptions and provide less information about the population parameter than do large-sample inferences. Nevertheless, the *t*-test is a method of testing a hypothesis about a population mean of a normal distribution when only a small number of observations are available. What can be done if you know that the population relative frequency distribution is decidedly nonnormal, say highly skewed?

What Can Be Done If the Population Relative Frequency Distribution Departs Greatly from Normal?

Answer: Use one of the nonparametric statistical methods of Chapter 15.

Exercises 7.47–7.63

Learning the Mechanics

7.47 **a.** Consider testing $H_0: \mu = 80$. Under what conditions should you use the t-distribution to conduct the test?
  b. In what ways are the distributions of the z-statistic and t-test statistic alike? How do they differ?

7.48 For each of the following rejection regions, sketch the sampling distribution of t and indicate the location of the rejection region on your sketch:
  a. $t > 1.440$ where df $= 6$
  b. $t < -1.782$ where df $= 12$
  c. $t < -2.060$ or $t > 2.060$ where df $= 25$
  d. For each of parts **a–c,** what is the probability that a Type I error will be made?

7.49 A random sample of n observations is selected from a normal population to test the null hypothesis that $\mu = 10$. Specify the rejection region for each of the following combinations of H_a, α, and n:
  a. $H_a: \mu \neq 10; \alpha = .05; n = 14$
  b. $H_a: \mu > 10; \alpha = .01; n = 24$
  c. $H_a: \mu > 10; \alpha = .10; n = 9$
  d. $H_a: \mu < 10; \alpha = .01; n = 12$
  e. $H_a: \mu \neq 10; \alpha = .10; n = 20$
  f. $H_a: \mu < 10; \alpha = .05; n = 4$

7.50 A sample of five measurements, randomly selected from a normally distributed population, resulted in the following summary statistics: $\bar{x} = 4.8$, $s = 1.3$.
  a. Test the null hypothesis that the mean of the population is 6 against the alternative hypothesis, $\mu < 6$. Use $\alpha = .05$.
  b. Test the null hypothesis that the mean of the population is 6 against the alternative hypothesis, $\mu \neq 6$. Use $\alpha = .05$.
  c. Find the observed significance level for each test.

7.51 Suppose you conduct a t-test for the null hypothesis $H_0: \mu = 1,000$ versus the alternative hypothesis $H_a: \mu > 1,000$ based on a sample of 17 observations. The test results are $t = 1.89$ and p-value $= .038$.
  a. What assumptions are necessary for the validity of this procedure?
  b. Interpret the results of the test.
  c. Suppose the alternative hypothesis had been the two-tailed $H_a: \mu \neq 1,000$. If the t-statistic were unchanged, then what would the p-value be for this test? Interpret the p-value for the two-tailed test.

Applying the Concepts—Basic

7.52 **Lobster trap placement.** Refer to the *Bulletin of Marine Science* (April 2010) observational study of lobster trap placement by teams fishing for the red spiny lobster in Baja California Sur, Mexico, Exercise 6.29 (p. 318). Trap-spacing measurements (in meters) for a sample of seven teams of red spiny lobster fishermen are reproduced in the accompanying table. Let μ represent the average of the trap-spacing measurements for the population of red spiny lobster fishermen fishing in Baja California Sur, Mexico. In Exercise 6.29 you computed the mean and standard deviation of the sample measurements to be $\bar{x} = 89.9$ meters and $s = 11.6$ meters, respectively. Suppose you want to determine if the true value of μ differs from 95 meters.

93	99	105	94	82	70	86

Source: Based on Shester, G. G. "Explaining catch variation among Baja California lobster fishers through spatial analysis of trap-placement decisions," *Bulletin of Marine Science*, Vol. 86, No. 2, April 2010 (Table 1), pp. 479–498.

  a. Specify the null and alternative hypotheses for this test.
  b. Since $\bar{x} = 89.9$ is less than 95, a fisherman wants to reject the null hypothesis. What are the problems with using such a decision rule?
  c. Compute the value of the test statistic.
  d. Find the approximate p-value of the test.
  e. Select a value of α, the probability of a Type I error. Interpret this value in the words of the problem.
  f. Give the appropriate conclusion, based on the results of parts **d** and **e.**
  g. What conditions must be satisfied for the test results to be valid?
  h. In Exercise 6.29 you found a 95% confidence interval for μ. Does this interval support your conclusion in part **f?**

7.53 **Radon exposure in Egyptian tombs.** Refer to the *Radiation Protection Dosimetry* (December 2010) study of radon exposure in Egyptian tombs, Exercise 6.30 (p. 318). The radon levels—measured in becquerels per cubic meter (Bq/m^3)—in the inner chambers of a sample of 12 tombs are listed in the table (next page). For the safety of the guards and visitors, the Egypt Tourism Authority (ETA) will temporarily close the tombs if the true mean level of radon exposure in the tombs rises to

One-Sample Statistics

	N	Mean	Std. Deviation	Std. Error Mean
RADON	12	3642.50	4486.929	1295.265

One-Sample Test

	Test Value = 6000					
					95% Confidence Interval of the Difference	
	t	df	Sig. (2-tailed)	Mean Difference	Lower	Upper
RADON	-1.820	11	.096	-2357.500	-5208.36	493.36

SPSS output for Exercise 7.53

One-Sample T: ROUGH

Test of mu = 2 vs not = 2

Variable	N	Mean	StDev	SE Mean	95% CI	T	P
ROUGH	20	1.88100	0.52391	0.11715	(1.63580, 2.12620)	-1.02	0.322

Minitab output for Exercise 7.55

6,000 Bq/m³. Consequently, the ETA wants to conduct a test to determine if the true mean level of radon exposure in the tombs is less than 6,000 Bq/m³, using a Type I error probability of .10. An SPSS analysis of the data is shown (bottom, p. 384). Specify all the elements of the test: H_0, H_a, test statistic, *p*-value, α, and your conclusion.

50	910	180	580	7800	4000
390	12100	3400	1300	11900	1100

7.54 A new dental bonding agent. When bonding teeth, orthodontists must maintain a dry field. A new bonding adhesive (called *Smartbond*) has been developed to eliminate the necessity of a dry field. However, there is concern that the new bonding adhesive is not as strong as the current standard, a composite adhesive (*Trends in Biomaterials & Artificial Organs*, Jan. 2003). Tests on a sample of 10 extracted teeth bonded with the new adhesive resulted in a mean breaking strength (after 24 hours) of $\bar{x} = 5.07$ Mpa and a standard deviation of $s = .46$ Mpa. Orthodontists want to know if the true mean breaking strength of the new bonding adhesive is less than 5.70 Mpa, the mean breaking strength of the composite adhesive.
a. Set up the null and alternative hypotheses for the test.
b. Find the rejection region for the test using $\alpha = .01$.
c. Compute the test statistic.
d. Give the appropriate conclusion for the test.
e. What conditions are required for the test results to be valid?

7.55 Surface roughness of pipe. Refer to the *Anti-corrosion Methods and Materials* (Vol. 50, 2003) study of the surface roughness of coated interior pipe used in oil fields, Exercise 6.33 (p. 318). The data (in micrometers) for 20 sampled pipe sections are reproduced in the next table.
a. Give the null and alternative hypotheses for testing whether the mean surface roughness of coated interior pipe, μ, differs from 2 micrometers.
b. Find the test statistic for the hypothesis test.
c. Give the rejection region for the hypothesis test, using $\alpha = .05$.
d. State the appropriate conclusion for the hypothesis test.
e. A Minitab printout giving the test results is shown at the top of the page. Find and interpret the *p*-value of the test.
f. In Exercise 6.33 you found a 95% confidence interval for μ. Explain why the confidence interval and test lead to the same conclusion about μ.

1.72	2.50	2.16	2.13	1.06	2.24	2.31	2.03	1.09	1.40
2.57	2.64	1.26	2.05	1.19	2.13	1.27	1.51	2.41	1.95

Source: Data from Farshad, F., & Pesacreta, T. "Coated pipe interior surface roughness as measured by three scanning probe instruments," *Anti-corrosion Methods and Materials*, Vol. 50, No. 1, 2003 (Table III).

7.56 Performance of stock screeners. Recall, from Exercise 6.34 (p. 318), that stock screeners are automated tools used by investment companies to help clients select a portfolio of stocks to invest in. The data on the annualized percentage return on investment (as compared to the Standard & Poor's 500 Index) for 13 randomly selected stock screeners provided by the American Association of Individual Investors (AAII)

	B	C	D	E	F	G
XLSTAT 2011.4.02 - One-sample t-test and z-test						
Theoretical mean: 0						
Significance level (%): 5						
Summary statistics	▼					
Summary statistics:						
Variable	Observations	Minimum	Maximum	Mean	Std. deviation	
ROI	13	-1.6000	24.8000	10.8231	7.7115	
One-sample t-test / Upper-tailed test:						
95% confidence interval on the mean:						
(7.0112, +Inf)						
Difference	10.8231					
t (Observed value)	5.0604					
t (Critical value)	1.7823					
DF	12					
p-value (one-tailed)	0.0001					
alpha	0.05					

XLSTAT output for Exercise 7.56

are repeated in the accompanying table. You want to determine whether μ, the average annualized return for all AAII stock screeners, is positive (which implies that the stock screeners perform better, on average, than the S&P 500). An XLSTAT printout of the analysis is shown on the bottom of page 385.

| 9.0 | −.1 | −1.6 | 14.6 | 16.0 | 7.7 | 19.9 | 9.8 | 3.2 | 24.8 | 17.6 | 10.7 | 9.1 |

a. State H_0 and H_a for this test.

b. Locate the values of $\bar{x}$ and s on the printout, and then use these values to compute the test statistic. Verify that your calculation is correct by comparing it to the test statistic value shown on the printout.

c. Locate the observed significance level (p-value) on the printout.

d. Give the appropriate conclusion if you test using $\alpha = .05$.

e. What assumption about the data must hold in order for the inference derived from the test to be valid?

Applying the Concepts—Intermediate

7.57 **Water distillation with solar energy.** In countries with a water shortage, converting salt water to potable water is big business. The standard method of water distillation is with a single-slope solar still. Several enhanced solar energy water distillation systems were investigated in *Applied Solar Energy* (Vol. 46, 2010). One new system employs a sun-tracking meter and a step-wise basin. The new system was tested over 3 randomly selected days at a location in Amman, Jordan. The daily amounts of distilled water collected by the new system over the 3 days were 5.07, 5.45, and 5.21 liters per square meter (l/m^2). Suppose it is known that the mean daily amount of distilled water collected by the standard method at the same location in Jordan is $\mu = 1.4$ l/m^2.

a. Set up the null and alternative hypotheses for determining whether the mean daily amount of distilled water collected by the new system is greater than 1.4.

b. For this test, give a practical interpretation of the value $\alpha = .10$.

c. Find the mean and standard deviation of the distilled water amounts for the sample of 3 days.

d. Use the information from part **c** to calculate the test statistic.

e. Find the observed significance level (p-value) of the test.

f. State, practically, the appropriate conclusion.

7.58 **Shopping vehicle and judgment.** Refer to the *Journal of Marketing Research* (Dec. 2011) study of when grocery store shoppers' judgments, Exercise 2.85 (p. 85). For one part of the study, 11 consumers were told to put their arm in a flex position (similar to a shopping basket) and then each consumer was offered several choices between a vice product and a virtue product (e.g., a movie ticket vs. a shopping coupon, pay later with a larger amount vs. pay now). Based on these choices, a vice choice score was determined on a scale of 0 to 100 (where higher scores indicate a greater preference for vice options). The data in the next table are (simulated) choice scores for the 11 consumers. Suppose that the average choice score

for consumers with an extended arm position (similar to pushing a shopping cart) is known to be $\mu = 50$. The researchers theorize that the mean choice score for consumers shopping with a flexed arm will be higher than 43 (reflecting their higher propensity to select a vice product. Test the theory at $\alpha = .05$.

| 56 | 76 | 62 | 57 | 55 | 61 | 62 | 43 | 57 | 61 | 58 |

7.59 **Minimizing tractor skidding distance.** Refer to the *Journal of Forest Engineering* (July 1999) study of minimizing tractor skidding distances along a new road in a European forest, Exercise 6.35 (p. 319). The skidding distances (in meters) were measured at 20 randomly selected road sites. The data are repeated below. Recall that a logger working on the road claims the mean skidding distance is at least 425 meters. Is there sufficient evidence to refute this claim? Use $\alpha = .10$.

| 488 | 350 | 457 | 199 | 285 | 409 | 435 | 574 | 439 | 546 |
| 385 | 295 | 184 | 261 | 273 | 400 | 311 | 312 | 141 | 425 |

Source: Based on Tujek, J., & Pacola, E. "Algorithms for skidding distance modeling on a raster digital terrain model," *Journal of Forest Engineering,* Vol. 10, No. 1, July 1999 (Table 1).

7.60 **Crude oil biodegradation.** Refer to the *Journal of Petroleum Geology* (April 2010) study of the environmental factors associated with biodegradation in crude oil reservoirs, Exercise 6.37 (p. 319). Recall that 16 water specimens were randomly selected from various locations in a reservoir on the floor of a mine and that the amount of dioxide (milligrams/liter)—a measure of biodegradation—as well as presence of oil were determined for each specimen. These data are reproduced in the accompanying table.

a. Conduct a test to determine if the true mean amount of dioxide present in water specimens that contained oil was less than 3 milligrams/liter. Use $\alpha = .10$.

b. Repeat part **a** for water specimens that did not contain oil.

Dioxide Amount	Crude Oil Present
3.3	No
0.5	Yes
1.3	Yes
0.4	Yes
0.1	No
4.0	No
0.3	No
0.2	Yes
2.4	No
2.4	No
1.4	No
0.5	Yes
0.2	Yes
4.0	No
4.0	No
4.0	No

Source: Based on Permanyer, A., et al. "Crude oil biodegradation and environmental factors at the Riutort oil shale mine, SE Pyrenees," *Journal of Petroleum Geology,* Vol. 33, No. 2, April 2010 (Table 1).

7.61 **Crack intensity of paved highways.** The Mississippi Department of Transportation collected data on the number of cracks (called *crack intensity*) in an undivided two-lane highway using van-mounted, state-of-the-art video technology (*Journal of Infrastructure Systems,* Mar. 1995). The mean number of cracks found in a sample of eight 50-meter sections of the highway was $\bar{x} = .210$, with a variance of $s^2 = .011$. Suppose the American Association of State Highway and Transportation Officials (AASHTO) recommends a maximum mean crack intensity of .100 for safety purposes. Is there evidence to say that the true mean crack intensity of the Mississippi highway exceeds the AASHTO recommended maximum? Use $\alpha = .01$ in the test.

7.62 **Active nuclear power plants.** Refer to the U.S. Energy Information Administration's list of active nuclear power plants operating in each of a sample of 20 states, Exercise 2.54 (p. 73). The data are reproduced in the next table.

NUKES

a. Is there sufficient evidence to claim that the mean number of active nuclear power plants operating in all states exceeds 3? Test using $\alpha = .10$.

b. Are the conditions required for a valid small-sample test reasonably satisfied? Explain.

c. Eliminate the lowest two values and the highest two values from the data set, then conduct the test of part **a** on the smaller data set. What impact does this have on the test results?

d. Why is it dangerous to eliminate data points in order to satisfy an assumption for a test of hypothesis?

State	Number of Power Plants	State	Number of Power Plants
Alabama	5	New Hampshire	1
Arizona	2	New York	6
California	4	North Carolina	5
Florida	5	Ohio	3
Georgia	4	Pennsylvania	9
Illinois	11	South Carolina	7
Kansas	1	Tennessee	3
Louisiana	2	Texas	4
Massachusetts	1	Vermont	1
Mississippi	1	Wisconsin	3

Source: Data from *Statistical Abstract of the United States,* 2010 (Table 906). U.S. Energy Information Administration. Electric Power Annual.

Applying the Concepts—Advanced

7.63 **Arsenic in smelters.** The Occupational Safety and Health Act (OSHA) allows issuance of engineering standards to ensure safe workplaces for all Americans. The maximum allowable mean level of arsenic in smelters, herbicide production facilities, and other places where arsenic is used is .004 milligrams per cubic meter of air. Suppose smelters at two plants are being investigated to determine whether they are meeting OSHA standards. Two analyses of the air are made at each plant, and the results (in milligrams per cubic meter of air) are shown in the table. A claim is made that the OSHA standard is violated at Plant 2 but not at Plant 1. Do you agree?

OSHA

Plant 1		Plant 2	
Observation	Arsenic Level	Observation	Arsenic Level
1	.01	1	.05
2	.005	2	.09

7.6 Large-Sample Test of Hypothesis about a Population Proportion

Inferences about population proportions (or percentages) are often made in the context of the probability, *p*, of "success" for a binomial distribution. We saw how to use large samples from *binomial* distributions to form confidence intervals for *p* in Section 6.4. We now consider tests of hypotheses about *p*.

For example, consider the problem of *insider trading* in the stock market. Insider trading is the buying and selling of stock by an individual privy to inside information in a company, usually a high-level executive in the firm. The Securities and Exchange Commission (SEC) imposes strict guidelines about insider trading so that all investors can have equal access to information that may affect the stock's price. An investor wishing to test the effectiveness of the SEC guidelines monitors the market for a period of a year and records the number of times a stock price increases the day following a significant purchase of stock by an insider. For a total of 576 such transactions, the stock increased the following day 327 times. Does this sample provide evidence that the stock price may be affected by insider trading?

We first view this as a binomial experiment, with the 576 transactions as the trials, and with success representing an increase in the stock's price the following day. Let *p* represent the probability that the stock price will increase following a large insider purchase. If the insider purchase has no effect on the stock price (that is, if the information available to the insider is identical to that available to the general market), then the investor expects the probability of a stock increase to be the same as that of a decrease, or $p = .5$. On the other hand, if insider trading affects the stock price (indicating that the market has not fully accounted for the information known to the insiders), then the investor expects the stock either to decrease or to increase more than half the time following significant insider transactions; that is, $p \neq .5$.

We can now place the problem in the context of a test of hypothesis:

$H_0: p = .5$ (Probability of stock increase equals .5—
i.e., insider purchase has no effect on stock price.)

$H_a: p \neq .5$ (Probability of stock increase differs from .5—
i.e., insider trading effects stock price.)

Recall (Section 5.4) that the sample proportion, $\hat{p}$, is really just the sample mean of the outcomes of the individual binomial trials and, as such, is approximately normally distributed (for large samples) according to the Central Limit Theorem. Thus, for large samples, we can use the standard normal z as the test statistic:

$$\text{Test statistic: } z = \frac{\text{Sample proportion} - \text{Null hypothesized proportion}}{\text{Standard deviation of sample proportion}}$$

$$= \frac{\hat{p} - p_0}{\sigma_{\hat{p}}}$$

where we use the symbol p_0 to represent the null hypothesized value of p.

Figure 7.20

Rejection region for insider trading example

Rejection region: We use the standard normal distribution to find the appropriate rejection region for the specified value of α. Using $\alpha = .05$, the two-tailed rejection region is

$$z < -z_{\alpha/2} = -z_{.025} = -1.96 \text{ or } z > z_{\alpha/2} = z_{.025} = 1.96$$

See Figure 7.20.

We are now prepared to calculate the value of the test statistic. Before doing so, we want to be sure that the sample size is large enough to ensure that the normal approximation for the sampling distribution of $\hat{p}$ is reasonable. Recall from Section 6.4 that we require both np and nq to be at least 15. Because the null hypothesized value, p_0, is assumed to be the true value of p until our test procedure indicates otherwise, we check to see if $np_0 \geq 15$ and $nq_0 \geq 15$ (where $q_0 = 1 - p_0$). Now, $np_0 = (576)(.5) = 288$ and $nq_0 = (576)(.5) = 288$; therefore, the normal distribution will provide a reasonable approximation for the sampling distribution of $\hat{p}$.

Returning to the hypothesis test at hand, the proportion of the sampled transactions that resulted in a stock increase is

$$\hat{p} = \frac{327}{576} = .568$$

Finally, we calculate the number of standard deviations (the z-value) between the sampled and hypothesized values of the binomial proportion:

$$z = \frac{\hat{p} - p_0}{\sigma_{\hat{p}}} = \frac{\hat{p} - p_0}{\sqrt{p_0 q_0/n}} = \frac{.568 - .5}{.021} = \frac{.068}{.021} = 3.24$$

The implication is that the observed sample proportion is (approximately) 3.24 standard deviations above the null hypothesized proportion .5 (Figure 7.20). Therefore, we reject the null hypothesis, concluding at the .05 level of significance that the true probability of an increase or decrease in a stock's price differs from .5 the day following insider purchase of the stock. It appears that an insider purchase significantly increases the probability that the stock price will increase the following day. (To estimate the magnitude of the probability of an increase, a confidence interval can be constructed.)

The test of hypothesis about a population proportion p is summarized in the next box. Note that the procedure is entirely analogous to that used for conducting large-sample tests about a population mean.

Large-Sample Test of Hypothesis about p: Normal (z) Statistic

One-Tailed Test	Two-Tailed Test
H_0: $p = p_0$	H_0: $p = p_0$
H_a: $p < p_0$ (or H_a: $p > p_0$)	H_a: $p \neq p_0$
Test statistic: $z = \dfrac{\hat{p} - p_0}{\sigma_{\hat{p}}}$	Test statistic: $z = \dfrac{\hat{p} - p_0}{\sigma_{\hat{p}}}$

where, according to H_0, $\sigma_{\hat{p}} = \sqrt{p_0 q_0 / n}$ and $q_0 = 1 - p_0$

Rejection region:	Rejection region: $|z| > z_{\alpha/2}$
$z < -z_\alpha$ (or $z > z_\alpha$ when H_a: $p > p_0$)	

Note: p_0 is the symbol for the numerical value of p assigned in the null hypothesis.

Conditions Required for a Valid Large-Sample Hypothesis Test for p

1. A random sample is selected from a binomial population.
2. The sample size n is large. (This condition will be satisfied if both $np_0 \geq 15$ and $nq_0 \geq 15$.)

Example 7.10

Hypothesis Test for p—Proportion of Defective Batteries

Problem The reputations (and hence sales) of many businesses can be severely damaged by shipments of manufactured items that contain a large percentage of defectives. For example, a manufacturer of alkaline batteries may want to be reasonably certain that fewer than 5% of its batteries are defective. Suppose 300 batteries are randomly selected from a very large shipment; each is tested, and 10 defective batteries are found. Does this provide sufficient evidence for the manufacturer to conclude that the fraction defective in the entire shipment is less than .05? Use $\alpha = .01$.

Solution The objective of the sampling is to determine whether there is sufficient evidence to indicate that the fraction defective, p, is less than .05. Consequently, we will test the null hypothesis that $p = .05$ against the alternative hypothesis that $p < .05$. The elements of the test are

H_0: $p = .05$ (Fraction of defective batteries equals .05.)

H_a: $p < .05$ (Fraction of defective batteries is less than .05.)

Test statistic: $z = \dfrac{\hat{p} - p_0}{\sigma_{\hat{p}}}$

Rejection region: $z < -z_{.01} = -2.326$ (see Figure 7.21)

Before conducting the test, we check to determine whether the sample size is large enough to use the normal approximation to the sampling distribution of $\hat{p}$. Because $np_0 = (300)(.05) = 15$ and $nq_0 = (300)(.95) = 285$ are both at least 15, the normal approximation will be adequate.

We now calculate the test statistic:

$$z = \frac{\hat{p} - .05}{\sigma_{\hat{p}}} = \frac{(10/300) - .05}{\sqrt{p_0 q_0 / n}} = \frac{.03333 - .05}{\sqrt{p_0 q_0 / 300}}$$

Notice that we use p_0 to calculate $\sigma_{\hat{p}}$ because, in contrast to calculating $\sigma_{\hat{p}}$ for a confidence interval, the test statistic is computed on the assumption that the null hypothesis is true—that is, $p = p_0$. Therefore, substituting the values for $\hat{p}$ and p_0 into the z-statistic, we obtain

$$z \approx \frac{-.01667}{\sqrt{(.05)(.95)/300}} = \frac{-.01667}{.0126} = -1.32$$

As shown in Figure 7.21, the calculated z-value does not fall in the rejection region. Therefore, there is insufficient evidence at the .01 level of significance to indicate that the shipment contains fewer than 5% defective batteries.

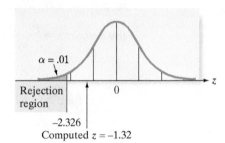

Figure 7.21
Rejection region for Example 7.10

-2.326
Computed $z = -1.32$

■ **Now Work Exercise 7.64a, b**

| Example | 7.11 |

The _p_-Value for a Test about a Population Proportion _p_

Figure 7.22

The observed significance level for Example 7.11

Problem In Example 7.10 we found that we did not have sufficient evidence, at the $\alpha = .01$ level of significance, to indicate that the fraction defective p of alkaline batteries was less than $p = .05$. How strong was the weight of evidence favoring the alternative hypothesis ($H_a: p < .05$)? Find the observed significance level for the test.

Solution The computed value of the test statistic z was $z = -1.32$. Therefore, for this lower-tailed test, the observed significance level is

$$\text{Observed significance level} = P(z \leq -1.32)$$

This lower-tail area is shown in Figure 7.22. The area between $z = 0$ and $z = 1.32$ is given in Table II in Appendix D as .4066. Therefore, the observed significance level is $.5 - .4066 = .0934$.

Note: The observed significance level can also be obtained with statistical software. The Minitab printout shown in Figure 7.23 gives the p-value (highlighted).

Test and CI for One Proportion

Test of p = 0.05 vs p < 0.05

				95% Upper		
Sample	X	N	Sample p	Bound	Z-Value	P-Value
1	10	300	0.033333	0.050380	-1.32	0.093

Using the normal approximation.

Figure 7.23
Minitab lower-tailed test of p, Example 7.11

Look Back Although we did not reject $H_0: p = .05$ at $\alpha = .01$, the probability of observing a z-value as small as or smaller than -1.32 is only .0934 if, in fact, H_0 is true. Therefore, we would reject H_0 if we choose $\alpha = .10$ (because the observed significance level is less than .10), and we would not reject H_0 (the conclusion of Example 7.10) if we choose $\alpha = .05$ or $\alpha = .01$.

■ **Now Work Exercise 7.64c**

Small-sample test procedures are also available for p, although most surveys use samples that are large enough to employ the large-sample tests presented in this section. A test of proportions that can be applied to small samples is discussed in Chapter 10.

STATISTICS
in ACTION
REVISITED

Testing a Population Proportion

In the previous Statistics in Action Revisited (p. 375), we investigated Kimberly-Clark Corporation's assertion that the company should put more than 60 tissues in a cold-care box of Kleenex® tissues. We did this by testing the claim that the mean number of tissues used by a person with a cold is $\mu = 60$, using data collected from a survey of 250 Kleenex® users. Another approach to the problem is to consider the proportion of Kleenex® users who use more than 60 tissues when they have a cold. Now the population parameter of interest is p, the proportion of all Kleenex® users who use more than 60 tissues when they have a cold.

Kimberly-Clark Corporation's belief that the company should put more than 60 tissues in a cold-care box will be supported if over half of the Kleenex® users surveyed used more than 60 tissues (i.e., if $p > .5$). Is there evidence to indicate that the population proportion exceeds .5? To answer this question, we set up the following null and alternative hypotheses:

$$H_0: p = .5 \quad H_a: p > .5$$

Recall that the survey results for the 250 sampled Kleenex® users are stored in the **TISSUE** data file. In addition to the number of tissues used by each person, the file contains a qualitative variable—called USED60—representing whether the person used fewer or more than 60 tissues. (The values of USED60 in the data set are "LESS" or "MORE.") A Minitab analysis of this variable yielded the printout displayed in Figure SIA7.2.

On the Minitab printout, x represents the number of the 250 people with colds who used more than 60 tissues. Note that $x = 154$. This value is used to compute the test statistic $z = 3.67$, highlighted on the printout. The p-value of the test, also highlighted on the printout, is p-value $= .000$. Since this value is less than $\alpha = .05$, there is sufficient evidence (at $\alpha = .05$) to reject H_0; we conclude that the proportion of all Kleenex® users who use more than 60 tissues when they have a cold exceeds 5. This conclusion supports again the company's decision to put more than 60 tissues in a cold-care box of Kleenex.

Test and CI for One Proportion: USED60

Test of p = 0.5 vs p > 0.5

Event = MORE

Variable	X	N	Sample p	95% Lower Bound	Z-Value	P-Value
USED60	154	250	0.616000	0.565404	3.67	0.000

Using the normal approximation.

Figure SIA7.2

Minitab test of $p = .5$ for Kleenex survey

Data Set: TISSUE

Exercises 7.64–7.81

Learning the Mechanics

7.64 Suppose a random sample of 100 observations from a binomial
NW population gives a value of $\hat{p} = .63$ and you wish to test the null hypothesis that the population parameter p is equal to .70 against the alternative hypothesis that p is less than .70.
  a. Noting that $\hat{p} = .63$, what does your intuition tell you? Does the value of $\hat{p}$ appear to contradict the null hypothesis?
  b. Use the large-sample z-test to test $H_0: p = .70$ against the alternative hypothesis, $H_a: p < .70$. Use $\alpha = .05$. How do the test results compare with your intuitive decision from part **a**?
  c. Find and interpret the observed significance level of the test you conducted in part **b**.

7.65 Suppose the sample in Exercise 7.64 has produced $\hat{p} = .83$ and we wish to test $H_0: p = .9$ against the alternative $H_a: p < .9$.
  a. Calculate the value of the z-statistic for this test.
  b. Note that the numerator of the z-statistic ($\hat{p} - p_0 = .83 - .90 = -.07$) is the same as for Exercise 7.64. Considering this, why is the absolute value of z for this exercise larger than that calculated in Exercise 7.64?
  c. Complete the test using $\alpha = .05$ and interpret the result.
  d. Find the observed significance level for the test and interpret its value.

7.66 A statistics student used a computer program to test the null hypothesis $H_0: p = .5$ against the one-tailed alternative,

$H_a: p > .5$. A sample of 500 observations are input into SPSS, which returns the following results: $z = .44$, two-tailed p-value = .33.

a. The student concludes, based on the p-value, that there is a 33% chance that the alternative hypothesis is true. Do you agree? If not, correct the interpretation.

b. How would the p-value change if the alternative hypothesis was two-tailed, $H_a: p \neq .5$? Interpret this p-value.

7.67 Refer to Exercise 6.44 (p. 325), in which 50 consumers taste-tested a new snack food. Their responses (where 0 = do not like; 1 = like; 2 = indifferent) are reproduced below.

SNACK

a. Test $H_0: p = .5$ against $H_a: p > .5$, where p is the proportion of customers who do not like the snack food. Use $\alpha = .10$.

b. Find the observed significance level of your test.

1	0	0	1	2	0	1	1	0	0	0	1
0	2	0	2	2	0	0	1	1	0	0	0
0	1	0	2	0	0	0	1	0	0	1	0
0	1	0	1	0	2	0	0	1	1	0	0
0	1										

7.68 For the binomial sample sizes and null hypothesized values of p in each part, determine whether the sample size is large enough to use the normal approximation methodology presented in this section to conduct a test of the null hypothesis $H_0: p = p_0$.

a. $n = 900, p_0 = .975$ b. $n = 125, p_0 = .01$

c. $n = 40, p_0 = .75$ d. $n = 15, p_0 = .75$

e. $n = 12, p_0 = .62$

● Applet Exercise 7.5

Use the applet *Hypotheses Test for a Proportion* to investigate the relationships between the probabilities of Type I and Type II errors occurring at levels .05 and .01. For this exercise, use $n = 100$, true $p = 0.5$, and alternative *not equal*.

a. Set null $p = .5$. What happens to the proportion of times the null hypothesis is rejected at the .05 level and at the .01 level as the applet is run more and more times? What type of error has occurred when the null hypothesis is rejected in this situation? Based on your results, is this type of error more likely to occur at level .05 or at level .01? Explain.

b. Set null $p = .6$. What happens to the proportion of times the null hypothesis is *not* rejected at the .05 level and at the .01 level as the applet is run more and more times? What type of error has occurred when the null hypothesis is *not* rejected in this situation? Based on your results, is this type of error more likely to occur at level .05 or at level .01? Explain.

c. Use your results from parts **a** and **b** to make a general statement about the probabilities of Type I and Type II errors at levels .05 and .01.

● Applet Exercise 7.6

Use the applet *Hypotheses Test for a Proportion* to investigate the effect of the true population proportion p on the probability of a Type I error occurring. For this exercise, use $n = 100$, and alternative *not equal*.

a. Set true $p = .5$ and null $p = .5$. Run the applet several times and record the proportion of times the null hypothesis is rejected at the .01 level.

b. Clear the applet and repeat part **a** for true $p = .1$ and null $p = .1$. Then repeat one more time for true $p = .01$ and null $p = .01$.

c. Based on your results from parts **a** and **b**, what can you conclude about the probability of a Type I error occurring as the true population proportion gets closer to 0?

Applying the Concepts—Basic

7.69 **Paying for music downloads.** If you use the Internet, have you ever paid to access or download music? This was one of the questions of interest in a *Pew Internet & American Life Project Survey* (October 2010). In a representative sample of 755 adults who use the Internet, 506 admitted that they have paid to download music. Let p represent the true proportion of all Internet-using adults who have paid to download music.

a. Compute a point estimate of p.

b. Set up the null and alternative hypotheses for testing whether the true proportion of all Internet-using adults who have paid to download music exceeds .7.

c. Compute the test statistic for part **b**.

d. Find the rejection region for the test if $\alpha = .01$.

e. Find the p-value for the test.

f. Make the appropriate conclusion using the rejection region.

g. Make the appropriate conclusion using the p-value.

7.70 **Satellite radio in cars.** A spokesperson for the National Association of Broadcasters (NAB) claims that 80% of all satellite radio subscribers have a satellite radio receiver in their car. In a recent survey of 501 satellite radio subscribers, 396 have a satellite receiver in their car. Consider a test of the NAB spokesperson's claim.

a. Define the parameter of interest to the NAB spokesperson.

b. Set up the null hypothesis for testing the claim.

c. Specify the alternative hypothesis if you believe that the spokesperson's claim is too high.

d. Compute the value of the test statistic.

e. Determine the rejection region for the test using $\alpha = .10$.

f. Compute the p-value of the test.

g. Make the appropriate conclusion. Show that the decision based on the rejection region agrees with the decision based on the p-value.

7.71 **History of corporate acquisitions.** Refer to the *Academy of Management Journal* (Aug. 2008) investigation of the performance and timing of corporate acquisitions, Exercise 6.53 (p. 326). Recall that the investigation discovered that in a random sample of 2,778 firms, 748 announced one or more acquisitions during the year 2000. Does the sample provide sufficient evidence to indicate that the true percentage of all firms that announced one or more acquisitions during the year 2000 is less than 30%? Use $\alpha = .05$ to make your decision.

7.72 **Gummi Bears: Red or yellow?** Companies that produce candies typically offer different colors of their candies to provide consumers a choice. Presumably, the consumer will

SECTION 7.6 □ Large-Sample Test of Hypothesis about a Population Proportion **393**

choose one color over another because of taste. *Chance* (Winter 2010) presented an experiment designed to test this taste theory. Students were blindfolded and then given a red-colored or yellow-colored Gummi Bear to chew. (Half the students were randomly assigned to receive the red Gummi Bear and half to receive the yellow Bear. The students could not see what color Gummi Bear they were given.) After chewing, the students were asked to guess the color of the candy based on the flavor. Of the 121 students who participated in the study, 97 correctly identified the color of the Gummi Bear.

a. If there is no relationship between color and Gummi Bear flavor, what proportion of the population of students would correctly identify the color?

b. Specify the null and alternative hypotheses for testing whether color and flavor are related.

c. Carry out the test and give the appropriate conclusion at $\alpha = .01$. Use the p-value of the test, shown on the accompanying SPSS printout, to make your decision.

Binomial Test

		Category	N	Observed Prop.	Test Prop.	Exact Sig. (2-tailed)
ID_Color	Group 1	Yes	97	.80	.50	.000
	Group 2	No	24	.20		
	Total		121	1.00		

7.73 Toothpaste brands with the ADA seal. *Consumer Reports* evaluated and rated 46 brands of toothpaste. One attribute examined in the study was whether or not a toothpaste brand carries an American Dental Association (ADA) seal verifying effective decay prevention. The data for the 46 brands (coded 1 = ADA seal, 0 = no ADA seal) are listed here.

```
0   0   0   0   0   0   1   1   1   0   0   1
0   1   0   0   0   0   1   1   1   0   1   1
1   1   0   0   0   0   0   1   0   0   1   1
1   0   1   0   1   1   1   0   0   0
```

a. Give the null and alternative hypotheses for testing whether the true proportion of toothpaste brands with the ADA seal verifying effective decay prevention is less than .5.

b. Locate the p-value on the Minitab printout below.

c. Make the appropriate conclusion using $\alpha = .10$.

```
Test of p = 0.5 vs p < 0.5

Event = 1

                                95%
                              Upper    Exact
Variable   X   N   Sample p   Bound   P-Value
ADASEAL   20  46  0.434783  0.566289  0.231
```

7.74 Vacation-home owners. The National Association of Realtors (NAR) reported the results of a March 2010 survey of home buyers. In a random sample of 1,982 residential properties purchased during the year, 198 were purchased as a vacation home. Five years ago, 14% of residential properties were vacation homes.

a. Do the survey results allow the NAR to conclude (at $\alpha = .01$) that the percentage of all residential properties purchased for vacation homes is less that 14%.

b. The NAR sent the survey questionnaire to a nationwide sample of 45,000 new home owners, of which 1,982 responded to the survey. How might this bias the results?

Applying the Concepts—Intermediate

7.75 Organic-certified coffee. Coffee markets that conform to organic standards focus on the environmental aspects of coffee growing, such as the use of shade trees and a reduced reliance on chemical pesticides. A study of organic coffee growers was published in *Food Policy* (Vol. 36, 2010). In a representative sample of 845 coffee growers from southern Mexico, 417 growers were certified to sell to organic coffee markets while 77 growers were transitioning to become organic certified. In the United States, 60% of coffee growers are organic certified. Is there evidence to indicate that fewer than 60% of the coffee growers in southern Mexico are either organic certified or transitioning to become organic certified? State your conclusion so that there is only a 5% chance of making a Type I error.

7.76 Unemployment and a reduced workweek. In an effort to increase employment, France mandated in February 2000 that all companies with 20 or more employees reduce the workweek to 35 hours. The economic impact of the shortened workweek was analyzed in *Economic Policy* (July 2008). The researchers focused on several key variables such as hourly wages, dual-job holdings, and level of employment. Assume that in the year prior to the 35-hour-workweek law, unemployment in France was at 12%. Suppose that in a random sample of 500 French citizens (eligible workers) taken several years after the law was enacted, 53 were unemployed. Conduct a test of hypothesis to determine if the French unemployment rate dropped after the enactment of the 35-hour-workweek law. Test using $\alpha = .05$.

7.77 Effectiveness of skin cream. Pond's Age-Defying Complex, a cream with alpha hydroxy acid, advertised that it could reduce wrinkles and improve the skin. In a study published in *Archives of Dermatology* (June 1996), 33 middle-aged women used a cream with alpha hydroxy acid for 22 weeks. At the end of the study period, a dermatologist judged whether each woman exhibited skin improvement. The results for the 33 women (where I = improved skin and N = no improvement) are listed in the next table. [*Note:* Pond's recently discontinued the production of this cream product, replacing it with Age-Defying Towlettes.]

a. Do the data provide sufficient evidence to conclude that the cream improved the skin of more than 60% of middle-aged women? Test using $\alpha = .05$.

b. Find and interpret the p-value of the test.

7.78 Detection of motorcycles while driving. Motorcycle fatalities have increased dramatically over the past decade. As a result, manufacturers of powered two-wheelers (PTWs)

are tweaking with their design in order to improve visibility by automobile drivers. The factors that impact the visibility of PTWs on the road were investigated in *Accident Analysis and Prevention* (Vol. 44, 2012). A visual search study was conducted in which viewers were presented with pictures of driving scenarios and asked to identify the presence or absence of a PTW. Of interest to the researchers is the detection rate, i.e., the proportion of pictures showing a PTW in which the viewer actually detected the presence of the PTW. Suppose that, in theory, the true detection rate for pictures of PTWs is .70. The study revealed that in a sample of 2,376 pictures that included a PTW, only 1,554 were detected by the viewers. Use this results to test the theory at $\alpha = .10$.

7.79 **TVs with DVRs.** According to Nielsen's *Television Audience Report* (2011), 41% of all households with televisions in the United States have a digital video recorder (DVR). Develop a sampling plan that will allow you to test this claim. Identify the target population, experimental units, variable to be measured, parameter of interest, null and alternative hypotheses, and the form of the test statistic.

Applying the Concepts—Advanced

7.80 **Choosing portable grill displays.** Refer to the *Journal of Consumer Research* (Mar. 2003) experiment on influencing the choices of others by offering undesirable alternatives, Exercise 3.23 (p. 142). Recall that each of 124 college students selected three portable grills from five to display on the showroom floor. The students were instructed to include Grill #2 (a smaller-sized grill) and select the remaining two grills in the display to maximize purchases of Grill #2. If the six possible grill display combinations (1-2-3, 1-2-4, 1-2-5, 2-3-4, 2-3-5, and 2-4-5) were selected at random, then the proportion of students selecting any display was $\frac{1}{6} = .167$. One theory tested by the researcher was that the students would tend to choose the three-grill display so that Grill #2 was a compromise between a more desirable and a less desirable grill (i.e., display 1-2-3, 1-2-4, or 1-2-5). Of the 124 students, 85 selected a three-grill display that was consistent with this theory. Use this information to test the theory proposed by the researcher at $\alpha = .05$.

7.81 **The Pepsi Challenge.** "Take the Pepsi Challenge" was a famous marketing campaign used by the Pepsi-Cola Company. Coca-Cola drinkers participated in a blind taste test where they were asked to taste unmarked cups of Pepsi and Coke and were asked to select their favorite. In one Pepsi television commercial, an announcer stated that "in recent blind taste tests, more than half the Diet Coke drinkers surveyed said they preferred the taste of Diet Pepsi." Suppose 100 Diet Coke drinkers took the Pepsi Challenge and 56 preferred the taste of Diet Pepsi. Determine if more than half of all Diet Coke drinkers selected Diet Pepsi in the blind taste test. Select α to minimize the probability of a Type I error. What were the consequences of the test results from Coca-Cola's perspective?

7.7 Test of Hypothesis about a Population Variance

Although many practical problems involve inferences about a population mean (or proportion), it is sometimes of interest to make an inference about a population variance, σ^2. To illustrate, a quality-control supervisor in a cannery knows that the exact amount each can contains will vary because there are certain uncontrollable factors that affect the amount of fill. The mean fill per can is important, but equally important is the variation of fill. If σ^2, the variance of the fill, is large, some cans will contain too little and others too much. Suppose regulatory agencies specify that the standard deviation of the amount of fill should be less than .1 ounce. To determine whether the process is meeting this specification, the supervisor randomly selects 10 cans and weighs the contents of each. The results are given in Table 7.6.

Table 7.6	Fill Weights (in Ounces) of 10 Cans								
16.00	16.06	15.95	16.04	16.10	16.05	16.02	16.03	15.99	16.02

Data Set: FILLWT

Do these data provide sufficient evidence to indicate that the variability is as small as desired? To answer this question, we need a procedure for testing a hypothesis about σ^2.

Intuitively, it seems that we should compare the sample variance σ^2 to the hypothesized value of σ^2 (or s to σ) in order to make a decision about the population's variability. The quantity

$$\frac{(n-1)s^2}{\sigma^2}$$

is known to have a **chi-square (χ^2) sampling distribution** when the population from which the sample is taken is *normally distributed*. (Chi-square distributions were introduced in Section 6.6.)

Since the distribution of $\frac{(n-1)s^2}{\sigma^2}$ is known, we can use this quantity as a test statistic in a test of hypothesis for a population variance, as illustrated in the next example.

> **BIOGRAPHY**
>
> **FRIEDRICH R. HELMERT (1843–1917)**
> *Helmert Transformations*
>
> German Friedrich Helmert studied engineering sciences and mathematics at Dresden University, where he earned his PhD, then accepted a position as a professor of geodesy—the scientific study of the earth's size and shape—at the technical school in Aachen. Helmert's mathematical solutions to geodesy problems led him to several statistics-related discoveries. His greatest statistical contribution occurred in 1876, when he was the first to prove that the sampling distribution of the sample variance, s^2, is a chi-square distribution. Helmert used a series of mathematical transformations to obtain the distribution of s^2—transformations that have since been named "Helmert transformations" in his honor. Later in life, Helmert was appointed professor of advanced geodesy at the prestigious University of Berlin and director of the Prussian Geodesic Institute.

Example 7.12

Test for σ^2—Fill Weight Variance

Problem Refer to the fill weights for the sample of ten 16-ounce cans in Table 7.6. Do the data provide sufficient evidence to indicate that the true standard deviation σ of the fill measurements of all 16-ounce cans is less than .1 ounce?

Solution Here, we want to test whether $\sigma < .1$. Because the null and alternative hypotheses must be stated in terms of σ^2 rather than σ, we want to test the null hypothesis that $\sigma^2 = (.1)^2 = .01$ against the alternative that $\sigma^2 < .01$. Therefore, the elements of the test are

$H_0: \sigma^2 = .01$ (Fill variance equals .01—i.e., process specifications are not met.)

$H_a: \sigma^2 < .01$ (Fill variance is less than .01—i.e., process specifications are met.)

Test statistic: $\chi^2 = \dfrac{(n-1)s^2}{\sigma^2}$

Assumption: The distribution of the amounts of fill is approximately normal.

Rejection region: The smaller the value of s^2 we observe, the stronger the evidence in favor of H_a. Thus, we reject H_0 for "small values" of the test statistic. Recall (Section 6.6) that the chi-square distribution depends on $(n-1)$ degrees of freedom. With $\alpha = .05$ and $(n-1) = 9$ df, the χ^2 value for rejection is found in Table IV and pictured in Figure 7.24. We will reject H_0 if $\chi^2 < 3.32511$.

[*Note:* The area given in Table IV is the area to the *right* of the numerical value in the table. Thus, to determine the lower-tail value, which has $\alpha = .05$ to its *left*, we used the $\chi^2_{.95}$ column in Table IV.]

A Minitab analysis of the data in Table 7.6 is displayed in Figure 7.25. The value of s (highlighted) on the printout is $s = .0412$. Substituting into the formula for the test statistic, we have

Figure 7.24

Rejection region for Example 7.12

$$\chi^2 = \frac{(n-1)s^2}{\sigma^2} = \frac{9(.0412)^2}{.01} = 1.53$$

Test and CI for One Variance: WEIGHT

```
Method

Null hypothesis        Sigma = 0.1
Alternative hypothesis  Sigma < 0.1

The chi-square method is only for the normal distribution.
The Bonett method is for any continuous distribution.


Statistics

Variable   N   StDev   Variance
WEIGHT    10  0.0412   0.00169


95% One-Sided Confidence Intervals

                       Upper Bound   Upper Bound
Variable   Method       for StDev    for Variance
WEIGHT     Chi-Square      0.0677        0.00458
           Bonett          0.0732        0.00536


Tests

                           Test
Variable   Method       Statistic   DF   P-Value
WEIGHT     Chi-Square        1.52    9     0.003
           Bonett              –     –     0.010
```

Figure 7.25

Minitab analysis of fill weight variance, Example 7.12

Because the test statistic falls into the rejection region, we reject H_0 in favor of H_a—that is, the supervisor can conclude that the variance σ^2 of the population of all amounts of fill is less than .01 ($\sigma < .1$) with probability of a Type I error equal to $\alpha = .05$. If this procedure is repeatedly used, it will incorrectly reject H_0 only 5% of the time. Thus, the quality-control supervisor is confident in the decision that the cannery is operating within the desired limits of variability.

Look Back Note that both the test statistic (rounded) and the lower-tailed p-value of the test (.003) are highlighted at the bottom of the printout, Figure 7.25. Because $\alpha = .05$ exceeds the p-value, our decision to reject H_0 is confirmed.

■ **Now Work Exercise 7.87**

One-tailed and two-tailed tests of hypothesis for σ^2 are given in the following box.

Test of a Hypothesis about σ^2

One-Tailed Test	Two-Tailed Test
$H_0: \sigma^2 = \sigma_0^2$	$H_0: \sigma^2 = \sigma_0^2$
$H_a: \sigma^2 < \sigma_0^2$ (or $H_a: \sigma^2 > \sigma_0^2$)	$H_a: \sigma^2 \neq \sigma_0^2$
Test statistic: $\chi^2 = \dfrac{(n-1)s^2}{\sigma_0^2}$	Test statistic: $\chi^2 = \dfrac{(n-1)s^2}{\sigma_0^2}$
Rejection region: $\chi^2 < \chi_{(1-\alpha)}^2$	Rejection region: $\chi^2 < \chi_{(1-\alpha/2)}^2$ or
(or $\chi^2 > \chi_\alpha^2$ when $H_a: \sigma^2 > \sigma_0^2$)	$\chi^2 > \chi_{(\alpha/2)}^2$

where σ_0^2 is the hypothesized variance and the distribution of χ^2 is based on $(n-1)$ degrees of freedom.

> **Conditions Required for a Valid Hypothesis Test for s^2**
>
> **1.** A random sample is selected from the target population.
> **2.** The population from which the sample is selected has a distribution that is approximately normal.

> ⚠ **CAUTION** The procedure for conducting a hypothesis test for σ^2 in the above examples requires an assumption regardless of whether the sample size n is large or small. We must assume that the population from which the sample is selected has an approximate normal distribution. Unlike small-sample tests for μ based on the t-statistic, *slight to moderate departures from normality will render the chi-square test invalid.*

Exercises 7.82–7.95

Learning the Mechanics

7.82 Let χ_0^2 be a particular value of χ^2. Find the value of χ_0^2 such that
  a. $P(\chi^2 > \chi_0^2) = .10$ for $n = 12$
  b. $P(\chi^2 > \chi_0^2) = .05$ for $n = 9$
  c. $P(\chi^2 > \chi_0^2) = .025$ for $n = 5$

7.83 A random sample of n observations is selected from a normal population to test the null hypothesis that $\sigma^2 = 25$. Specify the rejection region for each of the following combinations of H_a, α, and n:
  a. H_a: $\sigma^2 \neq 25$; $\alpha = .05$; $n = 16$
  b. H_a: $\sigma^2 > 25$; $\alpha = .01$; $n = 23$
  c. H_a: $\sigma^2 > 25$; $\alpha = .10$; $n = 15$
  d. H_a: $\sigma^2 < 25$; $\alpha = .01$; $n = 13$
  e. H_a: $\sigma^2 \neq 25$; $\alpha = .10$; $n = 7$
  f. H_a: $\sigma^2 < 25$; $\alpha = .05$; $n = 25$

7.84 A random sample of seven measurements gave $\bar{x} = 9.4$ and $s^2 = 4.84$.
  a. What assumptions must you make concerning the population in order to test a hypothesis about σ^2?
  b. Suppose the assumptions in part **a** are satisfied. Test the null hypothesis, $\sigma^2 = 1$, against the alternative hypothesis, $\sigma^2 > 1$. Use $\alpha = .05$.
  c. Test the null hypothesis that $\sigma^2 = 1$ against the alternative hypothesis that $\sigma^2 \neq 1$. Use $\alpha = .05$.

7.85 Refer to Exercise 7.84. Suppose we had $n = 100$, $\bar{x} = 9.4$, and $s^2 = 4.84$.
  a. Test the null hypothesis, H_0: $\sigma^2 = 1$, against the alternative hypothesis, H_a: $\sigma^2 > 1$.
  b. Compare your test result with that of Exercise 7.84.

7.86 A random sample of $n = 7$ observations from a normal population produced the following measurements: 4, 0, 6, 3, 3, 5, 9. Do the data provide sufficient evidence to indicate that $\sigma^2 < 1$? Test using $\alpha = .05$.

Applying the Concepts—Basic

7.87 **Trading skills of institutional investors.** Refer to *The* *Journal of Finance* (April 2011) analysis of trading skills of institutional investors, Exercise 7.36 (p. 377). Recall that the study focused on "round-trip" trades, i.e., trades in which the same stock was both bought and sold in the same quarter. In a random sample of 200 round-trip trades made by institutional investors, the sample standard deviation of the rates of return was 8.82%. One property of a consistent performance of institutional investors is a small variance in the rates of return of round-trip trades, say, a standard deviation of less than 10%.
  a. Specify the null and alternative hypotheses for determining whether the population of institutional investors performs consistently.
  b. Find the rejection region for the test using $\alpha = .05$.
  c. Interpret the value of α in the words of the problem.
  d. A Minitab printout of the analysis is shown below. Locate the test statistic and p-value on the printout.
  e. Give the appropriate conclusion in the words of the problem.
  f. What assumptions about the data are required for the inference to be valid?

Test and CI for One Variance

Method

Null hypothesis   Sigma = 10
Alternative hypothesis Sigma < 10

The chi-square method is only for the normal distribution.
The Bonett method cannot be calculated with summarized data.

Statistics

N	StDev	Variance
200	8.82	77.8

Tests

Method	Test Statistic	DF	P-Value
Chi-Square	154.81	199	0.009

7.88 Lobster trap placement. Refer to the *Bulletin of Marine Science* (April 2010) observational study of lobster trap placement by teams fishing for the red spiny lobster in Baja California Sur, Mexico, Exercise 7.52 (p. 384). Trap-spacing measurements (in meters) for a sample of seven teams of red spiny lobster fishermen are repeated in the table. (These measurements are for the BT cooperative in the accompanying data file.) The researchers want to know whether σ^2, the variation in the population of trap-spacing measurements, is larger than 10 m². They will conduct a test of hypothesis using $\alpha = .05$.

93	99	105	94	82	70	86

Source: Based on Shester, G. G. "Explaining catch variation among Baja California lobster fishers through spatial analysis of trap-placement decisions," *Bulletin of Marine Science*, Vol. 86, No. 2, April 2010 (Table 1), pp. 479–498.

a. Specify the null and alternative hypotheses for this test.
b. Find the variance of the sample data, s^2.
c. Note that $s^2 > 10$. Consequently, a fisherman wants to reject the null hypothesis. What are the problems with using such a decision rule?
d. Compute the value of the test statistic.
e. Use statistical software to find the *p*-value of the test.
f. Give the appropriate conclusion.
g. What conditions must be satisfied for the test results to be valid?

7.89 Golf tees produced from an injection mold. Refer to Exercise 7.37 (p. 378) and the weights of tees produced by an injection mold process. If operating correctly, the process will produce tees with a weight variance of .000004 (ounces)². If the weight variance differs from .000004, the injection molder is out of control.

a. Set up the null and alternative hypotheses for testing whether the injection mold process is out of control.
b. Use the data saved in the accompanying file to conduct the test, part **a**. Use $\alpha = .01$.
c. What conditions are required for inferences derived from the test to be valid? Are they reasonably satisfied?

7.90 A new dental bonding agent. Refer to the *Trends in Biomaterials & Artificial Organs* (Jan. 2003) study of a new dental bonding adhesive (called *Smartbond*), Exercise 7.54 (p. 385). Recall that tests on a sample of 10 extracted teeth bonded with the new adhesive resulted in a mean breaking strength (after 24 hours) of $\bar{x} = 5.07$ Mpa and a standard deviation of $s = .46$ Mpa. The manufacturer must demonstrate that the breaking strength variance of the new adhesive is less than the variance of the standard composite adhesive, $\sigma^2 = .25$.

a. Set up the null and alternative hypotheses for the test.
b. Find the rejection region for the test using $\alpha = .01$.
c. Compute the test statistic.
d. Give the appropriate conclusion for the test.
e. What conditions are required for the test results to be valid?

Applying the Concepts—Intermediate

7.91 Jitter in a water power system. Refer to the *Journal of Applied Physics* investigation of throughput jitter in the opening switch of a prototype water power system, Exercise 6.100 (p. 340). Recall that low throughput jitter is critical to successful waterline technology. An analysis of conduction time for a sample of 18 trials of the prototype system yielded $\bar{x} = 334.8$ nanoseconds and $s = 6.3$ nanoseconds. (Conduction time is defined as the length of time required for the downstream current to equal 10% of the upstream current.) A system is considered to have low throughput jitter if the true conduction time standard deviation is less than 7 nanoseconds. Does the prototype system satisfy this requirement? Test using $\alpha = .01$.

7.92 Drug content assessment. Refer to the *Analytical Chemistry* (Dec. 15, 2009) study of a new method used by GlaxoSmithKline Medicines Research Center to determine the amount of drug in a tablet, Exercise 6.101 (p. 340). Drug concentrations (measured as a percentage) for 50 randomly selected tablets are repeated in the accompanying table. The standard method of assessing drug content yields a concentration variance of 9. Can the scientists at GlaxoSmithKline conclude that the new method of determining drug concentration is less variable than the standard method? Test using $\alpha = .01$.

91.28	92.83	89.35	91.90	82.85	94.83	89.83	89.00	84.62
86.96	88.32	91.17	83.86	89.74	92.24	92.59	84.21	89.36
90.96	92.85	89.39	89.82	89.91	92.16	88.67	89.35	86.51
89.04	91.82	93.02	88.32	88.76	89.26	90.36	87.16	91.74
86.12	92.10	83.33	87.61	88.20	92.78	86.35	93.84	91.20
93.44	86.77	83.77	93.19	81.79				

Source: Based on Borman, P. J., Marion, J. C., Damjanov, I., & Jackson, P. "Design and analysis of method equivalence studies," *Analytical Chemistry*, Vol. 81, No. 24, December 15, 2009 (Table 3).

7.93 Do ball bearings conform to specifications? It is essential in the manufacture of machinery to use parts that conform to specifications. In the past, diameters of the ball bearings produced by a certain manufacturer had a variance of .00156. To cut costs, the manufacturer instituted a less expensive production method. The variance of the diameters of 100 randomly sampled bearings produced by the new process was .00211. Do the data provide sufficient evidence to indicate that diameters of ball bearings produced by the new process are more variable than those produced by the old process?

7.94 Cooling method for gas turbines. Refer to the *Journal of Engineering for Gas Turbines and Power* (Jan. 2005) study of the performance of augmented gas turbine engines, Exercise 7.40 (p. 378). Recall that performance for each in a sample of 67 gas turbines was measured by heat rate (kilojoules per kilowatt per hour). The data are saved in the accompanying file. Suppose that standard gas turbines have heat rates with a standard deviation of 1,500 kJ/kWh. Is there sufficient evidence to indicate that the heat rates of the augmented gas turbine engine are more variable than the heat rates of the standard gas turbine engine? Test using $\alpha = .05$.

Applying the Concepts—Advanced

7.95 **Why do small firms export?** Refer to the *Journal of Small Business Management* (Vol. 40, 2002) study of what motivates small firms to export, Exercise 7.45 (p. 379). Recall that in a survey of 137 exporting firms, each CEO was asked to respond to the statement "Management believes that the firm can achieve economies of scale by exporting" on a scale of 1 (strongly disagree) to 5 (strongly agree). Summary statistics for the $n = 137$ scale scores were reported as $\bar{x} = 3.85$ and $s = 1.5$.

a. Explain why the researcher will be unable to conclude that the true mean scale score exceeds 3.5 (as in Exercise 7.45) if the standard deviation of the scale scores is too large.

b. Give the largest value of the true standard deviation, σ, for which you will reject the null hypothesis $H_0: \mu = 3.5$ in favor of the alternative hypothesis $H_a: \mu > 3.5$ using $\alpha = .01$.

c. Based on the study results, is there evidence (at $\alpha = .01$) to indicate that σ is smaller than the value you determined in part **b**?

7.8 Calculating Type II Error Probabilities: More about β^*

In our introduction to hypothesis testing in Section 7.1, we showed that the probability of committing a Type I error, α, can be controlled by the selection of the rejection region for the test. Thus, when the test statistic falls in the rejection region and we make the decision to reject the null hypothesis, we do so knowing the error rate for incorrect rejections of H_0. The situation corresponding to accepting the null hypothesis, and thereby risking a Type II error, is not generally as controllable. For that reason, we adopted a policy of nonrejection of H_0 when the test statistic does not fall in the rejection region, rather than risking an error of unknown magnitude.

To see how β, the probability of a Type II error, can be calculated for a test of hypothesis, recall the example in Section 7.1 in which a city tests a manufacturer's sewer pipe to see whether it meets the requirement that the mean strength exceeds 2,400 pounds per linear foot. The setup for the test is as follows:

$$H_0: \mu = 2{,}400$$

$$H_a: \mu > 2{,}400$$

Test statistic: $z = \dfrac{\bar{x} - 2{,}400}{\sigma / \sqrt{n}}$

Rejection region: $z > 1.645$ for $\alpha = .05$

Figure 7.26a shows the rejection region for the **null distribution**—that is, the distribution of the test statistic assuming the null hypothesis is true. The area in the rejection region is .05, and this area represents α, the probability that the test statistic leads to rejection of H_0 when in fact H_0 is true.

The Type II error probability β is calculated assuming that the null hypothesis is false because it is defined as the *probability of accepting H_0 when it is false*. Because H_0 is false for any value of μ exceeding 2,400, one value of β exists for each possible value of μ greater than 2,400 (an infinite number of possibilities). Figures 7.26b–d show three of the possibilities, corresponding to alternative hypothesis values of μ equal to 2,425, 2,450, and 2,475, respectively. Note that β is the area in the *nonrejection* (or *acceptance*) *region* in each of these distributions and that β decreases as the true value of μ moves farther from the null hypothesized value of $\mu = 2,400$. This is sensible because the probability of incorrectly accepting the null hypothesis should decrease as the distance between the null and alternative values of μ increases.

In order to calculate the value of β for a specific value of μ in H_a, we proceed as follows:

1. Calculate the value of $\bar{x}$ that corresponds to the border between the acceptance and rejection regions. For the sewer pipe example, this is the value of $\bar{x}$ that lies 1.645 standard deviations above $\mu = 2,400$ in the sampling distribution of $\bar{x}$.

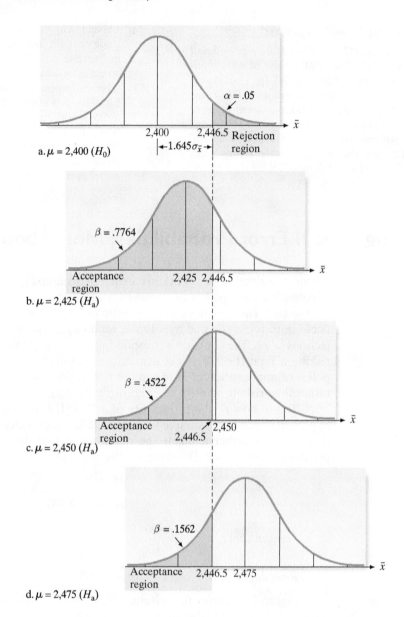

Figure 7.26

Values of α and β for various values of μ

a. $\mu = 2,400$ (H_0)

b. $\mu = 2,425$ (H_a)

c. $\mu = 2,450$ (H_a)

d. $\mu = 2,475$ (H_a)

Denoting this value by $\bar{x}_0$, corresponding to the largest value of $\bar{x}$ that supports the null hypothesis, we find (recalling that $s = 200$ and $n = 50$)

$$\bar{x}_0 = \mu_0 + 1.645\sigma_{\bar{x}} = 2,400 + 1.645\left(\frac{\sigma}{\sqrt{n}}\right)$$

$$\approx 2,400 + 1.645\left(\frac{s}{\sqrt{n}}\right) = 2,400 + 1.645\left(\frac{200}{\sqrt{50}}\right)$$

$$= 2,400 + 1.645(28.28) = 2,446.5$$

2. For a particular alternative distribution corresponding to a value of μ, denoted by μ_a, we calculate the z-value corresponding to $\bar{x}_0$, the border between the rejection and acceptance regions. We then use this z-value and Table II in Appendix D to determine the area in the *acceptance region* under the alternative distribution. This area is the value of β corresponding to the particular alternative μ_a. For example, for the alternative $\mu_a = 2,425$, we calculate

$$z = \frac{\bar{x}_0 - 2,425}{\sigma_{\bar{x}}} = \frac{\bar{x}_0 - 2,425}{\sigma/\sqrt{n}}$$

$$\approx \frac{\bar{x}_0 - 2,425}{\sigma_{\bar{x}}} = \frac{2,446.5 - 2,425}{28.28} = .76$$

Note in Figure 7.26b that the area in the acceptance region is the area to the left of $z = .76$. This area is

$$\beta = .5 + .2764 = .7764$$

Thus, the probability that the test procedure will lead to an incorrect acceptance of the null hypothesis $\mu = 2,400$ when in fact $\mu = 2,425$ is about .78. As the average strength of the pipe increases to 2,450, the value of β decreases to .4522 (Figure 7.26c). If the mean strength is further increased to 2,475, the value of β is further decreased to .1562 (Figure 7.26d). Thus, even if the true mean strength of the pipe exceeds the minimum specification by 75 pounds per linear foot, the test procedure will lead to an incorrect acceptance of the null hypothesis (rejection of the pipe) approximately 16% of the time. The upshot is that the pipe must be manufactured so that the mean strength well exceeds the minimum requirement if the manufacturer wants the probability of its acceptance by the city to be large (i.e., β to be small).

The steps for calculating β for a large-sample test about a population mean and a population proportion are summarized in the following boxes.

Steps for Calculating β for a Large-Sample Test about μ

1. Calculate the value(s) of $\bar{x}$ corresponding to the border(s) of the rejection region. There will be one border value for a one-tailed test and two for a two-tailed test. The formula is one of the following, corresponding to a test with level of significance α:

$$\text{Upper-tailed test: } \bar{x}_0 = \mu_0 + z_\alpha \sigma_{\bar{x}} \approx \mu_0 + z_\alpha \left(\frac{s}{\sqrt{n}} \right)$$
$$(H_a: \mu > \mu_0)$$

$$\text{Lower-tailed test: } \bar{x}_0 = \mu_0 - z_\alpha \sigma_{\bar{x}} \approx \mu_0 - z_\alpha \left(\frac{s}{\sqrt{n}} \right)$$
$$(H_a: \mu < \mu_0)$$

$$\text{Two-tailed test: } \bar{x}_{0,L} = \mu_0 - z_{\alpha/2} \sigma_{\bar{x}} \approx \mu_0 - z_{\alpha/2} \left(\frac{s}{\sqrt{n}} \right)$$
$$(H_a: \mu \neq \mu_0)$$

$$\bar{x}_{0,U} = \mu_0 + z_{\alpha/2} \sigma_{\bar{x}} \approx \mu_0 + z_{\alpha/2} \left(\frac{s}{\sqrt{n}} \right)$$

2. Specify the value of μ_a in the alternative hypothesis for which the value of β is to be calculated. Then convert the border value(s) of $\bar{x}_0$ to z-value(s) using the alternative distribution with mean μ_a. The general formula for the z-value is

$$z = \frac{\bar{x}_0 - \mu_a}{\sigma_{\bar{x}}}$$

3. Sketch the alternative distribution (centered at μ_a), and shade the area in the acceptance (nonrejection) region. Use the z-statistic(s) and Table II of Appendix D to find the shaded area, which is β.

$$\text{Lower-tailed test: } \beta = P\left(z > \frac{\bar{x}_0 - \mu_a}{\sigma_{\bar{x}}} \right)$$
$$(H_a: \mu < \mu_0)$$

$$\text{Upper-tailed test: } \beta = P\left(z < \frac{\bar{x}_0 - \mu_a}{\sigma_{\bar{x}}} \right)$$
$$(H_a: \mu > \mu_0)$$

$$\text{Two-tailed test: } \beta = P\left(\frac{\bar{x}_{0,L} - \mu_a}{\sigma_{\bar{x}}} < z < \frac{\bar{x}_{0,U} - \mu_a}{\sigma_{\bar{x}}} \right)$$
$$(H_a: \mu \neq \mu_0)$$

Steps for Calculating β for a Large-Sample Test about p

1. Calculate the value(s) of $\hat{p}$ corresponding to the border(s) of the rejection region. There will be one border for a one-tailed test and two for a two-tailed test. The formula is one of the following, corresponding to a test with level of significance α.

$$\textit{Upper-tailed test: } \hat{p}_0 = p_0 + z_\alpha \sigma_p = p_0 + z_\alpha \sqrt{\frac{p_0 q_0}{n}}$$
$$(H_a: p > p_0)$$

$$\textit{Lower-tailed test: } \hat{p}_0 = p_0 - z_\alpha \sigma_p = p_0 + z_\alpha \sqrt{\frac{p_0 q_0}{n}}$$
$$(H_a: p < p_0)$$

$$\textit{Two-tailed test: } \hat{p}_{0,L} = p_0 - z_{\alpha/2} \sigma_p = p_0 - z_{\alpha/2} \sqrt{\frac{p_0 q_0}{n}}$$
$$(H_a: p \neq p_0)$$

$$\hat{p}_{0,U} = p_0 + z_{\alpha/2} \sigma_p = p_0 + z_{\alpha/2} \sqrt{\frac{p_0 q_0}{n}}$$

2. Specify the value of p_a in the alternative hypothesis for which the value of β is to be calculated. Then covert the border values of $\hat{p}_0$ to z-value(s), using the alternative distribution with mean p_a. The general formula for the z-value is:

$$z = (\hat{p}_0 - p_a)/\sigma_p = \frac{\hat{p}_0 - p_a}{\sqrt{\dfrac{p_0 q_0}{n}}}$$

3. Sketch the alternative distribution (centered at p_a), and shade the area in the acceptance (nonrejection) region. Use the z-statistic(s) and Table II of Appendix D to find the shaded area, which is β.

$$\textit{Upper-tailed test: } \beta = P\left(z < \frac{\hat{p}_0 - p_a}{\sqrt{\dfrac{p_0 q_0}{n}}} \right)$$

$$(H_a: p > p_0)$$

$$\textit{Lower-tailed test: } \beta = P\left(z > \frac{\hat{p}_0 - p_a}{\sqrt{\dfrac{p_0 q_0}{n}}} \right)$$

$$(H_a: p < p_0)$$

$$\textit{Two-tailed test: } \beta = P\left(\frac{\hat{p}_{0,L} - p_a}{\sqrt{\dfrac{p_0 q_0}{n}}} < z < \frac{p_{0,U} - p_a}{\sqrt{\dfrac{p_0 q_0}{n}}} \right)$$

$$(H_a: p \neq p_0)$$

Following the calculation of β for a particular value of the parameter in H_a you should interpret the value in the context of the hypothesis-testing application. It is often useful to interpret the value of $1 - \beta$, which is known as the **power of the test** corresponding to a particular alternative, say, μ_a for a population mean. Since β is the probability of accepting the null hypothesis when the alternative hypothesis is true with $\mu = \mu_a$, $1 - \beta$ is the probability of the complementary event, or the probability of rejecting the null hypothesis when the alternative $H_a: \mu = \mu_a$ is true. That is, the power $(1 - \beta)$ measures the likelihood that the test procedure will lead to the correct decision (reject H_0) for a particular value of the mean (or proportion) in the alternative hypothesis.

> The **power of a test** is the probability that the test will correctly lead to the rejection of the null hypothesis for a particular value of μ or p in the alternative hypothesis. The power is equal to $(1 - \beta)$ for the particular alternative considered.

For example, in the sewer pipe example we found that $\beta = .7764$ when $\mu = 2{,}425$. This is the probability that the test leads to the (incorrect) acceptance of the null hypothesis when $\mu = 2{,}425$. Or, equivalently, the power of the test is $1 - .7764 = .2236$, which means that the test will lead to the (correct) rejection of the null hypothesis only 22% of the time when the pipe exceeds specifications by 25 pounds per linear foot. When the manufacturer's pipe has a mean strength of 2,475 (that is, 75 pounds per linear foot in excess of specifications), the power of the test increases to $1 - .1562 = .8438$—that is, the test will lead to the acceptance of the manufacturer's pipe 84% of the time if $\mu = 2{,}475$.

Example 7.13	**Problem** Recall the quality-control study in Example 7.5, in which we tested to determine whether a cereal box filling machine was deviating from the specified mean fill of $\mu = 12$ ounces. The test setup is repeated here:
The Power of a Test— Quality-Control Study	

$$H_0: \mu = 12$$
$$H_a: \mu \neq 12 \text{ (i.e., } \mu < 12 \text{ or } \mu > 12)$$

$$\text{Test statistic: } z = \frac{\bar{x} - 12}{\sigma_{\bar{x}}}$$

$$\text{Rejection region: } z < -1.96 \text{ or } z > 1.96 \text{ for } \alpha = .05$$
$$z < -2.575 \text{ or } z > 2.575 \text{ for } \alpha = .01$$

Note that two rejection regions have been specified corresponding to values of $\alpha = .05$ and $\alpha = .01$, respectively. Assume that $n = 100$ and $s = .5$.

a. Suppose the machine is underfilling the boxes by an average of .1 ounce (i.e., $\mu = 11.9$). Calculate the values of β corresponding to the two rejection regions. Discuss the relationship between the values of α and β.

b. Calculate the power of the test for each of the rejection regions when $\mu = 11.9$.

Solution

a. We first consider the rejection region corresponding to $\alpha = .05$. The first step is to calculate the border values of $\bar{x}$ corresponding to the two-tailed rejection region, $z < -1.96$ or $z > 1.96$:

$$\bar{x}_{0,L} = \mu_0 - 1.96\sigma_{\bar{x}} \approx \mu_0 - 1.96\left(\frac{s}{\sqrt{n}}\right) = 12 - 1.96\left(\frac{.5}{10}\right) = 11.902$$

$$\bar{x}_{0,U} = \mu_0 + 1.96\sigma_{\bar{x}} \approx \mu_0 + 1.96\left(\frac{s}{\sqrt{n}}\right) = 12 + 1.96\left(\frac{.5}{10}\right) = 12.098$$

These border values are shown in Figure 7.27a.

Next, we convert these values to z-values in the alternative distribution with $\mu_a = 11.9$:

$$z_L = \frac{x_{0,L} - \mu_a}{\sigma_{\bar{x}}} \approx \frac{11.902 - 11.9}{.05} = .04$$

$$z_U = \frac{x_{0,U} - \mu_a}{\sigma_{\bar{x}}} \approx \frac{12.098 - 11.9}{.05} = 3.96$$

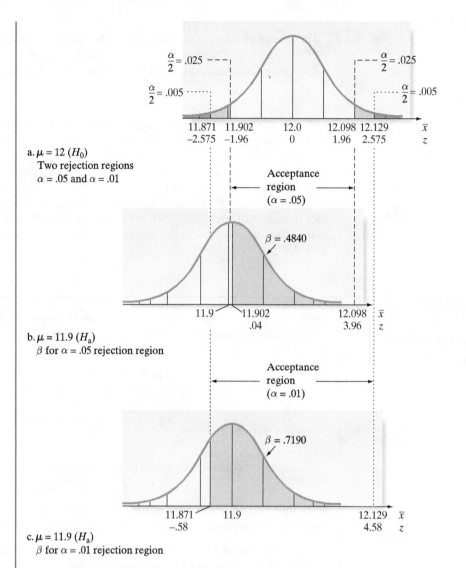

a. $\mu = 12\ (H_0)$
   Two rejection regions
   $\alpha = .05$ and $\alpha = .01$

b. $\mu = 11.9\ (H_a)$
   β for $\alpha = .05$ rejection region

c. $\mu = 11.9\ (H_a)$
   β for $\alpha = .01$ rejection region

Figure 7.27

Calculation of β for filling machine process, Example 7.13

These z-values are shown in Figure 7.27b: You can see that the acceptance (or nonrejection) region is the area between them. Using Table II in Appendix D, we find that the area between $z = 0$ and $z = .04$ is .0160, and the area between $z = 0$ and $z = 3.96$ is (approximately) .5 (because $z = 3.96$ is off the scale of Table II). Then the area between $z = .04$ and $z = 3.96$ is, approximately,

$$\beta = .5 - .0160 = .4840$$

Thus, the test with $\alpha = .05$ will lead to a Type II error about 48% of the time when the machine is underfilling, on average, by .1 ounce.

For the rejection region corresponding to $\alpha = .01$, $z < -2.575$, or $z > 2.575$, we find

$$\bar{x}_{0,\mathrm{L}} = 12 - 2.575\left(\frac{.5}{10}\right) = 11.871$$

$$\bar{x}_{0,\mathrm{U}} = 12 + 2.575\left(\frac{.5}{10}\right) = 12.129$$

These border values of the rejection region are shown in Figure 7.27c.

Converting these two border values to z-values in the alternative distribution with $\mu_a = 11.9$, we find $z_{\mathrm{L}} = -.58$ and $z_{\mathrm{U}} = 4.58$. The area between these values is, approximately,

$$\beta = P(-.58 < z < 4.58) = .2190 + .5 = .7190$$

Thus, the chance that the test procedure with $\alpha = .01$ will lead to an incorrect acceptance of H_0 is about 72%.

Note that the value of β increases from .4840 to .7190 when we decrease the value of α from .05 to .01. This is a general property of the relationship between α and β: *as α is decreased (increased), β is increased (decreased).*

b. The power is defined to be the probability of (correctly) rejecting the null hypothesis when the alternative is true. When $\mu = 11.9$ and $\alpha = .05$, we find

$$\text{Power} = 1 - \beta = 1 - .4840 = .5160$$

When $\mu = 11.9$ and $\alpha = .01$, we find

$$\text{Power} = 1 - \beta = 1 - .7190 = .2810$$

You can see that the power of the test is decreased as the level of α is decreased. This means that as the probability of incorrectly rejecting the null hypothesis is decreased, the probability of correctly accepting the null hypothesis for a given alternative is also decreased.

Look Back A key point of this example is that the value of α must be selected carefully, with the realization that a test is made less capable of detecting departures from the null hypothesis when the value of α is decreased.

■ **Now Work Exercise 7.102**

Note: Most statistical software packages now have options for computing the power of standard tests of hypothesis. Usually you will need to specify the type of test (z-test or t-test), form of H_a ($<$, $>$, or $\neq$), standard deviation, sample size, and the value of the parameter in H_a (or the difference between the value in H_0 and the value in H_a). The Minitab power analysis for Example 7.13 when $\alpha = .05$ is displayed in Figure 7.28. The power of the test (.516) is highlighted on the printout.

Power and Sample Size

1-Sample Z Test

Testing mean = null (versus not = null)
Calculating power for mean = null + difference
Alpha = 0.05 Assumed standard deviation = 0.5

Difference	Sample Size	Power
0.1	100	0.516005

Figure 7.28

Minitab power analysis for Example 7.13

We have shown that the probability of committing a Type II error, β, is inversely related to α (Example 7.13) and that the value of β decreases as the value of μ_a moves farther from the null hypothesis value (sewer pipe example). The sample size n also affects β. Remember that the standard deviation of the sampling distribution of $\bar{x}$ is inversely proportional to the square root of the sample size ($\sigma_{\bar{x}} = \sigma/\sqrt{n}$). Thus, as illustrated in Figure 7.29, the variability of both the null and alternative sampling distributions is decreased as n is increased. If the value of α is specified and remains fixed, the value of β decreases as n increases, as illustrated in Figure 7.29. Conversely, the power of the test for a given alternative hypothesis is increased as the sample size is increased. The properties of β and power are summarized in the box.

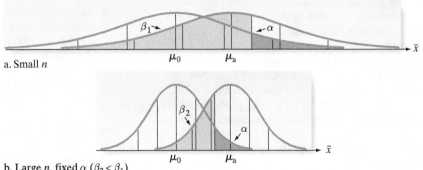

a. Small n

b. Large n, fixed α ($\beta_2 < \beta_1$)

Figure 7.29

Relationship between α, β, and n

> ### Properties of β and Power
>
> 1. For fixed n and α, the value of β decreases, and the power increases as the distance between the specified null value μ_0 (or, p_0) and the specified alternative value μ_a (or, p_a) increases (see Figure 7.26).
> 2. For fixed n and values of μ_0 and μ_a (or, p_0 and p_a), the value of β increases, and the power decreases as the value of α is decreased (see Figure 7.27).
> 3. For fixed α and values of μ_0 and μ_a (or, p_0 and p_a), the value of β decreases, and the power increases as the sample size n is increased (see Figure 7.29).

Exercises 7.96–7.107

Learning the Mechanics

7.96
  a. List three factors that will increase the power of a test.
  b. What is the relationship between β, the probability of committing a Type II error, and the power of a test?

7.97 Suppose you want to test $H_0: \mu = 500$ against $H_a: \mu > 500$ using $\alpha = .05$. The population in question is normally distributed with standard deviation 100. A random sample of size $n = 25$ will be used.
  a. Sketch the sampling distribution of $\bar{x}$ assuming that H_0 is true.
  b. Find the value of $\bar{x}_0$, that value of $\bar{x}$ above which the null hypothesis will be rejected. Indicate the rejection region on your graph of part **a**. Shade the area above the rejection region and label it α.
  c. On your graph of part **a,** sketch the sampling distribution of $\bar{x}$ if $\mu = 550$. Shade the area under this distribution that corresponds to the probability that $\bar{x}$ falls in the nonrejection region when $\mu = 550$. Label this area β.
  d. Find β.
  e. Compute the power of this test for detecting the alternative $H_a: \mu = 550$.

7.98 Refer to Exercise 7.97.
  a. If $\mu = 575$ instead of 550, what is the probability that the hypothesis test will incorrectly fail to reject H_0? That is, what is β?
  b. If $\mu = 575$, what is the probability that the test will correctly reject the null hypothesis? That is, what is the power of the test?
  c. Compare β and the power of the test when $\mu = 575$ to the values you obtained in Exercise 7.97 for $\mu = 550$. Explain the differences.

7.99 It is desired to test $H_0: \mu = 75$ against $H_a: \mu < 75$ using $\alpha = .10$. The population in question is uniformly distributed with standard deviation 15. A random sample of size 49 will be drawn from the population.
  a. Describe the (approximate) sampling distribution of $\bar{x}$ under the assumption that H_0 is true.
  b. Describe the (approximate) sampling distribution of $\bar{x}$ under the assumption that the population mean is 70.
  c. If μ were really equal to 70, what is the probability that the hypothesis test would lead the investigator to commit a Type II error?
  d. What is the power of this test for detecting the alternative $H_a: \mu = 70$?

7.100 Refer to Exercise 7.99.
  a. Find β for each of the following values of the population mean: 74, 72, 70, 68, and 66.
  b. Plot each value of β you obtained in part **a** against its associated population mean. Show β on the vertical axis and μ on the horizontal axis. Draw a curve through the five points on your graph.
  c. Use your graph of part **b** to find the approximate probability that the hypothesis test will lead to a Type II error when $\mu = 73$.
  d. Convert each of the β values you calculated in part **a** to the power of the test at the specified value of μ. Plot the power on the vertical axis against μ on the horizontal axis. Compare the graph of part **b** to the *power curve* of this part.
  e. Examine the graphs of parts **b** and **d**. Explain what they reveal about the relationships among the distance between the true mean μ and the null hypothesized mean μ_0, the value of β, and the power.

7.101 Suppose you want to conduct the two-tailed test of $H_0: p = .7$ against $H_a: p \neq .7$ using $\alpha = .05$. A random sample of size 100 will be drawn from the population in question.
  a. Describe the sampling distribution of $\hat{p}$ under the assumption that H_0 is true.
  b. Describe the sampling distribution of $\hat{p}$ under the assumption that $p = .65$.
  c. If p were really equal to .65, find the value of β associated with the test.
  d. Find the value of β for the alternative $H_a: p = .71$.

Applying the Concepts—Intermediate

7.102 **Square footage of new California homes.** The average size of single-family homes built in the United States is 2,390 square feet (*Statistical Abstract of the United States*, 2011). A random sample of 100 new homes sold in California yielded the following size information: $\bar{x} = 2,507$ square feet and $s = 257$ square feet.
  a. Assume the average size of U.S. homes is known with certainty. Do the sample data provide sufficient evidence to conclude that the mean size of California homes built exceeds the national average? Test using $\alpha = .01$.
  b. Suppose the actual mean size of new California homes was 2,490 square feet. What is the power of the test in part **a** to detect this 100-square-foot difference?

c. If the California mean were actually 2,440 square feet, what is the power of the test in part **a** to detect this 50-square-foot difference?

7.103 Manufacturers that practice sole sourcing. If a manufacturer (the vendee) buys all items of a particular type from a particular vendor, the manufacturer is practicing *sole sourcing* (Schonberger and Knod, *Operations Management,* 2001). As part of a sole-sourcing arrangement, a vendor agrees to periodically supply its vendee with sample data from its production process. The vendee uses the data to investigate whether the mean length of rods produced by the vendor's production process is truly 5.0 millimeters (mm) or more, as claimed by the vendor and desired by the vendee.

    a. If the production process has a standard deviation of .01 mm, the vendor supplies $n = 100$ items to the vendee, and the vendee uses $\alpha = .05$ in testing H_0: $\mu = 5.0$ mm against H_a: $\mu < 5.0$ mm, what is the probability that the vendee's test will fail to reject the null hypothesis when in fact $\mu = 4.9975$ mm? What is the name given to this type of error?

    b. Refer to part **a.** What is the probability that the vendee's test will reject the null hypothesis when in fact $\mu = 5.0$? What is the name given to this type of error?

    c. What is the power of the test to detect a departure of .0025 mm below the specified mean rod length of 5.0 mm?

7.104 Satellite radio in cars. Refer to the National Association of Broadcasters (NAB) survey of 501 satellite radio subscribers, Exercise 7.70 (p. 392). Recall that an NAB spokesperson claims that 80% of all satellite radio subscribers have a satellite radio receiver in their car. You conducted a test to determine if the claimed value is too high using $\alpha = .10$. What is the probability that the test will conclude that the claim is too high, if in fact the true percentage of all satellite radio subscribers who have a satellite radio receiver in their car is 82%?

7.105 Gummi Bears: Red or yellow? Refer to the *Chance* (Winter 2010) experiment to determine if color of a Gummi Bear is related to its flavor, Exercise 7.72 (p. 392). You tested the null hypothesis of $p = .5$ against the two-tailed alternative hypothesis of $p \neq .5$ using $\alpha = .01$, where p represents the true proportion of blind folded students who correctly identified the color of the Gummi Bear. Recall that of the 121 students who participated in the study, 97 correctly identified the color. Find the power of the test if the true proportion is $p = .65$.

7.106 Fuel economy of the Honda Civic. According to the Environmental Protection Agency (EPA) *Fuel Economy Guide,* the 2011 Honda Civic automobile obtains a mean of 36 miles per gallon (mpg) on the highway. Suppose Honda claims that the EPA has underestimated the Civic's mileage. To support its assertion, the company selects $n = 50$ model 2011 Civic cars and records the mileage obtained for each car over a driving course similar to the one used by the EPA. The following data resulted: $\bar{x} = 38.3$ mpg, $s = 6.4$ mpg.

    a. If Honda wishes to show that the mean mpg for 2011 Civic autos is greater than 36 mpg, what should the alternative hypothesis be? The null hypothesis?

    b. Do the data provide sufficient evidence to support the auto manufacturer's claim? Test using $\alpha = .05$. List any assumptions you make in conducting the test.

    c. Calculate the power of the test for the mean values of 36.5, 37.0, 37.5, 38.0, and 38.5, assuming $s = 6.4$ is a good estimate of σ.

    d. Plot the power of the test on the vertical axis against the mean on the horizontal axis. Draw a curve through the points.

    e. Use the power curve of part **d** to estimate the power for the mean value $\mu = 37.75$. Calculate the power for this value of μ and compare it to your approximation.

    f. Use the power curve to approximate the power of the test when $\mu = 41$. If the true value of the mean mpg for this model is really 41, what (approximately) are the chances that the test will fail to reject the null hypothesis that the mean is 36?

7.107 Solder-joint inspections. Refer to Exercise 7.44 (p. 379), in which the performance of a particular type of laser-based inspection equipment was investigated. Assume that the standard deviation of the number of solder joints inspected on each run is 1.2. If $\alpha = .05$ is used in conducting the hypothesis test of interest using a sample of 48 circuit boards, and if the true mean number of solder joints that can be inspected is really equal to 9.5, what is the probability that the test will result in a Type II error?

◻ Chapter Notes

Key Terms

Note: Asterisks (*) denote items from the optional sections of this chapter.

Alternative (research) hypothesis 357
Chi-square sampling distribution 395
Conclusions 360
Hypothesis 356
Level of significance 361
Lower-tailed test 362
Null distribution 399
Null hypothesis 356
Observed significance level (*p*-value) 367

One-tailed (one-sided) statistical test 361
*Power of the test 402
Rejection region 358
Test of hypothesis 356
Test statistic 357
Two-tailed (two-sided) hypothesis 361
Type I error 358
Type II error 359
Upper-tailed test 362

Key Symbols

μ	Population mean
p	Population proportion, $P(\text{Success})$, in binomial trial
σ^2	Population variance
$\bar{x}$	Sample mean (estimator of μ)
$\hat{p}$	Sample proportion (estimator of p)
s^2	Sample variance (estimator of σ^2)
H_0	Null hypothesis
H_a	Alternative hypothesis
α	Probability of a Type I error
β	Probability of a Type II error
χ^2	Chi-square (sampling distribution of s^2 for normal data)

Key Ideas

Key Words for Identifying the Target Parameter

μ — Mean, Average
p — Proportion, Fraction, Percentage, Rate, Probability
σ^2 — Variance, Variability, Spread

Elements of a Hypothesis Test

1. *Null hypothesis* (H_0)
2. *Alternative hypothesis* (H_a)
3. *Test statistic* $(z, t, or \chi^2)$
4. *Significance level* (α)
5. *p-value*
6. *Conclusion*

Probabilities in Hypothesis Testing

$\alpha = P(\textbf{Type I Error}) = P(\text{Reject } H_0 \text{ when } H_0 \text{ is true})$
$\beta = P(\textbf{Type II Error}) = P(\text{Accept } H_0 \text{ when } H_0 \text{ is false})$
$1 - \beta = \textbf{Power of a Test} = P(\text{Reject } H_0 \text{ when } H_0 \text{ is false})$

Forms of Alternative Hypothesis

Lower-tailed: H_a: $\mu < 50$
Upper-tailed: H_a: $\mu > 50$
Two-tailed: H_a: $\mu \neq 50$

Using p-Values to Decide

1. Choose significance level (α)
2. Obtain *p*-value of the test
3. If $\alpha > p$-value, reject H_0

Guide to Selecting a One-Sample Hypothesis Test

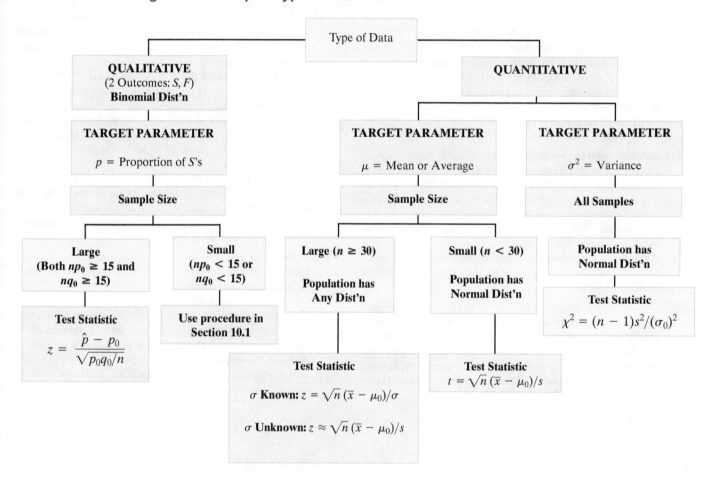

Supplementary Exercises 7.108–7.145

Note: List the assumptions necessary for the valid implementation of the statistical procedures you use in solving all these exercises. Exercises marked with an asterisk (*) are from the optional section in this chapter.

Learning the Mechanics

7.108 Specify the differences between a large-sample and small-sample test of hypothesis about a population mean μ. Focus on the assumptions and test statistics.

7.109 *Complete the following statement:* The smaller the *p*-value associated with a test of hypothesis, the stronger the support for the _____ hypothesis. Explain your answer.

7.110 Which of the elements of a test of hypothesis can and should be specified *prior* to analyzing the data that are to be used to conduct the test?

7.111 If you select a very small value for α when conducting a hypothesis test, will β tend to be big or small? Explain.

7.112 If the rejection of the null hypothesis of a particular test would cause your firm to go out of business, would you want α to be small or large? Explain.

7.113 A random sample of 20 observations selected from a normal population produced $\bar{x} = 72.6$ and $s^2 = 19.4$.
 a. Test $H_0: \mu = 80$ against $H_a: \mu < 80$. Use $\alpha = .05$.
 b. Test $H_0: \mu = 80$ against $H_a: \mu \neq 80$. Use $\alpha = .01$.

7.114 A random sample of 175 measurements possessed a mean $\bar{x} = 8.2$ and a standard deviation $s = .79$.
 a. Test $H_0: \mu = 8.3$ against $H_a: \mu \neq 8.3$. Use $\alpha = .05$.
 b. Test $H_0: \mu = 8.4$ against $H_a: \mu \neq 8.4$. Use $\alpha = .05$.
 c. Test $H_0: \sigma = 1$ against $H_a: \sigma \neq 1$. Use $\alpha = .05$.
 *d. Find the power of the test, part **a,** if $\mu_a = 8.5$.

7.115 A random sample of $n = 200$ observations from a binomial population yields $\hat{p} = .29$.
 a. Test $H_0: p = .35$ against $H_a: p < .35$. Use $\alpha = .05$.
 b. Test $H_0: p = .35$ against $H_a: p \neq .35$. Use $\alpha = .05$.

7.116 A t-test is conducted for the null hypothesis $H_0: \mu = 10$ versus the alternative $H_a: \mu > 10$ for a random sample of $n = 17$ observations. The test results are $t = 1.174$, p-value $= .1288$.
 a. Interpret the p-value.
 b. What assumptions are necessary for the validity of this test?
 c. Calculate and interpret the p-value assuming the alternative hypothesis was instead $H_a: \mu \neq 10$.

7.117 A random sample of 41 observations from a normal population possessed a mean $\bar{x} = 88$ and a standard deviation $s = 6.9$.
 a. Test $H_0: \sigma^2 = 30$ against $H_a: \sigma^2 > 30$. Use $\alpha = .05$.
 b. Test $H_0: \sigma^2 = 30$ against $H_a: \sigma^2 \neq 30$. Use $\alpha = .05$.

Applying the Concepts—Basic

7.118 **Latex allergy in health care workers.** Refer to the *Current Allergy & Clinical Immunology* (Mar. 2004) study of $n = 46$ hospital employees who were diagnosed with a latex allergy from exposure to the powder on latex gloves, Exercise 6.112 (p. 343). The number of latex gloves used per week by the sampled workers is summarized as follows: $\bar{x} = 19.3$ and $s = 11.9$. Let μ represent the mean number of latex gloves used per week by all hospital employees. Consider testing $H_0: \mu = 20$ against $H_a: \mu < 20$.
 a. Give the rejection region for the test at a significance level of $\alpha = .01$.
 b. Calculate the value of the test statistic.
 c. Use the results, parts **a** and **b,** to make the appropriate conclusion.

7.119 **Latex allergy in health care workers (cont'd).** Refer to Exercise 7.118. Let σ^2 represent the variance in the number of latex gloves used per week by all hospital employees. Consider testing $H_0: \sigma^2 = 100$ against $H_a: \sigma^2 \neq 100$.
 a. Give the rejection region for the test at a significance level of $\alpha = .01$.
 b. Calculate the value of the test statistic.
 c. Use the results, parts **a** and **b,** to make the appropriate conclusion.

7.120 **"Made in the USA" survey.** Refer to the *Journal of Global Business* (Spring 2002) study of what "Made in the USA" means to consumers, Exercise 2.152 (p. 116). Recall that 64 of 106 randomly selected shoppers believed "Made in the USA" means 100% of labor and materials are from the United States. Let p represent the true proportion of consumers who believe "Made in the USA" means 100% of labor and materials are from the United States.
 a. Calculate a point estimate for p.
 b. A claim is made that $p = .70$. Set up the null and alternative hypotheses to test this claim.
 c. Calculate the test statistic for the test, part **b.**
 d. Find the rejection region for the test if $\alpha = .01$.
 e. Use the results, parts **c** and **d,** to make the appropriate conclusion.

7.121 **Beta value of a stock.** The "beta coefficient" of a stock is a measure of the stock's volatility (or risk) relative to the market as a whole. Stocks with beta coefficients greater than 1 generally bear greater risk (more volatility) than the market, whereas stocks with beta coefficients less than 1 are less risky (less volatile) than the overall market (Alexander, Sharpe, and Bailey, *Fundamentals of Investments,* 2000). A random sample of 15 high-technology stocks was selected at the end of 2009, and the mean and standard deviation of the beta coefficients were calculated: $\bar{x} = 1.23$, $s = .37$.
 a. Set up the appropriate null and alternative hypotheses to test whether the average high-technology stock is riskier than the market as a whole.
 b. Establish the appropriate test statistic and rejection region for the test. Use $\alpha = .10$.
 c. What assumptions are necessary to ensure the validity of the test?
 d. Calculate the test statistic and state your conclusion.
 e. What is the approximate p-value associated with this test? Interpret it.
 f. Conduct a test to determine if the variance of the stock beta values differs from .15. Use $\alpha = .05$.

7.122 **Accuracy of price scanners at Wal-Mart.** Refer to Exercise 6.127 (p. 345) and the study of the accuracy of checkout scanners at Wal-Mart stores in California. Recall that the National Institute for Standards and Technology (NIST) mandates that for every 100 items scanned through the electronic checkout scanner at a retail store, no more than two should have an inaccurate price. A study of random items purchased at California Wal-Mart stores found that 8.3% had the wrong price (*Tampa Tribune,* Nov. 22, 2005). Assume that the study included 1,000 randomly selected items.
 a. Identify the population parameter of interest in the study.
 b. Set up H_0 and H_a for a test to determine if the true proportion of items scanned at California Wal-Mart stores exceeds the 2% NIST standard.
 c. Find the test statistic and rejection region (at $\alpha = .05$) for the test.
 d. Give a practical interpretation of the test.
 e. What conditions are required for the inference, part **d,** to be valid? Are these conditions met?

7.123 **A camera that detects liars.** According to *New Scientist* (Jan. 2, 2002), a new thermal imaging camera that detects small temperature changes is now being used as a polygraph device. The U.S. Department of Defense Polygraph Institute (DDPI) claims the camera can correctly detect liars 75% of the time by monitoring the temperatures of their faces.

a. Give the null hypothesis for testing the claim made by the DDPI.

b. What is a Type I error for this problem? A Type II error?

7.124 Size of diamonds sold at retail. Refer to the *Journal of Statistics Education* data on diamonds saved in the file. In Exercise 6.120 (p. 344) you selected a random sample of 30 diamonds from the 308 diamonds and found the mean and standard deviation of the number of carats per diamond for the sample. Let μ represent the mean number of carats in the population of 308 diamonds. Suppose you want to test $H_0: \mu = .6$ against $H_a: \mu \neq .6$.

a. In the words of the problem, define a Type I error and a Type II error.

b. Use the sample information to conduct the test at a significance level of $\alpha = .05$.

c. Conduct the test, part **b**, using $\alpha = .10$.

d. What do the results suggest about the choice of α in a test of hypothesis?

7.125 Cost-of-living index. Each year, Kiplinger's complies its list of *Best Value Cities*. One of the statistics used in the rankings is the cost-of-living index, complied by the U.S. Bureau of Labor Statistics. The index measures the cost of living in a city relative to the national average of 100. In 2011, the New York metropolitan area had a cost-of-living index of 218, the highest in the nation. This means that the cost of living in New York City is 118% higher than the average cost of living for the nation. In contrast, Pueblo, Colorado, had the lowest cost-of-living index (84). The table lists the cost-of-living index for each in a sample of seven Southeastern cities.

City	Cost-of-living Index (U.S. mean = 100)
Charlotte, NC	93.0
Birmingham, AL	89.6
Florence, SC	100.0
Tampa, FL	92.1
Atlanta, GA	95.2
Knoxville, TN	89.7
Miami, FL	107.7

Source: Data from U.S. Bureau of Labor Statistics, 2011.

a. Specify the null and alternative hypotheses for testing whether the true mean cost-of-living index for Southeastern cities differs from the national cost-of-living index of 100.

b. What assumptions about the sample and population must hold in order for the test, part **a,** to yield valid results?

c. Conduct the hypothesis test using $\alpha = .05$.

d. Is the observed significance level of the test greater or less than .05? Justify your answer.

Applying the Concepts—Intermediate

7.126 Consumers' use of discount coupons. In 1894, druggist Asa Candler began distributing handwritten tickets to his customers for free glasses of Coca-Cola at his soda fountain. That was the genesis of the discount coupon. In 1975, it was estimated that 65% of U.S. consumers regularly used discount coupons when shopping. In a more recent consumer survey, 72% said they regularly redeem coupons

(Prospectiv 2008 Consumer Coupon Poll). Assume the recent survey consisted of a random sample of 1,000 shoppers.

a. Does the survey provide sufficient evidence that the percentage of shoppers using cents-off coupons exceeds 65%? Test using $\alpha = .05$.

b. Is the sample size large enough to use the inferential procedures presented in this section? Explain.

c. Find the observed significance level for the test you conducted in part **a** and interpret its value.

7.127 Errors in medical tests. Medical tests have been developed to detect many serious diseases. A medical test is designed to minimize the probability that it will produce a "false positive" or a "false negative." A *false positive* refers to a positive test result for an individual who does not have the disease, whereas a false negative is a negative test result for an individual who does have the disease.

a. If we treat a medical test for a disease as a statistical test of hypothesis, what are the null and alternative hypotheses for the medical test?

b. What are the Type I and Type II errors for the test? Relate each to false positives and false negatives.

c. Which of the errors has graver consequences? Considering this error, is it more important to minimize α or β? Explain.

7.128 Drivers' use of the Lincoln Tunnel. The Lincoln Tunnel (under the Hudson River) connects suburban New Jersey to midtown Manhattan. On Mondays at 8:30 A.M., the mean number of cars waiting in line to pay the Lincoln Tunnel toll is 1,220. Because of the substantial wait during rush hour, the Port Authority of New York and New Jersey is considering raising the amount of the toll between 7:30 and 8:30 A.M. to encourage more drivers to use the tunnel at an earlier or later time. Suppose the Port Authority experiments with peak-hour pricing for 6 months, increasing the toll from $4 to $7 during the rush hour peak. On 10 different workdays at 8:30 A.M. aerial photographs of the tunnel queues are taken and the number of vehicles counted. The results follow:

1,260 1,052 1,201 942 1,062 999 931 849 867 735

Analyze the data for the purpose of determining whether peak-hour pricing succeeded in reducing the average number of vehicles attempting to use the Lincoln Tunnel during the peak rush hour.

7.129 Point spreads of NFL games. Refer to the *Chance* (Fall 1998) study of point-spread errors in NFL games, Exercise 7.41 (p. 379). Recall that the difference between the actual game outcome and the point spread established by odds makers—the point-spread error—was calculated for 240 NFL games. The results are summarized as follows: $\bar{x} = -1.6, s = 13.3$. Suppose the researcher wants to know whether the true standard deviation of the point-spread errors exceeds 15. Conduct the analysis using $\alpha = .10$.

7.130 Improving the productivity of chickens. Refer to the *Applied Animal Behaviour Science* (Oct. 2000) study of the color of string preferred by pecking domestic chickens, Exercise 6.122 (p. 344). Recall that $n = 72$ chickens were exposed to blue string and the number of pecks each chicken took at the string over a specified time interval had a mean of $\bar{x} = 1.13$ pecks and a standard deviation of $s = 2.21$ pecks. Also recall that previous research had shown that $\mu = 7.5$ pecks if chickens are exposed to white string.

a. Conduct a test (at $\alpha = .01$) to determine if the true mean number of pecks at blue string is less than $\mu = 7.5$ pecks.

b. In Exercise 6.122, you used a 99% confidence interval as evidence that chickens are more apt to peck at white string than blue string. Do the test results, part **a**, support this conclusion? Explain.

7.131 Are manufacturers satisfied with trade promotions? Sales promotions that are used by manufacturers to entice retailers to carry, feature, or push the manufacturer's products are called *trade promotions.* A survey of 132 manufacturers conducted by Nielsen found that 36% of the manufacturers were satisfied with their spending for trade promotions (*Survey of Trade Promotion Practices,* 2004). Is this sufficient evidence to reject a previous claim by the American Marketing Association that no more than half of all manufacturers are dissatisfied with their trade promotion spending?

a. Conduct the appropriate hypothesis test at $\alpha = .02$. Begin your analysis by determining whether the sample size is large enough to apply the testing methodology presented in this chapter.

b. Report the observed significance level of the test and interpret its meaning in the context of the problem.

c. Calculate β, the probability of a Type II error, if in fact 55% of all manufacturers are dissatisfied with their trade promotion spending.

7.132 Arresting shoplifters. Shoplifting in the United States costs retailers about $35 million a day. Despite the seriousness of the problem, the National Association of shoplifting Prevention (NASP) claims that only 50% of all shoplifters are turned over to police (www.shopliftingprevention.org). A random sample of 40 U.S. retailers were questioned concerning the disposition of the most recent shoplifter they apprehended. A total of 24 were turned over to police. Do these data provide sufficient evidence to contradict the NASP?

a. Conduct a hypothesis test to answer the question of interest. Use $\alpha = .05$.

b. Is the sample size large enough to use the inferential procedure of part **a**?

c. Find the observed significance level of the hypothesis test in part **a**. Interpret the value.

d. For what values of α would the observed significance level be sufficient to reject the null hypothesis of the test you conducted in part **b**?

*7.133 Arresting shoplifters (cont'd). Refer to Exercise 7.132.

a. Describe a Type II error in terms of this application.

b. Calculate the probability β of a Type II error for this test assuming that the true fraction of shoplifters turned over to the police is $p = .55$.

c. Suppose the number of retailers sampled is increased from 40 to 100. How does this affect the probability of a Type II error for $p = .55$?

7.134 Frequency marketing programs by restaurants. To instill customer loyalty, airlines, hotels, rental car companies, and credit card companies (among others) have initiated *frequency marketing programs* that reward their regular

customers. More than 80 million people are members of the frequent flier programs of the airline industry (www.frequentflier.com). A large fast-food restaurant chain wished to explore the profitability of such a program. They randomly selected 12 of their 1,200 restaurants nationwide and instituted a frequency program that rewarded customers with a $5.00 gift certificate after every 10 meals purchased at full price. They ran the trial program for 3 months. The restaurants not in the sample had an average increase in profits of $1,050 over the previous 3 months, whereas the restaurants in the sample had the following changes in profit.

$2,232.90	$ 545.47	$3,440.70	$1,809.10
$6,552.70	$4,798.70	$2,965.00	$2,610.70
$3,381.30	$1,591.40	$2,376.20	$-2,191.00

Note that the last number is negative, representing a decrease in profits.

a. Specify the appropriate null and alternative hypotheses for determining whether the mean profit change for restaurants with frequency programs was significantly greater (in a statistical sense) than $1,050.

b. Conduct the test of part **b** using $\alpha = .05$. Does it appear that the frequency program would be profitable for the company if adopted nationwide?

7.135 EPA limits on vinyl chloride. The EPA sets an airborne limit of 5 parts per million (ppm) on vinyl chloride, a colorless gas used to make plastics, adhesives, and other chemicals. It is both a carcinogen and a mutagen (New Jersey Department of Health, *Hazardous Substance Fact Sheet,* 2010). A major plastics manufacturer, attempting to control the amount of vinyl chloride its workers are exposed to, has given instructions to halt production if the mean amount of vinyl chloride in the air exceeds 3.0 ppm. A random sample of 50 air specimens produced the following statistics: $\bar{x} = 3.1$ ppm, $s = .5$ ppm.

a. Do these statistics provide sufficient evidence to halt the production process? Use $\alpha = .01$.

b. If you were the plant manager, would you want to use a large or a small value for α for the test in part **a**? Explain.

c. Find the p-value for the test and interpret its value.

*7.136 EPA limits vinyl chloride (cont'd). Refer to Exercise 7.135.

a. In the context of the problem, define a Type II error.

b. Calculate β for the test described in part **a** of Exercise 7.135, assuming that the true mean is $\mu = 3.1$ ppm.

c. What is the power of the test to detect a departure from the manufacturer's 3.0 ppm limit when the mean is 3.1 ppm?

d. Repeat parts **b** and **c** assuming that the true mean is 3.2 ppm. What happens to the power of the test as the plant's mean vinyl chloride level departs further from the limit?

*7.137 EPA limits on vinyl chloride (cont'd). Refer to Exercises 7.135 and 7.136.

a. Suppose an α value of .05 is used to conduct the test. Does this change favor halting production? Explain.

b. Determine the value of β and the power for the test when $\alpha = .05$ and $\mu = 3.1$.

c. What happens to the power of the test when α is increased?

7.138 Evaluating a measuring instrument. One way of evaluating a measuring instrument is to repeatedly measure the same item and compare the average of these measurements to the item's known measured value. The difference is used to assess the instrument's accuracy (American Society for Quality). To evaluate a particular Metlar scale, an item whose weight is known to be 16.01 ounces is weighed five times by the same operator. The measurements (in ounces) follow:

15.99	16.00	15.97	16.01	15.96

a. In a statistical sense, does the average measurement differ from 16.01? Conduct the appropriate hypothesis test at $\alpha = .05$. What does your analysis suggest about the accuracy of the instrument?

b. List any assumptions you make in conducting the hypothesis test, part **a.**

c. Evaluate the instrument's precision by testing whether the standard deviation of the weight measurements is greater than .01. Use $\alpha = .05$.

7.139 Graduation rates of student-athletes. Are student-athletes at Division I universities poorer students than non-athletes? The National Collegiate Athletic Association (NCAA) measures the academic outcomes of student-athletes with the Graduation Success Rate (GSR). The GSR is measured as the percentage of eligible athletes who graduate within 6 years of entering college. It is well known that the GSR for all students at Division I colleges is 60%.

a. Suppose the NCAA reports that in a sample of 500 student-athletes, 315 graduated within 6 years. Is this sufficient information to conclude that the GSR for all student athletes at Division I institutions differs from 60%? Test using $\alpha = .01$.

b. The GSR statistics are also broken down by gender and sport. It is known that the GSR for all male college students is 58%. In a sample of 200 male basketball players at Division I institutions, 84 graduated within 6 years. Is this sufficient information to conclude that the GSR for all male basketball players at Division I institutions differs from 58%? Test using $\alpha = .01$.

7.140 Feminized faces in TV commercials. Television commercials most often employ females or "feminized" males to pitch a company's product. Research published in *Nature* (Aug. 27, 1998) revealed that people are, in fact, more attracted to "feminized" faces, regardless of gender. In one experiment, 50 human subjects viewed both a Japanese female face and a Caucasian male face on a computer. Using special computer graphics, each subject could morph the faces (by making them more feminine or more masculine) until they attained the "most attractive" face. The level of feminization x (measured as a percentage) was measured.

a. For the Japanese female face, $\bar{x} = 10.2\%$ and $s = 31.3\%$. The researchers used this sample information to test the null hypothesis of a mean level of feminization equal to 0%. Verify that the test statistic is equal to 2.3.

b. Refer to part **a.** The researchers reported the *p*-value of the test as $p = .021$. Verify and interpret this result.

c. For the Caucasian male face, $\bar{x} = 15.0\%$ and $s = 25.1\%$. The researchers reported the test statistic (for the test of the null hypothesis stated in part **a**) as 4.23 with an associated *p*-value of approximately 0. Verify and interpret these results.

7.141 Identifying type of urban land cover. For planning purposes, urban land cover must be identified as either grassland, commercial, or residential. This is typically done using remote sensing data from satellite pictures. In *Geographical Analysis* (Oct. 2006), researchers from Arizona State, Florida State, and Louisiana State universities collaborated on a new method for analyzing remote sensing data. A satellite photograph of an urban area was divided into 4×4 meter areas (called pixels). Of interest is a numerical measure of the distribution of gaps or hole sizes in the pixel, called *lacunarity*. The mean and standard deviation of the lacunarity measurements for a sample of 100 pixels randomly selected from a specific urban area are 225 and 20, respectively. It is known that the mean lacunarity measurement for all grassland pixels is 220. Do the data suggest that the area sampled is grassland? Test at $\alpha = .01$.

Applying the Concepts—Advanced

7.142 Ages of cable TV shoppers. In a paper presented at the 2000 Conference of the International Association for Time Use Research, professor Margaret Sanik of Ohio State University reported the results of her study on American cable TV viewers who purchase items from one of the home shopping channels. She found that the average age of these cable TV shoppers was 51 years. Suppose you want to test the null hypothesis, $H_0: \mu = 51$, using a sample of $n = 50$ cable TV shoppers.

a. Find the *p*-value of a two-tailed test if $\bar{x} = 52.3$ and $s = 7.1$.

b. Find the *p*-value of an upper-tailed test if $\bar{x} = 52.3$ and $s = 7.1$.

c. Find the *p*-value of a two-tailed test if $\bar{x} = 52.3$ and $s = 10.4$.

d. For each of the tests, parts **a–c,** give a value of α that will lead to a rejection of the null hypothesis.

e. If $\bar{x} = 52.3$, give a value of s that will yield a two-tailed *p*-value of .01 or less.

7.143 Factors that inhibit learning in marketing. What factors inhibit the learning process in the classroom? To answer this question, researchers at Murray State University surveyed 40 students from a senior-level marketing class (*Marketing Education Review*). Each student was given a list of factors and asked to rate the extent to which each factor inhibited the learning process in courses offered in their department. A 7-point rating scale was used, where 1 = "not at all" and 7 = "to a great extent." The factor with the highest rating was instructor related: "Professors who place too much emphasis on a single right answer rather than overall thinking and creative ideas." Summary statistics for the student ratings of this factor are $\bar{x} = 4.70, s = 1.62$.

a. Conduct a test to determine if the true mean rating for this instructor-related factor exceeds 4. Use $\alpha = .05$. Interpret the test results.

b. Examine the results of the study from a practical view, then discuss why "statistically significant" does not always imply "practically significant."

c. Because the variable of interest, rating, is measured on a 7-point scale, it is unlikely that the population of ratings will be normally distributed. Consequently, some analysts may perceive the test, part **a**, to be invalid and search for alternative methods of analysis. Defend or refute this argument.

7.144 Testing the placebo effect. The *placebo effect* describes the phenomenon of improvement in the condition of a patient taking a placebo—a pill that looks and tastes real but contains no medically active chemicals. Physicians at a clinic in La Jolla, California, gave what they thought were drugs to 7,000 asthma, ulcer, and herpes patients. Although the doctors later learned that the drugs were really placebos, 70% of the patients reported an improved condition. Use this information to test (at $\alpha = .05$) the placebo effect at the clinic. Assume that if the placebo is ineffective, the probability of a patient's condition improving is .5.

Critical Thinking Challenge

7.145 The hot tamale caper. "Hot tamales" are chewy, cinnamon-flavored candies. A bulk vending machine is known to dispense, on average, 15 hot tamales per bag with a standard deviation of 3 per bag. *Chance* (Fall 2000) published an article on a classroom project in which students were required to purchase bags of hot tamales from the machine and count the number of candies per bag. One student group claimed they purchased five bags that had the following candy counts: 25, 23, 21, 21, and 20. These data are saved in the file. There was some question as to whether the students had fabricated the data. Use a hypothesis test to gain insight into whether or not the data collected by the students were fabricated. Use a level of significance that gives the benefit of the doubt to the students.

Activity 7.1 *Challenging a Company's Claim:* Tests of Hypotheses

Use the Internet or a newspaper or magazine to find an example of a claim made by a company about the reliability or efficiency of one of its products. In this activity, you represent a consumer group that believes the claim may be false.

1. In your example, what kinds of evidence might exist that would cause one to suspect that the claim might be false and therefore worthy of a statistical study? Be specific. If the claim were false, how would consumers be hurt?

2. Describe what data are relevant and how those data may be collected.

3. Explain the steps necessary to reject the company's claim at level α. State the null and alternative hypotheses. If you reject the claim, does it mean that the claim is false?

4. If you reject the claim when the claim is actually true, what type of error has occurred? What is the probability of this error occurring?

5. If you were to file a lawsuit against the company based on your rejection of its claim, how might the company use your results to defend itself?

Activity 7.2 *Keep the Change:* Tests of Hypotheses

In this activity, we will test claims that the mean amount transferred for any single purchase is $0.50 and that the mean amount that Bank of America matches for a customer during the first 90 days of enrollment is at least $25. We will be working with data sets from Activity 1.1, page 29 and Activity 2.2, page 120.

1. Based on the assumption that all transfer amounts between $0.00 and $0.99 seem to be equally likely to occur, one may conclude that the mean of the amounts transferred is about $0.50. Explain how someone who doesn't believe this conclusion would use a test of hypothesis to argue that the conclusion is false.

2. Suppose that your original data set *Amounts Transferred* from Activity 1.1 represents a random sample of amounts transferred for all Bank of America customers' purchases. Does your sample meet the requirements for performing either a large-sample or a small-sample test of hypothesis about the population mean? Explain. If your data meet the criteria for one of the tests, perform that test at $\alpha = .05$.

3. Use the pooled data set of *Amounts Transferred* from Activity 4.2 to represent a random sample of amounts transferred for all Bank of America customers' purchases. Explain how the conditions for the large-sample test of hypothesis about a population mean are met. Then perform the test at $\alpha = .05$. Do your results suggest that the mean may be something other than $0.50? Explain.

4. A friend suggests to you that the mean amount the bank matches for a customer during the first 90 days is at least $25. Explain how you could use a test of hypothesis to argue that your friend is wrong.

5. Suppose that your data set *Bank Matching* from Activity 1.1 represents a random sample of all Bank of America customers' bank matching. Perform an appropriate test of hypothesis at $\alpha = .05$ against your friend's claim. Assume that the underlying distribution is normal, if necessary. Does the test provide evidence that your friend's claim is false?

Keep the results from this activity for use in other activities.

References

Snedecor, G. W., & Cochran, W. G. *Statistical Methods,* 7th ed. Ames: Iowa State University Press, 1980.

Wackerly, D., Mendenhall, W., & Scheaffer, R. *Mathematical Statistics with Applications,* 7th ed. Belmont, CA: Thomson, Brooks/Cole, 2008.

SPSS: Tests of Hypotheses

Note: SPSS cannot currently conduct a test for a population variance.

Testing μ

Step 1 Access the SPSS spreadsheet file that contains the sample data.

Step 2 Click on the "Analyze" button on the SPSS menu bar and then click on "Compare Means" and "One-Sample T Test," as shown in Figure 7.S.1.

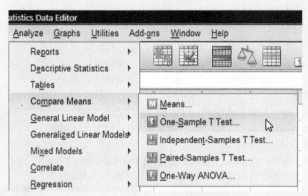

Figure 7.S.1 SPSS menu options for a test on a mean

Step 3 On the resulting dialog box (shown in Figure 7.S.2), specify the quantitative variable of interest in the "Test Variable(s)" box and the value of μ_0 for the null hypothesis in the "Test Value" box.

Figure 7.S.2 SPSS 1-sample *t*-test for mean dialog box

Step 4 Click "OK." SPSS will automatically conduct a two-tailed test of hypothesis.

Important Note: The SPSS one-sample *t*-procedure uses the *t*-statistic to conduct the test of hypothesis. When the sample size *n* is small, this is the appropriate method. When the sample size *n* is large, the *t*-value will be approximately equal to the large-sample *z*-value and the resulting test will still be valid.

Testing *p*

Step 1 Access the SPSS spreadsheet file that contains the sample data.

Step 2 Click on the "Analyze" button on the SPSS menu bar, then click on "Nonparametric Tests," "Legacy Dialogs," and "Binomial" (see Figure 7.S.3).

Figure 7.S.3 SPSS menu options for test on a proportion

Step 3 On the resulting dialog box (shown in Figure 7.S.4), specify the binomial variable of interest in the "Test Variable List" box and the value of p_0 for the null hypothesis in the "Test Proportion" box.

Figure 7.S.4 SPSS binomial test for proportion dialog box

Step 4 Click "OK" to generate the two-tailed test of hypothesis.

Important: SPSS requires the binomial variable to be entered as a quantitative variable. Typically, this is accomplished by entering two numerical values (e.g., 0 and 1) for the two outcomes of the variable. If the data have been entered in this fashion, select the "Get from data" option in the "Define Dichotomy" area of the dialog box.

You can also create the two outcome values for a quantitative variable by selecting the "Cut point" option in the "Define Dichotomy" area and specifying a numerical value. All values of the variables less than or equal to the cut point value are assigned to one group (success), and all other values are assigned to the other group (failure).

Minitab: Tests of Hypotheses

Testing μ

Step 1 Access the Minitab data worksheet that contains the sample data.

Step 2 Click on the "Stat" button on the Minitab menu bar and then click on "Basic Statistics" and "1-Sample t," as shown in Figure 7.M.1.

Figure 7.M.1 Minitab menu options for a test on a mean

Step 3 On the resulting dialog box (shown in Figure 7.M.2), click on "Samples in columns" and then specify the quantitative variable of interest in the open box.

Figure 7.M.2 Minitab 1-sample *t*-test for mean dialog box

Step 4 Check "Perform hypothesis test" and then specify the value of μ_0 for the null hypothesis in the "Hypothesized mean" box.

Step 5 Click on the "Options" button at the bottom of the dialog box and specify the form of the alternative hypothesis, as shown in Figure 7.M.3.

Figure 7.M.3 Minitab 1-sample *t*-test options

Step 6 Click "OK" to return to the "1-Sample t" dialog box and then click "OK" again to produce the hypothesis test.

Note: If you want to produce a test for the mean from summary information (e.g., the sample mean, sample standard deviation, and sample size), click on "Summarized data" in the "1-Sample t" dialog box, enter the values of the summary statistics and μ_0, and then click "OK."

Important: The Minitab one-sample *t*-procedure uses the *t*-statistic to generate the hypothesis test. When the sample size *n*

is small, this is the appropriate method. When the sample size *n* is large, the *t*-value will be approximately equal to the large-sample *z*-value, and the resulting test will still be valid. If you have a large sample and you know the value of the population standard deviation σ (which is rarely the case), select "1-Sample Z" from the "Basic Statistics" menu options (see Figure 7.M.1) and make the appropriate selections.

Testing *p*

Step 1 Access the Minitab data worksheet that contains the sample data.

Step 2 Click on the "Stat" button on the Minitab menu bar and then click on "Basic Statistics" and "1 Proportion" (see Figure 7.M.1).

Step 3 On the resulting dialog box (shown in Figure 7.M.4), click on "Samples in columns," and then specify the qualitative variable of interest in the open box.

Figure 7.M.4 Minitab 1 proportion test dialog box

Step 4 Check "Perform hypothesis test" and then specify the null hypothesis value p_0 in the "Hypothesized proportion" box.

Step 5 Click "Options," then specify the form of the alternative hypothesis in the resulting dialog box, as shown in Figure 7.M.5. Also, check the "Use test and interval based on normal distribution" box at the bottom.

Figure 7.M.5 Minitab 1 proportion test options

Step 6 Click "OK" to return to the "1 Proportion" dialog box and then click "OK" again to produce the test results.

Note: If you want to produce a confidence interval for a proportion from summary information (e.g., the number of successes and the sample size), click on "Summarized data" in the "1 Proportion" dialog box (see Figure 7.M.4). Enter the value for the number of trials (i.e., the sample size) and the number of events (i.e., the number of successes), and then click "OK."

Testing σ^2

Step 1 Access the Minitab data worksheet that contains the sample data set.

Step 2 Click on the "Stat" button on the Minitab menu bar and and then click on "Basic Statistics" and "1 Variance" (see Figure 7.M.1).

Step 3 Once the resulting dialog box appears (see Figure 7.M.6), click on "Samples in columns" and then specify the quantitative variable of interest in the open box.

Figure 7.M.6 Minitab 1 variance test dialog box

Step 4 Check "Perform hypothesis test" and specify the null hypothesis value of the standard deviation σ_0 in the open box.

Step 5 Click on the "Options" button at the bottom of the dialog box and specify the form of the alternative hypothesis (similar to Figure 7.M.3).

Step 6 Click "OK" twice to produce the hypothesis test.

Note: If you want to produce a test for the variance from summary information (e.g., the sample standard deviation and sample size), click on "Summarized data" in the "1 Variance" dialog box (Figure 7.M.6) and enter the values of the summary statistics.

Excel/XLSTAT: Tests of Hypotheses

Currently, tests of hypothesis for a population variance are not available in XLSTAT.

Testing μ

Step 1 Click the "XLSTAT" button on the Excel main menu bar, select "Parametric tests," and then click "One-sample t-test and z-test," as shown in Figure 7.E.1.

Step 2 When the resulting dialog box appears, highlight the column that contains the values of the quantitative variable you want to analyze so that the column appears in the appropriate entry (see, for example, Figure 7.E.2).

Figure 7.E.2 XLSTAT test mean dialog box

Step 3 Click the "Options" tab, then specify the form of the alternative hypothesis, value of the hypothesized (theoretical) mean, and the value of α (significance level) in the appropriate boxes, as shown in Figure 7.E.3.

Figure 7.E.3 XLSTAT options for testing a mean

Step 4 Click "OK," then "Continue" to display the test results.

Testing p

[*Note:* To conduct a test of hypothesis for a binomial proportion using XLSTAT, you will need summary information on your qualitative data, e.g., the sample size and either the number of successes or proportion of successes in the sample.]

Step 1 Click the "XLSTAT" button on the Excel main menu bar, select "Parametric tests," and then click "Tests for one proportion," as shown in Figure 7.E.4.

Figure 7.E.1 XLSTAT menu options for testing a mean

Figure 7.E.4 XLSTAT menu options for a binomial proportion

Step 2 When the resulting dialog box appears, check "Frequency" in the "Data format" area, enter the number of successes and the sample size in the "Frequency" and "Sample size" boxes, respectively, and then specify the value of the hypothesized (test) proportion, as shown in Figure 7.E.5. (Alternatively, you can check "Proportion" in the "Data format" area and enter the sample proportion in the Test "proportion" box.)

Figure 7.E.5 XLSTAT test for proportion dialog box

Step 3 Click the "Options" tab, specify the form of the alternative hypothesis, and then enter "0" for the hypothesized difference and the value of α (significance level) in the appropriate boxes, as shown in Figure 7.E.6.

Figure 7.E.6 XLSTAT options for testing a proportion

Step 4 Click "OK" to display the test results.

TI-84 Graphing Calculator: Tests of Hypotheses

Note: The TI-84 graphing calculator cannot currently conduct a test for a population variance.

Hypothesis Test for a Population Mean (Large-Sample Case)

Step 1 *Enter the Data (Skip to Step 2 if you have summary statistics, not raw data)*

- Press **STAT** and select **1:Edit**

Note: If the list already contains data, clear the old data. Use the up **ARROW** to highlight "**L1.**"

- Press **CLEAR ENTER**
- Use the **ARROW** and **ENTER** keys to enter the data set into **L1**

Step 2 *Access the Statistical Tests Menu*

- Press **STAT**
- Arrow right to **TESTS**
- Press **ENTER** to select either **Z-Test** (if large sample and known) or **T-Test** (if unknown)

Step 3 *Choose "Data" or "Stats." ("Data" is selected when you have entered the raw data into a List. "Stats" is selected when you are given only the mean, standard deviation, and sample size.)*

- Press **ENTER**

If you selected "Data," enter the values for the hypothesis test where μ_0 = the value for μ in the null hypothesis, σ = assumed value of the population standard deviation.

- Set **List** to **L1**
- Set **Freq** to **1**
- Use the **ARROW** to highlight the appropriate alternative hypothesis
- Press **ENTER**
- Arrow down to "**Calculate**"
- Press **ENTER**

If you selected "Stats," enter the values for the hypothesis test where μ_0 = the value for μ in the null hypothesis, σ = assumed value of the population standard deviation.

- Enter the sample mean, sample standard deviation, and sample size
- Use the **ARROW** to highlight the appropriate alternative hypothesis
- Press **ENTER**
- Arrow down to "**Calculate**"
- Press **ENTER**

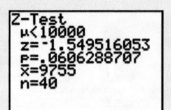

```
Z-Test
 μ<10000
 z=-1.549516053
 P=.0606288707
 x̄=9755
 n=40
```

The chosen test will be displayed as well as the z (or t) test statistic, the p-value, the sample mean, and the sample size.

Testing p

Step 1 *Enter the Data (Skip to Step 2 if you have summary statistics, not raw data)*

- Press **STAT** and select **1:Edit**

Note: If the list already contains data, clear the old data. Use the up **ARROW** to highlight "**L1.**"

- Press **CLEAR ENTER**
- Use the **ARROW** and **ENTER** keys to enter the data set into **L1**

Step 2 *Access the Statistical Tests Menu*

- Press **STAT**
- Arrow right to **TESTS**
- Press **ENTER** after selecting **1-Prop Z Test**

Step 3 *Enter the hypothesized proportion p_0, the number of success x, and the sample size n*

- Use the **ARROW** to highlight the appropriate alternative hypothesis
- Press **ENTER**
- Arrow down to "**Calculate**"
- Press **ENTER**

The chosen test will be displayed as well as the z-test statistic and the p-value.

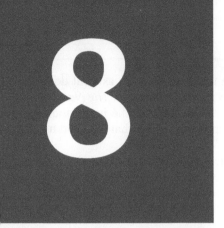

8

CONTENTS

Where We've Been

- Explored two methods for making statistical inferences: *confidence intervals* and *tests of hypotheses*
- Studied confidence intervals and tests for a single population mean μ, a single population proportion p, and a single population variance σ^2
- Learned how to select the sample size necessary to estimate a population parameter with a specified margin of error

Where We're Going

- Learn how to identify the target parameter for comparing two populations (8.1)
- Learn how to compare two population means using confidence intervals and tests of hypotheses (8.2–8.3)
- Apply these inferential methods to problems where we want to compare two population proportions or two population variances (8.4, 8.6)
- Determine the sizes of the samples necessary to estimate the difference between two population parameters with a specified margin of error (8.5)

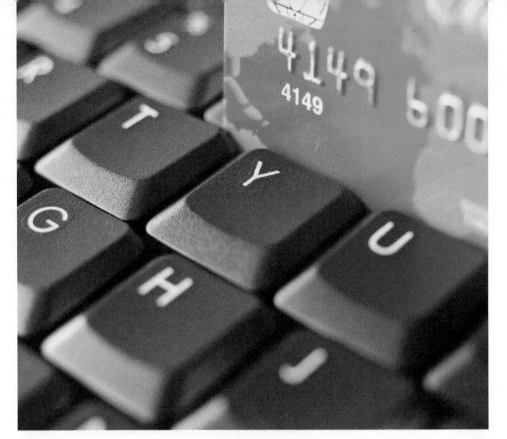

☐ Inferences Based on Two Samples *Confidence Intervals*

and Tests of Hypotheses

STATISTICS in ACTION *ZixIt Corp. v. Visa USA Inc.* — A Libel Case

The National Law Journal *(Aug. 26–Sep. 2, 2002) reported on an interesting court case involving ZixIt Corp., a start-up Internet credit card clearing center. ZixIt claimed that its new online credit card processing system would allow Internet shoppers to make purchases without revealing their credit card numbers. This claim violated the established protocols of most major credit card companies, including Visa. Without the company's knowledge, a Visa vice president for technology research and development began writing e-mails and Web site postings on a Yahoo! message board for ZixIt investors, challenging ZixIt's claim and urging investors to sell their ZixIt stock. The Visa executive posted more than 400 e-mails and notes before he was caught. Once it was discovered that a Visa executive was responsible for the postings, ZixIt filed a lawsuit against Visa Corp., alleging that Visa—using the executive as its agent—had engaged in a "malicious two-part scheme to disparage and interfere with ZixIt" and its efforts to market the new online credit card processing system. In the libel case ZixIt asked for $699 million in damages.*

Dallas lawyers Jeff Tillotson and Mike Lynn, of the law firm Lynn Tillotson & Pinker, were hired to defend Visa in the lawsuit. The lawyers, in turn, hired Dr. James McClave (coauthor of this text) as their expert statistician. McClave testified in court on an "event study" he did matching the Visa executive's e-mail postings with movement of ZixIt's stock price the next business day. McClave's testimony,

419

STATISTICS in ACTION CONTINUED

showing that there was an equal number of days when the stock went up as went down after a posting, helped the lawyers representing Visa to prevail in the case. *The National Law Journal* reported that, after two-and-a-half days of deliberation, "the jurors found [the Visa executive] was not acting in the scope of his employment and that Visa had not defamed ZixIt or interfered with its business."

In this chapter, we demonstrate several of the statistical analyses McClave used to infer that the Visa executive's postings had no effect on ZixIt's stock price. The daily ZixIt stock prices as well as the timing of the Visa executive's postings are saved in the **ZIXITVISA** file.* We apply the statistical methodology presented in this chapter to this data set in two Statistics in Action Revisited examples.

STATISTICS in ACTION REVISITED

□ Comparing Mean Price Changes **(p. 430)**

□ Comparing Proportions **(p. 452)**

Data Set: ZIXVSA □

8.1 Identifying the Target Parameter

Many experiments involve a comparison of two populations. For instance, a realtor may want to estimate the difference in mean sales price between city and suburban homes. A consumer group might test whether two major brands of food freezers differ in the average amount of electricity they use. A television market researcher wants to estimate the difference in the proportions of younger and older viewers who regularly watch a popular TV program. A golf ball supplier may be interested in comparing the variability in the distance that two competing brands of golf balls travel when struck with the same club. In this chapter, we consider techniques for using two samples to compare the populations from which they were selected.

The same procedures that are used to estimate and test hypotheses about a single population can be modified to make inferences about two populations. As in Chapters 6 and 7, the methodology used will depend on the sizes of the samples and the parameter of interest (i.e., the *target parameter*). Some key words and the type of data associated with the parameters covered in this chapter are listed in the box.

Determining the Target Parameter

Parameter	Key Words or Phrases	Type of Data
$\mu_1 - \mu_2$	Mean difference; difference in averages	Quantitative
$p_1 - p_2$	Difference between proportions, percentages, fractions, or rates; compare proportions	Qualitative
$(\sigma_1)^2/(\sigma_2)^2$	Ratio of variances; difference in variability or spread; compare variation	Quantitative

---

You can see that the key words *difference* and *compare* help identify the fact that two populations are to be compared. For the examples given above, the words *mean* in *mean sales price* and *average* in *average amount of electricity* imply that the target parameter is the difference in population means, $\mu_1 - \mu_2$. The word *proportions* in *proportions of younger and older viewers* indicates that the target parameter is the difference in proportions, $p_1 - p_2$. Finally, the key word *variability* in *variability in the distance* identifies the ratio of population variances, $(\sigma_1)^2/(\sigma_2)^2$, as the target parameter.

As with inferences about a single population, the type of data (quantitative or qualitative) collected on the two samples is also indicative of the target parameter. With

*Data provided (with permission) from Info Tech, Inc., Gainesville, Florida.

quantitative data, you are likely to be interested in comparing the means or variances of the data. With qualitative data with two outcomes (success or failure), a comparison of the proportions of successes is likely to be of interest.

We consider methods for comparing two population means in Sections 8.2 and 8.3. A comparison of population proportions is presented in Section 8.4 and population variances in Section 8.6. We show how to determine the sample sizes necessary for reliable estimates of the target parameters in Section 8.5.

8.2 Comparing Two Population Means: Independent Sampling

In this section we develop both large-sample and small-sample methodologies for comparing two population means. In the large-sample case, we use the z-statistic (where $z \approx t$ when the population variances are unknown), while in the small-sample case we use the t-statistic.

Large Samples

Example 8.1

Large-Sample Confidence Interval for $(\mu_1 - \mu_2)$—Comparing Mean Car Prices

Problem In recent years, the United States and Japan have engaged in intense negotiations regarding restrictions on trade between the two countries. One of the claims made repeatedly by U.S. officials is that many Japanese manufacturers price their goods higher in Japan than in the United States, in effect subsidizing low prices in the United States by extremely high prices in Japan. According to the U.S. argument, Japan accomplishes this by keeping competitive U.S. goods from reaching the Japanese marketplace.

An economist decided to test the hypothesis that higher retail prices are being charged for Japanese automobiles in Japan than in the United States. She obtained independent random samples of 50 retail sales in the United States and 50 retail sales in Japan over the same time period and for the same model of automobile and converted the Japanese sales prices from yen to dollars using current conversion rates. The data, saved in the **AUTOS** file, are listed in Table 8.1. Form a 95% confidence interval for the difference between the population mean retail prices of this automobile model for the two countries. Interpret the result.

Solution Recall that the general form of a large-sample confidence interval for a single mean μ is $\bar{x} \pm z_{\alpha/2}\sigma_{\bar{x}}$—that is, we add and subtract $z_{\alpha/2}$ standard deviations of the sample estimate, $\bar{x}$, to the value of the estimate. We employ a similar procedure to form the confidence interval for the difference between two population means.

Let μ_1 represent the mean of the population of retail sales prices for this car model sold in the United States. Let μ_2 be similarly defined for retail sales in Japan. We wish to form a confidence interval for $(\mu_1 - \mu_2)$. An intuitively appealing estimator for

Table 8.1	Automobile Retail Prices (Thousands of Dollars)								
USA Sales:	18.2	16.2	17.2	18.7	18.4	16.6	14.9	16.8	12.1	10.8
	18.5	15.5	16.2	16.3	18.2	19.5	13.2	16.8	12.9	17.2
	18.2	16.3	16.8	16.4	18.6	15.6	17.1	18.1	18.9	19.0
	17.3	18.8	14.9	16.7	20.3	17.1	14.6	17.2	13.0	18.4
	16.9	13.3	16.3	15.9	16.6	17.6	16.0	17.1	14.6	18.0
Japan Sales:	18.5	14.0	18.2	21.1	13.9	18.7	14.9	16.4	16.3	18.0
	16.8	19.8	17.3	16.6	14.9	16.3	16.5	15.4	17.6	20.1
	16.4	18.0	17.5	18.4	19.8	14.8	18.2	16.7	20.2	16.2
	20.4	17.9	15.5	15.4	17.7	17.1	17.9	17.4	18.2	16.2
	18.5	16.9	17.6	14.4	21.6	18.6	16.2	14.3	12.5	20.0

Data Set: AUTOS

Group Statistics

	COUNTRY	N	Mean	Std. Deviation	Std. Error Mean
PRICE	USA	50	16596.00	1981.440	280.218
	JAPAN	50	17236.00	1974.093	279.179

Independent Samples Test

		Levene's Test for Equality of Variances		t-test for Equality of Means						95% Confidence Interval of the Difference	
		F	Sig.	t	df	Sig. (2-tailed)	Mean Difference	Std. Error Difference		Lower	Upper
PRICE	Equal variances assumed	.118	.732	-1.618	98	.109	-640.000	395.554		-1424.964	144.964
	Equal variances not assumed			-1.618	97.999	.109	-640.000	395.554		-1424.964	144.964

Figure 8.1

SPSS summary statistics and confidence interval for automobile price study

$(\mu_1 - \mu_2)$ is the difference between the sample means, $(\bar{x}_1 - \bar{x}_2)$. Thus, we will form the confidence interval of interest by

$$(\bar{x}_1 - \bar{x}_2) \pm z_{\alpha/2}\sigma_{(\bar{x}_1 - \bar{x}_2)}$$

Assuming the two samples are independent, the standard deviation of the difference between the sample means is

$$\sigma_{(\bar{x}_1 - \bar{x}_2)} = \sqrt{\frac{\sigma_1^2}{n_1} + \frac{\sigma_2^2}{n_2}} \approx \sqrt{\frac{s_1^2}{n_1} + \frac{s_2^2}{n_2}}$$

Note that we have substituted s_1^2 and s_2^2 for the usually unknown values of σ_1^2 and σ_2^2, respectively. With large samples, this will be a good approximation.

Summary statistics for the car sales data are displayed in the SPSS printout, Figure 8.1. Note that $\bar{x}_1 = \$16,596$, $\bar{x}_2 = \$17,236$, $s_1 = \$1,981$, and $s_2 = \$1,974$. Using these values and noting that $\alpha = .05$ and $z_{.025} = 1.96$, we find that the 95% confidence interval is, approximately,

$$(16,596 - 17,236) \pm 1.96\sqrt{\frac{(1,981)^2}{50} + \frac{(1,974)^2}{50}} = -640 \pm (1.96)(396)$$

$$= -640 \pm 776$$

or $(-1416, 136)$. This interval is also given at the bottom of Figure 8.1. (Differences in the results are due to rounding and normal approximation.)

Using this estimation procedure over and over again for different samples, we know that approximately 95% of the confidence intervals formed in this manner will enclose the difference in population means $(\mu_1 - \mu_2)$. Therefore, we are highly confident that the difference in mean retail prices in the United States and Japan is between $-\$1,416$ and $\$136$. Because 0 falls in this interval, it is possible for the difference to be 0 (i.e., for $\mu_1 = \mu_2$); thus, the economist cannot conclude that a significant difference exists between the mean retail prices in the two countries.

Look Back If the confidence interval for $(\mu_1 - \mu_2)$ contains all positive numbers [e.g., $(527, 991)$], then we would conclude that the difference between the means is positive and that $\mu_1 > \mu_2$. Alternatively, if the interval contains all negative numbers [e.g., $(-722, -145)$], then we would conclude that the difference between the means is negative and that $\mu_1 < \mu_2$.

■ **Now Work Exercise 8.3a**

The justification for the procedure used in Example 8.1 to estimate $(\mu_1 - \mu_2)$ relies on the properties of the sampling distribution of $(\bar{x}_1 - \bar{x}_2)$. The performance of the estimator in repeated sampling is pictured in Figure 8.2, and its properties are summarized in the box on the next page.

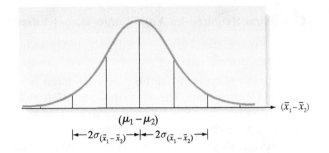

Figure 8.2

Sampling distribution of $(\bar{x}_1 - \bar{x}_2)$

Properties of the Sampling Distribution of $(\bar{x}_1 - \bar{x}_2)$

1. The mean of the sampling distribution $(\bar{x}_1 - \bar{x}_2)$ is $(\mu_1 - \mu_2)$.

2. If the two samples are independent, the standard deviation of the sampling distribution is

$$\sigma_{(\bar{x}_1 - \bar{x}_2)} = \sqrt{\frac{\sigma_1^2}{n_1} + \frac{\sigma_2^2}{n_2}}$$

where σ_1^2 and σ_2^2 are the variances of the two populations being sampled, and n_1 and n_2 are the respective sample sizes. We also refer to $\sigma_{(\bar{x}_1 - \bar{x}_2)}$ as the **standard error** of the statistic $(\bar{x}_1 - \bar{x}_2)$.

3. The sampling distribution of $(\bar{x}_1 - \bar{x}_2)$ is approximately normal for *large samples* by the Central Limit Theorem.

In Example 8.1, we noted the similarity in the procedures for forming a large-sample confidence interval for one population mean and a large-sample confidence interval for the difference between two population means. When we are testing hypotheses, the procedures are again very similar. The general large-sample procedures for forming confidence intervals and testing hypotheses about $(\mu_1 - \mu_2)$ are summarized in the following boxes.

Large, Independent Samples Confidence Interval for $(\mu_1 - \mu_2)$: Normal (z) Statistic

$$\sigma_1^2 \text{ and } \sigma_2^2 \text{ known: } (\bar{x}_1 - \bar{x}_2) \pm z_{\alpha/2}\sigma_{(\bar{x}_1 - \bar{x}_2)} = (\bar{x}_1 - \bar{x}_2) \pm z_{\alpha/2}\sqrt{\frac{\sigma_1^2}{n_1} + \frac{\sigma_2^2}{n_2}}$$

$$\sigma_1^2 \text{ and } \sigma_2^2 \text{ unknown: } (\bar{x}_1 - \bar{x}_2) \pm z_{\alpha/2}\sigma_{(\bar{x}_1 - \bar{x}_2)} \approx (\bar{x}_1 - \bar{x}_2) \pm z_{\alpha/2}\sqrt{\frac{s_1^2}{n_1} + \frac{s_2^2}{n_2}}$$

Large, Independent Samples Test of Hypothesis for $(\mu_1 - \mu_2)$: Normal (z) Statistic

One-Tailed Test	Two-Tailed Test
$H_0: (\mu_1 - \mu_2) = D_0$	$H_0: (\mu_1 - \mu_2) = D_0$
$H_a: (\mu_1 - \mu_2) < D_0$	$H_a: (\mu_1 - \mu_2) \neq D_0$
[or $H_a: (\mu_1 - \mu_2) > D_0$]	

where D_0 = Hypothesized difference between the means (this difference is often hypothesized to be equal to 0)

Test statistic:

$$z = \frac{(\bar{x}_1 - \bar{x}_2) - D_0}{\sigma_{(\bar{x}_1 - \bar{x}_2)}} \quad \text{where} \quad \sigma_{(\bar{x}_1 - \bar{x}_2)} = \sqrt{\frac{\sigma_1^2}{n_1} + \frac{\sigma_2^2}{n_2}} \text{ if } \sigma_1^2 \text{ and } \sigma_2^2 \text{ are known}$$

$$\approx \sqrt{\frac{s_1^2}{n_1} + \frac{s_2^2}{n_2}} \text{ if } \sigma_1^2 \text{ and } \sigma_2^2 \text{ are unknown}$$

Rejection region: $z < -z_{\alpha}$
[or $z > z_{\alpha}$ when
$H_a: (\mu_1 - \mu_2) > D_0$]

Rejection region: $|z| > z_{\alpha/2}$

> **Conditions Required for Valid Large-Sample Inferences about $(\mu_1 - \mu_2)$**
>
> 1. The two samples are randomly selected in an independent manner from the two target populations.
> 2. The sample sizes, n_1 and n_2, are both large (i.e., $n_1 \geq 30$ and $n_2 \geq 30$). [Due to the Central Limit Theorem, this condition guarantees that the sampling distribution of $(\bar{x}_1 - \bar{x}_2)$ will be approximately normal regardless of the shapes of the underlying probability distributions of the populations. Also, s_1^2 and s_2^2 will provide good approximations to σ_1^2 and σ_2^2 when the samples are both large.]

Example 8.2 **Large-Sample Test for $(\mu_1 - \mu_2)$—Comparing Mean Car Prices**	**Problem** Refer to the study of retail prices of an automobile sold in the United States and Japan, Example 8.1. Another way to compare the mean retail prices for the two countries is to conduct a test of hypothesis. Use the information on the SPSS printout, Figure 8.1, to conduct the test. Use $\alpha = .05$.

Solution Again, we let μ_1 and μ_2 represent the population mean retail sales prices in the United States and Japan, respectively. If the claim made by the U.S. government is true, then the mean retail price in Japan will exceed the mean in the United States [i.e., $\mu_1 < \mu_2$ or $(\mu_1 - \mu_2) < 0$]. Thus, the elements of the test are as follows:

H_0: $(\mu_1 - \mu_2) = 0$ (i.e., $\mu_1 = \mu_2$; note that $D_0 = 0$ for this hypothesis test)

H_a: $(\mu_1 - \mu_2) < 0$ (i.e., $\mu_1 < \mu_2$)

Test statistic: $z = \dfrac{(\bar{x}_1 - \bar{x}_2) - D_0}{\sigma_{(\bar{x}_1 - \bar{x}_2)}} = \dfrac{(\bar{x}_1 - \bar{x}_2) - 0}{\sigma_{(\bar{x}_1 - \bar{x}_2)}}$

Rejection region: $z < -z_{.05} = -1.645$ (see Figure 8.3)

Substituting the summary statistics given in Figure 8.1 into the test statistic, we obtain

$$z = \frac{(\bar{x}_1 - \bar{x}_2) - 0}{\sigma_{(\bar{x}_1 - \bar{x}_2)}} = \frac{(16{,}596 - 17{,}236)}{\sqrt{\dfrac{\sigma_1^2}{n_1} + \dfrac{\sigma_2^2}{n_2}}}$$

$$\approx \frac{-640}{\sqrt{\dfrac{s_1^2}{n_1} + \dfrac{s_2^2}{n_2}}} = \frac{-640}{\sqrt{\dfrac{(1{,}981)^2}{50} + \dfrac{(1{,}974)^2}{50}}} = \frac{-640}{396} = -1.62$$

[*Note:* This value of the test statistic is shown (highlighted) at the bottom of the SPSS printout, Figure 8.1 (p. 422).]

Figure 8.3

Rejection region for Example 8.2

As you can see in Figure 8.3, the calculated z-value does not fall in the rejection region. Therefore, the samples do not provide sufficient evidence, at $\alpha = .05$, for the economist to conclude that the mean retail price in Japan exceeds that in the United States.

Look Back First, note that this conclusion agrees with the inference drawn from the 95% confidence interval in Example 8.1. Generally, however, a confidence interval will provide more information on the difference in means than a test. A test can detect only whether or not a difference between the means exists, while the confidence interval provides information on the magnitude of the difference. Second, a one-tailed hypothesis test and a confidence interval (which is two-tailed) may not always agree. However, a two-tailed test of hypothesis and a confidence interval will *always* give the same inference about the target parameter, as long as the value of α is the same for both.

Example	8.3

The *p*-Value of a Test for
$(\mu_1 - \mu_2)$

Problem Find the observed significance level for the test in Example 8.2. Interpret the result.

Solution The alternative hypothesis in Example 8.2, H_a: $(\mu_1 - \mu_2) < 0$, required a lower one-tailed test using

$$z = \frac{\bar{x}_1 - \bar{x}_2}{\sigma_{(\bar{x}_1 - \bar{x}_2)}}$$

as a test statistic. Because the approximate *z*-value calculated from the sample data was -1.62, the observed significance level (*p*-value) for the lower-tailed test is the probability of observing a value of *z* more contradictory to the null hypothesis as $z = -1.62$; that is,

$$p\text{-value} = P(z < -1.62)$$

This probability is computed assuming H_0 is true and is equal to the shaded area shown in Figure 8.4.

The tabulated area corresponding to $z = 1.62$ in Table II in Appendix D is .4474. Therefore, the observed significance level of the test is

$$p\text{-value} \approx .5 - .4474 = .0526$$

Because our selected α value, .05, is less than this *p*-value, we have insufficient evidence to reject H_0: $(\mu_1 - \mu_2) = 0$ in favor of H_a: $(\mu_1 - \mu_2) < 0$.

Figure 8.4

The observed significance level for Example 8.2

Look Back The *p*-value of the test is more easily obtained from a statistical software package. A Minitab printout for the hypothesis test is displayed in Figure 8.5. The one-tailed *p*-value, highlighted on the printout, is .054, which agrees (except for rounding) with our approximated *p*-value.

Two-Sample T-Test and CI: USA, JAPAN

```
Two-sample T for USA vs JAPAN

        N    Mean   StDev  SE Mean
USA    50   16596    1981      280
JAPAN  50   17236    1974      279


Difference = mu (USA) - mu (JAPAN)
Estimate for difference:  -640.000
95% upper bound for difference:  16.838
T-Test of difference = 0 (vs <): T-Value = -1.62   P-Value = 0.054   DF = 98
Both use Pooled StDev = 1977.7703
```

Figure 8.5

Minitab analysis for comparing U.S. and Japan mean auto prices

■ **Now Work Exercise 8.3b**

Small Samples

When comparing two population means with small samples (say, $n_1 < 30$ or $n_2 < 30$), the methodology of the previous three examples is invalid. The reason? When the sample sizes are small, estimates of σ_1^2 and σ_2^2 are unreliable, and the Central Limit Theorem (which guarantees that the *z*-statistic is normal) can no longer be applied. But as in the case of a single mean (Section 7.5), we use the familiar Student's *t*-distribution.

To use the t-distribution, both sampled populations must be approximately nor-mally distributed with equal population variances, and the random samples must be

selected independently of each other. The normality and equal variances assumptions imply relative frequency distributions for the populations that would appear as shown in Figure 8.6.

Because we assume the two populations have equal variances ($\sigma_1^2 = \sigma_2^2 = \sigma^2$), it is reasonable to use the information contained in *both* samples to construct a **pooled sample estimator of σ^2** for use in confidence intervals and test statistics.* Thus, if s_1^2 and s_2^2 are the two sample variances (both estimating the variance σ^2 common to both populations), the pooled estimator of σ^2, denoted as s_p^2, is

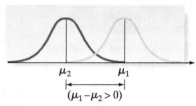

Figure 8.6

Assumptions for the two-sample *t:* (1) normal populations, (2) equal variances

$$s_p^2 = \frac{(n_1 - 1)s_1^2 + (n_2 - 1)s_2^2}{(n_1 - 1) + (n_2 - 1)} = \frac{(n_1 - 1)s_1^2 + (n_2 - 1)s_2^2}{n_1 + n_2 - 2}$$

or

From sample 1   From sample 2

$$s_p^2 = \frac{\sum(x_1 - \bar{x}_1)^2 + \sum(x_2 - \bar{x}_2)^2}{n_1 + n_2 - 2}$$

where x_1 represents a measurement from sample 1 and x_2 represents a measurement from sample 2. Recall that the term *degrees of freedom* was defined in Section 6.2 as 1 less than the sample size. Thus, in this case, we have $(n_1 - 1)$ degrees of freedom for sample 1 and $(n_2 - 1)$ degrees of freedom for sample 2. Because we are pooling the information on σ^2 obtained from both samples, the degrees of freedom associated with the pooled variance s_p^2 is equal to the sum of the degrees of freedom for the two samples, namely, the denominator of s_p^2; that is, $(n_1 - 1) + (n_2 - 1) = n_1 + n_2 - 2$.

Note that the second formula given for s_p^2 shows that the pooled variance is simply a *weighted average* of the two sample variances, s_1^2 and s_2^2. The weight given each variance is proportional to its degrees of freedom. If the two variances have the same number of degrees of freedom (i.e., if the sample sizes are equal), then the pooled variance is a simple average of the two sample variances. The result is an average or "pooled" variance that is a better estimate of σ^2 than either s_1^2 or s_2^2 alone.

Both the confidence interval and the test of hypothesis procedures for comparing two population means with small samples are summarized in the following boxes.

Small, Independent Samples Confidence Interval for ($\mu_1 - \mu_2$): Student's *t*-Statistic

$$(\bar{x}_1 - \bar{x}_2) \pm t_{\alpha/2}\sqrt{s_p^2\left(\frac{1}{n_1} + \frac{1}{n_2}\right)}$$

where $s_p^2 = \dfrac{(n_1 - 1)s_1^2 + (n_2 - 1)s_2^2}{n_1 + n_2 - 2}$

and $t_{\alpha/2}$ is based on $(n_1 + n_2 - 2)$ degrees of freedom.

*s_p^2 can be shown to be the minimum-variance unbiased estimator (MVUE) of σ^2 when $\sigma^2 = \sigma_1^2 = \sigma_2^2$.

Small, Independent Samples Test of Hypothesis for $(\mu_1 - \mu_2)$: Student's t-Statistic

One-Tailed Test	Two-Tailed Test
$H_0: (\mu_1 - \mu_2) = D_0$	$H_0: (\mu_1 - \mu_2) = D_0$
$H_a: (\mu_1 - \mu_2) < D_0$	$H_a: (\mu_1 - \mu_2) \neq D_0$
[or $H_a: (\mu_1 - \mu_2) > D_0$]	

$$\text{Test statistic: } t = \frac{(\bar{x}_1 - \bar{x}_2) - D_0}{\sqrt{s_p^2\left(\dfrac{1}{n_1} + \dfrac{1}{n_2}\right)}}$$

Rejection region: $t < -t_\alpha$ Rejection region: $|t| > t_{\alpha/2}$
   [or $t > t_\alpha$ when $H_a: (\mu_1 - \mu_2) > D_0$]
where t_α and $t_{\alpha/2}$ are based on $(n_1 + n_2 - 2)$ degrees of freedom.

Conditions Required for Valid Small-Sample Inferences about $(\mu_1 - \mu_2)$

1. The two samples are randomly selected in an independent manner from the two target populations.
2. Both sampled populations have distributions that are approximately normal.
3. The population variances are equal (i.e., $\sigma_1^2 = \sigma_2^2$).

Example 8.4

Small-Sample Confidence Interval for $(\mu_1 - \mu_2)$ — Managerial Success

Problem Behavioral researchers have developed an index designed to measure managerial success. The index (measured on a 100-point scale) is based on the manager's length of time in the organization and his or her level within the firm; the higher the index, the more successful the manager. Suppose a researcher wants to compare the average success index for two groups of managers at a large manufacturing plant. Managers in group 1 engage in a high volume of interactions with people outside the manager's work unit. (Such interactions include phone and face-to-face meetings with customers and suppliers, outside meetings, and public relations work.) Managers in group 2 rarely interact with people outside their work unit. Independent random samples of 12 and 15 managers are selected from groups 1 and 2, respectively, and the success index of each is recorded. The results of the study are given in Table 8.2.

a. Use the data in the table to estimate the true mean difference between the success indexes of managers in the two groups. Use a 95% confidence interval.
b. Interpret the interval, part **a**.
c. What assumptions must be made so that the estimate is valid? Are they reasonably satisfied?

Table 8.2	Managerial Success Indexes for Two Groups of Managers										
	Group 1						Group 2				
	Interaction with Outsiders						Few Interactions				
	65	58	78	60	68	69	62	53	36	34	56	50
	66	70	53	71	63	63	42	57	46	68	48	42
							52	53	43			

Data Set: SUCCES

```
Two-sample T for SUCCESS

GROUP   N    Mean   StDev  SE Mean
1       12   65.33   6.61      1.9
2       15   49.47   9.33      2.4


Difference = mu (1) - mu (2)
Estimate for difference:  15.87
95% CI for difference:  (9.29, 22.45)
T-Test of difference = 0 (vs not =): T-Value = 4.97  P-Value = 0.000  DF = 25
Both use Pooled StDev = 8.2472
```

Figure 8.7

Minitab printout for Example 8.4

Solution

a. For this experiment, let μ_1 and μ_2 represent the mean success index of group 1 and group 2 managers, respectively. Then, the objective is to obtain a 95% confidence interval for $(\mu_1 - \mu_2)$.

The first step in constructing the confidence interval is to obtain summary statistics (e.g., $\bar{x}$ and s) on the success index for each group of managers. The data of Table 8.2 were entered into a computer, and Minitab was used to obtain these descriptive statistics. The Minitab printout appears in Figure 8.7. Note that $\bar{x}_1 = 65.33, s_1 = 6.61, \bar{x}_2 = 49.47,$ and $s_2 = 9.33$.

Next, we calculate the pooled estimate of variance:

$$s_p^2 = \frac{(n_1 - 1)s_1^2 + (n_2 - 1)s_2^2}{n_1 + n_2 - 2}$$

$$= \frac{(12 - 1)(6.61)^2 + (15 - 1)(9.33)^2}{12 + 15 - 2} = 67.97$$

where s_p^2 is based on $(n_1 + n_2 - 2) = (12 + 15 - 2) = 25$ degrees of freedom. Also, we find $t_{\alpha/2} = t_{.025} = 2.06$ (based on 25 degrees of freedom) from Table III in Appendix D.

Finally, the 95% confidence interval for $(\mu_1 - \mu_2)$, the difference between mean managerial success indexes for the two groups, is

$$(\bar{x}_1 - \bar{x}_2) \pm t_{\alpha/2}\sqrt{s_p^2\left(\frac{1}{n_1} + \frac{1}{n_2}\right)} = 65.33 - 49.47 \pm t_{.025}\sqrt{67.97\left(\frac{1}{12} + \frac{1}{15}\right)}$$

$$= 15.86 \pm (2.06)(3.19)$$

$$= 15.86 \pm 6.58$$

or $(9.28, 22.44)$. This interval agrees (except for rounding) with the one shown at the bottom of the Minitab printout, Figure 8.7.

b. Notice that the confidence interval includes positive differences only. Consequently, we are 95% confident that $(\mu_1 - \mu_2)$ exceeds 0. In fact, we estimate the mean success index, μ_1, for managers with a high volume of outsider interaction (group 1) to be anywhere between 9.28 and 22.44 points higher than the mean success index, μ_2, of managers with few interactions (group 2).

c. To properly use the small-sample confidence interval, the following assumptions must be satisfied:

1. The samples of managers are randomly and independently selected from the populations of group 1 and group 2 managers.

2. The success indexes are normally distributed for both groups of managers.

3. The variance of the success indexes is the same for the two populations (i.e., $\sigma_1^2 = \sigma_2^2$).

Figure 8.8

Minitab normal probability plots for manager success index

The first assumption is satisfied, based on the information provided about the sampling procedure in the problem description. To check the plausibility of the remaining two assumptions, we resort to graphical methods. Figure 8.8 is a Minitab printout that displays normal probability plots for the success indexes of the two samples of managers. The near straight-line trends on both plots indicate that the success index distributions are approximately mound-shaped and symmetric. Consequently, each sample data set appears to come from a population that is approximately normal.

One way to check assumption #3 is to test the null hypothesis $H_0: \sigma_1^2 = \sigma_2^2$. This test is covered in Section 8.6. Another approach is to examine box plots for the sample data. Figure 8.9 is a Minitab printout that shows side-by-side vertical box plots for the success indexes in the two samples. Recall from Section 2.7 that the box plot represents the "spread" of a data set. The two box plots appear to have about the same spread; thus, the samples appear to come from populations with approximately the same variance.

Figure 8.9

Minitab box plots for manager success index

Look Back All three assumptions appear to be reasonably satisfied for this application of the small-sample confidence interval.

◾ **Now Work Exercise 8.7**

The two-sample t-statistic is a powerful tool for comparing population means when the assumptions are satisfied. It has also been shown to retain its usefulness when the sampled populations are only approximately normally distributed. And when the sample sizes are equal, the assumption of equal population variances can be relaxed— that is, if $n_1 = n_2$, then σ_1^2 and σ_2^2 can be quite different, and the test statistic will still possess, approximately, a Student's t-distribution. In the case where $\sigma_1^2 \neq \sigma_2^2$ and $n_1 \neq n_2$, an approximate small-sample confidence interval or test can be obtained by modifying the degrees of freedom associated with the t-distribution.

The next box gives the approximate small-sample procedures to use when the assumption of equal variances is violated. The test for the "unequal sample sizes" case is based on Satterthwaite's (1946) approximation.

Approximate Small-Sample Procedures when $\sigma_1^2 \neq \sigma_2^2$

1. **Equal sample sizes $(n_1 = n_2 = n)$**

   Confidence interval: $(\bar{x}_1 - \bar{x}_2) \pm t_{\alpha/2}\sqrt{(s_1^2 + s_2^2)/n}$

   Test statistic for H_0: $(\mu_1 - \mu_2) = 0$: $t = (\bar{x}_2 - \bar{x}_2)/\sqrt{(s_1^2 + s_2^2)/n}$

   where t is based on $\nu = n_1 + n_2 - 2 = 2(n - 1)$ degrees of freedom.

2. **Unequal sample sizes $(n_1 \neq n_2)$**

   Confidence interval: $(\bar{x}_1 - \bar{x}_2) \pm t_{\alpha/2}\sqrt{(s_1^2/n_1) + (s_2^2/n_2)}$

   Test statistic for H_0: $(\mu_1 - \mu_2) = 0$: $t = (\bar{x}_1 - \bar{x}_2)/\sqrt{(s_1^2/n_1) + (s_2^2/n_2)}$ where t is based on degrees of freedom equal to

   $$\nu = \frac{(s_1^2/n_1 + s_2^2/n_2)^2}{\dfrac{(s_1^2/n_1)^2}{n_1 - 1} + \dfrac{(s_1^2/n_2)^2}{n_2 - 1}}$$

Note: The value of ν will generally not be an integer. Round ν down to the nearest integer to use the t-table.

When the assumptions are clearly not satisfied, you can select larger samples from the populations or you can use other available statistical tests (nonparametric statistical tests, which are described in Chapter 15).

What Should You Do if the Assumptions Are Not Satisfied?

Answer: If you are concerned that the assumptions are not satisfied, use the Wilcoxon rank sum test for independent samples to test for a shift in population distributions. See Chapter 15.

STATISTICS in ACTION REVISITED

Comparing Mean Price Changes

Refer to the *ZixIt v. Visa* court case described in the Statistics in Action (pp. 419–420). Recall that a Visa executive wrote e-mails and made Web site postings in an effort to undermine a new online credit card processing system developed by ZixIt. ZixIt sued Visa for libel, asking for $699 million in damages. An expert statistician, hired by the defendants (Visa), performed an "event study" in which he matched the Visa executive's e-mail postings with movement of ZixIt's stock price the next business day. The data were collected daily from September 1 to December 30, 1999 (an 83-day period) and are available in the **ZIXVSA** file. In addition to daily closing price (dollars) of ZixIt stock, the file contains a variable for whether or not the Visa executive posted an e-mail and the change in price of the stock the following business day. During the 83-day period, the executive posted e-mails on 43 days and had no postings on 40 days.

If the daily postings by the Visa executive had a negative impact on ZixIt stock, then the average price change following nonposting days should exceed the average

Two-Sample T-Test and CI: PriceChange, Posting

```
Two-sample T for PriceChange

Posting   N   Mean  StDev  SE Mean
NO       40  -0.13   3.46     0.55
POST     43   0.06   2.20     0.34


Difference = mu (NO) - mu (POST)
Estimate for difference:  -0.188
95% CI for difference:  (-1.470, 1.093)
T-Test of difference = 0 (vs not =): T-Value = -0.29  P-Value = 0.770  DF = 65
```

Figure SIA8.1

Minitab comparison of two price change means

price change following posting days. Consequently, one way to analyze the data is to conduct a comparison of two population means through either a confidence interval or a test of hypothesis. Here, we let μ_1 represent the mean price change of ZixIt stock following all nonposting days and μ_2 represent the mean price change of ZixIt stock following posting days. If, in fact, the charges made by ZixIt are true, then μ_1 will exceed μ_2. However, if the data do not support ZixIt's claim, then we will not be able to reject the null hypothesis H_0: $(\mu_1 - \mu_2) = 0$ in favor of H_a: $(\mu_1 - \mu_2) > 0$. Similarly, if a confidence interval for $(\mu_1 - \mu_2)$ contains the value 0, then there will be no evidence to support ZixIt's claim.

Because both sample sizes ($n_1 = 40$ and $n_2 = 43$) are large, we can apply the large-sample z-test or large-sample confidence interval procedure for independent samples. A Minitab printout for this analysis is shown in Figure SIA8.1. Both the 95% confidence interval and p-value for a two-tailed test of hypothesis are highlighted on the printout. Note that the 95% confidence interval, ($-\$1.47$, $\$1.09$), includes the value $\$0$, and the p-value for the two-tailed hypothesis test (.770) implies that the two population means are not significantly different. Also, interestingly, the sample mean price change after posting days ($\bar{x}_1 = \$.06$) is small and positive, while the sample mean price change after nonposting days ($\bar{x}_2 = -\$.13$) is small and negative, totally contradicting ZixIt's claim.

The statistical expert for the defense presented these results to the jury, arguing that the "average price change following posting days is small and similar to the average price change following nonposting days" and "the difference in the means is not statistically significant."

Note: The statistician also compared the mean ZixIt trading volume (number of ZixIt stock shares traded) after posting days to the mean trading volume after nonposting days. These results are shown in Figure SIA8.2. You can see that the 95% confidence interval for the difference in mean trading volume (highlighted) includes 0, and the p-value for a two-tailed test of hypothesis for a difference in means (also highlighted) is not statistically significant. These results were also presented to the jury in defense of Visa.

```
Two-sample T for VolumeAfter

Posting   N    Mean   StDev  SE Mean
NO       40  719645  430837    68121
POST     43  578665  333921    50922


Difference = mu (NO) - mu (POST)
Estimate for difference:  140980
95% CI for difference:  (-28526, 310485)
T-Test of difference = 0 (vs not =): T-Value = 1.66  P-Value = 0.102  DF = 73
```

Figure SIA8.2

Minitab comparison of two trading volume means analysis

Data Set: ZIXVSA

Exercises 8.1–8.25

Learning the Mechanics

8.1 The purpose of this exercise is to compare the variability of $\bar{x}_1$ and $\bar{x}_2$ with the variability of $(\bar{x}_1 - \bar{x}_2)$.

    a. Suppose the first sample is selected from a population with mean $\mu_1 = 150$ and variance $\sigma_1^2 = 900$. Within what range should the sample mean vary about 95% of the time in repeated samples of 100 measurements from this distribution? That is, construct an interval extending 2 standard deviations of $\bar{x}_1$ on each side of μ_1.

    b. Suppose the second sample is selected independently of the first from a second population with mean $\mu_2 = 150$ and variance $\sigma_2^2 = 1,600$. Within what range should the sample mean vary about 95% of the time in repeated samples of 100 measurements from this distribution? That is, construct an interval extending 2 standard deviations of $\bar{x}_2$ on each side of μ_2.

    c. Now consider the difference between the two sample means $(\bar{x}_1 - \bar{x}_2)$. What are the mean and standard deviation of the sampling distribution of $(\bar{x}_1 - \bar{x}_2)$?

    d. Within what range should the difference in sample means vary about 95% of the time in repeated independent samples of 100 measurements each from the two populations?

    e. What, in general, can be said about the variability of the difference between independent sample means relative to the variability of the individual sample means?

8.2 Independent random samples of 64 observations each are chosen from two normal populations with the following means and standard deviations:

Population 1	Population 2
$\mu_1 = 12$	$\mu_2 = 10$
$\sigma_1 = 4$	$\sigma_2 = 3$

Let $\bar{x}_1$ and $\bar{x}_2$ denote the two sample means.

    a. Give the mean and standard deviation of the sampling distribution of $\bar{x}_1$.

    b. Give the mean and standard deviation of the sampling distribution of $\bar{x}_2$.

    c. Suppose you were to calculate the difference between the sample means $(\bar{x}_1 - \bar{x}_2)$. Find the mean and standard deviation of the sampling distribution of $(\bar{x}_1 - \bar{x}_2)$.

    d. Will the statistic $(\bar{x}_1 - \bar{x}_2)$ be normally distributed? Explain.

8.3 In order to compare the means of two populations, independent random samples of 400 observations are selected from each population, with the following results:

Sample 1	Sample 2
$\bar{x}_1 = 5,275$	$\bar{x}_2 = 5,240$
$s_1 = 150$	$s_2 = 200$

    a. Use a 95% confidence interval to estimate the difference between the population means $(\mu_1 - \mu_2)$. Interpret the confidence interval.

    b. Test the null hypothesis $H_0: (\mu_1 - \mu_2) = 0$ versus the alternative hypothesis $H_a: (\mu_1 - \mu_2) \neq 0$. Give the significance level of the test and interpret the result.

    c. Suppose the test in part **b** was conducted with the alternative hypothesis $H_a: (\mu_1 - \mu_2) > 0$. How would your answer to part **b** change?

    d. Test the null hypothesis $H_0: (\mu_1 - \mu_2) = 25$ versus $H_a: (\mu_1 - \mu_2) \neq 25$. Give the significance level and interpret the result. Compare your answer to the test conducted in part **b**.

    e. What assumptions are necessary to ensure the validity of the inferential procedures applied in parts **a–d**?

8.4 To use the t-statistic to test for a difference between the means of two populations, what assumptions must be made about the two populations? About the two samples?

8.5 Two populations are described in each of the following cases. In which cases would it be appropriate to apply the small-sample t-test to investigate the difference between the population means?

    a. Population 1: Normal distribution with variance σ_1^2. Population 2: Skewed to the right with variance $\sigma_2^2 = \sigma_1^2$.

    b. Population 1: Normal distribution with variance σ_1^2. Population 2: Normal distribution with variance $\sigma_2^2 \neq \sigma_1^2$.

    c. Population 1: Skewed to the left with variance σ_1^2. Population 2: Skewed to the left with variance $\sigma_2^2 = \sigma_1^2$.

    d. Population 1: Normal distribution with variance σ_1^2. Population 2: Normal distribution with variance $\sigma_2^2 = \sigma_1^2$.

    e. Population 1: Uniform distribution with variance σ_1^2. Population 2: Uniform distribution with variance $\sigma_2^2 = \sigma_1^2$.

8.6 Assume that $\sigma_1^2 = \sigma_2^2 = \sigma^2$. Calculate the pooled estimator of σ^2 for each of the following cases:

    a. $s_1^2 = 120, s_2^2 = 100, n_1 = n_2 = 25$

    b. $s_1^2 = 12, s_2^2 = 20, n_1 = 20, n_2 = 10$

    c. $s_1^2 = .15, s_2^2 = .20, n_1 = 6, n_2 = 10$

    d. $s_1^2 = 3,000, s_2^2 = 2,500, n_1 = 16, n_2 = 17$

Note that the pooled estimate is a weighted average of the sample variances. To which of the variances does the pooled estimate fall nearer in each of the above cases?

8.7 Independent random samples from normal populations produced the results shown in the next table.

Sample 1	Sample 2
1.2	4.2
3.1	2.7
1.7	3.6
2.8	3.9
3.0	

    a. Calculate the pooled estimate of σ^2.

    b. Do the data provide sufficient evidence to indicate that $\mu_2 > \mu_1$? Test using $\alpha = .10$.

    c. Find a 90% confidence interval for $(\mu_1 - \mu_2)$.

d. Which of the two inferential procedures, the test of hypothesis in part **b** or the confidence interval in part **c**, provides more information about $(\mu_1 - \mu_2)$?

8.8 Two independent random samples have been selected—100 observations from population 1 and 100 from population 2. Sample means $\bar{x}_1 = 26.6$ and $\bar{x}_2 = 15.5$ were obtained. From previous experience with these populations, it is known that the variances are $\sigma_1^2 = 9$ and $\sigma_2^2 = 16$.

a. Find $\sigma_{(\bar{x}_1 - \bar{x}_2)}$.

b. Sketch the approximate sampling distribution for $(\bar{x}_1 - \bar{x}_2)$ assuming $(\mu_1 - \mu_2) = 10$.

c. Locate the observed value of $(\bar{x}_1 - \bar{x}_2)$ on the graph you drew in part **b**. Does it appear that this value contradicts the null hypothesis $H_0: (\mu_1 - \mu_2) = 10$?

d. Use the z-table to determine the rejection region for the test of $H_0: (\mu_1 - \mu_2) = 10$ against $H_0: (\mu_1 - \mu_2) \neq 10$. Use $\alpha = .05$.

e. Conduct the hypothesis test of part **d** and interpret your result.

f. Construct a 95% confidence interval for $(\mu_1 - \mu_2)$. Interpret the interval.

g. Which inference provides more information about the value of $(\mu_1 - \mu_2)$—the test of hypothesis in part **e** or the confidence interval in part **f**?

8.9 Independent random samples of $n_1 = 233$ and $n_2 = 312$ are selected from two populations and used to test the hypothesis $H_0: (\mu_1 - \mu_2) = 0$ against the alternative $H_a: (\mu_1 - \mu_2) \neq 0$.

a. The two-tailed p-value of the test is .1150. Interpret this result.

b. If the alternative hypothesis had been $H_a: (\mu_1 - \mu_2) < 0$, how would the p-value change? Interpret the p-value for this one-tailed test.

8.10 Independent random samples from approximately normal populations produced the results shown below.

L08010

Sample 1				Sample 2			
52	33	42	44	52	43	47	56
41	50	44	51	62	53	61	50
45	38	37	40	56	52	53	60
44	50	43		50	48	60	55

a. Do the data provide sufficient evidence to conclude that $(\mu_2 - \mu_1) > 10$? Test using $\alpha = .01$.

b. Construct a 98% confidence interval for $(\mu_2 - \mu_1)$. Interpret your result.

8.11 Independent random samples selected from two normal populations produced the sample means and standard deviations shown below.

Sample 1	Sample 2
$n_1 = 17$	$n_2 = 12$
$\bar{x}_1 = 5.4$	$\bar{x}_2 = 7.9$
$s_1 = 3.4$	$s_2 = 4.8$

a. Conduct the test $H_0: (\mu_1 - \mu_2) = 0$ against $H_a: (\mu_1 - \mu_2) \neq 0$. Interpret the results.

b. Estimate $(\mu_1 - \mu_2)$ using a 95% confidence interval.

Applying the Concepts—Basic

8.12 Lobster trap placement. Refer to the *Bulletin of Marine Science* (April 2010) study of lobster trap placement, Exercise 6.29 (p. 318). Recall that the variable of interest was the average distance separating traps—called *trap spacing*—deployed by teams of fishermen fishing for the red spiny lobster in Baja California Sur, Mexico. The trap-spacing measurements (in meters) for a sample of seven teams from the Bahia Tortugas (BT) fishing cooperative are repeated in the table. In addition, trap-spacing measurements for eight teams from the Punta Abreojos (PA) fishing cooperative are listed. For this problem, we are interested in comparing the mean trap-spacing measurements of the two fishing cooperatives.

BT Cooperative:	93	99	105	94	82	70	86	
PA Cooperative:	118	94	106	72	90	66	153	98

Source: Based on Shester, G. G. "Explaining catch variation among Baja California lobster fishers through spatial analysis of trap-placement decisions," *Bulletin of Marine Science,* Vol. 86, No. 2, April 2010 (Table 1).

a. Identify the target parameter for this study.

b. Compute a point estimate of the target parameter.

c. What is the problem with using the normal (z) statistic to find a confidence interval for the target parameter?

d. Find a 90% confidence interval for the target parameter.

e. Use the interval, part **d**, to make a statement about the difference in mean trap-spacing measurements of the two fishing cooperatives.

f. What conditions must be satisfied for the inference, part **e**, to be valid?

8.13 Last name and acquisition timing. The speed with which consumers decide to purchase a product was investigated in the *Journal of Consumer Research* (August 2011). The researchers theorized that consumers with last names that begin with letters later in the alphabet will tend to acquire items faster than those whose last names begin with letters earlier in the alphabet—called the *last name effect*. MBA students were offered up to four free tickets to attend a top-ranked women's college basketball game for which there was a limited supply of tickets. The first letter of the last name of those who responded to an e-mail offer in time to receive the tickets was noted as well as the response time (measured in minutes). The researchers compared the response times for two groups of MBA students: (1) those with last names beginning with one of the first nine letters of the alphabet and (2) those with last names beginning with one of the last nine letters of the alphabet. Summary statistics for the two groups are provided in the table.

	First 9 Letters: A–I	Last 9 Letters: R–Z
Sample size:	25	25
Mean response time (minutes):	25.08	19.38
Standard deviation (minutes):	10.41	7.12

Source: Based on Carlson, K. A., & Conrad, J. M. "The last name effect: How last name influences acquisition timing," *Journal of Consumer Research,* Vol. 38, No. 2, August 2011.

a. Construct a 95% confidence interval for the difference between the true mean response times for MBA students in the two groups.

b. Based on the interval, part **a,** which group has the shorter mean response time? Does this result support the researchers' *last name effect* theory? Explain.

8.14 Effectiveness of teaching software. Educational software—ranging from video-game-like programs played on Sony PlayStations to rigorous drilling exercises used on computers—has become very popular in school districts across the country. The U.S. Department of Education (DOE) recently conducted a national study of the effectiveness of educational software. In one phase of the study, a sample of 1,516 first-grade students in classrooms that used educational software was compared to a sample of 1,103 first-grade students in classrooms that did not use the technology. In its *Report to Congress* (March 2007), the DOE concluded that "[mean] test scores [of students on the SAT reading test] were not significantly higher in classrooms using reading...software products" than in classrooms that did not use educational software.

a. Identify the parameter of interest to the DOE.

b. Specify the null and alternative hypotheses for the test conducted by the DOE.

c. The *p*-value for the test was reported as .62. Based on this value, do you agree with the conclusion of the DOE? Explain.

8.15 Children's recall of TV ads. Marketing professors at Robert Morris and Kent State Universities examined children's recall and recognition of television advertisements (*Journal of Advertising,* Spring 2006). Two groups of children were shown a 60-second commercial for Sunkist FunFruit Rock-n-Roll Shapes. One group (the A/V group) was shown the ad with both audio and video; the second group (the video only group) was shown only the video portion of the commercial. Following the viewing, the children were asked to recall 10 specific items from the ad. The number of the 10 items recalled correctly by each child is summarized in the table. The researchers theorized that "children who receive an audiovisual presentation will have the same level of mean recall of ad information as those who receive only the visual aspects of the ad."

Video Only Group	A/V Group
$n_1 = 20$	$n_2 = 20$
$\bar{x}_1 = 3.70$	$\bar{x}_2 = 3.30$
$s_1 = 1.98$	$s_2 = 2.13$

Source: Based on Maher, J. K., Hu, M. Y., & Kolbe, R. H. "Children's recall of television ad elements," *Journal of Advertising,* Spring 2006, Volume 35(1).

a. Set up the appropriate null and alternative hypotheses to test the researchers' theory.

b. Find the value of the test statistic.

c. Give the rejection region for $\alpha = .10$.

d. Make the appropriate inference. What can you say about the researchers' theory?

e. The researchers reported the *p*-value of the test as *p*-value = .542. Interpret this result.

f. What conditions are required for the inference to be valid?

8.16 Drug content assessment. Refer to Exercise 4.123 (p. 240) and the *Analytical Chemistry* (Dec. 15, 2009) study in which scientists used high-performance liquid chromatography to determine the amount of drug in a tablet. Twenty-five tablets were produced at each of two different, independent sites. Drug concentrations (measured as a percentage) for the tablets produced at the two sites are listed in the table below. The scientists want to know whether there is any difference between the mean drug concentration in tablets produced at Site 1 and the corresponding mean at Site 2. Use the accompanying Minitab printout to help the scientists draw a conclusion.

Site 1

91.28	92.83	89.35	91.90	82.85	94.83	89.83	89.00	84.62
86.96	88.32	91.17	83.86	89.74	92.24	92.59	84.21	89.36
90.96	92.85	89.39	89.82	89.91	92.16	88.67		

Site 2

89.35	86.51	89.04	91.82	93.02	88.32	88.76	89.26	90.36
87.16	91.74	86.12	92.10	83.33	87.61	88.20	92.78	86.35
93.84	91.20	93.44	86.77	83.77	93.19	81.79		

Source: Borman, P. J., Marion, J. C., Damjanov, I., & Jackson, P. "Design and analysis of method equivalence studies," *Analytical Chemistry,* Vol. 81, No. 24, December 15, 2009 (Table 3).

Two-Sample T-Test and CI: Content, Site

```
Two-sample T for Content

Site   N    Mean   StDev  SE Mean
1      25   89.55  3.07   0.61
2      25   89.03  3.34   0.67


Difference = mu (1) - mu (2)
Estimate for difference:   0.515
95% CI for difference:   (-1.308, 2.338)
T-Test of difference = 0 (vs not =): T-Value = 0.57  P-Value = 0.573  DF = 48
Both use Pooled StDev = 3.2057
```

Minitab output for Exercise 8.16

8.17 Buy-side vs. sell-side analysts' earnings forecasts. Refer to the *Financial Analysts Journal* (Jul./Aug. 2008) study of financial analysts' forecast earnings, Exercise 2.86 (p. 86). Recall that data were collected on 3,526 forecasts made by buy-side analysts and 58,562 forecasts made by sell-side analysts, and the relative absolute forecast error was determined for each. The mean and standard deviation of forecast errors for both types of analysts are given in the table.

	Buy-Side Analysts	Sell-Side Analysts
Sample Size	3,526	58,562
Mean	0.85	−0.05
Standard Deviation	1.93	0.85

Source: Groysberg, B., Healy, P., & Chapman, C. "Buy-side vs. sell-side analysts' earnings forecasts," *Financial Analysts Journal*, Vol. 64, No. 4, Jul./Aug. 2008.

a. Construct a 95% confidence interval for the difference between the mean forecast error of buy-side analysts and the mean forecast error of sell-side analysts.

b. Based on the interval, part **a,** which type of analysis has the greater mean forecast error? Explain.

c. What assumptions about the underlying populations of forecast errors (if any) are necessary for the validity of the inference, part **b**?

Applying the Concepts—Intermediate

8.18 Homework assistance for accounting students. How much assistance should accounting professors provide students for completing homework? Is too much assistance counterproductive? These were some of the questions of interest in a *Journal of Accounting Education* (Vol. 25, 2007) article. A total of 75 junior-level accounting majors who were enrolled in Intermediate Financial Accounting participated in an experiment. All students took a pretest on a topic not covered in class; then each was given a homework problem to solve on the same topic. However, the students were randomly assigned different levels of assistance on the homework. Some (20 students) were given the completed solution, some (25 students) were given check figures at various steps of the solution, and the rest (30 students) were given no help. After finishing the homework, each student was given a posttest on the subject. One of the variables of interest to the researchers was the knowledge gain (or, test score improvement), measured as the difference between the posttest and pretest scores. The sample mean knowledge gains for the three groups of students are provided in the table.

	No Solutions	Check Figures	Completed Solutions
Sample Size	30	25	20
Sample Mean	2.43	2.72	1.95

Source: Based on Lindquist, T. M., & Olsen, L. M. "How much help, is too much help? An experimental investigation of the use of check figures and completed solutions in teaching intermediate accounting," *Journal of Accounting Education,* Vol. 25, No. 3, 2007, pp. 103–117 (Table 1, Panel B).

a. The researchers theorized that as the level of homework assistance increased, the test score improvement from pretest to posttest would decrease. Do the sample means reported in the table support this theory?

b. What is the problem with using only the sample means to make inferences about the population mean knowledge gains for the three groups of students?

c. The researchers conducted a statistical test of hypothesis to compare the mean knowledge gain of students in the "no solutions" group to the mean knowledge gain of students in the "check figures" group. Based on the theory, part **a,** set up the null and alternative hypotheses for the test.

d. The observed significance level of the t-test of part *c* was reported as .8248. Using $\alpha = .05$, interpret this result.

e. The researchers conducted a statistical test of hypothesis to compare the mean knowledge gain of students in the "completed solutions" group to the mean knowledge gain of students in the "check figures" group. Based on the theory, part **a,** set up the null and alternative hypotheses for the test.

f. The observed significance level of the *t*-test of part **e** was reported as .1849. Using $\alpha = .05$, interpret this result.

g. The researchers conducted a statistical test of hypothesis to compare the mean knowledge gain of students in the "no solutions" group to the mean knowledge gain of students in the "completed solutions" group. Based on the theory, part **a,** set up the null and alternative hypotheses for the test.

h. The observed significance level of the *t*-test of part **g** was reported as .2726. Using $\alpha = .05$, interpret this result.

8.19 Patent infringement case. *Chance* (Fall 2002) described a lawsuit where Intel Corp. was charged with infringing on a patent for an invention used in the automatic manufacture of computer chips. In response, Intel accused the inventor of adding material to his patent notebook after the patent was witnessed and granted. The case rested on whether a patent witness' signature was written on top of key text in the notebook or under the key text. Intel hired a physicist who used an X-ray beam to measure the relative concentration of certain elements (e.g., nickel, zinc, potassium) at several spots on the notebook page. The zinc measurements for three notebook locations—on a text line, on a witness line, and on the intersection of the witness and text lines—are provided in the table.

Text Line	.335	.374	.440			
Witness Line	.210	.262	.188	.329	.439	.397
Intersection	.393	.353	.285	.295	.319	

a. Use a test or a confidence interval (at $\alpha = .05$) to compare the mean zinc measurement for the text line with the mean for the intersection.

b. Use a test or a confidence interval (at $\alpha = .05$) to compare the mean zinc measurement for the witness line with the mean for the intersection.

c. From the results, parts **a** and **b,** what can you infer about the mean zinc measurements at the three notebook locations?

d. What assumptions are required for the inferences to be valid? Are they reasonably satisfied?

Data for Exercise 8.21

Control Group:

1	24	5	16	21	7	20	1	9	20	19	10	23	16	0	4	9	13	17	13	0	2	12	11	7	3	11
1	19	9	12	18	5	21	30	15	4	2	12	11	10	13	11	3	6	10	13	16	12	28	19	12	20	

Rudeness Condition:

4	11	18	11	9	6	5	11	9	12	7	5	7	3	11	1	9	11	10	7	8	9	10	7
11	4	13	5	4	7	8	3	8	15	9	16	10	0	7	15	13	9	2	13	10			

8.20 Producer willingness to supply biomass. The conversion of biomass to energy is critical for producing transportation fuels. How willing are producers to supply biomass products such as cereal straw, corn stover, and surplus hay? To answer this question, economists conducted a survey of producers in both mid-Missouri and southern Illinois (*Biomass and Energy,* Vol. 36, 2012). Independent samples of 431 Missouri producers and 508 Illinois producers participated in the survey. Each producer was asked to give the maximum proportion of hay produced that he or she would be willing to sell to the biomass market. Summary statistics for the two groups of producers are listed in the table. Does the mean amount of surplus that hay producers are willing to sell to the biomass market differ for the two areas, Missouri and Illinois? Use $\alpha = .05$ to make the comparison.

	Missouri Producers	Illinois Producers
Sample Size	431	508
Mean Amount of Hay (%)	21.5	22.2
Standard Deviation (%)	33.4	34.9

Source: Based on Altman, I., & Sanders, D. "Producer willingness and ability to supply biomass: Evidence from the U.S. Midwest," *Biomass and Energy,* Vol. 36, No. 8, 2012 (Tables 3 and 7).

8.21 Does rudeness really matter in the workplace? Studies have established that rudeness in the workplace can lead to retaliatory and counterproductive behavior. However, there has been little research on how rude behaviors influence a victim's task performance. Such a study was conducted, with the results published in the *Academy of Management Journal* (Oct. 2007). College students enrolled in a management course were randomly assigned to one of two experimental conditions: rudeness condition (45 students) and control group (53 students). Each student was asked to write down as many uses for a brick as possible in 5 minutes. For those students in the rudeness condition, the facilitator displayed rudeness by generally berating students for being irresponsible and unprofessional (due to a late-arriving confederate). No comments were made about the late-arriving confederate to students in the control group. The number of different uses for a brick was recorded for each of the 98 students and is shown at the top of the page. Conduct a statistical analysis (at $\alpha = .01$) to determine if the true mean performance level for students in the rudeness condition is lower than the true mean performance level for students in the control group.

8.22 Service without a smile. "Service with a smile" is a slogan that many businesses adhere to. However, there are some jobs (e.g., those of judges, law enforcement officers, pollsters) that require neutrality when dealing with the public. An organization will typically provide "display rules" to guide employees on what emotions they should use when interacting with the public. A *Journal of Applied Psychology* (Vol. 96, 2011) study compared the results of surveys conducted using two different types of display rules: positive (requiring a strong display of positive emotions) and neutral (maintaining neutral emotions at all times). In this designed experiment, 145 undergraduate students were randomly assigned to either a positive display rule condition ($n_1 = 78$) or a neutral display rule condition ($n_2 = 67$). Each participant was trained on how to conduct the survey using the display rules. As a manipulation check, the researchers asked each participant to rate, on a scale of 1 = "strongly agree" to 5 = "strongly disagree," the statement, "This task requires me to be neutral in my expressions."

a. If the manipulation of the participants was successful, which group should have the larger mean response? Explain.

b. The data for the study (simulated based on information provided in the journal article) are listed in the table below. Access the data and run an analysis to determine if the manipulation was successful. Conduct a test of hypothesis using $\alpha = .05$.

c. What assumptions, if any, are required for the inference from the test to be valid?

Data for Exercise 8.22

Positive Display Rule:

2	4	3	3	3	3	4	4	4	4	4	4	4	4	4	4	4	4	4	5
4	4	4	4	4	4	4	4	4	4	4	4	4	4	4	5	5	5	5	5
5	5	5	5	5	5	5	5	5	5	5	5	5	5	5	5	5	5	5	5
5	5	5	5	5	5	5	5	5	5	5	5	5	5	5	5	5			

Neutral Display Rule:

3	3	2	1	2	1	1	1	2	2	1	2	2	2	3	2	2	1	2
2	2	2	2	1	2	2	2	2	2	2	1	2	2	2	2	2	2	2
3	2	1	2	2	2	1	2	1	2	2	3	2	2	2	2	2	2	2
2	2	2	1	2	2	2	2	2	2									

8.23 Is honey a cough remedy? Refer to the *Archives of Pediatrics and Adolescent Medicine* (Dec. 2007) study of honey as a children's cough remedy, Exercise 2.30 (p. 61). Children who were ill with an upper respiratory tract infection and their parents participated in the study. Parents were instructed to give their sick child a dosage of liquid "medicine" prior to bedtime. Unknown to the parents, some were given a dosage of dextromethorphan (DM)—an over-the-counter cough medicine—while others were given a similar dose of honey. (*Note:* A third group gave their children no medicine.) Parents then rated their children's cough symptoms, and the improvement in total cough symptoms score was determined for each child. The data (improvement scores) for the 35 children in the DM dosage group and the 35 children in the honey dosage group are reproduced in the table below. Do you agree with the statement (extracted from the article), "Honey may be a preferable treatment for the cough and sleep difficulty associated with childhood upper respiratory tract infection"? Use the comparison of two means methodology presented in this section to answer the question.

Honey Dosage:

12 11 15 11 10 13 10 4 15 16 9 14 10 6 10 8 11
12 12 8 12 9 11 15 10 15 9 13 8 12 10 8 9 5 12

DM Dosage:

 4 6 9 4 7 7 7 9 12 10 11 6 3 4 9 7 8
12 12 4 12 13 7 10 13 9 4 4 10 15 9 12 6

Source: Paul, I. M., et al. "Effect of honey, dextromethorphan, and no treatment on nocturnal cough and sleep quality for coughing children and their parents," *Archives of Pediatrics and Adolescent Medicine,* Vol. 161, No. 12, Dec. 2007 (data simulated).

8.24 Cooling method for gas turbines. Refer to the *Journal of Engineering for Gas Turbines and Power* (Jan. 2005) study of gas turbines augmented with high-pressure inlet fogging, Exercise 7.40 (p. 378). The researchers classified gas turbines into three categories: traditional, advanced, and aeroderivative. Summary statistics on heat rate (kilojoules per kilowatt per hour) for each of the three types of gas turbines are shown in the Minitab printout (at the top of the next column).

a. Is there sufficient evidence of a difference between the mean heat rates of traditional augmented gas turbines and aeroderivative augmented gas turbines? Test using $\alpha = .05$.

b. Is there sufficient evidence of a difference between the mean heat rates of advanced augmented gas turbines and aeroderivative augmented gas turbines? Test using $\alpha = .05$.

Minitab Output for Exercise 8.24

Descriptive Statistics: HEATRATE

Variable	ENGINE	N	Mean	StDev	Minimum	Maximum
HEATRATE	Advanced	21	9764	639	9105	11588
	Aeroderiv	7	12312	2652	8714	16243
	Traditional	39	11544	1279	10086	14796

Applying the Concepts—Advanced

8.25 Ages of self-employed immigrants. Is self-employment for immigrant workers a faster route to economic advancement in the country? This was one of the questions studied in research published in the *International Journal of Manpower* (Vol. 32, 2011). One aspect of the study involved comparing the ages of self-employed and wage-earning immigrants. The researcher found that in Sweden, native wage earners tend to be younger than self-employed natives. However, immigrant wage earners tend to be older than self-employed immigrants. This inference was based on summary statistics for male Swedish immigrants shown in the table.

	Self-Employed Immigrants	Wage-Earning Immigrants
Sample Size	870	84,875
Mean Age (years)	44.88	46.79

Source: Based on Andersson, L. "Occupational choice and returns to self-employment among immigrants," *International Journal of Manpower,* Vol. 32, No. 8, 2011 (Table I).

a. Based on the information given, why is it impossible to provide a measure of reliability for the inference "Self-employed immigrants are younger, on average, than wage-earning immigrants in Sweden"?

b. What information do you need to obtain a measure of reliability for the inference, part **a**?

c. Give a value of the test statistic that would lead you to conclude that the true mean age of self-employed immigrants is less than the true mean age of wage-earning immigrants if you are willing to risk a Type I error rate of .01.

d. Assume that σ, the standard deviation of the ages, is the same for both self-employed and wage-earning immigrants. Give an estimate of σ that would lead you to conclude that the true mean age of self-employed immigrants is less than the true mean age of wage-earning immigrants using $\alpha = .01$.

e. Is the true value of σ likely to be larger or smaller than the one you calculated in part **d**?

8.3	**Comparing Two Population Means: Paired Difference Experiments**

Suppose you want to compare the mean daily sales of two restaurants located in the same city. If you were to record the restaurants' total sales for each of 12 randomly selected days during a 6-month period, the results might appear as shown in Table 8.3. Do these data provide evidence of a difference between the mean daily sales of the two restaurants?

Table 8.3	Daily Sales for Two Restaurants	
Day	Restaurant 1 (x_1)	Restaurant 2 (x_2)
1 (Wednesday)	$1,005	$ 918
2 (Saturday)	2,073	1,971
3 (Tuesday)	873	825
4 (Wednesday)	1,074	999
5 (Friday)	1,932	1,827
6 (Thursday)	1,338	1,281
7 (Thursday)	1,449	1,302
8 (Monday)	759	678
9 (Friday)	1,905	1,782
10 (Monday)	693	639
11 (Saturday)	2,106	2,049
12 (Tuesday)	981	933

Data Set: SALES2

We want to test the null hypothesis that the mean daily sales, μ_1 and μ_2, for the two restaurants are equal against the alternative hypothesis that they differ; that is,

$$H_0: (\mu_1 - \mu_2) = 0$$
$$H_a: (\mu_1 - \mu_2) \neq 0$$

Many researchers mistakenly use the *t*-statistic for two independent samples (Section 8.2) to conduct this test. The analysis is shown on the Excel/XLSTAT printout, Figure 8.10. The test statistic, $t = .38$, is highlighted on the printout, as well as the *p*-value of the test, *p*-value = .7047. At $\alpha = .10$, the *p*-value exceeds α. Thus, from *this* analysis we might conclude that insufficient evidence exists to infer that there is a difference in mean daily sales for the two restaurants.

Summary statistics:

Variable	Observations	Minimum	Maximum	Mean	Std. deviation
SALES1	12	693.0000	2106.0000	1349.0000	530.0744
SALES2	12	639.0000	2049.0000	1267.0000	516.0370

t-test for two independent samples / Two-tailed test:

95% confidence interval on the difference between the means:
   (−360.8877 , 524.8877)

Difference	82.0000
t (Observed value)	0.3840
|t| (Critical value)	2.0739
DF	22
p-value (Two-tailed	0.7047
alpha	0.05

Figure 8.10

Excel/XLSTAT printout of an invalid analysis of the data in Table 8.3

If you carefully examine the data in Table 8.3, however, you will find this conclusion difficult to accept. The sales of restaurant 1 exceed those of restaurant 2 *for every one of the randomly selected 12 days.* This, in itself, is strong evidence to indicate that μ_1 differs from μ_2, and we will subsequently confirm this fact. Why, then, was the *t*-test unable to detect this difference? The answer is, *the independent samples* t-*test is not a valid procedure to use with this set of data.*

The *t*-test is inappropriate because the assumption of independent samples is invalid. We have randomly chosen *days;* thus, once we have chosen the sample of days for restaurant 1, we have *not* independently chosen the sample of days for restaurant 2.

The dependence between observations within days can be seen by examining the pairs of daily sales, which tend to rise and fall together as we go from day to day. This pattern provides strong visual evidence of a violation of the assumption of independence required for the two-sample t-test of Section 8.2. Also, substituting $s_1^2 = 530.07$ and $s_2^2 = 516.04$ (obtained from the printout, Figure 8.10) into the formula for s_p^2, we obtain

$$s_p^2 = \frac{(n_1 - 1)s_1^2 + (n_2 - 1)s_2^2}{n_1 + n_2 - 2}$$

$$= \frac{(12 - 1)(530.07)^2 + (12 - 1)(516.04)^2}{12 + 12 - 2} = 273{,}635.7$$

Thus, there is a *large variation within samples* (reflected by the large value of s_p^2) in comparison to the relatively *small difference between the sample means.* Because s_p^2 is so large, the t-test of Section 8.2 is unable to detect a possible difference between μ_1 and μ_2.

Table 8.4	Daily Sales and Differences for Two Restaurants		
Day	Restaurant 1 (x_1)	Restaurant 2 (x_2)	Difference $d = x_1 - x_2$
1 (Wednesday)	$1,005	$ 918	$ 87
2 (Saturday)	2,073	1,971	102
3 (Tuesday)	873	825	48
4 (Wednesday)	1,074	999	75
5 (Friday)	1,932	1,827	105
6 (Thursday)	1,338	1,281	57
7 (Thursday)	1,449	1,302	147
8 (Monday)	759	678	81
9 (Friday)	1,905	1,782	123
10 (Monday)	693	639	54
11 (Saturday)	2,106	2,049	57
12 (Tuesday)	981	933	48

We now consider a valid method of analyzing the data of Table 8.3. In Table 8.4, we add the column of differences between the daily sales of the two restaurants, $d = x_1 - x_2$. We can regard these daily differences in sales as a random sample of all daily differences, past and present. Then we can use this sample to make inferences about the mean of the population of differences, μ_d, which is equal to the difference $(\mu_1 - \mu_2)$—that is, the mean of the population (and sample) of differences equals the difference between the population (and sample) means. Thus, our test becomes

$$H_0: \mu_d = 0 \ [\text{i.e., } (\mu_1 - \mu_2) = 0]$$
$$H_a: \mu_d \neq 0 \ [\text{i.e., } (\mu_1 - \mu_2) \neq 0]$$

The test statistic is a one-sample t (Section 7.5) because we are now analyzing a single sample of differences for small n:

$$\text{Test statistic: } t = \frac{\bar{d} - 0}{s_d / \sqrt{n_d}}$$

where $\bar{d}$ = Sample mean difference
s_d = Sample standard deviation of differences
n_d = Number of differences = number of pairs

Assumptions: The population of differences in daily sales is approximately normally distributed. The sample differences are randomly selected from the population differences. [*Note:* We do not need to make the assumption that $\sigma_1^2 = \sigma_2^2$.]

Rejection region: At significance level $\alpha = .05$, we will reject H_0 if $|t| > t_{.05}$, where $t_{.05}$ is based on $(n_d - 1)$ degrees of freedom.

Referring to Table III in Appendix D, we find the t-value corresponding to $\alpha = .025$ and $n_d - 1 = 12 - 1 = 11$ df to be $t_{.025} = 2.201$. Then we will reject the null hypothesis if

$|t| > 2.201$ (see Figure 8.11). Note that the number of degrees of freedom has decreased from $n_1 + n_2 - 2 = 22$ to 11 when we use the paired difference experiment rather than the two independent random samples design.

Summary statistics for the $n = 12$ differences are shown on the Minitab printout, Figure 8.12. Note that $\bar{d} = 82.0$ and $s_d = 32.0$ (rounded). Substituting these values into the formula for the test statistic, we have

$$t = \frac{\bar{d} - 0}{s_d/\sqrt{n_d}} = \frac{82}{32/\sqrt{12}} = 8.88$$

Figure 8.11

Rejection region for restaurant sales example

Because this value of t falls in the rejection region, we conclude (at $\alpha = .05$) that the difference in population mean daily sales for the two restaurants differs from 0. We can reach the same conclusion by noting that the p-value of the test, highlighted in Figure 8.12, is approximately 0. The fact that $(\bar{x}_1 - \bar{x}_2) = \bar{d} = \$82.00$ strongly suggests that the mean daily sales for restaurant 1 exceed the mean daily sales for restaurant 2.

```
Paired T for SALES1 - SALES2

             N    Mean   StDev  SE Mean
SALES1      12    1349    530      153
SALES2      12    1267    516      149
Difference  12   82.00   31.99     9.23


95% CI for mean difference: (61.68, 102.32)
T-Test of mean difference = 0 (vs not = 0): T-Value = 8.88  P-Value = 0.000
```

Figure 8.12

Minitab analysis of differences in daily restaurant sales

This kind of experiment, in which observations are paired and the differences are analyzed, is called a **paired difference experiment.** In many cases, a paired difference experiment can provide more information about the difference between population means than an independent samples experiment. The idea is to compare population means by comparing the differences between pairs of experimental units (objects, people, etc.) that were very similar prior to the experiment. The differencing removes sources of variation that tend to inflate σ^2. For instance, in the restaurant example, the day-to-day variability in daily sales is removed by analyzing the differences between the restaurants' daily sales. Making comparisons within groups of similar experimental units is called **blocking,** and the paired difference experiment is an example of a **randomized block experiment.** In our example, the days represent the blocks.

Some other examples for which the paired difference experiment might be appropriate are the following:

1. Suppose you want to estimate the difference $(\mu_1 - \mu_2)$ in mean price per gallon between two major brands of premium gasoline. If you choose two independent random samples of stations for each brand, the variability in price due to geographic location may be large. To eliminate this source of variability, you could choose pairs of stations of similar size, one station for each brand, in close geographic proximity and use the sample of differences between the prices of the brands to make an inference about $(\mu_1 - \mu_2)$.

2. A college placement center wants to estimate the difference $(\mu_1 - \mu_2)$ in mean starting salaries for men and women graduates who seek jobs through the center. If it independently samples men and women, the starting salaries may vary because of their different college majors and differences in grade point averages. To eliminate these sources of variability, the placement center could match male and female job seekers according to their majors and grade point

averages. Then the differences between the starting salaries of each pair in the sample could be used to make an inference about $(\mu_1 - \mu_2)$.

3. To compare the performance of two automobile salespeople, we might test a hypothesis about the difference $(\mu_1 - \mu_2)$ in their respective mean monthly sales. If we randomly choose n_1 months of salesperson 1's sales and independently choose n_2 months of salesperson 2's sales, the month-to-month variability caused by the seasonal nature of new car sales might inflate s_p^2 and prevent the two-sample t-statistic from detecting a difference between μ_1 and μ_2, if such a difference actually exists. However, by taking the difference in monthly sales for the two salespeople for each of n months, we eliminate the month-to-month variability (seasonal variation) in sales, and the probability of detecting a difference between μ_1 and μ_2, if a difference exists, is increased.

The hypothesis-testing procedures and the method of forming confidence intervals for the difference between two means using a paired difference experiment are summarized in the following boxes for both large and small n.

Paired Difference Confidence Interval for $\mu_d = (\mu_1 - \mu_2)$

Large Sample, Normal (z) Statistic:

$$\bar{d} \pm z_{\alpha/2} \frac{\sigma_d}{\sqrt{n_d}} \approx \bar{d} \pm z_{\alpha/2} \frac{s_d}{\sqrt{n_d}}$$

Small Sample, Student's t-Statistic:

$$\bar{d} \pm t_{\alpha/2} \frac{s_d}{\sqrt{n_d}}$$

where $t_{\alpha/2}$ is based on $(n_d - 1)$ degrees of freedom.

Paired Difference Test of Hypothesis for $\mu_d = (\mu_1 - \mu_2)$

One-Tailed Test	Two-Tailed Test
$H_0: \mu_d = D_0$	$H_0: \mu_d = D_0$
$H_a: \mu_d < D_0$	$H_a: \mu_d \neq D_0$
[or $H_a: \mu_d > D_0$]	

Large Sample, Normal (z) Statistic

Test statistic: $z = \dfrac{\bar{d} - D_0}{\sigma_d/\sqrt{n_d}} \approx \dfrac{\bar{d} - D_0}{s_d/\sqrt{n_d}}$

Rejection region: $z < -z_\alpha$	Rejection region: $\lvert z \rvert > z_{\alpha/2}$
[or $z > z_\alpha$ when $H_a: \mu_d > D_0$]	

Small Sample, Student's t-Statistic

Test statistic: $t = \dfrac{\bar{d} - D_0}{s_d/\sqrt{n_d}}$

Rejection region: $t < -t_\alpha$	Rejection region: $\lvert t \rvert > t_{\alpha/2}$
[or $t > t_\alpha$ when $H_a: \mu_d > D_0$]	

where t_α and $t_{\alpha/2}$ are based on $(n_d - 1)$ degrees of freedom

---

Conditions Required for Valid Large-Sample Inferences about μ_d

1. A random sample of differences is selected from the target population of differences.

2. The sample size n_d is large (i.e., $n_d \geq 30$). (By the Central Limit Theorem, this condition guarantees that the test statistic will be approximately normal regardless of the shape of the underlying probability distribution of the population.)

> **Conditions Required for Valid Small-Sample Inferences about μ_d**
>
> 1. A random sample of differences is selected from the target population of differences.
> 2. The population of differences has a distribution that is approximately normal.

Example 8.5

Confidence Interval for μ_d—Comparing Mean Salaries of Males and Females

Problem An experiment is conducted to compare the starting salaries of male and female college graduates who find jobs. Pairs are formed by choosing a male and a female with the same major and similar grade point averages (GPAs). Suppose a random sample of 10 pairs is formed in this manner and the starting annual salary of each person is recorded. The results are shown in Table 8.5. Compare the mean starting salary, μ_1, for males to the mean starting salary, μ_2, for females using a 95% confidence interval. Interpret the results.

Table 8.5	Data on Annual Salaries for Matched Pairs of College Graduates		
Pair	Male x_1	Female x_2	Difference $d = x_1 - x_2$
1	$29,300	$28,800	$500
2	41,500	41,600	−100
3	40,400	39,800	600
4	38,500	38,500	0
5	43,500	42,600	900
6	37,800	38,000	−200
7	69,500	69,200	300
8	41,200	40,100	1,100
9	38,400	38,200	200
10	59,200	58,500	700

Data Set: PAIRS

Solution Because the data on annual salary are collected in pairs of males and females matched on GPA and major, a paired difference experiment is performed. To conduct the analysis, we first compute the differences between the salaries, as shown in Table 8.5. Summary statistics for these $n = 10$ differences are displayed in the Minitab printout, Figure 8.13.

```
Paired T for MALE - FEMALE

                 N    Mean   StDev  SE Mean
MALE            10   43930   11665     3689
FEMALE          10   43530   11617     3674
Difference      10     400     435      137


95% CI for mean difference: (89, 711)
T-Test of mean difference = 0 (vs not = 0): T-Value = 2.91   P-Value = 0.017
```

Figure 8.13
Minitab analysis of salary differences

The 95% confidence interval for $\mu_d = (\mu_1 - \mu_2)$ for this small sample is

$$\bar{d} \pm t_{\alpha/2} \frac{s_d}{\sqrt{n_d}}$$

where $t_{\alpha/2} = t_{.025} = 2.262$ (obtained from Table III Appendix D) is based on $n_d - 1 = 9$ degrees of freedom. Substituting the values of $\bar{d} = 400$ and $s_d = 435$ shown on the printout, we obtain

$$\bar{d} \pm t_{.025} \frac{s_d}{\sqrt{n_d}} = 400 \pm 2.262 \left(\frac{435}{\sqrt{10}} \right)$$

$$= 400 \pm 311 = (\$89, \$711)$$

[*Note:* This interval is also shown on the Minitab printout, Figure 8.13.] Our interpretation is that the true mean difference between the starting salaries of males and females falls between $89 and $711, with 95% confidence. Because the interval falls above 0, we infer that $\mu_1 - \mu_2 > 0$; that is, that the mean salary for males exceeds the mean salary for females.

Look Back Remember that $\mu_d = \mu_1 - \mu_2$. So, if $\mu_d > 0$, then $\mu_1 > \mu_2$. Alternatively, if $\mu_d < 0$, then $\mu_1 < \mu_2$.

■ **Now Work Exercise 8.39**

To measure the amount of information about $(\mu_1 - \mu_2)$ gained by using a paired difference experiment in Example 8.5 rather than an independent samples experiment, we can compare the relative widths of the confidence intervals obtained by the two methods. A 95% confidence interval for $(\mu_1 - \mu_2)$ using the paired difference experiment is, from Example 8.5, ($89, $711). If we mistakenly analyzed the same data as though this were an independent samples experiment,* we would first obtain the descriptive statistics shown in the SPSS printout, Figure 8.14.

Then we would substitute the sample means and standard deviations shown on the printout into the formula for a 95% confidence interval for $(\mu_1 - \mu_2)$ using independent samples:

$$(\bar{x}_1 - \bar{x}_2) \pm t_{.025}\sqrt{s_p^2\left(\frac{1}{n_1} + \frac{1}{n_2}\right)}$$

where

$$s_p^2 = \frac{(n_1 - 1)s_1^2 + (n_2 - 1)s_2^2}{n_1 + n_2 - 2}$$

SPSS performed these calculations and obtained the interval ($-$10,537.50, $11,337.50). This interval is highlighted in Figure 8.14.

Notice that the independent samples interval includes 0. Consequently, if we were to use this interval to make an inference about $(\mu_1 - \mu_2)$, we would incorrectly conclude that the mean starting salaries of males and females do not differ! You can see that the confidence interval for the independent sampling experiment is about five times wider than for the corresponding paired difference confidence interval. Blocking out the variability due to differences in majors and grade point averages significantly increases the information about the difference in male and female mean starting salaries by providing a much more accurate (smaller confidence interval for the same confidence coefficient) estimate of $(\mu_1 - \mu_2)$.

Group Statistics

	GENDER	N	Mean	Std. Deviation	Std. Error Mean
SALARY	M	10	43930.00	11665.148	3688.844
	F	10	43530.00	11616.946	3673.601

Independent Samples Test

		Levene's Test for Equality of Variances		t-test for Equality of Means							
										95% Confidence Interval of the Difference	
		F	Sig.	t	df	Sig. (2-tailed)	Mean Difference	Std. Error Difference	Lower	Upper
SALARY	Equal variances assumed	.000	.991	.077	18	.940	400.00	5206.046	-10537.5	11337.50
	Equal variances not assumed			.077	18.000	.940	400.00	5206.046	-10537.5	11337.51

Figure 8.14

SPSS analysis of salaries, assuming independent samples

*This is done only to provide a measure of the increase in the amount of information obtained by a paired design in comparison to an unpaired design. Actually, if an experiment is designed using pairing, an unpaired analysis would be invalid because the assumption of independent samples would not be satisfied.

You may wonder whether conducting a paired difference experiment is always superior to an independent samples experiment. The answer is—most of the time but not always. We sacrifice half the degrees of freedom in the t-statistic when a paired difference design is used instead of an independent samples design. This is a loss of information, and unless this loss is more than compensated for by the reduction in variability obtained by blocking (pairing), the paired difference experiment will result in a net loss of information about $(\mu_1 - \mu_2)$. Thus, we should be convinced that the pairing will significantly reduce variability before performing the paired difference experiment. Most of the time this will happen.

ETHICS in STATISTICS

In a two-group analysis, intentionally pairing observations after the data have been collected in order to produce a desired result is considered *unethical statistical practice*.

One final note: The pairing of the observations is determined before the experiment is performed (that is, by the *design* of the experiment). A paired difference experiment is *never* obtained by pairing the sample observations after the measurements have been acquired.

> **What Do You Do When the Assumption of a Normal Distribution for the Population of Differences Is Not Satisfied?**
>
> *Answer:* Use the Wilcoxon signed rank test for the paired difference design (Chapter 15).

Exercises 8.26–8.42

Learning the Mechanics

8.26 A paired difference experiment produced the following results:

$$n_d = 38 \quad \bar{x}_1 = 92 \quad \bar{x}_2 = 95.5 \quad \bar{d} = -3.5 \quad s_d^2 = 21$$

a. Determine the values of z for which the null hypothesis, $\mu_1 - \mu_2 = 0$, would be rejected in favor of the alternative hypothesis, $\mu_1 - \mu_2 < 0$. Use $\alpha = .10$.

b. Conduct the paired difference test described in part **a.** Draw the appropriate conclusions.

c. What assumptions are necessary so that the paired difference test will be valid?

d. Find a 90% confidence interval for the mean difference μ_d.

e. Which of the two inferential procedures, the confidence interval of part **d** or the test of hypothesis of part **b**, provides more information about the differences between the population means?

8.27 A paired difference experiment yielded n_d pairs of observations. In each case, what is the rejection region for testing $H_0: \mu_d > 2$?

a. $n_d = 12, \alpha = .05$
b. $n_d = 24, \alpha = .10$
c. $n_d = 4, \alpha = .025$
d. $n_d = 80, \alpha = .01$

8.28 The data for a random sample of six paired observations
NW are shown in the next table.

L08028

a. Calculate the difference between each pair of observations by subtracting observation 2 from observation 1. Use the differences to calculate $\bar{d}$ and s_d^2.

b. If μ_1 and μ_2 are the means of populations 1 and 2, respectively, express μ_d in terms of μ_1 and μ_2.

Pair	Sample from Population 1 (Observation 1)	Sample from Population 2 (Observation 2)
1	7	4
2	3	1
3	9	7
4	6	2
5	4	4
6	8	7

c. Form a 95% confidence interval for μ_d.

d. Test the null hypothesis $H_0: \mu_d = 0$ against the alternative hypothesis $H_a: \mu_d \neq 0$. Use $\alpha = .05$.

8.29 The data for a random sample of 10 paired observations
are shown in the table below.

L08029

Pair	Sample from Population 1	Sample from Population 2
1	19	24
2	25	27
3	31	36
4	52	53
5	49	55
6	34	34
7	59	66
8	47	51
9	17	20
10	51	55

a. If you wish to test whether these data are sufficient to indicate that the mean for population 2 is larger than that for population 1, what are the appropriate null and alternative hypotheses? Define any symbols you use.

b. Conduct the test, part **a,** using $\alpha = .10$.

c. Find a 90% confidence interval for μ_d. Interpret this result.

d. What assumptions are necessary to ensure the validity of this analysis?

8.30 A paired difference experiment yielded the following results:

$$n_d = 40 \quad \Sigma d = 468 \quad \Sigma d^2 = 6,880$$

a. Test $H_0: \mu_d = 10$ against $H_a: \mu_d \neq 10$, where $\mu_d = (\mu_1 - \mu_2)$. Use $\alpha = .05$.

b. Report the p-value for the test you conducted in part **a.** Interpret the p-value.

c. Do you need to assume that the population of differences is normally distributed? Explain.

Applying the Concepts—Basic

8.31 **Summer weight-loss camp.** Camp Jump Start is an 8-week summer camp for overweight and obese adolescents. Counselors develop a weight-management program for each camper that centers on nutrition education and physical activity. To justify the cost of the camp, counselors must provide empirical evidence that the weight-management program is effective. In a study published in *Pediatrics* (April 2010), the body mass index (BMI) was measured for each of 76 campers both at the start and end of camp. Summary statistics on BMI measurements are shown in the table.

	Mean	Standard Deviation
Starting BMI	34.9	6.9
Ending BMI	31.6	6.2
Paired Differences	3.3	1.5

Source: Based on Huelsing, J., Kanafani, N., Mao, J., & White, N. H. "Camp Jump Start: Effects of a residential summer weight-loss camp for older children and adolescents," *Pediatrics,* Vol. 125, No. 4, April 2010 (Table 3).

a. Give the null and alternative hypotheses for determining whether the mean BMI at the end of camp is less than the mean BMI at the start of camp.

b. How should the data be analyzed, as an independent samples test or as a paired difference test? Explain.

c. Calculate the test statistic using the formula for an independent samples test. (*Note:* This is *not* how the test should be conducted.)

d. Calculate the test statistic using the formula for a paired difference test.

e. Compare the test statistics, parts **c** and **d.** Which test statistic provides more evidence in support of the alternative hypothesis?

f. The p-value of the test, part **d,** was reported as $p < .0001$. Interpret this result assuming $\alpha = .01$.

g. Do the differences in BMI values need to be normally distributed in order for the inference, part **f,** to be valid? Explain.

h. Find a 99% confidence interval for the true mean change in BMI for Camp Jump Start campers. Interpret the result.

8.32 **Performance ratings of government agencies.** The U.S. Office of Management and Budget (OMB) requires government agencies to produce annual performance and accounting reports (PARS) each year. A research team at George Mason University evaluated the quality of the PARS for 24 government agencies (*The Public Manager,* Summer 2008), where evaluation scores ranged from 12 (lowest) to 60 (highest). The accompanying file contains evaluation scores for all 24 agencies for two consecutive years. (See Exercise 2.129, p. 105.) Data for a random sample of five of these agencies are shown in the accompanying table. Suppose you want to conduct a paired difference test to determine whether the true mean evaluation score of government agencies in year 2 exceeds the true mean evaluation score in year 1.

Agency	Year 1 Score	Year 2 Score
GSA	34	40
Agriculture	33	35
Social Security	33	33
USAID	32	42
Defense	17	32

Source: Ellig, J., & Wray, H. "Measuring performance reporting quality," *The Public Manager,* Vol. 37, No. 2, Summer 2008 (p. 66). Copyright © 2008 by Jerry Ellig. Reprinted with permission.

a. Explain why the data should be analyzed using a paired difference test.

b. Compute the difference between the year 2 score and the year 1 score for each sampled agency.

c. Find the mean and standard deviation of the differences, part **b.**

d. Use the summary statistics, part **c,** to find the test statistic.

e. Give the rejection region for the test using $\alpha = .10$.

f. Make the appropriate conclusion in the words of the problem.

8.33 **Twinned drill holes.** A traditional method of verifying mineralization grades in mining is to drill twinned holes, i.e., the drilling of a new hole, or "twin," next to an earlier drill hole. The use of twinned drill holes was investigated in *Exploration and Mining Geology* (Vol. 18, 2009). Geologists use data collected at both holes to estimate the total amount of heavy minerals (THM) present at the drilling site. The data in the table on the next page (based on information provided in the journal article) represent THM percentages for a sample of 15 twinned holes drilled at a diamond mine in Africa. The geologists want to know if there is any evidence of a difference in the true THM means of all original holes and their twin holes drilled at the mine.

a. Explain why the data should be analyzed as paired differences.

b. Compute the difference between the "1st Hole" and "2nd Hole" measurements for each drilling location.

c. Find the mean and standard deviation of the differences, part **b.**

d. Use the summary statistics, part **c,** to find a 90% confidence interval for the true mean difference ("1st Hole" minus "2nd Hole") in THM measurements.

e. Interpret the interval, part **d.** Can the geologists conclude that there is no evidence of a difference in the true THM means of all original holes and their twin holes drilled at the mine?

Location	1st Hole	2nd Hole
1	5.5	5.7
2	11.0	11.2
3	5.9	6.0
4	8.2	5.6
5	10.0	9.3
6	7.9	7.0
7	10.1	8.4
8	7.4	9.0
9	7.0	6.0
10	9.2	8.1
11	8.3	10.0
12	8.6	8.1
13	10.5	10.4
14	5.5	7.0
15	10.0	11.2

8.34 **Packaging of a children's health food.** Refer to the *Journal of Consumer Behaviour* (Vol. 10, 2011) study of packaging of a children's health food product, Exercise 7.33 (p. 376). Recall that a fictitious brand of a healthy food product—sliced apples—was packaged to appeal to children (a smiling cartoon apple was on the front of the package). The researchers compared the appeal of this fictitious brand to the appeal of a commercially available brand of sliced apples, which was not packaged for children. Each of 408 schoolchildren rated both brands on a 5-point "willingness to eat" scale, with 1 = "not willing at all" and 5 = "very willing." The fictitious brand had a sample mean score of 3.69, while the commercially available brand had a sample mean score of 3.00. The researchers wanted to compare the population mean score for the fictitious brand, μ_F, to the population mean score for the commercially available brand, μ_C. They theorized that μ_F would be greater than μ_C.
a. Specify the null and alternative hypotheses for the test.
b. Explain how the researchers should analyze the data and why.
c. The researchers reported a test statistic value of 5.71. Interpret this result. Use $\alpha = .05$ to make your conclusion.
d. Find the approximate *p*-value of the test.
e. Could the researchers have tested at $\alpha = .01$ and arrived at the same conclusion?

8.35 **"I am not selling anything" surveys.** To improve response rates in telephone surveys, interviewers are often instructed by the polling company to state, "I am not selling anything" at the outset of the call. The effectiveness of the "I am not selling anything" strategy was investigated in the *International Journal of Public Opinion Research* (Winter 2004). The sample consisted of 29 different telephone surveys. However, in each survey about half the people were contacted by interviewers using the "I am not selling anything" introduction and the other half were contacted by interviewers using the standard (no mention of "not selling") introduction. Thus, for each of the 29 surveys, both the "not selling" and standard interviewing techniques were employed. Summary statistics on response

rates (proportion of people called who actually responded to the survey questions) are given in the accompanying table. The goal of the researchers was to compare the mean response rates of the two interviewing methods with the specific purpose to determine if the mean response rate for "not selling" was higher than that for the standard.

	"Not selling" Introduction	Standard Introduction
Number of Surveys	29	29
Mean Response Rate	.262	.246
Standard Deviation	.12	.11

Source: De Leeuw, E. D., & Hox, J. J. "I am not selling anything: 29 experiments in telephone introductions," *International Journal of Public Opinion Research*, Vol. 16, No. 4, Winter 2004, pp. 464–473 (Table 1). Copyright © 2004 by Oxford University Press. Reprinted with permission.

a. Explain why the data should be analyzed as a paired difference experiment.
b. Analyze the data in the table using the independent samples *t*-test. Do you detect a significant difference between the mean response rates of the two methods using $\alpha = .05$?
c. The researchers applied the paired difference *t* procedure and obtained an observed significance level of *p*-value = .001. Interpret this result if $\alpha = 0.5$.
d. Compare the inferences you made in parts **b** and **c**.

8.36 **NHTSA new car crash tests.** Refer to the National Highway Traffic Safety Administration (NHTSA) crash-test data for new cars saved in the file. Crash-test dummies were placed in the driver's seat and front passenger's seat of a new car model, and the car was steered by remote control into a head-on collision with a fixed barrier while traveling at 35 miles per hour. Two of the variables measured for each of the 98 new cars in the data set are (1) the severity of the driver's chest injury and (2) the severity of the passenger's chest injury. (The more points assigned to the chest injury rating, the more severe the injury.) Suppose the NHTSA wants to determine whether the true mean driver chest injury rating exceeds the true mean passenger chest injury rating and, if so, by how much.
a. State the parameter of interest to the NHTSA.
b. Explain why the data should be analyzed as matched pairs.
c. Find a 99% confidence interval for the true difference between the mean chest injury ratings of drivers and front-seat passengers.
d. Interpret the interval, part **c.** Does the true mean driver chest injury rating exceed the true mean passenger chest injury rating? If so, by how much?
e. What conditions are required for the analysis to be valid? Do these conditions hold for these data?

Applying the Concepts—Intermediate

8.37 **Taking "power naps" during work breaks.** Lack of sleep costs companies about $18 billion a year in lost productivity, according to the National Sleep Foundation. Companies are waking up to the problem, however. Some even have quiet rooms available for study or sleep. "Power naps" are in vogue (*Athens Daily News,* Jan. 9, 2000). A major airline recently began encouraging reservation agents to nap during their breaks. The accompanying table lists the number of complaints received about each of a sample of 10 reservation agents during the 6 months before naps were encouraged and during the 6 months after the policy change.

a. Do the data present sufficient evidence to conclude that the new napping policy reduced the mean number of customer complaints about reservation agents? Test using $\alpha = .05$.

b. What assumptions must hold to ensure the validity of the test?

c. What variables, not controlled in the study, could lead to an invalid conclusion?

Operator	Before Policy	After Policy
1	10	5
2	3	0
3	16	7
4	11	4
5	8	6
6	2	4
7	1	2
8	14	3
9	5	5
10	6	1

8.38 **Acidity of mouthwash.** Acid has been found to be a primary cause of dental caries (cavities). It is theorized that oral mouthwashes contribute to the development of caries due to the antiseptic agent oxidizing into acid over time. This theory was tested in the *Journal of Dentistry, Oral Medicine and Dental Education* (Vol. 3, 2009). Three bottles of mouthwash, each of a different brand, were randomly selected from a drugstore. The pH level (where lower pH levels indicate higher acidity) of each bottle was measured on the date of purchase and after 30 days. The data are shown in the table. Conduct an analysis to determine if the mean initial pH level of mouthwash differs significantly from the mean pH level after 30 days. Use $\alpha = .05$ as your level of significance.

Mouthwash Brand	Initial pH	Final pH
LMW	4.56	4.27
SMW	6.71	6.51
RMW	5.65	5.58

Source: Based on Chunhye, K. L., & Schmitz, B. C. "Determination of pH, total acid, and total ethanol in oral health products: Oxidation of ethanol and recommendations to mitigate its association with dental caries," *Journal of Dentistry, Oral Medicine and Dental Education,* Vol. 3, No. 1, 2009 (Table 1).

8.39 **Testing electronic circuits.** Japanese researchers have developed a compression/depression method of testing electronic circuits based on Huffman coding (*IEICE Transactions on Information & Systems,* Jan. 2005). The new method is designed to reduce the time required for input decompression and output compression—called the *compression ratio.* Experimental results were obtained by testing a sample of 11 benchmark circuits (all of different sizes) from a SUN Blade 1000 workstation. Each circuit was tested using the standard compression/depression method and the new Huffman-based coding method, and the compression ratio was recorded. The data are given in the accompanying table. Compare the two methods with a 95% confidence interval. Which method has the smaller mean compression ratio?

Circuit	Standard Method	Huffman-coding Method
1	.80	.78
2	.80	.80
3	.83	.86
4	.53	.53
5	.50	.51
6	.96	.68
7	.99	.82
8	.98	.72
9	.81	.45
10	.95	.79
11	.99	.77

Source: Based on Ichihara, H., Shintani, M., & Inoue, T. "Huffman-based test response coding," *IEICE Transactions on Information & Systems,* Vol. E88-D, No. 1, Jan. 2005 (Table 3).

8.40 **Impact of red light cameras on car crashes.** To combat red-light-running crashes—the phenomenon of a motorist entering an intersection after the traffic signal turns red and causing a crash—many states are adopting photo-red enforcement programs. In these programs, red light cameras installed at dangerous intersections photograph the license plates of vehicles that run the red light. How effective are photo-red enforcement programs in reducing red-light-running crash incidents at intersections? The Virginia Department of Transportation (VDOT) conducted a comprehensive study of its newly adopted photo-red enforcement program and published the results in a June 2007 report. In one portion of the study, the VDOT provided crash data both before and after installation of red light cameras at several intersections. The data (measured as the number of crashes caused by red light running per intersection per year) for 13 intersections in Fairfax County, Virginia, are given in the table. Analyze the data for the VDOT. What do you conclude?

Intersection	Before Camera	After Camera
1	3.60	1.36
2	0.27	0
3	0.29	0
4	4.55	1.79
5	2.60	2.04
6	2.29	3.14
7	2.40	2.72
8	0.73	0.24
9	3.15	1.57
10	3.21	0.43
11	0.88	0.28
12	1.35	1.09
13	7.35	4.92

Source: Based on "Research report: The impact of red light cameras (photo-red enforcement) on crashes in Virginia" from Virginia Transportation Research Council.

8.41 **Evaluating a new drug.** Merck Research Labs conducted an experiment to evaluate the effect of a new drug using the single-T swim maze. Nineteen impregnated dam rats were captured and allocated a dosage of 12.5 milligrams of the drug. One male and one female rat pup were randomly selected from each resulting litter to perform in the swim maze. Each pup was placed in the water at one end of the maze and allowed to swim until it escaped at the opposite end. If the pup failed to escape after a certain period of time, it was placed at the beginning of the maze and given another chance. The experiment was repeated until each pup accomplished three successful escapes. The table below reports the number of swims required by each pup to perform three successful escapes. Is there sufficient evidence of a difference between the mean number of swims required by male and female pups? Conduct the test (at $\alpha = .10$). Comment on the assumptions required for the test to be valid.

Litter	Male	Female	Litter	Male	Female
1	8	5	11	6	5
2	8	4	12	6	3
3	6	7	13	12	5
4	6	3	14	3	8
5	6	5	15	3	4
6	6	3	16	8	12
7	3	8	17	3	6
8	5	10	18	6	4
9	4	4	19	9	5
10	4	4			

Source: Copyright © 2012 by Merck Research Laboratories. Reprinted with permission.

Applying the Concepts—Advanced

8.42 **Alcoholic fermentation in wines.** Determining alcoholic fermentation in wine is critical to the wine-making process.
WINE40 Must/wine density is a good indicator of the fermentation point because the density value decreases as sugars are

converted into alcohol. For decades, winemakers have measured must/wine density with a hydrometer. Although accurate, the hydrometer employs a manual process that is very time-consuming. Consequently, large wineries are searching for more rapid measures of density measurement. An alternative method uses the hydrostatic balance instrument (similar to the hydrometer but digital). A winery in Portugal collected the must/wine density measurements for white wine samples randomly selected from the fermentation process for a recent harvest. For each sample, the density of the wine at 20°C was measured with both the hydrometer and the hydrostat balance. The densities for 40 wine samples are saved in the file. The first five and last five observations are shown in the table. The winery will use the alternative method of measuring wine density only if it can be demonstrated that the mean difference between the density measurements of the two methods does not exceed .002. Perform the analysis for the winery. Provide the winery with a written report of your conclusions.

Sample	Hydrometer	Hydrostatic
1	1.08655	1.09103
2	1.00270	1.00272
3	1.01393	1.01274
4	1.09467	1.09634
5	1.10263	1.10518
⋮	⋮	⋮
36	1.08084	1.08097
37	1.09452	1.09431
38	0.99479	0.99498
39	1.00968	1.01063
40	1.00684	1.00526

Source: Cooperative Cellar of Borba (*Adega Cooperative de Borba*), Portugal.

<h1>8.4   Comparing Two Population Proportions: Independent Sampling</h1>

Suppose a personal water craft (PWC) manufacturer wants to compare the potential market for its products in the northeastern United States to the market in the southeastern United States. Such a comparison would help the manufacturer decide where to concentrate sales efforts. Using telephone directories, the company randomly chooses 1,000 households in the southeast (SE) and 1,000 households in the northeast (NE) and determines whether each household plans to buy a PWC within the next 5 years. The objective is to use this sample information to make an inference about the difference $(p_1 - p_2)$ between the proportion p_1 of *all* households in the SE and the proportion p_2 of *all* households in the NE that plan to purchase a PWC within 5 years.

The two samples represent independent binomial experiments. (See Section 4.3 for the characteristics of binomial experiments.) The binomial random variables are the numbers x_1 and x_2 of the 1,000 sampled households in each area that indicate they will purchase a PWC within 5 years. The results are summarized in Table 8.6.

We can now calculate the sample proportions $\hat{p}_1$ and $\hat{p}_2$ of the households in the SE and NE, respectively, that are prospective buyers:

Table 8.6	Results of Telephone Survey

SE	NE
$n_1 = 1{,}000$	$n_2 = 1{,}000$
$x_1 = 42$	$x_2 = 24$

$$\hat{p}_1 = \frac{x_1}{n_1} = \frac{42}{1{,}000} = .042$$

$$\hat{p}_2 = \frac{x_2}{n_2} = \frac{24}{1{,}000} = .024$$

The difference between the sample proportions $(\hat{p}_1 - \hat{p}_2)$ makes an intuitively appealing point estimator of the difference between the population parameters $(p_1 - p_2)$. For our example, the estimate is

$$(\hat{p}_1 - \hat{p}_2) = .042 - .024 = .018$$

To judge the reliability of the estimator $(\hat{p}_1 - \hat{p}_2)$, we must observe its performance in repeated sampling from the two populations—that is, we need to know the sampling distribution of $(\hat{p}_1 - \hat{p}_2)$. The properties of the sampling distribution are given in the next box. Remember that $\hat{p}_1$ and $\hat{p}_2$ can be viewed as means of the number of successes per trial in the respective samples, so the Central Limit Theorem applies when the sample sizes are large.

Properties of the Sampling Distribution of $(p_1 - p_2)$

1. The mean of the sampling distribution of $(\hat{p}_1 - \hat{p}_2)$ is $(p_1 - p_2)$; that is,

$$E(\hat{p}_1 - \hat{p}_2) = p_1 - p_2$$

Thus, $(\hat{p}_1 - \hat{p}_2)$ is an unbiased estimator of $(p_1 - p_2)$.

2. The standard deviation of the sampling distribution of $(\hat{p}_1 - \hat{p}_2)$ is

$$\sigma_{(\hat{p}_1 - \hat{p}_2)} = \sqrt{\frac{p_1 q_1}{n_1} + \frac{p_2 q_2}{n_2}}$$

3. If the sample sizes n_1 and n_2 are large (see Section 6.4 for a guideline), the sampling distribution of $(\hat{p}_1 - \hat{p}_2)$ is approximately normal.

Because the distribution of $(\hat{p}_1 - \hat{p}_2)$ in repeated sampling is approximately normal, we can use the z-statistic to derive confidence intervals for $(p_1 - p_2)$ or test a hypothesis about $(p_1 - p_2)$.

For the PWC example, a 95% confidence interval for the difference $(p_1 - p_2)$ is

$$(\hat{p}_1 - \hat{p}_2) \pm 1.96\sigma_{(\hat{p}_1 - \hat{p}_2)} \quad \text{or} \quad (\hat{p}_1 - \hat{p}_2) \pm 1.96\sqrt{\frac{p_1 q_1}{n_1} + \frac{p_2 q_2}{n_2}}$$

The quantities $p_1 q_1$ and $p_2 q_2$ must be estimated to complete the calculation of the standard deviation $\sigma_{(\hat{p}_1 - \hat{p}_2)}$ and hence the calculation of the confidence interval. In Section 6.4 we showed that the value of pq is relatively insensitive to the value chosen to approximate p. Therefore, $\hat{p}_1 \hat{q}_1$ and $\hat{p}_2 \hat{q}_2$ will provide satisfactory estimates to approximate $p_1 q_1$ and $p_2 q_2$, respectively. Then

$$\sqrt{\frac{p_1 q_1}{n_1} + \frac{p_2 q_2}{n_2}} \approx \sqrt{\frac{\hat{p}_1 \hat{q}_1}{n_1} + \frac{\hat{p}_2 \hat{q}_2}{n_2}}$$

and we will approximate the 95% confidence interval by

$$(\hat{p}_1 - \hat{p}_2) \pm 1.96\sqrt{\frac{\hat{p}_1 \hat{q}_1}{n_1} + \frac{\hat{p}_2 \hat{q}_2}{n_2}}$$

Substituting the sample quantities yields

$$(.042 - .024) \pm 1.96\sqrt{\frac{(.042)(.958)}{1,000} + \frac{(.024)(.976)}{1,000}}$$

or, $.018 \pm .016$. Thus, we are 95% confident that the interval from .002 to .034 contains $(p_1 - p_2)$. We infer that there are between .2% and 3.4% more households in the southeast than in the northeast that plan to purchase PWCs in the next 5 years.

The general form of a confidence interval for the difference $(p_1 - p_2)$ between population proportions is given in the following box.

Large-Sample $(1 - \alpha)\%$ Confidence Interval for $(p_1 - p_2)$: Normal (z) Statistic

$$(\hat{p}_1 - \hat{p}_2) \pm z_{\alpha/2}\sigma_{(\hat{p}_1 - \hat{p}_2)} = (\hat{p}_1 - \hat{p}_2) \pm z_{\alpha/2}\sqrt{\frac{p_1 q_1}{n_1} + \frac{p_2 q_2}{n_2}}$$

$$\approx (\hat{p}_1 - \hat{p}_2) \pm z_{\alpha/2}\sqrt{\frac{\hat{p}_1 \hat{q}_1}{n_1} + \frac{\hat{p}_2 \hat{q}_2}{n_2}}$$

Conditions Required for Valid Large-Sample Inferences about $(p_1 - p_2)$

1. The two samples are randomly selected in an independent manner from the two target populations.
2. The sample sizes, n_1 and n_2, are both large so that the sampling distribution of $(\hat{p}_1 - \hat{p}_2)$ will be approximately normal. (This condition will be satisfied if both $n_1\hat{p}_1 \geq 15, n_1\hat{q}_1 \geq 15,$ and $n_2\hat{p}_2 \geq 15, n_2\hat{q}_2 \geq 15$.)

The z-statistic,

$$z = \frac{(\hat{p}_1 - \hat{p}_2) - (p_1 - p_2)}{\sigma_{(\hat{p}_1 - \hat{p}_2)}}$$

is used to test the null hypothesis that $(p_1 - p_2)$ equals some specified difference, say D_0. For the special case where $D_0 = 0$—that is, where we want to test the null hypothesis $H_0: (p_1 - p_2) = 0$ (or, equivalently, $H_0: p_1 = p_2$)—the best estimate of $p_1 = p_2 = p$ is obtained by dividing the total number of successes $(x_1 + x_2)$ for the two samples by the total number of observations $(n_1 + n_2)$; that is,

$$\hat{p} = \frac{x_1 + x_2}{n_1 + n_2} \quad \text{or} \quad \hat{p} = \frac{n_1\hat{p}_1 + n_2\hat{p}_2}{n_1 + n_2}$$

The second equation shows that $\hat{p}$ is a weighted average of $\hat{p}_1$ and $\hat{p}_2$, with the larger sample receiving more weight. If the sample sizes are equal, then $\hat{p}$ is a simple average of the two sample proportions of successes.

We now substitute the weighted average $\hat{p}$ for both p_1 and p_2 in the formula for the standard deviation of $(\hat{p}_1 - \hat{p}_2)$:

$$\sigma_{(\hat{p}_1 - \hat{p}_2)} = \sqrt{\frac{p_1 q_1}{n_1} + \frac{p_2 q_2}{n_2}} \approx \sqrt{\frac{\hat{p}\hat{q}}{n_1} + \frac{\hat{p}\hat{q}}{n_2}} = \sqrt{\hat{p}\hat{q}\left(\frac{1}{n_1} + \frac{1}{n_2}\right)}$$

The test is summarized in the next box.

Large-Sample Test of Hypothesis about $(p_1 - p_2)$: Normal (z) Statistic

One-Tailed Test	Two-Tailed Test
$H_0: (p_1 - p_2) = 0$*	$H_0: (p_1 - p_2) = 0$
$H_a: (p_1 - p_2) < 0$	$H_a: (p_1 - p_2) \neq 0$
[or $H_a: (p_1 - p_2) > 0$]	

Test statistic: $z = \dfrac{(\hat{p}_1 - \hat{p}_2)}{\sigma_{(\hat{p}_1 - \hat{p}_2)}}$

Rejection region: $z < -z_\alpha$	Rejection region: $|z| > z_{\alpha/2}$
[or $z > z_\alpha$ when $H_a: (p_1 - p_2) > 0$]	

Note: $\sigma_{(\hat{p}_1 - \hat{p}_2)} = \sqrt{\dfrac{p_1 q_1}{n_1} + \dfrac{p_2 q_2}{n_2}} \approx \sqrt{\hat{p}\hat{q}\left(\dfrac{1}{n_1} + \dfrac{1}{n_2}\right)}$, where $\hat{p} = \dfrac{x_1 + x_2}{n_1 + n_2}$.

---

*The test can be adapted to test for a difference $D_0 \neq 0$. Because most applications call for a comparison of p_1 and p_2, implying $D_0 = 0$, we will confine our attention to this case.

| **Example** | **8.6** |

Large-Sample Test about $(p_1 - p_2)$—Comparing Car Repair Rates

Problem A consumer advocacy group wants to determine whether there is a difference between the proportions of the two leading automobile models that need major repairs (more than $500) within 2 years of their purchase. A sample of 400 two-year owners of model 1 is contacted, and a sample of 500 two-year owners of model 2 is contacted. The numbers x_1 and x_2 of owners who report that their cars needed major repairs within the first 2 years are 53 and 78, respectively. Test the null hypothesis that no difference exists between the proportions in populations 1 and 2 needing major repairs against the alternative that a difference does exist. Use $\alpha = .10$.

Solution If we define p_1 and p_2 as the true proportions of model 1 and model 2 owners, respectively, whose cars needed major repairs within 2 years, the elements of the test are

$$H_0: (p_1 - p_2) = 0$$
$$H_a: (p_1 - p_2) \neq 0$$
$$\text{Test statistic: } z = \frac{(\hat{p}_1 - \hat{p}_2) - 0}{\sigma_{(\hat{p}_1 - \hat{p}_2)}}$$

Rejection region ($\alpha = .10$): $|z| > z_{\alpha/2} = z_{.05} = 1.645$ (see Figure 8.15)

We now calculate the sample proportions of owners who needed major car repairs,

$$\hat{p}_1 = \frac{x_1}{n_1} = \frac{53}{400} = .1325$$

$$\hat{p}_2 = \frac{x_2}{n_2} = \frac{78}{500} = .1560$$

Then

$$z = \frac{(\hat{p}_1 - \hat{p}_2) - 0}{\sigma_{(\hat{p}_1 - \hat{p}_2)}} \approx \frac{(\hat{p}_1 - \hat{p}_2)}{\sqrt{\hat{p}\hat{q}\left(\frac{1}{n_1} + \frac{1}{n_2}\right)}}$$

Figure 8.15

Rejection region for Example 8.6

where

$$\hat{p} = \frac{x_1 + x_2}{n_1 + n_2} = \frac{53 + 78}{400 + 500} = .1456$$

Note that $\hat{p}$ is a weighted average of $\hat{p}_1$ and $\hat{p}_2$, with more weight given to the larger sample of model 2 owners.

Thus, the computed value of the test statistic is

$$z = \frac{.1325 - .1560}{\sqrt{(.1456)(.8544)\left(\frac{1}{400} + \frac{1}{500}\right)}} = \frac{-.0235}{.0237} = -.99$$

The samples provide insufficient evidence at $\alpha = .10$ to detect a difference between the proportions of the two models that needed repairs within 2 years.

Look Back Even though 2.35% more sampled owners of model 2 found they needed major repairs, this difference is less than 1 standard deviation ($z = -.99$) from the hypothesized zero difference between the true proportions. Thus, a 95% confidence interval for $(p_1 - p_2)$ would include 0—also implying no evidence of a difference.

■ **Now Work Exercise 8.49**

<table>
<tr><td>

Example   8.7

Finding the Observed Significance Level of a Test for $p_1 - p_2$

</td><td>

Problem Use a statistical software package to conduct the test in Example 8.6. Find and interpret the p-value of the test.

Solution We entered the sample sizes (n_1 and n_2) and number of successes (x_1 and x_2) into Excel/XLSTAT and obtained the printout shown in Figure 8.16. The test statistic for this two-tailed test is shaded on the printout, as well as the observed significance level (p-value). Note that p-value $= .3205$ exceeds $\alpha = .10$. Consequently, there is no evidence of a difference between the true population proportions.

</td></tr>
</table>

z-test for two proportions / Two-tailed test:

95% confidence interval on the difference between the proportions:
(−0.0699 , 0.0229)

Difference	−0.0235
z (Observed value)	−0.9934
z (Critical value)	1.9600
p-value (Two-tailed)	0.3205
alpha	0.05

Figure 8.16
Excel/XLSTAT printout for test of two proportions

Comparing Proportions

In the first Statistics in Action Revisited in this chapter (p. 430), we demonstrated how the expert statistician used a comparison of two means to defend Visa in a libel case. Recall that ZixIt claimed that a Visa executive's e-mail postings had a negative impact on ZixIt's attempt to develop a new online credit card processing system. Here, we demonstrate another way to analyze the data, one successfully presented in court by the statistician.

In addition to daily closing price and trading volume of ZixIt stock, the **ZIXVSA** file also contains a qualitative variable that indicates whether the stock price increased or not (decreased or stayed the same) on the following day. This variable was created by the statistician to compare the proportion of days on which ZixIt stock went up for posting and nonposting days. Let p_1 represent the proportion of days where the ZixIt stock price increased following all nonposting days and p_2 represent the proportion of days where the ZixIt stock price increased following posting days. Then, if the charges made by ZixIt were true (i.e., that postings had a negative impact on ZixIt stock), p_1 will exceed p_2. Thus, a comparison of two population proportions is appropriate. Recall that during the 83-day period of interest, the executive posted e-mails on 43 days and had no postings on 40 days. Again, both sample sizes ($n_1 = 40$ and $n_2 = 43$) are large, so we can apply the large-sample z-test or large-sample confidence interval procedure for independent samples. (Can you demonstrate this?) A Minitab printout for this analysis is shown in Figure SIA8.3.

From the printout you can see that following the 40 nonposting days, the price increased on 20 days; following the 43 posting days, the stock price increased on 18 days. Thus, the sample proportions are $p_1 = 20/40 = .5$ and $p_2 = 18/43 = .42$. Are these sample proportions different enough for us to conclude that the population proportions are different and that ZixIt's claim was true? Not according to the statistical analysis. Note that the 95% confidence interval for ($p_1 - p_2$), (−.133, .295), includes the value 0, and the p-value for the two-tailed test of H_0: ($p_1 - p_2$) = 0, p-value = .456, exceeds, say $\alpha = .05$. Both imply that the two population proportions are not significantly different.

Test and CI for Two Proportions: Up/Down, Posting

```
Event = UP

Posting    X    N    Sample p
NO        20   40    0.500000
POST      18   43    0.418605


Difference = p (NO) - p (POST)
Estimate for difference:  0.0813953
95% CI for difference:  (-0.132500, 0.295291)
Test for difference = 0 (vs not = 0):  Z = 0.75   P-Value = 0.456

Fisher's exact test: P-Value = 0.513
```

Figure SIA8.3

Minitab comparison of two proportions analysis

Also, neither sample proportion is significantly different from .5. (Can you demonstrate this?) Consequently, in courtroom testimony, the statistical expert used these results to conclude that "the direction of ZixIt's stock price movement following days with postings is random, just like days with no postings."

Data Set: ZIXVSA

Exercises 8.43–8.60

Learning the Mechanics

8.43 Consider making an inference about $p_1 - p_2$, where there are x_1 successes in n_1 binomial trials and x_2 successes in n_2 binomial trials.

a. Describe the distributions of x_1 and x_2.

b. Explain why the Central Limit Theorem is important in finding an approximate distribution for $(\hat{p}_1 - \hat{p}_2)$.

8.44 For each of the following values of α, find the values of z for which $H_0: (p_1 - p_2) = 0$ would be rejected in favor of $H_a: (p_1 - p_2) < 0$.

a. $\alpha = .01$ **b.** $\alpha = .025$

c. $\alpha = .05$ **d.** $\alpha = .10$

8.45 In each case, determine whether the sample sizes are large enough to conclude that the sampling distribution of $(\hat{p}_1 - \hat{p}_2)$ is approximately normal.

a. $n_1 = 12, n_2 = 14, \hat{p}_1 = .42, \hat{p}_2 = .57$

b. $n_1 = 12, n_2 = 14, \hat{p}_1 = .92, \hat{p}_2 = .86$

c. $n_1 = n_2 = 30, \hat{p}_1 = .70, \hat{p}_2 = .73$

d. $n_1 = 100, n_2 = 250, \hat{p}_1 = .93, \hat{p}_2 = .97$

e. $n_1 = 125, n_2 = 200, \hat{p}_1 = .08, \hat{p}_2 = .12$

8.46 Construct a 95% confidence interval for $(p_1 - p_2)$ in each of the following situations:

a. $n_1 = 400, \hat{p}_1 = .65; n_2 = 400, \hat{p}_2 = .58$

b. $n_1 = 180, \hat{p}_1 = .31; n_2 = 250, \hat{p}_2 = .25$

c. $n_1 = 100, \hat{p}_1 = .46; n_2 = 120, \hat{p}_2 = .61$

8.47 Independent random samples, each containing 800 observations, were selected from two binomial populations. The samples from populations 1 and 2 produced 320 and 400 successes, respectively.

a. Test $H_0: (p_1 - p_2) = 0$ against $H_a: (p_1 - p_2) > 0$. Use $\alpha = .05$.

b. Test $H_0: (p_1 - p_2) = 0$ against $H_a: (p_1 - p_2) \neq 0$. Use $\alpha = .01$.

c. Test $H_0: (p_1 - p_2) = 0$ against $H_a: (p_1 - p_2) < 0$. Use $\alpha = .01$.

d. Form a 90% confidence interval for $(p_1 - p_2)$.

8.48 Random samples of size $n_1 = 55$ and $n_2 = 65$ were drawn from populations 1 and 2, respectively. The samples yielded $\hat{p}_1 = .7$ and $\hat{p}_2 = .6$. Test $H_0: (p_1 - p_2) = 0$ against $H_a: (p_1 - p_2) > 0$ using $\alpha = .05$.

Applying the Concepts—Basic

8.49 **The "winner's curse" in auction bidding.** In auction bidding, the "winner's curse" is the phenomenon of the winning (or highest) bid price being above the expected value of the item being auctioned. *The Review of Economics and Statistics* (Aug. 2001) published a study on whether bid experience impacts the likelihood of the winner's curse occurring. Two groups of bidders in a sealed-bid auction were compared: (1) super-experienced bidders and (2) less-experienced bidders. In the super-experienced group, 29 of 189 winning bids were above the item's expected value; in the less-experienced group, 32 of 149 winning bids were above the item's expected value.

a. Find an estimate of p_1, the true proportion of super-experienced bidders who fell prey to the winner's curse.

b. Find an estimate of p_2, the true proportion of less-experienced bidders who fell prey to the winner's curse.

c. Construct a 90% confidence interval for $p_1 - p_2$.

d. Give a practical interpretation of the confidence interval, part **c**. Make a statement about whether bid experience impacts the likelihood of the winner's curse occurring.

8.50 **Is steak your favorite barbeque food?** July is National Grilling Month in the United States. On July 1, 2008, *The Harris Poll #70* reported on a survey of Americans' grilling preferences. When asked about their favorite food prepared on a barbeque, 662 of 1,250 randomly sampled Democrats preferred steak, as compared to 586 of 930 randomly sampled Republicans.

a. Give a point estimate for the proportion of all Democrats who prefer steak as their favorite barbeque food.

b. Give a point estimate for the proportion of all Republicans who prefer steak as their favorite barbeque food.

c. Give a point estimate for the difference between the proportions of all Democrats and all Republicans who prefer steak as their favorite barbeque food.

d. Construct a 95% confidence interval for the difference between the proportions of all Democrats and all Republicans who prefer steak as their favorite barbeque food.

e. Give a practical interpretation of the interval, part **d**.

f. Explain the meaning of the phrase 95% confident in your answer to part **e**.

8.51 **Producer willingness to supply biomass.** Refer to the *Biomass and Energy* (Vol. 36, 2012) study of the willingness of producers to supply biomass products such as surplus hay, Exercise 8.20 (p. 436). Recall that independent samples of Missouri producers and Illinois producers were surveyed. Another aspect of the study focused on the services producers were willing to supply. One key service involves windrowing (mowing and piling) of hay. Of the 558 Missouri producers surveyed, 187 were willing to offer windrowing services; of the 940 Illinois producers surveyed, 380 were willing to offer windrowing services. The researchers want to know if the proportion of producers who were willing to offer windrowing services to the biomass market differs for the two areas, Missouri and Illinois.

a. Specify the parameter of interest to the researchers.

b. Set up the null and alternative hypotheses for testing whether the proportion of producers who were willing to offer windrowing services differs in Missouri and Illinois.

c. A Minitab analysis of the data is shown below. Locate the test statistic on the printout.

d. Give the rejection region for the test using $\alpha = .01$.

e. Locate the p-value of the test on the printout.

f. Make the appropriate conclusion using both the p-value and rejection region approach. Your conclusions should agree.

```
Test and CI for Two Proportions

Sample   X     N    Sample p
1       187   558   0.335125
2       380   940   0.404255


Difference = p (1) - p (2)
Estimate for difference:  -0.0691299
99% CI for difference:  (-0.135079, -0.00318070)
Test for difference = 0 (vs not = 0):  Z = -2.67  P-Value = 0.008

Fisher's exact test: P-Value = 0.008
```

8.52 **Planning habits survey.** *American Demographics* (Jan. 2002) reported the results of a survey on the planning habits of men and women. In response to the question, "What is your preferred method of planning and keeping track of meetings, appointments, and deadlines?," 56% of the men and 46% of the women answered, "Keep them in my head." A nationally representative sample of 1,000 adults participated in the survey; therefore, assume that 500 were men and 500 were women.

a. Set up the null and alternative hypotheses for testing whether the percentage of men who prefer keeping track of appointments in their head is larger than the corresponding percentage of women.

b. Compute the test statistic for the test.

c. Give the rejection region for the test using $\alpha = .01$.

d. Find the p-value for the test.

e. Make the appropriate conclusion.

8.53 **Hospital administration of malaria patients.** One of the most serious health problems in India is malaria. Consequently, Indian hospital administrators must have the resources to treat the high volume of malaria patients that are admitted. Research published in the *National Journal of Community Medicine* (Vol. 1, 2010) investigated whether the malaria admission rate is higher in some months than in others. In a sample of 192 hospital patients admitted in January, 32 were treated for malaria. In an independent sample of 403 patients admitted in May (4 months later), 34 were treated for malaria.

a. Describe the two populations of interest in this study.

b. Give a point estimate of the difference in the malaria admission rates in January and May.

c. Find a 90% confidence interval for the difference in the malaria admission rates in January and May.

d. Based on the interval, part **c**, can you conclude that a difference exists in the true malaria admission rates in January and May? Explain.

Applying the Concepts—Intermediate

8.54 **Electronic vs. printed surveys.** The rapid evolution of computer hardware and software has made it easy for businesses to conduct computer-based and Web-based (i.e., electronic) surveys. Professors at Michigan State and DePaul Universities collaborated on a study designed to compare the response rates of electronic surveys and traditional print surveys (Decision Sciences Institute, *Decision Line,* July 2001). The two surveys were developed for customers who had purchased products over the Internet from a leading retailer of office supplies. Of the 631 customers mailed the printed survey, 261 returned usable responses. Of the 414 customers who were sent a computer disk with the electronic survey, 155 returned usable responses.

a. Estimate the difference between the response rates of the two survey types using a 90% confidence interval. Interpret the result.

b. If the difference in response rates is 5% or less, the researchers will infer that there is no "practical" difference in response rates for the two surveys. Are the researchers able to make this inference? Explain.

8.55 **Salmonella in produce.** Salmonella is the most common type of bacterial food-borne illness in the United States. How prevalent is salmonella in produce grown in the major agricultural region of Monterey, California? Researchers from the U.S. Department of Agriculture (USDA) conducted tests for salmonella in produce grown in the region and published their results in *Applied and Environmental Microbiology* (April 2011). In a sample of 252 cultures obtained from water used to irrigate the region, 18 tested positive for salmonella. In an independent sample of 476 cultures obtained from the region's wildlife (e.g., birds), 20 tested positive for salmonella. Is this sufficient evidence for the USDA to state that the prevalence of salmonella in the region's water differs from the prevalence of salmonella in the region's wildlife? Use $\alpha = .01$ to make your decision.

8.56 Angioplasty's benefits challenged. More than 1 million heart patients each year undergo an angioplasty. The benefits of an angioplasty were challenged in a recent study of 2,287 patients (2007 Annual Conference of the American College of Cardiology, New Orleans). All the patients had substantial blockage of the arteries but were medically stable. All were treated with medication such as aspirin and beta-blockers. However, half the patients were randomly assigned to get an angioplasty and half were not. After 5 years, the researchers found that 211 of the 1,145 patients in the angioplasty group had subsequent heart attacks compared to 202 of 1,142 patients in the medication-only group. Do you agree with the study's conclusion, "There was no significant difference in the rate of heart attacks for the two groups"? Support your answer with a 95% confidence interval.

8.57 Entrepreneurial careers of MBA alumni. Are African American MBA students more likely to begin their careers as entrepreneurs than white MBA students? This was a question of interest to the Graduate Management Admission Council (GMAC). *GMAC Research Reports* (Oct. 3, 2005) published the results of a survey of MBA alumni. Of the 1,304 African Americans who responded to the survey, 209 reported their employment status after graduation as self-employed or a small business owner. Of the 7,120 whites who responded to the survey, 356 reported their employment status after graduation as self-employed or a small business owner. Use this information to answer the research question.

8.58 Predicting software defects. Refer to the PROMISE Software Engineering Repository data on 498 modules of software code written in "C" language for a NASA spacecraft instrument, saved in the file. (See Exercise 3.76, p. 168) Recall that the software code in each module was evaluated for defects; 49 were classified as "true" (i.e., module has defective code), and 449 were classified as "false" (i.e., module has correct code). Consider these to be independent random samples of software code modules. Researchers predicted the defect status of each module using the simple algorithm, "If number of lines of code in the module exceeds 50, predict the module to have a defect." The accompanying SPSS printout shows the number of modules in each of the two samples that were predicted to have defects (PRED_LOC = "yes") and predicted to have no defects (PRED_LOC = "no"). Now, define the *accuracy rate* of the algorithm as the proportion of modules that were correctly predicted. Compare the accuracy rate of the algorithm when applied to modules with defective code to the accuracy rate of the algorithm when applied to modules with correct code. Use a 99% confidence interval.

DEFECT * PRED_LOC Crosstabulation

Count

		PRED_LOC		
		no	yes	Total
DEFECT	false	400	49	449
	true	29	20	49
Total		429	69	498

Applying the Concepts—Advanced

8.59 Food craving study. Do you have an insatiable craving for chocolate or some other food? Because many North Americans apparently do, psychologists are designing scientific studies to examine the phenomenon. According to the *New York Times* (Feb. 22, 1995), one of the largest studies of food cravings involved a survey of 1,000 McMaster University (Canada) students. The survey revealed that 97% of the women in the study acknowledged specific food cravings while only 67% of the men did.

a. How large do n_1 and n_2 need to be to conclude that the true proportion of women who acknowledged having food cravings exceeds the corresponding proportion of men? Assume $\alpha = .01$.

b. Why is it dangerous to conclude from the study that women have a higher incidence of food cravings than men?

8.60 Religious symbolism in TV commercials. Gonzaga University professors conducted a study of television commercials and published their results in the *Journal of Sociology, Social Work and Social Welfare* (Vol. 2, 2008). The key research question was: "Do television advertisers use religious symbolism to sell goods and services?" In a sample of 797 TV commercials collected in 1998, only 16 commercials used religious symbolism. Of the sample of 1,499 TV commercials examined in the more recent study, 51 commercials used religious symbolism. Conduct an analysis to determine if the percentage of TV commercials that use religious symbolism has changed since the 1998 study. If you detect a change, estimate the magnitude of the difference and attach a measure of reliability to the estimate.

8.5 Determining the Required Sample Size

You can find the appropriate sample size to estimate the difference between a pair of parameters with a specified margin of error (ME) and degree of reliability by using the method described in Section 6.5 — that is, to estimate the difference between a pair of parameters correct to within ME units with confidence level $(1 - \alpha)$, let $z_{\alpha/2}$ standard deviations of the sampling distribution of the estimator equal ME. Then solve for the sample size. To do this, you have to solve the problem for a specific ratio between n_1 and n_2. Most often, you will want to have equal sample sizes—that is, $n_1 = n_2 = n$. We will illustrate the procedure with two examples.

Example 8.8

Finding the Sample Sizes for Estimating $(\mu_1 - \mu_2)$— Comparing Mean Crop Yields

Problem New fertilizer compounds are often advertised with the promise of increased crop yields. Suppose we want to compare the mean yield μ_1 of wheat when a new fertilizer is used to the mean yield μ_2 with a fertilizer in common use. The estimate of the difference in mean yield per acre is to be correct to within .25 bushel with a confidence coefficient of .95. If the sample sizes are to be equal, find $n_1 = n_2 = n$, the number of 1-acre plots of wheat assigned to each fertilizer.

Solution To solve the problem, you need to know something about the variation in the bushels of yield per acre. Suppose from past records you know the yields of wheat possess a range of approximately 10 bushels per acre. You could then approximate $\sigma_1 = \sigma_2 = \sigma$ by letting the range equal 4σ. Thus,

$$4\sigma \approx 10 \text{ bushels}$$

$$\sigma \approx 2.5 \text{ bushels}$$

The next step is to solve the equation

$$z_{\alpha/2}\sigma_{(\bar{x}_1 - \bar{x}_2)} = \text{ME} \qquad \text{or} \qquad z_{\alpha/2}\sqrt{\frac{\sigma_1^2}{n_1} + \frac{\sigma_2^2}{n_2}} = \text{ME}$$

for n, where $n = n_1 = n_2$. Because we want the estimate to lie within $\text{ME} = .25$ of $(\mu_1 - \mu_2)$ with confidence coefficient equal to .95, we have $z_{\alpha/2} = z_{.025} = 1.96$. Then, letting $\sigma_1 = \sigma_2 = 2.5$ and solving for n, we have

$$1.96\sqrt{\frac{(2.5)^2}{n} + \frac{(2.5)^2}{n}} = .25$$

$$1.96\sqrt{\frac{2(2.5)^2}{n}} = .25$$

$$n = 768.32 \approx 769 \text{ (rounding up)}$$

Consequently, you will have to sample 769 acres of wheat for each fertilizer to estimate the difference in mean yield per acre to within .25 bushel.

Look Back Because $n = 769$ would necessitate extensive and costly experimentation, you might decide to allow a larger margin of error (say, $\text{ME} = .50$ or $\text{ME} = 1$) to reduce the sample size, or you might decrease the confidence coefficient. The point is that we can obtain an idea of the experimental effort necessary to achieve a specified precision in our final estimate by determining the approximate sample size *before* the experiment is started.

■ **Now Work Exercise 8.62a**

Example 8.9

Finding the Sample Sizes for Estimating $(p_1 - p_2)$— Comparing Defect Rates of Two Machines

Problem A production supervisor suspects a difference exists between the proportions p_1 and p_2 of defective items produced by two different machines. Experience has shown that the proportion defective for each of the two machines is in the neighborhood of .03. If the supervisor wants to estimate the difference in the proportions to within .005 using a 95% confidence interval, how many items must be randomly sampled from the production of each machine? (Assume that the supervisor wants $n_1 = n_2 = n$.)

Solution In this sampling problem, the margin of error is $\text{ME} = .005$, and for the specified level of reliability, $(1 - \alpha) = .95$, $z_{\alpha/2} = z_{.025} = 1.96$. Then, letting $p_1 = p_2 = .03$ and $n_1 = n_2 = n$, we find the required sample size per machine by solving the following equation for n:

$$z_{\alpha/2}\sigma_{(\hat{p}_1 - \hat{p}_2)} = \text{ME}$$

or

$$z_{\alpha/2} \sqrt{\frac{p_1 q_1}{n_1} + \frac{p_2 q_2}{n_2}} = \text{ME}$$

$$1.96 \sqrt{\frac{(.03)(.97)}{n} + \frac{(.03)(.97)}{n}} = .005$$

$$1.96 \sqrt{\frac{2(.03)(.97)}{n}} = .005$$

$$n = 8{,}943.2$$

Look Back This large n will likely result in a tedious sampling procedure. If the supervisor insists on estimating $(p_1 - p_2)$ correct to within .005 with 95% confidence, approximately 9,000 items will have to be inspected for each machine.

■ **Now Work Exercise 8.61a**

You can see from the calculations in Example 8.9 that $\sigma_{(\hat{p}_1 - \hat{p}_2)}$ (and hence the solution, $n_1 = n_2 = n$) depends on the actual (but unknown) values of p_1 and p_2. In fact, the required sample size $n_1 = n_2 = n$ is largest when $p_1 = p_2 = .5$. Therefore, if you have no prior information on the approximate values of p_1 and p_2, use $p_1 = p_2 = .5$ in the formula for $\sigma_{(\hat{p}_1 - \hat{p}_2)}$. If p_1 and p_2 are in fact close to .5, then the values of n_1 and n_2 that you have calculated will be correct. If p_1 and p_2 differ substantially from .5, then your solutions for n_1 and n_2 will be larger than needed. Consequently, using $p_1 = p_2 = .5$ when solving for n_1 and n_2 is a conservative procedure because the sample sizes n_1 and n_2 will be at least as large as (and probably larger than) needed.

The procedures for determining the sample sizes necessary for estimating $(\mu_1 - \mu_2)$ or $(p_1 - p_2)$ for the case $n_1 = n_2$ are given in the boxes that follow.

Determination of Sample Size for Estimating $(\mu_1 - \mu_2)$

To estimate $(\mu_1 - \mu_2)$ with a given margin of error ME and with confidence level $(1 - \alpha)$, use the following formula to solve for equal sample sizes that will achieve the desired reliability:

$$n_1 = n_2 = \frac{(z_{\alpha/2})^2 (\sigma_1^2 + \sigma_2^2)}{(\text{ME})^2}$$

You will need to substitute estimates for the values of σ_1^2 and σ_2^2 before solving for the sample size. These estimates might be sample variances s_1^2 and s_2^2 from prior sampling (e.g., a pilot sample) or from an educated (and conservatively large) guess based on the range—that is, $s \approx R/4$.

Determination of Sample Size for Estimating $(p_1 - p_2)$

To estimate $(p_1 - p_2)$ with a given margin of error ME and with confidence level $(1 - \alpha)$, use the following formula to solve for equal sample sizes that will achieve the desired reliability:

$$n_1 = n_2 = \frac{(z_{\alpha/2})^2 (p_1 q_1 + p_2 q_2)}{(\text{ME})^2}$$

You will need to substitute estimates for the values of p_1 and p_2 before solving for the sample size. These estimates might be based on prior samples, obtained from educated guesses, or, most conservatively, specified as $p_1 = p_2 = .5$.

Exercises 8.61–8.72

Learning the Mechanics

8.61 Assuming that $n_1 = n_2$, find the sample sizes needed to estimate $(p_1 - p_2)$ for each of the following situations:

NW **a.** Margin of error = .01 with 99% confidence. Assume that $p_1 \approx .4$ and $p_2 \approx .7$.

  b. A 90% confidence interval of width .05. Assume that there is no prior information available to obtain approximate values of p_1 and p_2.

  c. Margin of error = .03 with 90% confidence. Assume that $p_1 \approx .2$ and $p_2 \approx .3$.

8.62 Find the appropriate values of n_1 and n_2 (assume $n_1 = n_2$) needed to estimate $(\mu_1 - \mu_2)$ for each of the following situations:

NW **a.** A margin of error equal to 3.2 with 95% confidence. From prior experience it is known that $\sigma_1 \approx 15$ and $\sigma_2 \approx 17$.

  b. A margin of error equal to 8 with 99% confidence. The range of each population is 60.

  c. A 90% confidence interval of width 1.0. Assume that $\sigma_1^2 \approx 5.8$ and $\sigma_2^2 \approx 7.5$.

8.63 Suppose you want to estimate the difference between two population means correct to within 1.8 with a 95% confidence interval. If prior information suggests that the population variances are approximately equal to $\sigma_1^2 = \sigma_2^2 = 14$ and you want to select independent random samples of equal size from the populations, how large should the sample sizes, n_1 and n_2, be?

8.64 Enough money has been budgeted to collect independent random samples of size $n_1 = n_2 = 100$ from populations 1 and 2 to estimate $(\mu_1 - \mu_2)$. Prior information indicates that $\sigma_1 = \sigma_2 = 10$. Have sufficient funds been allocated to construct a 90% confidence interval for $(\mu_1 - \mu_2)$ of width 5 or less? Justify your answer.

Applying the Concepts—Basic

8.65 **Last name and acquisition timing.** Refer to the *Journal of Consumer Research* (August 2011) study of the *last name effect* in acquisition timing, Exercise 8.13 (p. 433). Recall that the mean response times (in minutes) to acquire basketball tickets were compared for two groups of MBA students—those students with last names beginning with one of the first nine letters of the alphabet and those with last names beginning with one of the last nine letters of the alphabet. How many MBA students from each group would need to be selected to estimate the difference in mean times to within 2 minutes of its true value with 95% confidence? (Assume equal sample sizes were selected for each group and that the response time standard deviation for both groups is $\sigma \approx 9$ minutes.)

8.66 **Homework assistance for accounting students.** Refer to the *Journal of Accounting Education* (Vol. 25, 2007) study of providing homework assistance to accounting students, Exercise 8.18 (p. 435). Recall that one group of students was given a completed homework solution and another group was given only check figures at various steps of the solution. The researchers wanted to compare the average test score improvement of the two groups. How many students should be sampled in each group to estimate the

difference in the averages to within .5 point with 99% confidence? Assume that the standard deviations of the test score improvements for the two groups are approximately equal to 1.

8.67 **Electronic vs. printed surveys.** Refer to the *Decision Line* (July 2001) study designed to compare the response rates of electronic surveys and traditional print surveys, Exercise 8.54 (p. 454). Recall that the two surveys were developed for customers who had purchased products over the Internet from a leading retailer of office supplies. How many customers should be sampled to estimate the difference between the response rates of the two survey types to within .01 using a 90% confidence interval? Assume the same number of customers should be sampled for each survey.

8.68 **Conducting a political poll.** A pollster wants to estimate the difference between the proportions of men and women who favor a particular national candidate using a 90% confidence interval of width .04. Suppose the pollster has no prior information about the proportions. If equal numbers of men and women are to be polled, how large should the sample sizes be?

Applying the Concepts—Intermediate

8.69 **Life expectancies of working women and housewives.** Is housework hazardous to your health? A study in *Public Health Reports* compared the life expectancies of 25-year-old white women in the labor force to those who are housewives. How large a sample would have to be taken from each group in order to be 95% confident that the estimate of difference in average life expectancies for the two groups is within 1 year of the true difference in average life expectancies? Assume that equal sample sizes will be selected from the two groups and that the standard deviation for both groups is approximately 15 years.

8.70 **Users of home shopping services.** All cable companies carry at least one home shopping channel. Who uses these home shopping services? Are the shoppers primarily men or women? Suppose you want to estimate the difference in the proportions of men and women who say they have used or expect to use televised home shopping using an 80% confidence interval of width .06 or less.

  a. Approximately how many people should be included in your samples?

  b. Suppose you want to obtain individual estimates for the two proportions of interest. Will the sample size found in part **a** be large enough to provide estimates of each proportion correct to within .02 with probability equal to .90? Justify your response.

8.71 **Angioplasty's benefits challenged.** Refer to the study of patients with substantial blockage of the arteries presented at the 2007 Annual Conference of the American College of Cardiology, Exercise 8.56 (p. 455). Recall that half the patients were randomly assigned to get an angioplasty and half were not. The researchers compared the proportion of patients with subsequent heart attacks for the two groups and reported no significant difference between the two proportions. Although the study involved over

2,000 patients, the sample size may have been too small to detect a difference in heart attack rates.

a. How many patients must be sampled in each group to estimate the difference in heart attack rates to within .015 with 95% confidence? (Use summary data from Exercise 8.56 in your calculation.)

b. Comment on the practicality of carrying out the study with the sample sizes determined in part **a**.

c. Comment on the practical significance of the difference detected in the confidence interval for the study, part **a**.

8.72 **Average housing space per person.** Even though Japan is an economic superpower, Japanese workers are in many ways worse off than their U.S. and European counterparts. For example, the estimated average housing space per person (in square feet) is 645 in the United States but only 344 in Japan (Diawa House Industry, Co., Japan). Suppose a team of economists and sociologists from the United Nations plans to reestimate the difference in the mean housing space per person for U.S. and Japanese workers. Assume that equal sample sizes will be used for each country and that the standard deviation is 35 square feet for Japan and 80 for the United States. How many people should be sampled in each country to estimate the difference to within 10 square feet with 95% confidence?

8.6 Comparing Two Population Variances: Independent Sampling

Many times, it is of practical interest to use the techniques developed in this chapter to compare the means or proportions of two populations. However, there are also important instances when we wish to compare two population variances. For example, when two devices are available for producing precision measurements (scales, calipers, thermometers, etc.), we might want to compare the variability of the measurements of the devices before deciding which one to purchase. Or when two standardized tests can be used to rate job applicants, the variability of the scores for both tests should be taken into consideration before deciding which test to use.

For problems like these, we need to develop a statistical procedure to compare population variances. The common statistical procedure for comparing population variances, σ_1^2 and σ_2^2, makes an inference about the ratio $\frac{\sigma_1^2}{\sigma_2^2}$. In this section, we will show how to test the null hypothesis that the ratio $\frac{\sigma_1^2}{\sigma_2^2}$ equals 1 (the variances are equal) against the alternative hypothesis that the ratio differs from 1 (the variances differ):

$$H_0: \frac{\sigma_1^2}{\sigma_2^2} = 1 \quad (\sigma_1^2 = \sigma_2^2)$$

$$H_a: \frac{\sigma_1^2}{\sigma_2^2} \neq 1 \quad (\sigma_1^2 \neq \sigma_2^2)$$

To make an inference about the ratio $\frac{\sigma_1^2}{\sigma_2^2}$, it seems reasonable to collect sample data and use the ratio of the sample variances, $\frac{s_1^2}{s_2^2}$. We will use the test statistic

$$F = \frac{s_1^2}{s_2^2}$$

To establish a rejection region for the test statistic, we need to know the sampling distribution of $\frac{s_1^2}{s_2^2}$. As you will subsequently see, the sampling distribution of $\frac{s_1^2}{s_2^2}$ is based on two of the assumptions already required for the t-test:

1. The two sampled populations are normally distributed.

2. The samples are randomly and independently selected from their respective populations.

When these assumptions are satisfied and when the null hypothesis is true (that is, $\sigma_1^2 = \sigma_2^2$), the sampling distribution of $F = \frac{s_1^2}{s_2^2}$ is the **F-distribution** with $(n_1 - 1)$ numerator degrees of freedom and $(n_2 - 1)$ denominator degrees of freedom, respectively. The shape of the F-distribution depends on the degrees of freedom associated with s_1^2 and s_2^2—that is, on $(n_1 - 1)$ and $(n_2 - 1)$. An F-distribution with 7 and 9 df is shown in Figure 8.17. As you can see, the distribution is skewed to the right because $\frac{s_1^2}{s_2^2}$ cannot be less than 0 but can increase without bound.

Figure 8.17

An F-distribution with 7 numerator and 9 denominator degrees of freedom

We need to be able to find F values corresponding to the tail areas of this distribution to establish the rejection region for our test of hypothesis because we expect the ratio F of the sample variances to be either very large or very small when the population variances are unequal. The upper-tail F values for $\alpha = .10, .05, .025,$ and $.01$ can be found in Tables V, VI, VII, and VIII in Appendix D. Table VI is partially reproduced in Table 8.7. It gives F values that correspond to $\alpha = .05$ upper-tail areas for different degrees of freedom ν_1 for the numerator sample variance, s_1^2, whereas the rows correspond to the degrees of freedom ν_2 for the denominator sample variance, s_2^2. Thus, if the numerator degrees of freedom is $\nu_1 = 7$ and the denominator degrees of freedom is $\nu_2 = 9$, we look in the seventh column and ninth row to find $F_{.05} = 3.29$. As shown in Figure 8.18, $\alpha = .05$ is the tail area to the right of 3.29 in the F-distribution with 7 and 9 df—that is, if $\sigma_1^2 = \sigma_2^2$, then the probability that the F-statistic will exceed 3.29 is $\alpha = .05$.

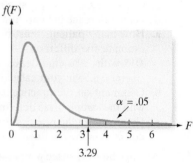

Figure 8.18

An F-distribution for $\nu_1 = 7$ df and $\nu_2 = 9$ df; $\alpha = .05$

GEORGE W. SNEDECOR
(1882–1974)
Snedecor's F-test

George W. Snedecor's education began at the University of Alabama, where he obtained his bachelor's degree in mathematics and physics. He went on to the University of Michigan for his master's degree in physics and finally earned his PhD in mathematics at the University of Kentucky. Snedecor learned of an opening for an assistant professor of mathematics at the University of Iowa, packed his belongings in his car, and began driving to apply for the position. By mistake, he ended up in Ames, Iowa, home of Iowa State University—then an agricultural school that had no need for a mathematics teacher. Nevertheless, Snedecor stayed and founded a statistics laboratory, eventually teaching the first course in statistics at Iowa State in 1915. In 1933, Snedecor turned the statistics laboratory into the first-ever Department of Statistics in the United States. During his tenure as chair of the department, Snedecor published his landmark textbook, *Statistical Methods* (1937). The text contained the first published reference for a test of hypothesis to compare two variances. Although Snedecor named it the *F*-test in honor of statistician R. A. Fisher (who had developed the *F*-distribution a few years earlier), many researchers still refer to it as Snedecor's *F*-test. Now in its ninth edition, *Statistical Methods* (with William Cochran as a coauthor) continues to be one of the most frequently cited texts in the statistics field.

Table 8.7 | **Reproduction of Part of Table VI in Appendix D: Percentage Points of the *F*-Distribution, $\alpha = .05$**

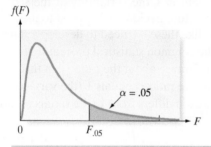

	Numerator Degrees of Freedom								
ν_1 / ν_2	1	2	3	4	5	6	7	8	9
1	161.4	199.5	215.7	224.6	230.2	234.0	236.8	238.9	240.5
2	18.51	19.00	19.16	19.25	19.30	19.33	19.35	19.37	19.38
3	10.13	9.55	9.28	9.12	9.01	8.94	8.89	8.85	8.81
4	7.71	6.94	6.59	6.39	6.26	6.16	6.09	6.04	6.00
5	6.61	5.79	5.41	5.19	5.05	4.95	4.88	4.82	4.77
6	5.99	5.14	4.76	4.53	4.39	4.28	4.21	4.15	4.10
7	5.59	4.74	4.35	4.12	3.97	3.87	3.79	3.73	3.68
8	5.32	4.46	4.07	3.84	3.69	3.58	3.50	3.44	3.39
9	5.12	4.26	3.86	3.63	3.48	3.37	3.29	3.23	3.18
10	4.96	4.10	3.71	3.48	3.33	3.22	3.14	3.07	3.02
11	4.84	3.98	3.59	3.36	3.20	3.09	3.01	2.95	2.90
12	4.75	3.89	3.49	3.25	3.11	3.00	2.91	2.85	2.80
13	4.67	3.81	3.41	3.18	3.03	2.92	2.83	2.77	2.71
14	4.60	3.74	3.34	3.11	2.96	2.85	2.76	2.70	2.65

Denominator Degrees of Freedom

Example 8.10

An *F*-Test Application—Comparing Paper Mill Production Variation

Problem A manufacturer of paper products wants to compare the variation in daily production levels at two paper mills. Independent random samples of days are selected from each mill, and the production levels (in units) are recorded. The data are shown in Table 8.8. Do these data provide sufficient evidence to indicate a difference in the variability of production levels at the two paper mills? (Use $\alpha = .10$.)

Table 8.8	Production Levels at Two Paper Mills							
Mill 1:	34	18	28	21	40	23	29	
	25	10	38	32	22	22		
Mill 2:	31	13	27	19	22	18	23	22	21
	18	15	24	13	19	18	19	23	13

Data Set: PAPER

Solution Let

$$\sigma_1^2 = \text{Population variance of production levels at mill 1}$$
$$\sigma_2^2 = \text{Population variance of production levels at mill 2}$$

The hypotheses of interest, then, are

$$H_0: \frac{\sigma_1^2}{\sigma_2^2} = 1 \qquad (\sigma_1^2 = \sigma_2^2)$$

$$H_a: \frac{\sigma_1^2}{\sigma_2^2} \neq 1 \qquad (\sigma_1^2 \neq \sigma_2^2)$$

The nature of the *F*-tables given in Appendix D affects the form of the test statistic. To form the rejection region for a two-tailed *F*-test, we want to make certain that the upper tail is used because only the upper-tail values of *F* are shown in the tables in Appendix D. To accomplish this, *we will always place the larger sample variance in the numerator of the F-test statistic.* This doubles the tabulated value for α because we double the probability that the *F*-ratio will fall in the upper tail by always placing the larger sample variance in the numerator—that is, we establish a one-tailed rejection region by putting the larger variance in the numerator rather than establishing rejection regions in both tails.

Thus, for our example, we have a numerator s_1^2 with df $= \nu_1 = n_1 - 1 = 12$ and a denominator s_2^2 with df $= \nu_2 = n_2 - 1 = 17$. Therefore, the test statistic will be

$$F = \frac{\text{Larger sample variance}}{\text{Smaller sample variance}} = \frac{s_1^2}{s_2^2}$$

and we will reject $H_0: \sigma_1^2 = \sigma_2^2$ for $\alpha = .10$ when the calculated value of *F* exceeds the tabulated value:

$$F_{\alpha/2} = F_{.05} = 2.38 \qquad \text{(see Figure 8.19)}$$

Figure 8.19

Rejection region for Example 8.10

To calculate the value of the test statistic, we require the sample variances. Summary statistics for the data in Table 8.8 are shown on the Minitab printout, Figure 8.20. The sample standard deviations (shaded) are $s_1 = 8.36$ and $s_2 = 4.85$. Therefore,

$$F = \frac{s_1^2}{s_2^2} = \frac{(8.36)^2}{(4.85)^2} = 2.97$$

When we compare this result to the rejection region shown in Figure 8.19, we see that $F = 2.97$ falls in the rejection region. Therefore, the data provide sufficient evidence to indicate that the population variances differ. It appears that the variation in production levels at mill 1 tends to be higher than the variation at mill 2.

Descriptive Statistics: LEVEL

```
Variable  MILL   N   Mean   StDev   Minimum  Median  Maximum
LEVEL      1    13  26.31   8.36     10.00   25.00   40.00
           2    18  19.89   4.85     13.00   19.00   31.00
```

Figure 8.20

Minitab summary statistics for data in Table 8.8

Look Back What would you have concluded if the value of F calculated from the samples had not fallen in the rejection region? Would you have concluded that the null hypothesis of equal variances is true? No, because then you risk the possibility of a Type II error (accepting H_0 if H_a is true) without knowing the value of β, the probability of accepting H_0: $\sigma_1^2 = \sigma_2^2$ if, in fact, it is false. Because we will not consider the calculation of β for specific alternatives in this text, when the F-statistic does not fall in the rejection region, we simply conclude that insufficient sample evidence exists to refute the null hypothesis that $\sigma_1^2 = \sigma_2^2$.

◼ **Now Work Exercise 8.78a**

The F-test for equal population variances is summarized in the following boxes.*

F-Test for Equal Population Variances

One-Tailed Test	Two-Tailed Test>
H_0: $\sigma_1^2 = \sigma_2^2$	H_0: $\sigma_1^2 = \sigma_2^2$
H_a: $\sigma_1^2 < \sigma_2^2$ (or H_a: $\sigma_1^2 > \sigma_2^2$)	H_a: $\sigma_1^2 \neq \sigma_2^2$
Test statistic:	*Test statistic:*
$F = \dfrac{s_2^2}{s_1^2}$	$F = \dfrac{\text{Larger sample variance}}{\text{Smaller sample variance}}$
$\left(\text{or } F = \dfrac{s_1^2}{s_2^2} \text{ when } H_a: \sigma_1^2 > \sigma_2^2\right)$	$= \dfrac{s_1^2}{s_2^2}$ when $s_1^2 > s_2^2$
	$\left(\text{or } \dfrac{s_2^2}{s_1^2} \text{ when } s_2^2 > s_1^2\right)$
Rejection region:	*Rejection region:*
$F > F_\alpha$	$F > F_{\alpha/2}$

where F_α and $F_{\alpha/2}$ are based on ν_1 = numerator degrees of freedom and ν_2 = denominator degrees of freedom; ν_1 and ν_2 are the degrees of freedom for the numerator and denominator sample variances, respectively.

Conditions Required for a Valid F-Test for Equal Variances

1. Both sampled populations are normally distributed.
2. The samples are random and independent.

Example 8.11	

The Observed Significance Level of an F-Test

Problem Find the p-value for the test in Example 8.10 using the F-tables in Appendix D. Compare this to the exact p-value obtained from a computer printout.

Solution Because the observed value of the F-statistic in Example 8.10 was 2.97, the observed significance level of the test would equal the probability of observing a value of F at least as contradictory to H_0: $\sigma_1^2 = \sigma_2^2$ as $F = 2.97$, if, in fact, H_0 is true. Because we give the F-tables in Appendix D only for values of α equal to .10, .05, .025, and .01, we can only approximate the observed significance level. Checking Tables VII and VIII, we find $F_{.025} = 2.82$ and $F_{.01} = 3.46$. Because the observed value of F exceeds $F_{.025}$ but

---

*Although a test of a hypothesis of equality of variances is the most common application of the F-test, it can also be used to test a hypothesis that the ratio between the population variances is equal to some specified value: H_0: $\sigma_1^2/\sigma_2^2 = k$. The test is conducted in exactly the same way as specified in the box, except that we use the test statistic

$$F = \frac{s_1^2}{s_2^2}\left(\frac{1}{k}\right)$$

is less than $F_{.01}$, the observed significance level for the test is less than $2(.025) = .05$ but greater than $2(.01) = .02$ — that is,

$$.02 < p\text{-value} < .05$$

The exact p-value of the test is shown on the Minitab printout, Figure 8.21. This value (highlighted) is .04.

Test for Equal Variances: LEVEL versus MILL

95% Bonferroni confidence intervals for standard deviations

```
MILL   N    Lower     StDev     Upper
   1  13  5.73182   8.36047  14.9507
   2  18  3.49950   4.84936   7.7455
```

F-Test (normal distribution)
Test statistic = 2.97, p-value = 0.040

Levene's Test (any continuous distribution)
Test statistic = 3.78, p-value = 0.062

Figure 8.21

Minitab F-test for equal variances

Look Back We double the α value shown in Tables VII and VIII because this is a two-tailed test.

■ **Now Work Exercise 8.78b**

As a final example of an application, consider the comparison of population variances as a check of the assumption $\sigma_1^2 = \sigma_2^2$ needed for the two-sample t-test. Rejection of the null hypothesis $\sigma_1^2 = \sigma_2^2$ would indicate that the assumption is invalid. [*Note:* Nonrejection of the null hypothesis does *not* imply that the assumption is valid.] We illustrate with an example.

Example 8.12

Checking the Assumption of Equal Variances

Problem In Example 8.4 (Section 8.2) we used the two-sample t-statistic to compare the success indexes of two groups of managers. The data are repeated in Table 8.9 for convenience. The use of the t-statistic was based on the assumption that the population variances of the managerial success indexes were equal for the two groups. Conduct a test of hypothesis to check this assumption at $\alpha = .10$.

Table 8.9	Managerial Success Indexes for Two Groups of Managers										
	Group 1						Group 2				
	Interaction with Outsiders						Few Interactions				
65	58	78	60	68	69		62	53	36	34	56	50
66	70	53	71	63	63		42	57	46	68	48	42
							52	53	43			

Data Set: SUCCES

Solution We want to test

$$H_0: \sigma_1^2 = \sigma_2^2$$
$$H_a: \sigma_1^2 \neq \sigma_2^2$$

This F-test is shown on the Excel/XLSTAT printout, Figure 8.22. Both the test statistic, $F = .5$, and two-tailed p-value, p-value $= .2554$, are highlighted on the printout. Because $\alpha = .10$ is less than the p-value, we do not reject the null hypothesis that the population variances of the success indexes are equal. It is here that the temptation to misuse the F-test is strongest. *We cannot conclude that the data justify the use of the t-statistic.* This is equivalent to accepting H_0, and we have repeatedly warned against this conclusion because the probability of a Type II error, β, is unknown. The α level of .10 protects us only against rejecting H_0 if it is true. This use of the F-test may prevent us from abusing the t-procedure when we obtain a value of F that leads to a rejection of the assumption that $\sigma_1^2 = \sigma_2^2$. But when the F-statistic does not fall in the rejection region, we know little more about the validity of the assumption than before we conducted the test.

Summary statistics:

Variable	Observations	Minimum	Maximum	Mean	Std. deviation
SUCCESS|1	12	53.0000	78.0000	65.3333	6.6104
SUCCESS|2	15	34.0000	68.0000	49.4667	9.3340

Fisher's F-test / Two-tailed test:

90% confidence interval on the ratio of variances:
(0.1955, 1.3736)

Ratio	0.5016
F (Observed value)	0.5016
F (Critical value)	2.5655
DF1	11
DF2	14
p-value (Two-tailed)	0.2554
alpha	0.1

Figure 8.22

Excel/XLSTAT analysis for testing assumption of equal variances

Look Back A 90% confidence interval for the ratio σ_1^2/σ_2^2 is shown in the middle of the Excel/XLSTAT printont of Figure 8.22. Note that the interval (.196, 1.374) includes 1; hence, we cannot conclude that the ratio differs from 1. Thus, the confidence interval leads to the same conclusion as the two-tailed test does: There is insufficient evidence of a difference between the population variances.

━━ ■ **Now Work Exercise 8.84**

What Do You Do If the Assumption of Normal Population Distributions Is Not Satisfied?

Answer: The F-test is much less robust (i.e., much more sensitive) to departures from normality than the t-test for comparing the population means (Section 8.2). If you have doubts about the normality of the population frequency distributions, use a **nonparametric method** (e.g., *Levene's test*) for comparing the two population variances. This method can be found in the nonparametric statistics texts listed in the references for Chapter 15.

Exercises 8.73–8.88

Learning the Mechanics

8.73 Use Tables V, VI, VII, and VIII in Appendix D to find each
NW of the following F-values:
  a. $F_{.05}$ where $\nu_1 = 9$ and $\nu_2 = 6$
  b. $F_{.01}$ where $\nu_1 = 18$ and $\nu_2 = 14$
  c. $F_{.025}$ where $\nu_1 = 11$ and $\nu_2 = 4$
  d. $F_{.10}$ where $\nu_1 = 20$ and $\nu_2 = 5$

8.74 Given ν_1 and ν_2, find the following probabilities:
  a. $\nu_1 = 2, \nu_2 = 30, P(F \geq 5.39)$
  b. $\nu_1 = 24, \nu_2 = 10, P(F < 2.74)$
  c. $\nu_1 = 7, \nu_2 = 1, P(F \leq 236.8)$
  d. $\nu_1 = 40, \nu_2 = 40, P(F > 2.11)$

8.75 For each of the following cases, identify the rejection region that should be used to test $H_0: \sigma_1^2 = \sigma_2^2$ against $H_a: \sigma_1^2 > \sigma_2^2$. Assume $\nu_1 = 30$ and $\nu_2 = 20$.
- **a.** $\alpha = .10$
- **b.** $\alpha = .05$
- **c.** $\alpha = .025$
- **d.** $\alpha = .01$

8.76 For each of the following cases, identify the rejection region that should be used to test $H_0: \sigma_1^2 = \sigma_2^2$ against $H_a: \sigma_1^2 \neq \sigma_2^2$. Assume $\nu_1 = 10$ and $\nu_2 = 12$.
- **a.** $\alpha = .20$
- **b.** $\alpha = .10$
- **c.** $\alpha = .05$
- **d.** $\alpha = .02$

8.77 Specify the appropriate rejection region for testing $H_0: \sigma_1^2 = \sigma_2^2$ in each of the following situations:
- **a.** $H_a: \sigma_1^2 > \sigma_2^2; \alpha = .05, n_1 = 25, n_2 = 20$
- **b.** $H_a: \sigma_1^2 < \sigma_2^2; \alpha = .05, n_1 = 10, n_2 = 15$
- **c.** $H_a: \sigma_1^2 \neq \sigma_2^2; \alpha = .10, n_1 = 21, n_2 = 31$
- **d.** $H_a: \sigma_1^2 < \sigma_2^2; \alpha = .01, n_1 = 31, n_2 = 41$
- **e.** $H_a: \sigma_1^2 \neq \sigma_2^2; \alpha = .05, n_1 = 7, n_2 = 16$

8.78 Independent random samples were selected from each of two normally distributed populations, $n_1 = 12$ from population 1 and $n_2 = 27$ from population 2. The means and variances for the two samples are shown in the table.

Sample 1	Sample 2
$n_1 = 12$	$n_2 = 27$
$\bar{x}_1 = 31.7$	$\bar{x}_2 = 37.4$
$s_1^2 = 3.87$	$s_2^2 = 8.75$

- **a.** Test the null hypothesis $H_0: \sigma_1^2 = \sigma_2^2$ against the alternative hypothesis $H_a: \sigma_1^2 \neq \sigma_2^2$. Use $\alpha = .10$.
- **b.** Find and interpret the approximate p-value of the test.

8.79 Independent random samples were selected from each of two normally distributed populations, $n_1 = 6$ from population 1 and $n_2 = 5$ from population 2. The data are shown in the table.

Sample 1	Sample 2
3.1	2.3
4.4	1.4
1.2	3.7
1.7	8.9
.7	5.5
3.4	

- **a.** Test $H_0: \sigma_1^2 = \sigma_2^2$ against $H_a: \sigma_1^2 < \sigma_2^2$. Use $\alpha = .01$.
- **b.** Find and interpret the approximate p-value of the test.

Applying the Concepts — Basic

8.80 **Lobster trap placement.** Refer to the *Bulletin of Marine Science* (April 2010) study of lobster trap placement, Exercise 8.12 (p. 433). The data are repeated here (next column). You used the small-sample t-statistic to form a confidence interval for the difference between the mean trap-spacing measurements of the two fishing cooperatives. This method requires the variance of the population of trap spacings for the BT cooperative, $(\sigma_{BT})^2$, to be the same as the population variance for the PA cooperative, $(\sigma_{PA})^2$.

BT Cooperative:	93	99	105	94	82	70	86	
PA Cooperative:	118	94	106	72	90	66	153	98

Source: Shester, G. G. "Explaining catch variation among Baja California lobster fishers through spatial analysis of trap-placement decisions," *Bulletin of Marine Science,* Vol. 86, No. 2, April 2010 (Table 1).

- **a.** Set up the null and alternative hypotheses for testing the equality of variances.
- **b.** Find the sample variances for the two cooperatives.
- **c.** Compute the test statistic.
- **d.** Find the approximate p-value of the test.
- **e.** Make the appropriate conclusion using $\alpha = .01$.

8.81 **Children's recall of TV ads.** Refer to the *Journal of Advertising* (Spring 2006) study of children's recall of television commercials, Exercise 8.15 (p. 434). You used a small-sample t-test to test the null hypothesis $H_0: (\mu_1 - \mu_2) = 0$, where μ_1 = mean number of ads recalled by children in the video only group and μ_2 = mean number of ads recalled by children in the A/V group. Summary statistics for the study are reproduced in the table below. The validity of the inference derived from the test is based on the assumption of equal group variances, i.e., $\sigma_1^2 = \sigma_2^2$.
- **a.** Set up the null and alternative hypotheses for testing this assumption.
- **b.** Compute the test statistic.
- **c.** Find the rejection region for the test using $\alpha = .10$.
- **d.** Make the appropriate conclusion in the words of the problem.
- **e.** Comment on the validity of the inference derived about the difference in population means in Exercise 8.15.

Video Only Group	A/V Group
$n_1 = 20$	$n_2 = 20$
$\bar{x}_1 = 3.70$	$\bar{x}_2 = 3.30$
$s_1 = 1.98$	$s_2 = 2.13$

8.82 **Mental health of workers and the unemployed.** A study in the *Journal of Occupational and Organizational Psychology* investigated the relationship of employment status and mental health. A sample of working and unemployed people was selected, and each person was given a mental health examination using the General Health Questionnaire (GHQ), a widely recognized measure of mental health. Although the article focused on comparing the mean GHQ levels, a comparison of the variability of GHQ scores for employed and unemployed men and women is of interest as well.
- **a.** In general terms, what does the amount of variability in GHQ scores tell us about the group?
- **b.** What are the appropriate null and alternative hypotheses to compare the variability of the mental health scores of the employed and unemployed groups? Define any symbols you use.
- **c.** The standard deviation for a sample of 142 employed men was 3.26, while the standard deviation for 49 unemployed men was 5.10. Conduct the test you set up in part **b** using $\alpha = .05$. Interpret the results.
- **d.** What assumptions are necessary to ensure the validity of the test?

8.83 Drug content assessment. Refer to Exercise 8.16 (p. 434) and the *Analytical Chemistry* (Dec. 15, 2009) study in which scientists used high-performance liquid chromatography to determine the amount of drug in a tablet. Recall that 25 tablets were produced at each of two different, independent sites. The researchers want to determine if the two sites produced drug concentrations with different variances. A Minitab printout of the analysis follows. Locate the test statistic and *p*-value on the printout. Use these values and $\alpha = .05$ to conduct the appropriate test for the researchers.

Test and CI for Two Variances: Content vs Site

```
Method

Null hypothesis          Variance(1) / Variance(2) = 1
Alternative hypothesis   Variance(1) / Variance(2) not = 1
Significance level       Alpha = 0.05


Statistics

Site  N   StDev  Variance
1     25  3.067  9.406
2     25  3.339  11.147

Ratio of standard deviations = 0.919
Ratio of variances = 0.844


95% Confidence Intervals

                                  CI for
Distribution   CI for StDev       Variance
of Data        Ratio              Ratio
Normal         (0.610, 1.384)     (0.372, 1.915)
Continuous     (0.497, 1.315)     (0.247, 1.729)


Tests

                                     Test
Method                     DF1 DF2 Statistic P-Value
F Test (normal)             24  24    0.84    0.681
Levene's Test (any continuous) 1 48   0.64    0.427
```

Applying the Concepts—Intermediate

8.84 Patent infringement case. Refer to the *Chance* (Fall 2002) description of a patent infringement case against Intel Corp., Exercise 8.19 (p. 435). The zinc measurements for three locations on the original inventor's notebook—on a text line, on a witness line, and on the intersection of the witness and text line—are reproduced in the table.

Text Line	.335	.374	.440			
Witness Line	.210	.262	.188	.329	.439	.397
Intersection	.393	.353	.285	.295	.319	

a. Use a test (at $\alpha = .05$) to compare the variation in zinc measurements for the text line with the corresponding variation for the intersection.

b. Use a test (at $\alpha = .05$) to compare the variation in zinc measurements for the witness line with the corresponding variation for the intersection.

c. From the results, parts **a** and **b**, what can you infer about the variation in zinc measurements at the three notebook locations?

d. What assumptions are required for the inferences to be valid? Are they reasonably satisfied? (You checked these assumptions when answering Exercise 8.19d.)

8.85 Analyzing human inspection errors. Tests of product quality using human inspectors can lead to serious inspection error problems (*Journal of Quality Technology*). To evaluate the performance of inspectors in a new company, a quality manager had a sample of 12 novice inspectors evaluate 200 finished products. The same 200 items were evaluated by 12 experienced inspectors. The quality of each item—whether defective or nondefective—was known to the manager. The table lists the number of inspection errors (classifying a defective item as nondefective or vice versa) made by each inspector.

Novice Inspectors				Experienced Inspectors			
30	35	26	40	31	15	25	19
36	20	45	31	28	17	19	18
33	29	21	48	24	10	20	21

a. Prior to conducting this experiment, the manager believed the variance in inspection errors was lower for experienced inspectors than for novice inspectors. Do the sample data support her belief? Test using $\alpha = .05$.

b. What is the appropriate *p*-value of the test you conducted in part **a?**

8.86 Cooling method for gas turbines. Refer to the *Journal of Engineering for Gas Turbines and Power* (Jan. 2005) study of gas turbines augmented with high-pressure inlet fogging, Exercise 8.24 (p. 437). Heat rate data (kilojoules per kilowatt per hour) for each of three types of gas turbines (advanced, aeroderivative, traditional) are saved in the accompanying file. In order to compare the mean heat rates of two types of gas turbines, you assumed that the heat rate variances were equal.

a. Conduct a test (at $\alpha = .05$) for equality of heat rate variances for traditional and aeroderivative augmented gas turbines. Use the result to make a statement about the validity of the inference derived in Exercise 8.24a.

b. Conduct a test (at $\alpha = .05$) for equality of heat rate variances for advanced and aeroderivative augmented gas turbines. Use the result to make a statement about the validity of the inference derived in Exercise 8.24b.

8.87 "Just-in-time" deliveries from factories to foxholes. Following the initial Persian Gulf War, the Pentagon changed its logistics processes to be more corporate-like. The extravagant "just-in-case" mentality was replaced with "just-in-time" systems. Emulating FedEx and United Parcel Service, deliveries from factories to foxholes are now expedited using bar codes, laser cards, radio tags, and databases to track supplies. The table below contains order-to-delivery times (in days) for a sample of shipments from the United States to the Persian Gulf and a sample of shipments to Bosnia.

Persian Gulf	Bosnia
28.0	15.1
20.0	6.4
26.5	5.0
10.6	11.4
9.1	6.5
35.2	6.5
29.1	3.0
41.2	7.0
27.5	5.5

Source: Based on Crock, S. "The Pentagon goes to B-school," *Business Week*, December 11, 1995, p. 98.

a. Is there sufficient evidence to indicate that the variances in order-to-delivery times for Persian Gulf and Bosnia shipments differ? Use $\alpha = .05$.

b. Given your answer to part **a,** is it appropriate to construct a confidence interval for the difference between the mean order-to-delivery times? Explain.

8.88 Is honey a cough remedy? Refer to the *Archives of Pediatrics and Adolescent Medicine* (Dec. 2007) study HCOUGH of honey as a children's cough remedy, Exercise 8.23 (p. 437). The data (cough improvement scores) for the 33 children in the DM dosage group and the 35 children in the honey dosage group are reproduced in the table below. In Exercise 8.23, you used a comparison of two means to determine whether "honey may be a preferable treatment for the cough and sleep difficulty associated with childhood upper respiratory tract infection." The researchers also want to know if the variability in coughing improvement scores differs for the two groups. Conduct the appropriate analysis, using $\alpha = .10$.

Honey Dosage:	12	11	15	11	10	13	10	4	15	16	9	14	10	6	10	11	12	15
	12	9	11	15	10	9	13	8	12	10	8	9	5	12	8	12	8	
DM Dosage:	4	6	9	4	7	7	7	9	12	10	11	3	9	7	8	12	12	
	13	7	10	13	9	4	4	10	15	9	6	4	12	6	12	4		

Source: Paul, I. M., et al. "Effect of honey, dextromethorphan, and no treatment on nocturnal cough and sleep quality for coughing children and their parents," *Archives of Pediatrics and Adolescent Medicine*, Vol. 161, No. 12, Dec. 2007 (data simulated).

■ Chapter Notes

Key Terms

Blocking 440
F-distribution 459
Nonparametric method 464
Paired difference experiment 440

Pooled sample estimator of σ^2 426
Randomized block experiment 440
Standard error 423

Key Symbols

$\mu_1 - \mu_2$	Difference between population means
μ_d	Paired difference in population means
$p_1 - p_2$	Difference between population proportions
$\frac{\sigma_1^2}{\sigma_2^2}$	Ratio of population variances
D_0	Hypothesized value of difference
$\bar{x}_1 - \bar{x}_2$	Difference between sample means
$\bar{d}$	Mean of sample differences
$\hat{p}_1 - \hat{p}_2$	Difference between sample proportions
$\frac{s_1^2}{s_2^2}$	Ratio of sample variances
$\sigma_{(\bar{x}_1 - \bar{x}_2)}$	Standard error for $\bar{x}_1 - \bar{x}_2$
$\sigma_{\bar{d}}$	Standard error for $\bar{d}$
$\sigma_{(\hat{p}_1 - \hat{p}_2)}$	Standard error for $\hat{p}_1 - \hat{p}_2$
F_α	Critical value for *F*-distribution
ν_1	Numerator degrees of freedom for *F*-distribution
ν_2	Denominator degrees of freedom for *F*-distribution
ME	Margin of error in estimation

Key Ideas

Key Words for Identifying the Target Parameter

$\mu_1 - \mu_2$	Difference in means or averages
μ_d	Paired difference in means or averages
$p_1 - p_2$	Difference in proportions, fractions, percentages, rates
$\frac{\sigma_1^2}{\sigma_2^2}$	Ratio (or difference) in variances, spreads

Determining the Sample Size

Estimating $\mu_1 - \mu_2$: $n_1 = n_2 = (z_{\alpha/2})^2(\sigma_1^2 + \sigma_2^2)/(ME)^2$
Estimating $p_1 - p_2$: $n_1 = n_2 = (z_{\alpha/2})^2(p_1q_1 + p_2q_2)/(ME)^2$

Conditions Required for Inferences about $\mu_1 - \mu_2$

Large samples:
1. Independent random samples
2. $n_1 \geq 30, n_2 \geq 30$

Small samples:
1. Independent random samples
2. Both populations normal
3. $\sigma_1^2 = \sigma_2^2$

Conditions Required for Inferences about $\frac{\sigma_1^2}{\sigma_2^2}$

Large or small samples:
1. Independent random samples
2. Both populations normal

Conditions Required for Inferences about μ_d

Large samples:
1. Random sample of paired differences
2. $n_d \geq 30$

Small samples:
1. Random sample of paired differences
2. Population of differences is normal

Conditions Required for Inferences about $p_1 - p_2$

Large samples:
1. Independent random samples
2. $n_1p_1 \geq 15, n_1q_1 \geq 15$
3. $n_2p_2 \geq 15, n_2q_2 \geq 15$

Using a Confidence Interval for $(\mu_1 - \mu_2)$ or $(p_1 - p_2)$ to Determine whether a Difference Exists

1. If the confidence interval includes all *positive* numbers $(+, +)$: $\rightarrow$ Infer $\mu_1 > \mu_2$ or $p_1 > p_2$
2. If the confidence interval includes all *negative* numbers $(-, -)$: $\rightarrow$ Infer $\mu_1 < \mu_2$ or $p_1 < p_2$
3. If the confidence interval includes 0 $(-, +)$: $\rightarrow$ Infer no evidence of a difference

Guide to Selecting a Two-Sample Hypothesis Test and Confidence Interval

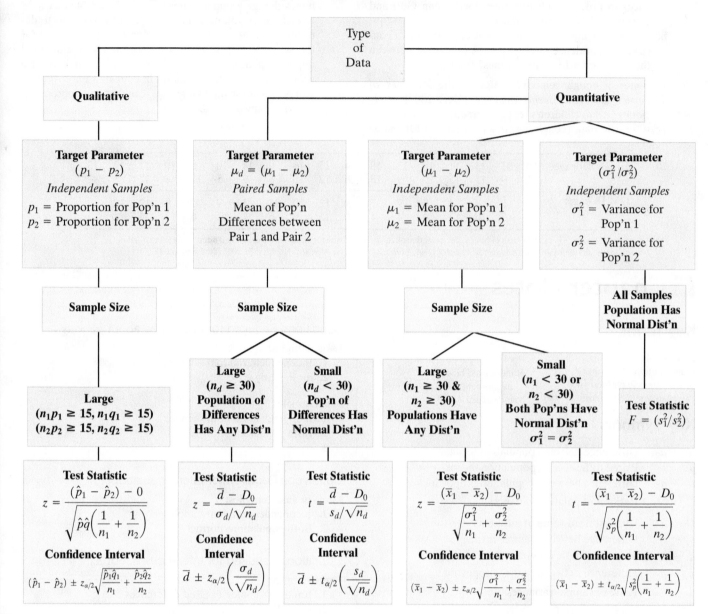

Supplementary Exercises 8.89–8.123

Learning the Mechanics

8.89 List the assumptions necessary for each of the following inferential techniques:

a. Large-sample inferences about the difference $(\mu_1 - \mu_2)$ between population means using a two-sample z-statistic

b. Small-sample inferences about $(\mu_1 - \mu_2)$ using an independent samples design and a two-sample t-statistic

c. Small-sample inferences about $(\mu_1 - \mu_2)$ using a paired difference design and a single-sample t-statistic to analyze the differences

d. Large-sample inferences about the differences $(p_1 - p_2)$ between binomial proportions using a two-sample z-statistic

e. Inferences about the ratio $\frac{\sigma_1^2}{\sigma_2^2}$ of two population variances using an F-test.

8.90 Two independent random samples were selected from normally distributed populations with means and variances (μ_1, σ_1^2) and (μ_2, σ_2^2), respectively. The sample sizes, means, and variances are shown in the following table.

Sample 1	Sample 2
$n_1 = 20$	$n_2 = 15$
$\bar{x}_1 = 123$	$\bar{x}_2 = 116$
$s_1^2 = 31.3$	$s_2^2 = 120.1$

a. Test $H_0: \sigma_1^2 = \sigma_2^2$ against $H_a: \sigma_1^2 \neq \sigma_2^2$. Use $\alpha = .05$.

b. Would you be willing to use a small sample t-test to test the null hypothesis $H_0: (\mu_1 - \mu_2) = 0$ against the alternative hypothesis $H_a: (\mu_1 - \mu_2) \neq 0$? Why?

8.91 Independent random samples were selected from two normally distributed populations with means μ_1 and μ_2, respectively. The sample sizes, means, and variances are shown in the following table.

Sample 1	Sample 2
$n_1 = 12$	$n_2 = 14$
$\bar{x}_1 = 17.8$	$\bar{x}_2 = 15.3$
$s_1^2 = 74.2$	$s_2^2 = 60.5$

a. Test $H_0: (\mu_1 - \mu_2) = 0$ against $H_a: (\mu_1 - \mu_2) > 0$. Use $\alpha = .05$.

b. Form a 99% confidence interval for $(\mu_1 - \mu_2)$.

c. How large must n_1 and n_2 be if you wish to estimate $(\mu_1 - \mu_2)$ to within 2 units with 99% confidence? Assume that $n_1 = n_2$.

8.92 Independent random samples were selected from two binomial populations. The sizes and number of observed successes for each sample are shown in the following table.

Sample 1	Sample 2
$n_1 = 200$	$n_2 = 200$
$x_1 = 110$	$x_2 = 130$

a. Test $H_0: (p_1 - p_2) = 0$ against $H_a: (p_1 - p_2) < 0$. Use $\alpha = .10$.

b. Form a 95% confidence interval for $(p_1 - p_2)$.

c. What sample sizes would be required if we wish to use a 95% confidence interval of width .01 to estimate $(p_1 - p_2)$?

8.93 Two independent random samples are taken from two populations. The results of these samples are summarized in the next table.

Sample 1	Sample 2
$n_1 = 135$	$n_2 = 148$
$\bar{x}_1 = 12.2$	$\bar{x}_2 = 8.3$
$s_1^2 = 2.1$	$s_2^2 = 3.0$

a. Form a 90% confidence interval for $(\mu_1 - \mu_2)$.

b. Test $H_0: (\mu_1 - \mu_2) = 0$ against $H_a: (\mu_1 - \mu_2) \neq 0$. Use $\alpha = .01$.

c. What sample sizes would be required if you wish to estimate $(\mu_1 - \mu_2)$ to within .2 with 90% confidence? Assume that $n_1 = n_2$.

8.94 A random sample of five pairs of observations were selected, one of each pair from a population with mean μ_1, the other from a population with mean μ_2. The data are shown in the accompanying table.

L08094

Pair	Value from Population 1	Value from Population 2
1	28	22
2	31	27
3	24	20
4	30	27
5	22	20

a. Test the null hypothesis $H_0: \mu_d = 0$ against $H_a: \mu_d \neq 0$, where $\mu_d = \mu_1 - \mu_2$. Use $\alpha = .05$.

b. Form a 95% confidence interval for μ_d.

c. When are the procedures you used in parts **a** and **b** valid?

Applying the Concepts—Basic

8.95 **Determining the target parameter.** For each of the following studies, give the parameter of interest and state any assumptions that are necessary for the inferences to be valid.

a. To investigate a possible link between jet lag and memory impairment, a University of Bristol (England) neurologist recruited 20 female flight attendants who worked flights across several time zones. Half of the attendants had only a short recovery time between flights and half had a long recovery time between flights. The average size of the right temporal lobe of the brain for the short-recovery group was significantly smaller than the average size of the right temporal lobe of the brain for the long-recovery group (*Tampa Tribune*, May 23, 2001).

b. In a study presented at the March 2001 meeting of the Association for the Advancement of Applied Sport Psychology, researchers revealed that the proportion of athletes who have a good self-image of their body is 20% higher than the corresponding proportion of nonathletes.

c. A University of Florida animal sciences professor has discovered that feeding chickens corn oil causes them to produce larger eggs (*UF News*, April 11, 2001). The weight of eggs produced by each of a sample of chickens on a regular feed diet was recorded. Then, the same chickens were fed a diet supplemented by corn oil, and the weight of eggs produced by each was recorded. The mean weight of the eggs produced with corn oil was 3 grams heavier than the mean weight produced with the regular diet.

8.96 **Financial incentives for college students.** A study reported in *Inside Higher Education News* (May 22, 2006) found that financial incentives can improve low-income college students' grades and retention. As part of their "Opening Doors" program, a Louisiana community college offered to pay students $1,000 per semester on condition that they maintain at least half-time enrollment and at least a 2.0 grade point average (GPA).

a. About 61% of Opening Doors students enrolled full time as opposed to about 52% of traditional students. Identify the target parameter for this comparison.

b. The mean GPA of Opening Doors students was 2.3 as compared to the mean GPA of 2.1 for traditional students. Identify the target parameter for this comparison.

8.97 **Rating service at five-star hotels.** A study published in *The Journal of American Academy of Business, Cambridge* (March 2002) examined whether the perception of service quality at five-star hotels in Jamaica differed by gender. Hotel guests were randomly selected from the lobby and restaurant areas and asked to rate 10 service-related items (e.g., "The personal attention you received from our employees"). Each item was rated on a 5-point scale (1 = "much worse than I expected," 5 = "much better than I expected"), and the sum of the items for each guest was determined. A summary of the guest scores is provided in the table.

Gender	Sample Size	Mean Score	Standard Deviation
Males	127	39.08	6.73
Females	114	38.79	6.94

a. Construct a 90% confidence interval for the difference between the population mean service-rating scores given by male and female guests at Jamaican five-star hotels.

b. Conduct a test to determine if the service-rating score variances differ by gender. Use $\alpha = .10$

c. Use the results, parts **a** and **b,** to make an inference about whether the perception of service quality at five-star hotels in Jamaica differs by gender.

8.98 **Hull failures of oil tankers.** Refer to the *Marine Technology* (Jan. 1995) study of major oil spills from tankers and carriers, Exercise 2.159 (p. 117). The data for the 42 recent spills are saved in the accompanying file.

HULL

a. Construct a 90% confidence interval for the difference between the mean spillage amount of accidents caused by collision and the mean spillage amount of accidents caused by fire/explosion. Interpret the result.

b. Conduct a test of hypothesis to compare the mean spillage amount of accidents caused by grounding to the corresponding mean of accidents caused by hull failure. Use $\alpha = .05$.

c. Refer to parts **a** and **b.** State any assumptions required for the inferences derived from the analyses to be valid. Are these assumptions reasonably satisfied?

d. Conduct a test of hypothesis to compare the variation in spillage amounts for accidents caused by collision and accidents caused by grounding. Use $\alpha = .02$.

8.99 **Financial incentives for college students.** Do students who play virtual-reality educational software games perform better in school? If so, software designers will use this information to create more attractive and motivating educational software. In a study published in *Educational Technology & Society* (April 2005), a class of 90 elementary schoolchildren were randomly divided into two groups of 45. One group used a virtual-reality game called VR-ENGAGE to learn about geography. The other group learned geography on the computer with a simple user interface. All students were given an exam at the beginning and the end of the learning period. The difference in test scores was used to find the percentage improvement in scores for each student. The following table summarizes the results for the two groups.

	VR-ENGAGE	Simple User Interface
n:	45	45
$\bar{x}:$	43.15	32.48
s:	12.57	9.26

Source: Based on Virvou, M., Katsionis, G., & Manos, K. "Combining software games with education: Evaluation of its educational effectiveness," *Educational Technology & Society,* Vol. 8, No. 2, April 2005 (Table 2).

a. Visually inspect the summary results. Does it appear that the mean improvement in scores for the virtual-reality group is greater than the mean for the simple user interface group?

b. Conduct an analysis (either a confidence interval or a test of hypothesis) at $\alpha = .05$ to support your observation in part **a.**

8.100 **Durability of shock absorbers.** A manufacturer of automobile shock absorbers was interested in comparing the durability of its shocks with that of the shocks produced

SHOCK

by its biggest competitor. To make the comparison, one of the manufacturer's and one of the competitor's shocks were randomly selected and installed on the rear wheels of each of six cars. After the cars had been driven 20,000 miles, the strength of each test shock was measured, coded, and recorded. Results of the examination are shown in the table.

Car Number	Manufacturer's Shock	Competitor's Shock
1	8.8	8.4
2	10.5	10.1
3	12.5	12.0
4	9.7	9.3
5	9.6	9.0
6	13.2	13.0

a. Explain why the data are collected as matched pairs.

b. Do the data present sufficient evidence to conclude that there is a difference in the mean strength of the two types of shocks after 20,000 miles of use? Use $\alpha = .05$.

c. Find the approximate observed significance level for the test and interpret its value.

d. What assumptions are necessary to apply a paired difference analysis to the data?

e. Construct a 95% confidence interval for μ_d. Interpret the confidence interval.

f. Suppose the data are based on independent random samples. Construct a 95% confidence interval for $(\mu_1 - \mu_2)$. Interpret your result.

g. Compare the confidence intervals you obtained in parts **e** and **f.** Which is wider? To what do you attribute the difference in width? Assuming in each case that the appropriate assumptions are satisfied, which interval provides you with more information about $(\mu_1 - \mu_2)$? Explain.

h. Are the results of an unpaired analysis valid if the data come from a paired experiment?

8.101 **Life expectancy of Oscar winners.** Movie actors who win an Oscar usually can command a greater fee for their next motion picture. Does winning an Academy of Motion Picture Arts and Sciences award (aka, an Oscar) lead to long-term mortality for movie actors? In an article in the *Annals of Internal Medicine* (May 15, 2001), researchers sampled 762 Academy Award winners and matched each one with another actor of the same sex who was in the same winning film and was born in the same era. The life expectancy (age) of each pair of actors was compared.

a. Explain why the data should be analyzed as a paired difference experiment.

b. Set up the null hypothesis for a test to compare the mean life expectancies of Academy Award winners and nonwinners.

c. The sample mean life expectancies of Academy Award winners and nonwinners were reported as 79.7 years and 75.8 years, respectively. The *p*-value for comparing the two population means was reported as $p = .003$. Interpret this value in the context of the problem.

8.102 **Diamonds sold at retail.** Refer to the data for 308 diamonds saved in the file. Two quantitative variables in the data set are number of carats and selling price. One of the qualitative variables is the independent certification body

DIAMND

that assessed each of the stones. Three certification bodies were used: GIA, IGI, and HRD. The Minitab printout shown below gives the means and standard deviations of the quantitative variables for each certification body.

Descriptive Statistics: CARAT, PRICE

Variable	CERT	N	Mean	StDev
CARAT	GIA	151	0.6723	0.2456
	HRD	79	0.8129	0.1831
	IGI	78	0.3665	0.2163
PRICE	GIA	151	5310	3247
	HRD	79	7181	2898
	IGI	78	2267	2121

a. Construct a 95% confidence interval for the difference between the mean carat size of diamonds certified by GIA and the mean carat size of diamonds certified by HRD.

b. Interpret the result, part a. Specifically, which (if either) of the two population means compared is larger and by how much?

c. Construct a 95% confidence interval for the difference between the mean carat size of diamonds certified by GIA and the mean carat size of diamonds certified by IGI.

d. Interpret the result, part c. Specifically, which (if either) of the two population means is larger and by how much?

e. Construct a 95% confidence interval for the difference between the mean selling price of diamonds certified by HRD and the mean selling price of diamonds certified by IGI.

f. Interpret the result, part e. Specifically, which (if either) of the two population means is larger and by how much?

g. Conduct a test to determine whether the variation in carat size differs for diamonds certified by GIA and diamonds certified by HRD. Use $\alpha = .05$.

h. Conduct a test to determine whether the variation in carat size differs for diamonds certified by GIA and diamonds certified by IGI. Use $\alpha = .05$.

i. Conduct a test to determine whether the variation in selling price differs for diamonds certified by HRD and diamonds certified by IGI. Use $\alpha = .05$.

j. Use a statistical software package (and the data in the accompanying file) to determine whether the assumption of normally distributed data for each certification group is reasonably satisfied.

8.103 **Ages of cable TV shoppers.** Refer to the International Association for Time Use Research study on cable TV viewers who purchase items from one of the home shopping channels, Exercise 7.142 (p. 412). The 1,600 sampled viewers described their motivation for watching cable TV shopping networks by giving their level of agreement (on a 5-point scale, where 1 = strongly disagree and 5 = strongly agree) with the statement, "I have nothing else to do." The researcher wanted to compare the mean responses of viewers who watch the shopping network at noon with those viewers who do not watch at noon.

a. Give the null and alternative hypotheses for determining whether the mean response of noontime watchers differs from the mean response of non-noontime watchers.

b. The researcher found the p-value for the test, part a, to be .02. Interpret this result, assuming $\alpha = .05$.

c. Interpret the result, part b, assuming $\alpha = .01$.

d. The sample means for noontime watchers and non-watchers were found to be 3.3 and 3.4, respectively. Comment on the practical significance of this result.

8.104 **Career success expectations.** In evaluating the usefulness and validity of a questionnaire, researchers often pretest the questionnaire on different independently selected samples of respondents. Knowledge of the differences and similarities of the samples and their respective populations is important for interpreting the questionnaire's validity. *Educational and Psychological Measurement* (Feb. 1998) reported on a questionnaire developed for measuring the career success expectations of employees. The instrument was tested on the two independent samples described in the following table.

	Managers and Professionals	Part-Time MBA Students
Sample size	162	109
Gender (% males)	95.0	68.9
Marital status (% married)	91.2	53.4

Source: Based on Stephens, G. K., Szajna, B., & Broome, K. M., "The career success expectation scale: An exploratory and confirmatory factor analysis," *Educational and Psychological Measurement,* Vol. 58, No. 1, Feb. 1998, pp.129–141.

a. Does the population of managers and professionals from which the sample was drawn consist of more males than the part-time MBA population does? Conduct the appropriate test using $\alpha = .05$.

b. Describe any assumptions you made in conducting the test of part a and why you made them.

c. Does the population of managers and professionals consist of more married individuals than the part-time MBA population does? Conduct the appropriate hypothesis test using $\alpha = .01$.

d. What assumptions must hold for the test of part c to be valid?

8.105 **Likelihood of getting a routine medical checkup.** Who is more likely to get a routine medical checkup—employed or unemployed people? To answer this question, a team of physicians and public health professors collected data on a sample of over 2,200 individuals (*American Journal of Public Health,* Jan. 2002). Of the 1,140 individuals who were employed, 642 visited a physician for a routine checkup within the past year. In contrast, 740 of the 1,106 unemployed individuals had a routine medical checkup within the past year.

a. Specify the parameter of interest to the research team.

b. Set up the null and alternative hypotheses for testing whether there is a difference between the percentages of employed and unemployed people who had a recent routine medical checkup.

c. Compute the test statistic for the test.

d. Give the rejection region for the test using $\alpha = .01$.

e. The research team reported the p-value for the test as p-value ≈ 0. Do you agree?

f. Make the appropriate conclusion.

8.106 **Turnover rates in the United States and Japan.** High job turnover rates are often associated with high product defect rates because high turnover rates mean more inexperienced workers who are unfamiliar with the company's product lines (Stevenson, *Production/Operations Management*, 2000). In a study, five Japanese and five U.S. plants that manufacture air conditioners were randomly sampled; their turnover rates are listed in the table.

U.S. Plants	Japanese Plants
7.11%	3.52%
6.06	2.02
8.00	4.91
6.87	3.22
4.77	1.92

a. Do the data provide sufficient evidence to indicate that the mean annual percentage turnover for U.S. plants exceeds the corresponding mean percentage for Japanese plants? Test using $\alpha = .05$.
b. Find and interpret the observed significance level of the test you conducted in part **a**.
c. List any assumptions you made in conducting the hypothesis test of part **a**. Comment on their validity for this application.

8.107 **Cell phone usage differs by gender.** The role of the cell phone in modern life was investigated by a Pew Internet & American Life Project (April 2006) survey. A total of 1,286 cell phone users were interviewed in the sample. One of the objectives was to compare male and female cell phone users. For example, 32% of men admitted they sometimes don't drive safely while talking or texting on a cell phone compared to 25% of women. Also, 71% of men used their cell phone in an emergency compared to 77% of women. Assume that half (643) of the cell phone users in the sample were men and half (643) were women.

a. Describe the two populations of interest in the survey.
b. Give an estimate of the proportion of men and the proportion of women who sometimes do not drive safely while talking or texting on a cell phone.
c. Find a 90% confidence interval for the difference between the proportions of men and women who sometimes do not drive safely while talking or texting on a cell phone.
d. From your answer to part **c**, can you conclude that men are more likely than women to sometimes not drive safely while talking or texting on a cell phone? Explain.
e. Give an estimate of the proportion of men and the proportion of women who used their cell phone in an emergency.
f. Conduct a test to determine whether the proportions of men and women who used their cell phone in an emergency differ. Use $\alpha = .10$.

Applying the Concepts—Intermediate

8.108 **Sampling plan for a movie promotion.** Advertising companies often try to characterize the average user of a client's product so ads can be targeted at particular segments of the buying community. A new movie is about to be released, and the advertising company wants to determine whether to aim the ad campaign at people under or over

25 years of age. It plans to arrange an advance showing of the movie to an audience from each group and then obtain an opinion about the movie from each individual. How many individuals should be included in each sample if the advertising company wants to estimate the difference in the proportions of viewers in each age group who will like the movie to within .05 with 90% confidence? Assume the sample size for each group will be the same and about half of each group will like the movie.

8.109 **Comparing purchasers and nonpurchasers of toothpaste.** Marketing strategists would like to predict consumer response to new products and their accompanying promotional schemes. Consequently, studies that examine the differences between buyers and nonbuyers of a product are of interest. One classic study conducted by Shuchman and Riesz (*Journal of Marketing Research*) was aimed at characterizing the purchasers and nonpurchasers of Crest toothpaste. The researchers demonstrated that both the mean household size (number of persons) and mean household income were significantly larger for purchasers than for nonpurchasers. A similar study used independent random samples of size 20 and yielded the data shown in the following table on the age of the householder primarily responsible for buying toothpaste.

a. Do the data present sufficient evidence to conclude there is a difference in the mean age of purchasers and nonpurchasers? Use $\alpha = .10$.
b. What assumptions are necessary in order to answer part **a**?
c. Find the observed significance level for the test and interpret its value.
d. Calculate and interpret a 90% confidence interval for the difference between the mean ages of purchasers and nonpurchasers.

Purchasers						Nonpurchasers					
34	35	23	44	52	46	28	22	44	33	55	63
28	48	28	34	33	52	45	31	60	54	53	58
41	32	34	49	50	45	52	52	66	35	25	48
29	59					59	61				

8.110 **Killing moths with carbon dioxide.** A University of South Florida biologist conducted an experiment to determine whether increased levels of carbon dioxide kill leaf-eating moths (*USF Magazine*, Winter 1999). Moth larvae were placed in open containers filled with oak leaves. Half the containers had normal carbon dioxide levels, while the other half had double the normal level of carbon dioxide. Ten percent of the larvae in the containers with high carbon dioxide levels died, compared to 5% in the containers with normal levels. Assume that 80 moth larvae were placed, at random, in each of the two types of containers. Do the experimental results demonstrate that an increased level of carbon dioxide is effective in killing a higher percentage of leaf-eating moth larvae? Test using $\alpha = .01$.

8.111 **Racial profiling by the LAPD.** *Racial profiling* is a term used to describe any police action that relies on ethnicity rather than behavior to target suspects engaged in criminal activities. Does the Los Angeles Police Department (LAPD) invoke racial profiling in stops and searches of LA drivers? This question was addressed in *Chance* (Spring 2006).

a. Data on stops and searches of both African Americans and white drivers are summarized in the accompanying table. Conduct a test (at $\alpha = .05$) to determine if there is a disparity in the proportions of African American and white drivers who are searched by the LA police after being stopped.

b. The LAPD defines a *hit rate* as the proportion of searches that result in a discovery of criminal activity. Use the data in the table to estimate the disparity in the hit rates for African American and white drivers using a 95% confidence interval. Interpret the results.

Race	Number Stopped	Number Searched	Number of "Hits"
African American	61,688	12,016	5,134
White	106,892	5,312	3,006

Source: Based on Khadjavi, L. S. "Driving while black in the City of Angels," *Chance,* Vol. 19, No. 2.

8.112 State SAT scores. Refer to Exercise 2.27 (p. 60) and the data on average math SAT scores for each of the 50 states and District of Columbia for the years 2001 and 2011. The data are saved in the file. (The first five observations and last two observations in the data set are shown in the table below.)

State	2001	2011
Alabama	554	541
Alaska	510	511
Arizona	525	523
Arkansas	550	570
California	517	515
⋮	⋮	⋮
Wisconsin	596	602
Wyoming	545	569

Source: Based on "SAT trends: Background on the SAT takers in the class of 2011," from The CollegeBoard.

a. In Exercise 2.27c, you computed the *paired differences* of SAT scores by subtracting the 2001 score from the 2011 score for each state. Find the mean of these 51 paired differences. This value is μ_d, the mean difference in SAT scores for the population of 50 states and the District of Columbia.

b. Explain why there is no need to employ the confidence interval or test procedures of this section to make an inference about μ_d.

c. Now, suppose the 50 paired differences of part **a** represent a sample of SAT score differences for 50 randomly selected high school students. Use the data in the file to make an inference about whether the true mean SAT score of high school students in 2011 differs from the true mean in 2001. Use a confidence level of .90.

8.113 Rat damage to sugarcane fields. Poisons are used to prevent rat damage in sugarcane fields. The U.S. Department of Agriculture is investigating whether the rat poison should be located in the middle of the field or on the outer perimeter. One way to answer this question is to determine where the greater amount of damage occurs. If damage is measured by the proportion of cane stalks that have been damaged by rats, how many stalks from each section of the field should be sampled to estimate the true difference between proportions of stalks damaged in the two sections to within .02 with 95% confidence?

8.114 Environmental impact study. Some power plants are located near rivers or oceans so that the available water can be used for cooling the condensers. Suppose that, as part of an environmental impact study, a power company wants to estimate the difference in mean water temperature between the discharge of its plant and the offshore waters. How many sample measurements must be taken at each site to estimate the true difference between means to within $.2°C$ with 95% confidence? Assume that the range in readings will be about $4°C$ at each site and the same number of readings will be taken at each site.

8.115 Instrument precision. When new instruments are developed to perform chemical analyses of products (food, medicine, etc.), they are usually evaluated with respect to two criteria: accuracy and precision. *Accuracy* refers to the ability of the instrument to identify correctly the nature and amounts of a product's components. *Precision* refers to the consistency with which the instrument will identify the components of the same material. Thus, a large variability in the identification of a single batch of a product indicates a lack of precision. Suppose a pharmaceutical firm is considering two brands of an instrument designed to identify the components of certain drugs. As part of a comparison of precision, 10 test-tube samples of a well-mixed batch of a drug are selected and then 5 are analyzed by instrument A and 5 by instrument B. The data shown below are the percentages of the primary component of the drug given by the instruments. Do these data provide evidence of a difference in the precision of the two machines? Use $\alpha = .10$.

Instrument A	Instrument B
43	46
48	49
37	43
52	41
45	48

8.116 Computer-mediated communication study. Computer-mediated communication (CMC) is a form of interaction that heavily involves technology (e.g., instant messaging, e-mail). A study was conducted to compare relational intimacy in people interacting via CMC to people meeting face-to-face (FTF) (*Journal of Computer-Mediated Communication,* April 2004). Participants were 48 undergraduate students, of which half were randomly assigned to the CMC group and half assigned to the FTF group. Each group was given a task that required communication with the group members. Those in the CMC group used the "chat" mode of instant-messaging software; those in the FTF group met in a conference room. The variable of interest, relational intimacy score, was measured (on a 7-point scale) for each participant after each of three different meeting sessions and is saved in the accompanying file. Scores for the first meeting session are given in the table on the next page. The researchers hypothesized that, after the first meeting, the mean relational intimacy score for participants in the CMC group would be lower than the mean relational intimacy score for participants in the FTF group. Test the researchers' hypothesis using $\alpha = .10$.

Data for Exercise 8.116

CMC	4	3	3	4	3	3	3	3	4	4	3	4
	3	3	2	4	2	4	5	4	4	4	5	3
FTF	5	4	4	4	3	3	3	4	3	3	3	3
	4	4	4	4	3	3	3	3	4	4	2	4

Note: Data simulated from descriptive statistics provided in article.

8.117 **Computer-mediated communication study (cont'd).** Refer to Exercise 8.116. The researchers also hypothesized that the mean relational intimacy score for participants in the CMC group would significantly increase between the first and third meetings, but the difference between the first and third meetings would not significantly change for participants in the FTF group.

    a. For the CMC group comparison, give the null and alternative hypotheses of interest.

    b. The researchers made the comparison, part **a,** using a paired *t*-test. Explain why the data should be analyzed as matched pairs.

    c. For the CMC group comparison, the reported test statistic was $t = 3.04$ with *p*-value = .003. Interpret these results. Is the researchers' hypothesis supported?

    d. For the FTF group comparison, give the null and alternative hypotheses of interest.

    e. For the FTF group comparison, the reported test statistic was $t = .39$ with *p*-value = .70. Interpret these results. Is the researchers' hypothesis supported?

8.118 **Positive spillover effects from self-managed work teams.** To improve quality, productivity, and timeliness, many American industries employ self-managed work teams (SMWTs). A team typically consists of 5 to 15 workers who are collectively responsible for making decisions and performing all tasks related to a particular project. Because SMWTs require that employees be trained in interpersonal skills, they can have potential positive spillover effects on a worker's family life. The link between SMWT work characteristics and workers' perceptions of positive spillover into family life was investigated in the *Quality Management Journal* (Summer 1995). Survey data were collected from 114 AT&T employees who work in 1 of 15 SMWTs at an AT&T technical division. The workers were divided into two groups: (1) those who reported positive spillover of work skills to family life and (2) those who did not report positive work spillover. The two groups were compared on a variety of job and demographic characteristics, one of which was the use of creative ideas (measured on a 7-point scale, where the larger the number, the more of the characteristic indicated). The data (simulated from summary information provided in the *Quality Management Journal* article) are saved in the file.

    a. One comparison of interest to the researchers is whether the mean creative use of ideas scale score for employees who report positive spillover of work skills to family life differs from the mean scale score for employees who did not report positive work spillover. Give the null and alternative hypotheses that will allow the researchers to make the comparison.

    b. Discuss whether it is appropriate to apply the large-sample z-test to test the hypotheses, part **a.**

    c. The results of the test are shown in the SPSS printout below. Interpret these results. Make the appropriate conclusion using $\alpha = .05$.

    d. A 95% confidence interval for the difference between the mean use of creative ideas scale scores is shown in the last column of the SPSS printout. Interpret this interval. Does the inference derived from the confidence interval agree with that from the hypothesis test?

    e. The data also include the qualitative variable, Gender, for each worker. The researchers want to know whether the proportion of male workers in the two groups are significantly different. A Minitab printout of the analysis is shown below. Fully interpret the results in the words of the problem.

Applying the Concepts—Advanced

8.119 **Impact of gender on advertising.** How does gender affect the type of advertising that proves to be most effective? An article in the *Journal of Advertising Research* (May/June 1990)

SPSS output for Exercise 8.118

Independent Samples Test

		Levene's Test for Equality of Variances		t-test for Equality of Means						95% Confidence Interval of the Difference	
		F	Sig.	t	df	Sig. (2-tailed)	Mean Difference	Std. Error Difference	Lower	Upper
CREATIVE	Equal variances assumed	16.479	.000	8.565	112	.000	.808	.094	.621	.994
	Equal variances not assumed			8.847	108.727	.000	.808	.091	.627	.988

Minitab output for Exercise 8.118

Test and CI for Two Proportions: GENDER, GROUP

```
Event = MALE


GROUP     X    N   Sample p
NOSPILL   59   67  0.880597
SPILLOV   39   47  0.829787


Difference = p (NOSPILL) - p (SPILLOV)
Estimate for difference:  0.0508098
95% CI for difference:  (-0.0817519, 0.183371)
Test for difference = 0 (vs not = 0):  Z = 0.75  P-Value = 0.453
```

makes reference to numerous studies that conclude males tend to be more competitive with others than with themselves. To apply this conclusion to advertising, the author created two ads promoting a new brand of soft drink:

Ad 1: Four men are shown competing in racquetball
Ad 2: One man is shown competing against himself in racquetball

The author hypothesized that the first ad would be more effective when shown to males. To test this hypothesis, 43 males were shown both ads and asked to measure their attitude toward the advertisement (Aad), their attitude toward the brand of soft drink (Ab), and their intention to purchase the soft drink (Intention). Each variable was measured using a 7-point scale, with higher scores indicating a more favorable attitude. The results are shown in the table below. Do you agree with the author's hypothesis?

	Sample Means		
	Aad	Ab	Intention
Ad 1	4.465	3.311	4.366
Ad 2	4.150	2.902	3.813
Level of Significance	$p = .091$	$p = .032$	$p = .050$

8.120 Salaries of postgraduates. Refer to the *Economics of Education Review* (Vol. 21, 2002) study of the relationship between education level and earnings, Exercise 7.46 (p. 379). A National Adult Literacy Survey revealed that males with a postgraduate degree had a sample mean salary of $61,340 (with standard error $s_{\bar{x}_M} = \$2,185$), while females with a postgraduate degree had a sample mean salary of $32,227 (with standard error $s_{\bar{x}_F} = \$932$). Let μ_M represent the population mean salary of all males with postgraduate degrees and μ_F represent the population mean salary of all females with postgraduate degrees.
   a. Set up the null and alternative hypotheses for determining whether μ_M exceeds μ_F.
   b. Calculate the test statistic for the test, part **a.** [*Note:* $s_{\bar{x}_M - \bar{x}_F} = \sqrt{(s_{\bar{x}_M}^2 + s_{\bar{x}_F}^2)}$.]
   c. Find the rejection region for the test using $\alpha = .01$.
   d. Use the results, parts **b** and **c,** to make the appropriate conclusion.

8.121 Gambling in public high schools. With the rapid growth in legalized gambling in the United States, there is concern that the involvement of youth in gambling activities is also increasing. University of Minnesota Professor Randy Stinchfield compared the rates of gambling among Minnesota public school students between 1992 and 1998 (*Journal of Gambling Studies,* Winter 2001). Based on survey data, the table (next column) shows the percentages of ninth-grade boys who gambled weekly or daily on any game (e.g., cards, sports betting, lotteries) for the 2 years.
   a. Are the percentages of ninth-grade boys who gambled weekly or daily on any game in 1992 and 1998 significantly different? (Use $\alpha = .01$.)
   b. Professor Stinchfield states that "because of the large sample sizes, even small differences may achieve statistical significance, so interpretations of the differences should include a judgment regarding the magnitude of the difference and its public health significance." Do you agree with this statement? If not, why not? If so,

obtain a measure of the magnitude of the difference between 1992 and 1998 and attach a measure of reliability to the difference.

	1992	1998
Number of Ninth-Grade Boys in Survey	21,484	23,199
Number Who Gambled Weekly/Daily	4,684	5,313

8.122 CareerBank.com annual salary survey. CareerBank.com conducts an annual salary survey of accounting, finance, and banking professionals. For one survey, data were collected for 2,800 responses submitted online by professionals across the country who voluntarily responded to CareerBank.com's Web-based survey. Salary comparisons were made by gender, education, and marital status. Some of the results are shown in the accompanying table.

	Males	Females
Mean Salary	$69,848	$52,012
Number of Respondents	1,400	1,400

   a. Suppose you want to make an inference about the difference between the mean salaries of male and female accounting/finance/banking professionals at a 95% level of confidence. Why is this impossible to do using the information in the table?
   b. Give values of the missing standard deviations that would lead you to conclude that the mean salary for males is significantly higher than the mean salary for females at a 95% level of confidence.
   c. In your opinion, are the sample standard deviations, part **b,** reasonable values for the salary data? Explain.
   d. How does the data-collection method impact any inferences derived from the data?

Critical Thinking Challenge

8.123 Facility layout study. Facility layout and material flowpath design are major factors in the productivity analysis of automated manufacturing systems. Facility layout is concerned with the location arrangement of machines and buffers for work-in-process. Flowpath design is concerned with the direction of manufacturing material flows (e.g., unidirectional or bidirectional; Lee, Lei, and Pinedo, *Annals of Operations Research,* 1997). A manufacturer of printed circuit boards is interested in evaluating two alternative existing layout and flowpath designs. The output of each design was monitored for 8 consecutive working days. The data (shown below) are saved in the file. Design 2 appears to be superior to Design 1. Do you agree? Explain fully.

Working Days	Design 1 (units)	Design 2 (units)
8/16	1,220	1,273
8/17	1,092	1,363
8/18	1,136	1,342
8/19	1,205	1,471
8/20	1,086	1,299
8/23	1,274	1,457
8/24	1,145	1,263
8/25	1,281	1,368

Activity 8.1 *Box Office Receipts:* Comparing Population Means

Use the Internet to find the daily box office receipts for two different hit movies during the first 8 weeks after their releases. In this activity, you will compare the mean daily box office receipts of these movies in two different ways.

1. Independently select random samples of size $n = 30$ from the data sets for each of the movies' daily box office receipts. Find the mean and standard deviation of each sample. Then find a confidence interval for the difference of the means.

2. Now pair the data for the two movies by day, that is, the box office receipts for the day of release for each movie are paired, the box office receipts for each movie's second day are paired, and so forth. Calculate the difference

in box office receipts for each day and select a random sample of size $n = 30$ from the daily differences. Then find a confidence interval for the sample mean.

3. Compare the confidence intervals from Exercises 1 and 2. Explain how the sampling for the paired difference experiment is different from the independent sampling. How might this sampling technique yield a better comparison of the two means in the box office example?

4. Compute the actual means for the daily box office receipts for each of the movies and then find the difference of the means. Does the difference of the means lie in both confidence intervals you found? Is the exact difference remarkably closer to one of the estimates? Explain.

Activity 8.2 *Keep the Change:* Inferences Based on Two Samples

In this activity, you will compare the mean amounts transferred for two different Bank of America customers as well as design some studies that might help the marketing department determine where to allocate more of its advertising budget. You will be working with data sets from Activity 1.1, *Keep the Change: Collecting Data,* on page 29.

1. You will need to work with another student in the class on this exercise. Each of you should use your data set *Amounts Transferred* from the Chapter 1 Activity as a random sample from a theoretically larger set of all your amounts ever transferred. Then the means and standard deviations of your data sets will be the sample means and standard deviations. Write a confidence interval for the difference of the two means at the 95% level. Does the interval contain 0? Are your mean amounts transferred significantly different? Explain.

2. Design a study to determine whether there is a significant difference in the mean amount of Bank of America matches for customers in California enrolled in the program and the mean amount of Bank of America matches for customers in Florida enrolled in the program. Be specific about sample sizes, tests used, and how a conclusion will be reached. How might the results of this study help Bank of America estimate costs in the program?

3. Design a study to determine whether there is a significant difference in the percentage of Bank of America customers in California enrolled in the program and the percentage of Bank of America customers in Florida enrolled in the program. Be specific about sample sizes, tests used, and how a conclusion will be reached. How might the results of this study help Bank of America's marketing department?

Keep the results from this activity for use in other activities.

References

Freedman, D., Pisani, R., & Purves, R. *Statistics.* New York: W. W. Norton and Co., 1978.

Gibbons, J. D. *Nonparametric Statistical Inference,* 2nd ed. New York: McGraw-Hill, 1985.

Hollander, M., & Wolfe, D. A. *Nonparametric Statistical Methods.* New York: Wiley, 1973.

Koehler, K. *Snedecor and Cochran's Statistical Methods,* 9th ed. New York: Blackwell Publishing, 2012.

Mendenhall, W., Beaver, R. J., & Beaver, B. M. *Introduction to Probability and Statistics,* 13th ed. Belmont, CA: Brooks/Cole, 2009.

Satterthwaite, F. W. "An approximate distribution of estimates of variance components," *Biometrics Bulletin,* Vol. 2, 1946, pp. 110–114.

Steel, R. G. D., & Torrie, J. H. *Principles and Procedures of Statistics,* 2nd ed. New York: McGraw-Hill, 1980.

USING TECHNOLOGY Technology images shown here are taken from SPSS Statistics Professional 20.0, Minitab 16, XLSTAT for Pearson, and Excel 2010.

SPSS: Two-Sample Inferences

SPSS can be used to make two-sample inferences about $\mu_1 - \mu_2$ for independent samples, μ_d for paired samples, $p_1 - p_2$, and $\frac{\sigma_1^2}{\sigma_2^2}$.

Comparing Means with Independent Samples

Step 1 Access the SPSS spreadsheet file that contains the sample data. The data file should contain one quantitative variable (which the means will be calculated on) and one qualitative variable with either two numerical coded values (e.g., 1 and 2) or two short categorical levels (e.g., "yes" and "no"). These two values represent the two groups or populations to be compared.

Step 2 Click on the "Analyze" button on the SPSS menu bar and then click on "Compare Means" and "Independent-Samples T Test," as shown in Figure 8.S.1.

Figure 8.S.1 SPSS menu options for comparing two means

Step 3 On the resulting dialog box (shown in Figure 8.S.2), specify the quantitative variable of interest in the "Test Variable(s)" box and the qualitative variable in the "Grouping Variable" box.

Figure 8.S.2 SPSS independent-samples T test dialog box

Step 4 Click the "Define Groups" button and specify the values of the two groups in the resulting dialog box (see Figure 8.S.3).

Figure 8.S.3 SPSS define groups dialog box

Step 5 Click "Continue" to return to the "Independent-Samples T Test" dialog screen. Without any further menu selections, SPSS will automatically conduct a two-tailed test of the null hypothesis, H_0: $\mu_1 - \mu_2 = 0$.

Step 6 If you want to generate a confidence interval for $\mu_1 - \mu_2$, click the "Options" button and specify the confidence level on the resulting menu screen, as shown in Figure 8.S.4. Click "Continue" to return to the "T Test" dialog box.

Figure 8.S.4 SPSS options dialog box

Step 7 Click "OK" to generate the SPSS printout.

Important Note: The SPSS two-sample *t*-procedure uses the *t*-statistic to conduct the test of hypothesis. When the sample sizes are small, this is the appropriate method. When the sample sizes are large, the *t*-value will be approximately equal to the large-sample *z*-value, and the resulting test will still be valid.

Comparing Means with Paired Samples

Step 1 Access the SPSS spreadsheet file that contains the sample data. The data file should contain two quantitative variables—one with the data values for the first group (or population) and one with the data values for the second group. (*Note:* The sample size should be the same for each group.)

Step 2 Click on the "Analyze" button on the SPSS menu bar and then click on "Compare Means" and "Paired-Samples T Test" (see Figure 8.S.1).

Step 3 On the resulting dialog box (shown in Figure 8.S.5), specify the two quantitative variables of interest in the "Paired Variables" box. Without any further menu selections, SPSS will automatically conduct a two-tailed test of the null hypothesis, H_0: $\mu_d = 0$.

Figure 8.S.5 SPSS paired-samples dialog box

Step 4 If you want to generate a confidence interval for μ_d, click the "Options" button and specify the confidence level on the resulting menu screen (as shown in Figure 8.S.4). Click "Continue" to return to the "Paired-Samples" dialog box.

Step 5 Click "OK" to generate the SPSS printout.

Comparing Proportions with Independent Samples

Step 1 SPSS requires summary data to compare population proportions. Create a data file with three variables (columns)—(1) SAMPLE, (2) OUTCOME, and (3) NUMBER—and four rows. Each row will give the sample number, outcome (success or failure), and number of observations. For example, Figure 8.S.6 shows the data file for a problem with 60 out of 100 successes for sample 1 and 50 out of 100 successes for sample 2.

SAMPLE	OUTCOME	NUMBER
1	S	60
1	F	40
2	S	50
2	F	50

Figure 8.S.6 SPSS data file for comparing two proportions

Step 2 Click on the "Data" button on the SPSS menu bar and then click on "Weight Cases". Enter the "Number" variable into the "Frequency Variable" box, then click "OK."

Step 3 Click on the "Analyze" button on the SPSS menu bar and then click on "Descriptive Statistics" and "Crosstabs." (See Figure 8.S.7.)

Figure 8.S.7 SPSS menu options for comparing two proportions

Step 4 On the resulting menu, specify "SAMPLE" in the "Row" box and "OUTCOME" in the "Column(s)" box as shown in Figure 8.S.8. Also, click the "Statistics" option button and select "Chi-square," then click the "Cells" option button and select "Observed Counts" and "Row Percentages."

Figure 8.S.8 SPSS menu options for comparing two proportions

Step 5 Click "Continue," then click "OK." On the resulting SPSS printout, look for the p-value associated with the "Likelihood Ratio" test (this is equivalent to the large-sample z-test).

Comparing Variances with Independent Samples

Follow the steps outlined for "Comparing Means with Independent Samples" above. On the resulting SPSS printout, there will be an F-test for comparing population variances. (This test, called Levene's Test, is a nonparametric test that is similar to the F-test presented in the text.)

Minitab: Two-Sample Inferences

Minitab can be used to make two-sample inferences about $\mu_1 - \mu_2$ or independent samples, μ_d for paired samples, $p_1 - p_2$ and $\frac{\sigma_1^2}{\sigma_2^2}$.

Comparing Means with Independent Samples

Step 1 Access the Minitab worksheet that contains the sample data.

Step 2 Click on the "Stat" button on the Minitab menu bar and then click on "Basic Statistics" and "2-Sample t," as shown in Figure 8.M.1. The resulting dialog box appears as shown in Figure 8.M.2.

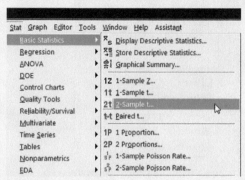

Figure 8.M.1 Minitab menu options for comparing two means

Figure 8.M.2 Minitab 2-sample t dialog box

Step 3a If the worksheet contains data for one quantitative variable (which the means will be computed on) and one qualitative variable (which represents the two groups or populations), select "Samples in one column" and then specify the quantitative variable in the "Samples" area and the qualitative variable in the "Subscripts" area. (See Figure 8.M.2.)

Step 3b If the worksheet contains the data for the first sample in one column and the data for the second sample in another column, select "Samples in different columns" and then specify the "First" and "Second" variables. Alternatively, if you have only summarized data (i.e., sample sizes, sample means, and sample standard deviations), select "Summarized data" and enter these summarized values in the appropriate boxes.

Step 4 Click the "Options" button on the Minitab "2-Sample t" dialog box. Specify the confidence level for a confidence interval, the null hypothesized value of the difference, $\mu_1 - \mu_2$, and the form of the alternative hypothesis (lower-tailed, two-tailed, or upper-tailed) in the resulting dialog box, as shown in Figure 8.M.3.

Figure 8.M.3 Minitab options dialog box

Step 5 Click "OK" to return to the "2-Sample t" dialog box and then click "OK" again to generate the Minitab printout.

Important Note: The Minitab two-sample *t*-procedure uses the *t*-statistic to conduct the test of hypothesis. When the sample sizes are small, this is the appropriate method. When the sample sizes are large, the *t*-value will be approximately equal to the large-sample *z*-value, and the resulting test will still be valid.

Comparing Means with Paired Samples

Step 1 Access the Minitab worksheet that contains the sample data. The data file should contain two quantitative variables—one with the data values for the first group (or population) and one with the data values for the second group. (*Note:* The sample size should be the same for each group.)

Step 2 Click on the "Stat" button on the Minitab menu bar and then click on "Basic Statistics" and "Paired t" (see Figure 8.M.1).

Step 3 On the resulting dialog box, select the "Samples in columns" option and specify the two quantitative variables of interest in the "First sample" and "Second sample" boxes, as shown in Figure 8.M.4. [Alternatively, if you have only summarized data of the paired differences, select the "Summarized data (differences)" option and enter the sample size, sample mean, and sample standard deviation in the appropriate boxes.]

Figure 8.M.4 Minitab paired-samples *t* dialog box

Step 4 Click the "Options" button and specify the confidence level for a confidence interval, the null hypothesized value of the difference, μ_d, and the form of the alternative hypothesis (lower-tailed, two-tailed, or upper-tailed) in the resulting dialog box. (See Figure 8.M.3.)

Step 5 Click "OK" to return to the "Paired t" dialog box and then click "OK" again to generate the Minitab printout.

Comparing Proportions with Large Independent Samples

Step 1 Access the Minitab worksheet that contains the sample data.

Step 2 Click on the "Stat" button on the Minitab menu bar and then click on "Basic Statistics" and "2 Proportions," as shown in Figure 8.M.1.

Step 3 On the resulting dialog box (shown in Figure 8.M.5), select the data option ("Samples in one column" or "Samples in different columns" or "Summarized data") and make the appropriate menu choices. (Figure 8.M.5 shows the menu options when you select "Summarized data.")

Figure 8.M.5 Minitab 2 proportions dialog box

Step 4 Click the "Options" button and specify the confidence level for a confidence interval, the null hypothesized value of the difference, and the form of the alternative hypothesis (lower-tailed, two-tailed, or upper-tailed) in the resulting dialog box, as shown in Figure 8.M.6. (If you desire a pooled estimate of *p* for the test, be sure to check the appropriate box.)

Figure 8.M.6 Minitab 2 proportions options

Step 5 Click "OK" to return to the "2 Proportions" dialog box and then click "OK" again to generate the Minitab printout.

Comparing Variances with Independent Samples

Step 1 Access the Minitab worksheet that contains the sample data.

Step 2 Click on the "Stat" button on the Minitab menu bar and then click on "Basic Statistics" and "2 Variances" (Figure 8.M.1.)

Step 3 On the resulting dialog box (shown in Figure 8.M.7), the menu selections and options are similar to those for the two-sample *t*-test.

Figure 8.M.7 Minitab 2 variances dialog box

Step 4 Click "OK" to produce the Minitab *F*-test printout.

Excel/XLSTAT: Two-Sample Inferences

Comparing Means with Independent Samples

Step 1 Click the "XLSTAT" button on the Excel main menu bar, select "Parametric tests," and then click "Two-sample t-test and z-test," as shown in Figure 8.E.1.

Figure 8.E.1 XLSTAT menu options for testing a mean

Step 2 When the resulting dialog box appears, select the proper "Data format" (e.g., "One column per variable"), and then select the appropriate columns (e.g., one column for the variable being analyzed and one for the variable that represents the two different samples). Also, check the "z test" box (if large samples) or the "Student's t test" box (if small samples). See, for example, Figure 8.E.2.

Figure 8.E.2 XLSTAT two-sample test dialog box

Step 3 Click the "Options" tab, then specify the form of the alternative hypothesis, the value of the hypothesized (theoretical) difference in means, and the value of α (significance level) in the appropriate boxes, as shown in Figure 8.E.3.

Figure 8.E.3 XLSTAT options for comparing two means

Step 4 Click "OK," then "Continue" to display the test results.

Comparing Means with Paired Samples

Step 1 Click the "XLSTAT" button on the Excel main menu bar, select "Parametric tests," then click "Two-sample t-test and z-test," as shown in Figure 8.E.1.

Step 2 When the resulting dialog box appears, select "Paired samples" as the "Data format," and then select the appropriate columns containing the data for the two samples, as shown in Figure 8.E.4. Also, check the "z test" box (if large samples) or the "Student's t test" box (if small samples).

Figure 8.E.4 XLSTAT options for paired samples

Step 3 Click the "Options" tab, and then specify the form of the alternative hypothesis, the value of the hypothesized (theoretical) difference in means, and the value of α (significance level) in the appropriate boxes, similar to Figure 8.E.3.

Step 4 Click "OK," then "Continue" to display the test results.

Comparing Proportions with Independent Samples

[*Note:* To compare two binomial proportions using XLSTAT, you will need summary information on your qualitative data, e.g., the sample sizes and either the number of successes or proportion of successes for both samples.]

Step 1 Click the "XLSTAT" button on the Excel main menu bar, select "Parametric tests," then click "Tests for two proportions," as shown in Figure 8.E.5.

Figure 8.E.5 XLSTAT menu options for comparing proportions

Step 2 When the resulting dialog box appears, check "Frequencies" in the "Data format" area, then enter the number of successes and the sample size for each sample in the appropriate boxes, as shown in Figure 8.E.6. (Alternatively, you can check "Proportions" in the "Data format" area and enter the sample proportions.)

Figure 8.E.6 XLSTAT test for two proportions dialog box

Step 3 Click the "Options" tab, specify the form of the alternative hypothesis, and then enter "0" for the hypothesized difference and the value of α (significance level) in the appropriate boxes, as shown in Figure 8.E.7.

Figure 8.E.7 XLSTAT options for testing proportions

Step 4 Click "OK" to display the test results.

Comparing Variances with Independent Samples

Step 1 Click the "XLSTAT" button on the Excel main menu bar, select "Parametric tests," then click "Two-sample comparison of variances" (see Figure 8.E.1).

Step 2 When the resulting dialog box appears, select the proper "Data format" (e.g., "One column per variable"), and then select the appropriate columns (e.g., one column for the variable being analyzed and one for the variable that represents the two different samples). Also, check the "Fisher's F-test" box, as shown in Figure 8.E.8.

Figure 8.E.8 XLSTAT two-sample variance test dialog box

Step 3 Click the "Options" tab, and then specify the form of the alternative hypothesis, the value of the hypothesized (theoretical) ratio of variances, and the value of α (significance level) in the appropriate boxes, as shown in Figure 8.E.9.

Figure 8.E.9 XLSTAT options for comparing two variances

Step 4 Click "OK," then "Continue" to display the test results.

TI-83/TI-84 Graphing Calculator: Two-Sample Inferences

The TI-84 graphing calculator can be used to conduct tests and form confidence intervals for the difference between two means with independent samples, the difference between two means with matched pairs, the difference between two proportions for large independent samples, and the ratio of two variances.

Confidence Interval for $\mu_1 - \mu_2$

Step 1 *Enter the data (Skip to Step 2 if you have summary statistics, not raw data)*

- Press **STAT** and select **1:Edit**

Note: If the lists already contain data, clear the old data. Use the up **ARROW** to highlight "L1."

- Press **CLEAR ENTER**
- Use the up **ARROW** to highlight "L2"
- Press **CLEAR ENTER**
- Use the **ARROW** and **ENTER** keys to enter the first data set into **L1**
- Use the **ARROW** and **ENTER** keys to enter the second data set into **L2**

Step 2 *Access the Statistical Tests Menu*

- Press **STAT**
- Arrow right to **TESTS**
- Arrow down to **2-SampTInt**
- Press **ENTER**

```
EDIT CALC TESTS
4↑2-SampTTest...
5:1-PropZTest...
6:2-PropZTest...
7:ZInterval...
8:TInterval...
9:2-SampZInt...
0:2-SampTInt...
```

Step 3 *Choose "Data" or "Stats" ("Data" is selected when you have entered the raw data into the Lists. "Stats" is selected when you are given only the means, standard deviations, and sample sizes.)*

- Press **ENTER**
- If you selected "Data," set **List1** to **L1** and **List2** to **L2**
- Set **Freq1** to **1** and set **Freq2** to **1**
- Set **C-Level** to the confidence level
- If you are assuming that the two populations have equal variances, select **Yes** for **Pooled**
- If you are not assuming equal variances, select **No**
- Press **ENTER**
- Arrow down to "**Calculate**"
- Press **ENTER**
- If you selected "Stats," enter the means, standard deviations, and sample sizes
- Set **C-Level** to the confidence level
- If you are assuming that the two populations have equal variances, select **Yes** for **Pooled**
- If you are not assuming equal variances, select **No**
- Press **ENTER**
- Arrow down to "**Calculate**"
- Press **ENTER**

```
2-SampTInt
 Inpt:Data Stats
 List1:L1
 List2:L2
 Freq1:1
 Freq2:1
 C-Level:.99
↓Pooled:No Yes
```

(The accompanying screen is set up for an example with a mean of 100, a standard deviation of 10, and a sample size of 15 for the first data set and a mean of 105, a standard deviation of 12, and a sample size of 18 for the second data set.)

The confidence interval will be displayed with the degrees of freedom, the sample statistics, and the pooled standard deviation (when appropriate).

Hypothesis Test for $\mu_1 - \mu_2$

Step 1 *Enter the data (Skip to Step 2 if you have summary statistics, not raw data)*

- Press **STAT** and select **1:Edit**

Note: If the lists already contain data, clear the old data. Use the up **ARROW** to highlight "**L1**."

- Press **CLEAR ENTER**
- Use the up **ARROW** to highlight "**L2**"
- Press **CLEAR ENTER**
- Use the **ARROW** and **ENTER** keys to enter the first data set into **L1**
- Use the **ARROW** and **ENTER** keys to enter the second data set into **L2**

Step 2 *Access the Statistical Tests Menu*

- Press **STAT**
- Arrow right to **TESTS**
- Arrow down to **2-SampTTest**
- Press **ENTER**

Step 3 *Choose "Data" or "Stats" ("Data" is selected when you have entered the raw data into the Lists. "Stats" is selected when you are given only the means, standard deviations, and sample sizes.)*

- Press **ENTER**
- If you selected "Data," set **List1** to **L1** and **List2** to **L2**
- Set **Freq1** to **1** and set **Freq2** to **1**
- Use the **ARROW** to highlight the appropriate alternative hypothesis
- Press **ENTER**
- If you are assuming that the two populations have equal variances, select **Yes** for **Pooled**
- If you are not assuming equal variances, select **No**
- Press **ENTER**
- Arrow down to "**Calculate**"
- Press **ENTER**
- If you selected "**Stats**," enter the means, standard deviations, and sample sizes

- Use the **ARROW** to highlight the appropriate alternative hypothesis
- Press **ENTER**
- If you are assuming that the two populations have equal variances, select **Yes** for **Pooled**
- If you are not assuming equal variances, select **No**
- Press **ENTER**
- Arrow down to "**Calculate**"
- Press **ENTER**

(The screen at the right is set up for an example with a mean of 100, a standard deviation of 10, and a sample size of 15 for the first data set and a mean of 120, a standard deviation of 12, and a sample size of 18 for the second data set.)

The results of the hypothesis test will be displayed with the *p*-value, degrees of freedom, the sample statistics, and the pooled standard deviation (when appropriate).

Confidence Interval for a Paired Difference Mean

Note: There is no paired difference option on the calculator. These instructions demonstrate how to calculate the differences and then use the 1-sample *t*-interval.

Step 1 *Enter the data and calculate the differences.*

- Press **STAT** and select **1:Edit**

Note: If the lists already contain data, clear the old data. Use the up **ARROW** to highlight "**L1**."

- Press **CLEAR ENTER**
- Use the up **ARROW** to highlight "**L2**"
- Press **CLEAR ENTER**
- Use the **ARROW** and **ENTER** keys to enter the first data set into **L1**
- Use the **ARROW** and **ENTER** keys to enter the second data set into **L2**
- The differences will be calculated in **L3**
- Use the up **ARROW** to highlight "**L3**"
- Press **CLEAR**— This will clear any old data, but **L3** will remain highlighted
- To enter the equation L3 = L1 − L2, use the following keystrokes:
  - Press **2ND** "**1**" (this will enter L1)
  - Press the **MINUS** button
  - Press **2ND** "**2**" (this will enter L2)

(Notice the equation at the bottom of the screen.)

L1	L2	L3	3
65	62	3	
58	53	5	
78	36	42	
60	34	26	
68	56	12	
69	50	19	
66	42	24	

L3 =L1−L2

- Press **ENTER** (the differences should be calculated in L3)

Step 2 *Access the Statistical Tests Menu*

- Press **STAT**
- Arrow right to **TESTS**
- Arrow down to **TInterval** (**even for large-sample case**)
- Press **ENTER**

| EDIT | CALC | **TESTS** |

```
2↑T-Test…
3:2-SampZTest…
4:2-SampTTest…
5:1-PropZTest…
6:2-PropZTest…
7:ZInterval…
8↓TInterval…
```

Step 3 *Choose "Data"*

- Press **ENTER**
- Set **List** to **L3**

- Set **Freq** to **1**
- Set **C-Level** to the confidence level
- Arrow down to "**Calculate**"
- Press **ENTER**

The confidence interval will be displayed with the mean, standard deviation, and sample size of the differences.

Hypothesis Test for a Paired Difference Mean

Note: There is no paired difference option on the calculator. These instructions demonstrate how to calculate the differences and then use the 1-sample *t*-test.

Step 1 *Enter the data and calculate the differences.*

- Press **STAT** and select **1:Edit**

Note: If the lists already contain data, clear the old data. Use the up **ARROW** to highlight "**L1.**"

- Press **CLEAR ENTER**
- Use the up **ARROW** to highlight "**L2**"
- Press **CLEAR ENTER**
- Use the **ARROW** and **ENTER** keys to enter the first data set into **L1**
- Use the **ARROW** and **ENTER** keys to enter the second data set into **L2**
- The differences will be calculated in **L3**
- Use the up **ARROW** to highlight "**L3**"
- Press **CLEAR**—this will clear any old data, but **L3** will remain highlighted
- To enter the equation L3 = L1 − L2, use the following keystrokes:
  - Press **2ND** "**1**" (this will enter L1)
  - Press the **MINUS** button
  - Press **2ND** "**2**" (this will enter L2)

(Notice the equation at the bottom of the screen.)

- Press **ENTER** (the differences should be calculated in L3)

Step 2 *Access the Statistical Tests Menu*

- Press **STAT**
- Arrow right to **TESTS**
- Arrow down to **T-Test** (even for large-sample case)
- Press **ENTER**

Step 3 *Choose "Data"*

- Press **ENTER**
- Enter the values for the hypothesis test, where μ_0 = the value for μ_d in the null hypothesis
- Set **List** to **L3**

- Set **Freq** to **1**
- Use the **ARROW** to highlight the appropriate alternative hypothesis
- Press **ENTER**
- Arrow down to "**Calculate**"
- Press **ENTER**

The test statistic and the *p*-value will be displayed, as well as the sample mean, standard deviation, and sample size of the differences.

Confidence Interval for $(p_1 - p_2)$

Step 1 *Access the Statistical Tests Menu*

- Press **STAT**
- Arrow right to **TESTS**
- Arrow down to **2-PropZInt**
- Press **ENTER**

Step 2 *Enter the values from the sample information and the confidence level*

where x_1 = number of successes in the first sample (e.g., 53)

n_1 = sample size for the first sample (e.g., 400)

x_2 = number of successes in the second sample (e.g., 78)

n_2 = sample size for the second sample (e.g., 500)

- Set **C-Level** to the confidence level
- Arrow down to "**Calculate**"
- Press **ENTER**

Hypothesis Test for $(p_1 - p_2)$

Step 1 *Access the Statistical Tests Menu*

- Press **STAT**
- Arrow right to **TESTS**
- Arrow down to **2-PropZ-Test**
- Press **ENTER**

Step 2 *Enter the values from the sample information and select the alternative hypothesis*

where x_1 = number of successes in the first sample (e.g., 53)

n_1 = sample size for the first sample (e.g., 400)

x_2 = number of successes in the second sample (e.g., 78)

n_2 = sample size for the second sample (e.g., 500)

- Use the **ARROW** to highlight the appropriate alternative hypothesis
- Press **ENTER**
- Arrow down to "**Calculate**"
- Press **ENTER**

Hypothesis Test for $\left(\frac{\sigma_1^2}{\sigma_2^2}\right)$

Step 1 *Enter the data (Skip to Step 2 if you have summary statistics, not raw data)*

- Press **STAT** and select **1:Edit**

Note: If the lists already contain data, clear the old data. Use the up **ARROW** to highlight "**L1.**"

- Press **CLEAR ENTER**
- Use the up **ARROW** to highlight "**L2**"
- Press **CLEAR ENTER**
- Use the **ARROW** and **ENTER** keys to enter the first data set into **L1**
- Use the **ARROW** and **ENTER** keys to enter the second data set into **L2**

Step 2 *Access the Statistical Tests Menu*

- Press **STAT**
- Arrow right to **TESTS**
- Arrow down to **2-SampFTest**
- Press **ENTER**

Step 3 *Choose "Data" or "Stats" ("Data" is selected when you have entered the raw data into the Lists. "Stats" is selected when you are given only the means, standard deviations, and sample sizes.)*

- Press **ENTER**
- If you selected "Data"
  - Set **List1** to **L1** and **List2** to **L2**
  - Set **Freq1** to **1** and set **Freq2** to **1**
  - Use the **ARROW** to highlight the appropriate alternative hypothesis
  - Press **ENTER**
  - Arrow down to "**Calculate**"
  - Press **ENTER**

- If you selected "Stats," enter the standard deviations and sample sizes
  - Use the **ARROW** to highlight the appropriate alternative hypothesis
  - Press **ENTER**
  - Arrow down to "**Calculate**"
  - Press **ENTER**

The results of the hypothesis test will be displayed with the *p*-value and the input data used.

[PART II] The Kentucky Milk Case

In The Kentucky Milk Case—Part I, you used graphical and numerical descriptive statistics to investigate bid collusion in the Kentucky school milk market. This case expands your previous analyses, incorporating inferential statistical methodology. The three areas of your focus are described below. (See p. 127 for the file layout of the **MILK** data.) Again, you should prepare a professional document that presents the results of the analyses and any implications regarding collusionary practices in the tri-county Kentucky milk market.

1. *Incumbency rates.* Recall from Part I that market allocation (where the same dairy controls the same school districts year after year) is a common form of collusive behavior in bid-rigging conspiracies. Market allocation is typically gauged by the incumbency rate for a market in a given school year—defined as the percentage of school districts that are won by the same milk vendor who won the previous year. Past experience with milk bids in a competitive market reveals that a "normal" incumbency rate is about .7—that is, 70% of the school districts are expected to purchase their milk from the same vendor who supplied the milk the previous year. In the 13-district tri-county Kentucky market, 13 vendor transitions potentially exist each year. Over the 1985–1988 period (when bid collusion was alleged to have occurred), there were 52 potential vendor transitions. Based on the actual number of vendor transitions that occurred each year and over the 1985–1988 period, make an inference regarding bid collusion.

2. *Bid price dispersion.* Recall that in competitive, sealed-bid markets, more dispersion or variability among the bids is observed than in collusive markets. (This is due to conspiring vendors sharing information about their bids.) Consequently, if collusion exists, the variation in bid prices in the tri-county market should be significantly smaller than the corresponding variation in the surrounding market. For each milk product, conduct an analysis to compare the bid price variances of the two markets each year. Make the appropriate inferences.

3. *Average winning bid price.* According to collusion theorists, the mean winning bid price in the "rigged" market will exceed the mean winning bid price in the competitive market for each year in which collusion occurs. In addition, the difference between the competitive average and the "rigged" average tends to grow over time when collusionary tactics are employed over several consecutive years. For each milk product, conduct an analysis to compare the winning bid price means of the tri-county and surrounding markets each year. Make the appropriate inferences.

Data Set: MILK

11

CONTENTS

Where We've Been

- Presented methods for estimating and testing population parameters
- Developed a test for relating two qualitative variables

Where We're Going

- Introduce the straight-line (*simple linear regression*) model as a means of relating one quantitative variable to another quantitative variable (11.1)
- Assess how well the simple linear regression model fits the sample data (11.2–11.4)
- Introduce the *correlation coefficient* as a means of relating one quantitative variable to another quantitative variable (11.5)
- Employ the simple linear regression model for predicting the value of one variable from a specified value of another variable (11.6–11.7)

☐ Simple Linear Regression

STATISTICS in ACTION **Legal Advertising—Does It Pay?**

According to the American Bar Association, there are over 1 million lawyers competing for your business. To gain a competitive edge, these lawyers aggressively advertise their services. The advertising of legal services has long been a controversial subject, with many believing that it constitutes an unethical (and in some cases even illegal) practice. Nonetheless, legal advertisements appear in nearly all media, ranging from the covers of telephone directories to infomercials on television, as well as a significant presence on the Internet. In fact, Erickson Marketing, Inc., reports that "attorneys are the #1 category of advertising in the Yellow Pages."

For this *Statistics in Action,* we present an actual recent case involving two former law partners. One partner (A) sued the other (B) over who should pay what share of the expenses of their former partnership. Partner A handled personal injury (PI) cases, while partner B handled only worker's compensation (WC) cases. The firm's advertising was focused on personal injury only, but partner A claimed that the ads resulted in the firm getting more WC cases for partner B, and therefore partner B should share the advertising expenses.

Table SIA11.1 shows the firm's new PI and WC cases each month over a 48-month period for this partnership. Also shown is the total expenditure on advertising each month and over the previous 6 months. Do these data provide support for the hypothesis that increased advertising expenditures are associated with more PI cases? With more WC cases? If advertising expenditures have a statistically significant association with the number of cases, does this necessarily mean that there is a causal relationship, that is, that spending more on advertising causes an increase in the number of cases? Based on these data, should partner A or partner B bear the brunt of the advertising expenditures?

Table SIA11.1	Legal Advertising Data			
Month	Advertising Expenditure ($)	New PI Cases	New WC Cases	6 Months Cumulative Adv. Exp. ($)
1	9,221.55	7	26	n/a
2	6,684.00	9	33	n/a
3	200.00	12	18	n/a
4	14,546.75	27	15	n/a
5	5,170.14	9	19	n/a
6	5,810.30	13	26	n/a
7	5,816.20	11	24	41,632.74
8	8,236.38	7	22	38,227.39
9	−2,089.55	13	12	39,779.77
10	29,282.24	7	15	37,490.22
11	9,193.58	9	21	52,225.71
12	9,499.18	8	24	56,249.15
13	11,128.76	18	25	59,938.03
14	9,057.64	9	19	65,250.59
15	13,604.54	25	12	66,071.85
16	14,411.76	26	33	81,765.94
17	13,724.28	27	32	66,895.46
18	13,419.42	12	21	71,426.16
19	17,372.33	14	18	75,346.40
20	6,296.35	5	25	81,589.97
21	13,191.59	22	12	78,828.68
22	26,798.80	15	7	78,415.73
23	18,610.95	12	22	90,802.77
24	829.53	18	27	95,689.44
25	16,976.53	20	25	83,099.55
26	14,076.98	38	26	82,703.75
27	24,791.75	13	28	90,484.38
28	9,691.25	18	31	102,084.54
29	28,948.25	21	40	84,976.99
30	21,373.52	7	39	95,314.29
31	9,675.25	16	41	115,858.28
32	33,213.55	12	48	108,557.00
33	19,859.85	15	28	127,693.57
34	10,475.25	18	29	122,761.67
35	24,790.84	30	20	123,545.67
36	36,660.94	12	27	119,388.26
37	8,812.50	30	26	134,675.68
38	41,817.75	20	45	133,812.93
39	27,399.33	19	30	142,417.13
40	25,723.10	29	33	149,956.61
41	16,312.10	58	24	165,204.46
42	26,332.78	42	40	156,725.72
43	60,207.58	24	36	146,397.56
44	42,485.39	47	29	197,792.64
45	35,601.92	24	17	198,460.28
46	72,071.50	14	13	206,662.87
47	12,797.11	31	15	253,011.27
48	12,310.50	26	16	249,496.28

Source: Info Tech, Inc.

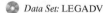 *Data Set:* LEGADV

The data for the case are saved in the **LEGADV** file. In the *Statistics in Action Revisited* sections of this chapter, we examine the relationship between monthly advertising expenditure and the number of new legal cases in an attempt to answer these questions.

STATISTICS in ACTION REVISITED

- ▫ Estimating a Straight-Line Regression Model **(p. 612)**
- ▫ Assessing How Well a Straight-Line Regression Model Fits Data **(p. 627)**
- ▫ Using the Coefficient of Correlation and the Coefficient of Determination **(p. 637)**
- ▫ Prediction Using the Straight-Line Model **(p. 645)**

In Chapters 6–9, we described methods for making inferences about population means. The mean of a population was treated as a *constant*, and we showed how to use sample data to estimate or to test hypotheses about this constant mean. In many applications, the mean of a population is not viewed as a constant but rather as a variable. For example, the mean sale price of residences sold this year in a large city might be treated as a variable that depends on the square feet of living space in the residence. For example, the relationship might be

$$\text{Mean sale price} = \$30,000 + \$60 \text{ (square feet)}$$

This formula implies that the mean sale price of 1,000-square-foot homes is \$90,000, the mean sale price of 2,000-square-foot homes is \$150,000, and the mean sale price of 3,000-square-foot homes is \$210,000.

In this chapter, we discuss situations in which the mean of the population is treated as a variable, dependent on the value of another variable. The dependence of residential sale price on the square feet of living space is one illustration. Other examples include the dependence of mean sales revenue of a firm on advertising expenditure, the dependence of mean starting salary of a college graduate on the student's GPA, and the dependence of mean monthly production of automobiles on the total number of sales in the previous month.

We begin our discussion with the simplest of all models relating a population mean to another variable—*the straight-line model.* We show how to use the sample data to estimate the straight-line relationship between the mean value of one variable, *y*, as it relates to a second variable, *x*. The methodology of estimating and using a straight-line relationship is referred to as *simple linear regression analysis.*

11.1 Probabilistic Models

An important consideration in merchandising a product is the amount of money spent on advertising. Suppose you want to model the monthly sales revenue of an appliance store as a function of the monthly advertising expenditure. The first question to be answered is this: "Do you think an exact relationship exists between these two variables?" That is, do you think it is possible to state the exact monthly sales revenue if the amount spent on advertising is known? We think you will agree with us that this is *not* possible for several reasons. Sales depend on many variables other than advertising expenditure—for example, time of year, the state of the general economy, inventory, and price structure. Even if many variables are included in a model (the topic of Chapter 12), it is still unlikely that we would be able to predict the monthly sales *exactly.* There will almost certainly be some variation in monthly sales due strictly to *random phenomena* that cannot be modeled or explained.

If we were to construct a model that hypothesized an exact relationship between variables, it would be called a **deterministic model.** For example, if we believe that *y*, the monthly sales revenue, will be exactly 15 times *x*, the monthly advertising expenditure, we write

$$y = 15x$$

This represents a *deterministic relationship* between the variables *y* and *x*. It implies that *y* can always be determined exactly when the value of *x* is known. *There is no allowance for error in this prediction.*

If, on the other hand, we believe there will be unexplained variation in monthly sales—perhaps caused by important but unincluded variables or by random phenomena—we discard the deterministic model and use a model that accounts for this **random error.** This **probabilistic model** includes both a deterministic component and a random error component. For example, if we hypothesize that the sales *y* are related to advertising expenditure *x* by

$$y = 15x + \text{Random error}$$

> **General Form of Probabilistic Models**
>
> $$y = \text{Deterministic component} + \text{Random error}$$
>
> where y is the variable of interest. We always assume that the mean value of the random error equals 0. This is equivalent to assuming that the mean value of y, $E(y)$, equals the deterministic component of the model; that is,
>
> $$E(y) = \text{Deterministic component}$$

we are hypothesizing a *probabilistic relationship* between y and x. Note that the deterministic component of this probabilistic model is $15x$.

Figure 11.1a shows the possible values of y and x for five different months, when the model is deterministic. All the pairs of (x, y) data points must fall exactly on the line because a deterministic model leaves no room for error.

Figure 11.1b shows a possible set of points for the same values of x when we are using a probabilistic model. Note that the deterministic part of the model (the straight line itself) is the same. Now, however, the inclusion of a random error component allows the monthly sales to vary from this line. Because we know that the sales revenue does vary randomly for a given value of x, the probabilistic model provides a more realistic model for y than does the deterministic model.

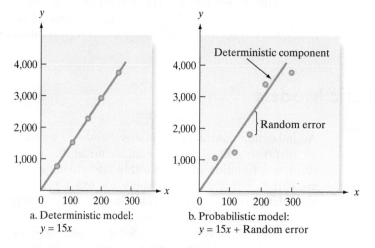

Figure 11.1

Possible sales revenues, y, for five different months, x

a. Deterministic model:
   $y = 15x$

b. Probabilistic model:
   $y = 15x + \text{Random error}$

In this chapter, we present the simplest of probabilistic models—the **straight-line model**—which derives its name from the fact that the deterministic portion of the model graphs as a straight line. Fitting this model to a set of data is an example of **regression analysis,** or **regression modeling.** The elements of the straight-line model are summarized in the next box.

> **A First-Order (Straight-Line) Probabilistic Model**
>
> $$y = \beta_0 + \beta_1 x + \varepsilon$$
>
> where
>
> $y = $ **Dependent** *or* **response variable** (variable to be modeled)
>
> $x = $ **Independent** *or* **predictor variable** (variable used as a predictor of y)*
>
> $E(y) = \beta_0 + \beta_1 x = $ Deterministic component
>
> ε (epsilon) $= $ Random error component
>
> β_0 (beta zero) $= $ **y-intercept of the line,** that is, the point at which the line *intercepts or cuts through the y-axis* (see Figure 11.2)

*The word *independent* should not be interpreted in a probabilistic sense, as defined in Chapter 3. The phrase *independent variable* is used in regression analysis to refer to a predictor variable for the response y.

FRANCIS GALTON (1822–1911)
The Law of Universal Regression

Francis Galton was the youngest of seven children born to a middle-class English family of Quaker faith. A cousin of Charles Darwin, Galton attended Trinity College (Cambridge, England) to study medicine. Due to the death of his father, Galton was unable to obtain his degree. His competence in both medicine and mathematics, however, led Galton to pursue a career as a scientist. Galton made major contributions to the fields of genetics, psychology, meteorology, and anthropology. Some consider Galton to be the first social scientist for his applications of the novel statistical concepts of the time—in particular, regression and correlation. While studying natural inheritance in 1886, Galton collected data on the heights of parents and adult children. He noticed the tendency for tall (or short) parents to have tall (or short) children, but the children were not as tall (or short), on average, as their parents. Galton called this phenomenon the "law of universal regression," for the average heights of adult children tend to "regress" to the mean of the population. Galton, with the help of his friend and disciple, Karl Pearson, applied the straight-line model to the height data, and the term *regression* model was coined.

β_1 (beta one) = **Slope of the line,** that is, the change (amount of increase or decrease) in the deterministic component of y for every 1-unit increase in x

[*Note:* A *positive* slope implies that $E(y)$ *increases* by the amount β_1 for each unit increase in x (see Figure 11.2). A *negative* slope implies that $E(y)$ *decreases* by the amount β_1.]

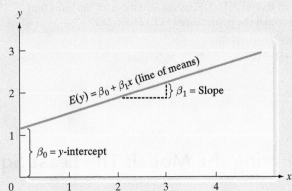

Figure 11.2
The straight-line model

In the probabilistic model, the deterministic component is referred to as the **line of means** because the mean of y, $E(y)$, is equal to the straight-line component of the model—that is,

$$E(y) = \beta_0 + \beta_1 x$$

Note that the Greek symbols β_0 and β_1, respectively, represent the y-intercept and slope of the model. They are population parameters that will be known only if we have access to the entire population of (x, y) measurements. Together with a specific value of the independent variable x, they determine the mean value of y, which is a specific point on the line of means (Figure 11.2).

The values of β_0 and β_1 will be unknown in almost all practical applications of regression analysis. The process of developing a model, estimating the unknown parameters, and using the model can be viewed as the five-step procedure shown in the next box.

Step 1: Hypothesize the deterministic component of the model that relates the mean, $E(y)$, to the independent variable x (Section 11.1).

Step 2: Use the sample data to estimate unknown parameters in the model (Section 11.2).

Step 3: Specify the probability distribution of the random error term and estimate the standard deviation of this distribution (Section 11.3).

Step 4: Statistically evaluate the usefulness of the model (Sections 11.4 and 11.5).

Step 5: When satisfied that the model is useful, use it for prediction, estimation, and other purposes (Section 11.6).

Exercises 11.1–11.9

Learning the Mechanics

11.1 In each case, graph the line that passes through the given points.
    a. $(1, 1)$ and $(5, 5)$ **b.** $(0, 3)$ and $(3, 0)$
    c. $(-1, 1)$ and $(4, 2)$ **d.** $(-6, -3)$ and $(2, 6)$

11.2 Give the slope and y-intercept for each of the lines graphed in Exercise 11.1.

11.3 The equation for a straight line (deterministic model) is

$$y = \beta_0 + \beta_1 x$$

If the line passes through the point $(-2, 4)$, then $x = -2$, $y = 4$ must satisfy the equation; that is,

$$4 = \beta_0 + \beta_1(-2)$$

Similarly, if the line passes through the point $(4, 6)$, then $x = 4$, $y = 6$ must satisfy the equation; that is,

$$6 = \beta_0 + \beta_1(4)$$

Use these two equations to solve for β_0 and β_1; then find the equation of the line that passes through the points $(-2, 4)$ and $(4, 6)$.

11.4 Refer to Exercise 11.3. Find the equations of the lines that pass through the points listed in Exercise 11.1.

11.5 Plot the following lines:
   a. $y = 4 + x$ **b.** $y = 5 - 2x$
   c. $y = -4 + 3x$ **d.** $y = -2x$
   e. $y = x$ **f.** $y = .50 + 1.5x$

11.6 Give the slope and y-intercept for each of the lines graphed in Exercise 11.5.

11.7 Why do we generally prefer a probabilistic model to a deterministic model? Give examples for when the two types of models might be appropriate.

11.8 What is the line of means?

11.9 If a straight-line probabilistic relationship relates the mean $E(y)$ to an independent variable x, does it imply that every value of the variable y will always fall exactly on the line of means? Why or why not?

11.2 Fitting the Model: The Least Squares Approach

After the straight-line model has been hypothesized to relate the mean $E(y)$ to the independent variable x, the next step is to collect data and to estimate the (unknown) population parameters, the y-intercept β_0 and the slope β_1.

To begin with a simple example, suppose an appliance store conducts a 5-month experiment to determine the effect of advertising on sales revenue. The results are shown in Table 11.1. (The number of measurements and the measurements themselves are unrealistically simple to avoid arithmetic confusion in this introductory example.) This set of data will be used to demonstrate the five-step procedure of regression modeling given in Section 11.1. In this section, we hypothesize the deterministic component of the model and estimate its unknown parameters (steps 1 and 2). The model assumptions and the random error component (step 3) are the subjects of Section 11.3, whereas Sections 11.4 and 11.5 assess the utility of the model (step 4). Finally, we use the model for prediction and estimation (step 5) in Section 11.6.

Step 1: *Hypothesize the deterministic component of the probabilistic model.* As stated before, we will consider only straight-line models in this chapter. Thus, the complete model to relate mean sales revenue $E(y)$ to advertising expenditure x is given by

$$E(y) = \beta_0 + \beta_1 x$$

Step 2: *Use sample data to estimate unknown parameters in the model.* This step is the subject of this section—namely, how can we best use the information in the sample of five observations in Table 11.1 to estimate the unknown y-intercept β_0 and slope β_1?

To determine whether a linear relationship between y and x is plausible, it is helpful to plot the sample data in a **scatterplot** (or **scattergram**). Recall (Section 2.9) that a scatterplot locates each of the five data points on a graph, as shown in Figure 11.3. Note that the scatterplot suggests a general tendency for y to increase as x increases. If you

Figure 11.3

Scatterplot for data in Table 11.1

Table 11.1	Advertising-Sales Data	
Month	Advertising Expenditure, x ($100s)	Sales Revenue, y ($1,000s)
1	1	1
2	2	1
3	3	2
4	4	2
5	5	4

Data Set: ADSALE

place a ruler on the scatterplot, you will see that a line may be drawn through three of the five points, as shown in Figure 11.4. To obtain the equation of this visually fitted line, note that the line intersects the y-axis at $y = -1$, so the y-intercept is -1. Also, y increases exactly 1 unit for every 1-unit increase in x, indicating that the slope is $+1$. Therefore, the equation is

$$\tilde{y} = -1 + 1(x) = -1 + x$$

where $\tilde{y}$ is used to denote the predicted y from the visual model.

One way to decide quantitatively how well a straight line fits a set of data is to note the extent to which the data points deviate from the line. For example, to evaluate the model in Figure 11.4, we calculate the magnitude of the *deviations* (i.e., the differences between the observed and the predicted values of y). These deviations, or **errors of prediction,** are the vertical distances between observed and predicted values (see Figure 11.4).*

Figure 11.4

Visual straight line fitted to the data in Figure 11.3

The observed and predicted values of y, their differences, and their squared differences are shown in Table 11.2. Note that the *sum of errors* equals 0 and the *sum of squares of the errors* (SSE), which gives greater emphasis to large deviations of the points from the line, is equal to 2.

Table 11.2	Comparing Observed and Predicted Values for the Visual Model			
x	y	$\tilde{y} = -1 + x$	$(y - \tilde{y})$	$(y - \tilde{y})^2$
1	1	0	$(1 - 0) = 1$	1
2	1	1	$(1 - 1) = 0$	0
3	2	2	$(2 - 2) = 0$	0
4	2	3	$(2 - 3) = -1$	1
5	4	4	$(4 - 4) = 0$	0
			Sum of errors $= 0$	Sum of squared errors (SSE) $= 2$

You can see by shifting the ruler around the graph that it is possible to find many lines for which the sum of errors is equal to 0, but it can be shown that there is one (and only one) line for which the SSE is a *minimum*. This line is called the **least squares line,** the **regression line,** or the **least squares prediction equation.** The methodology used to obtain this line is called the **method of least squares.**

Now Work Exercise 11.12a, b, c, d

To find the least squares prediction equation for a set of data, assume that we have a sample of n data points consisting of pairs of values of x and y, say (x_1, y_1), $(x_2, y_2), \ldots, (x_n, y_n)$. For example, the $n = 5$ data points shown in Table 11.2 are $(1, 1)$, $(2, 1)$, $(3, 2)$, $(4, 2)$, and $(5, 4)$. The fitted line, which we will calculate based on the five data points, is written as

$$\hat{y} = \hat{\beta}_0 + \hat{\beta}_1 x$$

The "hats" indicate that the symbols below them are estimates: $\hat{y}$ (y-hat) is an estimator of the mean value of y, $E(y)$, and a predictor of some future value of y; and $\hat{\beta}_0$ and $\hat{\beta}_1$ are estimators of β_0 and β_1, respectively.

For a given data point, say the point (x_i, y_i), the observed value of y is y_i, and the predicted value of y would be obtained by substituting x_i into the prediction equation:

$$\hat{y}_i = \hat{\beta}_0 + \hat{\beta}_1 x_i$$

*In Chapter 12, we refer to these errors of prediction as **regression residuals.** There, we learn that an analysis of residuals is essential in establishing a useful regression model.

And the deviation of the *i*th value of *y* from its predicted value is

$$(y_i - \hat{y}_i) = [y_i - (\hat{\beta}_0 + \hat{\beta}_1 x_i)]$$

Then the sum of squares of the deviations of the *y*-values about their predicted values for all the *n* points is

$$SSE = \sum [y_i - (\hat{\beta}_0 + \hat{\beta}_1 x_i)]^2$$

The quantities $\hat{\beta}_0$ and $\hat{\beta}_1$ that make the SSE a minimum are called the **least squares estimates** of the population parameters β_0 and β_1, and the prediction equation $\hat{y} = \hat{\beta}_0 + \hat{\beta}_1 x$ is called the *least squares line*.

The **least squares line** $\hat{y} = \hat{\beta}_0 + \hat{\beta}_1 x$ is one that has the following two properties:

1. The sum of the errors equals 0, i.e., mean error = 0.
2. The sum of squared errors (SSE) is smaller than for any other straight-line model, i.e., the error variance is minimum.

The values of $\hat{\beta}_0$ and $\hat{\beta}_1$ that minimize the SSE are (proof omitted) given by the formulas in the box.*

Formulas for the Least Squares Estimates

$$Slope: \hat{\beta}_1 = \frac{SS_{xy}}{SS_{xx}}$$

$$y\text{-}intercept: \hat{\beta}_0 = \bar{y} - \hat{\beta}_1 \bar{x}$$

$$\text{where}^\dagger \quad SS_{xy} = \sum (x_i - \bar{x})(y_i - \bar{y})$$

$$SS_{xx} = \sum (x_i - \bar{x})^2$$

$$n = \text{Sample size}$$

Example 11.1

Applying the Method of Least Squares— Advertising–Sales Data

Problem Refer to the advertising–monthly–sales data presented in Table 11.1. Consider the straight-line model, $E(y) = \beta_0 + \beta_1 x$, where y = sales revenue (thousands of dollars) and x = advertising expenditure (hundreds of dollars).

a. Use the method of least squares to estimate the values of β_0 and β_1.

b. Predict the sales revenue when advertising expenditure is $200 (i.e., when $x = 2$).

c. Find SSE for the analysis.

d. Give practical interpretations to β_0 and β_1.

Solution

a. We used Excel to make the preliminary computations for finding the least squares line. The Excel spreadsheet is shown in Figure 11.5. Using the values on the spreadsheet, we find

---

*Students who are familiar with calculus should note that the values of β_0 and β_1 that minimize SSE = $\sum (y_i - \hat{y}_i)^2$ are obtained by setting the two partial derivatives $\partial SSE/\partial \beta_0$ and $\partial SSE/\partial \beta_1$ equal to 0. The solutions to these two equations yield the formulas shown in the box. Furthermore, we denote the *sample* solutions to the equations by $\hat{\beta}_0$ and $\hat{\beta}_1$, where the "hat" denotes that these are sample estimates of the true population intercept β_0 and true population slope β_1.

†Alternatively, you can use the following "shortcut" formulas:

$$SS_{xy} = \sum x_i y_i - \frac{(\sum x_i)(\sum y_j)}{n}; \quad SS_{xx} = \sum x_i^2 - \frac{(\sum x_i)^2}{n}$$

Figure 11.5

Excel spreadsheet showing calculations for advertising-sales example

	A	B	C	D	E	F	G	H
1		AdvExp (X)	SalesRev (Y)	(X - 3)	(Y - 2)	(X-3)(Y-2)	(X-3)(X-3)	(Y-2)(Y-2)
2		1	1	-2	-1	2	4	1
3		2	1	-1	-1	1	1	1
4		3	2	0	0	0	0	0
5		4	2	1	0	0	1	0
6		5	4	2	2	4	4	4
7								
8	Totals	15	10	0	0	7	10	6
9	Mean	3	2					

$$\bar{x} = \frac{\Sigma x}{5} = \frac{15}{5} = 3$$

$$\bar{y} = \frac{\Sigma y}{5} = \frac{10}{5} = 2$$

$$SS_{xy} = \Sigma(x - \bar{x})(y - \bar{y}) = \Sigma(x - 3)(y - 2) = 7$$

$$SS_{xx} = \Sigma(x - \bar{x})^2 = \Sigma(x - 3)^2 = 10$$

Then the slope of the least squares line is

$$\hat{\beta}_1 = \frac{SS_{xy}}{SS_{xx}} = \frac{7}{10} = .7$$

and the y-intercept is

$$\hat{\beta}_0 = \bar{y} - \hat{\beta}_1\bar{x} = 2 - (.7)(3) = 2 - 2.1 = -.1$$

The least squares line is thus

$$\hat{y} = \hat{\beta}_0 + \hat{\beta}_1 x = -.1 + .7x$$

The graph of this line is shown in Figure 11.6.

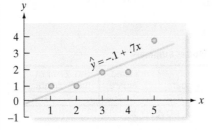

Figure 11.6

The line $\hat{y} = -.1 + .7x$ fitted to the data

b. The predicted value of y for a given value of x can be obtained by substituting into the formula for the least squares line. Substituting $x = 2$ into the least squares equation yields

$$\hat{y} = -.1 + .7x = -.1 + .7(2) = 1.3$$

Thus, when advertising expenditure is $200, we predict monthly sales revenue to be $1,300. We show how to find a prediction interval for y in Section 11.6.

c. The observed and predicted values of y, the deviations of the y values about their predicted values, and the squares of these deviations are shown in the Excel spreadsheet, Figure 11.7. Note that SSE = 1.10, and (as we would expect) this is less than the SSE = 2.0 obtained in Table 11.2 for the visually fitted line.

d. The estimated y-intercept, $\hat{\beta}_0 = -.1$, appears to imply that the estimated mean sales revenue is equal to -.1, or -$100, when the advertising expenditure, x, is equal to $0. Because negative sales revenues are not possible, this seems to make the model nonsensical. However, *the model parameters should be interpreted only within the*

	A	B	C	D	E	F
1	AdvExp (X)	SalesRev (Y)	Predicted Y=-.1+.7X	(Y-Yhat)	(Y-Yhat)(Y-Yhat)	
2	1	1	0.6	0.4	0.16	
3	2	1	1.3	-0.3	0.09	
4	3	2	2	0	0	
5	4	2	2.7	-0.7	0.49	
6	5	4	3.4	0.6	0.36	
7						
8			Sum	0	1.1	
9						
10						

Figure 11.7

Excel spreadsheet comparing observed and predicted values for advertising-sales example

sampled range of the independent variable—in this case, for advertising expenditures between $100 and $500. Thus, the y-intercept—which is, by definition, at $x = 0$ ($0 advertising expenditure)—is not within the range of the sampled values of x and is not subject to meaningful interpretation.

The slope of the least squares line, $\hat{\beta}_1 = .7$, implies that for every unit increase of x, the mean value of y is estimated to increase by .7 unit. In terms of this example, for every $100 increase in advertising, the mean sales revenue is estimated to increase by $700 *over the sampled range of advertising expenditures from $100 to $500.* Thus, the model does not imply that increasing the advertising expenditures from $500 to $1,000 will result in an increase in mean sales of $3,500, because the range of x in the sample does not extend to $1,000 ($x = 10$). Be careful to interpret the estimated parameters only within the sampled range of x.

Look Back The calculations required to obtain $\hat{\beta}_0$, $\hat{\beta}_1$, and SSE in simple linear regression, although straightforward, can become rather tedious. Even with the use of an Excel spreadsheet, the process is laborious, especially when the sample size is large. Fortunately, a statistical software package can significantly reduce the labor involved in regression calculations. The SPSS, Minitab, and Excel/XLSTAT outputs for the simple linear regression of the data in Table 11.1 are displayed in Figures 11.8a–c. The values of $\hat{\beta}_0$ and $\hat{\beta}_1$ are highlighted on the printouts. These values, $\hat{\beta}_0 = -.1$ and $\hat{\beta}_1 = .7$, agree exactly with our calculated values. The value of SSE = 1.10 is also highlighted on the printouts.

Model Summary

Model	R	R Square	Adjusted R Square	Std. Error of the Estimate
1	.904[a]	.817	.756	.606

a. Predictors: (Constant), ADVEXP_X

ANOVA[b]

Model		Sum of Squares	df	Mean Square	F	Sig.
1	Regression	4.900	1	4.900	13.364	.035[a]
	Residual	1.100	3	.367		
	Total	6.000	4			

a. Predictors: (Constant), ADVEXP_X

b. Dependent Variable: SALES_Y

Coefficients[a]

Model		Unstandardized Coefficients		Standardized Coefficients	t	Sig.
		B	Std. Error	Beta		
1	(Constant)	-.100	.635		-.157	.885
	ADVEXP_X	.700	.191	.904	3.656	.035

a. Dependent Variable: SALES_Y

Figure 11.8a

SPSS printout for the advertising-sales regression

Figure 11.8b

Minitab printout for the advertising-sales regression

```
Regression Analysis: SALES_Y versus ADVEXP_X

The regression equation is
SALES_Y = - 0.100 + 0.700 ADVEXP_X


Predictor      Coef   SE Coef       T      P
Constant    -0.1000    0.6351   -0.16  0.885
ADVEXP_X     0.7000    0.1915    3.66  0.035


S = 0.605530   R-Sq = 81.7%   R-Sq(adj) = 75.6%


Analysis of Variance

Source          DF       SS      MS       F      P
Regression       1   4.9000  4.9000   13.36  0.035
Residual Error   3   1.1000  0.3667
Total            4   6.0000
```

Figure 11.8c

XLSTAT printout of sales-advertising regression model

Regression of variable SALES_Y:

Goodness of fit statistics:

Observations	5.0000
Sum of weights	5.0000
DF	3.0000
R²	0.8167
Adjusted R²	0.7556
MSE	0.3667
RMSE	0.6055
DW	2.5091

Analysis of variance:

Source	DF	Sum of squares	Mean squares	F	Pr > F
Model	1	4.9000	4.9000	13.3636	0.0354
Error	3	1.1000	0.3667		
Corrected Total	4	6.0000			
Computed against model Y=Mean(Y)					

Model parameters:

Source	Value	Standard error	t	Pr > |t|	Lower bound (95%)	Upper bound (95%)
Intercept	−0.1000	0.6351	−0.1575	0.8849	−2.1211	1.9211
ADVEXP_X	0.7000	0.1915	3.6556	0.0354	0.0906	1.3094

Equation of the model:

SALES_Y = −0.10000+0.70000*ADVEXP_X

■ **Now Work Exercise 11.15**

Interpreting the Estimates of β_0 and β_1 in Simple Linear Regression

y-intercept: $\hat{\beta}_0$ represents the predicted value of *y* when $x = 0$ (*Caution:* This value will not be meaningful if the value $x = 0$ is nonsensical or outside the range of the sample data.)

slope: $\hat{\beta}_1$ represents the increase (or decrease) in *y* for every 1-unit increase in *x* (*Caution:* This interpretation is valid only for *x*-values within the range of the sample data.)

Even when the interpretations of the estimated parameters in a simple linear regression are meaningful, we need to remember that they are only estimates based on the sample. As such, their values will typically change in repeated sampling. How much confidence do we have that the estimated slope, $\hat{\beta}_1$, accurately approximates the true slope, β_1? This requires statistical inference, in the form of confidence intervals and tests of hypotheses, which we address in Section 11.4.

To summarize, we defined the best-fitting straight line to be the one that minimizes the sum of squared errors around the line, and we called it the *least squares line.* We should interpret the least squares line only within the sampled range of the independent variable. In subsequent sections, we show how to make statistical inferences about the model.

STATISTICS in ACTION REVISITED

Estimating a Straight-Line Regression Model

We return to the legal advertising case involving two former law partners (p. 601). Recall that partner A (who handled PI cases) sued partner B (who handled WC cases) over who should pay what share of the advertising expenses of their former partnership. Monthly data were collected on the number of new PI cases, number of new WC cases, and the total amount spent (in thousands of dollars) on advertising over the previous 6 months. These data (shown in Table SIA11.1, p. 602) are saved in the **LEGADV** file. Do these data provide support for the hypothesis that increased advertising expenditures are associated with more PI cases? Define y as the number of new PI cases per month and x as the cumulative 6-month advertising expenditures (in thousands of dollars). One way to investigate the link between these two variables is to fit the straight-line model, $E(y) = \beta_0 + \beta_1 x$, to the data in Table SIA11.1.

A Minitab scatterplot of the data and a simple linear regression printout are shown in Figure SIA11.1. Note that the least squares line is also displayed on the scatterplot. You can see that the line has a positive slope and, although there is some variation of the data points around the line, it appears that advertising expenditure (x) is fairly strongly related to the number of new PI cases (y). The estimated slope of the line (highlighted on Figure SIA11.1) is $\hat{\beta}_1 = .113$. Thus, we estimate a .113 increase in the number of new PI cases for every \$1,000 increase in cumulative advertising expenditures.

Does such a relationship also exist between number of new WC cases and advertising expenditure? Now let y = number of new WC cases per month and x = cumulative

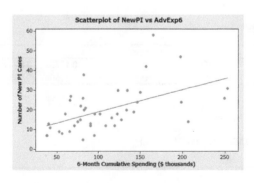

Regression Analysis: NewPI versus AdvExp6

```
The regression equation is
NewPI = 7.77 + 0.113 AdvExp6

Predictor    Coef   SE Coef     T      P
Constant    7.767    3.385    2.29  0.027
AdvExp6     0.11289  0.02793  4.04  0.000

S = 9.67521   R-Sq = 29.0%   R-Sq(adj) = 27.2%

Analysis of Variance

Source          DF     SS      MS      F      P
Regression       1   1529.5  1529.5  16.34  0.000
Residual Error  40   3744.4    93.6
Total           41   5273.9
```

Figure SIA11.1

Minitab analysis of new PI cases vs. 6-month cumulative advertising expenditure

Regression Analysis: NewWC versus AdvExp6

```
The regression equation is
NewWC = 24.6 + 0.0098 AdvExp6

Predictor    Coef   SE Coef     T      P
Constant    24.574   3.367    7.30  0.000
AdvExp6     0.00982  0.02778  0.35  0.725

S = 9.62296   R-Sq = 0.3%   R-Sq(adj) = 0.0%

Analysis of Variance

Source          DF     SS       MS     F      P
Regression       1    11.58   11.58  0.13  0.725
Residual Error  40  3704.06   92.60
Total           41  3715.64
```

Figure SIA11.2

Minitab analysis of new WC cases vs. 6-month cumulative advertising expenditure

6-month advertising expenditures. A Minitab scatterplot and simple linear regression analysis for these two variables are shown in Figure SIA11.2. Compared to the previous scatterplot, the slope of the least squares line shown in Figure SIA11.2 is much flatter, and the variation of the data points around the line is much larger. Consequently, it does not appear that number of new WC cases is very strongly related to advertising expenditure. In fact, the estimated slope (highlighted in Figure SIA11.2) implies that a $1,000 increase in cumulative advertising expenditures will lead to only a $\hat{\beta}_1 = .0098$ increase in the number of new WC cases per month.

Based on these descriptive statistics (scatterplots and least squares lines), it appears that partner A's argument that partner B should share the advertising expenses is weak, at best. In the *Statistics in Action Revisited* sections that follow, we will provide a measure of reliability to this inference and investigate the legal advertising data further.

Exercises 11.10–11.26

Learning the Mechanics

11.10 The following table is similar to Table 11.2. It is used for making the preliminary computations for finding the least squares line for the given pairs of x and y values.

x_i	y_i	x_i^2	$x_i y_i$
7	2		
4	4		
6	2		
2	5		
1	7		
1	6		
3	5		
Totals $\sum x_i =$	$\sum y_i =$	$\sum x_i^2 =$	$\sum x_i y_i =$

a. Complete the table.
b. Find SS_{xy}.
c. Find SS_{xx}.
d. Find $\hat{\beta}_1$.
e. Find $\bar{x}$ and $\bar{y}$.
f. Find $\hat{\beta}_0$.
g. Find the least squares line.

11.11 Refer to Exercise 11.10. After the least squares line has been obtained, the table below (which is similar to Table 11.2) can be used for (1) comparing the observed and the predicted values of y and (2) computing SSE.

x	y	$\hat{y}$	$(y - \hat{y})$	$(y - \hat{y})^2$
7	2			
4	4			
6	2			
2	5			
1	7			
1	6			
3	5			
			$\sum(y - \hat{y}) =$	$SSE = \sum(y - \hat{y})^2 =$

a. Complete the table.
b. Plot the least squares line on a scatterplot of the data. Plot the following line on the same graph: $\hat{y} = 14 - 2.5x$.
c. Show that SSE is larger for the line in part **b** than it is for the least squares line.

11.12 Construct a scatterplot for the data in the following table.

NW

x	.5	1	1.5
y	2	1	3

a. Plot the following two lines on your scatterplot:
$$y = 3 - x \quad \text{and} \quad y = 1 + x$$

b. Which of these lines would you choose to characterize the relationship between x and y? Explain.
c. Show that the sum of the errors of prediction for both of these lines equals 0.
d. Which of these lines has the smaller SSE?
e. Find the least squares line for the data and compare it to the two lines described in part **a**.

11.13 Consider the following pairs of measurements:

L11013

x	8	5	4	6	2	5	3
y	1	3	6	3	7	2	5

a. Construct a scatterplot for these data.
b. What does the scatterplot suggest about the relationship between x and y?
c. Find the least squares estimates of β_0 and β_1.
d. Plot the least squares line on your scatterplot. Does the line appear to fit the data well? Explain.

● Applet Exercise 11.1

Use the applet *Regression by Eye* to explore the relationship between the pattern of data in a scatterplot and the corresponding least squares model.

a. Run the applet several times. For each time, attempt to move the green line into a position that appears to minimize the vertical distances of the points from the line. Then click *Show regression line* to see the actual regression line. How close is your line to the actual line? Click *New data* to reset the applet.
b. Click the trash can to clear the graph. Use the mouse to place five points on the scatterplot that are approximately in a straight line. Then move the green line to approximate the regression line. Click *Show regression line* to see the actual regression line. How close were you this time?

c. Continue to clear the graph and plot sets of five points with different patterns among the points. Use the green line to approximate the regression line. How close do you come to the actual regression line each time?

d. Based on your experiences with the applet, explain why we need to use more reliable methods of finding the regression line than just "eyeing" it.

Applying the Concepts—Basic

11.14 In business, do nice guys finish first or last? Refer to the *Nature* (March 20, 2008) study of whether "nice guys finish last" in the business world, Exercise 2.123 (p. 104). Recall that college students repeatedly played a version of the game "prisoner's dilemma," where competitors choose cooperation, defection, or costly punishment. (Cooperation meant paying 1 unit for the opponent to receive 2 units, defection meant gaining 1 unit at a cost of 1 unit for the opponent, and punishment meant paying 1 unit for the opponent to lose 4 units.) At the conclusion of the games, the researchers recorded the average payoff and the number of times cooperation, defection, and punishment were used for each player. The scatterplots below plot average payoff (y) against level of cooperation use, defection use, and punishment use, respectively.

a. Consider cooperation use (x) as a predictor of average payoff (y). Based on the scatterplot, is there evidence of a linear trend?

b. Consider defection use (x) as a predictor of average payoff (y). Based on the scatterplot, is there evidence of a linear trend?

c. Consider punishment use (x) as a predictor of average payoff (y). Based on the scatterplot (reproduced from Exercise 2.123), is there evidence of a linear trend?

d. Refer to part **c**. Is the slope of the line relating punishment use (x) to average payoff (y) positive or negative?

11.15 State Math SAT scores. Refer to the data on average state Math SAT scores for 2001 and 2011, Exercise 2.27 (p. 60). The first five observations and last two observations in the file are reproduced in the next table. In Exercise 2.126 (p. 105), you examined the relationship between the 2001 Math SAT scores and the 2011 Math SAT scores with a scatterplot.

State	2001	2011
Alabama	554	541
Alaska	510	511
Arizona	525	523
Arkansas	550	570
California	517	515
⋮	⋮	⋮
Wisconsin	596	602
Wyoming	545	569

Source: Based on "SAT Trends: Background on the SAT Takers in the Class of 2011." The College Board.

a. Write the equation of a straight-line model relating 2011 Math SAT score (y) to 2001 Math SAT score (x).

b. An SPSS simple linear regression printout for the data is shown on the next page. Find the least squares prediction equation.

c. Give a practical interpretation of the y-intercept of the least squares line. If a practical interpretation is not possible, explain why.

d. Give a practical interpretation of the slope of the least squares line. Over what range of x is the interpretation meaningful?

11.16 Lobster fishing study. Refer to the *Bulletin of Marine Science* (April 2010) study of teams of fishermen fishing for the red spiny lobster in Baja California Sur, Mexico, Exercise 2.124 (p. 104). Two variables measured for each of 15 teams from two fishing cooperatives were y = total catch of lobsters (in kilograms) during the season and x = average percentage of traps allocated per day to exploring areas of unknown catch (called *search frequency*). These data are listed in the table.

Total Catch	Search Frequency	Total Catch	Search Frequency
9,998	18	6,535	21
7,767	14	6,695	26
8,764	4	4,891	29
9,077	18	4,937	23
8,343	9	5,727	17
9,222	5	7,019	21
6,827	8	5,735	20
2,785	35		

Source: Based on Shester, G. G. "Explaining catch variation among Baja California lobster fishers through spatial analysis of trap-placement decisions," *Bulletin of Marine Science,* Vol. 86, No. 2, April 2010 (Table 1).

a. Graph the data in a scatterplot. What type of trend, if any, do you observe?

b. A simple linear regression analysis was conducted using XLSTAT. A portion of the regression printout is shown on the next page. Find the estimates of β_0 and β_1 on the printout.

SPSS Output for Exercise 11.15

Coefficients[a]

Model		Unstandardized Coefficients		Standardized Coefficients	t	Sig.
		B	Std. Error	Beta		
1	(Constant)	-97.414	26.668		-3.653	.001
	MATH2001	1.188	.050	.959	23.830	.000

a. Dependent Variable: MATH2011

XLSTAT output for Exercise 11.16

Model parameters:

Source	Value	Standard error	t	Pr > |t|	Lower bound (95%)	Upper bound (95%)
Intercept	9877.8300	829.0411	11.9148	< 0.0001	8086.7957	11668.8643
SEARCHFR	-163.6024	41.9014	-3.9045	0.0018	-254.1249	-73.0799

Equation of the model:

CATCH = 9877.82997-163.60242*SEARCHFREQ

c. If possible, give a practical interpretation of the estimate of β_0. If no practical interpretation is possible, explain why.

d. If possible, give a practical interpretation of the estimate of β_1. If no practical interpretation is possible, explain why.

11.17 Drug controlled-release rate study. Researchers at Dow Chemical Co. investigated the effect of tablet surface area and volume on the rate at which a drug is released in a controlled-release dosage (*Drug Development and Industrial Pharmacy,* Vol. 28, 2002). Six similarly shaped tablets were prepared with different weights and thicknesses, and the ratio of surface area to volume was measured for each. Using a dissolution apparatus, each tablet was placed in 900 milliliters of deionized water, and the diffusional drug release rate (percentage of drug released divided by the square root of time) was determined. The experimental data are listed in the table below.

Drug Release Rate (% released/$\sqrt{\text{time}}$)	Surface Area to Volume (mm²/mm³)
60	1.50
48	1.05
39	.90
33	.75
30	.60
29	.65

Source: Reynolds, T., Mitchell, S., & Balwinski, K.M. "Investigation of the effect of table surface area/volume on drug release from hydroxypropyl-methylcellulose controlled-release matrix tablets," *Drug Development and Industrial Pharmacy,* Vol. 28, No. 4, 2002, pp. 457–466 (Figure 3). Reprinted by permission of the publisher (Taylor & Francis Group, www.informaworld.com).

a. Fit the simple linear model, $E(y) = \beta_0 + \beta_1 x$, where y = release rate and x = surface-area-to-volume ratio.

b. Interpret the estimates of β_0 and β_1.

c. Predict the drug release rate for a tablet that has a surface area/volume ratio of .50.

d. Comment on the reliability of the prediction in part **c.**

11.18 Extending the life of an aluminum smelter pot. An investigation of the properties of bricks used to line aluminum smelter pots was published in *The American Ceramic Society Bulletin* (Feb. 2005). Six different commercial bricks were evaluated. The life length of a smelter pot depends on the porosity of the brick lining (the less porosity, the longer the life); consequently, the researchers measured the apparent porosity of each brick specimen, as well as the mean pore diameter of each brick. The data are given in the accompanying table.

Brick	Apparent Porosity (%)	Mean Pore Diameter (micrometers)
A	18.8	12.0
B	18.3	9.7
C	16.3	7.3
D	6.9	5.3
E	17.1	10.9
F	20.4	16.8

Source: Based on Bonadia, P., et al. "Aluminosilicate refractories for aluminum cell linings," *The American Ceramic Society Bulletin,* Vol. 84, No. 2, Feb. 2005, pp. 26–31 (Table II).

a. Find the least squares line relating porosity (y) to mean pore diameter (x).

b. Interpret the y-intercept of the line.

c. Interpret the slope of the line.

d. Predict the apparent porosity percentage for a brick with a mean pore diameter of 10 micrometers.

11.19 Software millionaires and birthdays. In *Outliers: The Story of Success* (Little, Brown, 2008), the author notes that a disproportionate number of software millionaires were born around the year 1955. Is this a coincidence, or does birth year matter when gauging whether a software founder will be successful? On his Web blog (www.measuringusability.com), statistical consultant Jeff Sauro investigated this question by analyzing the data shown in the table on the next page.

Data for Exercise 11.19

Decade	Total U.S. Births (millions)	Number of Software Millionaire Birthdays	Number of CEO Birthdays (in a random sample of 70 companies from the *Fortune* 500 list)
1920	28.582	3	2
1930	24.374	1	2
1940	31.666	10	23
1950	40.530	14	38
1960	38.808	7	9
1970	33.309	4	0

Source: Sauro, J. "Were most software millionaires born around 1955?" *Measuring Usability,* November 17, 2010. Copyright © 2010 by Measuring Usability LLC. Reprinted with permission.

a. Fit a simple linear regression model relating number (y) of software millionaire birthdays in a decade to total number (x) of U.S. births. Give the least squares prediction equation.

b. Practically interpret the estimated y-intercept and slope of the model, part **a.**

c. Predict the number of software millionaire birthdays that will occur in a decade where the total number of U.S. births is 35 million.

d. Fit a simple linear regression model relating number (y) of software millionaire birthdays in a decade to number (x) of CEO birthdays. Give the least squares prediction equation.

e. Practically interpret the estimated y-intercept and slope of the model, part **d.**

f. Predict the number of software millionaire birthdays that will occur in a decade where the number of CEO birthdays (from a random sample of 70 companies) is 10.

Applying the Concepts—Intermediate

11.20 Public corruption and bad weather. The Federal Emergency Management Agency (FEMA) provides disaster relief for states impacted by natural disasters (e.g., hurricanes, tornados, floods). Do these bad weather windfalls lead to public corruption? This was the research question of interest in an article published in the *Journal of Law and Economics* (Nov. 2008). Data on y = average annual number of public corruption convictions (per 100,000 residents) and x = average annual FEMA relief (in dollars) per capita for each of the 50 states were used in the investigation.

a. Access the data, saved in the file, and construct a scatterplot. Do you observe a trend?

b. Fit the simple linear regression model, $E(y) = \beta_0 + \beta_1 x$, to the data and obtain estimates of the y-intercept and slope.

c. Practically interpret the estimated y-intercept and estimated slope.

11.21 Ranking driving performance of professional golfers. Refer to *The Sport Journal* (Winter 2007) study of a new method for ranking the total driving performance of golfers on the Professional Golf Association (PGA) tour, Exercise 2.50 (p. 72). Recall that the method computes a driving performance index based on a golfer's average driving distance (yards) and driving accuracy (percent of drives that land in the fairway). Data for the top 40 PGA golfers (as ranked by the new method) are saved in the

file. (The first five and last five observations are listed in the table.)

Rank	Player	Driving Distance (yards)	Driving Accuracy (%)	Driving Performance Index
1	Woods	316.1	54.6	3.58
2	Perry	304.7	63.4	3.48
3	Gutschewski	310.5	57.9	3.27
4	Wetterich	311.7	56.6	3.18
5	Hearn	295.2	68.5	2.82
⋮	⋮	⋮	⋮	⋮
36	Senden	291	66	1.31
37	Mickelson	300	58.7	1.30
38	Watney	298.9	59.4	1.26
39	Trahan	295.8	61.8	1.23
40	Pappas	309.4	50.6	1.17

Source: Wiseman, F., et al. "A new method for ranking total driving performance on the PGA Tour," *The Sport Journal,* Vol. 10, No. 1, Winter 2007 (Table 2).

a. Write the equation of a straight-line model relating driving accuracy (y) to driving distance (x).

b. Fit the model, part **a,** to the data using simple linear regression. Give the least squares prediction equation.

c. Interpret the estimated y-intercept of the line.

d. Interpret the estimated slope of the line.

e. In Exercise 2.132 (p. 106), you were informed that a professional golfer, practicing a new swing to increase his average driving distance, is concerned that his driving accuracy will be lower. Which of the two estimates, y-intercept or slope, will help you determine if the golfer's concern is a valid one? Explain.

11.22 Sweetness of orange juice. The quality of the orange juice produced by a manufacturer (e.g., Minute Maid, Tropicana) is constantly monitored. There are numerous sensory and chemical components that combine to make the best-tasting orange juice. For example, one manufacturer has developed a quantitative index of the "sweetness" of orange juice. (The higher the index, the sweeter the juice.) Is there a relationship between the sweetness index and a chemical measure such as the amount of water-soluble pectin (parts per million) in the orange juice? Data collected on these two variables for 24 production runs at a juice manufacturing plant are shown in the table on the next page. Suppose a manufacturer wants to use simple linear regression to predict the sweetness (y) from the amount of pectin (x).

Data for Exercise 11.22

Run	Sweetness Index	Pectin (ppm)
1	5.2	220
2	5.5	227
3	6.0	259
4	5.9	210
5	5.8	224
6	6.0	215
7	5.8	231
8	5.6	268
9	5.6	239
10	5.9	212
11	5.4	410
12	5.6	256
13	5.8	306
14	5.5	259
15	5.3	284
16	5.3	383
17	5.7	271
18	5.5	264
19	5.7	227
20	5.3	263
21	5.9	232
22	5.8	220
23	5.8	246
24	5.9	241

Note: The data in the table are authentic. For confidentiality reasons, the manufacturer cannot be disclosed.

a. Find the least squares line for the data.
b. Interpret $\hat{\beta}_0$ and $\hat{\beta}_1$ in the words of the problem.
c. Predict the sweetness index if amount of pectin in the orange juice is 300 ppm. [*Note:* A measure of reliability of such a prediction is discussed in Section 11.6]

11.23 Forecasting movie revenues with Twitter. Marketers are keenly interested in how social media (e.g., Facebook, Twitter) may influence consumers who buy their products. Researchers at HP Labs (Palo Alto, CA) investigated whether the volume of chatter on Twitter.com could be used to forecast the box office revenues of movies (*IEEE International Conference on Web Intelligence and*

Tweet Rate	Revenue (millions)
1365.8	142
1212.8	77
581.5	61
310.1	32
455	31
290	30
250	21
680.5	18
150	18
164.5	17
113.9	16
144.5	15
418	14
98	14
100.8	12
115.4	11
74.4	10
87.5	9
127.6	9
52.2	9
144.1	8
41.3	2
2.75	0.3

Intelligent Agent Technology, 2010). Opening weekend box office revenue data (in \$millions of dollars) were collected for a sample of 23 recent movies. In addition, the researchers computed each movie's *tweet rate,* i.e., the average number of tweets (at Twitter.com) referring to the movie per hour 1 week prior to the movie's release. The data (simulated based on information provided in the study) are listed in the accompanying table. Assuming that movie revenue and tweet rate are linearly related, how much do you estimate a movie's opening weekend revenue to change as the tweet rate for the movie increases by an average of 100 tweets per hour?

11.24 FCAT scores and poverty. In the state of Florida, elementary school performance is based on the average score obtained by students on a standardized exam, called the Florida Comprehensive Assessment Test (FCAT). An analysis of the link between FCAT scores and sociodemographic factors was published in the *Journal of Educational and Behavioral Statistics* (Spring 2004). Data on average math and reading FCAT scores of third graders, as well as the percentage of students below the poverty level, for a sample of 22 Florida elementary schools are listed in the table below.

a. Propose a straight-line model relating math score (y) to percentage (x) of students below the poverty level.
b. Fit the model to the data using the method of least squares.
c. Graph the least squares line on a scatterplot of the data. Is there visual evidence of a relationship between the two variables? Is the relationship positive or negative?
d. Interpret the estimates of the y-intercept and slope in the words of the problem.
e. Now consider a model relating reading score (y) to percentage (x) of students below the poverty level. Repeat parts **a–d** for this model.

Elementary School	FCAT-Math	FCAT-Reading	% Below Poverty
1	166.4	165.0	91.7
2	159.6	157.2	90.2
3	159.1	164.4	86.0
4	155.5	162.4	83.9
5	164.3	162.5	80.4
6	169.8	164.9	76.5
7	155.7	162.0	76.0
8	165.2	165.0	75.8
9	175.4	173.7	75.6
10	178.1	171.0	75.0
11	167.1	169.4	74.7
12	177.0	172.9	63.2
13	174.2	172.7	52.9
14	175.6	174.9	48.5
15	170.8	174.8	39.1
16	175.1	170.1	38.4
17	182.8	181.4	34.3
18	180.3	180.6	30.3
19	178.8	178.0	30.3
20	181.4	175.9	29.6
21	182.8	181.6	26.5
22	186.1	183.8	13.8

Source: Based on Tekwe, C. D., et al. "An empirical comparison of statistical models for value-added assessment of school performance," *Journal of Educational and Behavioral Statistics,* Vol. 29, No. 1, Spring 2004, pp. 11–36 (Table 2).

Data for Exercise 11.25

School	Enrollment (# full-time students)	Annual Tuition ($)	Mean GMAT	% with Job Offer	Avg. Salary ($)
Dartmouth	503	38,400	704	—	119,800
Michigan	1,873	33,076	690	91	105,986
Carnegie Mellon	661	38,800	691	93	95,531
Northwestern	2,650	38,844	700	94	117,060
Yale	468	36,800	696	86	104,018
Pennsylvania	1,840	40,458	716	92	117,471
Cal., Berkeley	1,281	21,512	701	92	112,699
Columbia	1,796	38,290	709	95	126,319
North Carolina	855	16,375	652	86	92,565
Southern Cal.	1,588	37,558	685	82	88,839

Source: "Wall Street Journal's annual rankings of business schools," *The Wall Street Journal,* Sep. 25, 2005. Copyright 2005 by Dow Jones & Company, Inc. Reproduced with permission.

11.25 Survey of the top business schools. Each year, the *Wall Street Journal* and *Harris Interactive* track the opinions and experiences of college recruiters for large corporations and summarize the results in the Business School Survey. One of these surveys included rankings of 76 business schools. Survey data for the top 10 business schools are given in the table above. All the data are saved in the file.
  a. Select one of the variables as the dependent variable, *y*, and another as the independent variable, *x*. Use your knowledge of the subject area and common sense to help you select the variables.
  b. Fit the simple linear model, $E(y) = \beta_0 + \beta_1 x$, to the data for all 76 business schools. Interpret the estimates of the slope and *y*-intercept.

Applying the Concepts—Advanced

11.26 Spreading rate of spilled liquid. Refer to the *Chemical Engineering Progress* (Jan. 2005) study of the rate at which a spilled volatile liquid will spread across a surface, Exercise 2.128 (p. 105). Recall that a DuPont Corp. engineer calculated the mass (in pounds) of a 50-gallon methanol spill

after a period of time ranging from 0 to 60 minutes. Do the data in the table below indicate that the mass of the spill tends to diminish as time increases? If so, how much will the mass diminish each minute?

Time (minutes)	Mass (pounds)	Time (minutes)	Mass (pounds)
0	6.64	22	1.86
1	6.34	24	1.60
2	6.04	26	1.37
4	5.47	28	1.17
6	4.94	30	0.98
8	4.44	35	0.60
10	3.98	40	0.34
12	3.55	45	0.17
14	3.15	50	0.06
16	2.79	55	0.02
18	2.45	60	0.00
20	2.14		

Source: Barry, J. "Estimating rates of spreading and evaporation of volatile liquids," *Chemical Engineering Progress,* Vol. 101, No. 1, Jan. 2005. Reproduced with permission. Copyright © 2005 AICHE.

11.3 Model Assumptions

In Section 11.2, we assumed that the probabilistic model relating the firm's sales revenue *y* to the advertising dollars is

$$y = \beta_0 + \beta_1 x + \varepsilon$$

We also recall that the least squares estimate of the deterministic component of the model, $\beta_0 + \beta_1 x$, is

$$\hat{y} = \hat{\beta}_0 + \hat{\beta}_1 x = -.1 + .7x$$

Now we turn our attention to the random component ε of the probabilistic model and its relation to the errors in estimating β_0 and β_1. We will use a probability distribution to characterize the behavior of ε. We will see how the probability distribution of ε determines how well the model describes the relationship between the dependent variable *y* and the independent variable *x*.

Step 3 in a regression analysis requires us to specify the probability distribution of the random error ε. We will make four basic assumptions about the general form of this probability distribution:

Assumption 1: The mean of the probability distribution of ε is 0—that is, the average of the values of ε over an infinitely long series of experiments is 0 for each setting of the independent variable x. This assumption implies that the mean value of y, $E(y)$, for a given value of x is $E(y) = \beta_0 + \beta_1 x$.

Assumption 2: The variance of the probability distribution of ε is constant for all settings of the independent variable x. For our straight-line model, this assumption means that the variance of ε is equal to a constant, say σ^2, for all values of x.

Assumption 3: The probability distribution of ε is normal.

Assumption 4: The values of ε associated with any two observed values of y are independent—that is, the value of ε associated with one value of y has no effect on the values of ε associated with other y values.

The implications of the first three assumptions can be seen in Figure 11.9, which shows distributions of errors for three values of x, namely, x_1, x_2, and x_3. Note that the relative frequency distributions of the errors are normal with a mean of 0 and a constant variance σ^2. (All the distributions shown have the same amount of spread or variability.) The straight line shown in Figure 11.9 is the line of means. It indicates the mean value of y for a given value of x. We denote this mean value as $E(y)$. Then, the line of means is given by the equation

$$E(y) = \beta_0 + \beta_1 x$$

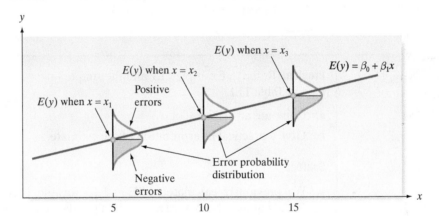

Figure 11.9

The probability distribution of ε

These assumptions make it possible for us to develop measures of reliability for the least squares estimators and to develop hypothesis tests for examining the usefulness of the least squares line. We have various techniques for checking the validity of these assumptions, and we have remedies to apply when they appear to be invalid. Several of these remedies are discussed in Chapter 12. Fortunately, the assumptions need not hold exactly in order for least squares estimators to be useful. The assumptions will be satisfied adequately for many applications encountered in practice.

It seems reasonable to assume that the greater the variability of the random error ε (which is measured by its variance σ^2), the greater will be the errors in the estimation of the model parameters β_0 and β_1 and in the error of prediction when $\hat{y}$ is used to predict y for some value of x. Consequently, you should not be surprised, as we proceed through this chapter, to find that σ^2 appears in the formulas for all confidence intervals and test statistics that we will be using.

In most practical situations, σ^2 is unknown, and we must use our data to estimate its value. The best estimate of σ^2, denoted by s^2, is obtained by dividing the sum of squares of the deviations of the y values from the prediction line,

$$\text{SSE} = \sum (y_i - \hat{y}_i)^2$$

by the number of degrees of freedom associated with this quantity. We use 2 df to estimate the two parameters β_0 and β_1 in the straight-line model, leaving $(n - 2)$ df for the error variance estimation.

Estimation of σ^2 for a (First-Order) Straight-Line Model

$$s^2 = \frac{\text{SSE}}{\text{Degrees of freedom for error}} = \frac{\text{SSE}}{n-2}$$

where $\text{SSE} = \Sigma(y_i - \hat{y}_i)^2 = \text{SS}_{yy} - \hat{\beta}_1\text{SS}_{xy}$

$$\text{SS}_{yy} = \Sigma(y_i - \bar{y})^2 *$$

To estimate the standard deviation σ of ε, we calculate

$$s = \sqrt{s^2} = \sqrt{\frac{\text{SSE}}{n-2}}$$

We will refer to s as the **estimated standard error of the regression model.**

 CAUTION When performing these calculations, you may be tempted to round the calculated values of SS_{yy}, $\hat{\beta}_1$, and SS_{xy}. Be certain to carry at least six significant figures for each of these quantities to avoid substantial errors in calculation of the SSE.

Example 11.2
Estimating σ — Advertising-Sales Regression

Problem Refer to Example 11.1 and the simple linear regression of the advertising-sales data in Table 11.1.

a. Compute an estimate of σ.

b. Give a practical interpretation of the estimate.

Solution

a. We previously calculated SSE = 1.10 for the least squares line $\hat{y} = -.1 + .7x$. Recalling that there were $n = 5$ data points, we have $n - 2 = 5 - 2 = 3$ df for estimating σ^2. Thus,

$$s^2 = \frac{\text{SSE}}{n-2} = \frac{1.10}{3} = .367$$

is the estimated variance, and

$$s = \sqrt{.367} = .61$$

is the standard error of the regression model.

b. You may be able to grasp s intuitively by recalling the interpretation of a standard deviation given in Chapter 2 and remembering that the least squares line estimates the mean value of y for a given value of x. Because s measures the spread of the distribution of y values about the least squares line, we should not be surprised to find that most of the observations lie within $2s$, or $2(.61) = 1.22$, of the least squares line. For this simple example (only five data points), all five sales revenue values fall within $2s$ (or \$1,220) of the least squares line. In Section 11.6, we use s to evaluate the error of prediction when the least squares line is used to predict a value of y to be observed for a given value of x.

Look Back The values of s^2 and s can also be obtained from a simple linear regression printout. The Minitab printout for the advertising-sales example is reproduced in Figure 11.10. The value of s^2 is highlighted at the bottom of the printout in the

---

*Alternatively, you can use the following "shortcut" formula:

$$\text{SS}_{yy} = \Sigma y^2 - \frac{(\Sigma y)^2}{n}$$

Regression Analysis: SALES_Y versus ADVEXP_X

```
The regression equation is
SALES_Y = - 0.100 + 0.700 ADVEXP_X


Predictor      Coef   SE Coef       T       P
Constant    -0.1000    0.6351   -0.16   0.885
ADVEXP_X     0.7000    0.1915    3.66   0.035


S = 0.605530   R-Sq = 81.7%   R-Sq(adj) = 75.6%


Analysis of Variance

Source           DF       SS       MS       F       P
Regression        1   4.9000   4.9000   13.36   0.035
Residual Error    3   1.1000   0.3667
Total             4   6.0000
```

Figure 11.10

Minitab printout for the advertising-sales regression

MS (Mean Square) column in the row labeled **Residual Error.** (In regression, the estimate of σ^2 is called Mean Square for Error, or MSE.) The value, $s^2 = .3667$, agrees with the one calculated by hand. The value of s is also highlighted in Figure 11.10. This value, $s = .60553$, agrees (except for rounding) with our hand-calculated value.

───■ **Now Work Exercise 11.32**

Interpretation of s, the Estimated Standard Deviation of ε

We expect most ($\approx 95\%$) of the observed y values to lie within $2s$ of their respective least squares predicted values, $\hat{y}$.

Exercises 11.27–11.40

Learning the Mechanics

11.27 Visually compare the scatterplots shown below. If a least squares line were determined for each data set, which do you think would have the smallest variance, s^2? Explain.

11.28 Calculate SSE and s^2 for each of the following cases:
  a. $n = 20$, $SS_{yy} = 95$, $SS_{xy} = 50$, $\hat{\beta}_1 = .75$
  b. $n = 40$, $\Sigma y^2 = 860$, $\Sigma y = 50$, $SS_{xy} = 2,700$, $\hat{\beta}_1 = .2$
  c. $n = 10$, $\Sigma(y_i - \bar{y})^2 = 58$, $SS_{xy} = 91$, $SS_{xx} = 170$

11.29 Suppose you fit a least squares line to 26 data points and the calculated value of SSE is 8.34.
  a. Find s^2, the estimator of σ^2 (the variance of the random error term ε).
  b. What is the largest deviation that you might expect between any one of the 26 points and the least squares line?

11.30 Refer to Exercise 11.10 (p. 613). Calculate SSE, s^2, and s for the least squares line. Use the value of s to determine where most of the errors of prediction lie.

a.

b.

c.

Scatterplots for Exercise 11.27

Applying the Concepts—Basic

11.31 Do nice guys really finish last in business? Refer to the *Nature* (March 20, 2008) study of whether "nice guys finish last" in business, Exercise 11.14 (p. 614). Recall that college students repeatedly played a version of the game "prisoner's dilemma," where competitors choose cooperation, defection, or costly punishment. At the conclusion of the games, the researchers recorded the average payoff and the number of times punishment was used for each player. Based on a scatterplot of the data, the simple linear regression relating average payoff (y) to punishment use (x) resulted in SSE = 1.04.

a. Assuming a sample size of $n = 28$, compute the estimated standard deviation of the error distribution, s.

b. Give a practical interpretation of s.

11.32 State Math SAT scores. Refer to the simple linear regression relating $y = 2011$ Math SAT scores to $x = 2001$ Math SAT scores, Exercise 11.15 (p. 614). A portion of the SPSS printout of the analysis is shown below.

Model Summary

Model	R	R Square	Adjusted R Square	Std. Error of the Estimate
1	.959[a]	.921	.919	11.912

a. Predictors: (Constant), MATH2001

ANOVA[a]

Model		Sum of Squares	df	Mean Square	F	Sig.
1	Regression	80575.988	1	80575.988	567.864	.000[b]
	Residual	6952.757	49	141.893		
	Total	87528.745	50			

a. Dependent Variable: MATH2011
b. Predictors: (Constant), MATH2001

a. Locate the values of SSE, s^2, and s on the SPSS printout.

b. Give a practical interpretation of the value of s.

11.33 Drug controlled-release rate study. Refer to the simple linear regression relating the drug release rate (y) to surface area-to-volume ratio (x), Exercise 11.17 (p. 615).

a. Find the value of s for the straight-line model fit in Exercise 11.17a.

b. Give a practical interpretation of the value of s.

11.34 Structurally deficient highway bridges. Refer to Exercise 1.28 (p. 27) and the data on structurally deficient highway bridges compiled by the Federal Highway Administration (FHWA) into the National Bridge Inventory (NBI). For each state, the NBI lists the number of structurally deficient bridges and the total area (thousands of square feet) of the deficient bridges. The data for the 50 states (plus the District of Columbia and Puerto Rico) are saved in the file. (The first five and last five observations are listed in the table in the next column.) For

State	Number	Area (thousands of sq. ft.)
Alabama	1,899	432.7
Alaska	155	60.9
Arizona	181	110.5
Arkansas	997	347.3
California	3,140	5,177.9
⋮	⋮	⋮
Washington	400	502.0
West Virginia	1,058	331.5
Wisconsin	1,302	399.8
Wyoming	389	143.4
Puerto Rico	241	195.4

future planning and budgeting, the FHWA wants to estimate the total area of structurally deficient bridges in a state based on the number of deficient bridges.

a. Write the equation of a straight-line model relating total area (y) to number of structurally deficient bridges (x).

b. The model, part **a,** was fit to the data using Minitab, as shown below. Find the least squares prediction equation on the printout.

c. List the assumptions required for the regression analysis.

d. Locate the estimated standard error of the regression model, s, on the printout.

e. Use the value of s to find a range where most (about 95%) of the errors of prediction will fall.

Regression Analysis: SDArea versus NumberSD

```
The regression equation is
SDArea = 120 + 0.346 NumberSD


Predictor     Coef   SE Coef     T       P
Constant     119.9     123.0   0.97   0.335
NumberSD   0.34560   0.06158   5.61   0.000


S = 635.187   R-Sq = 38.7%   R-Sq(adj) = 37.4%


Analysis of Variance

Source          DF        SS        MS       F       P
Regression       1  12710141  12710141   31.50   0.000
Residual Error  50  20173111    403462
Total           51  32883252
```

11.35 Software millionaires and birthdays. Refer to Exercise 11.19 (p. 615) and the study of software millionaires and their birthdays. The data are reproduced below.

a. Find SSE, s^2, and s for the simple linear regression model relating number (y) of software millionaire birthdays in a decade to total number (x) of U.S. births.

Data for Exercise 11.35

Decade	Total U.S. Births (millions)	Number of Software Millionaire Birthdays	Number of CEO Birthdays (in a random sample of 70 companies from the *Fortune* 500 list)
1920	28.582	3	2
1930	24.374	1	2
1940	31.666	10	23
1950	40.530	14	38
1960	38.808	7	9
1970	33.309	4	0

Source: Sauro, J. "Were most software millionaires born around 1955?" *Measuring Usability,* November 17, 2010. Copyright © 2010 by Measuring Usability LLC. Reprinted with permission.

b. Find SSE, s^2, and s for the simple linear regression model relating number (y) of software millionaire birthdays in a decade to number (x) of CEO birthdays.

c. Which of the two models' fit will have smaller errors of prediction? Why?

Applying the Concepts—Intermediate

11.36 Public corruption and bad weather. Refer to the *Journal of Law and Economics* (Nov. 2008) study of the link between Federal Emergency Management Agency (FEMA) disaster relief and public corruption, Exercise 11.20 (p. 616). You used the data in the file to fit a straight-line model relating a state's average annual number of public corruption convictions (y) to the state's average annual FEMA relief (x).

a. Estimate σ^2, the variance of the random error term in the model.

b. Estimate σ, the standard deviation of the random error term in the model.

c. Which of the estimates, part **a** or **b**, can be interpreted practically? Why?

d. Make a statement about how accurate the model is in predicting a state's average annual number of public corruption convictions.

11.37 Sweetness of orange juice. Refer to the study of the quality of orange juice produced at a juice manufacturing plant, Exercise 11.22 (p. 616). Recall that simple linear regression was used to predict the sweetness index (y) from the amount of pectin (x) in the orange juice.

a. Find the values of SSE, s^2, and s for this regression.

b. Explain why it is difficult to give a practical interpretation to s^2.

c. Give a practical interpretation of the value of s.

11.38 Are geography journals worth their cost? Refer to the *Geoforum* (Vol. 37, 2006) study of whether the price of a geography journal is correlated with quality, Exercise 2.127 (p. 105). Several quantitative variables were recorded for each in a sample of 28 geography journals: cost of a 1-year subscription (dollars); Journal Impact Factor (JIF)—the average number of times articles from the journal have been cited; number of citations for the journal over the past 5 years; and Relative Price Index (RPI). The data for the 28 journals are saved in the file. (Selected observations are listed below.)

Journal	Cost ($)	JIF	Cites	RPI
J. Econ. Geogr.	468	3.139	207	1.16
Prog. Hum. Geog.	624	2.943	544	0.77
T. I. Brit. Geogr.	499	2.388	249	1.11
Econ. Geogr.	90	2.325	173	0.30
A. A. A. Geogr.	698	2.115	377	0.93
Geogr. Anal.	213	0.902	106	0.88
Geogr. J.	223	0.857	81	0.94
Appl. Geogr.	646	0.853	74	3.38

Source: Based on Blomley, N. "Is this journal worth US$1118?" *Geoforum,* Vol. 37, 2006.

a. Fit a straight-line model relating cost (y) to JIF (x). Find an estimate of σ, the standard deviation of the error term, and interpret its value.

b. Fit a straight-line model relating cost (y) to number of citations (x). Find an estimate of σ, the standard deviation of the error term, and interpret its value.

c. Fit a straight-line model relating cost (y) to RPI (x). Find an estimate of σ, the standard deviation of the error term, and interpret its value.

d. Which predictor of cost—JIF, number of citations, or RPI—leads to a regression line with the smallest errors of prediction?

11.39 FCAT scores and poverty. Refer to the *Journal of Educational and Behavioral Statistics* (Spring 2004) study of scores on the Florida Comprehensive Assessment Test (FCAT), Exercise 11.24 (p. 617).

a. Consider the simple linear regression relating math score (y) to percentage (x) of students below the poverty level. Find and interpret the value of s for this regression.

b. Consider the simple linear regression relating reading score (y) to percentage (x) of students below the poverty level. Find and interpret the value of s for this regression.

c. Which dependent variable, math score or reading score, can be more accurately predicted by percentage (x) of students below the poverty level? Explain.

Applying the Concepts—Advanced

11.40 Life tests of cutting tools. To improve the quality of the output of any production process, it is necessary first to understand the capabilities of the process (Gitlow, et al., *Quality Management: Tools and Methods for Improvement,* 1995). In a particular manufacturing process, the useful life of a cutting tool is related to the speed at which the tool is operated. The data in the table below were derived from life tests for the two different brands of cutting tools currently used in the production process. For which brand would you feel more confident in using the least squares line to predict useful life for a given cutting speed? Explain.

Cutting Speed (meters per minute)	Useful Life (Hours) Brand A	Brand B
30	4.5	6.0
30	3.5	6.5
30	5.2	5.0
40	5.2	6.0
40	4.0	4.5
40	2.5	5.0
50	4.4	4.5
50	2.8	4.0
50	1.0	3.7
60	4.0	3.8
60	2.0	3.0
60	1.1	2.4
70	1.1	1.5
70	.5	2.0
70	3.0	1.0

Assessing the Utility of the Model: Making Inferences about the Slope β_1

Now that we have specified the probability distribution of ε and found an estimate of the variance σ^2, we are ready to make statistical inferences about the model's usefulness for predicting the response y. This is step 4 in our regression modeling procedure.

Refer again to the data of Table 11.1 and suppose the appliance store's sales revenue is *completely unrelated* to the advertising expenditure. What could be said about the values of β_0 and β_1 in the hypothesized probabilistic model

$$y = \beta_0 + \beta_1 x + \varepsilon$$

if x contributes no information for the prediction of y? The implication is that the mean of y—that is, the deterministic part of the model $E(y) = \beta_0 + \beta_1 x$—does not change as x changes. In the straight-line model, this means that the true slope, β_1, is equal to 0 (see Figure 11.11). Therefore, to test the null hypothesis that the linear model contributes no information for the prediction of y against the alternative hypothesis that the linear model is useful in predicting y, we test

$$H_0: \beta_1 = 0 \text{ against } H_a: \beta_1 \neq 0$$

Figure 11.11

Graph of the straight-line model when slope is zero, i.e., $y = \beta_0 + \varepsilon$

If the data support the alternative hypothesis, we will conclude that x does contribute information for the prediction of y using the straight-line model (although the true relationship between $E[y]$ and x could be more complex than a straight line). Thus, in effect, this is a test of the usefulness of the hypothesized model.

The appropriate test statistic is found by considering the sampling distribution of $\hat{\beta}_1$, the least squares estimator of the slope β_1, as shown in the following box.

Sampling Distribution of $\hat{\beta}_1$

If we make the four assumptions about ε (see Section 11.3), the sampling distribution of the least squares estimator $\hat{\beta}_1$ of the slope will be normal with mean β_1 (the true slope) and standard deviation

$$\sigma_{\hat{\beta}_1} = \frac{\sigma}{\sqrt{SS_{xx}}} \quad \text{(see Figure 11.12)}$$

We estimate $\sigma_{\hat{\beta}_1}$ by $s_{\hat{\beta}_1} = \dfrac{s}{\sqrt{SS_{xx}}}$ and refer to this quantity as the **estimated standard error of the least squares slope $\hat{\beta}_1$.**

Figure 11.12

Sampling distribution of $\hat{\beta}_1$

Because σ is usually unknown, the appropriate test statistic is a t-statistic, formed as follows:

$$t = \frac{\hat{\beta}_1 - \text{Hypothesized value of } \beta_1}{s_{\hat{\beta}_1}} \qquad \text{where } s_{\hat{\beta}} = \frac{s}{\sqrt{SS_{xx}}}$$

Thus,

$$t = \frac{\hat{\beta}_1 - 0}{s/\sqrt{SS_{xx}}}$$

Note that we have substituted the estimator s for σ and then formed the estimated standard error $s_{\hat{\beta}_1}$ by dividing s by $\sqrt{SS_{xx}}$. The number of degrees of freedom associated with this t-statistic is the same as the number of degrees of freedom associated with s. Recall that this number is $(n-2)$ df when the hypothesized model is a straight line (see Section 11.3). The setup of our test of the usefulness of the straight-line model is summarized in the following boxes.

A Test of Model Utility: Simple Linear Regression

One-Tailed Test	Two-Tailed Test
H_0: $\beta_1 = 0$	H_0: $\beta_1 = 0$
H_a: $\beta_1 < 0$ (or H_a: $\beta_1 > 0$)	H_a: $\beta_1 \neq 0$
	Test statistic: $t = \dfrac{\hat{\beta}_1}{s_{\hat{\beta}_1}} = \dfrac{\hat{\beta}_1}{s/\sqrt{SS_{xx}}}$
Rejection region: $t < -t_\alpha$	Rejection region: $|t| > t_{\alpha/2}$
(or $t > t_\alpha$ when H_a: $\beta_1 > 0$)	
where t_α and $t_{\alpha/2}$ are based on $(n-2)$ degrees of freedom	

Conditions Required for a Valid Test: Simple Linear Regression

Refer to the four assumptions about ε listed in Section 11.3.

Example 11.3

Testing the Regression Slope, β_1—Sales Revenue Model

Problem Refer to the simple linear regression analysis of the advertising-sales data, Examples 11.1 and 11.2. Conduct a test (at $\alpha = .05$) to determine if sales revenue (y) is linearly related to advertising expenditure (x).

Solution As stated previously, we want to test H_0: $\beta_1 = 0$ against H_a: $\beta_1 \neq 0$. For this example, $n = 5$. Thus t will be based on $n - 2 = 3$ df, and the rejection region (at $\alpha = .05$) will be

$$|t| > t_{.025} = 3.182$$

We previously calculated $\hat{\beta}_1 = .7$, $s = .61$, and $SS_{xx} = 10$. Thus, the test statistic is

$$t = \frac{\hat{\beta}_1}{s/\sqrt{SS_{xx}}} = \frac{.7}{.61/\sqrt{10}} = \frac{.7}{.19} = 3.7$$

Because this calculated t-value falls into the upper-tail rejection region (see Figure 11.13), we reject the null hypothesis and conclude that the slope β_1 is not 0. The sample evidence indicates that advertising expenditure x contributes information for the production of sales revenue y when a linear model is used.

[*Note:* We can reach the same conclusion by using the observed significance level (p-value) of the test from a computer printout. The Minitab printout for the advertising-sales example is reproduced in Figure 11.14. The test statistic and *two-tailed* p-value are highlighted on the printout. Because the p-value is smaller than $\alpha = .05$, we will reject H_0.]

Figure 11.13

Rejection region and calculated t-value for testing $H_0: \beta_1 = 0$ versus $H_a: \beta_1 \neq 0$

Regression Analysis: SALES_Y versus ADVEXP_X

```
The regression equation is
SALES_Y = - 0.100 + 0.700 ADVEXP_X


Predictor      Coef   SE Coef        T      P
Constant    -0.1000    0.6351    -0.16  0.885
ADVEXP_X     0.7000    0.1915     3.66  0.035


S = 0.605530   R-Sq = 81.7%   R-Sq(adj) = 75.6%


Analysis of Variance

Source          DF       SS       MS      F      P
Regression       1   4.9000   4.9000  13.36  0.035
Residual Error   3   1.1000   0.3667
Total            4   6.0000
```

Figure 11.14

Minitab printout for the advertising-sales regression

Look Back What conclusion can be drawn if the calculated t-value does not fall in the rejection region or if the observed significance level of the test exceeds α? We know from previous discussions of the philosophy of hypothesis testing that such a t-value does *not* lead us to accept the null hypothesis—that is, we do not conclude that $\beta_1 = 0$. Additional data might indicate that β_1 differs from 0, or a more complex relationship may exist between x and y, requiring the fitting of a model other than the straight-line model. We discuss several such models in Chapter 12.

■ **Now Work Exercise 11.46**

Interpreting p-Values for β Coefficients in Regression

Almost all statistical computer software packages report a *two-tailed* p-value for each of the β parameters in the regression model. For example, in simple linear regression, the p-value for the two-tailed test $H_0: \beta_1 = 0$ versus $H_a: \beta_1 \neq 0$ is given on the printout. If you want to conduct a *one-tailed* test of hypothesis, you will need to adjust the p-value reported on the printout as follows:

$$Upper\text{-}tailed\ test\ (H_a: \beta_1 > 0): \quad p\text{-value} = \begin{cases} p/2 & \text{if } t > 0 \\ 1 - p/2 & \text{if } t < 0 \end{cases}$$

$$Lower\text{-}tailed\ test\ (H_a: \beta_1 < 0): \quad p\text{-value} = \begin{cases} p/2 & \text{if } t < 0 \\ 1 - p/2 & \text{if } t > 0 \end{cases}$$

where p is the p-value reported on the printout and t is the value of the test statistic.

Another way to make inferences about the slope β_1 is to estimate it using a confidence interval. This interval is formed as shown in the next box.

A 100(1 − α)% Confidence Interval for the Simple Linear Regression Slope β_1

$$\hat{\beta}_1 \pm t_{\alpha/2}s_{\hat{\beta}_1}$$

where the estimated standard error $\hat{\beta}_1$ is calculated by

$$s_{\hat{\beta}_1} = \frac{s}{\sqrt{SS_{xx}}}$$

and $t_{\alpha/2}$ is based on $(n - 2)$ degrees of freedom.

Conditions Required for a Valid Confidence Interval: Simple Linear Regression

Refer to the four assumptions about ϵ listed in Section 11.3.

For the simple linear regression of sales revenue (Examples 11.1–11.3), $t_{\alpha/2}$ is based on $(n - 2) = 3$ degrees of freedom, and, for $\alpha = .05, t_{.025} = 3.182$. Therefore, a 95% confidence interval for the slope β_1, the expected change in sales revenue for a \$100 increase in advertising expenditure, is

$$\hat{\beta}_1 \pm (t_{.025})s_{\hat{\beta}_1} = .7 \pm 3.182\left(\frac{s}{\sqrt{SS_{xx}}}\right) = .7 \pm 3.182\left(\frac{.61}{\sqrt{10}}\right) = .7 \pm .61$$

Thus, the interval estimate of the slope parameter β_1 is .09 to 1.31. [*Note:* This interval can also be obtained using statistical software and is highlighted on the SPSS printout, Figure 11.15.] In terms of this example, the implication is that we can be 95% confident that the *true* mean increase in monthly sales revenue per additional \$100 of advertising expenditure is between \$90 and \$1,310. This inference is meaningful only over the sampled range of x—that is, from \$100 to \$500 of advertising expenditures.

Figure 11.15

SPSS printout with 95% confidence intervals for the advertising-sales regression β's

Coefficients^a

Model		Unstandardized Coefficients		Standardized Coefficients	t	Sig.	95% Confidence Interval for B	
		B	Std. Error	Beta			Lower Bound	Upper Bound
1	(Constant)	−.100	.635		−.157	.885	−2.121	1.921
	ADVEXP_X	.700	.191	.904	3.656	.035	.091	1.309

a. Dependent Variable: SALES_Y

Because all the values in this interval are positive, it appears that β_1 is positive and that the mean of y, $E(y)$, increases as x increases. However, the rather large width of the confidence interval reflects the small number of data points (and, consequently, a lack of information) in the experiment. Particularly bothersome is the fact that the lower end of the confidence interval implies that we are not even recovering our additional expenditure because a \$100 increase in advertising may produce as little as a \$90 increase in mean sales. If we wish to tighten this interval, we need to increase the sample size.

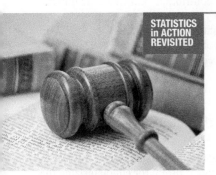

STATISTICS in ACTION REVISITED

Assessing How Well a Straight-Line Regression Model Fits Data

In the previous *Statistics in Action Revisited*, we fit the straight-line model, $E(y) = \beta_0 + \beta_1 x$, where x = cumulative 6-month advertising expenditures and y represents either the number of new PI cases or the number of new WC cases per month. The SPSS regression printouts for the two analyses are shown in Figure SIA11.3. (The regression for y = number of new PI cases is shown at the top, and the regression for y = number of new WC cases is shown at the bottom of the printout.) The objective is to determine whether one or both of the dependent variables are statistically linearly related to cumulative 6-month advertising expenditures.

The two-tailed p-values for testing the null hypothesis, H_0: $\beta_1 = 0$ (highlighted on the printouts), are p-value ≈ 0 for number of new PI cases and p-value $= .725$ for number

STATISTICS in ACTION REVISITED CONTINUED

Coefficients[a]

Model		Unstandardized Coefficients		Standardized Coefficients	t	Sig.	95% Confidence Interval for B	
		B	Std. Error	Beta			Lower Bound	Upper Bound
1	(Constant)	7.767	3.385		2.295	.027	.926	14.609
	CUM. ADV (thous)	.113	.028	.539	4.042	.000	.056	.169

a. Dependent Variable: New PI Cases

Coefficients[a]

Model		Unstandardized Coefficients		Standardized Coefficients	t	Sig.	95% Confidence Interval for B	
		B	Std. Error	Beta			Lower Bound	Upper Bound
1	(Constant)	24.574	3.367		7.299	.000	17.770	31.379
	CUM. ADV (thous)	.010	.028	.056	.354	.725	−.046	.066

a. Dependent Variable: New WC Cases

Figure SIA11.3

SPSS simple linear regressions for legal advertising data

of new WC cases. For y = number of new PI cases, there is sufficient evidence to reject H_0 (at $\alpha = .01$) and conclude that number of new PI cases is linearly related to cumulative 6-month advertising expenditures. In contrast, for y = number of WC cases, there is insufficient evidence to reject H_0 (at $\alpha = .01$); thus, there is no evidence of a linear relationship between the number of new WC cases and cumulative 6-month advertising expenditures.

We can gain further insight into this phenomenon by examining a 95% confidence interval for the slope, β_1. For y = number of new PI cases, the interval (highlighted on the SPSS printout) is (.056, .169). With 95% confidence, we can state that for every $1,000 increase in monthly advertising expenditures, the number of new PI cases each month will increase between .056 and .169. Now, a more realistic increase in cumulative 6-month advertising expenditures is, say, $20,000. Multiplying the endpoints of the interval by 20, we see that this increase in advertising spending leads to an increase of anywhere between 1 and 3 new PI cases.

Now, for y = number of new WC cases, the 95% confidence interval for the slope (also highlighted on the SPSS printout) is ($-.046, .066$). Because the interval spans the value 0, we draw the same conclusion as we did with the hypothesis test—there is no statistical evidence of a linear relationship between the number of new WC cases and cumulative 6-month advertising expenditures.

Recall that partner A (who handled the PI cases) sued partner B (who handled the WC cases) for not paying a fair share of the advertising expenses. These results do not support partner A's argument because there is no evidence that partner B benefitted from advertising.

Exercises 11.41–11.58

Learning the Mechanics

11.41 Construct both a 95% and a 90% confidence interval for β_1 for each of the following cases:
  a. $\hat{\beta}_1 = 31, s = 3, SS_{xx} = 35, n = 10$
  b. $\hat{\beta}_1 = 64, SSE = 1,960, SS_{xx} = 30, n = 14$
  c. $\hat{\beta}_1 = -8.4, SSE = 146, SS_{xx} = 64, n = 20$

11.42 Consider the following pairs of observations:

L11042

x	1	4	3	2	5	6	0
y	1	3	3	1	4	7	2

  a. Construct a scatterplot for the data.
  b. Use the method of least squares to fit a straight line to the seven data points in the table.
  c. Plot the least squares line on your scatterplot of part **a.**
  d. Specify the null and alternative hypotheses you would use to test whether the data provide sufficient evidence

to indicate that x contributes information for the (linear) prediction of y.
  e. What is the test statistic that should be used in conducting the hypothesis test of part **d?** Specify the degrees of freedom associated with the test statistic.
  f. Conduct the hypothesis test of part **d** using $\alpha = .05$.

11.43 Refer to Exercise 11.42. Construct an 80% and a 98% confidence interval for β_1.

11.44 Do the accompanying data provide sufficient evidence to conclude that a straight line is useful for characterizing the relationship between x and y?

L11044

x	4	2	4	3	2	4
y	1	6	5	3	2	4

Applying the Concepts—Basic

11.45 State Math SAT Scores. Refer to the SPSS simple linear regression relating y = average state SAT Math score in 2011 with x = average state SAT Math score in 2001, Exercise 11.15 (p. 614).
  a. Give the null and alternative hypotheses for determining whether a positive linear relationship exists between y and x.
  b. Locate the p-value of the test on the SPSS printout. Interpret the result if $\alpha = .05$.
  c. Find a 95% confidence interval for the slope, β_1. Interpret the result.

11.46 Lobster fishing study. Refer to the *Bulletin of Marine Science* (April 2010) study of teams of fishermen fishing for the red spiny lobster in Baja California Sur, Mexico, Exercise 11.16 (p. 614). A simple linear regression model relating y = total catch of lobsters (in kilograms) and x = average percentage of traps allocated per day to exploring areas of unknown catch (called *search frequency*) was fit to the data in the file. A portion of the XLSTAT printout is reproduced at the bottom of the page.
  a. Give the null and alternative hypotheses for testing whether total catch (y) is negatively linearly related to search frequency (x).
  b. Find the p-value of the test on the XLSTAT printout.
  c. Give the appropriate conclusion of the test, part **c**, using $\alpha = .05$.

11.47 Congress voting on women's issues. The *American Economic Review* (March 2008) published research on how the gender mix of a U.S. legislator's children can influence the legislator's votes in Congress. Specifically, the researcher investigated how having daughters influences voting on women's issues. The American Association of University Women (AAUW) uses voting records of each member of Congress to compute an AAUW score, where higher scores indicate more favorable voting for women's rights. The researcher modeled AAUW score (y) as a function of the number of daughters (x) a legislator has. Data collected for the 434 members of the 107th Congress were used to fit the straight-line model, $E(y) = \beta_0 + \beta_1 x$.
  a. If it is true that having daughters influences voting on women's issues, will the sign of β_1 be positive or negative? Explain.
  b. The following statistics were reported in the article: $\hat{\beta}_1 = .27$ and $s_{\hat{\beta}_1} = .74$. Find a 95% confidence interval for β_1.

  c. Use the result, part **b**, to make an inference about the model. [*Note:* We will return to this problem in Chapter 12 and consider a more complex model for AAUW score.]

11.48 Generation Y's entitlement mentality. The current workforce is dominated by "Generation Y"—people born between 1982 and 1999. These workers have a reputation as having an entitlement mentality (e.g., they believe they have a right to a high-paying job, without the work ethic). The reasons behind this phenomenon were investigated in *Proceedings of the Academy of Educational Leadership* (Vol. 16, 2011). A sample of 272 undergraduate business students was administered a questionnaire designed to capture the behaviors that lead to an entitlement mentality. The responses were used to measure the following two quantitative variables for each student: entitlement score (y)—where higher scores indicate a greater level of entitlement, and "helicopter parents" score (x)—where higher scores indicate that the student's parents had a higher level of involvement in his or her everyday experiences and problems.
  a. Give the equation of a simple linear regression model relating y to x.
  b. The researchers theorize that helicopter parents lead to an entitlement mentality. Based on this theory, would you expect β_0 to be positive or negative (or are you unsure)? Would you expect β_1 to be positive or negative (or are you unsure)? Explain.
  c. The p-value for testing H_0: $\beta_1 = 0$ versus H_a: $\beta_1 > 0$ was reported as .002. Use this result to test the researchers' entitlement theory at $\alpha = .01$.

11.49 Drug controlled-release rate study. Refer to the simple linear regression analysis relating y = drug release rate to x = surface-area-to-volume ratio, Exercise 11.17 (p. 615). Use the results of the regression to form a 90% confidence interval for the slope, β_1. Interpret the result.

11.50 Sweetness of orange juice. Refer to the simple linear regression relating y = sweetness index of an orange juice sample with x = amount of water-soluble pectin, Exercise 11.22 (p. 616). Use the results of the regression to form a 95% confidence interval for the slope, β_1. Interpret the result.

Applying the Concepts—Intermediate

11.51 Software millionaires and birthdays. Refer to Exercise 11.19 (p. 615) and the study of whether birth decade can predict the number of software millionaires born in the decade. The data are reproduced in the next table (p. 630).

Model parameters:

Source	Value	Standard error	t	Pr > |t|	Lower bound (95%)	Upper bound (95%)
Intercept	9877.8300	829.0411	11.9148	< 0.0001	8086.7957	11668.8643
SEARCHFR	-163.6024	41.9014	-3.9045	0.0018	-254.1249	-73.0799

Equation of the model:

CATCH = 9877.82997-163.60242*SEARCHFREQ

XLSTAT output for Exercise 11.46

Data for Exercise 11.51

Decade	Total U.S. Births (millions)	Number of Software Millionaire Birthdays	Number of CEO Birthdays (in a random sample of 70 companies from the *Fortune* 500 list)
1920	28.582	3	2
1930	24.374	1	2
1940	31.666	10	23
1950	40.530	14	38
1960	38.808	7	9
1970	33.309	4	0

Source: Sauro, J. "Were most software millionaires born around 1955?" *Measuring Usability,* November 17, 2010. Copyright © 2010 by Measuring Usability LLC. Reprinted with permission.

a. Construct a 95% confidence interval for the slope of the model, $E(y) = \beta_0 + \beta_1 x$, where $x =$ total number of U.S. births and $y =$ number of software millionaire birthdays. Give a practical interpretation of the interval.

b. Construct a 95% confidence interval for the slope of the model, $E(y) = \beta_0 + \beta_1 x$, where $x =$ number of CEO birthdays (in a sample of 70 companies) and $y =$ number of software millionaire birthdays. Give a practical interpretation of the interval.

c. Can you conclude that number of software millionaires born in a decade is linearly related to total number of people born in the United States? Number of CEOs born in the decade?

11.52 Beauty and electoral success. Are good looks an advantage when running for political office? This was the question of interest in an article published in the *Journal of Public Economics* (Feb. 2010). The researchers focused on a sample of 641 nonincumbent candidates for political office in Finland. Photos of each candidate were evaluated by non-Finnish subjects; each evaluator assigned a beauty rating—measured on a scale of 1 (lowest rating) to 5 (highest rating)—to each candidate. The beauty ratings for each candidate were averaged, then the average was divided by the standard deviation for all candidates to yield a beauty index for each candidate. (*Note:* A 1-unit increase in the index represents a 1-standard-deviation increase in the beauty rating.) The relative success (measured as a percentage of votes obtained) of each candidate was used as the dependent variable (y) in a regression analysis. One of the independent variables in the model was beauty index (x).

a. Write the equation of a simple linear regression relating y to x.

b. Does the y-intercept of the equation, part **a,** have a practical interpretation? Explain.

c. The article reported the estimated slope of the equation, part **a,** as 22.91. Give a practical interpretation of this value.

d. The standard error of the slope estimate was reported as 3.73. Use this information and the estimate from part **c** to conduct a test for a positive slope at $\alpha = .01$. Give the appropriate conclusion in the words of the problem.

11.53 Ranking driving performance of professional golfers. Refer to *The Sport Journal* (Winter 2007) study of a new method for ranking the total driving performance of golfers on the PGA tour, Exercise 11.21 (p. 616). You fit a straight-line model relating driving accuracy (y) to driving distance (x) to the data saved in the file.

a. Give the null and alternative hypotheses for testing whether driving accuracy (y) decreases linearly as driving distance (x) increases.

b. Find the test statistic and p-value of the test, part **a.**

c. Make the appropriate conclusion at $\alpha = .01$.

11.54 Are geography journals worth their cost? Refer to the *Geoforum* (Vol. 37, 2006) study of whether the price of a geography journal is correlated with quality, Exercise 11.38 (p. 623).

a. In Exercise 11.38a, you fit a straight-line model relating cost (y) to JIF (x). Find and interpret a 95% confidence interval for the slope of the line.

b. In Exercise 11.38b, you fit a straight-line model relating cost (y) to number of citations (x). Find and interpret a 95% confidence interval for the slope of the line.

c. In Exercise 11.38c, you fit a straight-line model relating cost (y) to RPI (x). Find and interpret a 95% confidence interval for the slope of the line.

11.55 Survey of the top business schools. Refer to the *Wall Street Journal* (Sep. 25, 2005) Business School Survey, Exercise 11.25 (p. 618). If you pay more in tuition to go to a top business school, will it necessarily result in a higher probability of a job offer at graduation? Let $y =$ percentage of graduates with job offers and $x =$ tuition cost; then fit the simple linear model, $E(y) = \beta_0 + \beta_1 x$, to the data in the file. Is there sufficient evidence (at $\alpha = .10$) of a positive linear relationship between y and x?

11.56 Public corruption and bad weather. Refer to the *Journal of Law and Economics* (Nov. 2008) study of the link between Federal Emergency Management Agency (FEMA) disaster relief and public corruption, Exercise 11.20 (p. 616). Evaluate the overall adequacy of the straight-line model relating a state's average annual number of public corruption convictions (y) to the state's average annual FEMA relief (x). Use $\alpha = .01$.

Applying the Concepts—Advanced

11.57 Does elevation impact hitting performance in baseball? Refer to the *Chance* (Winter 2006) investigation of the effects of elevation on slugging percentage in Major League Baseball, Exercise 2.125 (p. 104). Recall that data were compiled on players' composite slugging percentage at each of 29 cities for a recent season, as well as each city's elevation (feet above sea level). The data are saved in the file. (Selected observations are shown in the table on the following page.) Consider a straight-line model relating slugging percentage (y) to elevation (x).

a. Is there sufficient evidence (at $\alpha = .01$) of a positive linear relationship between elevation (x) and slugging percentage (y)?.

Selected data for Exercise 11.57

City	Slug Pct.	Elevation
Anaheim	.480	160
Arlington	.605	616
Atlanta	.530	1,050
Baltimore	.505	130
Boston	.505	20
⋮	⋮	⋮
Denver	.625	5,277
⋮	⋮	⋮
Seattle	.550	350
San Francisco	.510	63
St. Louis	.570	465
Tampa	.500	10
Toronto	.535	566

Source: Based on Schaffer, J., & Heiny, E.L. "The effects of elevation on slugging percentage in Major League Baseball," *Chance,* Vol. 19, No. 1, Winter 2006 (adapted from Figure 2, p. 30).

b. Construct a scatterplot for the data and draw the least squares line on the graph. Locate the data point for Denver on the graph. What do you observe?

c. You learned in Exercise 2.125 that the Colorado Rockies, who play their home games in Coors Field, Denver, typically lead the league in team slugging percentage. Many baseball experts attribute this to the "thin air" of Denver—called the "mile-high" city due to its elevation. Remove the data point for Denver from the data set and refit the straight-line model to the remaining data. What conclusions can you draw about the "thin air" theory from this analysis?

11.58 Spreading rate of spilled liquid. Refer to the *Chemical Engineering Progress* (Jan. 2005) study of the rate at which a spilled volatile liquid will spread across a surface, Exercise 11.26 (p. 618). Recall that the data on mass of the spill and elapsed time of the spill are saved in the file. Is there sufficient evidence (at $\alpha = .05$) to indicate that the mass of the spill tends to diminish linearly as time increases? If so, give an interval estimate (with 95% confidence) of the decrease in spill mass for each minute of elapsed time.

11.5 The Coefficients of Correlation and Determination

In this section, we present two statistics that describe the adequacy of a model: the *coefficient of correlation* and the *coefficient of determination.*

Coefficient of Correlation

Recall (from Section 2.10) that a **bivariate relationship** describes a relationship—or correlation—between two variables, x and y. Scatterplots are used to graphically describe a bivariate relationship. In this section, we will discuss the concept of **correlation** and show how it can be used to measure the linear relationship between two variables x and y. A numerical descriptive measure of the linear association between x and y is provided by the *coefficient of correlation, r.*

The **coefficient of correlation,** * r, is a measure of the strength of the *linear* relationship between two variables x and y. It is computed (for a sample of n measurements on x and y) as follows:

$$r = \frac{SS_{xy}}{\sqrt{SS_{xx}SS_{yy}}}$$

where

$$SS_{xy} = \Sigma(x - \bar{x})(y - \bar{y})$$

$$SS_{xx} = \Sigma(x - \bar{x})^2$$

$$SS_{yy} = \Sigma(y - \bar{y})^2$$

Note that the computational formula for the correlation coefficient r given in the definition involves the same quantities that were used in computing the least squares prediction equation. In fact, because the numerators of the expressions for $\hat{\beta}_1$ and r are

*The value of r is often called the *Pearson correlation coefficient* to honor its developer, Karl Pearson. (See Biography, p. 566.)

identical, you can see that $r = 0$ when $\hat{\beta}_1 = 0$ (the case where x contributes no information for the prediction of y), and r is positive when the slope is positive and negative when the slope is negative. Unlike $\hat{\beta}_1$, the correlation coefficient r is *scaleless* and assumes a value between -1 and $+1$, regardless of the units of x and y.

A value of r near or equal to 0 implies little or no linear relationship between y and x. In contrast, the closer r comes to 1 or -1, the stronger the linear relationship between y and x. And if $r = 1$ or $r = -1$, all the sample points fall exactly on the least squares line. Positive values of r imply a positive linear relationship between y and x; that is, y increases as x increases. Negative values of r imply a negative linear relationship between y and x; that is, y decreases as x increases. Each of these situations is portrayed in Figure 11.16.

Now Work Exercise 11.60

We demonstrate how to calculate the coefficient of correlation r using the data in Table 11.1 for the advertising-sales example. The quantities needed to calculate r are SS_{xy}, SS_{xx}, and SS_{yy}. The first two quantities have been calculated previously as $SS_{xy} = 7$ and $SS_{xx} = 10$. The calculation for $SS_{yy} = \Sigma(y - \bar{y})^2$ is shown on the last column of the Excel spreadsheet, Figure 11.5 (p. 000). The result is $SS_{yy} = 6$.

We now find the coefficient of correlation:

$$r = \frac{SS_{xy}}{\sqrt{SS_{xx}SS_{yy}}} = \frac{7}{\sqrt{(10)(6)}} = \frac{7}{\sqrt{60}} = .904$$

The fact that r is positive and near 1 in value indicates that the sales revenue y tends to increase as advertising expenditure x increases—*for this sample of 5 months*. This is the same conclusion we reached when we found the calculated value of the least squares slope to be positive.

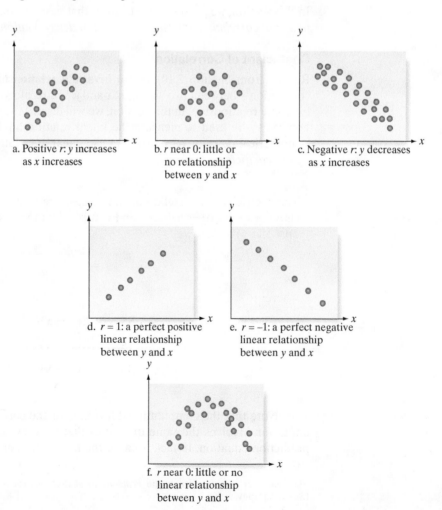

a. Positive r: y increases as x increases

b. r near 0: little or no relationship between y and x

c. Negative r: y decreases as x increases

d. $r = 1$: a perfect positive linear relationship between y and x

e. $r = -1$: a perfect negative linear relationship between y and x

f. r near 0: little or no linear relationship between y and x

Figure 11.16

Values of r and their implications

Example 11.4

Using the Correlation Coefficient—Relating Crime Rate and Casino Employment

Problem Legalized gambling is available on several riverboat casinos operated by a city in Mississippi. The mayor of the city wants to know the correlation between the number of casino employees and the yearly crime rate. The records for the past 10 years are examined, and the results listed in Table 11.3 are obtained. Calculate the coefficient of correlation r for the data. Interpret the result.

Table 11.3	Data on Casino Employees and Crime Rate, Example 11.4	
Year	Number of Casino Employees, x (thousands)	Crime Rate, y (number of crimes per 1,000 population)
2003	15	1.35
2004	18	1.63
2005	24	2.33
2006	22	2.41
2007	25	2.63
2008	29	2.93
2009	30	3.41
2010	32	3.26
2011	35	3.63
2012	38	4.15

Data Set: CASINO

Solution Rather than use the computing formula given in the definition, we resort to using a statistical software package. The data of Table 11.3 were entered into a computer, and Minitab was used to compute r. The Minitab printout is shown in Figure 11.17.

Correlations: EMPLOYEES, CRIMERAT

```
Pearson correlation of EMPLOYEES and CRIMERAT = 0.987
P-Value = 0.000
```

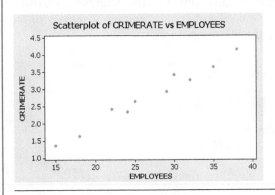

Figure 11.17
Minitab correlation printout for Example 11.4

The coefficient of correlation, highlighted at the top on the printout, is $r = .987$. Thus, the size of the casino workforce and crime rate in this city are very highly correlated—at least over the past 10 years. The implication is that a strong positive linear relationship exists between these variables (see the scatterplot at the bottom of Figure 11.17). We must be careful, however, not to jump to any unwarranted conclusions. For instance, the mayor may be tempted to conclude that hiring more casino workers next year will increase the crime rate—that is, that there is a *causal relationship* between the two variables. However, high correlation does not imply causality. The fact is, many things have probably contributed both to the increase in the casino workforce and to the increase in crime rate. The city's tourist trade has undoubtedly grown since riverboat casinos were legalized, and it is likely that the casinos have expanded both in services offered and in number. *We cannot infer a causal relationship on the basis of high sample correlation. When a high correlation is observed in the sample data, the only safe conclusion is that a linear trend may exist between* x *and* y.

ETHICS in STATISTICS

Intentionally using the correlation coefficient only to make an inference about the relationship between two variables in situations where a nonlinear relationship may exist is considered *unethical statistical practice.*

Look Back Another variable, such as the increase in tourism, may be the underlying cause of the high correlation between x and y.

◼ **Now Work Exercise 11.75**

> ⚠ **CAUTION** When using the sample correlation coefficient, r, to infer the nature of the relationship between x and y, two caveats exist: (1) A *high correlation* does not necessarily imply that a causal relationship exists between x and y—only that a linear trend may exist; (2) a *low correlation* does not necessarily imply that x and y are unrelated—only that x and y are not strongly *linearly* related.

Keep in mind that the correlation coefficient r measures the linear association between x values and y values in the sample, and a similar linear coefficient of correlation exists for the population from which the data points were selected. The **population correlation coefficient** is denoted by the symbol ρ (rho). As you might expect, ρ is estimated by the corresponding sample statistic, r. Or, instead of estimating ρ, we might want to test the null hypothesis $H_0: \rho = 0$ against $H_a: \rho \neq 0$—that is, we can test the hypothesis that x contributes no information for the prediction of y by using the straight-line model against the alternative that the two variables are at least linearly related.

However, we already performed this *identical* test in Section 11.4 when we tested $H_0: \beta_1 = 0$ against $H_a: \beta_1 \neq 0$—that is, the null hypothesis $H_0: \rho = 0$ is equivalent to the hypothesis $H_0: \beta_1 = 0$.* When we tested the null hypothesis $H_0: \beta_1 = 0$ in connection with the advertising-sales example, the data led to a rejection of the null hypothesis at the $\alpha = .05$ level. This rejection implies that the null hypothesis of a 0 correlation between the two variables (sales revenue and advertising expenditure) can also be rejected at the $\alpha = .05$ level. The only real difference between the least squares slope $\hat{\beta}_1$ and the coefficient of correlation r is the measurement scale. Therefore, the information they provide about the usefulness of the least squares model is to some extent redundant. Consequently, we will use the slope to make inferences about the existence of a positive or negative linear relationship between two variables.

For the sake of completeness, a summary of the test for linear correlation is provided in the following boxes.

A Test for Linear Correlation

One-Tailed Test	Two-Tailed Test
$H_0: \rho = 0$	$H_0: \rho = 0$
$H_a: \rho > 0$ (or $H_a: \rho < 0$)	$H_a: \rho \neq 0$

$$\text{Test statistic: } t = \frac{r\sqrt{n-2}}{\sqrt{1-r^2}} = \frac{\hat{\beta}_1}{s_{\hat{\beta}_1}}$$

Rejection region: $t > t_\alpha$ (or $t < -t_\alpha$)   Rejection region: $|t| > t_{\alpha/2}$

where the distribution of t depends on $(n - 2)$ df.

Condition Required for a Valid Test of Correlation

The sample of (x, y) values is randomly selected from a normal population.

Coefficient of Determination

Another way to measure the usefulness of the model is to measure the contribution of x in predicting y. To accomplish this, we calculate how much the errors of prediction of y were reduced by using the information provided by x. To illustrate, consider the sample

---

*The two tests are equivalent in simple linear regression only.

shown in the scatterplot of Figure 11.18a. If we assume that x contributes no information for the prediction of y, the best prediction for a value of y is the sample mean $\bar{y}$, which is shown as the horizontal line in Figure 11.18b. The vertical line segments in Figure 11.18b are the deviations of the points about the mean $\bar{y}$. Note that the sum of squares of deviations for the prediction equation $\hat{y} = \bar{y}$ is

$$SS_{yy} = \sum (y_i - \bar{y})^2$$

Now suppose you fit a least squares line to the same set of data and locate the deviations of the points about the line as shown in Figure 11.18c. Compare the deviations about the prediction lines in Figures 11.18b and 11.18c. You can see that

1. If x contributes little or no information for the prediction of y, the sums of squares of deviations for the two lines,

$$SS_{yy} = \sum (y_i - \bar{y})^2 \quad \text{and} \quad SSE = \sum (y_i - \hat{y}_i)^2$$

will be nearly equal.

2. If x does contribute information for the prediction of y, the SSE will be smaller than SS_{yy}. In fact, if all the points fall on the least squares line, then SSE = 0.

Then the reduction in the sum of squares of deviations that can be attributed to x, expressed as a proportion of SS_{yy}, is

$$\frac{SS_{yy} - SSE}{SS_{yy}}$$

Note that SS_{yy} is the "total sample variation" of the observations around the mean $\bar{y}$ and that SSE is the remaining "unexplained sample variability" after fitting the line $\bar{y}$. Thus,

a. Scatterplot of data   b. Assumption: x contributes no information
for predicting y, $\hat{y} = \bar{y}$

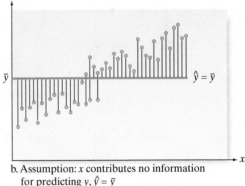

c. Assumption: x contributes information
for predicting y, $\hat{y} = \hat{\beta}_0 + \hat{\beta}_1 x$

Figure 11.18

A comparison of the sum of squares
of deviations for two models

the difference (SS_{yy} − SSE) is the "explained sample variability" attributable to the linear relationship with x. Then a verbal description of the proportion is

$$\frac{SS_{yy} - SSE}{SS_{yy}} = \frac{\text{Explained sample variability}}{\text{Total sample variablity}}$$

$$= \text{Proportion of total sample variability explained by the linear relationship}$$

In simple linear regression, it can be shown that this proportion—called the *coefficient of determination*—is equal to the square of the simple linear coefficient of correlation r.

> **Coefficient of Determination**
>
> $$r^2 = \frac{SS_{yy} - SSE}{SS_{yy}} = 1 - \frac{SSE}{SS_{yy}}$$
>
> It represents the proportion of the total sample variability around $\bar{y}$ that is explained by the linear relationship between y and x. (In simple linear regression, it may also be computed as the square of the coefficient of correlation r.)

Note that r^2 is always between 0 and 1 because r is between −1 and +1. Thus, an r^2 of .60 means that the sum of squares of deviations of the y values about their predicted values has been reduced 60% by the use of the least squares equation $\hat{y}$, instead of $\bar{y}$, to predict y.

Example 11.5

Obtaining the Value of r^2—Sales Revenue Model

Problem Calculate the coefficient of determination for the advertising-sales example. The data are repeated in Table 11.4 for convenience. Interpret the result.

Table 11.4	Advertising-Sales Data
Advertising Expenditure, x ($100s)	Sales Revenue, y ($1,000s)
1	1
2	1
3	2
4	2
5	4

 Data Set: ADSALE

Solution From previous calculations,

$$SS_{yy} = 6 \quad \text{and} \quad SSE = \sum(y - \hat{y})^2 = 1.10$$

Then, from the definition, the coefficient of determination is given by

$$r^2 = \frac{SS_{yy} - SSE}{SS_{yy}} = \frac{6.0 - 1.1}{6.0} = \frac{4.9}{6.0} = .82$$

Another way to compute r^2 is to recall (Section 11.2) that $r = .904$. Then we have $r^2 = (.904)^2 = .82$. A third way to obtain r^2 is from a computer printout. This value is highlighted on the SPSS printout reproduced in Figure 11.19. Our interpretation is as follows: We know that using advertising expenditure, x, to predict y with the least squares line

$$\hat{y} = -.1 + .7x$$

Model Summary

Figure 11.19

Portion of SPSS printout for advertising-sales regression

Model	R	R Square	Adjusted R Square	Std. Error of the Estimate
1	.904ª	.817	.756	.606

a. Predictors: (Constant), ADVEXP_X

accounts for 82% of the total sum of squares of deviations of the five sample y values about their mean. Or, stated another way, 82% of the sample variation in sales revenue (y) can be "explained" by using advertising expenditure (x) in a straight-line model.

■ Now Work Exercise 11.64a

> **Practical Interpretation of the Coefficient of Determination, r^2**
>
> About $100(r^2)\%$ of the sample variation in y (measured by the total sum of squares of deviations of the sample y values about their mean $\bar{y}$) can be explained by (or attributed to) using x to predict y in the straight-line model.

STATISTICS in ACTION REVISITED

Using the Coefficient of Correlation and the Coefficient of Determination

In the previous *Statistics in Action Revisited* (p. 627), we discovered that cumulative 6-month advertising expenditures was a statistically useful linear predictor of number of new PI cases but not a useful linear predictor of number of new WC cases. Both the coefficients of correlation and determination (highlighted on the Minitab printouts in Figures SIA11.4 and SIA11.5) also support this conclusion.

Regression Analysis: NewPI versus AdvExp6

```
The regression equation is
NewPI = 7.77 + 0.113 AdvExp6

Predictor      Coef   SE Coef      T      P
Constant      7.767     3.385   2.29  0.027
AdvExp6     0.11289   0.02793   4.04  0.000

S = 9.67521   R-Sq = 29.0%   R-Sq(adj) = 27.2%

Analysis of Variance

Source          DF       SS      MS      F      P
Regression       1   1529.5  1529.5  16.34  0.000
Residual Error  40   3744.4    93.6
Total           41   5273.9
```

Correlations: NewPI, AdvExp6

```
Pearson correlation of NewPI and AdvExp6 = 0.539
P-Value = 0.000
```

Figure SIA11.4

Minitab printout with coefficients of correlation and determination for y = number of new PI cases

Regression Analysis: NewWC versus AdvExp6

```
The regression equation is
NewWC = 24.6 + 0.0098 AdvExp6

Predictor      Coef   SE Coef      T      P
Constant     24.574     3.367   7.30  0.000
AdvExp6     0.00982   0.02778   0.35  0.725

S = 9.62296   R-Sq = 0.3%   R-Sq(adj) = 0.0%

Analysis of Variance

Source          DF       SS      MS      F      P
Regression       1    11.58   11.58   0.13  0.725
Residual Error  40  3704.06   92.60
Total           41  3715.64
```

Figure SIA11.5

Minitab printout with coefficients of correlation and determination for y = number of new WC cases

Correlations: NewWC, AdvExp6

```
Pearson correlation of NewWC and AdvExp6 = 0.056
P-Value = 0.725
```

> STATISTICS
> in ACTION
> REVISITED
> CONTINUED

For y = number of new PI cases, the correlation coefficient value of $r = .539$ is statistically significantly different from 0 and indicates a moderate positive linear relationship between the variables. The coefficient of determination, $r^2 = .29$, implies that almost 30% of the sample variation in number of new PI cases can be explained by using advertising expenditure (x) in the straight-line model. In contrast, for y = number of new WC cases, $r = .056$ is not statistically different from 0 and $r^2 = .003$ implies that only 0.3% of the sample variation in number of new WC cases can be explained by using advertising expenditure (x) in the straight-line model.

Exercises 11.59–11.75

Learning the Mechanics

11.59 Describe the slope of the least squares line if
 a. $r = .7$ **b.** $r = -.7$
 c. $r = 0$ **d.** $r^2 = .64$

11.60 Explain what each of the following sample correlation coefficients tells you about the relationship between the x and y values in the sample:
 a. $r = 1$ **b.** $r = -1$
 c. $r = 0$ **d.** $r = -.90$
 e. $r = .10$ **f.** $r = -.88$

11.61 Calculate r^2 for the least squares line in each of the following exercises. Interpret their values.
 a. Exercise 11.10   **b.** Exercise 11.13

11.62 Construct a scatterplot for each data set. Then calculate r and r^2 for each data set. Interpret their values.

 a.

x	−2	−1	0	1	2
y	−2	1	2	5	6

 b.

x	−2	−1	0	1	2
y	6	5	3	2	0

 c.

x	1	2	2	3	3	3	4
y	2	1	3	1	2	3	2

 d.

x	0	1	3	5	6
y	0	1	2	1	0

◉ Applet Exercise 11.2

Use the applet *Correlation by Eye* to explore the relationship between the pattern of data in a scatterplot and the corresponding correlation coefficient.

 a. Run the applet several times. Each time, guess the value of the correlation coefficient. Then click *Show r* to see the actual correlation coefficient. How close is your value to the actual value of r? Click *New data* to reset the applet.
 b. Click the trash can to clear the graph. Use the mouse to place five points on the scatterplot that are approximately in a straight line. Then guess the value of the correlation coefficient. Click *Show r* to see the actual correlation coefficient. How close were you this time?
 c. Continue to clear the graph and plot sets of five points with different patterns among the points. Guess the value of r. How close do you come to the actual value of r each time?
 d. Based on your experiences with the applet, explain why we need to use more reliable methods of finding the correlation coefficient than just "eyeing" it.

Applying the Concepts—Basic

11.63 Going for it on fourth-down in the NFL. Each week coaches in the National Football League (NFL) face a decision during the game. On fourth-down, should the team punt the ball or go for a first-down? To aid in the decision-making process, statisticians at California State University, Northridge, developed a regression model for predicting the number of points scored (y) by a team that has a first-down with a given number of yards (x) from the opposing goal line (*Chance*, Winter 2009). One of the models fit to data collected on five NFL teams from a recent season was the simple linear regression model, $E(y) = \beta_0 + \beta_1 x$. The regression yielded the following results: $\hat{y} = 4.42 - 048x, r^2 = .18$.
 a. Give a practical interpretation of the coefficient of determination, r^2.
 b. Compute the value of the coefficient of correlation, r, from the value of r^2. Is the value of r positive or negative? Why?

11.64 Lobster fishing study. Refer to the *Bulletin of Marine Science* (April 2010) study of teams of fishermen fishing for the red spiny lobster in Baja California Sur, Mexico, Exercise 11.46 (p. 629). Recall that simple linear regression was used to model y = total catch of lobsters (in kilograms) during the season as a function of x = average percentage of traps allocated per day to exploring areas of unknown catch (called *search frequency*). Another portion of the XLSTAT printout of the analysis is shown on the next page.
 a. Locate and interpret the coefficient of determination, r^2, on the printout.
 b. Locate and interpret the coefficient of correlation, r, on the printout.
 c. In Exercise 11.46, you conducted a test to determine that total catch (y) is negatively linearly related to search frequency (x). Which of the two statistics, r or r^2, can be used to partially support this inference? Explain.

XLSTAT output for Exercise 11.64

Correlation matrix:

Variables	SEARCHFREQ	CATCH
SEARCHFREQ	**1.0000**	−0.7347
CATCH	−0.7347	**1.0000**

Regression of variable CATCH:

Goodness of fit statistics:

Observations	15.0000
Sum of weights	15.0000
DF	13.0000
R^2	0.5397
Adjusted R^2	0.5043
MSE	1902741.2024
RMSE	1379.3989
DW	1.4475

11.65 RateMyProfessors.com. A popular Web site among college students is RateMyProfessors.com (RMP). Established over 10 years ago, RMP allows students to post quantitative ratings of their instructors. In *Practical Assessment, Research & Evaluation* (May 2007), University of Maine researchers investigated whether instructor ratings posted on RMP are correlated with the formal in-class student evaluations of teaching (SET) that all universities are required to administer at the end of the semester. Data collected for $n = 426$ University of Maine instructors yielded a correlation between RMP and SET ratings of .68.

a. Give the equation of a linear model relating SET rating (y) to RMP rating (x).

b. Give a practical interpretation of the value $r = .68$.

c. Is the estimated slope of the line, part **a**, positive or negative? Explain.

d. A test of the null hypothesis H_0: $\rho = 0$ yielded a p-value of .001. Interpret this result.

e. Compute the coefficient of determination, r^2, for the regression analysis. Interpret the result.

11.66 In business, do nice guys finish first or last? Refer to the *Nature* (March 20, 2008) study of the use of punishment in cooperation games, Exercise 11.14 (p. 614). Recall that college students repeatedly played a version of the game "prisoner's dilemma," and the researchers recorded the average payoff and the number of times cooperation, defection, and punishment were used for each player.

a. A test of no correlation between cooperation use (x) and average payoff (y) yielded a p-value of .33. Interpret this result.

b. A test of no correlation between defection use (x) and average payoff (y) yielded a p-value of .66. Interpret this result.

c. A test of no correlation between punishment use (x) and average payoff (y) yielded a p-value of .001. Interpret this result.

11.67 Women in top management. An empirical analysis of women in upper management positions at U.S. firms was published in the *Journal of Organizational Culture, Communications and Conflict* (July 2007). Monthly data ($n = 252$ months) were collected for several variables, including the number of females in managerial positions, the number of females with a college degree, and the number of female high school graduates with no college degree. Similar data were collected for males.

a. The correlation coefficient relating number of females in managerial positions and number of females with a college degree was reported as $r = .983$. Interpret this result.

b. The correlation coefficient relating number of females in managerial positions and number of female high school graduates with no college degree was reported as $r = .074$. Interpret this result.

c. The correlation coefficient relating number of males in managerial positions and number of males with a college degree was reported as $r = .722$. Interpret this result.

d. The correlation coefficient relating number of males in managerial positions and number of male high school graduates with no college degree was reported as $r = .528$. Interpret this result.

11.68 Last name and acquisition timing. Refer to the *Journal of Consumer Research* (August 2011) study of the speed with which consumers decide to purchase a product, Exercise 8.13 (p. 433). Recall that the researchers theorized that consumers with last names that begin with letters later in the alphabet would tend to acquire items faster than those whose last names begin with letters earlier in the alphabet (i.e., the *last name effect*). Each in a sample of 50 MBA students was offered free tickets to attend a college basketball game for which there was a limited supply of tickets. The first letter of the last name of those who responded to an e-mail offer in time to receive the tickets was noted and given a numerical value (e.g., "A" = 1, "B" = 2, etc.). Each student's response time (measured in minutes) was also recorded.

a. The researchers computed the correlation between the two variables as $r = -.271$. Interpret this result.

b. The observed significance level for testing for a negative correlation in the population was reported as p-value = .018. Interpret this result for $\alpha = .05$.

c. Does this analysis support the researchers' *last name effect* theory? Explain.

Applying the Concepts—Intermediate

11.69 Software millionaires and birthdays. Refer to Exercise 11.19 (p. 615) and the study of the seemingly disproportionate number of software millionaires born around the year 1955. The data are reproduced in the table on the following page.

a. Find the coefficient of determination for the simple linear regression model relating number (y) of software millionaire birthdays in a decade to total number (x) of U.S. births. Interpret the result.

b. Find the coefficient of determination for the simple linear regression model relating number (y) of software millionaire birthdays in a decade to number (x) of CEO birthdays. Interpret the result.

c. The consulting statistician argued that the software industry appears to be no different from any other industry with respect to producing millionaires in a decade. Do you agree? Explain.

Data for Exercise 11.69

Decade	Total U.S. Births (millions)	Number of Software Millionaire Birthdays	Number of CEO Birthdays (in a random sample of 70 companies from the *Fortune* 500 list)
1920	28.582	3	2
1930	24.374	1	2
1940	31.666	10	23
1950	40.530	14	38
1960	38.808	7	9
1970	33.309	4	0

Source: Sauro, J. "Were most software millionaires born around 1955?" *Measuring Usability,* November 17, 2010. Copyright © 2010 by Measuring Usability LLC. Reprinted with permission.

11.70 Child labor in diamond mines. The role of child laborers on Africa's colonial-era diamond mines was the subject of research published in the *Journal of Family History* (Vol. 35, 2010). One particular mining company lured children to the mines by offering incentives for adult male laborers to relocate their families close to the diamond mine. The success of the incentive program was examined by determining the annual *accompaniment rate,* i.e., the percentage of wives (or sons, or daughters) who accompanied their husbands (or fathers) in relocating to the mine. Information from the journal article was used to simulate accompaniment rates for nine consecutive years. Those rates are shown in the table below.

a. Find the correlation coefficient relating the accompaniment rates for wives and sons. Interpret this value.

b. Find the correlation coefficient relating the accompaniment rates for wives and daughters. Interpret this value.

c. Find the correlation coefficient relating the accompaniment rates for sons and daughters. Interpret this value.

Year	Wives	Sons	Daughters
1	28.7	2.4	14.3
2	41.6	1.7	13.1
3	37.2	0.5	10
4	39.3	3.7	19.6
5	39.5	5.6	19.4
6	39.9	11.2	21.7
7	40.2	12.1	15.3
8	31.3	8.8	15.1
9	25.3	7.6	19.6

Source: Based on Cleveland, T., "Minors in name only: Child laborers on the diamond mines of the *Companhia de Diamantes de Angola* (Diamang), 1917–1975." *Journal of Family History,* Vol. 35, No. 1, 2010 (Table 1).

11.71 Sweetness of orange juice. Refer to the simple linear regression relating y = sweetness index of an orange juice sample with x = amount of water-soluble pectin, Exercise 11.22 (p. 616) and the data saved in the file. Find and interpret the coefficient of determination, r^2, and the coefficient of correlation, r.

11.72 Performance ratings of government agencies. The U.S. Office of Management and Budget (OMB) requires government agencies to produce annual performance and accounting reports (PARS) each year. Refer to *The Public Manager* (Summer 2008) listing of PARS evaluation scores for 24 government agencies, Exercise 2.129 (p. 105). Recall that evaluation scores ranged from 12 (lowest) to 60 (highest). The PARS evaluation scores for two consecutive years are reproduced in the following table.

a. Calculate and interpret the coefficient of correlation between the PARS scores in year 1 and year 2.

b. Is there sufficient evidence of a positive linear relationship between year 2 PARS score (y) and year 1 PARS score (x)? Test using $\alpha = .05$.

Agency	Year 1	Year 2
Transportation	55	53
Labor	53	51
Veterans	51	51
NRC	39	34
Commerce	37	36
HHS	37	35
DHS	37	30
Justice	35	37
Treasury	35	35
GSA	34	40
Agriculture	33	35
EPA	33	36
Social Security	33	33
USAID	32	42
Education	32	36
Interior	32	31
NASA	32	32
Energy	31	34
HUD	31	30
NSF	31	31
State	31	50
OPM	27	28
SBA	22	31
Defense	17	32

Source: Ellig, J., & Wray, H. "Measuring performance reporting quality," *The Public Manager,* Vol. 37, No. 2, Summer 2008 (p. 66). Copyright © 2008 by Jerry Ellig. Reprinted with permission.

11.73 Survey of the top business schools. Refer to the *Wall Street Journal* (Sep. 25, 2005) Business School Survey, Exercise 11.25 (p. 618) and the data saved in the file. Find and interpret r and r^2 for the simple linear regression relating y = percentage of graduates with job offers and x = tuition cost and then fit the simple linear model.

11.74 Spreading rate of spilled liquid. Refer to the *Chemical Engineering Progress* (Jan. 2005) study of the rate at which a spilled volatile liquid will spread across a surface, Exercise 11.26 (p. 618) and the data saved in the file. Find and interpret r and r^2 for the simple linear regression y = mass of the spill and x = elapsed time of the spill.

Applying the Concepts—Advanced

11.75 Salary linked to height. Are short people short-changed
when it comes to salary? According to Business Professors
T. A. Judge (University of Florida) and D. M. Cable
(University of North Carolina), tall people tend to earn
more money over their careers than short people (*Journal
of Applied Psychology*, June 2004). Using data collected
from participants in the National Longitudinal Surveys
begun in 1979, the researchers computed the correlation
between average earnings from 1985 to 2000 (in dollars) and
height (in inches) for several occupations. The results are
given in the table. Are average earnings positively related
to height? For all occupations? If so, can you conclude that
a person taller than you will earn a higher salary? Explain.

Occupation	Correlation, r	Sample Size, n
Sales	.41	117
Managers	.35	455
Blue Collar	.32	349
Service Workers	.31	265
Professional/ Technical	.30	453
Clerical	.25	358
Crafts/ Forepersons	.24	250

Source: Judge, T. A., & Cable, D. M. "The effect of physical height
on workplace success and income: Preliminary test of a theoretical
model," *Journal of Applied Psychology*, Vol. 89, No. 3, June 2004
(Table 5).

11.6 Using the Model for Estimation and Prediction

If we are satisfied that a useful model has been found to describe the relationship between x and y, we are ready for step 5 in our regression modeling procedure: using the
model for estimation and prediction.

*The most common uses of a probabilistic model for making inferences can be
divided into two categories. The first is using the model to estimate the mean value of* y,
E(y), *for a specific value of* x. For our advertising-sales example, we may want to estimate the mean sales revenue for *all* months during which \$400 ($x = 4$) is expended on
advertising.

The second use of the model entails predicting a new individual y *value for a given* x.
That is, if we decide to expend \$400 in advertising next month, we may want to predict
the firm's sales revenue for that month.

In the first case, we are attempting to *estimate the mean value of* y *for a very large
number of experimental units at the given* x *value.* In the second case, we are trying to
predict the outcome for a single experimental unit at the given x *value.* Which of these
model uses—estimating the mean value of y or predicting an individual new value of y
(for the same value of x)—can be accomplished with the greater accuracy?

Before answering this question, we first consider the problem of choosing an
estimator (or predictor) of the mean (or a new individual) y value. We will use the least
squares prediction equation

$$\hat{y} = \hat{\beta}_0 + \hat{\beta}_1 x$$

both to estimate the mean value of y and to predict a specific new value of y for a given
value of x. For our example, we found

$$\hat{y} = -.1 + .7x$$

so that the estimated mean sales revenue for all months when $x = 4$ (advertising is
\$400) is

$$\hat{y} = -.1 + .7(4) = 2.7$$

or \$2,700. (Recall that the units of y are thousands of dollars.) The same value is used to
predict a new y value when $x = 4$—that is, both the estimated mean and the predicted
value of y are $\hat{y} = 2.7$ when $x = 4$, as shown in Figure 11.20.

The difference between these two model uses lies in the relative accuracy of the
estimate and the prediction. These accuracies are best measured by using the sampling
errors of the least squares line when it is used as an estimator and as a predictor, respectively. These errors are reflected in the standard deviations given in the next box.

Figure 11.20

Estimated mean value and
predicted individual value of sales
revenue y for $x = 4$

Sampling Errors for the Estimator of the Mean of y and the Predictor of an Individual New Value of y

1. The *standard deviation* of the sampling distribution of the estimator $\hat{y}$ of the *mean value of y* at a specific value of x, say x_p, is

$$\sigma_{\hat{y}} = \sigma\sqrt{\frac{1}{n} + \frac{(x_p - \bar{x})^2}{SS_{xx}}}$$

where σ is the standard deviation of the random error ε. We refer to $\sigma_{\hat{y}}$ as the **standard error of $\hat{y}$.**

2. The *standard deviation* of the prediction error for the predictor $\hat{y}$ of an individual *new y value* at a specific value of x is

$$\sigma_{(y-\hat{y})} = \sigma\sqrt{1 + \frac{1}{n} + \frac{(x_p - \bar{x})^2}{SS_{xx}}}$$

where σ is the standard deviation of the random error ε. We refer to $\sigma_{(y-\hat{y})}$ as the **standard error of the prediction.**

The true value of σ is rarely known, so we estimate σ by s and calculate the estimation and prediction intervals as shown in the next two boxes.

A 100(1 − α)% Confidence Interval for the Mean Value of y at x = x_p

$$\hat{y} \pm t_{\alpha/2}\,(\text{Estimated standard error of } \hat{y})$$

or

$$\hat{y} \pm t_{\alpha/2}s\sqrt{\frac{1}{n} + \frac{(x_p - \bar{x})^2}{SS_{xx}}}$$

where $t_{\alpha/2}$ is based on $(n - 2)$ degrees of freedom.

A 100(1 − α)% Prediction Interval* for an Individual New Value of y at x = x_p

$$\hat{y} \pm t_{\alpha/2}\,(\text{Estimated standard error of prediction})$$

or

$$\hat{y} \pm t_{\alpha/2}s\sqrt{1 + \frac{1}{n} + \frac{(x_p - \bar{x})^2}{SS_{xx}}}$$

where $t_{\alpha/2}$ is based on $(n - 2)$ degrees of freedom.

Example 11.6

Estimating the Mean of y—Sales Revenue Model

Problem Refer to the sales-appraisal simple linear regression in previous examples. Find a 95% confidence interval for the mean monthly sales when the appliance store spends $400 on advertising.

Solution Here, we desire a confidence interval for the mean, $E(y)$, for *all* months when the store spends $400 on advertising. For a $400 advertising expenditure, $x = 4$, and the confidence interval for the mean value of y is

$$\hat{y} \pm t_{\alpha/2}s\sqrt{\frac{1}{n} + \frac{(x_p - \bar{x})^2}{SS_{xx}}} = \hat{y} \pm t_{.025}s\sqrt{\frac{1}{5} + \frac{(4 - \bar{x})^2}{SS_{xx}}}$$

---

*The term *prediction interval* is used when the interval formed is intended to enclose the value of a random variable. The term *confidence interval* is reserved for the estimation of population parameters (such as the mean).

where $t_{.025}$ is based on $n - 2 = 5 - 2 = 3$ degrees of freedom. Recall that $\hat{y} = 2.7$, $s = .61, \bar{x} = 3$, and $SS_{xx} = 10$. From Table III in Appendix D, $t_{.025} = 3.182$. Thus, we have

$$2.7 \pm (3.182)(.61)\sqrt{\frac{1}{5} + \frac{(4-3)^2}{10}} = 2.7 \pm (3.182)(.61)(.55)$$

$$= 2.7 \pm (3.182)(.34)$$

$$= 2.7 \pm 1.1 = (1.6, 3.8)$$

Therefore, when the store spends $400 a month on advertising, we are 95% confident that the mean sales revenue for these months is between $1,600 and $3,800.

Look Back Note that we used a small amount of data (small in size) for purposes of illustration in fitting the least squares line. The interval would probably be narrower if more information had been obtained from a larger sample.

◾ **Now Work Exercise 11.76a–d**

| **Example** | **11.7** |

Predicting an Individual value of y—Sales Revenue Model

Problem Refer, again, to the sales-appraisal regression. Predict the monthly sales for next month if $400 is spent on advertising. Use a 95% prediction interval.

Solution Here, our focus is on a *single* month when the store spends $400 on advertising. To predict the sales for a particular month for which $x_p = 4$, we calculate the 95% prediction interval as

$$\hat{y} \pm t_{\alpha/2}s\sqrt{1 + \frac{1}{n} + \frac{(x_p - \bar{x})^2}{SS_{xx}}} = 2.7 \pm (3.182)(.61)\sqrt{1 + \frac{1}{5} + \frac{(4-3)^2}{10}}$$

$$= 2.7 \pm (3.182)(.61)(1.14)$$

$$= 2.7 \pm (3.182)(.70)$$

$$= 2.7 \pm 2.2 = (.5, 4.9)$$

Therefore, we predict with 95% confidence that the sales revenue next month (a month in which we spend $400 in advertising) will fall in the interval from $500 to $4,900.

Look Back Like the confidence interval for the mean value of y, the prediction interval for y is quite large. This is because we have chosen a simple example (only five data points) to fit the least squares line. The width of the prediction interval could be reduced by using a larger number of data points.

◾ **Now Work Exercise 11.76e**

Both the confidence interval for $E(y)$ and prediction interval for y can be obtained using a statistical software package. Figure 11.21 is a Minitab printout showing the confidence interval and prediction interval for the data in the advertising-sales example. The 95% confidence interval for $E(y)$ when $x = 4$, highlighted under "95% CI" in Figure 11.21, is (1.645, 3.755). The 95% prediction interval for y when $x = 4$, highlighted in Figure 11.21 under "95% PI," is (.503, 4.897). Both intervals agree with the ones computed in Examples 11.6–11.7.

```
Predicted Values for New Observations

New
Obs    Fit  SE Fit     95% CI          95% PI
  1  2.700   0.332  (1.645, 3.755)  (0.503, 4.897)


Values of Predictors for New Observations

New
Obs  ADVEXP_X
  1     4.00
```

Figure 11.21

Minitab printout giving 95% confidence interval for $E(y)$ and 95% prediction interval for y

Note that the prediction interval for an individual new value of y is *always* wider than the corresponding confidence interval for the mean value of y. To see this, consider the following. The error in estimating the mean value of y, $E(y)$, for a given value of x, say x_p, is the distance between the least squares line and the true line of means, $E(y) = \beta_0 + \beta_1 x$. This error, $[\hat{y} - E(y)]$, is shown in Figure 11.22. In contrast, *the error* $(y_p - \hat{y})$ *in predicting some future value of* y *is the sum of two errors*—the error of estimating the mean of y, $E(y)$, plus the random error that is a component of the value of y to be predicted (see Figure 11.23). Consequently, the error of predicting a particular value of y will be larger than the error of estimating the mean value of y for a particular value of x. Note from their formulas that both the error of estimation and the error of prediction take their smallest values when $x_p = \bar{x}$. The farther x_p lies from $\bar{x}$, the larger will be the errors of estimation and prediction. You can see why this is true by noting the deviations for different values of x_p between the line of means $E(y) = \beta_0 + \beta_1 x$ and the predicted line of means $\hat{y} = \hat{\beta}_0 + \hat{\beta}_1 x$ shown in Figure 11.23. The deviation is larger at the extremes of the interval where the largest and smallest values of x in the data set occur.

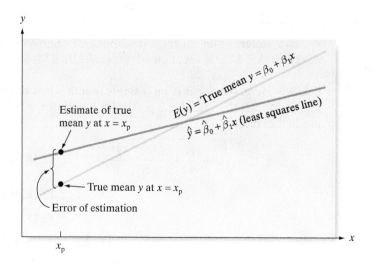

Figure 11.22

Error of estimating the mean value of y for a given value of x

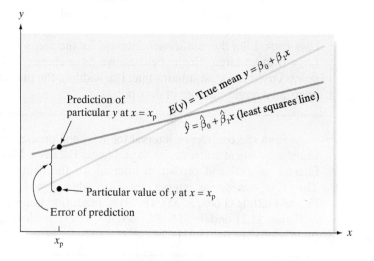

Figure 11.23

Error of predicting a future value of y for a given value of x

Both the confidence intervals for mean values and the prediction intervals for new values are depicted over the entire range of the regression line in Figure 11.24. You can see that the confidence interval is always narrower than the prediction interval, and they are both narrowest at the mean $\bar{x}$, increasing steadily as the distance $|x - \bar{x}|$ increases. In fact, when x is selected far enough away from $\bar{x}$ so that it falls outside the range of the sample data, it is dangerous to make any inferences about $E(y)$ or y.

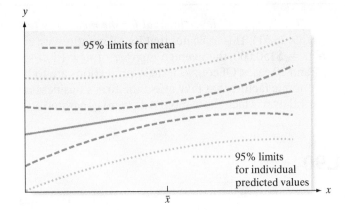

Figure 11.24

Confidence intervals for mean values and prediction intervals for new values

> ⚠ **CAUTION** Using the least squares prediction equation to estimate the mean value of y or to predict a particular value of y for values of x that fall *outside the range* of the values of x contained in your sample data may lead to errors of estimation or prediction that are much larger than expected. Although the least squares model may provide a very good fit to the data over the range of x values contained in the sample, it could give a poor representation of the true model for values of x outside this region.

The confidence interval width grows smaller as n is increased; thus, in theory, you can obtain as precise an estimate of the mean value of y as desired (at any given x) by selecting a large enough sample. The prediction interval for a new value of y also grows smaller as n increases, but there is a lower limit on its width. If you examine the formula for the prediction interval, you will see that the interval can get no smaller than $\hat{y} \pm z_{\alpha/2}\sigma$.* Thus, the only way to obtain more accurate predictions for new values of y is to reduce the standard deviation of the regression model, σ. This can be accomplished only by improving the model, either by using a curvilinear (rather than linear) relationship with x or by adding new independent variables to the model, or both. Methods of improving the model are discussed in Chapter 12.

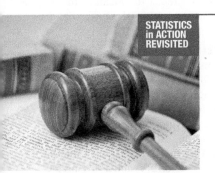

STATISTICS in ACTION REVISITED

Prediction Using the Straight-Line Model

In the two previous *Statistics in Action Revisited* sections, we demonstrated that x = cumulative 6-month advertising expenditures is a useful linear predictor of y = the number of new PI cases. The Minitab printout shown in Figure SIA11.6 gives a 95% prediction interval for the number of new PI cases in a month where cumulative spending on advertising over the past 6 months is x = $150,000. The highlighted interval is (4.78, 44.62). Thus, we can be 95% confident that for a given month with a 6-month cumulative advertising expenditure of $150,000, the law firm will add between 5 and 44 new PI cases that month.

```
Predicted Values for New Observations

New
Obs    Fit   SE Fit      95% CI           95% PI
  1   24.70   1.89   (20.89, 28.51)   (4.78, 44.62)


Values of Predictors for New Observations

New
Obs   AdvExp6
  1     150
```

Figure SIA11.6

Minitab prediction interval for legal advertising straight-line model

---

*The result follows from the facts that, for large n, $t_{\alpha/2} \approx z_{\alpha/2}$, $s \approx \sigma$, and the last two terms under the radical in the standard error of the predictor are approximately 0.

STATISTICS in ACTION REVISITED CONTINUED

The 95% *confidence interval for the mean of y* (also highlighted on the printout) is (20.89, 28.51). This indicates that for all months with cumulative spending on advertising of $x = \$150,000$, the average number of new PI cases each month will range between 21 and 28 cases. Of course, if these projections are to be useful for future planning, other economic factors that may affect the firm's business must be similar to those during the period over which the sample data were generated. □

Exercises 11.76–11.90

Learning the Mechanics

11.76 Consider the following pairs of measurements:

L11076

x	−2	0	2	4	6	8	10
y	0	3	2	3	8	10	11

a. Construct a scatterplot for these data.
b. Find the least squares line and plot it on your scatterplot.
c. Find s^2 and s.
d. Find a 90% confidence interval for the mean value of y when $x = 3$. Plot the upper and lower bounds of the confidence interval on your scatterplot.
e. Find a 90% prediction interval for a new value of y when $x = 3$. Plot the upper and lower bounds of the prediction interval on your scatterplot.
f. Compare the widths of the intervals you constructed in parts **d** and **e**. Which is wider and why?

11.77 Consider the pairs of measurements shown in the table. For these data, $SS_{xx} = 38.9$, $SS_{yy} = 33.6$, $SS_{xy} = 32.8$, and $\hat{y} = -.414 + .843x$.

L11077

x	4	6	0	5	2	3	2	6	2	1
y	3	5	−1	4	3	2	0	4	1	1

a. Construct a scatterplot for these data.
b. Plot the least squares line on your scatterplot.
c. Use a 95% confidence interval to estimate the mean value of y when $x_p = 6$. Plot the upper and lower bounds of the interval on your scatterplot.
d. Repeat part **c** for $x_p = 3.2$ and $x_p = 0$.
e. Compare the widths of the three confidence intervals you constructed in parts **c** and **d** and explain why they differ.

11.78 Refer to Exercise 11.77.
a. Using no information about x, estimate and calculate a 95% confidence interval for the mean value of y. [*Hint:* Use the one-sample *t* methodology of Section 5.4.]
b. Plot the estimated mean value and the confidence interval as horizontal lines on your scatterplot.
c. Compare the confidence intervals you calculated in parts **c** and **d** of Exercise 11.77 with the one you calculated in part **a** of this exercise. Does x appear to contribute information about the mean value of y?
d. Check the answer you gave in part **c** with a statistical test of the null hypothesis $H_0: \beta_1 = 0$ against $H_a: \beta_1 \neq 0$. Use $\alpha = .05$.

11.79 In fitting a least squares line to $n = 10$ data points, the following quantities were computed:
$$SS_{xx} = 32 \quad \bar{x} = 3 \quad SS_{yy} = 26 \quad \bar{y} = 4 \quad SS_{xy} = 28$$
a. Find the least squares line.
b. Graph the least squares line.
c. Calculate SSE.
d. Calculate s^2.
e. Find a 95% confidence interval for the mean value of y when $x_p = 2.5$.
f. Find a 95% prediction interval for y when $x_p = 4$.

Applying the Concepts—Basic

11.80 In business, do nice guys finish first or last? Refer to the *Nature* (March 20, 2008) study of the use of punishment in cooperation games, Exercise 11.14 (p. 614). Recall that simple linear regression was used to model a player's average payoff (y) as a straight-line function of the number of times punishment was used (x) by the player.
a. If the researchers want to predict average payoff for a single player who used punishment 10 times, how should they proceed?
b. If the researchers want to predict the mean of the average payoffs for all players who used punishment 10 times, how should they proceed?

11.81 Lobster fishing study. Refer to the *Bulletin of Marine Science* (April 2010) study of teams of fishermen fishing for the red spiny lobster in Baja California Sur, Mexico, Exercise 11.16 (p. 614). Recall that simple linear regression was used to model y = total catch of lobsters (in kilograms) during the season as a function of x = average percentage of traps allocated per day to exploring areas of unknown catch (called *search frequency*). A portion of the Minitab printout giving a 95% confidence interval for $E(y)$ and a 95% prediction interval for y when $x = 25$ is shown below.

```
Predicted Values for New Observations

New Obs   Fit   SE Fit     95% CI          95% PI
    1    5788    465   (4783, 6792)   (2643, 8933)


Values of Predictors for New Observations

New Obs   SEARCHFREQ
    1        25.0
```

a. Locate and interpret the 95% confidence interval for $E(y)$.
b. Locate and interpret the 95% prediction interval for y.

XLSTAT output for Exercise 11.82

Predictions for the new observations:

Observation	Pred(RelRate)	Lower bound 90% (Mean)	Upper bound 90% (Mean)	Lower bound 90% (Observation)	Upper bound 90% (Observation)
1.5	61.08	57.26	64.91	55.33	66.83
1.05	44.92	42.99	46.85	40.21	49.63
0.9	39.53	37.78	41.29	34.90	44.17
0.75	34.15	32.17	36.12	29.42	38.87
0.6	28.76	26.27	31.25	23.80	33.72
0.65	30.55	28.26	32.85	25.69	35.42

11.82 Drug controlled-release rate study. Refer to the *Drug Development and Industrial Pharmacy* (Vol. 28, 2002) drug controlled-release rate study, Exercise 11.17 (p. 615). Recall that data for six drug tablets were used to fit the simple linear model, $E(y) = \beta_0 + \beta_1 x$, where y = drug release rate and x = surface-area-to-volume ratio. An Excel/XLSTAT printout giving a 90% prediction interval for each of the $n = 6$ observations in the sample is shown above. Select an observation and give a practical interpretation for this prediction interval.

11.83 Sweetness of orange juice. Refer to the simple linear regression of sweetness index y and amount of pectin x for $n = 24$ orange juice samples, Exercise 11.22 (p. 616). A 90% confidence interval for the mean sweetness index, $E(y)$, for each of the first 12 runs is shown on the SPSS spreadsheet below. Select an observation and interpret this interval.

11.84 Public corruption and bad weather. Refer to the *Journal of Law and Economics* (Nov. 2008) study of the link between Federal Emergency Management Agency (FEMA) disaster relief and public corruption, Exercise 11.56 (p. 630). You determined that the *p*-value for testing the adequacy of the straight-line model relating a state's average annual number of public corruption convictions (y) to the state's

average annual FEMA relief (x) was $p = .102$. Based on this result, would you recommend using the model to predict the number of public corruption convictions in a state with an annual FEMA relief of $x = 5$ thousand dollars? Explain.

Applying the Concepts—Intermediate

11.85 Software millionaires and birthdays. Refer to Exercise 11.35 (p. 622) and the study of software millionaires and their birthdays. The data are reproduced on the next page. Recall that simple linear regression was used to model number (y) of software millionaire birthdays in a decade as a straight-line function of number (x) of CEO birthdays.

a. Consider a future decade where the number of CEO birthdays (in a random sample of 70 companies) is 25. Find a 95% prediction interval for the number of software millionaire birthdays in this decade. Interpret the result.

b. Consider another future decade where the number of CEO birthdays (in a random sample of 70 companies) is 10. Will the 95% prediction interval for the number of software millionaire birthdays in this decade be narrower or wider than the interval, part **b?** Explain.

	run	sweet	pectin	lower90m	upper90m
1	1	5.2	220	5.64898	5.83848
2	2	5.5	227	5.63898	5.81613
3	3	6.0	259	5.57819	5.72904
4	4	5.9	210	5.66194	5.87173
5	5	5.8	224	5.64337	5.82560
6	6	6.0	215	5.65564	5.85493
7	7	5.8	231	5.63284	5.80379
8	8	5.6	268	5.55553	5.71011
9	9	5.6	239	5.61947	5.78019
10	10	5.9	212	5.65946	5.86497
11	11	5.4	410	5.05526	5.55416
12	12	5.6	256	5.58517	5.73592
13	13	5.8	306	5.43785	5.65219
14	14	5.5	259	5.57819	5.72904
15	15	5.3	284	5.50957	5.68213
16	16	5.3	383	5.15725	5.57694
17	17	5.7	271	5.54743	5.70434
18	18	5.5	264	5.56591	5.71821
19	19	5.7	227	5.63898	5.81613
20	20	5.3	263	5.56843	5.72031
21	21	5.9	232	5.63125	5.80075
22	22	5.8	220	5.64898	5.83848
23	23	5.8	246	5.60640	5.76091
24	24	5.9	241	5.61587	5.77454

SPSS output for Exercise 11.83

Data for Exercise 11.85

Decade	Total U.S. Births (millions)	Number of Software Millionaire Birthdays	Number of CEO Birthdays (in a random sample of 70 companies from the *Fortune* 500 list)
1920	28.582	3	2
1930	24.374	1	2
1940	31.666	10	23
1950	40.530	14	38
1960	38.808	7	9
1970	33.309	4	0

Source: Sauro, J. "Were most software millionaires born around 1955?" *Measuring Usability,* November 17, 2010. Copyright © 2010 by Measuring Usability LLC. Reprinted with permission.

11.86 Ranking driving performance of professional golfers. Refer to *The Sport Journal* (Winter 2007) study of a new method for ranking the total driving performance of golfers on the PGA tour, Exercise 11.21 (p. 616). You fit a straight-line model relating driving accuracy (y) to driving distance (x) to the data saved in the file. Of interest is predicting y and estimating $E(y)$ when $x = 300$ yards.
a. Find and interpret a 95% prediction interval for y.
b. Find and interpret a 95% confidence interval for $E(y)$.
c. If you are interested in knowing the average driving accuracy of all PGA golfers who have a driving distance of 300 yards, which of the intervals is relevant? Explain.

11.87 Spreading rate of spilled liquid. Refer to the *Chemical Engineering Progress* (Jan. 2005) study of the rate at which a spilled volatile liquid will spread across a surface, Exercise 11.26 (p. 618). Recall that simple linear regression was used to model y = mass of the spill as a function of x = elapsed time of the spill.
a. Find a 99% confidence interval for the mean mass of all spills with an elapsed time of 15 minutes. Interpret the result.
b. Find a 99% prediction interval for the mass of a single spill with an elapsed time of 15 minutes. Interpret the result.
c. Compare the intervals, parts **a** and **b**. Which interval is wider? Will this always be the case? Explain.

11.88 Forecasting managerial needs. Managers are an important part of any organization's resource base. Accordingly, the organization should be just as concerned about forecasting its future managerial needs as it is with forecasting its needs for, say, the natural resources used in its production process (Northcraft and Neale, *Organizational Behavior: A Management Challenge,* 2001). A common forecasting procedure is to model the relationship between sales and the number of managers needed because the demand for managers is the result of the increases and decreases in the demand for products and services that a firm offers its customers. To develop this relationship, the data shown in the following table are collected from a firm's records.
a. Test the usefulness of the model. Use $\alpha = .05$. State your conclusion in the context of the problem.
b. The company projects that it will sell 39 units next month. Use the least squares model to construct a 90% prediction interval for the number of managers needed next month.
c. Interpret the interval in part **b**. Use the interval to determine the reliability of the firm's projection.

Units Sold, x	Managers, y	Units Sold, x	Managers, y
5	10	30	22
4	11	31	25
8	10	36	30
7	10	38	30
9	9	40	31
15	10	41	31
20	11	51	32
21	17	40	30
25	19	48	32
24	21	47	32

11.89 Predicting quit rates in manufacturing. The reasons given by workers for quitting their jobs generally fall into one of two categories: (1) worker quits to seek or take a different job, or (2) worker quits to withdraw from the labor force. Economic theory suggests that wages and quit rates are related. The table below lists quit rates (quits per 100 employees) and the average hourly wage in a sample of 15 manufacturing industries. Consider the simple linear regression of quit rate y on average wage x.

Industry	Quit Rate, y	Average Wage, x
1	1.4	$ 8.20
2	.7	10.35
3	2.6	6.18
4	3.4	5.37
5	1.7	9.94
6	1.7	9.11
7	1.0	10.59
8	.5	13.29
9	2.0	7.99
10	3.8	5.54
11	2.3	7.50
12	1.9	6.43
13	1.4	8.83
14	1.8	10.93
15	2.0	8.80

a. Do the data present sufficient evidence to conclude that average hourly wage rate contributes useful information for the prediction of quit rates? What does your model suggest about the relationship between quit rates and wages?
b. Find a 95% prediction interval for the quit rate in an industry with an average hourly wage of $9.00. Interpret the result.
c. Find a 95% confidence interval for the mean quit rate for industries with an average hourly wage of $9.00. Interpret this result.

Applying the Concepts—Advanced

11.90 Life tests of cutting tools. Refer to the data saved in the file, Exercise 11.40 (p. 623).

TOOLS **a.** Use a 90% confidence interval to estimate the mean useful life of a brand A cutting tool when the cutting speed is 45 meters per minute. Repeat for brand B. Compare the widths of the two intervals and comment on the reasons for any difference.

b. Use a 90% prediction interval to predict the useful life of a brand A cutting tool when the cutting speed is 45 meters per minute. Repeat for brand B. Compare the widths of the two intervals to each other and to the two intervals you calculated in part **a.** Comment on the reasons for any differences.

c. Note that the estimation and prediction you performed in parts **a** and **b** were for a value of x that was not included in the original sample—that is, the value x = 45 was not part of the sample. However, the value is within the range of x values in the sample, so the regression model spans the x value for which the estimation and prediction were made. In such situations, estimation and prediction represent *interpolations.* Suppose you were asked to predict the useful life of a brand A cutting tool for a cutting speed of x = 100 meters per minute. Because the given value of x is outside the range of the sample x values, the prediction is an example of **extrapolation.** Predict the useful life of a brand A cutting tool that is operated at 100 meters per minute and construct a 95% prediction interval for the actual useful life of the tool. What additional assumption do you have to make in order to ensure the validity of an extrapolation?

11.7 A Complete Example

In the preceding sections, we have presented the basic elements necessary to fit and use a straight-line regression model. In this section, we will assemble these elements by applying them in an example with the aid of a computer.

Suppose a fire insurance company wants to relate the amount of fire damage in major residential fires to the distance between the burning house and the nearest fire station. The study is to be conducted in a large suburb of a major city; a sample of 15 recent fires in this suburb is selected. The amount of damage, y, and the distance between the fire and the nearest fire station, x, are recorded for each fire. The results are shown in Table 11.5 and saved in the **RFIRES** file.

Step 1: First, we hypothesize a model to relate fire damage, y, to the distance from the nearest fire station, x. We hypothesize a straight-line probabilistic model:

$$y = \beta_0 + \beta_1 x + \varepsilon$$

Step 2: Next, we open the **RFIRES** file and use a statistical software package to estimate the unknown parameters in the deterministic component of the hypothesized model. The Excel printout for the simple linear regression analysis is

Table 11.5	Fire Damage Data
Distance from Fire Station, x (miles)	Fire Damage, y (thousands of dollars)
3.4	26.2
1.8	17.8
4.6	31.3
2.3	23.1
3.1	27.5
5.5	36.0
.7	14.1
3.0	22.3
2.6	19.6
4.3	31.3
2.1	24.0
1.1	17.3
6.1	43.2
4.8	36.4
3.8	26.1

Data Set: RFIRES

Regression Analysis					
Regression Statistics					
Multiple R	0.960977715				
R Square	0.923478169				
Adjusted R Square	0.917591874				
Standard Error	2.316346184				
Observations	15				
ANOVA					
	df	*SS*	*MS*	*F*	*Significance F*
Regression	1	841.766358	841.766358	156.8861596	1.2478E-08
Residual	13	69.75097535	5.365459643		
Total	14	911.5173333			

	Coefficients	*Standard Error*	*t Stat*	*P-value*	*Lower 95%*	*Upper 95%*
Intercept	10.27792855	1.420277811	7.236562082	6.58556E-06	7.209605476	13.34625162
DISTANCE	4.919330727	0.392747749	12.52542054	1.2478E-08	4.070850963	5.767810491

Figure 11.25

Excel printout for fire damage regression analysis

Figure 11.26

Minitab scatterplot with least squares line for fire damage regression analysis

shown in Figure 11.25. The least squares estimates of the slope β_1 and intercept β_0, highlighted on the printout, are

$$\hat{\beta}_1 = 4.919331$$
$$\hat{\beta}_0 = 10.277929$$

and the least squares equation is (rounded)

$$\hat{y} = 10.278 + 4.919x$$

This prediction equation is graphed in the Minitab scatterplot, Figure 11.26.

The least squares estimate of the slope, $\hat{\beta}_1 = 4.919$, implies that the estimated mean damage increases by \$4,919 for each additional mile from the fire station. This interpretation is valid over the range of x, or from .7 to 6.1 miles from the station. The estimated y-intercept, $\hat{\beta}_0 = 10.278$, has the interpretation that a fire 0 miles from the fire station has an estimated mean damage of \$10,278. Although this would seem to apply to the fire station itself, remember that the y-intercept is meaningfully interpretable only if $x = 0$ is within the sampled range of the independent variable. Because $x = 0$ is outside the range in this case, $\hat{\beta}_0$ has no practical interpretation.

Step 3: Now we specify the probability distribution of the random error component ε. The assumptions about the distribution are identical to those listed in Section 11.3. Although we know that these assumptions are not completely satisfied (they rarely are for practical problems), we are willing to assume they are approximately satisfied for this example. The estimate of the standard deviation σ of ε, highlighted on the Excel printout (Figure 11.25) is

$$s = 2.31635$$

This implies that most of the observed fire damage (y) values will fall within approximately $2s = 4.64$ thousand dollars of their respective predicted values when using the least squares line. [*Note:* A more precise prediction interval for y is given in step 5.]

Step 4: We can now check the usefulness of the hypothesized model—that is, whether x really contributes information for the prediction of y using the straight-line model. First, test the null hypothesis that the slope β_1 is 0—that is, that there is no linear relationship between fire damage and the distance from the nearest fire station, against the alternative hypothesis that fire damage increases as the distance increases. We test

$$H_0: \beta_1 = 0$$

$$H_a: \beta_1 > 0$$

The test statistic value (highlighted on the printout) is $t = 12.53$. Also, the two-tailed observed significance level for testing $H_a: \beta_1 \neq 0$, (highlighted on the printout) is approximately 0. When we divide this value in half, the p-value for our one-tailed test is also approximately 0. This small p-value leaves little doubt that mean fire damage and distance between the fire and station are at least linearly related, with mean fire damage increasing as the distance increases.

We gain additional information about the relationship by forming a 95% confidence interval for the slope β_1. The lower and upper endpoints of this interval are highlighted on the Excel printout shown in Figure 11.25.

This yields the interval (4.070, 5.768). We estimate (with 95% confidence) that the interval from \$4,070 to \$5,768 encloses the mean increase (β_1) in fire damage per additional mile distance from the fire station.

Another measure of the utility of the model is the coefficient of determination, r^2. The value (highlighted on Figure 11.25) is $r^2 = .9235$, which implies that about 92% of the sample variation in fire damage (y) is explained by the distance (x) between the fire and the fire station.

The coefficient of correlation, r, that measures the strength of the linear relationship between y and x is not shown on the Excel printout and must be calculated. Using the facts that $r = \sqrt{r^2}$ in simple linear regression and that r and $\hat{\beta}_1$ have the same sign, we find

$$r = +\sqrt{r^2} = \sqrt{.9235} = .96$$

The high correlation confirms our conclusion that β_1 is greater than 0; it appears that fire damage and distance from the fire station are positively correlated. All signs point to a strong linear relationship between y and x.

Step 5: We are now prepared to use the least squares model. Suppose the insurance company wants to predict the fire damage if a major residential fire were to occur 3.5 miles from the nearest fire station. A 95% confidence interval for $E(y)$ and prediction interval for y when $x = 3.5$ are shown on the Minitab printout, Figure 11.27. The predicted value (highlighted on the printout) is $\hat{y} = 27.496$, while the 95% prediction interval (also highlighted) is (22.3239, 32.6672). Therefore, with 95% confidence we predict fire damage in a major residential fire 3.5 miles from the nearest station to be between \$22,324 and \$32,667.

```
Predicted Values for New Observations

New
Obs    Fit  SE Fit     95% CI          95% PI
  1  27.496  0.604  (26.190, 28.801)  (22.324, 32.667)


Values of Predictors for New Observations

New
Obs  DISTANCE
  1    3.50
```

Figure 11.27

Minitab confidence and prediction intervals for fire damage regression

> ⚠ **CAUTION** We would not use this prediction model to make predictions outside the scope of the model, i.e., for homes less than .7 mile or more than 6.1 miles from the nearest fire station. A look at the data in Table 11.7 reveals that all the x values fall between .7 and 6.1. It is dangerous to use the model to make predictions outside the region in which the sample data fall. A straight line might not provide a good model for the relationship between the mean value of y and the value of x when stretched over a wider range of x values.

Exercises 11.91–11.93

Applying the Concepts—Intermediate

11.91 Prices of recycled materials. Prices of recycled materials (e.g., plastics, paper, and glass) are highly volatile due to the fact that supply is constant, rather than tied to demand. An exploratory study of the prices of recycled products in the United Kingdom was published in *Resources, Conservation, and Recycling* (Vol. 60, 2012). The researchers employed simple linear regression to model $y =$ the monthly price of recycled colored plastic bottles as a function of $x =$ the monthly price of naphtha (a primary material in plastics). The following results were obtained for monthly data collected over a recent 10-year period ($n = 120$ months):

$\hat{y} = -32.35 + 4.82x$, $t = 16.60$ (for testing H_0: $\beta_1 = 0$)
$r = .83$, $r^2 = .69$

Use this information to conduct the first four steps of a complete simple linear regression analysis. Give your conclusions in the words of the problem.

11.92 Forecasting movie revenues with Twitter. Refer to the *IEEE International Conference on Web Intelligence and Intelligent Agent Technology* (2010) study of how social media (e.g., Twitter.com) may influence the products consumers buy, Exercise 11.23 (p. 617). Recall that opening weekend box office revenue (in millions of dollars) and *tweet rate* (average number of tweets referring to the movie per hour) were collected for a sample of 23 recent movies. The data are reproduced in the table. Conduct a complete simple linear regression analysis of the relationship between revenue (y) and tweet rate (x). Write all your conclusions in the words of the problem.

11.93 An MBA's work-life balance. The importance of having employees with a healthy work-life balance has been recognized by U.S. companies for decades. Many business schools offer courses that assist MBA students with developing good work-life balance habits, and most large companies have developed work-life balance programs for their employees. In April 2005, the Graduate Management Admission Council (GMAC) conducted a survey of over 2,000 MBA alumni to explore the work-life balance issue. (For example, one question asked alumni to state their level of agreement with the statement "My personal and work demands are overwhelming.") Based on these responses, the GMAC determined a work-life balance scale score for each MBA alumnus. Scores ranged from 0 to 100, with lower scores indicating a higher imbalance between work and life. Many other variables, including average number of hours worked per week, were also measured. The data for the work-life balance study are saved in the file. (The first 15 observations are listed in the accompanying table.) Let $x =$ average number of hours worked per week and $y =$ work-life balance scale score for each MBA alumnus. Investigate the link between these two variables by conducting a complete simple linear regression analysis of the data. Summarize your findings in a professional report.

Tweet Rate	Revenue (millions)
1365.8	142
1212.8	77
581.5	61
310.1	32
455	31
290	30
250	21
680.5	18
150	18
164.5	17
113.9	16
144.5	15
418	14
98	14
100.8	12
115.4	11
74.4	10
87.5	9
127.6	9
52.2	9
144.1	8
41.3	2
2.75	0.3

WLB Score	Hours
75.22	50
64.98	45
49.62	50
44.51	55
70.10	50
54.74	60
55.98	55
21.24	60
59.86	50
70.10	50
29.00	70
64.98	45
36.75	40
35.45	40
45.75	50

Source: Schoenfeld, G. "Work-life balance: An MBA alumni report," *Graduate Management Admission Council (GMAC) Research Report* (Oct. 13, 2005). Copyright © 2005 by the Graduate Management Admissions Council (GMAC). Reprinted with permission.

■ Chapter Notes

Key Terms

Key Symbols/Notation

y	Dependent variable (variable to be predicted)
x	Independent variable (variable used to predict y)
$E(y)$	Expected value (mean) of y
β_0	y-intercept of true line
β_1	Slope of true line
$\hat{\beta}_0$	Least squares estimate of y-intercept
$\hat{\beta}_1$	Least squares estimate of slope
ε	Random error
$\hat{y}$	Predicted value of y for a given x-value
$(y - \hat{y})$	Estimated error of prediction
SSE	Sum of squared errors of prediction
r	Coefficient of correlation
r^2	Coefficient of determination
x_p	Value of x used to predict y
$r^2 = \dfrac{\text{SS}_{yy} - \text{SSE}}{\text{SS}_{yy}}$	Coefficient of determination

$$\hat{y} \pm t_{\alpha/2} s \sqrt{\frac{1}{n} + \frac{(x_p - \bar{x})^2}{\text{SS}_{xx}}}$$ 100%$(1 - \alpha)$ confidence interval for $E(y)$ when $x = x_p$

$$\hat{y} \pm t_{\alpha/2} s \sqrt{1 + \frac{1}{n} + \frac{(x_p - \bar{x})^2}{\text{SS}_{xx}}}$$ 100%$(1 - \alpha)$ prediction interval for y when $x = x_p$

Key Ideas

Simple Linear Regression variables

y = **Dependent** variable (quantitative)
x = **Independent** variable (quantitative)

Method of Least Squares Properties

1. average error of prediction = 0
2. sum of squared errors is minimum

Practical Interpretation of y-Intercept

Predicted y-value when $x = 0$

(no practical interpretation if $x = 0$ is either nonsensical or outside range of sample data)

Practical Interpretation of Slope

Increase (or decrease) in mean y for every 1-unit increase in x

First-Order (Straight-Line) Model

$$E(y) = \beta_0 + \beta_1 x$$

where $E(y)$ = mean of y

β_0 = **y-intercept** of line (point where line intecepts y-axis)
β_1 = **slope** of line (change in mean of y for every 1-unit change in x)

Coefficient of Correlation, r

1. ranges between -1 and $+1$
2. measures strength of *linear relationship* between y and x

Coefficient of Determination, r^2

1. ranges between 0 and 1
2. measures proportion of sample variation in y "explained" by the model

Practical Interpretation of Model Standard Deviation, s

Ninety-five percent of y-values fall within $2s$ of their respected predicted values

Width of *confidence interval for $E(y)$* will always be **narrower** than width of prediction interval for y

Guide to Simple Linear Regression

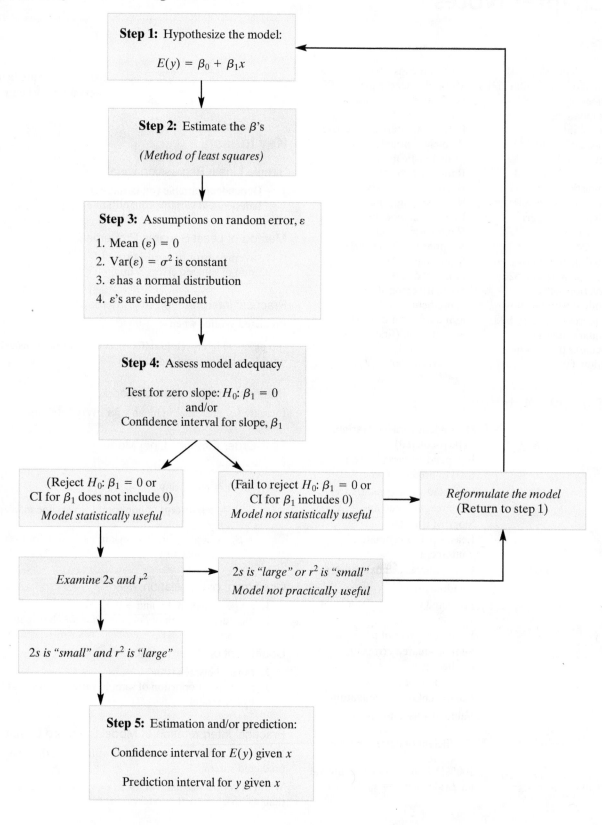

Step 1: Hypothesize the model:

$$E(y) = \beta_0 + \beta_1 x$$

Step 2: Estimate the β's

(Method of least squares)

Step 3: Assumptions on random error, ε

1. Mean $(\varepsilon) = 0$
2. Var$(\varepsilon) = \sigma^2$ is constant
3. ε has a normal distribution
4. ε's are independent

Step 4: Assess model adequacy

Test for zero slope: $H_0: \beta_1 = 0$
and/or
Confidence interval for slope, β_1

(Reject $H_0: \beta_1 = 0$ or
CI for β_1 does not include 0)
Model statistically useful

(Fail to reject $H_0: \beta_1 = 0$ or
CI for β_1 includes 0)
Model not statistically useful

Reformulate the model
(Return to step 1)

Examine 2s and r^2

2s is "large" or r^2 is "small"
Model not practically useful

2s is "small" and r^2 is "large"

Step 5: Estimation and/or prediction:

Confidence interval for $E(y)$ given x

Prediction interval for y given x

Supplementary Exercises 11.94–11.112

Learning the Mechanics

11.94 Consider the following sample data:

y	5	1	3
x	5	1	3

a. Construct a scatterplot for the data.
b. It is possible to find many lines for which $\Sigma(y - \hat{y}) = 0$. For this reason, the criterion $\Sigma(y - \hat{y}) = 0$ is not used for identifying the "best-fitting" straight line. Find two lines that have $\Sigma(y - \hat{y}) = 0$.
c. Find the least squares line.
d. Compare the value of SSE for the least squares line to that of the two lines you found in part **b**. What principle of least squares is demonstrated by this comparison?

11.95 In fitting a least squares line to $n = 15$ data points, the following quantities were computed: $SS_{xx} = 55$, $SS_{yy} = 198$, $SS_{xy} = -88$, $\bar{x} = 1.3$, and $\bar{y} = 35$.
a. Find the least squares line.
b. Graph the least squares line.
c. Calculate SSE.
d. Calculate s^2.
e. Find a 90% confidence interval for β_1. Interpret this estimate.
f. Find a 90% confidence interval for the mean value of y when $x = 15$.
g. Find a 90% prediction interval for y when $x = 15$.

11.96 Consider the following 10 data points:

L11096

x	3	5	6	4	3	7	6	5	4	7
y	4	3	2	1	2	3	3	5	4	2

a. Plot the data on a scatterplot.
b. Calculate the values of r and r^2.
c. Is there sufficient evidence to indicate that x and y are linearly correlated? Test at the $\alpha = .10$ level of significance.

Applying the Concepts—Basic

11.97 "Metaskills" and career management. Effective management of one's own career requires a skill set that includes adaptability, tolerance for ambiguity, self-awareness, and ability to identify change. Management professors at Pace University (New York) used correlation coefficients to investigate the relationship between these "metaskills" and effective career management (*International Journal of Manpower*, Aug. 2000). Data were collected for 446 business graduates who had all completed a management metaskills course. Two of the many variables measured were self-knowledge skill level (x) and goal-setting ability (y). The correlation coefficient for these two variables was $r = .70$.
a. Give a practical interpretation of the value of r.
b. The p-value for a test of no correlation between the two variables was reported as p-value $= .001$. Interpret this result.
c. Find the coefficient of determination, r^2, and interpret the result.

11.98 Burnout of human services professionals. Emotional exhaustion, or *burnout*, is a significant problem for people with careers in the field of human services. Regression analysis was used to investigate the relationship between burnout and aspects of the human services professional's job and job-related behavior (*Journal of Applied Behavioral Science*, Vol. 22, 1986). Emotional exhaustion was measured with the Maslach Burnout Inventory, a questionnaire. One of the independent variables considered, called *concentration*, was the proportion of social contacts with individuals who belong to a person's work group. The next table lists the values of the emotional exhaustion index (higher values indicate greater exhaustion) and concentration for a sample of 25 human services professionals who work in a large public hospital. A Minitab printout of the simple linear regression is provided below.

BRNOUT

Exhaustion Index, y	Concentration, x	Exhaustion Index, y	Concentration, x
100	20%	493	86%
525	60	892	83
300	38	527	79
980	88	600	75
310	79	855	81
900	87	709	75
410	68	791	77
296	12	718	77
120	35	684	77
501	70	141	17
920	80	400	85
810	92	970	96
506	77		

```
The regression equation is
EXHAUST = - 29 + 8.87 CONCEN


Predictor   Coef   SE Coef      T      P
Constant   -29.5    106.7   -0.28   0.785
CONCEN     8.865    1.471    6.03   0.000


S = 174.207    R-Sq = 61.2%    R-Sq(adj) = 59.5%


Analysis of Variance

Source          DF       SS       MS      F      P
Regression       1  1102408  1102408  36.33  0.000
Residual Error  23   698009    30348
Total           24  1800417


Predicted Values for New Observations

New
Obs    Fit  SE Fit       95% CI           95% PI
  1  679.7    38.7  (599.7, 759.8)  (310.6, 1048.9)


Values of Predictors for New Observations

New
Obs   CONCEN
  1     80.0
```

a. Construct a scatterplot for the data. Do the variables x and y appear to be related?

b. Find the correlation coefficient for the data and interpret its value. Does your conclusion mean that concentration causes emotional exhaustion? Explain.

c. Test the usefulness of the straight-line relationship with concentration for predicting burnout. Use $\alpha = .05$.

d. Find the coefficient of determination for the model and interpret it.

e. Find a 95% confidence interval for the slope β_1. Interpret the result.

f. Use a 95% confidence interval to estimate the mean exhaustion level for all professionals who have 80% of their social contacts within their work groups. Interpret the interval.

11.99 Retaliation against company "whistle-blowers." Individuals who report perceived wrongdoing of a corporation or public agency are known as *whistle-blowers.* Two researchers developed an index to measure the extent of retaliation against a whistle-blower (*Journal of Applied Psychology,* 1986). The index was based on the number of forms of reprisal actually experienced, the number of forms of reprisal threatened, and the number of people within the organization (e.g., coworkers or immediate supervisor) who retaliated against them. The table below lists the retaliation index (higher numbers indicate more extensive retaliation) and salary for a sample of 15 whistle-blowers from federal agencies.

Retaliation Index	Salary	Retaliation Index	Salary
301	$62,000	535	$19,800
550	36,500	455	44,000
755	21,600	615	46,600
327	24,000	700	15,100
500	30,100	650	70,000
377	35,000	630	21,000
290	47,500	360	16,900
452	54,000		

Source: Based on Near, J. P., & Miceli, M. P. "Retaliation against whistle blowers: Predictors and effects," *Journal of Applied Psychology,* Vol. 71, No. 1, 1986, pp. 137–145.

a. Construct a scatterplot for the data. Does it appear that the extent of retaliation increases, decreases, or stays the same with an increase in salary? Explain.

b. Use the method of least squares to fit a straight line to the data.

c. Graph the least squares line on your scatterplot. Does the least squares line support your answer to the question in part **a**? Explain.

d. Interpret the y-intercept, $\hat{\beta}_0$ of the least squares line in terms of this application. Is the interpretation meaningful?

e. Interpret the slope, $\hat{\beta}_1$, of the least squares line in terms of this application. Over what range of x is this interpretation meaningful?

f. Test the adequacy of the model using $\alpha = .05$.

11.100 Buying income of households. *Sales and Marketing Management* determined the "effective buying income" (EBI) of the average household in a state. Can the EBI be used to predict retail sales per household in the store-group category "eating and drinking places"?

a. Use the data for 13 states given in the table below to find the least squares line relating retail sales per household (y) to average household EBI (x).

b. Plot the least squares line, as well as the actual data points, on a scatterplot.

c. Based on the graph, part **b**, give your opinion regarding the predictive ability of the least squares line.

d. Find a 95% confidence interval for the slope of the line.

e. Use the results, part **d**, to assess the adequacy of the straight-line model.

State	Average Household Buying Income ($)	Retail Sales: Eating and Drinking Places ($ per household)
Connecticut	60,998	2,553.8
New Jersey	63,853	2,154.8
Michigan	46,915	2,523.3
Minnesota	44,717	2,278.6
Florida	42,442	2,475.8
South Carolina	37,848	2,358.4
Mississippi	34,490	1,538.4
Oklahoma	34,830	2,063.1
Texas	44,729	2,363.5
Colorado	44,571	3,214.9
Utah	43,421	2,653.8
California	50,713	2,215.0
Oregon	40,597	2,144.0

Source: "The survey of buying power," *Sales and Marketing Management,* 1995. Copyright © 1995 by Sales and Marketing Management. Reprinted with permission.

11.101 Diamonds sold at retail. Refer to the *Journal of Statistics Education* study of 308 diamonds sold on the open market, Exercise 2.158 (p. 117). Recall that you related the size of the diamond (number of carats) to the asking price (dollars) using a scatterplot.

a. Write the equation of a straight-line model relating asking price (y) to number of carats (x).

b. An XLSTAT simple linear regression printout for the analysis is shown on the following page. Find the equation of the least squares line.

c. Give a practical interpretation of the y-intercept of the least squares line. If a practical interpretation is not possible, explain why.

d. Locate a 95% confidence interval for the slope of the least squares line on the printout and practically interpret the result. Over what range is the interpretation meaningful?

e. Locate the estimated standard deviation of the random error on the printout and practically interpret this value.

f. Specify the null and alternative hypotheses for determining whether a positive linear relationship exists between asking price and size.

g. Locate the p-value of the test, part **f**, on the printout. Interpret the result if $\alpha = .05$.

h. Locate the coefficient of determination, r^2, on the printout and interpret the result.

i. Locate the coefficient of correlation, r, on the printout and interpret the result.

j. Locate a 95% prediction interval for the asking price when carat size is .5 on the printout and practically interpret the result.

XLSTAT output for Exercise 11.101

Variables	CARAT	PRICE
CARAT	**1.0000**	0.9447
PRICE	0.9447	**1.0000**

Regression of variable PRICE:

Goodness of fit statistics:

Observatic	308.0000
Sum of we	308.0000
DF	306.0000
R²	0.8925
Adjusted R	0.8922
MSE	1248949.7531
RMSE	1117.5642
DW	1.2156

Analysis of variance:

Source	DF	Sum of squares	Mean squares	F	Pr > F
Model	1	3173248722.4667	3173248722.4667	2540.7337	< 0.0001
Error	306	382178624.4521	1248949.7531		
Corrected	307	3555427346.9188			

Computed against model Y=Mean(Y)

Model parameters:

Source	Value	Standard error	t	Pr > |t|	Lower bound (95%)	Upper bound (95%)
Intercept	-2298.3576	158.5306	-14.4979	< 0.0001	-2610.3056	-1986.4096
CARAT	11598.8840	230.1106	50.4057	< 0.0001	11146.0846	12051.6834

Equation of the model:

PRICE = -2298.35760+11598.88401*CARAT

Predictions for the new observations:

Observation	Pred(PRICE)	Lower bound 95% (Mean)	Upper bound 95% (Mean)	Lower bound 95% (Observation)	Upper bound 95% (Observation)
0.5	3501.0844	3362.4870	3639.7018	1297.6366	5704.5322

k. Locate a 95% confidence interval for the mean asking price when carat size is .5 on the printout and practically interpret the result.

11.102 Sports news on local TV broadcasts. *The Sports Journal* (Winter 2004) published the results of a study conducted to assess the factors that impact the time allotted to sports news on local television news broadcasts. Information on total time (in minutes) allotted to sports and audience ratings of the TV news broadcast (measured on a 100-point scale) was obtained from a national sample of 163 news directors. A correlation analysis on the data yielded $r = .43$.
a. Interpret the value of the correlation coefficient, r.
b. Find and interpret the value of the coefficient of determination, r^2.

Applying the Concepts—Intermediate

11.103 Evaluating managerial success. H. Mintzberg's classic book *The Nature of Managerial Work* (1973) identified the roles found in all managerial jobs. An observational study of 19 managers from a medium-sized manufacturing plant extended Mintzberg's work by investigating which activities *successful* managers actually perform (*Journal of Applied Behavioral Science*, Aug. 1985). To measure success, the researchers devised an index based on the manager's length of time in the organization and his or her level within the firm; the higher the index, the more successful the manager. The table on the following page presents data that can be used to determine whether managerial success is related to the extensiveness of a manager's network-building interactions with people outside the manager's work unit. Such interactions include phone and face-to-face meetings with customers and suppliers, attending outside meetings, and doing public relations work.
a. Construct a scatterplot for the data.
b. Find the prediction equation for managerial success.
c. Find s for your prediction equation. Interpret the standard deviation s in the context of this problem.
d. Plot the least squares line on your scatterplot of part **a.** Does it appear that the number of interactions

Data for Exercise 11.103

Manager	Manager Success Index, y	Number of Interactions with Outsiders, x
1	40	12
2	73	71
3	95	70
4	60	81
5	81	43
6	27	50
7	53	42
8	66	18
9	25	35
10	63	82
11	70	20
12	47	81
13	80	40
14	51	33
15	32	45
16	50	10
17	52	65
18	30	20
19	42	21

with outsiders contributes information for the prediction of managerial success? Explain.

e. Conduct a formal statistical hypothesis test to answer the question posed in part d. Use $\alpha = .05$.

f. Construct a 95% confidence interval for β_1. Interpret the interval in the context of the problem.

g. A particular manager was observed for 2 weeks, as in the *Journal of Applied Behavioral Science* study. She made 55 contacts with people outside her work unit. Predict the value of the manager's success index. Use a 90% prediction interval.

h. A second manager was observed for 2 weeks. This manager made 110 contacts with people outside his work unit. Why should caution be exercised in using the least squares model developed from the given data set to construct a prediction interval for this manager's success index?

i. In the context of this problem, determine the value of x for which the associated prediction interval for y is the narrowest.

11.104 Doctors and ethics. Refer to the *Journal of Medical Ethics* (Vol. 32, 2006) study of physicians' use of ethics consultation, Exercise 2.131 (p. 106). Recall that the medical researchers measured the *length of time in practice* (i.e., years of experience) and the *amount of exposure to ethics in medical school* (number of hours) for a sample of 118 physicians. Consider a straight-line regression model relating hours of exposure (y) to time in practice (x).

a. Fit the model to the data saved in the file and conduct a test (at $\alpha = .05$) for a linear relationship between the two variables.

b. In Exercise 2.132 you identified a highly suspect outlier for hours of exposure. Remove this outlier from the data set and rerun the analysis, part a. What do you observe?

11.105 Do New Jersey banks serve minority communities? Financial institutions have a legal and social responsibility to serve all communities. Do banks adequately serve both inner-city and suburban neighborhoods, both poor and wealthy communities? In New Jersey, banks have been charged with withdrawing from urban areas with a high percentage of minorities. To examine this charge, a regional New Jersey newspaper, the *Asbury Park Press,* compiled county-by-county data on the number (y) of people in each county per branch bank in the county and the percentage (x) of the population in each county that is minority. These data for each of New Jersey's 21 counties are provided in the table below.

County	Number of People per Bank Branch	Percentage of Minority Population
Atlantic	3,073	23.3
Bergen	2,095	13.0
Burlington	2,905	17.8
Camden	3,330	23.4
Cape May	1,321	7.3
Cumberland	2,557	26.5
Essex	3,474	48.8
Gloucester	3,068	10.7
Hudson	3,683	33.2
Hunterdon	1,998	3.7
Mercer	2,607	24.9
Middlesex	3,154	18.1
Monmouth	2,609	12.6
Morris	2,253	8.2
Ocean	2,317	4.7
Passaic	3,307	28.1
Salem	2,511	16.7
Somerset	2,333	12.0
Sussex	2,568	2.4
Union	3,048	25.6
Warren	2,349	2.8

Source: D'Ambrosio, P., & Chambers, S. "No checks and balances," *Asbury Park Press,* September 10, 1995. Copyright © 1995 by Asbury Park Press. Reprinted with permission.

a. Plot the data in a scatterplot. What pattern, if any, does the plot reveal?

b. Consider the linear model $E(y) = \beta_0 + \beta_1 x$. If, in fact, the charge against the New Jersey banks is true, then an increase in the percentage of minorities (x) will lead to a decrease in the number of bank branches in a county and therefore will result in an increase in the number of people (y) per branch. Will the value of β_1 be positive or negative in this situation?

c. Do these data support or refute the charge made against the New Jersey banking community? Test using $\alpha = .01$.

11.106 Monetary values of NFL teams. Refer to the *Forbes* magazine 2011 report on the financial standings of each team in the National Football League (NFL), Exercise 2.26 (p. 60). The table listing the current value (without deduction for debt, except stadium debt) and operating income for each team is reproduced on the next page.

a. Propose a straight-line model relating an NFL team's current value (y) to its operating income (x).

b. Fit the model to the data using the method of least squares.

c. Interpret the least squares estimates of the slope and y-intercept in the words of the problem.

d. Statistically assess the adequacy of the model. Do you recommend using it to predict an NFL team's value?

Data for Exercise 11.106

Rank	Team	Current Value ($mil)	1-Yr Value Change (%)	Debt/Value (%)	Revenue ($mil)	Operating Income ($mil)
1	Dallas Cowboys	1,850	2	18	406	119
2	Washington Redskins	1,555	0	26	352	65.6
3	New England Patriots	1,400	2	19	333	42.9
4	New York Giants	1,300	10	50	293	40.6
5	New York Jets	1,223	7	61	285	25.1
6	Houston Texans	1,202	3	17	283	41
7	Philadelphia Eagles	1,164	4	9	274	28.9
8	Chicago Bears	1,093	2	11	266	43.4
9	Green Bay Packers	1,089	7	2	259	12
10	Baltimore Ravens	1,088	1	25	262	24.9
11	Indianapolis Colts	1,057	2	4	252	32.8
12	Denver Broncos	1,046	0	14	255	28.5
13	Pittsburgh Steelers	1,018	2	25	255	28.3
14	Miami Dolphins	1,012	0	40	253	12.9
15	Carolina Panthers	1,002	−3	19	257	31.2
16	Seattle Seahawks	997	1	12	249	7.8
17	San Francisco 49ers	990	7	14	234	1.5
18	Kansas City Chiefs	986	2	14	252	14.5
19	Tampa Bay Buccaneers	981	−5	18	245	50.8
20	Cleveland Browns	977	−4	15	247	−2.9
21	New Orleans Saints	965	1	13	261	28.9
22	Tennessee Titans	964	−3	13	250	21.8
23	San Diego Chargers	920	1	14	241	34.2
24	Arizona Cardinals	901	−2	17	240	56.4
25	Cincinnati Bengals	875	−3	11	236	44.7
26	Detroit Lions	844	3	33	228	−7.7
27	Atlanta Falcons	814	−2	34	233	27.2
28	Minnesota Vikings	796	3	41	227	3.7
29	Buffalo Bills	792	−1	16	236	40.9
30	St. Louis Rams	775	−1	15	228	24.6
31	Oakland Raiders	761	0	16	217	23
32	Jacksonville Jaguars	725	0	17	236	32.8

Source: Based on "Football's Most Valuable Teams," *Forbes,* September 7, 2011.

11.107 Evaluating a truck weigh-in-motion program. The
Minnesota Department of Transportation installed a
WEIGHN state-of-the-art weigh-in-motion scale in the concrete
surface of the eastbound lanes of Interstate 494 in
Bloomington, Minnesota. After installation, a study was
undertaken to determine whether the scale's readings

Trial Number	Static Weight of Truck, x (thousand pounds)	Weigh-in-Motion Reading Prior to Calibration Adjustment, y_1 (thousand pounds)	Weigh-in-Motion Reading After Calibration Adjustment, y_2 (thousand pounds)
1	27.9	26.0	27.8
2	29.1	29.9	29.1
3	38.0	39.5	37.8
4	27.0	25.1	27.1
5	30.3	31.6	30.6
6	34.5	36.2	34.3
7	27.8	25.1	26.9
8	29.6	31.0	29.6
9	33.1	35.6	33.0
10	35.5	40.2	35.0

Source: Based on Wright, J. L., Owen, F., and Pena, D. "Status of MN/DOT's
weigh-in-motion program," St. Paul: Minnesota Department of Transportation,
January 1983.

correspond with the static weights of the vehicles being
monitored. (Studies of this type are known as *calibration studies.*) After some preliminary comparisons using
a two-axle, six-tire truck carrying different loads (see the
accompanying table), calibration adjustments were made
in the software of the weigh-in-motion system, and the
scales were reevaluated.

a. Construct two scatterplots, one of y_1 versus x and the
other of y_2 versus x.

b. Use the scatterplots of part **a** to evaluate the performance of the weigh-in-motion scale both before and
after the calibration adjustment.

c. Calculate the correlation coefficient for both sets of
data and interpret their values. Explain how these
correlation coefficients can be used to evaluate the
weigh-in-motion scale.

d. Suppose the sample correlation coefficient for y_2 and
x was 1. Could this happen if the static weights and the
weigh-in-motion readings disagreed? Explain.

11.108 Energy efficiency of buildings. Firms planning to build
new plants or make additions to existing facilities have
BTU become very conscious of the energy efficiency of proposed new structures and are interested in the relation
between yearly energy consumption and the number of
square feet of building shell. The table on the next page
lists the energy consumption in British thermal units
(a BTU is the amount of heat required to raise 1 pound

of water 1°F) for 22 buildings that were all subjected to the same climatic conditions. Consider a straight-line model relating BTU consumption, y, to building shell area, x.

a. Find the least squares estimates of the intercept β_0 and the slope β_1.

b. Investigate the usefulness of the model you developed in part **a**. Is yearly energy consumption positively linearly related to the shell area of the building? Test using $\alpha = .10$.

c. Find the observed significance level of the test of part **b**. Interpret its value.

d. Find the coefficient of determination r^2 and interpret its value.

e. A company wishes to build a new warehouse that will contain 8,000 square feet of shell area. Find the predicted value of energy consumption and associated 95% prediction interval. Comment on the usefulness of this interval.

f. The application of the model you developed in part **a** to the warehouse problem of part **e** is appropriate only if certain assumptions can be made about the new warehouse. What are these assumptions?

BTU/Year (thousands)	Shell Area (square feet)
3,870,000	30,001
1,371,000	13,530
2,422,000	26,060
672,200	6,355
233,100	4,576
218,900	24,680
354,000	2,621
3,135,000	23,350
1,470,000	18,770
1,408,000	12,220
2,201,000	25,490
2,680,000	23,680
337,500	5,650
567,500	8,001
555,300	6,147
239,400	2,660
2,629,000	19,240
1,102,000	10,700
423,500	9,125
423,500	6,510
1,691,000	13,530
1,870,000	18,860

11.109 Foreign investment risk. One of the most difficult tasks of developing and managing a global portfolio is assessing the risks of potential foreign investments. Duke University researcher C. R. Henry collaborated with two First Chicago Investment Management Company directors to examine the use of country credit ratings as a means of evaluating foreign investments (*Journal of Portfolio Management,* Winter 1995). To be effective, such a measure should help explain and predict the volatility of the foreign market in question. Data on annualized risk (y) and average credit rating (x) for 40 fictitious countries (based on the study results) are saved in the file. (The first and last five countries are shown in the table.)

a. Do the data provide sufficient evidence to conclude that country credit risk (x) contributes information for the prediction of market volatility (y)?

Country	Annualized Risk (%)	Average Credit Rating
1	85.9	30.7
2	25.8	77.1
3	25.2	82.7
4	20.9	77.3
5	63.7	35.1
⋮	⋮	⋮
36	73.0	31.5
37	20.7	86.5
38	14.3	95.3
39	44.9	43.9
40	34.5	23.4

b. Use a graph to visually locate any unusual data points (outliers).

c. Eliminate the outlier(s), part **b**, from the data set and rerun the simple linear regression analysis. Note any dramatic changes in the results.

Applying the Concepts—Advanced

11.110 Regression through the origin. Sometimes it is known from theoretical considerations that the straight-line relationship between two variables, x and y, passes through the origin of the xy-plane. Consider the relationship between the total weight of a shipment of 50-pound bags of flour, y, and the number of bags in the shipment, x. Because a shipment containing $x = 0$ bags (i.e., no shipment at all) has a total weight of $y = 0$, a straight-line model of the relationship between x and y should pass through the point $x = 0$, $y = 0$. In such a case, you could assume $\beta_0 = 0$ and characterize the relationship between x and y with the following model:

$$y = \beta_1 x + \varepsilon$$

The least squares estimate of β_1 for this model is

$$\hat{\beta}_1 = \frac{\sum x_i y_i}{\sum x_i^2}$$

From the records of past flour shipments, 15 shipments were randomly chosen, and the data shown in the table below were recorded.

Weight of Shipment	Number of 50-Pound Bags in Shipment
5,050	100
10,249	205
20,000	450
7,420	150
24,685	500
10,206	200
7,325	150
4,958	100
7,162	150
24,000	500
4,900	100
14,501	300
28,000	600
17,002	400
16,100	400

a. Find the least squares line for the given data under the assumption that $\beta_0 = 0$. Plot the least squares line on a scatterplot of the data.

b. Find the least squares line for the given data using the model

$$y = \beta_0 + \beta_1 x + \varepsilon$$

(i.e., do not restrict β_0 to equal 0). Plot this line on the same scatterplot you constructed in part **a.**

c. Refer to part **b.** Why might $\hat{\beta}_0$ be different from 0 even though the true value of β_0 is known to be 0?

d. The estimated standard error of $\hat{\beta}_0$ is equal to

$$s\sqrt{\frac{1}{n} + \frac{\bar{x}^2}{SS_{xx}}}$$

Use the t-statistic

$$t = \frac{\hat{\beta}_0 - 0}{s\sqrt{(1/n) + (\bar{x}^2/SS_{xx})}}$$

to test the null hypothesis H_0: $\beta_0 = 0$ against the alternative H_a: $\beta_0 \neq 0$. Use $\alpha = .10$. Should you include β_0 in your model?

Critical Thinking Challenges

11.111 Comparing cost functions. Managers are interested in modeling past cost behavior in order to make more accurate predictions of future costs. Models of past cost behavior are called *cost functions*. Factors that influence costs are called *cost drivers* (Horngren, Datar, and Rajan, *Cost Accounting*, 2011). The cost data shown below are from a rug manufacturer. Indirect manufacturing labor costs consist of machine maintenance costs and setup labor costs. Machine-hours and direct manufacturing labor-hours are cost drivers. Your task is to estimate and compare two alternative cost functions for indirect manufacturing labor costs. In the first, machine-hours is the independent variable; in the second, direct manufacturing labor-hours is the independent variable. Prepare a report that compares the two cost functions and recommends which should be used to explain and predict indirect manufacturing labor costs. Be sure to justify your choice.

Week	Indirect Manufacturing Labor Costs	Machine-Hours	Direct Manufacturing Labor-Hours
1	$1,190	68	30
2	1,211	88	35
3	1,004	62	36
4	917	72	20
5	770	60	47
6	1,456	96	45
7	1,180	78	44
8	710	46	38
9	1,316	82	70
10	1,032	94	30
11	752	68	29
12	963	48	38

Source: Based on Horngren, C. T., Datar, S. M., & Rajan, M. *Cost Accounting: A Managerial Emphasis*, 14th ed. Upper Saddle River, N.J.: Prentice Hall, 2011.

11.112 Spall damage in bricks. A civil suit revolved around a five-building brick apartment complex located in the Bronx, New York, which began to suffer *spalling* damage (i.e., a separation of some portion of the face of a brick from its body). The owner of the complex alleged that the bricks were defectively manufactured. The brick manufacturer countered that poor design and shoddy management led to the damage. To settle the suit, an estimate of the rate of damage per 1,000 bricks, called the *spall rate*, was required (*Chance*, Summer 1994). The owner estimated the spall rate using several *scaffold-drop* surveys. (With this method, an engineer lowers a scaffold down at selected places on building walls and counts the number of visible spalls for every 1,000 bricks in the observation area.) The brick manufacturer conducted its own survey by dividing the walls of the complex into 83 wall segments and taking a photograph of each wall segment. (The number of spalled bricks that could be made out from each photo was recorded, and the sum over all 83 wall segments was used as an estimate of total spall damage.) In this court case, the jury was faced with the following dilemma: The scaffold-drop survey provided the most accurate estimate of spall rates in a given wall segment. Unfortunately, the drop areas were not selected at random from the entire complex; rather, drops were made at areas with high spall concentrations, leading to an overestimate of the total damage. On the other hand, the photo survey was complete in that all 83 wall segments in the complex were checked for spall damage. But the spall rate estimated by the photos, at least in areas of high spall concentration, was biased low (spalling damage cannot always be seen from a photo), leading to an underestimate of the total damage.

Drop Location	Drop Spall Rate (per 1,000 bricks)	Photo Spall Rate (per 1,000 bricks)
1	0	0
2	5.1	0
3	6.6	0
4	1.1	.8
5	1.8	1.0
6	3.9	1.0
7	11.5	1.9
8	22.1	7.7
9	39.3	14.9
10	39.9	13.9
11	43.0	11.8

Source: Fairley, W. B., et al. "Bricks, buildings, and the Bronx: Estimating masonry deterioration," *Chance*, Vol. 7. No. 3, Summer 1994, p. 36 (Figure 3). Reprinted with permission from *Chance*. © 1994 by the American Statistical Association. All rights reserved. [*Note:* The data points are estimated from the points shown on a scatterplot.]

The data in the table are the spall rates obtained using the two methods at 11 drop locations. Use the data, as did expert statisticians who testified in the case, to help the jury estimate the true spall rate at a given wall segment. Then explain how this information, coupled with the data (not given here) on all 83 wall segments, can provide a reasonable estimate of the total spall damage (i.e., total number of damaged bricks).

Activity 11.1 Applying Simple Linear Regression to Your Favorite Data

Many dependent variables in business serve as the subjects of regression modeling efforts. We list five such variables here:

1. Rate of return of a stock
2. Annual unemployment rate
3. Grade point average of an accounting student
4. Gross domestic product of the United States
5. Salary cap space available for your favorite NFL team

Choose one of these dependent variables, or choose some other dependent variable, for which you want to construct a prediction model. There may be a large number of independent variables that should be included in a prediction equation for the dependent variable you choose. List three potentially important independent variables, x_1, x_2, and x_3, that you think might be (individually) strongly related to your dependent variable. Next, obtain 25 data values, each of which consists of a measure of your dependent variable y and the corresponding values of x_1, x_2, and x_3.

a. Use the least squares formulas given in this chapter to fit three straight-line models–one for each independent variable–for predicting y.

b. Interpret the sign of the estimated slope coefficient $\hat{\beta}_1$ in each case, and test the utility of each model by testing $H_0: \beta_1 = 0$ against $H_a: \beta_1 \neq 0$. What assumptions must be satisfied to ensure the validity of these tests?

c. Calculate the coefficient of determination, r^2, for each model. Which of the independent variables predicts y best for the 25 sampled sets of data? Is this variable necessarily best in general (i.e., for the entire population)? Explain.

Be sure to keep the data and the results of your calculations, since you will need them for the Activity section in Chapter 12.

References

Chatterjee, S., & Price, B. *Regression Analysis by Example,* 2nd ed. New York: Wiley, 1991.

Draper, N., & Smith, H. *Applied Regression Analysis,* 3rd ed. New York: Wiley, 1987.

Gitlow, H., Oppenheim, A., & Oppenheim, R. *Quality Management: Tools and Methods for Improvement,* 2nd ed. Burr Ridge, Ill.: Irwin, 1995.

Graybill, F. *Theory and Application of the Linear Model.* North Scituate, Mass.: Duxbury, 1976.

Kleinbaum, D., & Kupper, L. *Applied Regression Analysis and Other Multivariable Methods,* 2nd ed. North Scituate, Mass.: Duxbury, 1997.

Kutner, M., Nachtsheim, C., Neter, J., & Li, W. *Applied Linear Statistical Models,* 5th ed. New York: McGraw-Hill, 2006.

Mendenhall, W. *Introduction to Linear Models and the Design and Analysis of Experiments.* Belmont, CA.: Wadsworth, 1968.

Mendenhall, W., & Sincich, T. A. *Second Course in Statistics: Regression Analysis,* 7th ed. Upper Saddle River, N.J.: Prentice Hall, 2011.

Montgomery, D., Peck, E., & Vining, G. *Introduction to Linear Regression Analysis,* 3rd ed. New York: Wiley, 2001.

Mosteller, F., & Tukey, J. W. *Data Analysis and Regression: A Second Course in Statistics.* Reading, Mass.: Addison-Wesley, 1977.

Rousseeuw, P. J., & Leroy, A. M. *Robust Regression and Outlier Detection.* New York: Wiley, 1987.

Weisburg, S. *Applied Linear Regression,* 2nd ed. New York: Wiley, 1985.

USING TECHNOLOGY Technology images shown here are taken from SPSS Statistics Professional 20.0, Minitab 16, XLSTAT for Pearson, and Excel 2010.

SPSS: Simple Linear Regression

Regression Analysis

Step 1 Access the SPSS spreadsheet file that contains the two quantitative variables (dependent and independent variables).

Step 2 Click on the "Analyze" button on the SPSS menu bar and then click on "Regression" and "Linear," as shown in Figure 11.S.1.

Figure 11.S.1 SPSS menu options for regression

Step 3 On the resulting dialog box (see Figure 11.S.2), specify the dependent variable in the "Dependent" box and the independent variable in the "Independent(s)" box. Be sure to select "Enter" in the "Method" box.

Figure 11.S.2 SPSS linear regression dialog box

Step 4 To produce confidence intervals for the model parameters, click the "Statistics" button and check the appropriate menu items in the resulting menu list.

Step 5 To obtain prediction intervals for y and confidence intervals for $E(y)$, click the "Save" button and check the appropriate items in the resulting menu list, as shown in Figure 11.S.3. (The prediction intervals will be added as new columns to the SPSS data spreadsheet.)

Figure 11.S.3 SPSS linear regression save dialog box

Step 6 To return to the main Regression dialog box from any of these optional screens, click "Continue." Click "OK" on the Regression dialog box to view the linear regression results.

Correlation Analysis

Step 1 Click on the "Analyze" button on the main menu bar and then click on "Correlate" (see Figure 11.S.1).

Step 2 Click on "Bivariate." The resulting dialog box appears in Figure 11.S.4.

Step 3 Enter the variables of interest in the "Variables" box and check the "Pearson" option.

Step 4 Click "OK" to obtain a printout of the correlation.

Figure 11.S.4 SPSS correlation dialog box

Minitab: Simple Linear Regression

Regression Analysis

Step 1 Access the Minitab worksheet file that contains the two quantitative variables (dependent and independent variables).

Step 2 Click on the "Stat" button on the Minitab menu bar and then click on "Regression" and "Regression" again, as shown in Figure 11.M.1.

Figure 11.M.1 Minitab menu options for regression

Step 3 On the resulting dialog box (see Figure 11.M.2), specify the dependent variable in the "Response" box and the independent variable in the "Predictors" box.

Figure 11.M.2 Minitab regression dialog box

Step 4 To produce prediction intervals for y and confidence intervals for $E(y)$, click the "Options" button. The resulting dialog box is shown in Figure 11.M.3.

Step 5 Check "Confidence limits" and/or "Prediction limits," specify the "Confidence level," and enter the value of x in the "Prediction intervals for new observations" box.

Figure 11.M.3 Minitab regression options

Step 6 Click "OK" to return to the main Regression dialog box and then click "OK" again to produce the Minitab simple linear regression printout.

Correlation Analysis

Step 1 Click on the "Stat" button on the Minitab main menu bar, then click on "Basic Statistics," and then click on "Correlation," as shown in Figure 11.M.4.

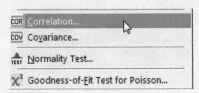

Figure 11.M.4 Minitab menu options for correlation

Step 2 On the resulting dialog box (see Figure 11.M.5), enter the two variables of interest in the "Variables" box.

Figure 11.M.5 Minitab correlation dialog box

Step 3 Click "OK" to obtain a printout of the correlation.

Excel/XLSTAT: Simple Linear Regression

Regression/Correlation Analysis

Step 1 First, create a workbook with two columns, one representing the quantitative dependent variable and the other the quantitative independent variable.

Step 2 Click the "XLSTAT" button on the Excel main menu bar, select "Modeling data," then click "Linear regression," as shown in Figure 11.E.1.

Figure 11.E.1 XLSTAT menu options for simple linear regression

Step 3 When the resulting dialog box appears (Figure 11.E.2), enter the column containing the dependent variable in the "Y / Dependent variables" box. Check the "Quantitative" option and then enter the column containing the independent variable in the "X / Explanatory variables" box.

Figure 11.E.2 XLSTAT dialog box for linear regression

Step 4 To obtain prediction/confidence intervals, select the "Prediction" tab, then enter the column with the values of the independent variable for which you want to make predictions in the "X / Explanatory variables" and "Quantitative" box, as shown in Figure 11.E.3.

Figure 11.E.3 XLSTAT dialog box for predictions

Step 5 Click "OK," then "Continue" to display the test results.

TI-84 Graphing Calculator: Simple Linear Regression

Finding the Least Squares Regression Equation

Step 1 *Enter the data*
- Press **STAT** and select **1:Edit**

Note: If a list already contains data, clear the old data.

- Use the up arrow to highlight the list name, "**L1**" or "**L2**"
- Press **CLEAR ENTER**
- Enter your *x*-data in **L1** and your *y*-data in **L2**

Step 2 *Find the equation*

- Press **STAT** and highlight **CALC**
- Press **4** for **LinReg(ax + b)**
- Press **ENTER**
- The screen will show the values for *a* and *b* in the equation $y = ax + b$.

Finding r and r^2

Use this procedure if r and r^2 do not already appear on the LinReg screen from part I:

Step 1 *Turn the diagnostics feature on*

- Press **2nd 0** for **CATALOG**
- Press the **ALPHA** key and x^{-1} for **D**
- Press the down **ARROW** until **DiagnosticsOn** is highlighted
- Press **ENTER** twice

Step 2 *Find the regression equation as shown in part I above*

The values for r and r^2 will appear on the screen as well.

Graphing the Least Squares Line with the Scatterplot

Step 1 *Enter the data as shown in part I above*

Step 2 *Set up the data plot*

- Press **Y=** and **CLEAR** all func
- Press **2nd Y=** for **STAT PLO**
- Press **1** for **Plot1**
- Set the cursor so that **ON** is flashing
- For **Type,** use the **ARROW** and **ENTER** keys to highlight and select the scatterplot (first icon in the first row)
- For **Xlist,** choose the column containing the *x*-data
- For **Ylist,** choose the column containing the *y*-data

Step 3 *Find the regression equation and store the equation in Y1*

- Press **STAT** and highlight **CALC**
- Press **4** for **LinReg (ax + b)** (Note: Don't press ENTER here because you want to store the regression equation in Y1.)
- Press **VARS**
- Use the right arrow to highlight **Y-VARS**
- Press **ENTER** to select **1:Function**
- Press **ENTER** to select **1:Y1**
- Press **ENTER**

Step 4 *View the scatterplot and regression line*

- Press **ZOOM** and then press **9** to select **9:ZoomStat**

You should see the data graphed along with the regression line.

12

CONTENTS

Where We've Been

- Introduced the straight-line model relating a dependent variable y to a single independent variable x
- Demonstrated how to estimate the parameters of the straight-line model using the method of least squares
- Showed how to statistically assess the adequacy of the model
- Showed how to use the model to Estimate E(y) and predict y for a given value of x

☐ Multiple Regression and Model Building

| STATISTICS in ACTION | **Bid Rigging in the Highway Construction Industry** |

In the United States, commercial contractors bid for the right to construct state highways and roads. A state government agency, usually the Department of Transportation (DOT), notifies various contractors of the state's intent to build a highway. Sealed bids are submitted by the contractors, and the contractor with the lowest bid (building cost) is awarded the road construction contract. The bidding process works extremely well in competitive markets but has the potential to increase construction costs if the markets are noncompetitive or if collusive practices are present. The latter occurred in the 1980s in Florida. Numerous road contractors either admitted or were found guilty of price fixing (i.e., setting the cost of construction above the fair, or competitive, cost through bid rigging or other means).

This Statistics in Action involves data collected by the Florida attorney general shortly following the price-fixing crisis. The attorney general's objective is to build a model for the cost (y) of a road construction contract awarded using the sealed-bid system. The **FLAG** file contains data for a sample of 235 road contracts. The variables measured for each contract are listed in Table SIA12.1. Ultimately, the attorney general wants to use the model to predict the costs of future road contracts in the state.

In several Statistics in Action Revisited sections in this chapter, we show how to analyze the data using a multiple regression analysis.

Table SIA12.1	Variables in the FLAG Data File	
Variable Name	Type	Description
CONTRACT	Quantitative	Road contract number
COST	Quantitative	Low bid contract cost (thousands of dollars)
DOTEST	Quantitative	DOT engineer's cost estimate (thousands of dollars)
STATUS	Qualitative	Bid status (1 = fixed, 0 = competitive)
B2B1RAT	Quantitative	Ratio of second lowest bid to low bid
B3B1RAT	Quantitative	Ratio of third lowest bid to low bid
BHB1RAT	Quantitative	Ratio of highest bid to low bid
DISTRICT	Qualitative	Location of road (1 = south Florida, 0 = north Florida)
BTPRATIO	Quantitative	Ratio of number of bidders to number of plan holders
DAYSEST	Quantitative	DOT engineer's estimate of number of workdays required

Data Set: FLAG

STATISTICS in ACTION REVISITED

- Evaluating a First-Order Model **(p. 687)**
- Variable Screening and Model Building **(p. 735)**
- A Residual Analysis **(p. 752)**

12.1 Multiple Regression Models

Most practical applications of regression analysis employ models that are more complex than the simple straight-line model. For example, a realistic probabilistic model for monthly sales revenue would include more than just the amount of advertising expenditure. Factors such as last month's sales, number of sales competitors, and advertising medium are some of the many variables that might be related to sales revenue. Thus, we would want to incorporate these and other potentially important independent variables into the model in order to make accurate predictions.

Probabilistic models that include more than one independent variable are called **multiple regression models.** The general form of these models is

$$y = \beta_0 + \beta_1 x_1 + \beta_2 x_2 + \cdots + \beta_k x_k + \varepsilon$$

The dependent variable *y* is now written as a function of *k* independent variables, $x_1, x_2, \ldots, x_k$. The random error term is added to make the model probabilistic rather than deterministic. The value of the coefficient β_i determines the contribution of the independent variable x_i, and β_0 is the *y*-intercept. The coefficients $\beta_0, \beta_1, \ldots, \beta_k$ are usually unknown because they represent population parameters.

At first glance it might appear that the regression model shown above would not allow for anything other than straight-line relationships between *y* and the independent variables, but this is not true. Actually, $x_1, x_2, \ldots, x_k$ can be functions of variables as long as the functions do not contain unknown parameters. For example, the monthly sales revenue, *y*, could be a function of the independent variables

$$x_1 = \text{Advertising expenditure}$$
$$x_2 = \text{Number of sales competitors}$$
$$x_3 = (x_1)^2$$
$$x_4 = 1 \text{ if TV advertising, 0 if not}$$

The x_3 term is called a **higher-order term** because it is the value of a quantitative variable (x_1) squared (i.e., raised to the second power). The x_4 term is a **coded variable** representing a qualitative variable (advertising medium). The multiple regression model is quite versatile and can be made to model many different types of response variables.

The General Multiple Regression Model*

$$y = \beta_0 + \beta_1 x_1 + \beta_2 x_2 + \cdots + \beta_k x_k + \varepsilon$$

where

y is the dependent variable.

$x_1, x_2, \ldots, x_k$ are the independent variables.

$E(y) = \beta_0 + \beta_1 x_1 + \beta_2 x_2 + \cdots + \beta_k x_k$ is the deterministic portion of the model.

β_i determines the contribution of the independent variable x_i.

Note: The symbols $x_1, x_2, \ldots, x_k$ may represent higher-order terms for quantitative predictors or terms that represent qualitative predictors.

As shown in the box, the steps used to develop the multiple regression model are similar to those used for the simple linear regression model.

Analyzing a Multiple Regression Model

Step 1 Hypothesize the deterministic component of the model. This component relates the mean, $E(y)$, to the independent variables $x_1, x_2, \ldots, x_k$. This involves the choice of the independent variables to be included in the model (Sections 12.2, 12.5–12.10).

Step 2 Use the sample data to estimate the unknown model parameters $\beta_0, \beta_1, \beta_2, \ldots, \beta_k$ in the model (Section 12.2).

Step 3 Specify the probability distribution of the random error term, ε, and estimate the standard deviation of this distribution, σ (Section 12.3).

Step 4 Check that the assumptions on ε are satisfied and make model modifications if necessary (Section 12.11).

Step 5 Statistically evaluate the usefulness of the model (Sections 12.3).

Step 6 When satisfied that the model is useful, use it for prediction, estimation, and other purposes (Section 12.4).

The assumptions we make about the random error ε of the multiple regression model are also similar to those in a simple linear regression (see Section 11.3). These are summarized below.

Assumptions for Random Error ε

For any given set of values of $x_1, x_2, \ldots, x_k$, the random error ε has a probability distribution with the following properties:

1. Mean equal to 0

2. Variance equal to σ^2

3. Normal distribution

4. Random errors are independent (in a probabilistic sense).

Throughout this chapter, we introduce several different types of models that form the foundation of **model building** (or useful model construction). In the next several sections, we consider the most basic multiple regression model, called the *first-order model.*

*Technically, this model is referred to as a general multiple *linear* regression model since the equation is a linear function of the β's.

PART I: FIRST-ORDER MODELS WITH QUANTITATIVE INDEPENDENT VARIABLES

12.2 Estimating and Making Inferences about the β Parameters

BIOGRAPHY

GEORGE U. YULE (1871–1951)
Yule Processes

Born on a small farm in Scotland, George Yule received an extensive childhood education. After graduating from University College (London), where he studied civil engineering, Yule spent a year employed in engineering workshops. However, he made a career change in 1893, accepting a teaching position back at University College under the guidance of statistician Karl Pearson (see p. 566). Inspired by Pearson's work, Yule produced a series of important articles on the statistics of regression and correlation. Yule is considered the first to apply the method of least squares in regression analysis, and he developed the theory of multiple regression. He eventually was appointed a lecturer in statistics at Cambridge University and later became the president of the prestigious Royal Statistical Society. Yule made many other contributions to the field, including the invention of time series analysis and the development of Yule processes and the Yule distribution.

A model that includes terms only for *quantitative* independent variables, called a **first-order model**, is described in the box. Note that the first-order model does not include any higher-order terms (such as x_1^2).

> **A First-Order Model in Five Quantitative Independent (Predictor) Variables***
>
> $$E(y) = \beta_0 + \beta_1 x_1 + \beta_2 x_2 + \beta_3 x_3 + \beta_4 x_4 + \beta_5 x_5$$
>
> where $x_1, x_2, \ldots, x_5$ are all quantitative variables that *are not* functions of other independent variables.
>
> *Note:* β_i represents the slope of the line relating y to x_i when all the other x's are held fixed.

The method of fitting first-order models—and multiple regression models in general—is identical to that of fitting the simple straight-line model: the **method of least squares**—that is, we choose the estimated model

$$\hat{y} = \hat{\beta}_0 + \hat{\beta}_1 x_1 + \cdots + \hat{\beta}_k x_k$$

that   (1) has an average error of prediction of 0, i.e., $\Sigma(y - \hat{y}) = 0$
and   (2) minimizes SSE $= (y - \hat{y})^2$

As in the case of the simple linear model, the sample estimates $\hat{\beta}_0, \hat{\beta}_1, \ldots, \hat{\beta}_k$ are obtained as a solution to a set of simultaneous linear equations.[†]

The primary difference between fitting the simple and multiple regression models is computational difficulty. The $(k + 1)$ simultaneous linear equations that must be solved to find the $(k + 1)$ estimated coefficients $\hat{\beta}_0, \hat{\beta}_1, \ldots, \hat{\beta}_k$ cannot be written in simple equation form; rather, the estimates are obtained using matrices and matrix algebra. Instead of presenting the complex matrix algebra required to fit the models, we resort to statistical software and present output from SPSS, Minitab, and Excel.

Example 12.1

Fitting a First-Order Model: Price of an Antique Clock

Problem A collector of antique grandfather clocks sold at auction believes that the price received for the clocks depends on both the age of the clocks and the number of bidders at the auction. Thus, he hypothesizes the first-order model

$$y = \beta_0 + \beta_1 x_1 + \beta_2 x_2 + \varepsilon$$

where

$$y = \text{Auction price (dollars)}$$
$$x_1 = \text{Age of clock (years)}$$
$$x_2 = \text{Number of bidders}$$

A sample of 32 auction prices of grandfather clocks, along with their age and the number of bidders, is given in Table 12.1.

a. Use scatterplots to plot the sample data. Interpret the plots.

b. Use the method of least squares to estimate the unknown parameters β_0, β_1, and β_2 of the model.

---

*The terminology *first order* is derived from the fact that each x in the model is raised to the first power.

[†]Students who are familiar with calculus should note that $\hat{\beta}_0, \hat{\beta}_1, \ldots, \hat{\beta}_k$ are the solutions to the set of equations $\partial \text{SSE}/\partial \hat{\beta}_0 = 0, \partial \text{SSE}/\partial \hat{\beta}_1 = 0, \ldots, \partial \text{SSE}/\partial \hat{\beta}_k = 0$. The solution is usually given in matrix form, but we do not present the details here. See the references for details.

Table 12.1	Auction Price Data				
Age, x_1	Number of Bidders, x_2	Auction Price, y	Age, x_1	Number of Bidders, x_2	Auction Price, y
127	13	$1,235	170	14	$2,131
115	12	1,080	182	8	1,550
127	7	845	162	11	1,884
150	9	1,522	184	10	2,041
156	6	1,047	143	6	845
182	11	1,979	159	9	1,483
156	12	1,822	108	14	1,055
132	10	1,253	175	8	1,545
137	9	1,297	108	6	729
113	9	946	179	9	1,792
137	15	1,713	111	15	1,175
117	11	1,024	187	8	1,593
137	8	1,147	111	7	785
153	6	1,092	115	7	744
117	13	1,152	194	5	1,356
126	10	1,336	168	7	1,262

Data Set: CLOCKS

c. Find the value of SSE that is minimized by the least squares method.

d. Estimate σ, the standard deviation of the model, and interpret the result.

Solution

a. Minitab side-by-side scatterplots for examining the bivariate relationships between y and x_1, and between y and x_2, are shown in Figure 12.1. Of the two variables, age (x_1) appears to have the stronger linear relationship with auction price (y).

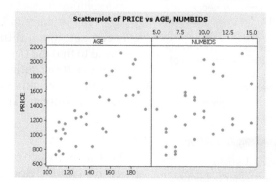

Figure 12.1

Minitab side-by-side scatterplots for the data of Table 12.1

b. The model hypothesized is fit to the data of Table 12.1 with Minitab. A portion of the printout is reproduced in Figure 12.2. The least squares estimates of the β parameters (highlighted) are $\hat{\beta}_0 = -1,339$, $\hat{\beta}_1 = 12.74$, and $\hat{\beta}_2 = 85.95$. Therefore, the equation that minimizes SSE for this data set (i.e., the **least squares prediction equation**) is

$$\hat{y} = -1,339 + 12.74x_1 + 85.95x_2$$

c. The minimum value of the sum of the squared errors, also highlighted in Figure 12.2, is SSE = 516,727.

d. Recall that the estimator of σ^2 for the straight-line model is $s^2 = \text{SSE}/(n-2)$, and note that the denominator is (n − number of estimated β parameters), which is ($n-2$) in the straight-line model. Because we must estimate the three parameters β_0, β_1, and β_2 for the first-order model, the estimator of σ^2 is

$$s^2 = \frac{\text{SSE}}{n-3} = \frac{\text{SSE}}{32-3} = \frac{516,727}{29} = 17,818$$

This value, often called the **mean square for error (MSE)**, is also highlighted at the bottom of the Minitab printout in Figure 12.2. The estimate of σ, then, is

$$s = \sqrt{17,818} = 133.5$$

Regression Analysis: PRICE versus AGE, NUMBIDS

```
The regression equation is
PRICE = - 1339 + 12.7 AGE + 86.0 NUMBIDS


Predictor    Coef   SE Coef      T       P
Constant   -1339.0    173.8   -7.70   0.000
AGE        12.7406   0.9047   14.08   0.000
NUMBIDS     85.953    8.729    9.85   0.000


S = 133.485   R-Sq = 89.2%   R-Sq(adj) = 88.5%


Analysis of Variance

Source        DF        SS       MS       F       P
Regression     2   4283063  2141531  120.19   0.000
Residual Error 29   516727    17818
Total         31   4799790
```

Figure 12.2

Minitab analysis of the auction price model

which is highlighted in the middle of the Minitab printout in Figure 12.2. One useful interpretation of the estimated standard deviation s is that the interval $\pm 2s$ will provide a rough approximation to the accuracy with which the model will predict future values of y for given values of x. Thus, we expect the model to provide predictions of auction price to within about $\pm 2s = \pm 2(133.5) = \pm 267$ dollars.*

Look Back As with simple linear regression, we will use the estimator of σ^2 both to check the utility of the model (Section 12.3) and to provide a measure of reliability of predictions and estimates when the model is used for those purposes (Section 12.4). Thus, you can see that the estimation of σ^2 plays an important part in the development of a regression model.

■ **Now Work Exercise 12.2a–c**

Estimator of σ^2 for a Multiple Regression Model with k Independent Variables

$$s^2 = \frac{\text{SSE}}{n - \text{number of estimated } \beta \text{ parameters}} = \frac{\text{SSE}}{n - (k + 1)}$$

After obtaining the least squares prediction equation, the analyst will usually want to make meaningful interpretations of the β estimates. Recall that in the straight-line model (Chapter 11)

$$y = \beta_0 + \beta_1 x + \varepsilon$$

β_0 represents the y-intercept of the line, and β_1 represents the slope of the line. From our discussion in Chapter 11, β_1 has a practical interpretation—it represents the mean change in y for every 1-unit increase in x. When the independent variables are quantitative, the β parameters in the first-order model specified in Example 12.1 have similar interpretations. The difference is that when we interpret the β that multiplies one of the variables (e.g., x_1), we must be certain to hold the values of the remaining independent variables (e.g., x_2, x_3) fixed.

To see this, suppose that the mean $E(y)$ of a response y is related to two quantitative independent variables, x_1 and x_2, by the first-order model

$$E(y) = 1 + 2x_1 + x_2$$

In other words, $\beta_0 = 1$, $\beta_1 = 2$, and $\beta_2 = 1$.

Now, when $x_2 = 0$, the relationship between $E(y)$ and x_1 is given by

$$E(y) = 1 + 2x_1 + (0) = 1 + 2x_1$$

---

*The $\pm 2s$ approximation will improve as the sample size is increased. We will provide more precise methodology for the construction of prediction intervals in Section 12.4.

A Minitab graph of this relationship (a straight line) is shown in Figure 12.3. Similar graphs of the relationship between $E(y)$ and x_1 for $x_2 = 1$,

$$E(y) = 1 + 2x_1 + (1) = 2 + 2x_1$$

and for $x_2 = 2$,

$$E(y) = 1 + 2x_1 + (2) = 3 + 2x_1$$

also are shown in Figure 12.3. Note that the slopes of the three lines are all equal to $\beta_1 = 2$, the coefficient that multiplies x_1.

Figure 12.3

Minitab graph of
$E(y) = 1 + 2x_1 + x_2$ for
$x_2 = 0, 1, 2$

Figure 12.3 exhibits a characteristic of all first-order models: If you graph $E(y)$ versus any one variable—say, x_1—for fixed values of the other variables, the result will always be a *straight line* with slope equal to β_1. If you repeat the process for other values of the fixed independent variables, you will obtain a set of *parallel* straight lines. This indicates that the effect of the independent variable x_i on $E(y)$ is independent of all the other independent variables in the model, and this effect is measured by the slope β_i (see the box on page 669).

A Minitab three-dimensional graph of the model $E(y) = 1 + 2x_1 + x_2$ is shown in Figure 12.4. Note that the model graphs as a plane. If you slice the plane at a particular value of x_2 (say, $x_2 = 0$), you obtain a straight line relating $E(y)$ to x_1 (e.g., $E[y] = 1 + 2x_1$). Similarly, if you slice the plane at a particular value of x_1, you obtain a straight line relating $E(y)$ to x_2. Because it is more difficult to visualize three-dimensional and, in general, k-dimensional surfaces, we will graph all the models presented in this chapter in two dimensions. *The key to obtaining these graphs is to hold fixed all but one of the independent variables in the model.*

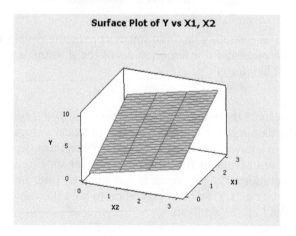

Figure 12.4

Minitab 3-dimensional graph of
$E(y) = 1 + 2x_1 + x_2$

Example 12.2

Interpreting the
β Estimates: Clock
Auction Price Model

Problem Refer to the first-order model for auction price *(y)* considered in Example 12.1. Interpret the estimates of the β parameters in the model.

Solution The least squares prediction equation, as given in Example 12.1, is $\hat{y} = -1,339 + 12.74x_1 + 85.95x_2$. We know that with first-order models, β_1 represents the slope of the line relating y to x_1 for fixed x_2. That is, β_1 measures the change in $E(y)$ for every 1-unit increase in x_1 when the other independent variable in the model is held fixed. A similar statement can be made about β_2: β_2 measures the change in $E(y)$ for every 1-unit increase in x_2 when the other x in the model is held fixed. Consequently, we obtain the following interpretations:

> $\hat{\beta}_1 = 12.74$: We estimate the mean auction price $E(y)$ of an antique clock to increase \$12.74 for every 1-year increase in age (x_1) when the number of bidders (x_2) is held fixed.

> $\hat{\beta}_2 = 85.95$: We estimate the mean auction price $E(y)$ of an antique clock to increase \$85.95 for every 1-bidder increase in the number of bidders (x_2) when age (x_1) is held fixed.

The value $\hat{\beta}_0 = -1{,}339$ does not have a meaningful interpretation in this example. To see this, note that $\hat{y} = \hat{\beta}_0$ when $x_1 = x_2 = 0$. Thus, $\hat{\beta}_0 = -1{,}339$ represents the estimated mean auction price when the values of all the independent variables are set equal to 0. Because an antique clock with these characteristics — an age of 0 years and 0 bidders on the clock — is not practical, the value of $\hat{\beta}_0$ has no meaningful interpretation.

Look Back In general, $\hat{\beta}_0$ will not have a practical interpretation unless it makes sense to set the values of the x's simultaneously equal to 0.

■ Now Work Exercise 12.14a, b

 CAUTION The interpretation of the β parameters in a multiple regression model will depend on the terms specified in the model. The interpretations above are for a first-order linear model only. In practice, you should be sure that a first-order model is the correct model for $E(y)$ before making these β interpretations. (We discuss alternative models for $E(y)$ in Sections 12.5–12.8.)

Inferences about the individual β parameters in a model are obtained using either a confidence interval or a test of hypothesis, as outlined in the following two boxes.*

A 100(1 − α)% Confidence Interval for a β Parameter

$$\hat{\beta}_i \pm t_{\alpha/2}s_{\hat{\beta}_i}$$

where $t_{\alpha/2}$ is based on $n - (k + 1)$ degrees of freedom and

$\quad n$ = Number of observations

$\quad k + 1$ = Number of β parameters in the model

Test of an Individual Parameter Coefficient in the Multiple Regression Model

One-Tailed Test	Two-Tailed Test
H_0: $\beta_i = 0$	H_0: $\beta_i = 0$
H_a: $\beta_i < 0$ [or H_a: $\beta_i > 0$]	H_a: $\beta_i \neq 0$

$$\text{Test statistic: } t = \frac{\hat{\beta}_i}{s_{\hat{\beta}_i}}$$

Rejection region: $t < -t_\alpha$	Rejection region: $|t| > t_{\alpha/2}$
[or $t > t_\alpha$ when H_a: $\beta_i > 0$]	

where t_α and $t_{\alpha/2}$ are based on $n - (k + 1)$ degrees of freedom and

$\quad n$ = Number of observations

$\quad k + 1$ = Number of β parameters in the model

---

*The formulas for computing $\hat{\beta}_i$ and its standard error are so complex that the only reasonable way to present them is by using matrix algebra. We do not assume a prerequisite of matrix algebra for this text, and, in any case, we think the formulas can be omitted in an introductory course without serious loss. They are programmed into almost all statistical software packages with multiple regression routines and are presented in some of the texts listed in the references.

> **Conditions Required for Valid Inferences about the β Parameters**
>
> Refer to the four assumptions about the probability distribution for the random error ε. (p. 668).

We illustrate these methods with another example.

Example   12.3

Inferences about the β Parameters—Auction Price Model

Problem Refer to Examples 12.1 and 12.2. The collector of antique grandfather clocks knows that the price (y) received for the clocks increases linearly with the age (x_1) of the clocks. Moreover, the collector hypothesizes that the auction price (y) will increase linearly as the number of bidders (x_2) increases. Use the information on the Minitab printout shown in Figure 12.2 (p. 671) to

a. Test the hypothesis that the mean auction price of a clock increases as the number of bidders increases when age is held constant, that is, test $\beta_2 > 0$. Use $\alpha = .05$.

b. Form a 90% confidence interval for β_1 and interpret the result.

Solution

a. The hypotheses of interest concern the parameter β_2. Specifically,

$$H_0: \beta_2 = 0$$
$$H_a: \beta_2 > 0$$

The test statistic is a t-statistic formed by dividing the sample estimate $\hat{\beta}_2$ of the parameter β_2 by the estimated standard error of $\hat{\beta}_2$ (denoted $s_{\hat{\beta}_2}$). These estimates, $\hat{\beta}_2 = 85.953$ and $s_{\hat{\beta}_2} = 8.729$, as well as the calculated t-value,

$$\textit{Test statistic: } t = \frac{\hat{\beta}_2}{s_{\hat{\beta}_2}} = \frac{85.953}{8.729} = 9.85$$

are highlighted on the Minitab printout in Figure 12.2.

The rejection region for the test is found in exactly the same way as the rejection regions for the t-tests in previous chapters—that is, we consult Table III in Appendix D to obtain an upper-tail value of t. This is a value t_α such that $P(t > t_\alpha) = \alpha$. We can then use this value to construct rejection regions for either one-tailed or two-tailed tests.

For $\alpha = .05$ and $n - (k + 1) = 32 - (2 + 1) = 29$ df, the critical t-value obtained from Table III is $t_{.05} = 1.699$. Therefore,

Rejection region: $t > 1.699$ (see Figure 12.5)

Because the test statistic value, $t = 9.85$, falls in the rejection region, we have sufficient evidence to reject H_0. Thus, the collector can conclude that the mean auction price of a clock increases as the number of bidders increases, when age is held constant. Note that the two-tailed observed significance level of the test is also highlighted on the printout. Because the one-tailed p-value (half this value) is p-value ≈ 0, any nonzero α (e.g., $\alpha = .01$) will lead us to reject H_0.

Figure 12.5

Rejection region for $H_0: \beta_2 = 0$ vs. $H_a: \beta_2 > 0$

b. A 90% confidence interval for β_1 is:

$$\hat{\beta}_1 \pm t_{\alpha/2}s_{\hat{\beta}_1} = \hat{\beta}_1 \pm t_{.05}s_{\hat{\beta}_1}$$

Substituting $\hat{\beta}_1 = 12.74$, $s_{\hat{\beta}_1} = .905$ (both obtained from the Minitab printout, Figure 12.2), and $t_{.05} = 1.699$ (from part **a**) into the equation, we obtain

$$12.74 \pm 1.699(.905) = 12.74 \pm 1.54$$

or (11.20, 14.28). Thus, we are 90% confident that β_1 falls between 11.20 and 14.28. Because β_1 is the slope of the line relating auction price (y) to age of the clock (x_1), we conclude that the price increases between \$11.20 and \$14.28 for every 1-year increase in age, holding number of bidders (x_2) constant.

Look Back When interpreting the β multiplied by one x, be sure to hold fixed the values of the other x's in the model.

◼ **Now Work Exercise 12.14c, d**

12.3 Evaluating Overall Model Utility

In Section 12.2, we demonstrated the use of t-tests in making inferences about β parameters in the multiple regression model. There are caveats, however, with conducting these t-tests for the purposes of determining which x's are useful for predicting y. Several of these are listed next.

> **Use Caution when Conducting t-Tests on the β Parameters**
>
> It is dangerous to conduct t-tests on the individual β parameters in a *first-order linear model* for the purpose of determining which independent variables are useful for predicting y and which are not. If you fail to reject H_0: $\beta_i = 0$, several conclusions are possible:
>
> **1.** There is no relationship between y and x_i.
>
> **2.** A straight-line relationship between y and x exists (holding the other x's in the model fixed), but a Type II error occurred.
>
> **3.** A relationship between y and x_i (holding the other x's in the model fixed) exists but is more complex than a straight-line relationship (e.g., a curvilinear relationship may be appropriate). The most you can say about a β parameter test is that there is either sufficient (if you reject H_0: $\beta_i = 0$) or insufficient (if you do not reject H_0: $\beta_i = 0$) evidence of a *linear (straight-line)* relationship between y and x_i.

In addition, conducting t-tests on each β parameter in a model is *not* the best way to determine whether the overall model is contributing information for the prediction of y. If we were to conduct a series of t-tests to determine whether the independent variables are contributing to the predictive relationship, we would be very likely to make one or more errors in deciding which terms to retain in the model and which to exclude.

For example, suppose you fit a first-order model in 10 quantitative x variables and decide to conduct t-tests on all 10 of the individual β's in the model, each at $\alpha = .05$. Even if all the β parameters (except β_0) are equal to 0, approximately 40% of the time you will incorrectly reject the null hypothesis at least once and conclude that some β parameter differs from 0.* Thus, in multiple regression models for which a large number

*The proof of this result (assuming independence of tests) proceeds as follows:

$P(\text{Reject } H_0 \text{ at least once} \mid \beta_1 = \beta_2 = \cdots = \beta_{10} = 0)$
$= 1 - P(\text{Reject } H_0 \text{ no times} \mid \beta_1 = \beta_2 = \cdots = \beta_{10} = 0)$
$\leq 1 - [P(\text{Accept } H_0: \beta_1 = 0 \mid \beta_1 = 0) \cdot P(\text{Accept } H_0: \beta_2 = 0 \mid \beta_2 = 0) \cdot \cdots \cdot P(\text{Accept } H_0: \beta_{10} = 0 \mid \beta_{10} = 0)]$
$= 1 - [(1 - \alpha)^{10}] = 1 - (.95)^{10} = .401$

For dependent tests, the Bonferroni inequality states that
$P(\text{Reject } H_0 \text{ at least once} \mid \beta_1 = \beta_2 = \cdots = \beta_{10} = 0) \leq 10(\alpha) = 10(.05) = .50.$

of independent variables are being considered, conducting a series of t-tests may include a large number of insignificant variables and exclude some useful ones. To test the utility of a multiple regression model, we need a *global test* (one that encompasses all the β parameters). We would also like to find some statistical quantity that measures how well the model fits the data.

We commence with the easier problem—finding a measure of how well a linear model fits a set of data. For this we use the multiple regression equivalent of r^2, the coefficient of determination for the straight-line model (Chapter 11), as shown in the box.

The **multiple coefficient of determination, R^2,** is defined as

$$R^2 = 1 - \frac{\text{SSE}}{\text{SS}_{yy}} = \frac{\text{SS}_{yy} - \text{SSE}}{\text{SS}_{yy}} = \frac{\text{Explained variablilty}}{\text{Total variability}}$$

Just like r^2 in the simple linear model, R^2 represents the fraction of the sample variation of the y values (measured by SS_{yy}) that is explained by the least squares prediction equation. Thus, $R^2 = 0$ implies a complete lack of fit of the model to the data, and $R^2 = 1$ implies a perfect fit, with the model passing through every data point. In general, the larger the value of R^2, the better the model fits the data.

To illustrate, the value $R^2 = .892$ for the auction price model of Examples 12.1–12.3 is highlighted on the SPSS printout for the analysis shown in Figure 12.6. This high value of R^2 implies that using the independent variables age and number of bidders in a first-order model explains 89.2% of the total *sample variation* (measured by SS_{yy}) in auction price (y). Thus, R^2 is a sample statistic that tells how well the model fits the data and thereby represents a measure of the usefulness of the entire model.

Model Summary

Model	R	R Square	Adjusted R Square	Std. Error of the Estimate
1	.945[a]	.892	.885	133.485

a. Predictors: (Constant), NUMBIDS, AGE

ANOVA[b]

Model		Sum of Squares	df	Mean Square	F	Sig.
1	Regression	4283062.960	2	2141531.480	120.188	.000[a]
	Residual	516726.540	29	17818.157		
	Total	4799789.500	31			

a. Predictors: (Constant), NUMBIDS, AGE

b. Dependent Variable: PRICE

Coefficients[a]

Model		Unstandardized Coefficients		Standardized Coefficients	t	Sig.	95% Confidence Interval for B	
		B	Std. Error	Beta			Lower Bound	Upper Bound
1	(Constant)	−1338.951	173.809		−7.704	.000	−1694.432	−983.471
	AGE	12.741	.905	.887	14.082	.000	10.890	14.591
	NUMBIDS	85.953	8.729	.620	9.847	.000	68.101	103.805

a. Dependent Variable: PRICE

Figure 12.6

SPSS analysis of the auction price model

A large value of R^2 computed from the *sample* data does not necessarily mean that the model provides a good fit to all of the data points in the *population*. For example, a first-order linear model that contains three parameters will provide a perfect fit to a sample of three data points, and R^2 will equal 1. Likewise, you will always obtain a perfect fit ($R^2 = 1$) to a set of n data points if the model contains exactly n parameters. Consequently, if you want to use the value of R^2 as a measure of how useful the model will be for predicting y, it should be based on a sample that contains substantially more data points than the number of parameters in the model.

⚠ **CAUTION** In a multiple regression analysis, use the value of R^2 as a measure of how useful a linear model will be for predicting y only if the sample contains substantially more data points than the number of β parameters in the model.

As an alternative to using R^2 as a measure of model adequacy, the *adjusted multiple coefficient of determination*, denoted R_a^2, is often reported. The formula for R_a^2 is shown in the box.

The **adjusted multiple coefficient of determination** is given by

$$R_a^2 = 1 - \left[\frac{(n-1)}{n-(k+1)} \right] \left(\frac{SSE}{SS_{yy}} \right)$$

$$= 1 - \left[\frac{(n-1)}{n-(k+1)} \right] (1 - R^2)$$

Note: $R_a^2 \leq R^2$

R^2 and R_a^2 have similar interpretations. However, unlike R^2, R_a^2 takes into account ("adjusts" for) both the sample size n and the number of β parameters in the model. R_a^2 will always be smaller than R^2 and, more importantly, cannot be "forced" to 1 by simply adding more and more independent variables to the model. Consequently, analysts prefer the more conservative R_a^2 when choosing a measure of model adequacy. The value of R_a^2 is also highlighted in Figure 12.6. Note that $R_a^2 = .885$, a value only slightly smaller than R^2.

Despite their utility, R^2 and R_a^2 are only sample statistics. Therefore, it is dangerous to judge the global usefulness of a model based solely on these values. A better method is to conduct a test of hypothesis involving *all* the β parameters (except β_0) in a model. In particular, for the general multiple regression model $E(y) = \beta_0 + \beta_1 x_1 + \beta_2 x_2 + \cdots + \beta_k x_k$, we would test

$$H_0: \beta_1 = \beta_2 = \cdots = \beta_k = 0$$

H_a: At least one of the coefficients is nonzero.

The test statistic used to test this hypothesis is an F-statistic, and several equivalent versions of the formula can be used (although we will usually rely on the computer to calculate the F-statistic):

$$\textit{Test statistic: } F = \frac{(SS_{yy} - SSE)/k}{SSE/[n-(k+1)]}$$

$$= \frac{\text{Mean Square (Model)}}{\text{Mean Square (Error)}} = \frac{R^2/k}{(1-R^2)/[n-(k+1)]}$$

These formulas indicate that the F-statistic is the ratio of the *explained* variability divided by the model degrees of freedom to the *unexplained* variability divided by the error degrees of freedom. Thus, the larger the proportion of the total variability accounted for by the model, the larger the F-statistic.

To determine when the ratio becomes large enough that we can confidently reject the null hypothesis and conclude that the model is more useful than no model at all for predicting y, we compare the calculated F-statistic to a tabulated F value with k df in the numerator and $[n-(k+1)]$ df in the denominator. Recall that tabulations of the F-distribution for various values of α are given in Tables V, VI, VII, and VIII in Appendix D.

Rejection region: $F > F_\alpha$, where F is based on k numerator and $n - (k + 1)$ denominator degrees of freedom.

The analysis of variance F-test for testing the usefulness of the model is summarized in the next box.

Testing Global Usefulness of the Model: The Analysis of Variance *F*-Test

$H_0: \beta_1 = \beta_2 = \cdots = \beta_k = 0$ (All model terms are unimportant for predicting y.)

H_a: At least one $\beta_i \neq 0$ (At least one model term is useful for predicting y.)

$$\text{Test statistic: } F = \frac{(SS_{yy} - SSE)/k}{SSE/[n - (k + 1)]} = \frac{R^2/k}{(1 - R^2)/[n - (k + 1)]}$$

$$= \frac{\text{Mean Square (Model)}}{\text{Mean Square (Error)}}$$

where n is the sample size and k is the number of terms in the model.

Rejection region: $F > F_\alpha$, with k numerator degrees of freedom and $[n - (k + 1)]$ denominator degrees of freedom.

Conditions Required for the Global *F*-Test in Regression to Be Valid

refer to the standard regression assumptions about the random error component (Section 12.1).

⚠ **CAUTION** A rejection of the null hypothesis $H_0: \beta_1 = \beta_2 = \cdots = \beta_k$ in the *global F-test* leads to the conclusion [with $100(1 - \alpha)\%$ confidence] that the model is statistically useful. However, statistically "useful" does not necessarily mean "best." Another model may prove even more useful in terms of providing more reliable estimates and predictions. This global *F*-test is usually regarded as a test that the model *must* pass to merit further consideration.

Example 12.4

Assessing Overall Adequacy—Clock Auction Price Model

Problem Refer to Examples 12.1–12.3, in which an antique collector modeled the auction price (y) of grandfather clocks as a function of the age of the clock (x_1) and the number of bidders (x_2). Recall that the hypothesized first-order model is

$$y = \beta_0 + \beta_1 x_1 + \beta_2 x_2 + \varepsilon$$

The SPSS printout for the analysis is shown in Figure 12.6 (p. 676).

a. Find and interpret the adjusted coefficient of determination R_a^2.

b. Conduct the global *F*-test of model usefulness at the $\alpha = .05$ level of significance.

Solution

a. The R_a^2 value (highlighted in Figure 12.6) is .885. This implies that the least squares model has explained about 88.5% of the total sample variation in y values (auction prices), after adjusting for sample size and number of independent variables in the model.

b. The elements of the global test of the model follow:

$H_0: \beta_1 = \beta_2 = 0$ (*Note: k = 2*)

H_a: At least one of the two model coefficients, β_1 and β_2, is nonzero.

$$\text{Test statistic: } F = \frac{\text{MS (Model)}}{\text{MSE}} = \frac{2,141,531}{17,818} = 120.19 \text{ (see Figure 12.6)}$$

p-value ≈ 0

Conclusion: Because $\alpha = .05$ exceeds the observed significance level, $(p \approx 0)$, the data provide strong evidence that at least one of the model coefficients is nonzero. The overall model appears to be statistically useful for predicting auction prices.

Look Back Can we be sure that the best prediction model has been found if the global F-test indicates that a model is useful? Unfortunately, we cannot. The addition of other independent variables may improve the usefulness of the model. (See the box on p. 678.) We consider more complex multiple regression models in Sections 12.5–12.8.

━━━━━━━━━━━━━━━━━━━━━━━━━━ ◼ **Now Work Exercise 12.15d–h**

In this section, we discussed several different statistics for assessing the utility of a multiple regression model: t-tests on individual β parameters, R^2, R_a^2, and the global F-test. Both R^2 and R_a^2 are indicators of how well the prediction equation fits the data. Intuitive evaluations of the contribution of the model based on R^2 must be examined with care. Unlike R_a^2, the value of R^2 increases as more and more variables are added to the model. Consequently, you could force R^2 to take a value very close to 1 even though the model contributes no information for the prediction of y. In fact, R^2 equals 1 when the number of terms in the model (including β_0) equals the number of data points. Therefore, you should not rely solely on the value of R^2 (or even R_a^2) to tell you whether the model is useful for predicting y.

Conducting t-tests on all of the individual β parameters is also not the best method of testing the global utility of the model because these multiple tests result in a high probability of making at least one Type I error. Use the F-test for testing the global utility of the model.

After we have determined that the overall model is useful for predicting y using the F-test, we may elect to conduct one or more t-tests on the individual β parameters. However, the test (or tests) to be conducted should be decided a priori—that is, prior to fitting the model. Also, we should limit the number of t-tests conducted to avoid the potential problem of making too many Type I errors. Generally, the regression analyst will conduct t-tests only on the "most important" β's. We provide insight in identifying the most important β's in a linear model in Sections 12.5–12.8.

Recommendation for Checking the Utility of a Multiple Regression Model

1. First, conduct a test of overall model adequacy using the F-test—that is, test

$$H_0: \beta_1 = \beta_2 = \cdots = \beta_k = 0$$

If the model is deemed adequate (that is, if you reject H_0), then proceed to step 2. Otherwise, you should hypothesize and fit another model. The new model may include more independent variables or higher-order terms.

2. Conduct t-tests on those β parameters in which you are particularly interested (that is, the "most important" β's). As we will see in Sections 12.5 and 12.6, these usually involve only the β's associated with higher-order terms (x^2, x_1x_2, etc.). However, it is a safe practice to limit the number of β's that are tested. Conducting a series of t-tests leads to a high overall Type I error rate α.

Exercises 12.1–12.24

Learning the Mechanics

12.1 Write a first-order model relating $E(y)$ to
  a. two quantitative independent variables.
  b. four quantitative independent variables.
  c. five quantitative independent variables.

12.2 Minitab was used to fit the model
  NW $\quad E(y) = \beta_0 + \beta_1x_1 + \beta_2x_2$ to $n = 20$ data points, and the printout shown on the next page was obtained.

a. What are the sample estimates of β_0, β_1, and β_2?
b. What is the least squares prediction equation?
c. Find SSE, MSE, and s. Interpret the standard deviation in the context of the problem.
d. Test $H_0: \beta_1 = 0$ against $H_0: \beta_1 \neq 0$. Use $\alpha = .05$.
e. Use a 95% confidence interval to estimate β_2.
f. Find R^2 and R_a^2 and interpret these values.
g. Find the test statistic for testing $H_0: \beta_1 = \beta_2 = 0$.
h. Find the observed significance level of the test, part **g**. Interpret the result.

Minitab output for Exercise 12.2

```
The regression equation is
Y = 506.35 - 941.9 X1 - 429.1 X2


Predictor    Coef   SE Coef     T      P
Constant   506.346   45.17   11.21  0.000
X1        -941.900  275.08   -3.42  0.003
X2        -429.060  379.83   -1.13  0.274


S = 94.251    R-Sq = 45.9%    R-Sq(adj) = 39.6%


Analysis of Variance

Source        DF     SS       MS      F      P
Regression     2   128329   64165   7.22  0.005
Residual Error 17  151016    8883
Total         19   279345
```

12.3 Suppose you fit the multiple regression model

$$y = \beta_0 + \beta_1 x_1 + \beta_2 x_2 + \beta_3 x_3 + \varepsilon$$

to $n = 30$ data points and obtain the following result:

$$\hat{y} = 3.4 - 4.6x_1 + 2.7x_2 + .93x_3$$

The estimated standard errors of $\hat{\beta}_2$ and $\hat{\beta}_3$ are 1.86 and .29, respectively.

a. Test the null hypothesis $H_0: \beta_2 = 0$ against the alternative hypothesis $H_a: \beta_2 \neq 0$. Use $\alpha = .05$.

b. Test the null hypothesis $H_0: \beta_3 = 0$ against the alternative hypothesis $H_a: \beta_3 \neq 0$. Use $\alpha = .05$.

c. The null hypothesis $H_0: \beta_2 = 0$ is not rejected. In contrast, the null hypothesis $H_0: \beta_3 = 0$ is rejected. Explain how this can happen even though $\hat{\beta}_2 > \hat{\beta}_3$.

12.4 Suppose you fit the first-order multiple regression model

$$y = \beta_0 + \beta_1 x_1 + \beta_2 x_2 + \varepsilon$$

to $n = 25$ data points and obtain the prediction equation

$$\hat{y} = 6.4 + 3.1x_1 + .92x_2$$

The estimated standard deviations of the sampling distributions of $\hat{\beta}_1$ and $\hat{\beta}_2$ are 2.3 and .27, respectively.

a. Test $H_0: \beta_1 = 0$ against $H_a: \beta_1 > 0$. Use $\alpha = .05$.

b. Test $H_0: \beta_2 = 0$ against $H_a: \beta_2 \neq 0$. Use $\alpha = .05$.

c. Find a 90% confidence interval for β_1. Interpret the interval.

d. Find a 99% confidence interval for β_2. Interpret the interval.

12.5 How is the number of degrees of freedom available for estimating σ^2 (the variance of ε) related to the number of independent variables in a regression model?

12.6 Consider the first-order model equation in three quantitative independent variables

$$E(y) = 1 + 2x_1 + x_2 - 3x_3$$

a. Graph the relationship between y and x_1 for $x_2 = 1$ and $x_3 = 3$.

b. Repeat part **a** for $x_2 = -1$ and $x_3 = 1$.

c. How do the graphed lines in parts **a** and **b** relate to each other? What is the slope of each line?

d. If a linear model is first-order in three independent variables, what type of geometric relationship will you obtain when $E(y)$ is graphed as a function of one of the independent variables for various combinations of values of the other independent variables?

12.7 Suppose you fit the first-order model

$$y = \beta_0 + \beta_1 x_1 + \beta_2 x_2 + \beta_3 x_3 + \beta_4 x_4 + \beta_5 x_5 + \varepsilon$$

to $n = 30$ data points and obtain

$$SSE = .33 \quad R^2 = .92$$

a. Do the values of SSE and R^2 suggest that the model provides a good fit to the data? Explain.

b. Is the model of any use in predicting y? Test the null hypothesis $H_0: \beta_1 = \beta_2 = \beta_3 = \beta_4 = \beta_5 = 0$ against the alternative hypothesis H_a: At least one of the parameters $\beta_1, \beta_2, \ldots, \beta_5$ is nonzero. Use $\alpha = .05$.

12.8 If the analysis of variance F-test leads to the conclusion that at least one of the model parameters is nonzero, can you conclude that the model is the best predictor for the dependent variable y? Can you conclude that all of the terms in the model are important for predicting y? What is the appropriate conclusion?

Applying the Concepts—Basic

12.9 Usability professionals salary survey. The Usability Professionals' Association (UPA) supports people who research, design, and evaluate the user experience of products and services. Recently, the UPA conducted a salary survey of its members (*UPA Salary Survey*, August 18, 2009). One of the report's authors, Jeff Sauro, investigated how much having a PhD affects salaries in this profession and discussed his analysis on the blog, www.measuringusability.com. Sauro fit a first-order multiple regression model for salary (y, in dollars) as a function of years of experience (x_1), PhD status ($x_2 = 1$ if PhD, 0 if not), and manager status ($x_3 = 1$ if manager, 0 if not). The following prediction equation was obtained:

$$\hat{y} = 52{,}484 + 2{,}941x_1 + 16{,}880x_2 + 11{,}108x_3$$

a. Predict the salary of a UPA member with 10 years of experience who does not have a PhD, but is a manager.

b. Predict the salary of a UPA member with 10 years of experience who does have a PhD, but is not a manager.

c. The following coefficient was reported: $R_a^2 = .32$. Give a practical interpretation of this value.

d. A 95% confidence interval for β_1 was reported as (2700, 3200). Give a practical interpretation of this result.

e. A 95% confidence interval for β_2 was reported as (11,500, 22,300). Give a practical interpretation of this result.

f. A 95% confidence interval for β_3 was reported as (7,600, 14,600). Give a practical interpretation of this result.

12.10 Forecasting movie revenues with Twitter. Refer to the *IEEE International Conference on Web Intelligence and Intelligent Agent Technology* (2010) study on using the volume of chatter on Twitter.com to forecast movie box office revenue, Exercise 11.23 (p. 617). Recall that opening weekend box office revenue data (in millions of dollars) were collected for a sample of 24 recent movies. In addition to each movie's *tweet rate*, i.e., the average number of tweets referring to the movie per hour 1 week prior to the movie's release, the researchers also computed the ratio of positive to negative tweets (called the *PN-ratio*).

a. Give the equation of a first-order model relating revenue (y) to both tweet rate (x_1) and PN-ratio (x_2).

b. Which β in the model, part **a,** represents the change in revenue (y) for every 1-tweet increase in the tweet rate (x_1), holding PN-ratio (x_2) constant?

c. Which β in the model, part **a,** represents the change in revenue (y) for every 1-unit increase in the PN-ratio (x_2), holding tweet rate (x_1) constant?

d. The following coefficients were reported: $R^2 = .945$ and $R_a^2 = .940$. Give a practical interpretation for both R^2 and R_a^2.

e. Conduct a test of the null hypothesis, $H_0: \beta_1 = \beta_2 = 0$. Use $\alpha = .05$.

f. The researchers reported the p-values for testing $H_0: \beta_1 = 0$ and $H_0: \beta_2 = 0$ as both less than .0001. Interpret these results (use $\alpha = .01$).

12.11 Accounting and Machiavellianism. Refer to the *Behavioral Research in Accounting* (Jan. 2008) study of Machiavellian traits (e.g., manipulation, cunning, duplicity, deception, and bad faith) in accountants, Exercise 9.8 (p. 492). Recall that a Mach rating score was determined for each in a sample of accounting alumni of a large southwestern university. For one portion of the study, the researcher modeled an accountant's Mach score (y) as a function of age, gender, education, and income. Data on $n = 198$ accountants yielded the results shown in the table.

Independent Variable	t-value for $H_0: \beta_i = 0$	p-value
Age (x_1)	0.10	> .10
Gender (x_2)	−0.55	> .10
Education (x_3)	1.95	< .01
Income (x_4)	0.52	> .10

Overall model: $R^2 = .13$, $F = 4.74$ (p-value < .01)

a. Conduct a test of overall model utility. Use $\alpha = .05$.

b. Interpret the coefficient of determination, R^2.

c. Is there sufficient evidence (at $\alpha = .05$) to say that income is a statistically useful predictor of Mach score?

12.12 Characteristics of lead users. During new product development, companies often involve "lead users," i.e., creative individuals who are on the leading edge of an important market trend. *Creativity and Innovation Management* (Feb. 2008) published an article on identifying the social network characteristics of lead users of children's computer games. Data were collected for $n = 326$ children, and the following variables were measured: lead-user rating (y, measured on a 5-point scale), gender ($x_1 = 1$ if female, 0 if male), age (x_2, years), degree of centrality (x_3, measured as the number of direct ties to other peers in the network), and between-ness centrality (x_4, measured as the number of shortest paths between peers). A first-order model for y was fit to the data, yielding the following least squares prediction equation:

$$\hat{y} = 3.58 + .01x_1 - .06x_2 - .01x_3 + .42x_4$$

a. Give two properties of the errors of prediction that result from using the method of least squares to obtain the parameter estimates.

b. Give a practical interpretation of the estimate of β_4 in the model.

c. A test of $H_0: \beta_4 = 0$ resulted in a p-value of .002. Make the appropriate conclusion at $\alpha = .05$.

12.13 Highway crash data analysis. Researchers at Montana State University have written a tutorial on an empirical method for analyzing before and after highway crash data (Montana Department of Transportation, Research Report, May 2004). The initial step in the methodology is to develop a Safety Performance Function (SPF)—a mathematical model that estimates crash occurrence for a given roadway segment. Using data collected for over 100 roadway segments, the researchers fit the model, $E(y) = \beta_0 + \beta_1 x_1 + \beta_2 x_2$, where $y =$ number of crashes per 3 years, $x_1 =$ roadway length (miles), and $x_2 =$ AADT $=$ average annual daily traffic (number of vehicles). The results are shown in the following tables.

Interstate Highways

Variable	Parameter Estimate	Standard Error	t-value
Intercept	1.81231	.50568	3.58
Length (x_1)	.10875	.03166	3.44
AADT (x_2)	.00017	.00003	5.19

Noninterstate Highways

Variable	Parameter Estimate	Standard Error	t-value
Intercept	1.20785	.28075	4.30
Length (x_1)	.06343	.01809	3.51
AADT (x_2)	.00056	.00012	4.86

a. Give the least squares prediction equation for the interstate highway model.

b. Give practical interpretations of the β estimates, part **a.**

c. Refer to part **a.** Find a 99% confidence interval for β_1 and interpret the result.

d. Refer to part **a.** Find a 99% confidence interval for β_2 and interpret the result.

e. Repeat parts **a–d** for the noninterstate highway model.

12.14 Predicting runs scored in baseball. In *Chance* (Fall 2000), statistician Scott Berry built a multiple regression model for predicting total number of runs scored by a Major League Baseball team during a season. Using data on all teams over a 9-year period (a sample of $n = 234$), the results in the following table were obtained.

Independent Variable	β Estimate	Standard Error
Intercept	3.70	15.00
Walks (x_1)	.34	.02
Singles (x_2)	.49	.03
Doubles (x_3)	.72	.05
Triples (x_4)	1.14	.19
Home runs (x_5)	1.51	.05
Stolen bases (x_6)	.26	.05
Caught stealing (x_7)	−.14	.14
Strikeouts (x_8)	−.10	.01
Outs (x_9)	−.10	.01

Source: Table from Berry, S. M. "A statistician reads the sports pages: Modeling offensive ability in baseball," *Chance*, Vol. 13, No. 4, Fall 2000, pp. 56–59 (Table 2). Reprinted with permission from *Chance*. © 2000 by the American Statistical Association. Reprinted with permission.

a. Write the least squares prediction equation for y = total number of runs scored by a team in a season.

b. Interpret, practically, the β estimates in the model.

c. Conduct a test of $H_0: \beta_7 = 0$ against $H_a: \beta_7 < 0$ at $\alpha = .05$. Interpret the results.

d. Form a 95% confidence interval for β_5. Interpret the results.

Applying the Concepts—Intermediate

12.15 Novelty of a vacation destination. Many tourists choose a

NW vacation destination based on the newness or uniqueness (i.e., the novelty) of the itinerary. Texas A&M University professor J. Petrick investigated the relationship between novelty and vacationing golfers' demographics (*Annals of Tourism Research*, Vol. 29, 2002). Data were obtained from a mail survey of 393 golf vacationers to a large coastal resort in the southeastern United States. Several measures of novelty level (on a numerical scale) were obtained for each vacationer, including "change from routine," "thrill," "boredom-alleviation," and "surprise." The researcher employed four independent variables in a regression model to predict each of the novelty measures. The independent variables were x_1 = number of rounds of golf per year, x_2 = total number of golf vacations taken, x_3 = number of years played golf, and x_4 = average golf score.

a. Give the hypothesized equation of a first-order model for y = change from routine.

b. A test of $H_0: \beta_3 = 0$ versus $H_a: \beta_3 < 0$ yielded a p-value of .005. Interpret this result if $\alpha = .01$.

c. The estimate of β_3 was found to be negative. Based on this result (and the result of part **b**), the researcher concluded that "those who have played golf for more years are less apt to seek change from their normal routine in their golf vacations." Do you agree with this statement? Explain.

d. The regression results for three dependent novelty measures, based on data collected for $n = 393$ golf vacationers, are summarized in the table below. Give the null hypothesis for testing the overall adequacy of the first-order regression model.

e. Give the rejection region for the test, part **d**, for $\alpha = .01$.

f. Use the test statistics reported in the table and the rejection region from part **e** to conduct the test for each of the dependent measures of novelty.

g. Verify that the p-values reported in the table support your conclusions in part **f.**

h. Interpret the values of R^2 reported in the table.

Dependent Variable	F-value	p-value	R^2
Thrill	5.56	< .001	.055
Change from routine	3.02	.018	.030
Surprise	3.33	.011	.023

Source: Based on Petrick, J. F. "An examination of golf vacationers' novelty," *Annals of Tourism Research*, Vol. 29, No. 2, 2002, pp. 384–400.

12.16 Arsenic in groundwater. *Environmental Science & Technology*

○ (Jan. 2005) reported on a study of the reliability of a com-

WELLS mercial kit to test for arsenic in groundwater. The field kit was used to test a sample of 328 groundwater wells in

Bangladesh. In addition to the arsenic level (micrograms per liter), the latitude (degrees), longitude (degrees), and depth (feet) of each well were measured. The data are saved in the file. (The first and last 5 observations are listed in the table below.)

Well ID	Latitude	Longitude	Depth	Arsenic
10	23.7887	90.6522	60	331
14	23.7886	90.6523	45	302
30	23.7880	90.6517	45	193
59	23.7893	90.6525	125	232
85	23.7920	90.6140	150	19
⋮	⋮	⋮	⋮	⋮
7353	23.7949	90.6515	40	48
7357	23.7955	90.6515	30	172
7890	23.7658	90.6312	60	175
7893	23.7656	90.6315	45	624
7970	23.7644	90.6303	30	254

a. Write a first-order model for arsenic level (y) as a function of latitude, longitude, and depth.

b. Fit the model to the data using the method of least squares.

c. Give practical interpretations of the β estimates.

d. Find the model standard deviation, s, and interpret its value.

e. Find and interpret the values of R^2 and R_a^2.

f. Conduct a test of overall model utility at $\alpha = .05$.

g. Based on the results, parts **d–f**, would you recommend using the model to predict arsenic level (y)? Explain.

12.17 Reality TV and cosmetic surgery. How much influence

◉ does the media, especially reality television programs,

BDYIMG have on one's decision to undergo cosmetic surgery? This was the question of interest to psychologists who published an article in *Body Image: An International Journal of Research* (March 2010). In the study, 170 college students answered questions about their impressions of reality TV shows featuring cosmetic surgery, level of self-esteem, satisfaction with one's own body, and desire to have cosmetic surgery to alter one's body. The variables analyzed in the study were measured as follows: DESIRE—scale ranging from 5 to 25, where the higher the value, the greater the interest in having cosmetic surgery; GENDER—1 if male, 0 if female; SELFESTM—scale ranging from 4 to 40, where the higher the value, the greater the level of self-esteem; BODYSAT—scale ranging from 1 to 9, where the higher the value, the greater the satisfaction with one's own body; and IMPREAL—scale ranging from 1 to 7, where the higher the value, the more one believes reality television shows featuring cosmetic surgery are realistic. The data for the study (simulated based on statistics reported in the journal article) are saved in the file. Selected observations are listed in the next table on page 683. The psychologists used multiple regression to model desire to have cosmetic surgery (y) as a function of gender (x_1), self-esteem (x_2), body satisfaction (x_3), and impression of reality TV (x_4).

a. Fit the first-order model, $E(y) = \beta_0 + \beta_1 x_1 + \beta_2 x_2 + \beta_3 x_3 + \beta_4 x_4$, to the data in the file. Give the least squares prediction equation.

b. Interpret the β estimates in the words of the problem.

Data for Exercise 12.17 (first and last five observations)

STUDENT	DESIRE	GENDER	SELFESTM	BODYSAT	IMPREAL
1	11	0	24	3	4
2	13	0	20	3	4
3	11	0	25	4	5
4	11	1	22	9	4
5	18	0	8	1	6
⋮	⋮	⋮	⋮	⋮	⋮
166	18	0	25	3	5
167	13	0	26	4	5
168	9	1	13	5	6
169	14	0	20	3	2
170	6	1	27	8	3

River	Mile	Species	Length	Weight	DDT
FC	5	CHANNELCATFISH	42.5	732	10.00
FC	5	CHANNELCATFISH	44.0	795	16.00
FC	5	CHANNELCATFISH	41.5	547	23.00
FC	5	CHANNELCATFISH	39.0	465	21.00
FC	5	CHANNELCATFISH	50.5	1,252	50.00
⋮	⋮	⋮	⋮	⋮	⋮
TR	345	LARGEMOUTHBASS	23.5	358	2.00
TR	345	LARGEMOUTHBASS	30.0	856	2.20
TR	345	LARGEMOUTHBASS	29.0	793	7.40
TR	345	LARGEMOUTHBASS	17.5	173	0.35
TR	345	LARGEMOUTHBASS	36.0	1,433	1.90

c. Is the overall model statistically useful for predicting desire to have cosmetic surgery? Test using $\alpha = .01$.

d. Which statistic, R^2 or R_a^2, is the preferred measure of model fit? Practically interpret the value of this statistic.

e. Conduct a test to determine whether desire to have cosmetic surgery decreases linearly as level of body satisfaction increases. Use $\alpha = .05$.

f. Find a 95% confidence interval for β_4. Practically interpret the result.

12.18 Contamination from a plant's discharge. Refer to the U.S. Army Corps of Engineers data (Example 1.5, p. 13) on fish contaminated from the toxic discharges of a chemical plant located on the banks of the Tennessee River in Alabama. Recall that the engineers measured the length (in centimeters), weight (in grams), and DDT level (in parts per million) for 144 captured fish. In addition, the number of miles upstream from the river was recorded. The data are saved in the file. (The first and last five observations are shown in the table in the next column.)

a. Fit the first-order model, $E(y) = \beta_0 + \beta_1 x_1 + \beta_2 x_2 + \beta_3 x_3$, to the data, where $y =$ DDT level, $x_1 =$ mile, $x_2 =$ length, and $x_3 =$ weight. Report the least squares prediction equation.

b. Find the estimate of the standard deviation of ε for the model and give a practical interpretation of its value.

c. Conduct a test of the global utility of the model. Use $\alpha = .05$.

d. Do the data provide sufficient evidence to conclude that DDT level increases as length increases? Report the observed significance level of the test and reach a conclusion using $\alpha = .05$.

e. Find and interpret a 95% confidence interval for β_3.

12.19 Cooling method for gas turbines. Refer to the *Journal of Engineering for Gas Turbines and Power* (Jan. 2005) study of a high-pressure inlet fogging method for a gas turbine engine, Exercise 7.40 (p. 378). Recall that the heat rate (kilojoules per kilowatt per hour) was measured for each in a sample of 67 gas turbines augmented with high-pressure inlet fogging. In addition, several other variables were measured, including cycle speed (revolutions per minute), inlet temperature (°C), exhaust gas temperature (°C), cycle pressure ratio, and air mass flow rate (kilograms per second). The data are saved in the file. (The first and last five observations are listed in the table at the bottom of the page.)

a. Write a first-order model for heat rate (y) as a function of speed, inlet temperature, exhaust temperature, cycle pressure ratio, and airflow rate.

b. Fit the model to the data using the method of least squares.

c. Give practical interpretations of the β estimates.

d. Find the model standard deviation, s, and interpret its value.

e. Conduct a test for overall model utility using $\alpha = .01$.

f. Find and interpret R_a^2.

g. Is there sufficient evidence (at $\alpha = .01$) to indicate that heat rate (y) is linearly related to inlet temperature?

Data for Exercise 12.19 (selected observations)

RPM	CP Ratio	Inlet Temp.	Exhaust Temp.	Airflow	Heat Rate
27,245	9.2	1,134	602	7	14,622
14,000	12.2	950	446	15	13,196
17,384	14.8	1,149	537	20	11,948
11,085	11.8	1,024	478	27	11,289
14,045	13.2	1,149	553	29	11,964
⋮	⋮	⋮	⋮	⋮	⋮
18,910	14.0	1,066	532	8	12,766
3,600	35.0	1,288	448	152	8,714
3,600	20.0	1,160	456	84	9,469
16,000	10.6	1,232	560	14	11,948
14,600	13.4	1,077	536	20	12,414

Source: Based on Bhargava, R., & Meher-Homji, C. B. "Parametric analysis of existing gas turbines with inlet evaporative and overspray fogging," *Journal of Engineering for Gas Turbines and Power*, Vol. 127, No. 1, Jan. 2005, pp. 145–158.

12.20 Extracting water from oil. In the oil industry, water that mixes with crude oil during production and transportation must be removed. Chemists have found that the oil can be extracted from the water/oil mix electrically. Researchers at the University of Bergen (Norway) conducted a series of experiments to study the factors that influence the voltage (y) required to separate the water from the oil (*Journal of Colloid and Interface Science*, Aug. 1995). The seven independent variables investigated in the study are listed in the table below. (Each variable was measured at two levels—a "low" level and a "high" level.) Sixteen water/oil mixtures were prepared using different combinations of the independent variables; then each emulsion was exposed to a high electric field. In addition, three mixtures were tested when all independent variables were set to 0. The data for all 19 experiments are saved in the file (selected observations are shown in the table at the bottom of the page).

a. Propose a first-order model for y as a function of all seven independent variables.

b. Use a statistical software package to fit the model to the data in the table.

c. Fully interpret the β estimates.

d. Evaluate the overall utility of the model at $\alpha = .10$.

12.21 Occupational safety study. An important goal in occupational safety is "active caring." Employees demonstrate active caring (AC) about the safety of their coworkers when they identify environmental hazards and unsafe work practices and then implement appropriate corrective actions for these unsafe conditions or behaviors. Three factors hypothesized to increase the propensity for an employee to actively care for safety are (1) high self-esteem, (2) optimism, and (3) group cohesiveness. *Applied & Preventive Psychology* (Winter 1995) attempted to establish empirical support for the AC hypothesis by fitting the model $E(y) = \beta_0 + \beta_1 x_1 + \beta_2 x_2 + \beta_3 x_3$, where

y = AC score (active caring score, 15-point scale)

x_1 = Self-esteem score

x_2 = Optimism score

x_3 = Group cohesion score

The regression analysis, based on data collected for $n = 31$ hourly workers at a large fiber-manufacturing plant, yielded a multiple coefficient of determination of $R^2 = .362$.

a. Interpret the value of R^2.

b. Use the R^2 value to test the global utility of the model. Use $\alpha = .05$.

12.22 R^2 and model fit. Because the coefficient of determination R^2 always increases when a new independent variable is added to the model, it is tempting to include many variables in a model to force R^2 to be near 1. However, doing so reduces the degrees of freedom available for estimating σ^2, which adversely affects our ability to make reliable inferences. Suppose you want to use 18 economic indicators to predict next year's gross domestic product (GDP). You fit the model

$$y = \beta_0 + \beta_1 x_1 + \beta_2 x_2 + \cdots + \beta_{17} x_{17} + \beta_{18} x_{18} + \varepsilon$$

where y = GDP and $x_1, x_2, \ldots, x_{18}$ are the economic indicators. Only 20 years of data ($n = 20$) are used to fit the model, and you obtain $R^2 = .95$. Test to see whether this impressive-looking R^2 is large enough for you to infer that the model is useful—that is, that at least one term in the model is important for predicting GDP. Use $\alpha = .05$.

Applying the Concepts—Advanced

12.23 Bordeaux wine sold at auction. The vineyards in the Bordeaux region of France are known for producing excellent red wines. However, the uncertainty of the weather during the growing season, the phenomenon that wine tastes better with age, and the fact that some Bordeaux vineyards produce better wines than others encourage speculation concerning the value of a case of wine produced by a certain vineyard during a certain year (or vintage). As a result, many wine experts attempt to predict the auction price of a case of Bordeaux wine. The publishers of a newsletter titled *Liquid Assets: The International Guide to Fine Wine* discussed a multiple regression approach to predicting the London auction price of red Bordeaux wine in *Chance* (Fall 1995). The natural logarithm of the price y (in dollars) of a case containing a dozen bottles of red wine was modeled as a function of weather during growing season and age of vintage using data collected for the vintages of 1952–1980. Three models were fit to the data. The results of the regressions are summarized in the table on the next page.

Data for Exercise 12.20 (selected observations)

Experiment Number	Voltage, y (kw/cm)	Disperse Phase Volume, x_1 (%)	Salinity, x_2 (%)	Temperature, x_3 (°C)	Time Delay, x_4 (hours)	Surfactant Concentration, x_5 (%)	Span: Triton, x_6	Solid Particles, x_7 (%)
1	.64	40	1	4	.25	2	.25	.5
2	.80	80	1	4	.25	4	.25	2
3	3.20	40	4	4	.25	4	.75	.5
4	.48	80	4	4	.25	2	.75	2
5	1.72	40	1	23	.25	4	.75	2
⋮	⋮	⋮	⋮	⋮		⋮		
16	.72	80	4	23	24	4	.75	2
17	1.08	0	0	0	0	0	0	0
18	1.08	0	0	0	0	0	0	0
19	1.04	0	0	0	0	0	0	0

Source: Based on Førdedal, H., et al. "A multivariate analysis of W/O emulsions in high external electric fields as studied by means of dielectric time domain spectroscopy," *Journal of Colloid and Interface Science*, Vol. 173, No. 2, Aug. 1995, p. 398 (Table 2).

Results for Exercise 12.23

Independent Variables	Beta Estimates (Standard Errors)		
	Model 1	Model 2	Model 3
x_1 = Vintage year	.0354 (.0137)	.0238 (.00717)	.0240 (.00747)
x_2 = Average growing season temperature(°C)	(not included)	.616 (.0952)	.608 (.116)
x_3 = Sept./Aug. rainfall (cm)	(not included)	−.00386 (.00081)	−.00380 (.00095)
x_4 = Rainfall in months preceding vintage (cm)	(not included)	.0001173 (.000482)	.00115 (.000505)
x_5 = Average Sept. temperature(°C)	(not included)	(not included)	.00765 (.565)
	$R^2 = .212$	$R^2 = .828$	$R^2 = .828$
	$s = .575$	$s = .287$	$s = .293$

a. For each model, conduct a t-test (at $\alpha = .05$) for each of the β parameters in the model. Interpret the results.

b. When the natural log of y is used as a dependent variable, the antilogarithm of a β coefficient minus 1—that is $e^{\beta_i} - 1$—represents the percentage change in y for every 1-unit increase in the associated x value. Use this information to interpret the β estimates of each model.

c. Based on the values of R^2 and s, which of the three models would you recommend for predicting Bordeaux wine prices? Explain.

12.24 Cost analysis for a shipping department. Multiple regression is used by accountants in cost analysis to shed light on the factors that cause costs to be incurred and the magnitudes of their effects. Sometimes, it is desirable to use physical units instead of cost as the dependent variable in a cost analysis (e.g., if the cost associated with the activity of interest is a function of some physical unit, such as hours of labor). The advantage of this approach is that the regression model will provide estimates of the number of labor hours required under different circumstances, and these hours can then be costed at the current labor rate (Horngren, Foster, and Datar, *Cost Accounting*, 2006). The sample data shown in the table below have been collected from a firm's accounting and production records to provide cost information about the firm's shipping department. These data are saved in the file. Consider the model

$$y = \beta_0 + \beta_1 x_1 + \beta_2 x_2 + \beta_3 x_3 + \varepsilon$$

a. Find the least squares prediction equation.

b. Use an F-test to investigate the usefulness of the model specified in part **a.** Use $\alpha = .01$ and state your conclusion in the context of the problem.

c. Test $H_0: \beta_2 = 0$ versus $H_a: \beta_2 \neq 0$ using $\alpha = .05$. What do the results of your test suggest about the magnitude of the effects of x_2 on labor costs?

d. Find R^2 and interpret its value in the context of the problem.

e. If shipping department employees are paid $7.50 per hour, how much less, on average, will it cost the company per week if the average number of pounds per shipment increases from a level of 20 to 21? Assume that x_1 and x_2 remain unchanged. Your answer is an estimate of what is known in economics as the *expected marginal cost* associated with a 1-pound increase in x_3.

f. With what approximate precision can this model be used to predict the hours of labor? [*Note:* The precision of multiple regression predictions is discussed in Section 12.4.]

g. Can regression analysis alone indicate what factors *cause* costs to increase? Explain.

Data for Exercise 12.24

Week	Labor, y (hr)	Pounds Shipped, x_1 (1,000s)	Percentage of Units Shipped by Truck, x_2	Average Shipment Weight, x_3(/lb)
1	100	5.1	90	20
2	85	3.8	99	22
3	108	5.3	58	19
4	116	7.5	16	15
5	92	4.5	54	20
6	63	3.3	42	26
7	79	5.3	12	25
8	101	5.9	32	21
9	88	4.0	56	24
10	71	4.2	64	29
11	122	6.8	78	10
12	85	3.9	90	30
13	50	3.8	74	28
14	114	7.5	89	14
15	104	4.5	90	21
16	111	6.0	40	20
17	110	8.1	55	16
18	100	2.9	64	19
19	82	4.0	35	23
20	85	4.8	58	25

12.4 Using the Model for Estimation and Prediction

In Section 11.6, we discussed the use of the least squares line for estimating the mean value of y, $E(y)$, for some particular value of x, say $x = x_p$. We also showed how to use the same fitted model to predict, when $x = x_p$, some new value of y to be observed in the future. Recall that the least squares line yielded the same value for both the estimate of $E(y)$ and the prediction of some future value of y—that is, both are the result of substituting x_p into the prediction equation $\hat{y} = \hat{\beta}_0 + \hat{\beta}_1 x$ and calculating $\hat{y}_p$. There the equivalence ends. The confidence interval for the mean $E(y)$ is narrower than the prediction interval for y because of the additional uncertainty attributable to the random error ε when predicting some future value of y.

These same concepts carry over to the multiple regression model. Consider a first-order model relating sale price (y) of a residential property to land value (x_1), appraised improvements value (x_2), and home size (x_3). Suppose we want to estimate the mean sale price for a given property with $x_1 = \$15,000$, $x_2 = \$50,000$, and $x_3 = 1,800$ square feet. Assuming that the first-order model represents the true relationship between sale price and the three independent variables, we want to estimate

$$E(y) = \beta_0 + \beta_1 x_1 + \beta_2 x_2 + \beta_3 x_3 = \beta_0 + \beta_1(15,000) + \beta_2(50,000) + \beta_3(1,800)$$

After obtaining the least squares estimates $\hat{\beta}_0, \hat{\beta}_1, \hat{\beta}_2$, and $\hat{\beta}_3$, the estimate of $E(y)$ will be

$$\hat{y} = \hat{\beta}_0 + \hat{\beta}_1(15,000) + \hat{\beta}_2(50,000) + \hat{\beta}_3(1,800)$$

To form a confidence interval for the mean, we need to know the standard deviation of the sampling distribution for the estimator $\hat{y}$. For multiple regression models, the form of this standard deviation is rather complex. However, the regression routines of statistical computer software packages allow us to obtain the confidence intervals for mean values of y for any given combination of values of the independent variables. We illustrate with an example.

Example 12.5

Estimating E(y) and Predicting y—Auction Price Model

Problem Refer to Examples 12.1–12.4 and the first-order model, $E(y) = \beta_0 + \beta_1 x_1 + \beta_2 x_2$, where y = auction price of a grandfather clock, x_1 = age of the clock, and x_2 = number of bidders.

a. Estimate the average auction price for all 150-year-old clocks sold at auction with 10 bidders using a 95% confidence interval. Interpret the result.

b. Predict the auction price for a single 150-year-old clock sold at an auction with 10 bidders using a 95% prediction interval. Interpret the result.

c. Suppose you want to predict the auction price for one clock that is 50 years old and has 2 bidders. How should you proceed?

Solution

a. Here, the key words *average* and *for all* imply we want to estimate the mean of y, $E(y)$. We want a 95% confidence interval for $E(y)$ when $x_1 = 150$ years and $x_2 = 10$ bidders. A Minitab printout for this analysis is shown in Figure 12.7. The confidence interval (highlighted under **"95% CI"**) is (1,381.4, 1,481.9). Thus, we are 95% confident that the mean auction price for all 150-year-old clocks sold at an auction with 10 bidders lies between \$1,381.40 and \$1,481.90.

b. The key words *predict* and *for a single* imply that we want a 95% prediction interval for y when $x_1 = 150$ years and $x_2 = 10$ bidders. This interval (highlighted under "95% PI" on the Minitab printout, Figure 12.7) is (1,154.1, 1,709.3). We say, with 95% confidence, that the auction price for a single 150-year-old clock sold at an auction with 10 bidders falls between \$1,154.10 and \$1,709.30.

c. Now, we want to predict the auction price, y, for a single (*one*) grandfather clock when $x_1 = 50$ years and $x_2 = 2$ bidders. Consequently, we desire a 95% prediction interval for y. However, before we form this prediction interval, we should check

Figure 12.7

Minitab printout with 95% confidence intervals for grandfather clock model

```
Regression Analysis: PRICE versus AGE, NUMBIDS

The regression equation is
PRICE = - 1339 + 12.7 AGE + 86.0 NUMBIDS

Predictor       Coef  SE Coef      T      P
Constant     -1339.0    173.8  -7.70  0.000
AGE          12.7406   0.9047  14.08  0.000
NUMBIDS       85.953    8.729   9.85  0.000

S = 133.485    R-Sq = 89.2%    R-Sq(adj) = 88.5%

Analysis of Variance

Source          DF        SS       MS       F      P
Regression       2   4283063  2141531  120.19  0.000
Residual Error  29    516727    17818
Total           31   4799790

Predicted Values for New Observations

New
Obs     Fit  SE Fit      95% CI            95% PI
  1  1431.7    24.6  (1381.4, 1481.9)  (1154.1, 1709.3)

Values of Predictors for New Observations

New
Obs  AGE  NUMBIDS
  1  150     10.0
```

to make sure that the selected values of the independent variables, $x_1 = 50$ and $x_2 = 2$, are both reasonable and within their respective sample ranges. If you examine the sample data shown in Table 12.1 (p. 670), you will see that the range for age is $108 \le x_1 \le 194$, and the range for number of bidders is $5 \le x_2 \le 15$. Thus, both selected values fall well *outside* their respective ranges. Recall the *Caution* box in Section 11.6 (p. 645) warning about the dangers of using the model to predict y for a value of an independent variable that is not within the range of the sample data. Doing so may lead to an unreliable prediction.

Look Back If we want to make the prediction requested in part **c,** we would need to collect additional data on clocks with the requested characteristics (i.e., $x_1 = 50$ years and $x_2 = 2$ bidders) and then refit the model.

■ **Now Work Exercise 12.29**

STATISTICS
in ACTION
REVISITED

Evaluating a First-Order Model

The Florida attorney general wants to develop a model for the cost (y) of a road construction contract awarded using the sealed-bid system and to use the model to predict the costs of future road contracts in the state. In addition to contract cost, the **FLAG** file contains data on eight potential predictor variables for a sample of 235 road contracts. (See Table SIA12.1 on p. 667.) Minitab scatterplots (with the dependent variable, COST, plotted against each of the potential predictors) for the data are shown in Figure SIA12.1. From the scatterplots, it appears that the DOT engineer's cost estimate (DOTEST) and estimate of work days (DAYSEST) would be good predictors of contract cost. [In a future Statistics in Action Revisited section (p. 735), we will learn that the two best predictors of contract cost are actually DOTEST and the fixed or competitive status (STATUS) of the contract.] However, in this section, we will fit the first-order regression model using all eight independent variables.

The Minitab printout for the regression analysis is shown in Figure SIA12.2. The global F-statistic ($F = 1{,}166.68$) and associated p-value (.000) shown on the printout indicate that the overall model is statistically useful for predicting construction cost. The value of R^2 indicates that the model can explain 97.6% of the sample variation in contract cost. Both of these results provide strong statistical support for using the model for estimation and prediction.

STATISTICS
in ACTION
REVISITED
CONTINUED

Figure SIA12.1

Minitab scatterplots for **FLAG** data

a.

b.

c.

```
The regression equation is
COST = 124 + 0.906 DOTEST - 147 B2B1RAT - 84 B3B1RAT - 59.1 BHB1RAT + 148 STA>>
       + 37.8 DISTRICT + 218 BTPRATIO + 0.344 DAYSEST


Predictor     Coef   SE Coef      T      P
Constant     123.9     426.8   0.29  0.772
DOTEST     0.90647   0.01659  54.64  0.000
B2B1RAT     -147.1     419.0  -0.35  0.726
B3B1RAT      -83.8     245.4  -0.34  0.733
BHB1RAT     -59.09     54.90  -1.08  0.283
STATUS      148.16     51.48   2.88  0.004
DISTRICT     37.75     43.07   0.88  0.382
BTPRATIO     217.6     139.6   1.56  0.120
DAYSEST     0.3439    0.1803   1.91  0.058


S = 304.589   R-Sq = 97.6%   R-Sq(adj) = 97.6%


Analysis of Variance

Source          DF         SS         MS        F      P
Regression       8  865907936  108238492  1166.68  0.000
Residual Error 226   20967037      92774
Total          234  886874973
```

Figure SIA12.2

Minitab regression output for first-order model of road construction cost

[*Note:* Not all of the independent variables have statistically significant *t*-values. However, we caution against dropping the insignificant variables from the model at this stage. One reason (discussed in Section 12.3) is that performing a large number of *t*-tests will yield an inflated probability of at least one Type I error. In later sections of this chapter, we develop other reasons for why the multiple *t*-test approach is not a good strategy for determining which independent variables to keep in the model.]

The Minitab printout shown in Figure SIA12.3 gives a 95% prediction interval for cost and a 95% confidence interval for the mean cost for the *x*-values associated with the last observation (contract) in the **FLAG** file. These *x*-values are engineer's cost estimate (DOTEST) = 497 thousand dollars, ratio of second lowest bid to lowest bid (B2B1RAT) = 1.07, ratio of third lowest bid to lowest bid (B3B1RAT) = 1.08, ratio of highest bid to lowest bid (BHB1RAT) = 1.19, competitive bid (STATUS = 0), south

Florida contract (DISTRICT = 1), bidders to planholders ratio (BTPRATIO) = 0.5, and estimated work days (DAYSEST) = 90. The 95% confidence interval of (339.2, 528.2) implies that for all road contracts with these x-values, the mean contract cost falls between 339.2 and 528.2 thousand dollars, with 95% confidence.

```
Predicted Values for New Observations

New
Obs    Fit  SE Fit       95% CI             95% PI
  1  433.7    48.0  (339.2, 528.2)   (-173.9, 1041.2)


Values of Predictors for New Observations

New
Obs  DOTEST  B2B1RAT  B3B1RAT  BHB1RAT    STATUS  DISTRICT  BTPRATIO  DAYSEST
  1     497     1.07     1.08     1.19  0.000000      1.00     0.500     90.0
```

Figure SIA12.3

Minitab printout with 95% confidence and prediction intervals

The 95% prediction interval of $(-173.9, 1{,}041.2)$ implies that for an individual road contract with these x-values, the contract cost falls between 0 (because cost cannot be negative) and 1,041.2 thousand dollars, with 95% confidence. Note the wide range of the prediction interval. This is due to the large magnitude of the model standard deviation, $s = 305$ thousand dollars. Although the model is deemed statistically useful for predicting contract cost, it may not be "practically" useful. To reduce the magnitude of s, we will need to improve the model's predictive ability. (We consider such a model in the next Statistics in Action Revisited section.)

Data Set: FLAG

Exercises 12.25–12.33

Applying the Concepts—Basic

12.25 Characteristics of lead users. Refer to the *Creativity and Innovation Management* (Feb. 2008) study of lead users of children's computer games, Exercise 12.12 (p. 681). Recall that the researchers modeled lead-user rating (y, measured on a 5-point scale) as a function of gender ($x_1 = 1$ if female, 0 if male), age (x_2, years), degree of centrality (x_3, measured as the number of direct ties to other peers in the network), and betweenness centrality (x_4, measured as the number of shortest paths between peers). The least squares prediction equation was $\hat{y} = 3.58 + .01x_1 - .06x_2 - .01x_3 + .42x_4$.

a. Compute the predicted lead-user rating of a 10-year-old female child with 5 direct ties to other peers in her social network and with 2 shortest paths between peers.

b. Compute an estimate for the mean lead-user rating of all 8-year-old male children with 10 direct ties to other peers and with 4 shortest paths between peers.

12.26 Predicting runs scored in baseball. Refer to the *Chance* (Fall 2000) study of runs scored in Major League Baseball games, Exercise 12.14 (p. 681). Multiple regression was used to model total number of runs scored (y) of a team during the season as a function of number of walks (x_1), number of singles (x_2), number of doubles (x_3), number of triples

(x_4), number of home runs (x_5), number of stolen bases (x_6), number of times caught stealing (x_7), number of strikeouts (x_8), and total number of outs (x_9). Using the β estimates given in Exercise 12.14, predict the number of runs scored by your favorite Major League Baseball team last year. How close is the predicted value to the actual number of runs scored by your team? [*Note:* You can find data on your favorite team on the Internet at www.mlb.com.]

12.27 Reality TV and cosmetic surgery. Refer to the *Body Image: An International Journal of Research* (March 2010) study of the impact of reality TV shows on one's desire to undergo cosmetic surgery, Exercise 12.17 (p. 682). Recall that psychologists used multiple regression to model desire to have cosmetic surgery (y) as a function of gender (x_1), self-esteem (x_2), body satisfaction (x_3), and impression of reality TV (x_4). The SPSS printout below shows a confidence interval for $E(y)$ for each of the first five students in the study.

a. Interpret the confidence interval for $E(y)$ for student 1.

b. Interpret the confidence interval for $E(y)$ for student 4.

12.28 Chemical plant contamination. Refer to Exercise 12.18 (p. 683) and the U.S. Army Corps of Engineers study. You DDT fit the first-order model, $E(y) = \beta_0 + \beta_1 x_1 + \beta_2 x_2 + \beta_3 x_3$,

	STUDENT	DESIRE	GENDER	SELFESTM	BODYSAT	IMPREAL	Lower95CL_Mean	Upper95CL_Mean
1	1	11	0	24	3	4	13.42	14.31
2	2	13	0	20	3	4	13.56	14.55
3	3	11	0	25	4	5	13.42	14.56
4	4	11	1	22	9	4	8.79	10.89
5	5	18	0	8	1	6	15.18	17.34

SPSS output for Exercise 12.27

XLSTAT output for Exercise 12.28

Predictions for the new observations:					
Observation	Pred(DDT)	Lower bound 90% (Mean)	Upper bound 90% (Mean)	Lower bound 90% (Observation)	Upper bound 90% (Observation)
MILE=300, LNGTH=40, WT=1000	18.8803	3.8650	33.8956	-143.2178	180.9784

to the data, where y = DDT level (parts per million), x_1 = number of miles upstream, x_2 = length (centimeters), and x_3 = weight (grams). Use the Excel/XLSTAT printout above to predict, with 90% confidence, the DDT level of a fish caught 300 miles upstream with a length of 40 centimeters and a weight of 1,000 grams. Interpret the result.

12.29 Cooling method for gas turbines. Refer to the *Journal of Engineering for Gas Turbines and Power* (Jan. 2005) study of a high-pressure inlet fogging method for a gas turbine engine, Exercise 12.19 (p. 683). Recall that you fit a first-order model for heat rate (y) as a function of speed (x_1), inlet temperature (x_2), exhaust temperature (x_3), cycle pressure ratio (x_4), and airflow rate (x_5). A Minitab printout with both a 95% confidence interval for $E(y)$ and prediction interval for y for selected values of the x's is shown below.
a. Interpret the 95% prediction interval for y in the words of the problem.
b. Interpret the 95% confidence interval for $E(y)$ in the words of the problem.
c. Will the confidence interval for $E(y)$ always be narrower than the prediction interval for y? Explain.

```
Predicted Values for New Observations

New
Obs     Fit  SE Fit       95% CI              95% PI
  1  12632.5   237.3  (12157.9, 13107.1)  (11599.6, 13665.5)


Values of Predictors for New Observations

New
Obs   RPM  INLET-TEMP  EXH-TEMP  CPRATIO  AIRFLOW
  1  7500       1000       525     13.5     10.0
```

Applying the Concepts—Intermediate

12.30 Arsenic in groundwater. Refer to the *Environmental Science & Technology* (Jan. 2005) study of the reliability of a commercial kit to test for arsenic in groundwater, Exercise 12.16 (p. 682). You fit a first-order model for arsenic level (y) as a function of latitude, longitude, and depth. Based on the model statistics, the researchers concluded that the arsenic level is highest at a low latitude, high longitude, and low depth. Do you agree? If so, find a 95% prediction interval for arsenic level for the lowest latitude, highest longitude, and lowest depth that are within the range of the sample data. Interpret the result.

12.31 Pay-for-performance efficiency of CEOs. In Chapter 1 (p. 4), we presented *Forbes* magazine's "Executive Compensation Scoreboard." *Forbes* (April 13, 2011) determined which CEOs are worth their pay based on a comparison of the firm's stock performance and the CEO's annual salary. Data for 175 of the top performers are saved in the file. Some of the variables measured for each CEO include pay-for-performance efficiency rating (x_1), value of shares owned (x_2), age (x_3), and the CEO's average salary over

the past 5 years (y). (Recall that the lower the efficiency rating, the more the CEO is worth his/her pay.) Consider the first-order model $E(y) = \beta_0 + \beta_1 x_1 + \beta_2 x_2 + \beta_3 x_3$.
a. Fit the model to the data and give the least squares prediction equation.
b. Conduct a test of overall model adequacy using $\alpha = .05$.
c. Predict, with 95% confidence, the 5-year pay of a CEO with $x_1 = 173$, $x_2 = \$102.9$ million, and $x_3 = 59$ years. (*Note:* These values represent the data for Sam Palmisano, CEO of IBM.) Interpret the result.

12.32 Extracting water from oil. Refer to Exercise 12.20 (p. 684) and the study on separating water from oil. The researchers concluded that "in order to break a water-oil mixture with the lowest possible voltage, the volume fraction of the disperse phase (x_1) should be high, while the salinity (x_2) and the amount of surfactant (x_5) should be low." Use this information and the first-order model of Exercise 12.20 to find a 95% prediction interval for this "low" voltage (y). Interpret the interval.

12.33 Boiler drum production. In a production facility, an accurate estimate of man-hours needed to complete a task is crucial to management in making such decisions as the proper number of workers to hire, an accurate deadline to quote a client, or cost-analysis decisions regarding budgets. A manufacturer of boiler drums wants to use regression to predict the number of man-hours needed to erect the drums in future projects. To accomplish this, data for 35 boilers were collected. In addition to man-hours (y), the variables measured were boiler capacity (x_1 = lb/hr), boiler design pressure (x_2 = pounds per square inch or psi), boiler type (x_3 = 1 if industry field erected, 0 if utility field erected), and drum type (x_4 = 1 if steam, 0 if mud). The data are saved in the file. (The first five and last five observations are listed in the accompanying table.)
a. Fit the model $E(y) = \beta_0 + \beta_1 x_1 + \beta_2 x_2 + \beta_3 x_3 + \beta_4 x_4$ to the data. Give the estimates of the β's.
b. Conduct a test for the global utility of the model. Use $\alpha = .01$.
c. Find a 95% confidence interval for $E(y)$ when $x_1 = 150,000$, $x_2 = 500$, $x_3 = 1$, and $x_4 = 0$. Interpret the result.

Man-Hours, y	Boiler Capacity, x_1	Design Pressure, x_2	Boiler Type, x_3	Drum Type, x_4
3,137	120,000	375	1	1
3,590	65,000	750	1	1
4,526	150,000	500	1	1
10,825	1,073,877	2,170	0	1
4,023	150,000	325	1	1
⋮	⋮	⋮	⋮	⋮
4,206	441,000	410	1	0
4,006	441,000	410	1	0
3,728	627,000	1,525	0	0
3,211	610,000	1,500	0	0
1,200	30,000	325	1	0

Source: Dr. Kelly Uscategui.

PART II: MODEL BUILDING IN MULTIPLE REGRESSION

12.5 Interaction Models

In Section 12.2, we demonstrated the relationship between $E(y)$ and the independent variables in a first-order model. When $E(y)$ is graphed against any one variable (say, x_1) for fixed values of the other variables, the result is a set of *parallel* straight lines (see Figure 12.3, p. 672). When this situation occurs (as it always does for a first-order model), we say that the relationship between $E(y)$ and any one independent variable *does not depend* on the values of the other independent variables in the model.

However, if the relationship between $E(y)$ and x_1 does, in fact, depend on the values of the remaining x's held fixed, then the first-order model is not appropriate for predicting y. In this case, we need another model that will take into account this dependence. Such a model includes the *cross products* of two or more x's.

For example, suppose that the mean value $E(y)$ of a response y is related to two quantitative independent variables, x_1 and x_2, by the model

$$E(y) = 1 + 2x_1 - x_2 + 3x_1x_2$$

A graph of the relationship between $E(y)$ and x_1 for $x_2 = 0, 1$, and 2 is displayed in the Minitab graph, Figure 12.8.

Figure 12.8

Minitab graphs of $1 + 2x_1 - x_2 + 3x_1x_2$ for $x_2 = 0, 1, 2$

Note that the graph shows three nonparallel straight lines. You can verify that the slopes of the lines differ by substituting each of the values $x_2 = 0, 1$, and 2 into the equation.

For $x_2 = 0$:

$$E(y) = 1 + 2x_1 - (0) + 3x_1(0) = 1 + 2x_1 \quad (\text{slope} = 2)$$

For $x_2 = 1$,

$$E(y) = 1 + 2x_1 - (1) + 3x_1(1) = 0 + 5x_1 \quad (\text{slope} = 5)$$

For $x_2 = 2$,

$$E(y) = 1 + 2x_1 - (2) + 3x_1(2) = -1 + 8x_1 \quad (\text{slope} = 8)$$

Note that the slope of each line is represented by $\beta_1 + \beta_3x_2 = 2 + 3x_2$. Thus, the effect on $E(y)$ of a change in x_1 (i.e., the slope) now *depends* on the value of x_2. When this situation occurs, we say that x_1 and x_2 **interact.** The cross-product term, x_1x_2, is called an **interaction term,** and the model $E(y) = \beta_0 + \beta_1x_1 + \beta_2x_2 + \beta_3x_1x_2$ is called an **interaction model** with two quantitative variables.

An Interaction Model Relating $E(y)$ to Two Quantitative Independent Variables

$$E(y) = \beta_0 + \beta_1x_1 + \beta_2x_2 + \beta_3x_1x_2$$

where

$(\beta_1 + \beta_3x_2)$ represents the change in $E(y)$ for every 1-unit increase in x_1, holding x_2 fixed

$(\beta_2 + \beta_3x_1)$ represents the change in $E(y)$ for every 1-unit increase in x_2, holding x_1 fixed

A three-dimensional graph (generated in Minitab) of the interaction model in two quantitative x's is shown in Figure 12.9. Unlike the flat planar surface displayed in Figure 12.4, the interaction model traces a ruled surface (twisted plane) in three-dimensional space. If we slice the twisted plane at a fixed value of x_2, we obtain a straight line relating $E(y)$ to x_1; however, the slope of the line will change as we change the value of x_2. Consequently, an interaction model is appropriate when the linear relationship between y and one independent variable depends on the value of another independent variable. The next example illustrates this idea.

Figure 12.9

Minitab 3-dimensional graph of $1 + 2x_1 - x_2 + 3x_1x_2$

Example **12.6**

Evaluating an Interaction Model—Clock Auction Prices

Problem Refer to Examples 12.1–12.4. Suppose the collector of grandfather clocks, having observed many auctions, believes that the *rate of increase* of the auction price with age will be driven upward by a large number of bidders. Thus, instead of a relationship like that shown in Figure 12.10a, in which the rate of increase in price with age is the same for any number of bidders, the collector believes the relationship is like that shown in Figure 12.10b. Note that as the number of bidders increases from 5 to 15, the slope of the price versus age line increases.

Consequently, the interaction model is proposed:

$$y = \beta_0 = \beta_1 x_1 + \beta_2 x_2 + \beta_3 x_1 x_2 + \varepsilon$$

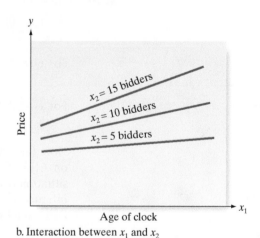

Figure 12.10

Examples of no-interaction and interaction models

a. No interaction between x_1 and x_2

b. Interaction between x_1 and x_2

The 32 data points listed in Table 12.1 (p. 670) were used to fit the model with interaction. A portion of the Minitab printout is shown in Figure 12.11.

a. Test the overall utility of the model using the global F-test at $\alpha = .05$.

b. Test the hypothesis (at $\alpha = .05$) that the price-age slope increases as the number of bidders increases—that is, that age and number of bidders, x_2, interact positively.

c. Estimate the change in auction price of a 150-year-old grandfather clock, y, for each additional bidder.

Regression Analysis: PRICE versus AGE, NUMBIDS, AGEBID

```
The regression equation is
PRICE = 320 + 0.88 AGE - 93.3 NUMBIDS + 1.30 AGEBID


Predictor    Coef   SE Coef      T      P
Constant    320.5    295.1    1.09   0.287
AGE         0.878    2.032     0.43   0.669
NUMBIDS    -93.26    29.89    -3.12   0.004
AGEBID     1.2978   0.2123     6.11   0.000


S = 88.9145   R-Sq = 95.4%   R-Sq(adj) = 94.9%


Analysis of Variance

Source          DF       SS        MS       F       P
Regression       3  4578427   1526142  193.04   0.000
Residual Error  28   221362      7906
Total           31  4799790
```

Figure 12.11

Minitab printout for interaction model of auction price

Solution

a. The global F-test is used to test the null hypothesis

$$H_0: \beta_1 = \beta_2 = \beta_3 = 0$$

The test statistic and p-value of the test (highlighted on the Minitab printout) are $F = 193.04$ and p-value $= 0$, respectively. Because $\alpha = .05$ exceeds the p-value, there is sufficient evidence to conclude that the model fit is a statistically useful predictor of auction price, y.

b. The hypotheses of interest to the collector concern the interaction parameter β_3. Specifically,

$$H_0: \beta_3 = 0$$
$$H_a: \beta_3 > 0$$

Because we are testing an individual β parameter, a t-test is required. The test statistic and two-tailed p-value (highlighted on the printout) are $t = 6.11$ and p-value $= 0$, respectively. The upper-tailed p-value, obtained by dividing the two-tailed p-value in half, is $0/2 = 0$. Because $\alpha = .05$ exceeds the p-value, the collector can reject H_0 and conclude that the rate of change of the mean price of the clocks with age increases as the number of bidders increases; that is, x_1 and x_2 interact positively. Thus, it appears that the interaction term should be included in the model.

c. To estimate the change in auction price, y, for every 1-unit increase in number of bidders, x_2, we need to estimate the slope of the line relating y to x_2 when the age of the clock, x_1, is 150 years old. An analyst who is not careful may estimate this slope as $\hat{\beta}_2 = -93.26$. Although the coefficient of x_2 is negative, this does *not* imply that auction price decreases as the number of bidders increases. Since interaction is present, the rate of change (slope) of mean auction price with the number of bidders *depends* on x_1, the age of the clock. For a fixed value of age (x_1), we can rewrite the interaction model as follows:

$$E(y) = \beta_0 + \beta_1 x_1 + \beta_2 x_2 + \beta_3 x_1 x_2 = \underbrace{(\beta_0 + \beta_1 x_1)}_{y\text{-intercept}} + \underbrace{(\beta_2 + \beta_3 x_1)}_{\text{slope}} x_2$$

Thus, the estimated rate of change of y for a 1-unit increase in x_2 (one new bidder) for a 150-year-old clock is

Estimated slope of the y versus x_2 line $= \hat{\beta}_2 + \hat{\beta}_3 x_1$

$$= -93.26 + 1.30(150) = 101.74$$

In other words, we estimate that the auction price of a 150-year-old clock will *increase* by about $101.74 for every additional bidder.

Look Back Although the rate of increase will vary as x_1 is changed, it will remain positive for the range of values of x_1 included in the sample. Extreme care is needed in interpreting the signs and sizes of coefficients in a multiple regression model.

◼ **Now Work Exercise 12.40**

Example 12.6 illustrates an important point about conducting t-tests on the β parameters in the interaction model. The key β parameter in this model is the interaction β, β_3. [Note that this β is also the one associated with the highest-order term in the model, x_1x_2.]* Consequently, we will want to test $H_0: \beta_3 = 0$ after we have determined that the overall model is useful for predicting y. Once interaction is detected (as in Example 12.6), however, tests on the first-order terms x_1 and x_2 should *not* be conducted because they are meaningless tests; the presence of interaction implies that both x's are important.

 CAUTION Once interaction has been deemed important in the model $E(y) = \beta_0 + \beta_1x_1 + \beta_2x_2 + \beta_3x_1x_2$, do not conduct t-tests on the β coefficients of the first-order terms x_1 and x_2. These terms should be kept in the model regardless of the magnitude of their associated p-values shown on the printout.

Exercises 12.34–12.48

Learning the Mechanics

12.34 Write an interaction model relating the mean value of y, $E(y)$ to
a. two quantitative independent variables
b. three quantitative independent variables [*Hint:* Include all possible two-way cross-product terms.]

12.35 Suppose the true relationship between $E(y)$ and the quantitative independent variables x_1 and x_2 is

$$E(y) = 3 + x_1 + 2x_2 - x_1x_2$$

a. Describe the corresponding three-dimensional response surface.
b. Plot the linear relationship between y and x_2 for $x_1 = 0, 1, 2$, where $0 \le x_2 \le 5$.
c. Explain why the lines you plotted in part **b** are not parallel.
d. Use the lines you plotted in part **b** to explain how changes in the settings of x_1 and x_2 affect $E(y)$.
e. Use your graph from part **b** to determine how much $E(y)$ changes when x_1 is changed from 2 to 0 and x_2 is simultaneously changed from 4 to 5.

12.36 Suppose you fit the interaction model

$$y = \beta_0 + \beta_1x_1 + \beta_2x_2 + \beta_3x_1x_2 + \varepsilon$$

to $n = 32$ data points and obtain the following results:

$$SS_{yy} = 479 \quad SSE = 21 \quad \hat{\beta}_3 = 10 \quad s_{\hat{\beta}_3} = 4$$

a. Find R^2 and interpret its value.
b. Is the model adequate for predicting y? Test at $\alpha = .05$.

c. Use a graph to explain the contribution of the x_1x_2 term to the model.
d. Is there evidence that x_1 and x_2 interact? Test at $\alpha = .05$.

12.37 The Minitab printout below was obtained from fitting the model

$$y = \beta_0 + \beta_1x_1 + \beta_2x_2 + \beta_3x_1x_2 + \varepsilon$$

to $n = 15$ data points.
a. What is the prediction equation for the response surface?
b. Describe the geometric form of the response surface of part **a**.

```
The regression equation is
Y = -2.55 + 3.82 X1 + 2.63 X2 -1.29 X1X2

Predictor    Coef   SE Coef      T      P
Constant   -2.550    1.142   -2.23  0.043
X1          3.815    0.529    7.22  0.000
X2          2.630    0.344    7.64  0.000
X1X2       -1.285    0.159   -8.06  0.000

S = 0.713    R-Sq = 85.6%    R-Sq(adj) = 81.6%

Analysis of Variance

Source         DF      SS      MS      F      P
Regression      3  33.149  11.050  21.75  0.000
Residual Error 11   5.587   0.508
Total          14  38.736
```

---

*The order of a term is equal to the sum of the exponents of the quantitative variables included in the term. Thus, when x_1 and x_2 are both quantitative variables, the cross product, x_1x_2, is a second-order term.

c. Plot the prediction equation for the case when $x_2 = 1$. Do this twice more on the same graph for the cases when $x_2 = 3$ and $x_2 = 5$.

d. Explain what it means to say that x_1 and x_2 interact. Explain why your graph of part **c** suggests that x_1 and x_2 interact.

e. Specify the null and alternative hypotheses you would use to test whether x_1 and x_2 interact.

f. Conduct the hypothesis test of part **e** using $\alpha = .01$.

Applying the Concepts—Basic

12.38 Tipping behavior in restaurants. By law, food servers at restaurants are not entitled to minimum wages since they are tipped by customers. Can food servers increase their tips by complimenting the customers they are waiting on? To answer this question, researchers collected data on the customer tipping behavior for a sample of 348 dining parties and reported their findings in the *Journal of Applied Social Psychology* (Vol. 40, 2010). Tip size (y, measured as a percentage of the total food bill) was modeled as a function of size of the dining party (x_1) and whether or not the server complimented the customers' choice of menu items (x_2). One theory states that the effect of size of the dining party on tip size is independent of whether or not the server compliments the customers' menu choices. A second theory hypothesizes that the effect of size of the dining party on tip size is greater when the server compliments the customers' menu choices as opposed to when the server refrains from complimenting menu choices.

a. Write a model for $E(y)$ as a function of x_1 and x_2 that corresponds to Theory 1.

b. Write a model for $E(y)$ as a function of x_1 and x_2 that corresponds to Theory 2.

c. The researchers summarized the results of their analysis with the following graph. Based on the graph, which of the two models would you expect to fit the data better? Explain.

12.39 Forecasting movie revenues with Twitter. Refer to the *IEEE International Conference on Web Intelligence and Intelligent Agent Technology* (2010) study on using the volume of chatter on Twitter.com to forecast movie box office revenue, Exercise 12.10 (p. 680). The researchers modeled a movie's opening weekend box office revenue (y) as a function of tweet rate (x_1) and ratio of positive to negative tweets (x_2) using a first-order model.

a. Write the equation of an interaction model for $E(y)$ as a function of x_1 and x_2.

b. In terms of the β's in the model, part **a**, what is the change in revenue (y) for every 1-tweet increase in the tweet rate (x_1), holding PN-ratio (x_2) constant at a value of 2.5?

c. In terms of the β's in the model, part **a,** what is the change in revenue (y) for every 1-tweet increase in the tweet rate (x_1), holding PN-ratio (x_2) constant at a value of 5.0?

d. In terms of the β's in the model, part **a,** what is the change in revenue (y) for every 1-unit increase in the PN-ratio (x_2), holding tweet rate (x_1) constant at a value of 100?

e. Give the null hypothesis for testing whether tweet rate (x_1) and PN-ratio (x_2) interact to affect revenue (y).

12.40 Role of retailer interest on shopping behavior. Retail interest is defined by marketers as the level of interest a consumer has in a given retail store. Marketing professors at the University of Tennessee at Chattanooga and the University of Alabama investigated the role of retailer interest in consumers' shopping behavior (*Journal of Retailing*, Summer 2006). Using survey data collected for $n = 375$ consumers, the professors developed an interaction model for $y =$ willingness of the consumer to shop at a retailer's store in the future (called *repatronage intentions*) as a function of $x_1 =$ consumer satisfaction and $x_2 =$ retailer interest. The regression results are shown below.

Variable	$\hat{\beta}$	t-value	p-value
Satisfaction (x_1)	.426	7.33	< .01
Retailer interest (x_2)	.044	0.85	> .10
Interaction (x_1x_2)	−.157	−3.09	< .01

$R^2 = .65$, $F = 226.35$, p-value < .001

a. Is the overall model statistically useful for predicting y? Test using $\alpha = .05$.

b. Conduct a test for interaction at $\alpha = .05$.

c. Use the β estimates to sketch the estimated relationship between repatronage intentions (y) and satisfaction (x_1) when retailer interest is $x_2 = 1$ (a low value).

d. Repeat part **c** when retailer interest is $x_2 = 7$ (a high value).

e. Sketch the two lines, parts **c** and **d,** on the same graph to illustrate the nature of the interaction.

12.41 Defects in nuclear missile housing parts. The technique of multivariable testing (MVT) was discussed in the *Journal of the Reliability Analysis Center* (First Quarter, 2004). MVT was shown to improve the quality of carbon-foam rings used in nuclear missile housings. The rings are produced via a casting process that involves mixing ingredients, oven curing, and carving the finished part. One type of defect analyzed was the number y of black streaks in the manufactured ring. Two variables found to impact the number of defects were turntable speed (revolutions per minute), x_1, and cutting-blade position (inches from center), x_2.

a. The researchers discovered "an interaction between blade position and turntable speed." Hypothesize a regression model for $E(y)$ that incorporates this interaction.

b. The researchers reported a positive linear relationship between number of defects (y) and turntable speed (x_1)

but found that the slope of the relationship was much steeper for lower values of cutting-blade position (x_2). What does this imply about the interaction term in the model, part **a**? Explain.

12.42 Consumer behavior while waiting in line. While waiting in a long line for service (e.g., to use an ATM or at the post office), at some point you may decide to leave the queue. The *Journal of Consumer Research* (Nov. 2003) published a study of consumer behavior while waiting in a queue. A sample of $n = 148$ college students was asked to imagine that they were waiting in line at a post office to mail a package and that the estimated waiting time is 10 minutes or less. After a 10-minute wait, students were asked about their level of negative feelings (annoyed, anxious) on a scale of 1 (strongly disagree) to 9 (strongly agree). Before answering, however, the students were informed about how many people were ahead of them and behind them in the line. The researchers used regression to relate negative feelings score (y) to number ahead in line (x_1) and number behind in line (x_2).

a. The researchers fit an interaction model to the data. Write the hypothesized equation of this model.

b. In the words of the problem, explain what it means to say that "x_1 and x_2 interact to affect y."

c. A t-test for the interaction β in the model resulted in a p-value greater than .25. Interpret this result.

d. From their analysis, the researchers concluded that "the greater the number of people ahead, the higher the negative feeling score" and "the greater the number of people behind, the lower the negative feeling score." Use this information to determine the signs of β_1 and β_2 in the model.

Applying the Concepts—Intermediate

12.43 Reality TV and cosmetic surgery. Refer to the *Body Image: An International Journal of Research* (March 2010) study of BDYIMG the impact of reality TV shows on a college student's decision to undergo cosmetic surgery, Exercise 12.17 (p. 682). Recall

that the data for the study (simulated based on statistics reported in the journal article) are saved in the file. Consider the interaction model, $E(y) = \beta_0 + \beta_1 x_1 + \beta_2 x_4 + \beta_3 x_1 x_4$, where y = desire to have cosmetic surgery (25-point scale), x_1 = {1 if male, 0 if female}, and x_4 = impression of reality TV (7-point scale). The model was fit to the data and the resulting SPSS printout appears at the bottom of the page.

a. Give the least squares prediction equation.

b. Find the predicted level of desire (y) for a male college student with an impression-of-reality-TV-scale score of 5.

c. Conduct a test of overall model adequacy. Use $\alpha = .10$.

d. Give a practical interpretation of R_a^2.

e. Give a practical interpretation of s.

f. Conduct a test (at $\alpha = .10$) to determine if gender (x_1) and impression of reality TV show (x_4) interact in the prediction of level of desire for cosmetic surgery (y).

12.44 Factors that impact an auditor's judgment. A study was conducted to determine the effects of linguistic delivery style and client credibility on auditors' judgments (*Advances in Accounting and Behavioral Research*, 2004). Two hundred auditors from Big 5 accounting firms were each asked to assume that he or she was an audit team supervisor of a new manufacturing client and was performing an analytical review of the client's financial statement. The researchers gave the auditors different information on the client's credibility and linguistic delivery style of the client's explanation. Each auditor then provided an assessment of the likelihood that the client-provided explanation accounted for the fluctuation in the financial statement. The three variables of interest—credibility (x_1), linguistic delivery style (x_2), and likelihood (y)—were all measured on a numerical scale. Regression analysis was used to fit the interaction model, $y = \beta_0 + \beta_1 x_1 + \beta_2 x_2 + \beta_3 x_1 x_2 + \varepsilon$. The results are summarized in the table on the next page.

Model Summary

Model	R	R Square	Adjusted R Square	Std. Error of the Estimate
1	.670[a]	.449	.439	2.350

a. Predictors: (Constant), GENDER_IMPREAL, IMPREAL, GENDER

ANOVA[a]

Model		Sum of Squares	df	Mean Square	F	Sig.
1	Regression	747.001	3	249.000	45.086	.000[b]
	Residual	916.787	166	5.523		
	Total	1663.788	169			

a. Dependent Variable: DESIRE

b. Predictors: (Constant), GENDER_IMPREAL, IMPREAL, GENDER

Coefficients[a]

Model		Unstandardized Coefficients		Standardized Coefficients		
		B	Std. Error	Beta	t	Sig.
1	(Constant)	11.779	.674		17.486	.000
	GENDER	−1.972	1.179	−.303	−1.672	.096
	IMPREAL	.585	.162	.258	3.617	.000
	GENDER_IMPREAL	−.553	.276	−.378	−2.004	.047

a. Dependent Variable: DESIRE

SPSS output for Exercise 12.43

Results for Exercise 12.44

	Beta Estimate	Std Error	t-statistic	p-value
Constant	15.865	10.980	1.445	0.150
Client credibility (x_1)	0.037	0.339	0.110	0.913
Linguistic delivery style (x_2)	−0.678	0.328	−2.064	0.040
Interaction (x_1x_2)	0.036	0.009	4.008	< 0.005

F-statistic = 55.35 $(p < 0.0005)$: $R_a^2 = .450$

a. Interpret the phrase *client credibility and linguistic delivery style interact* in the words of the problem.

b. Give the null and alternative hypotheses for testing the overall adequacy of the model.

c. Conduct the test, part **b**, using the information in the table.

d. Give the null and alternative hypotheses for testing whether client credibility and linguistic delivery style interact.

e. Conduct the test, part **d**, using the information in the table.

f. The researchers estimated the slope of the likelihood–linguistic delivery style line at a low level of client credibility $(x_1 = 22)$. Obtain this estimate and interpret it in the words of the problem.

g. The researchers also estimated the slope of the likelihood–linguistic delivery style line at a high level of client credibility $(x_1 = 46)$. Obtain this estimate and interpret it in the words of the problem.

12.45 Arsenic in groundwater. Refer to the *Environmental Science & Technology* (Jan. 2005) study of the reliability of a commercial kit to test for arsenic in groundwater, Exercise 12.16 (p. 682). Recall that you fit a first-order model for arsenic level (y) as a function of latitude (x_1), longitude (x_2), and depth (x_3).

a. Write a model for arsenic level (y) that includes first-order terms for latitude, longitude, and depth, as well as terms for interaction between latitude and depth and interaction between longitude and depth.

b. Use statistical software to fit the interaction model, part **a**, to the data. Give the least squares prediction equation.

c. Conduct a test (at $\alpha = .05$) to determine whether latitude and depth interact to affect arsenic level.

d. Conduct a test (at $\alpha = .05$) to determine whether longitude and depth interact to affect arsenic level.

e. Practically interpret the results of the tests, parts **c** and **d**.

12.46 Cooling method for gas turbines. Refer to the *Journal of Engineering for Gas Turbines and Power* (Jan. 2005) study of a high-pressure inlet fogging method for a gas turbine engine, Exercise 12.19 (p. 683). Recall that you fit a first-order model for heat rate (y) as a function of speed (x_1), inlet temperature (x_2), exhaust temperature (x_3), cycle pressure ratio (x_4), and airflow rate (x_5).

a. Researchers hypothesize that the linear relationship between heat rate (y) and temperature (both inlet and exhaust) depends on airflow rate. Write a model for heat rate that incorporates the researchers' theories.

b. Use statistical software to fit the interaction model, part **a**, to the data. Give the least squares prediction equation.

c. Conduct a test (at $\alpha = .05$) to determine whether inlet temperature and airflow rate interact to affect heat rate.

d. Conduct a test (at $\alpha = .05$) to determine whether exhaust temperature and airflow rate interact to affect heat rate.

e. Practically interpret the results of the tests, parts **c** and **d**.

12.47 Extracting water from oil. Refer to the *Journal of Colloid and Interface Science* study of water/oil mixtures, Exercise 12.20 (p. 684). Recall that three of the seven variables used to predict voltage (y) were volume (x_1), salinity (x_2), and surfactant concentration (x_5). The model the researchers fit is

$$E(y) = \beta_0 + \beta_1x_1 + \beta_2x_2 + \beta_3x_5 + \beta_4x_1x_2 + \beta_5x_1x_5$$

a. Note that the model includes interaction between disperse phase volume (x_1) and salinity (x_2) as well as interaction between disperse phase volume (x_1) and surfactant concentration (x_5). Discuss how these interaction terms affect the hypothetical relationship between y and x_1. Draw a sketch to support your answer.

b. Fit the interaction model to the data. Does this model appear to fit the data better than the first-order model in Exercise 12.20? Explain.

c. Interpret the β estimates of the interaction model.

12.48 Therapists' reactions to child-abuse reports. Licensed therapists are mandated by law to report child abuse by their clients. This requires the therapist to breach confidentiality and possibly lose the client's trust. A national survey of licensed psychotherapists was conducted to investigate clients' reactions to legally mandated child-abuse reports (*American Journal of Orthopsychiatry,* Jan. 1997). The sample consisted of 303 therapists who had filed a child-abuse report against one of their clients. The researchers were interested in finding the best predictors of a client's reaction (y) to the report, where y is measured on a 30-point scale. (The higher the value, the more favorable the client's response to the report.) The independent variables found to have the most predictive power are listed here.

x_1 = Therapist's age (years)

x_2 = Therapist's gender (1 if male, 0 if female)

x_3 = Degree of therapist's role strain (25-point scale)

x_4 = Strength of client-therapist relationship (40-point scale)

x_5 = Type of case (1 if family, 0 if not)

x_1x_2 = Age × gender interaction

a. Hypothesize a first-order model relating y to each of the five independent variables.

b. Give the null hypothesis for testing the contribution of x_4, strength of client-therapist relationship, to the model.

c. The test statistic for the test, part **b**, was $t = 4.408$ with an associated p-value of .001. Interpret this result.

d. The estimated β coefficient for the x_1x_2 interaction term was positive and highly significant $(p < .001)$. According to the researchers, "This interaction suggests that … as the age of the therapist increased, … male therapists were less likely to get negative client reactions than were female therapists." Do you agree?

e. For this model, $R^2 = .2946$. Interpret this value.

12.6 Quadratic and Other Higher-Order Models

All of the models discussed in the previous sections proposed straight-line relationships between $E(y)$ and each of the independent variables in the model. In this section, we consider models that allow for curvature in the two-dimensional relationship between y and an independent variable. Each of these models is a **second-order model** because it will include an x^2 term.

First, we consider a model that includes only one independent variable x. The form of this model, called the **quadratic model**, is

$$y = \beta_0 + \beta_1 x + \beta_2 x^2 + \varepsilon$$

The term involving x^2, called a **quadratic term** (or **second-order term**), enables us to hypothesize curvature in the graph of the response model relating y to x. Graphs of the quadratic model for two different values of β_2 are shown in Figure 12.12. When the curve opens upward, the sign of β_2 is positive (see Figure 12.12a); when the curve opens downward, the sign of β_2 is negative (see Figure 12.12b).

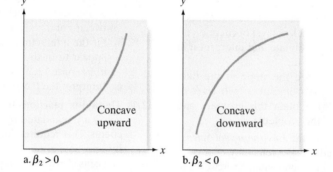

Figure 12.12

Graphs for two quadratic models

a. $\beta_2 > 0$ b. $\beta_2 < 0$

A Quadratic (Second-Order) Model in a Single Quantitative Independent Variable

$$E(y) = \beta_0 + \beta_1 x + \beta_2 x^2$$

where

β_0 is the y-intercept of the curve.

β_1 is a shift parameter.

β_2 is the rate of curvature.

Example 12.7

Analyzing a Quadratic Model—Predicting Electrical Usage

Problem In all-electric homes, the amount of electricity expended is of interest to consumers, builders, and groups involved with energy conservation. Suppose we wish to investigate the monthly electrical usage, y, in all-electric homes and its relationship to the size, x, of the home. Moreover, suppose we think that monthly electrical usage in all-electric homes is related to the size of the home by the quadratic model

$$y = \beta_0 + \beta_1 x + \beta_2 x^2 + \varepsilon$$

To fit the model, the values of y and x are collected for 15 homes during a particular month. The data are shown in Table 12.2.

a. Construct a scatterplot for the data. Is there evidence to support the use of a quadratic model?

b. Use the method of least squares to estimate the unknown parameters β_0, β_1, and β_2 in the quadratic model.

c. Graph the prediction equation and assess how well the model fits the data, both visually and numerically.

d. Interpret the β estimates.

Table 12.2	Home Size–Electrical Usage Data
Size of Home, x (sq. ft.)	Monthly Usage, y (kilowatt-hours)
1,290	1,182
1,350	1,172
1,470	1,264
1,600	1,493
1,710	1,571
1,840	1,711
1,980	1,804
2,230	1,840
2,400	1,986
2,710	2,007
2,930	1,984
3,000	1,960
3,210	2,001
3,240	1,928
3,520	1,945

💿 *Data Set:* KWHRS

e. Is the overall model useful (at $\alpha = .01$) for predicting electrical usage y?

f. Is there sufficient evidence of downward curvature in the home size–electrical usage relationship? Test using $\alpha = .01$.

Solution

a. A Minitab scatterplot for the data in Table 12.2 is shown in Figure 12.13. The figure illustrates that electrical usage appears to increase in a curvilinear manner with the size of the home. This provides some support for the inclusion of the quadratic term x^2 in the model.

Figure 12.13

Minitab scatterplot for electrical usage data

b. We used Excel to fit the model to the data in Table 12.2. Part of the Excel regression output is displayed in Figure 12.14. The least squares estimates of the β parameters (highlighted) are $\hat{\beta}_0 = -806.7$, $\hat{\beta}_1 = 1.9616$, and $\hat{\beta}_2 = -.00034$. Therefore, the equation that minimizes the SSE for the data is

$$\hat{y} = -806.7 + 1.9616x - .00034x^2$$

SUMMARY OUTPUT						
Regression Statistics						
Multiple R	0.988576					
R Square	0.977283					
Adjusted R Square	0.973496					
Standard Error	50.19975					
Observations	15					
ANOVA						
	df	*SS*	*MS*	*F*	*Significance F*	
Regression	2	1300900.218	650450.1	258.1135719	0.0000000001	
Residual	12	30240.18169	2520.015			
Total	14	1331140.4				
	Coefficients	*Standard Error*	*t Stat*	*P-value*	*Lower 95%*	*Upper 95%*
Intercept	−806.717	166.8720911	−4.83434	0.0004089596	−1170.299712	−443.134
SIZE	1.961617	0.152524384	12.861	0.0000000223	1.629294434	2.293939
SIZESQ	−0.00034	0.00003212	−10.599	0.0000001903	−0.000410426	−0.00027

Figure 12.14

Excel regression output for electrical usage model

c. Figure 12.15 is a Minitab graph of the least squares prediction equation. Note that the graph provides a good fit to the data of Table 12.2. A numerical measure of fit is obtained with the adjusted coefficient of determination, R_a^2. This value (highlighted on Figure 12.14) is $R_a^2 = .973$. This implies that about 97% of the sample variation in electrical usage (y) can be explained by the quadratic model (after adjusting for sample size and degrees of freedom).

Figure 12.15

Minitab plot of least squares model for electrical usage

d. The interpretation of the estimated coefficients in a quadratic model must be undertaken cautiously. First, the estimated y-intercept, $\hat{\beta}_0$, can be meaningfully interpreted only if the range of the independent variable includes zero—that is, if $x = 0$ is included in the sampled range of x. Although $\hat{\beta}_0 = -806.7$ seems to imply that the estimated electrical usage is negative when $x = 0$, this zero point is not in the range of the sample (the lowest value of x is 1,290 square feet), and the value is nonsensical (a home with 0 square feet); thus the interpretation of $\hat{\beta}_0$ is not meaningful.

The estimated coefficient of x is $\hat{\beta}_1 = 1.9616$, but in the presence of the quadratic term x^2, it no longer represents a slope.* The estimated coefficient of the first-order term x will not, in general, have a meaningful interpretation in the quadratic model.

The sign of the coefficient, $\hat{\beta}_2 = -.00034$, of the quadratic term, x^2, is the indicator of whether the curve is concave downward (mound-shaped) or concave upward (bowl-shaped). A negative $\hat{\beta}_2$ implies downward concavity, as in this example (Figure 12.15), and a positive $\hat{\beta}_2$ implies upward concavity. Rather than interpreting the numerical value of $\hat{\beta}_2$ itself, we employ a graphical representation of the model, as in Figure 12.15, to describe the model.

Note that Figure 12.15 implies that the estimated electrical usage is leveling off as the home sizes increase beyond 2,500 square feet. In fact, the convexity of the model would lead to decreasing usage estimates if we were to display the model out to 4,000 square feet and beyond (see Figure 12.16). However, model interpretations are not meaningful outside the range of the independent variable, which has a maximum value of 3,520 square feet in this example. Thus, although the model appears to support the hypothesis that the *rate of increase* per square foot *decreases* for home sizes near the high end of the sampled values, the conclusion that usage will actually begin to decrease for very large homes would be a *misuse* of the model because no homes of 3,600 square feet or more were included in the sample.

e. To test whether the quadratic model is statistically useful, we conduct the global F-test:

$$H_0: \beta_1 = \beta_2 = 0$$

$$H_a: \text{At least one of the above coefficients is nonzero.}$$

---

*For students with knowledge of calculus, note that the slope of the quadratic model is the first derivative $\partial y / \partial x = \beta_1 + 2\beta_2 x$. Thus, the slope varies as a function of x, rather than the constant slope associated with the straight-line model.

Figure 12.16

Potential misuse of quadratic model

From the Excel printout, Figure 12.14, the test statistic (highlighted) is $F = 258.11$ with an associated p-value of approximately 0. For any reasonable α, we reject H_0 and conclude that the overall model is a useful predictor of electrical usage, y.

f. Figure 12.15 shows concave downward curvature in the relationship between size of a home and electrical usage in the sample of 15 data points. To determine if this type of curvature exists in the population, we want to test

$$H_0: \beta_2 = 0 \text{ (no curvature in the response curve)}$$
$$H_a: \beta_2 < 0 \text{ (downward concavity exists in the response curve)}$$

The test statistic for testing β_2, highlighted on the printout, is $t = -10.599$, and the associated two-tailed p-value is .0000002. Because this is a one-tailed test, the appropriate p-value is $(.0000002)/2 = .0000001$. Now $\alpha = .01$ exceeds this p-value. Thus, there is very strong evidence of downward curvature in the population—that is, electrical usage increases more slowly per square foot for large homes than for small homes.

Look Back Note that the Excel printout in Figure 12.14 also provides the t-test statistic and corresponding two-tailed p-values for the tests of $H_0: \beta_0 = 0$ and $H_0: \beta_1 = 0$. Because the interpretation of these parameters is not meaningful for this model, the tests are not of interest.

◼ **Now Work Exercise 12.56**

When two or more quantitative independent variables are included in a second-order model, we can incorporate squared terms for each x in the model, as well as the interaction between the two independent variables. A model that includes all possible second-order terms in two independent variables—called a **complete second-order model**—is given in the box below.

Complete Second-Order Model with Two Quantitative Independent Variables

$$E(y) = \beta_0 + \beta_1 x_1 + \beta_2 x_2 + \beta_3 x_2 x_2 + \beta_4 x_1^2 + \beta_5 x_2^2$$

Comments on the Parameters

β_0: y-intercept, the value of $E(y)$ when $x_1 = x_2 = 0$

β_1, β_2: Changing β_1 and β_2 causes the surface to shift along the x_1- and x_2-axes

β_3: Controls the rotation of the surface

β_4, β_5: Signs and values of these parameters control the type of surface and the rates of curvature.

Three types of three-dimensional graphs (called **response surfaces**) are produced by a second-order model:* a **paraboloid** that opens upward (Figure 12.17a), a paraboloid that opens downward (Figure 12.17b), and a **saddle-shaped surface** (Figure 12.17c).

A complete second-order model is the three-dimensional equivalent of a quadratic model in a single quantitative variable. Instead of tracing parabolas, it traces paraboloids and saddle surfaces. Because only a portion of the complete surface is used to fit the data, this model provides a very large variety of gently curving surfaces that can be used to fit data. It is a good choice for a model if you expect curvature in the response surface relating $E(y)$ to x_1 and x_2.

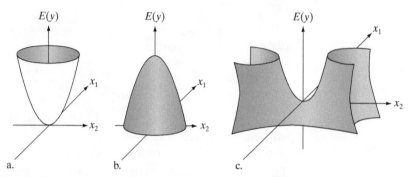

Figure 12.17

Graphs for three second-order surfaces

Example 12.8	

A More Complex Second-Order Model—Predicting Hours Worked per Week

Problem A social scientist would like to relate the number of hours worked per week (outside the home) by a married woman to the number of years of formal education she has completed and the number of children in her family.

a. Identify the dependent variable and the independent variables.

b. Write the first-order model for this example.

c. Modify the model in part **b** to include an interaction term.

d. Write a complete second-order model for $E(y)$.

Solution

a. The dependent variable is

y = Number of hours worked per week by a married woman

The two independent variables, both quantitative in nature, are

x_1 = Number of years of formal education completed by the woman

x_2 = Number of children in the family

b. The first-order model is

$$E(y) = \beta_0 + \beta_1 x_1 + \beta_2 x_2$$

This model would probably not be appropriate in this situation because x_1 and x_2 may interact and/or curvature terms corresponding to x_1^2 and x_2^2 may be needed to obtain a good model for $E(y)$.

c. Adding the interaction term, we obtain

$$E(y) = \beta_0 + \beta_1 x_1 + \beta_2 x_2 + \beta_3 x_1 x_2$$

This model should be better than the model in part **b** because we have now allowed for interaction between x_1 and x_2.

*The saddle-shaped surface (Figure 12.17c) is produced when $\beta_3^2 > 4\beta_4\beta_5$; the paraboloid opens upward (Figure 12.17a) when $\beta_4 + \beta_5 > 0$ and opens downward (Figure 12.17b) when $\beta_4 + \beta_5 < 0$.

d. The complete second-order model is

$$E(y) = \beta_0 + \beta_1 x_1 + \beta_2 x_2 + \beta_3 x_1 x_2 + \beta_4 x_1^2 + \beta_5 x_2^2$$

Because it would not be surprising to find curvature in the response surface, the complete second-order model would be preferred to the models in parts **b** and **c**.

Look Back How can we tell whether the complete second-order model really does provide better predictions of hours worked than the models in parts **b** and **c**? The answers to these and similar questions are examined in Section 12.9.

■ Now Work Exercise 12.59

Most relationships between $E(y)$ and two or more quantitative independent variables are second order and require the use of either the interactive or the complete second-order model to obtain a good fit to a data set. As in the case of a single quantitative independent variable, however, the curvature in the response surface may be very slight over the range of values of the variables in the data set. When this happens, a first-order model may provide a good fit to the data.

Exercises 12.49–12.65

Learning the Mechanics

12.49 Write a second-order model relating the mean of y, $E(y)$, to
  a. one quantitative independent variable
  b. two quantitative independent variables
  c. three quantitative independent variables [*Hint:* Include all possible two-way cross-product terms and squared terms.]

12.50 Suppose you fit the second-order model

$$y = \beta_0 + \beta_1 x + \beta_2 x^2 + \varepsilon$$

to $n = 25$ data points. Your estimate of β_2 is $\hat{\beta}_2 = .47$, and the estimated standard error of the estimate is .15.

  a. Test $H_0: \beta_2 = 0$ against $H_a: \beta_2 \neq 0$. Use $\alpha = .05$.
  b. Suppose you want to determine only whether the quadratic curve opens upward; that is, as x increases, the slope of the curve increases. Give the test statistic and the rejection region for the test for $\alpha = .05$. Do the data support the theory that the slope of the curve increases as x increases? Explain.

12.51 Suppose you fit the quadratic model

$$E(y) = \beta_0 + \beta_1 x + \beta_2 x^2$$

to a set of $n = 20$ data points and found $R^2 = .91$, $SS_{yy} = 29.94$, and $SSE = 2.63$.

  a. Is there sufficient evidence to indicate that the model contributes information for predicting y? Test using $\alpha = .05$.
  b. What null and alternative hypotheses would you test to determine whether upward curvature exists?
  c. What null and alternative hypotheses would you test to determine whether downward curvature exists?

12.52 Consider the following quadratic models:
  (1) $y = 1 - 2x + x^2$
  (2) $y = 1 + 2x + x^2$
  (3) $y = 1 + x^2$
  (4) $y = 1 - x^2$
  (5) $y = 1 + 3x^2$

  a. Graph each of the quadratic models, side by side, on the same sheet of graph paper.
  b. What effect does the first-order term ($2x$) have on the graph of the curve?
  c. What effect does the second-order term (x^2) have on the graph of the curve?

12.53 Minitab was used to fit the complete second-order model

$$E(y) = \beta_0 + \beta_1 x_1 + \beta_2 x_2 + \beta_3 x_1 x_2 + \beta_4 x_1^2 + \beta_5 x_2^2$$

to $n = 39$ data points. The printout is shown below.

```
The regression equation is
Y = -24.56 + 1.12 X1 + 27.99 X2 - 0.54 X1X2 - 0.004 X1SQ + 0.002 X2SQ


Predictor       Coef     SE Coef      T      P
Constant      -24.563      6.531   -3.76  0.001
X1             1.19848     0.1103   10.86  0.000
X2            27.988      79.489     0.35  0.727
X1X2          -0.5397      1.0338   -0.52  0.605
X1SQ          -0.0043      0.0004  -10.74  0.000
X2SQ           0.0020      0.0033    0.60  0.550


S = 2.762     R-Sq = 79.7%    R-Sq(adj) = 76.6%


Analysis of Variance

Source          DF      SS      MS      F      P
Regression       5   989.30  197.86  25.93  0.000
Residual Error  33   251.81    7.63
Total           38  1241.11
```

Minitab output for Exercise 12.53

a. Is there sufficient evidence to indicate that at least one of the parameters—$\beta_1, \beta_2, \beta_3, \beta_4,$ and β_5—is nonzero? Test using $\alpha = .05$.

b. Test $H_0: \beta_4 = 0$ against $H_a: \beta_4 \neq 0$. Use $\alpha = .01$.

c. Test $H_0: \beta_5 = 0$ against $H_a: \beta_5 \neq 0$. Use $\alpha = .01$.

d. Use graphs to explain the consequences of the tests in parts **b** and **c**.

Applying the Concepts—Basic

12.54 Personality traits and job performance. When attempting to predict job performance using personality traits, researchers typically assume that the relationship is linear. A study published in the *Journal of Applied Psychology* (Jan. 2011) investigated a curvilinear relationship between job task performance and a specific personality trait—conscientiousness. Using data collected for 602 employees of a large public organization, task performance was measured on a 30-point scale (where higher scores indicate better performance) and conscientiousness was measured on a scale of -3 to $+3$ (where higher scores indicate a higher level of conscientiousness).

a. The coefficient of correlation relating task performance score to conscientiousness score was reported as $r = .18$. Explain why the researchers should not use this statistic to investigate the curvilinear relationship between task performance and conscientiousness.

b. Give the equation of a curvilinear (quadratic) model relating task performance score (y) to conscientiousness score (x).

c. The researchers theorized that task performance increases as level of conscientiousness increases, but at a decreasing rate. Draw a sketch of this relationship.

d. If the theory in part **c** is supported, what is the expected sign of β_2 in the model, part **b**?

e. The researchers reported $\hat{\beta}_2 = -.32$ with an associated p-value of less than .05. Use this information to test the researchers' theory at $\alpha = .05$.

12.55 Going for it on fourth-down in the NFL. Refer to the *Chance* (Winter 2009) study of fourth-down decisions by coaches in the National Football League (NFL), Exercise 11.63 (p. 638). Recall that statisticians at California State University, Northridge, fit a straight-line model for predicting the number of points scored (y) by a team that has a first-down with a given number of yards (x) from the opposing goal line. A second model fit to data collected on five NFL teams from a recent season was the quadratic regression model, $E(y) = \beta_0 + \beta_1 x + \beta_2 x^2$. The regression yielded the following results: $\hat{y} = 6.13 + .141x - .0009x^2, R^2 = .226$.

a. If possible, give a practical interpretation of each of the β estimates in the model.

b. Give a practical interpretation of the coefficient of determination, R^2.

c. In Exercise 11.63, the coefficient of correlation for the straight-line model was reported as $R^2 = .18$. Does this statistic alone indicate that the quadratic model is a better fit than the straight-line model? Explain.

d. What test of hypothesis would you conduct to determine if the quadratic model is a better fit than the straight-line model?

12.56 Catalytic converters in cars. A quadratic model was applied to motor vehicle toxic emissions data collected in Mexico City (*Environmental Science & Engineering*, Sept. 1, 2000). The following equation was used to predict the percentage (y) of motor vehicles without catalytic converters in the Mexico City fleet for a given year (x):

$$\hat{y} = 325,790 - 321.67x + .0794x^2.$$

a. Explain why the value $\hat{\beta}_0 = 325,790$ has no practical interpretation.

b. Explain why the value $\hat{\beta}_1 = -321.67$ should not be interpreted as a slope.

c. Examine the value of $\hat{\beta}_2$ to determine the nature of the curvature (upward or downward) in the sample data.

d. The researchers used the model to estimate "that just after the year 2021 the fleet of cars with catalytic converters will completely disappear." Comment on the danger of using the model to predict y in the year 2021. (*Note:* The model was fit to data collected between 1984 and 1999.)

12.57 Testing tires for wear. Underinflated or overinflated tires can increase tire wear. A new tire was tested for wear at different pressures, with the results shown in the following table.

Pressure, x (pounds per square inch)	Mileage, y (thousands)
30	29
31	32
32	36
33	38
34	37
35	33
36	26

a. Plot the data on a scatterplot.

b. If you were given only the information for $x = 30, 31, 32, 33$, what kind of model would you suggest? For $x = 33, 34, 35, 36$? For all the data?

12.58 Assertiveness and leadership. Management professors at Columbia University examined the relationship between assertiveness and leadership (*Journal of Personality and Social Psychology,* Feb. 2007). The sample represented 388 people enrolled in a full-time MBA program. Based on answers to a questionnaire, the researchers measured two variables for each subject: assertiveness score (x) and leadership ability score (y). A quadratic regression model was fit to the data, with the following results:

Independent Variable	β Estimate	t-value	p-value
x	.57	2.55	.01
x^2	-.088	-3.97	$< .01$

Model $R^2 = .12$

a. Conduct a test of overall model utility. Use $\alpha = .05$.

b. The researchers hypothesized that leadership ability increases at a decreasing rate with assertiveness. Set up the null and alternative hypotheses to test this theory.

c. Use the reported results to conduct the test, part **b**. Give your conclusion (at $\alpha = .05$) in the words of the problem.

12.59 Goal congruence in top management teams. Do chief executive officers (CEOs) and their top managers always agree on the goals of the company? Goal importance congruence between CEOs and vice presidents (VPs) was studied in the *Academy of Management Journal* (Feb. 2008). The researchers used regression to model a VP's attitude toward the goal of improving efficiency (y) as a function of the two quantitative independent variables level of CEO leadership (x_1) and level of congruence between the CEO and the VP (x_2). A complete second-order model in x_1 and x_2 was fit to data collected for $n = 517$ top management team members at U.S. credit unions.

a. Write the complete second-order model for $E(y)$.

b. The coefficient of determination for the model, part **a**, was reported as $R^2 = .14$. Interpret this value.

c. The estimate of the β-value for the $(x_2)^2$ term in the model was found to be negative. Interpret this result, practically.

d. A t-test on the β-value for the interaction term in the model, x_1x_2, resulted in a p-value of .02. Practically interpret this result, using $\alpha = .05$.

Applying the Concepts—Intermediate

12.60 Shopping on Black Friday. Refer to the *International Journal of Retail and Distribution Management* (Vol. 39, 2011) study of shopping on Black Friday (the day after Thanksgiving), Exercise 6.16 (p. 309). Recall that researchers conducted interviews with a sample of 38 women shopping on Black Friday to gauge their shopping habits. Two of the variables measured for each shopper were age (x) and number of years shopping on Black Friday (y). Data on these two variables for the 38 shoppers are listed in the accompanying table.

a. Fit the quadratic model, $E(y) = \beta_0 + \beta_1x + \beta_2x^2$, to the data using statistical software. Give the prediction equation.

b. Conduct a test of the overall adequacy of the model. Use $\alpha = .01$.

c. Conduct a test to determine if the relationship between age (x) and number of years shopping on Black Friday (y) is best represented by a linear or quadratic function. Use $\alpha = .01$.

Age	Years	Age	Years
32	5	21	5
27	3	52	10
40	12	40	18
62	35	38	5
47	20	56	8
53	30	60	5
24	8	35	15
27	2	50	25
47	24	56	10
40	25	20	2
45	11	20	4
22	11	21	4
25	5	22	5
60	35	50	10
22	3	30	6
50	15	28	16
70	22	25	7
50	10	30	6
21	6	49	30

Source: Thomas, J. B., & Peters, C. "An exploratory investigation of Black Friday consumption rituals," *International Journal of Retail and Distribution Management*, Vol. 39, No. 7, 2011 (Table I). Copyright © 2011 by Emerald Group Publishing Limited. Reprinted with permission.

12.61 Revenues of popular movies. The *Internet Movie Database* (www.imdb.com) monitors the gross revenues for all major motion pictures. The accompanying table gives both the domestic (United States and Canada) and international gross revenues for a sample of 19 popular movies.

Movie Title (year)	Domestic Gross ($ millions)	International Gross ($ millions)
Avatar (2009)	760.5	2,021.0
Titanic (1997)	600.8	1,234.6
The Dark Knight (2008)	533.3	464.0
E.T. (1982)	439.9	321.8
Pirates of the Caribbean: Dead Man's Chest (2006)	423.0	642.9
Jurassic Park (1993)	356.8	563.0
Lion King (1994)	328.4	455.0
Harry Potter and the Sorcerer's Stone (2001)	317.6	651.1
Inception (2010)	291.4	468.2
The Hangover (2009)	277.3	201.6
Sixth Sense (1999)	293.5	368.0
Jaws (1975)	260.0	210.6
Ghost (1990)	217.6	300.0
Saving Private Ryan (1998)	216.1	263.2
Gladiator (2000)	187.7	268.6
Dances with Wolves (1990)	184.2	240.0
The Exorcist (1973)	204.6	153.0
My Big Fat Greek Wedding (2002)	241.4	115.1
Rocky IV (1985)	127.9	172.6

Source: Based on information from *The Internet Movie Database* (http://www.imdb.com).

a. Write a first-order model for foreign gross revenues (y) as a function of domestic gross revenues (x).

b. Write a second-order model for international gross revenues y as a function of domestic gross revenues x.

c. Construct a scatterplot for these data. Which of the models from parts **a** and **b** appears to be the better choice for explaining the variation in foreign gross revenues?

d. Fit the model of part **b** to the data and investigate its usefulness. Is there evidence of a curvilinear relationship between international and domestic gross revenues? Try using $\alpha = .05$.

e. Based on your analysis in part **d**, which of the models from parts **a** and **b** better explains the variation in international gross revenues? Compare your answer to your preliminary conclusion from part **c**.

12.62 Estimating change-point dosage. A standard method for studying toxic substances and their effects on humans is to observe the responses of rodents exposed to various doses of the substance over time. In the *Journal of Agricultural, Biological, and Environmental Statistics* (June 2005), researchers used least squares regression to estimate the *change-point* dosage—defined as the largest dose level that has no adverse effects. Data were obtained from a dose-response study of rats exposed to the toxic substance aconiazide. A sample of 50 rats was evenly divided into five dosage groups: 0, 100, 200, 500, and 750 milligrams per kilogram of body weight. The dependent variable y measured was the weight change (in grams) after a

2-week exposure. The researchers fit the quadratic model $E(y) = \beta_0 + \beta_1 x + \beta_2 x^2$, where x = dosage level, with the following results: $\hat{y} = 10.25 + .0053x - .0000266x^2$.

a. Construct a rough sketch of the least squares prediction equation. Describe the nature of the curvature in the estimated model.

b. Estimate the weight change (y) for a rat given a dosage of 500 mg/kg of aconiazide.

c. Estimate the weight change (y) for a rat given a dosage of 0 mg/kg of aconiazide. (This dosage is called the *control* dosage level.)

d. Of the five dosage groups in the study, find the largest dosage level x that yields an estimated weight change that is closest to but below the estimated weight change for the control group. This value is the *change-point* dosage.

12.63 Failure times of silicon wafer microchips. Researchers at National Semiconductor experimented with tin-lead solder bumps used to manufacture silicon wafer integrated circuit chips (International Wafer Level Packaging Conference, Nov. 3–4, 2005). The failure times of the microchips (in hours) was determined at different solder temperatures (degrees Celsius). The data for one experiment are given in the table. The researchers want to predict failure time (y) based on solder temperature (x).

a. Construct a scatterplot for the data. What type of relationship, linear or curvilinear, appears to exist between failure time and solder temperature?

b. Fit the model, $E(y) = \beta_0 + \beta_1 x + \beta_2 x^2$, to the data. Give the least squares prediction equation.

c. Conduct a test to determine if there is upward curvature in the relationship between failure time and solder temperature. (Use $\alpha = .05$.)

Temperature (°C)	Time to Failure (hours)
165	200
162	200
164	1,200
158	500
158	600
159	750
156	1,200
157	1,500
152	500
147	500
149	1,100
149	1,150
142	3,500
142	3,600
143	3,650
133	4,200
132	4,800
132	5,000
134	5,200
134	5,400
125	8,300
123	9,700

Source: Gee, S., & Nguyen, L. "Mean time to failure in wafer level-CSP packages with SnPb and SnAgCu solder bmps," International Wafer Level Packaging Conference, San Jose, CA, Nov. 3–4, 2005 (adapted from Figure 7). Reprinted with permission.

12.64 Public perceptions of health risks. In the *Journal of Experimental Psychology: Learning, Memory, and Cognition* (July 2005), University of Basel (Switzerland) psychologists tested the ability of people to judge risk of an infectious disease. The researchers asked German college students to estimate the number of people who are infected with a certain disease in a typical year. The median estimates as well as the actual incidence rate for each in a sample of 24 infections are provided in the table. Consider the quadratic model $E(y) = \beta_0 + \beta_1 x + \beta_2 x^2$, where y = actual incidence rate and x = estimated rate.

Infection	Incidence Rate	Estimate
Polio	0.25	300
Diphtheria	1	1,000
Trachoma	1.75	691
Rabbit fever	2	200
Cholera	3	17.5
Leprosy	5	0.8
Tetanus	9	1,000
Hemorrhagic fever	10	150
Trichinosis	22	326.5
Undulant fever	23	146.5
Well's disease	39	370
Gas gangrene	98	400
Parrot fever	119	225
Typhoid	152	200
Q fever	179	200
Malaria	936	400
Syphilis	1,514	1,500
Dysentery	1,627	1,000
Gonorrhea	2,926	6,000
Meningitis	4,019	5,000
Tuberculosis	12,619	1,500
Hepatitis	14,889	10,000
Gastroenteritis	203,864	37,000
Botulism	15	37,500

Source: Hertwig, R., Pachur, T., & Kurzenhauser, S. "Judgments of risk frequencies: Tests of possible cognitive mechanisms," *Journal of Experimental Psychology: Learning, Memory, and Cognition*, Vol. 31, No. 4, July 2005 (Table 1).

a. Fit the quadratic model to the data and then conduct a test to determine if incidence rate is curvilinearly related to estimated rate. (Use $\alpha = .05$.)

b. Construct a scatterplot for the data. Locate the data point for botulism on the graph. What do you observe?

c. Repeat part **a** but omit the data point for botulism from the analysis. Has the fit of the model improved? Explain.

12.65 Orange juice demand study. A chilled orange juice warehousing operation in New York City was experiencing too many out-of-stock situations with its 96-ounce containers. To better understand current and future demand for this product, the company examined the last 40 days of sales, which are shown in the table on the next page. One of the company's objectives is to model demand, y, as a function of sale day, x (where $x = 1, 2, 3, \ldots, 40$).

a. Construct a scatterplot for these data.

b. Does it appear that a second-order model might better explain the variation in demand than a first-order model? Explain.

c. Fit a first-order model to these data.

d. Fit a second-order model to these data.

e. Compare the results in parts **c** and **d** and decide which model better explains variation in demand. Justify your choice.

Data for Exercise 12.65

Sale Day, x	Demand for 96 oz. Containers, y (in cases)	Sale Day, x	Demand for 96 oz. Containers, y (in cases)
1	4,581	21	5,902
2	4,239	22	2,295
3	2,754	23	2,682
4	4,501	24	5,787
5	4,016	25	3,339
6	4,680	26	3,798
7	4,950	27	2,007
8	3,303	28	6,282
9	2,367	29	3,267
10	3,055	30	4,779
11	4,248	31	9,000
12	5,067	32	9,531
13	5,201	33	3,915
14	5,133	34	8,964
15	4,211	35	6,984
16	3,195	36	6,660
17	5,760	37	6,921
18	5,661	38	10,005
19	6,102	39	10,153
20	6,099	40	11,520

Source: Tom Metzler and Rick Campbell.

12.7 Qualitative (Dummy) Variable Models

Multiple regression models can also be written to include **qualitative** (or **categorical**) independent variables. Qualitative variables, unlike quantitative variables, cannot be measured on a numerical scale. Therefore, we must code the values of the qualitative variables (called **levels**) as numbers before we can fit the model. These coded qualitative variables are called **dummy** (or **indicator**) **variables** because the numbers assigned to the various levels are arbitrarily selected.

To illustrate, suppose a female executive at a certain company claims that male executives earn higher salaries, on average, than female executives with the same education, experience, and responsibilities. To support her claim, she wants to model the salary y of an executive using a qualitative independent variable representing the gender of an executive (male or female).

A convenient method of coding the values of a qualitative variable at two levels involves assigning a value of 1 to one of the levels and a value of 0 to the other. For example, the dummy variable used to describe gender could be coded as follows:

$$x = \begin{cases} 1 & \text{if male} \\ 0 & \text{if female} \end{cases}$$

The choice of which level is assigned to 1 and which is assigned to 0 is arbitrary. The model then takes the following form:

$$E(y) = \beta_0 + \beta_1 x$$

The advantage of using a 0–1 coding scheme is that the β coefficients are easily interpreted. The model above allows us to compare the mean executive salary $E(y)$ for males with the corresponding mean for females.

$$\text{Males } (x = 1): E(y) = \beta_0 + \beta_1(1) = \beta_0 + \beta_1$$
$$\text{Females } (x = 0): E(y) = \beta_0 + \beta_1(0) = \beta_0$$

These two means are illustrated in the bar graph in Figure 12.18.

First note that β_0 represents the mean salary for females (say, μ_F). When a 0–1 coding convention is used, β_0 will always represent the mean response associated with the level of the qualitative variable assigned the value 0 (called the **base level**).

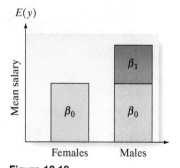

Figure 12.18

Bar graph comparing $E(y)$ for males and females

The difference between the mean salary for males and the mean salary for females, $\mu_M - \mu_F$, is represented by β_1—that is,

$$\mu_M - \mu_F = (\beta_0 + \beta_1) - (\beta_0) = \beta_1$$

This difference is shown in Figure 12.18.* With a 0–1 coding convention, β_1 will always represent the difference between the mean response for the level assigned the value 1 and the mean for the base level. Thus, for the executive salary model, we have

$$\beta_0 = \mu_F$$
$$\beta_1 = \mu_M - \mu_F$$

The model relating a mean response $E(y)$ to a qualitative independent variable at two levels is summarized in the following box.

A Model Relating $E(y)$ to a Qualitative Independent Variable with Two Levels

$$E(y) = \beta_0 + \beta_1 x$$

where

$$x = \begin{cases} 1 & \text{if level A} \\ 0 & \text{if level B} \end{cases}$$

Interpretation of β's:

$$\beta_0 = \mu_B \text{ (mean for base level)}$$
$$\beta_1 = \mu_A - \mu_B$$

Note: μ_i represents the mean of y, $E(y)$, for level i of the dummy variable.

Now carefully examine the model with a single qualitative independent variable at two levels; we will use exactly the same pattern for any number of levels. Moreover, the interpretation of the parameters will always be the same. One level (say, level A) is selected as the base level. Then for the 0–1 coding† for the dummy variables,

$$\mu_A = \beta_0$$

The coding for all dummy variables is as follows: To represent the mean value of y for a particular level, let that dummy variable equal 1; otherwise, the dummy variable is set equal to 0. Using this system of coding,

$$\mu_B = \beta_0 + \beta_1$$
$$\mu_C = \beta_0 + \beta_2$$

and so on. Because $\mu_A = \beta_0$, any other model parameter will represent the difference between means for that level and the base level:

$$\beta_1 = \mu_B - \mu_A$$
$$\beta_2 = \mu_C - \mu_A$$

and so on. Consequently, each β multiplied by a dummy variable represents the difference between $E(y)$ at one level of the qualitative variable and $E(y)$ at the base level.

A Model Relating $E(y)$ to One Qualitative Independent Variable with k Levels

Always use a number of dummy variables that is one less than the number of levels of the qualitative variable. Thus, for a qualitative variable with k levels, use $k - 1$ dummy variables:

$$E(y) = \beta_0 + \beta_1 x_1 + \beta_2 x_2 + \cdots + \beta_{k-1} x_{k-1}$$

---

*Note that β_1 could be negative. If β_1 were negative, the height of the bar corresponding to males would be *reduced* (rather than increased) from the height of the bar for females by the amount β_1. Figure 12.18 is constructed assuming that β_1 is a positive quantity.

†You do not have to use a 0–1 system of coding for the dummy variables. Any two-value system will work, but the interpretation given to the model parameters will depend on the code. Using the 0–1 system makes the model parameters easy to interpret.

where x_i is the dummy variable for level $i + 1$ and

$$x_i = \begin{cases} 1 & \text{if } y \text{ is observed at level } i + 1 \\ 0 & \text{otherwise} \end{cases}$$

Then, for this system of coding

$$\mu_A = \beta_0 \qquad \text{and} \qquad \beta_1 = \mu_B - \mu_A$$
$$\mu_B = \beta_0 + \beta_1 \qquad\qquad \beta_2 = \mu_C - \mu_A$$
$$\mu_C = \beta_0 + \beta_2 \qquad\qquad \beta_3 = \mu_D - \mu_A$$
$$\mu_D = \beta_0 + \beta_3 \qquad\qquad \vdots$$

Note: μ_i represents the mean of y, $E(y)$, for level i of the qualitative variable.

Example 12.9

A Model with One Qualitative Independent Variable—Credit Card Debt

Problem Suppose an economist wants to compare the mean dollar amounts owed by delinquent credit card customers in three different socioeconomic classes: (1) lower class, (2) middle class, and (3) upper class. A sample of 10 customers with delinquent accounts is selected from each group, and the amount owed by each is recorded, as shown in Table 12.3.

Table 12.3	Dollars Owed, Example 12.9	
Group 1 (lower class)	Group 2 (middle class)	Group 3 (upper class)
$148	$513	$335
76	264	643
393	433	216
520	94	536
236	535	128
134	327	723
55	214	258
166	135	380
415	280	594
153	304	465

Data Set: CCDEBT

a. Hypothesize a regression model for amount owed (y) using socioeconomic class as an independent variable.

b. Interpret the β's in the model.

c. Fit the model to the data and give the least squares prediction equation.

d. Use the model to determine if the mean dollar amounts owed by customers differ significantly for the three socioeconomic groups at $\alpha = .05$.

Solution

a. Note that socioeconomic status (low, middle, upper class) is a qualitative variable (measured on an ordinal scale). For a three-level qualitative variable, we need two dummy variables in the regression model. The model relating $E(y)$ to this single qualitative variable, socioeconomic group, is

$$E(y) = \beta_0 + \beta_1 x_1 + \beta_2 x_2$$

where (arbitrarily choosing group 1 as the base level)

$$x_1 = \begin{cases} 1 & \text{if group 2} \\ 0 & \text{if not} \end{cases} \qquad x_2 = \begin{cases} 1 & \text{if group 3} \\ 0 & \text{if not} \end{cases}$$

b. For this model

$$\beta_0 = \mu_1$$
$$\beta_1 = \mu_2 - \mu_1$$
$$\beta_2 = \mu_3 - \mu_1$$

where μ_1, μ_2, and μ_3 are the mean responses for socioeconomic groups 1, 2, and 3, respectively—that is, β_0 represents the mean amount owed for group 1 (lower class), β_1 represents the mean difference in amounts owed for group 2 (middle) and group 1 (lower), and β_2 represents the mean difference in amounts owed for group 3 (upper) and group 1 (lower).

c. The Minitab printout of the regression analysis is shown in Figure 12.19. The least squares estimates of the β's are highlighted on the printout, yielding the following least squares prediction equation:

$$\hat{y} = 229.6 + 80.3x_1 + 198.2x_2$$

Figure 12.19

Minitab output for model with dummy variables

Regression Analysis: Amount versus X1, X2

```
The regression equation is
Amount = 230 + 80.3 X1 + 198 X2

Predictor    Coef  SE Coef      T      P
Constant   229.60    53.43   4.30  0.000
X1          80.30    75.56   1.06  0.297
X2         198.20    75.56   2.62  0.014

S = 168.948   R-Sq = 20.5%   R-Sq(adj) = 14.6%

Analysis of Variance

Source          DF       SS      MS     F      P
Regression       2   198772   99386  3.48  0.045
Residual Error  27   770671   28543
Total           29   969443
```

Descriptive Statistics: Amount

```
Variable  Class   N    Mean   StDev  Minimum  Maximum
Amount      L     10  229.6   158.2     55.0    520.0
            M     10  309.9   147.9     94.0    535.0
            U     10  427.8   196.8    128.0    723.0
```

The interpretations of the β's in part **b** allow us to obtain the β estimates from the sample means associated with the different levels of the qualitative variable.*

Because $\beta_0 = \mu_1$, then the estimate of β_0 is the estimated mean delinquent amount for the lower-class group. This sample mean, highlighted at the bottom of the Minitab printout, is 229.6; thus $\hat{\beta}_0 = 229.6$.

Now $\beta_1 = \mu_2 - \mu_1$; therefore, the estimate of β_1 is the difference between the sample mean delinquent amounts for the middle- and lower-class groups. Based on the sample means highlighted at the bottom of the Minitab printout, we have $\hat{\beta}_1 = 309.9 - 229.6 = 80.3$.

Similarly, the estimate of $\beta_2 = \mu_3 - \mu_1$ is the difference between the sample mean delinquent amounts for the upper- and lower-class groups. From the sample means highlighted at the bottom of the Minitab printout, we have $\hat{\beta}_2 = 427.8 - 229.6 = 198.2$.

d. Testing the null hypothesis that the means for the three groups are equal—that is, $\mu_1 = \mu_2 = \mu_3$—is equivalent to testing

$$H_0: \beta_1 = \beta_2 = 0$$

You can see this by observing that if $\beta_1 = \mu_2 - \mu_1 = 0$, then $\mu_1 = \mu_2$. Similarly, if $\beta_2 = \mu_3 - \mu_1 = 0$, then $\mu_3 = \mu_1$. Thus, if H_0 is true, then μ_1, μ_2, and μ_3 must be equal. The alternative hypothesis is

H_a: At least one of the parameters, β_1 and β_2, differs from 0, which implies that at least two of the three means (μ_1, μ_2, and μ_3) differ.

*The least squares method and the sample means method will yield equivalent β estimates when the sample sizes associated with the different levels of the qualitative variable are equal.

To test this hypothesis, we conduct the global F-test for the model. The value of the F-statistic for testing the adequacy of the model, $F = 3.48$, and the observed significance level of the test, p-value $= .045$, are both highlighted on Figure 12.19. Because $\alpha = .05$ exceeds the p-value, we reject H_0 and conclude that at least one of the parameters, β_1 and β_2, differs from 0. Or, equivalently, we conclude that the data provide sufficient evidence to indicate that the mean indebtedness does vary from one socioeconomic group to another.

Look Back This global F-test is equivalent to the analysis of variance F-test for a completely randomized design of Chapter 9.

━■ Now Work Exercise 12.78

⚠ **CAUTION** A common mistake of regression analysts is to use a single dummy variable x for a qualitative variable at k levels, where $x = 1, 2, 3, \ldots, k$. Such a regression model will have unestimable β's and β's that are difficult to interpret. Remember, when modeling $E(y)$ with a single qualitative independent variable, the number of 0–1 dummy variables to include in the model will always be one less than the number of levels of the qualitative variable.

Exercises 12.66–12.81

Learning the Mechanics

12.66 Write a regression model relating the mean value of y to a qualitative independent variable that can assume two levels. Interpret all the terms in the model.

12.67 Write a regression model relating $E(y)$ to a qualitative independent variable that can assume three levels. Interpret all the terms in the model.

12.68 The Minitab printout below resulted from fitting the following model to $n = 15$ data points:

$$y = \beta_0 + \beta_1 x_1 + \beta_2 x_2 + \varepsilon$$

where

$$x_1 = \begin{cases} 1 & \text{if level 2} \\ 0 & \text{if not} \end{cases} \qquad x_2 = \begin{cases} 1 & \text{if level 3} \\ 0 & \text{if not} \end{cases}$$

a. Report the least squares prediction equation.
b. Interpret the values of β_1 and β_2.
c. Interpret the following hypotheses in terms of μ_1, μ_2, and μ_3:

```
The regression equation is
Y = 80.0 + 16.8 X1 + 40.4 X2


Predictor    Coef   SE Coef      T      P
Constant   80.000     4.082  19.60  0.000
X1         16.800     5.774   2.91  0.013
X2         40.400     5.774   7.00  0.000


S = 9.129    R-Sq = 80.5%   R-Sq(adj) = 77.2%

Analysis of Variance

Source         DF      SS      MS      F      P
Regression      2  4118.9  2059.5  24.72  0.000
Residual Error 12  1000.0    83.3
Total          14  5118.9
```

H_0: $\beta_1 = \beta_2 = 0$
H_a: At least one of the parameters β_1 and β_2 differs from 0

d. Conduct the hypothesis test of part **c**.

12.69 The following model was used to relate $E(y)$ to a single qualitative variable with four levels:

$$E(y) = \beta_0 + \beta_1 x_1 + \beta_2 x_2 + \beta_3 x_3$$

where

$$x_1 = \begin{cases} 1 & \text{if level 2} \\ 0 & \text{if not} \end{cases} \quad x_2 = \begin{cases} 1 & \text{if level 3} \\ 0 & \text{if not} \end{cases} \quad x_3 = \begin{cases} 1 & \text{if level 4} \\ 0 & \text{if not} \end{cases}$$

This model was fit to $n = 30$ data points, and the following result was obtained:

$$\hat{y} = 10.2 - 4x_1 + 12x_2 + 2x_3$$

a. Use the least squares prediction equation to find the estimate of $E(y)$ for each level of the qualitative independent variable.
b. Specify the null and alternative hypotheses you would use to test whether $E(y)$ is the same for all four levels of the independent variable.

Applying the Concepts—Basic

12.70 Can money spent on gifts buy love? Refer to the *Journal of Experimental Social Psychology* (Vol. 45, 2009) study of whether buying gifts truly buys love, Exercise 9.9 (p. 492). Recall that study participants were randomly assigned to play the role of gift-giver or gift-receiver. Gift-receivers were asked to provide the level of appreciation (measured on a 7-point scale where $1 =$ "not at all" and $7 =$ "to a great extent") they had for the last birthday gift they received from a loved one. Gift-givers were asked to recall the last birthday gift they gave to a loved one and to provide the level of appreciation the loved one had for the gift.

a. Write a dummy variable regression model that will allow the researchers to compare the average level of appreciation for birthday gift-givers (μ_G) to the average for birthday gift-receivers (μ_R).

b. Express each of the model's β parameters in terms of μ_G and μ_R.

c. The researchers hypothesize that the average level of appreciation is higher for birthday gift-givers than for birthday gift-receivers. Explain how to test this hypothesis using the regression model.

12.71 Production technologies, terroir, and quality of Bordeaux wine. In addition to state-of-the-art technologies, the production of quality wine is strongly influenced by the natural endowments of the grape-growing region—called the "terroir." *The Economic Journal* (May 2008) published an empirical study of the factors that yield a quality Bordeaux wine. A quantitative measure of wine quality (y) was modeled as a function of several qualitative independent variables, including grape-picking method (manual or automated), soil type (clay, gravel, or sand), and slope orientation (east, south, west, southeast, or southwest).

a. Create the appropriate dummy variables for each of the qualitative independent variables.

b. Write a model for wine quality (y) as a function of grape-picking method. Interpret the β's in the model.

c. Write a model for wine quality (y) as a function of soil type. Interpret the β's in the model.

d. Write a model for wine quality (y) as a function of slope orientation. Interpret the β's in the model.

12.72 Impact of race on football card values. University of Colorado sociologists investigated the impact of race on the value of professional football players' "rookie" cards (*Electronic Journal of Sociology*, 2007). The sample consisted of 148 rookie cards of National Football League (NFL) players who were inducted into the Football Hall of Fame. The price of the card (in dollars) was modeled as a function of several qualitative independent variables: race of player (black or white), card availability (high or low), and player position (quarterback, running back, wide receiver, tight end, defensive lineman, linebacker, defensive back, or offensive lineman).

a. Create the appropriate dummy variables for each of the qualitative independent variables.

b. Write a model for price (y) as a function of race. Interpret the β's in the model.

c. Write a model for price (y) as a function of card availability. Interpret the β's in the model.

d. Write a model for price (y) as a function of position. Interpret the β's in the model.

12.73 Accuracy of software effort estimates. Periodically, software engineers must provide estimates of their effort in developing new software. In the *Journal of Empirical Software Engineering* (Vol. 9, 2004), multiple regression was used to predict the accuracy of these effort estimates. The dependent variable, defined as the relative error in estimating effort,

$$y = (\text{actual effort} - \text{estimated effort})/(\text{actual effort})$$

was determined for each in a sample of $n = 49$ software development tasks. Several qualitative independent variables were evaluated as potential predictors of relative error. Some of these variables are described in the table.

Estimator role (developer or project leader)
Task complexity (low, medium, or high)
Contract type (fixed price or hourly rate)
Customer priority (time of delivery, cost, or quality)

a. Write a model for $E(y)$ as a function of estimator role. Interpret the β's.

b. Write a model for $E(y)$ as a function of task complexity. Interpret the β's.

c. Write a model for $E(y)$ as a function of contract type. Interpret the β's.

d. Write a model for $E(y)$ as a function of customer priority. Interpret the β's.

12.74 Buy-side vs. sell-side analysts' earnings forecasts. Refer to the *Financial Analysts Journal* (Jul./Aug. 2008) comparison of earnings forecasts of buy-side and sell-side analysts, Exercise 2.86 (p. 86). The Harvard Business School professors used regression to model the relative optimism (y) of the analysts' 3-month horizon forecasts. One of the independent variables used to model forecast optimism was the dummy variable $x = \{1$ if the analyst worked for a buy-side firm, 0 if the analyst worked for a sell-side firm$\}$.

a. Write the equation of the model for $E(y)$ as a function of type of firm.

b. Interpret the value of β_0 in the model, part **a.**

c. The professors write that the value of β_1 in the model, part **a,** "represents the mean difference in relative forecast optimism between buy-side and sell-side analysts." Do you agree?

d. The professors also argue that "if buy-side analysts make less optimistic forecasts than their sell-side counterparts, the [estimated value of β_1] will be negative." Do you agree?

12.75 Do blondes raise more funds? During fundraising, does the physical appearance of the solicitor impact the level of capital raised? An economist at the University of Nevada-Reno designed an experiment to answer this question and published the results in *Economic Letters* (Vol. 100, 2008). Each in a sample of 955 households was contacted by a female solicitor and asked to contribute to the Center for Natural Hazards Mitigation Research. The level of contribution (in dollars) was recorded as well as the hair color of the solicitor (blond Caucasian, brunette Caucasian, or minority female).

a. Consider a model for the mean level of contribution, $E(y)$, that allows for different means depending on the hair color of the solicitor. Create the appropriate number of dummy variables for hair color. (Use minority female as the base level.)

b. Write the equation of the model, part **a,** incorporating the dummy variables.

c. In terms of the β's in the model, what is the mean level of contribution for households contacted by a blond Caucasian solicitor?

d. In terms of the β's in the model, what is the difference between the mean level of contribution for households contacted by a blond solicitor and those contacted by a minority female?

e. One theory posits that blond solicitors will achieve the highest mean contribution level, but that there will be no difference between the mean contribution levels attained by brunette Caucasian and minority females. If this theory is true, give the expected signs of the β's in the model.

f. The researcher found the β-estimate for the dummy variable for blond Caucasian to be positive and significantly different from 0 (p-value $< .01$). The β-estimate for the dummy variable for brunette Caucasian was also positive, but not significantly different from 0 (p-value $> .10$). Do these results support the theory, part **e**?

Applying the Concepts—Intermediate

12.76 Deferred tax allowance study. A study was conducted to identify accounting choice variables that influence a manager's decision to change the level of the deferred tax asset allowance at the firm (*The Engineering Economist*, Jan./Feb. 2004). Data were collected for a sample of 329 firms that reported deferred tax assets in 2000. The dependent variable of interest (DTVA) is measured as the change in the deferred tax asset valuation allowance divided by the deferred tax asset. The independent variables used as predictors of DTVA are listed as follows:

LEVERAGE: x_1 = ratio of debt book value to shareholder's equity

BONUS: x_2 = 1 if firm maintains a management bonus plan, 0 if not

MVALUE: x_3 = market value of common stock

BBATH: x_4 = 1 if operating earnings negative and lower than last year, 0 if not

EARN: x_5 = change in operating earnings divided by total assets

A first-order model was fit to the data with the following results (p-values in parentheses):

$$R_a^2 = .280$$

$$\hat{y} = .044 + .006x_1 - .035x_2 - .001x_3 + .296x_4 + .010x_5$$
$$\quad (.070) \quad (.228) \quad (.157) \quad (.678) \quad (.001) \quad (.869)$$

a. Interpret the estimate of the β coefficient for x_4.

b. The "Big Bath" theory proposed by the researchers states that the mean DTVA for firms with negative earnings and earnings lower than last year will exceed the mean DTVA of other firms. Is there evidence to support this theory? Test using $\alpha = .05$.

c. Interpret the value of R_a^2.

12.77 Corporate sustainability and firm characteristics. Refer to the *Business and Society* (March 2011) study on how firm size and firm type impact corporate sustainability behaviors, Exercise 9.7 (p. 492). Recall that Certified Public Accountants (CPAs) were surveyed on their firms' likelihood of reporting sustainability policies (measured as a probability between 0 and 1). The CPAs were divided into four groups depending on firm size (large or small) and firm type (public or private): large/public, large/private, small/public, and small/private. One goal of the analysis is to determine whether the mean likelihood of reporting sustainability policies differs depending on firm size and firm type.

a. Consider a single qualitative variable representing the four size/type categories. Create the appropriate dummy variables for representing this qualitative variable as an independent variable in a regression model for predicting likelihood of reporting sustainability policies (y).

b. Give the equation of the model, part **a**, and interpret each of the model parameters.

c. The global F-test for the model resulted in p-value $< .001$. Give a practical interpretation of this result.

d. Now consider treating firm size and firm type as two different qualitative independent variables in a model for likelihood of reporting sustainability policies (y). Create the appropriate dummy variables for representing these qualitative variables in the model.

e. Refer to part **d**. Write a model for $E(y)$ as a function of firm size and firm type, but do not include interaction. (This model is called the *main effects* model.)

f. Refer to the model, part **e**. For each combination of firm size and firm type (e.g., large/public), write $E(y)$ as a function of the model parameters.

g. Use the results, part **f**, to show that for the main effects model, the difference between the mean likelihoods for large and small firms does not depend on firm type.

h. Write a model for $E(y)$ as a function of firm size, firm type, and size $\times$ type interaction.

i. Refer to the model, part **h**. For each combination of firm size and firm type (e.g., large/public), write $E(y)$ as a function of the model parameters.

j. Use the results, part **i**, to show that for the interaction model, the difference between the mean likelihoods for large and small firms does depend on firm type.

12.78 Homework assistance for accounting students. Refer to the *Journal of Accounting Education* (Vol. 25, 2007) study of assisting accounting students with their homework, Exercise 9.30 (p. 510). Recall that 175 accounting students took a pretest on a topic not covered in class and then each was given a homework problem to solve on the same topic. The students were assigned to one of three homework assistance groups. Some students received the completed solution, some were given check figures at various steps of the solution, and some received no help at all. After finishing the homework, the students were all given a posttest on the subject. The dependent variable of interest was the knowledge gain (or test score improvement). These data are saved in the file.

a. Propose a model for the knowledge gain (y) as a function of the qualitative variable, homework assistance group.

b. In terms of the β's in the model, give an expression for the difference between the mean knowledge gains of students in the "completed solution" and "no help" groups.

c. Fit the model to the data and give the least- diction equation.

d. Conduct
$\alpha = .05$. I

e. Show that
reached in

12.79 Comparing m
protect best a
REPELL 2000) tested 1
mosquito repe
lotion/cream o
dollars) was div
to cover expos
obtain a cost-pe
the maximum n

increments) provided when human testers exposed their arms to 200 mosquitoes. The data from the report are listed in the table.

Insect Repellent	Type	Cost/Use	Maximum Protection
Amway Hour Guard 12	Lotion/Cream	$2.08	13.5 hours
Avon Skin-So-Soft	Aerosol/Spray	0.67	0.5
Avon BugGuard Plus	Lotion/Cream	1.00	2.0
Ben's Backyard Formula	Lotion/Cream	0.75	7.0
Bite Blocker	Lotion/Cream	0.46	3.0
BugOut	Aerosol/Spray	0.11	6.0
Cutter Skinsations	Aerosol/Spray	0.22	3.0
Cutter Unscented	Aerosol/Spray	0.19	5.5
Muskoll Ultra6Hours	Aerosol/Spray	0.24	6.5
Natrapel	Aerosol/Spray	0.27	1.0
Off! Deep Woods	Aerosol/Spray	1.77	14.0
Off! Skintastic	Lotion/Cream	0.67	3.0
Sawyer Deet Formula	Lotion/Cream	0.36	7.0
Repel Permanone	Aerosol/Spray	2.75	24.0

Source: Based on "Buzz off and Insect repellants: Which keep bugs at bay?" *Consumer Reports*, June 2000.

a. Suppose you want to use repellent type to model the cost per use (y). Create the appropriate number of dummy variables for repellent type and write the model.

b. Fit the model, part **a**, to the data.

c. Give the null hypothesis for testing whether repellent type is a useful predictor of cost per use (y).

d. Conduct the test, part **c**, and give the appropriate conclusion. Use $\alpha = .10$.

e. Repeat parts **a–d** if the dependent variable is the maximum number of hours of protection (y).

Applying the Concepts—Advanced

12.80 Manipulating rates of return with stock splits. Some firms have been accused of using stock splits to manipulate their stock prices before being acquired by another firm. An article in *Financial Management* (Winter 2008) investigated the impact of stock splits on long-run stock performance for acquiring firms. A simplified version of the model fit by the researchers follows:

$$E(y) = \beta_0 + \beta_1 x_1 + \beta_2 x_2 + \beta_3 x_1 x_2,$$

where

$y =$ Firm's 3-year buy-and-hold return rate (%)
$x_1 = \{1$ if stock split prior to acquisition, 0 if not$\}$
$x_2 = \{1$ if firm's discretionary accrual is high, 0 if discretionary accrual is low$\}$

a. In terms of the β's in the model, what is the mean buy-and-hold return rate (BAR) for a firm with no stock split and a high discretionary accrual (DA)?

b. In terms of the β's in the model, what is the mean BAR for a firm with no stock split and a low DA?

c. For firms with no stock split, find the difference between the mean BAR for firms with high and low DA. (*Hint:* Use your answers to parts **a** and **b**.)

d. Repeat part **c** for firms with a stock split.

e. Note that the differences, parts **c** and **d**, are not the same. Explain why this illustrates the notion of interaction between x_1 and x_2.

f. A test for $H_0: \beta_3 = 0$ yielded a p-value of .027. Using $\alpha = .05$, interpret this result.

g. The researchers reported that the estimated values of both β_2 and β_3 are negative. Consequently, they conclude that "high-DA acquirers perform worse compared with low-DA acquirers. Moreover, the underperformance is even greater if high-DA acquirers have a stock split before acquistion." Do you agree?

12.81 Study of recall of TV commercials. Refer to the *Journal of Applied Psychology* (June 2002) study of recall of television commercials, Exercise 9.28 (p. 509). Participants were assigned to watch one of three types of TV programs, with nine commercials embedded in each show. Group V watched a TV program with a violent content code rating (e.g., *Tour of Duty*); group S viewed a show with a sex content code rating (e.g., *Strip Mall*); and group N watched a neutral TV program with neither a V nor an S rating (e.g., *Candid Camera*). The dependent variable measured for each participant was a score (y) on his/her recall of the brand names in the commercial messages, with scores ranging from 0 (no brands recalled) to 9 (all brands recalled).

a. Write a model for $E(y)$ as a function of viewer group.

b. Fit the model, part **a**, to the data saved in the file. Give the least squares prediction equation.

c. Conduct a test of overall model utility at $\alpha = .01$. Interpret the results.

d. The sample mean recall scores for the three groups were $\bar{y}_V = 2.08$, $\bar{y}_S = 1.71$, and $\bar{y}_N = 3.17$. Show how to find these sample means using only the β estimates obtained in part **b**.

Models with Both Quantitative and Qualitative Variables

Suppose you want to relate the mean monthly sales $E(y)$ of a company to monthly advertising expenditure x for three different advertising media (say newspaper, radio, and television) and you wish to use first-order (straight-line) models to model the responses for all three media. Graphs of these three relationships might appear as shown in Figure 12.20.

Because the lines in Figure 12.20 are hypothetical, a number of practical questions arise. Is one advertising medium as effective as any other? That is, do the three mean sales lines differ for the three advertising media? Do the increases in mean sales per dollar input in advertising differ for the three advertising media? That is, do the slopes of the three lines differ? Note that the two practical questions have been rephrased into questions about the parameters that define the three lines in Figure 12.20. To answer them, we must write a single regression model that will characterize the three lines of Figure 12.20 and that, by testing hypotheses about the lines, will answer the questions.

The response described previously, monthly sales, is a function of *two* independent variables, one quantitative (advertising expenditure x_1) and one qualitative (type of medium). We will proceed, in stages, to build a model relating $E(y)$ to these variables and will show graphically the interpretation we would give to the model at each stage. This will help you to see the contributions of the various terms in the model.

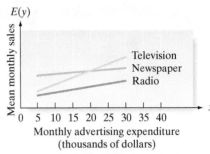

Figure 12.20

Graphs of the relationship between mean sales $E(y)$ and advertising expenditure x

1. The straight-line relationship between mean sales $E(y)$ and advertising expenditure is the same for all three media—that is, a single line will describe the relationship between $E(y)$ and advertising expenditure x_1 for all the media (see Figure 12.21).

$$E(y) = \beta_0 + \beta_1 x \qquad \text{where } x_1 = \text{advertising expenditure}$$

2. The straight lines relating mean sales $E(y)$ to advertising expenditure x_1 differ from one medium to another, but the rate of increase in mean sales per increase in dollar advertising expenditure x_1 is the same for all media—that is, the lines are parallel but possess different y-intercepts (see Figure 12.22).

$$E(y) = \beta_0 + \beta_1 x_1 + \beta_2 x_2 + \beta_3 x_3$$

where

$$x_1 = \text{advertising expenditure}$$

$$x_2 = \begin{cases} 1 & \text{if radio medium} \\ 0 & \text{if not} \end{cases}$$

$$x_3 = \begin{cases} 1 & \text{if television medium} \\ 0 & \text{if not} \end{cases}$$

Notice that this model is essentially a combination of a first-order model with a single quantitative variable and the model with a single qualitative variable:

First-order model with a single
quantitative variable: $E(y) = \beta_0 + \beta_1 x_1$

Model with single qualitative
variable at three levels: $E(y) = \beta_0 + \beta_2 x_2 + \beta_3 x_3$

where x_1, x_2, and x_3 are as just defined. The model described here implies no interaction between the two independent variables, which are advertising expenditure x_1 and the qualitative variable (type of advertising medium). The change in $E(y)$ for a 1-unit increase in x_1 is identical (the slopes of the lines are equal) for all three advertising media. The terms corresponding to each of the independent variables are called **main effect terms** because they imply no interaction.

3. The straight lines relating mean sales $E(y)$ to advertising expenditure x_1 differ for the three advertising media—that is, both the line intercepts and the slopes differ (see Figure 12.23). As you will see, this interaction model is obtained by

Figure 12.21

The relationship between $E(y)$ and x_1 is the same for all media

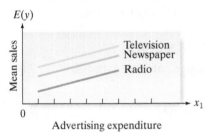

Figure 12.22

Parallel response lines for the three media

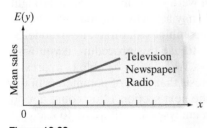

Figure 12.23

Different response lines for the three media

adding terms involving the cross-product terms, one each from each of the two independent variables:

$$E(y) = \overbrace{\beta_0 + \beta_1 x_1}^{\substack{\text{Main effect,}\\\text{advertising}\\\text{expenditure}}} + \overbrace{\beta_2 x_2 + \beta_3 x_3}^{\substack{\text{Main effect,}\\\text{type of}\\\text{medium}}} + \overbrace{\beta_4 x_1 x_2 + \beta_5 x_1 x_3}^{\text{Interaction}}$$

Note that each of the preceding models is obtained by adding terms to model 1, the single first-order model used to model the responses for all three media. Model 2 is obtained by adding the main effect terms for type of medium, the qualitative variable. Model 3 is obtained by adding the interaction terms to model 2.

Example 12.10

Interpreting the β's in a Model with Mixed Independent Variables

Problem Substitute the appropriate values of the dummy variables in model 3 (above) to obtain the equations of the three response lines in Figure 12.23.

Solution The complete model that characterizes the three lines in Figure 12.23 is

$$E(y) = \beta_0 + \beta_1 x_1 + \beta_2 x_2 + \beta_3 x_3 + \beta_4 x_1 x_2 + \beta_5 x_1 x_3$$

where

$$x_1 = \text{advertising expenditure}$$

$$x_2 = \begin{cases} 1 & \text{if radio medium} \\ 0 & \text{if not} \end{cases}$$

$$x_3 = \begin{cases} 1 & \text{if television medium} \\ 0 & \text{if not} \end{cases}$$

Examining the coding, you can see that $x_2 = x_3 = 0$ when the advertising medium is newspaper. Substituting these values into the expression for $E(y)$, we obtain the newspaper medium line:

$$E(y) = \beta_0 + \beta_1 x_1 + \beta_2(0) + \beta_3(0) + \beta_4 x_1(0) + \beta_5 x_1(0) = \beta_0 + \beta_1 x_1$$

Similarly, we substitute the appropriate values of x_2 and x_3 into the expression for $E(y)$ to obtain the radio medium line $(x_2 = 1, x_3 = 0)$:

$$E(y) = \beta_0 + \beta_1 x_1 + \beta_2(1) + \beta_3(0) + \beta_4 x_1(1) + \beta_5 x_1(0)$$

$$= \underbrace{(\beta_0 + \beta_2)}_{\textit{y-intercept}} + \underbrace{(\beta_1 + \beta_4)}_{\textit{Slope}} x_1$$

and the television medium line: $(x_2 = 0, x_3 = 1)$:

$$E(y) = \beta_0 + \beta_1 x_1 + \beta_2(0) + \beta_3(1) + \beta_4 x_1(0) + \beta_5 x_1(1)$$

$$= \underbrace{(\beta_0 + \beta_3)}_{\textit{y-intercept}} + \underbrace{(\beta_1 + \beta_5)}_{\textit{Slope}} x_1$$

Look Back If you were to fit model 3, obtain estimates of $\beta_0, \beta_1, \beta_2, \ldots, \beta_5$, and substitute them into the equations for the three media lines, you would obtain exactly the same prediction equations as you would obtain if you were to fit three separate straight lines, one to each of the three sets of media data. You may ask why we would not fit the three lines separately. Why bother fitting a model that combines all three lines (model 3) into the same equation? The answer is that you need to use this procedure if you wish to use statistical tests to compare the three media lines. We need to be able to express a practical question about the lines in terms of a hypothesis that a set of parameters in the model equals 0. (We demonstrate this procedure in the next section.) You could not do this if you were to perform three separate regression analyses and fit a line to each set of media data.

■ **Now Work Exercise 12.82**

Example 12.11

Testing for Two Different Slopes—Worker Productivity

Problem An industrial psychologist conducted an experiment to investigate the relationship between worker productivity and a measure of salary incentive for two manufacturing plants: One plant operates under "disciplined management practices," and the other plant uses a traditional management style. The productivity y per worker was measured by recording the number of machined castings that a worker could produce in a 4-week period of 40 hours per week. The incentive was the amount x_1 of bonus (in cents per casting) paid for all castings produced in excess of 1,000 per worker for the 4-week period. Nine workers were selected from each plant, and three from each group of nine were assigned to receive a 20¢ bonus per casting, three a 30¢ bonus, and three a 40¢ bonus. The productivity data for the 18 workers, three for each plant type and incentive combination, are shown in Table 12.4.

Table 12.4	Productivity Data for Example 12.11								
Management style	Incentive								
	20¢/casting			30¢/casting			40¢/casting		
Traditional	1,435	1,512	1,491	1,583	1,529	1,610	1,601	1,574	1,636
Disciplined	1,575	1,512	1,488	1,635	1,589	1,661	1,645	1,616	1,689

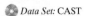

Data Set: CAST

a. Write a model for mean productivity, $E(y)$, assuming that the relationship between $E(y)$ and incentive x_1 is first-order.

b. Fit the model and graph the prediction equations for the disciplined and traditional management styles.

c. Do the data provide sufficient evidence to indicate that the rate of increase of worker productivity is different for disciplined and traditional plants? Test at $\alpha = .10$.

Solution

a. If we assume that a first-order model* is adequate to detect a change in mean productivity as a function of incentive x_1, then the model that produces two straight lines, one for each plant, is

$$E(y) = \beta_0 + \beta_1 x_1 + \beta_2 x_2 + \beta_3 x_1 x_2$$

where

$$x_1 = \text{incentive} \qquad x_2 = \begin{cases} 1 & \text{if disciplined management style} \\ 0 & \text{if traditional management style} \end{cases}$$

b. The SPSS printout for the regression analysis is shown in Figure 12.24. Reading the parameter estimates highlighted at the bottom of the printout, you can see that

$$\hat{y} = 1,365.833 + 6.217x_1 + 47.778x_2 + .033x_1 x_2$$

The prediction equation for the plant using a traditional management style can be obtained (see the coding) by substituting $x_2 = 0$ into the general prediction equation. Then

$$\hat{y} = \hat{\beta}_0 + \hat{\beta}_1 x_1 + \hat{\beta}_2(0) + \hat{\beta}_3 x_1(0) = \hat{\beta}_0 + \hat{\beta}_1 x_1$$
$$= 1,365.833 + 6.217x_1$$

---

*Although the model contains a term involving $x_1 x_2$, it is first-order (graphs as a straight line) in the quantitative variable x_1. The variable x_2 is a dummy variable that introduces or deletes terms in the model. The order of a model is determined only by the quantitative variables that appear in the model.

Model Summary

Model	R	R Square	Adjusted R Square	Std. Error of the Estimate
1	.843[a]	.711	.649	40.839

a. Predictors: (Constant), INC_PDUM, INCENTIV, PDUMMY

ANOVA[b]

Model		Sum of Squares	df	Mean Square	F	Sig.
1	Regression	57332.39	3	19110.796	11.459	.000[a]
	Residual	23349.22	14	1667.802		
	Total	80681.61	17			

a. Predictors: (Constant), INC_PDUM, INCENTIV, PDUMMY

b. Dependent Variable: CASTINGS

Coefficients[a]

Model		Unstandardized Coefficients		Standardized Coefficients	t	Sig.
		B	Std. Error	Beta		
1	(Constant)	1365.833	51.836		26.349	.000
	INCENTIV	6.217	1.667	.758	3.729	.002
	PDUMMY	47.778	73.308	.357	.652	.525
	INC_PDUM	.033	2.358	.008	.014	.989

a. Dependent Variable: CASTINGS

Figure 12.24

SPSS printout of the complete model for the casting data

Similarly, the prediction equation for the plant with a disciplined management style can be obtained by substituting $x_2 = 1$ into the general prediction equation. Then

$$\hat{y} = \hat{\beta}_0 + \hat{\beta}_1 x_1 + \hat{\beta}_2 x_2 + \hat{\beta}_3 x_1 x_2$$
$$= \hat{\beta}_0 + \hat{\beta}_1 x_1 + \hat{\beta}_2(1) + \hat{\beta}_3 x_1(1)$$
$$= \overbrace{(\beta_0 + \beta_2)}^{\text{y-intercept}} + \overbrace{(\beta_1 + \beta_3)x_1}^{\text{Slope}}$$
$$= (1{,}365.833 + 47.778) + (6.217 + .033)x_1$$
$$= 1{,}413.611 + 6.250x_1$$

A Minitab graph of these prediction equations is shown in Figure 12.25. Note that the slopes of the two lines are nearly identical (6.217 for traditional and 6.250 for disciplined).

Figure 12.25

Minitab plot of prediction equations for two plants

c. If the rate of increase of productivity with incentive (i.e., the slope) for plants with the disciplined management style is different from the corresponding slope for traditional plants, then the interaction β (i.e., β_3) will differ from 0. Consequently, we want to test

$$H_0: \beta_3 = 0$$
$$H_a: \beta_3 \neq 0$$

This test is conducted using the t-test of Section 12.3. From the SPSS printout, the test statistic and corresponding p-value are

$$t = .014 \qquad p = .989$$

Because $\alpha = .10$ is less than the p-value, we fail to reject H_0. There is insufficient evidence to conclude that the traditional and disciplined shapes differ. Thus, the test supports our observation of two nearly identical slopes in part **b.**

Look Back Because interaction is not significant, we will drop the $x_1 x_2$ term from the model and use the simpler model, $E(y) = \beta_0 + \beta_1 x_1 + \beta_2 x_2$, to predict productivity.

◼ **Now Work Exercise 12.88**

Models with both quantitative and qualitative x's may also include higher-order (e.g., second-order) terms. In the problem of relating mean monthly sales $E(y)$ of a company to monthly advertising expenditure x_1 and type of medium, suppose we think that the relationship between $E(y)$ and x_1 is curvilinear. We will construct the model, stage by stage, to enable you to compare the procedure with the stage-by-stage construction of the first-order model in the beginning of this section. The graphical interpretations will help you understand the contributions of the model terms.

1. The mean sales curves are identical for all three advertising media—that is, a single second-order curve will suffice to describe the relationship between $E(y)$ and x_1 for all the media (see Figure 12.26):

$$E(y) = \beta_0 + \beta_1 x_1 + \beta_2 x_1^2$$

where $x_1 =$ advertising expenditure

2. The response curves possess the same shapes but different y-intercepts (see Figure 12.27):

$$E(y) = \beta_0 + \beta_1 x_1 + \beta_2 x_1^2 + \beta_3 x_2 + \beta_4 x_3$$

where

$$x_1 = \text{advertising expenditure}$$

$$x_2 = \begin{cases} 1 & \text{if radio medium} \\ 0 & \text{if not} \end{cases}$$

$$x_3 = \begin{cases} 1 & \text{if television medium} \\ 0 & \text{if not} \end{cases}$$

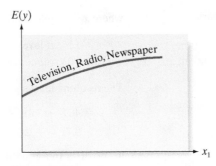

Figure 12.26

The relationship between $E(y)$ and x_1 is the same for all media

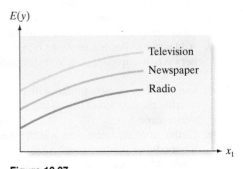

Figure 12.27

The response curves have the same shapes but different y-intercepts

3. The response curves for the three advertising media are different (i.e., advertising expenditure and type of medium interact), as shown in Figure 12.28:

$$E(y) = \beta_0 + \beta_1 x_1 + \beta_2 x_1^2 + \beta_3 x_2 + \beta_4 x_3 + \beta_5 x_1 x_2 + \beta_6 x_1 x_3 + \beta_7 x_1^2 x_2 + \beta_8 x_1^2 x_3$$

Now that you know how to write a model with two independent variables—one qualitative and one quantitative—we ask, Why do it? Why not write a separate second-order model for each type of medium where $E(y)$ is a function of only advertising expenditure? As stated earlier, one reason we wrote the single model representing all three response curves is so that we can test to determine whether the curves are different. We illustrate this procedure in Section 12.9. A second reason for writing a single model is that we obtain a pooled estimate of σ^2, the variance of the random error component ε. If the variance of ε is truly the same for each type of medium, the pooled estimate is superior to three separate estimates calculated by fitting a separate model for each type of medium.

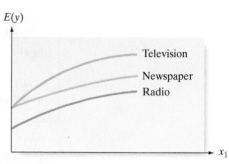

Figure 12.28

The response curves for the three media differ

Exercises 12.82–12.96

Learning the Mechanics

12.82 Consider a multiple regression model for a response y, with one quantitative independent variable x_1 and one qualitative variable at three levels.
  a. Write a first-order model that relates the mean response $E(y)$ to the quantitative independent variable.
  b. Add the main effect terms for the qualitative independent variable to the model of part **a.** Specify the coding scheme you use.
  c. Add terms to the model of part **b** to allow for interaction between the quantitative and qualitative independent variables.
  d. Under what circumstances will the response lines of the model in part **c** be parallel?
  e. Under what circumstances will the model in part **c** have only one response line?

12.83 Refer to Exercise 12.82.
  a. Write a complete second-order model that relates $E(y)$ to the quantitative variable.
  b. Add the main effect terms for the qualitative variable (at three levels) to the model of part **a.**
  c. Add terms to the model of part **b** to allow for interaction between the quantitative and qualitative independent variables.
  d. Under what circumstances will the response curves of the model have the same shape but different y-intercepts?
  e. Under what circumstances will the response curves of the model be parallel lines?
  f. Under what circumstances will the response curves of the model be identical?

12.84 Consider the model:
$$y = \beta_0 + \beta_1 x_1 + \beta_2 x_2 + \beta_3 x_3 + \varepsilon$$

where x_1 is a quantitative variable and x_2 and x_3 are dummy variables describing a qualitative variable at three levels using the coding scheme

$$x_2 = \begin{cases} 1 & \text{if level 2} \\ 0 & \text{otherwise} \end{cases} \qquad x_3 = \begin{cases} 1 & \text{if level 3} \\ 0 & \text{otherwise} \end{cases}$$

The resulting least squares prediction equation is

$$\hat{y} = 44.8 + 2.2 x_1 + 9.4 x_2 + 15.6 x_3$$

  a. What is the response line (equation) for $E(y)$ when $x_2 = x_3 = 0$? When $x_2 = 1$ and $x_3 = 0$? When $x_2 = 0$ and $x_3 = 1$?
  b. What is the least squares prediction equation associated with level 1? Level 2? Level 3? Plot these on the same graph.

12.85 Consider the model:
$$y = \beta_0 + \beta_1 x_1 + \beta_2 x_1^2 + \beta_3 x_2 + \beta_4 x_3 +$$
$$\beta_5 x_1 x_2 + \beta_6 x_1 x_3 + \beta_7 x_1^2 x_2 + \beta_8 x_1^2 x_3 + \varepsilon$$

where x_1 is a quantitative variable and

$$x_2 = \begin{cases} 1 & \text{if level 2} \\ 0 & \text{otherwise} \end{cases} \qquad x_3 = \begin{cases} 1 & \text{if level 3} \\ 0 & \text{otherwise} \end{cases}$$

The resulting least squares prediction equation is

$$\hat{y} = 48.8 - 3.4 x_1 + .07 x_1^2 - 2.4 x_2 - 7.5 x_3 +$$
$$3.7 x_1 x_2 + 2.7 x_1 x_3 - .02 x_1^2 x_2 - .04 x_1^2 x_3$$

  a. What is the equation of the response curve for $E(y)$ when $x_2 = 0$ and $x_3 = 0$? When $x_2 = 1$ and $x_3 = 0$? When $x_2 = 0$ and $x_3 = 1$?
  b. On the same graph, plot the least squares prediction equation associated with level 1, with level 2, and with level 3.

12.86 Write a model that relates $E(y)$ to two independent variables—one quantitative and one qualitative at four levels. Construct a model that allows the associated response curves to be second-order but does not allow for interaction between the two independent variables.

Applying the Concepts—Basic

12.87 Reality TV and cosmetic surgery. Refer to the *Body Image: An International Journal of Research* (March 2010) study of the impact of reality TV shows on a college student's decision to undergo cosmetic surgery, Exercise 12.43 (p. 696). The data saved in the file were used to fit the interaction model, $E(y) = \beta_0 + \beta_1 x_1 + \beta_2 x_4 + \beta_3 x_1 x_4$, where y = desire to have cosmetic surgery (25-point scale), $x_1 = \{1 \text{ if male, 0 if female}\}$, and x_4 = impression of reality TV (7-point scale). From the SPSS printout (p. 696), the estimated equation is:

$$\hat{y} = 11.78 - 1.97x_1 + .58x_4 - .55x_1 x_4$$

a. Give an estimate of the change in desire (y) for every 1-point increase in impression of reality TV show (x_4) for female students.

b. Repeat part **a** for male students.

12.88 Do blondes raise more funds? Refer to the *Economic Letters* (Vol. 100, 2008) study of whether the color of a female solicitor's hair impacts the level of capital raised, Exercise 12.75 (p. 712). Recall that 955 households were contacted by a female solicitor to raise funds for hazard mitigation research. In addition to the household's level of contribution (in dollars) and the hair color of the solicitor (blond Caucasian, brunette Caucasian, or minority female), the researcher also recorded the beauty rating of the solicitor (measured quantitatively, on a 10-point scale).

a. Write a first-order model (with no interaction) for mean contribution level, $E(y)$, as a function of a solicitor's hair color and her beauty rating.

b. Refer to the model, part **a**. For each hair color, express the change in contribution level for each 1-point increase in a solicitor's beauty rating in terms of the model parameters.

c. Write an interaction model for mean contribution level, $E(y)$, as a function of a solicitor's hair color and her beauty rating.

d. Refer to the model, part **c**. For each hair color, express the change in contribution level for each 1-point increase in a solicitor's beauty rating in terms of the model parameters.

e. Refer to the model, part **c**. Illustrate the interaction with a graph.

12.89 Impact of race on football card values. Refer to the *Electronic Journal of Sociology* (2007) study of the impact of race on the value of professional football players' "rookie" cards, Exercise 12.72 (p. 712). Recall that the sample consisted of 148 rookie cards of NFL players who were inducted into the Football Hall of Fame (HOF). The researchers modeled the natural logarithm of card price (y) as a function of the following independent variables:

Race:	$x_1 = 1$ if black, 0 if white
Card availability:	$x_2 = 1$ if high, 0 if low
Card vintage:	x_3 = year card printed
Finalist:	x_4 = natural logarithm of number of times player on final HOF ballot
Position-QB:	$x_5 = 1$ if quarterback, 0 if not
Position-RB:	$x_7 = 1$ if running back, 0 if not
Position-WR:	$x_8 = 1$ if wide receiver, 0 if not
Position-TE:	$x_9 = 1$ if tight end, 0 if not
Position-DL:	$x_{10} = 1$ if defensive lineman, 0 if not
Position-LB:	$x_{11} = 1$ if linebacker, 0 if not
Position-DB:	$x_{12} = 1$ if defensive back, 0 if not

[*Note:* For position, offensive lineman is the base level.]

a. The model $E(y) = \beta_0 + \beta_1 x_1 + \beta_2 x_2 + \beta_3 x_3 + \beta_4 x_4 + \beta_5 x_5 + \beta_6 x_6 + \beta_7 x_7 + \beta_8 x_8 + \beta_9 x_9 + \beta_{10} x_{10} + \beta_{11} x_{11} + \beta_{12} x_{12}$ was fit to the data with the following results: $R^2 = .705$, $R_a^2 = .681$, $F = 26.9$. Interpret the results, practically. Make an inference about the overall adequacy of the model.

b. Refer to part **a**. Statistics for the race variable were reported as follows: $\hat{\beta}_1 = -.147$, $s_{\hat{\beta}_1} = .145$, $t = -1.014$, p-value $= .312$. Use this information to make an inference about the impact of race on the value of professional football players' rookie cards.

c. Refer to part **a**. Statistics for the card vintage variable were reported as follows: $\hat{\beta}_3 = -.074$, $s_{\hat{\beta}_3} = .007$, $t = -10.92$, p-value $= .000$. Use this information to make an inference about the impact of card vintage on the value of professional football players' rookie cards.

d. Write a first-order model for $E(y)$ as a function of card vintage (x_3) and position (x_5–x_{12}) that allows for the relationship between price and vintage to vary depending on position.

12.90 Buy-side vs. sell-side analysts' earnings forecasts. Refer to the *Financial Analysts Journal* (Jul./Aug. 2008) comparison of earnings forecasts of buy-side and sell-side analysts, Exercise 12.74 (p. 712). Recall that the Harvard Business School professors used regression to model the relative optimism (y) of the analysts' 3-month horizon forecasts. The following model was fit to data collected on 11,121 forecasts: $E(y) = \beta_0 + \beta_1 x_1 + \beta_2 x_2 + \beta_3 x_3$, where

$x_1 = \{1$ if the analyst worked for a buy-side firm, 0 if the analyst worked for a sell-side firm$\}$

x_2 = number of days between forecast and fiscal year-end (i.e., forecast horizon)

x_3 = natural logarithm of the number of quarters the analyst had worked with the firm

a. The coefficient of determination for the model was reported as $R^2 = .069$. Interpret this value.

b. Use the value of R^2 in part **a** to conduct a test of the global utility of the model. Use $\alpha = .01$.

c. The value of β_1 was estimated as 1.07, with an associated t-value of 4.3. Use this information to test ($\alpha = .01$.) whether x_1 contributes significantly to the prediction of y.

d. The professors concluded that "after controlling for forecast horizon and analyst experience, earnings forecasts by the analysts at buy-side firms are more optimistic than forecasts made by analysts at sell-side firms." Do you agree?

12.91 Workplace bullying and intention to leave. Workplace bullying (e.g., work-related harassment, persistent criticism, withholding key information, spreading rumors, intimidation) has been shown to have a negative psychological effect on victims, often leading the victim to quit or resign. In *Human Resource Management Journal* (Oct. 2008), researchers employed multiple regression to examine whether perceived organizational support (POS) would moderate the relationship between workplace bullying and victims' intention to leave the firm. The dependent variable in the analysis, intention to leave (y), was measured on a quantitative scale. The two key independent variables in the study were bullying (x_1, measured on a quantitative scale) and perceived organizational support (measured qualitatively as "low," "neutral," or "high").

a. Set up the dummy variables required to represent POS in the regression model.

b. Write a model for $E(y)$ as a function of bullying and POS that hypothesizes three parallel straight lines, one for each level of POS.

c. Write a model for $E(y)$ as a function of bullying and POS that hypothesizes three nonparallel straight lines, one for each level of POS.

d. The researchers discovered that the effect of bullying on intention to leave was greater at the low level of POS than at the high level of POS. Which of the two models, parts **b** and **c**, support these findings?

Applying the Concepts—Intermediate

12.92 Agreeableness, gender, and wages. Do agreeable individuals get paid less, on average, than those who are less agreeable on the job? And is this gap greater for males than for females? These questions were addressed in the *Journal of Personality and Social Psychology* (Feb. 2012). Several variables were measured for each in a sample of individuals enrolled in the National Survey of Midlife Development in the U.S. Three of these variables are: (1) level of agreeableness score (where higher scores indicate a greater level of agreeableness), (2) gender (male or female), and (3) annual income (dollars). The researchers modeled mean income, $E(y)$, as a function of both agreeableness score (x_1) and a dummy variable for gender ($x_2 = 1$ if male, 0 if female). Data for a sample of 100 individuals (simulated, based on information provided in the study) are saved in the file. The first 10 observations are listed in the accompanying table.

Data for First 10 Individuals in Study

Income	Agree Score	Gender
44,770	3.0	1
51,480	2.9	1
39,600	3.3	1
24,370	3.3	0
15,460	3.6	0
43,730	3.8	1
48,330	3.2	1
25,970	2.5	0
17,120	3.5	0
20,140	3.2	0

a. Consider the model, $E(y) = \beta_0 + \beta_1 x_1 + \beta_2 x_2$. The researchers theorized that for either gender, income would decrease as agreeableness score increases. If this theory is true, what is the expected sign of β_1 in the model?

b. The researchers also theorized that the rate of decrease of income with agreeableness score would be steeper for males than for females (i.e., the income gap between males and females would be greater the less agreeable the individuals are). Can this theory be tested using the model, part **a**? Explain.

c. Consider the interaction model, $E(y) = \beta_0 + \beta_1 x_1 + \beta_2 x_2 + \beta_3 x_1 x_2$. If the theory, part **b**, is true, give the expected sign of β_1. The expected sign of β_3.

d. Fit the model, part **c**, to the sample data. Check the signs of the estimated β coefficients. How do they compare to the expected values, part **c**?

e. Refer to the interaction model, part **c**. Give the null and alternative hypotheses for testing whether the rate of decrease of income with agreeableness score is steeper for males than for females.

f. Conduct the test, part **e**. Use $\alpha = .05$. Is the researchers' theory supported?

12.93 Chemical plant contamination. Refer to Exercise 12.18 (p. 683) and the model relating the mean DDT level $E(y)$ of contaminated fish to $x_1 =$ miles captured upstream, $x_2 =$ length, and $x_3 =$ weight. Now consider a model for $E(y)$ as a function of both weight and species (channel catfish, largemouth bass, and smallmouth buffalo).

a. Set up the appropriate dummy variables for species.

b. Write the equation of a model that proposes parallel straight-line relationships between mean DDT level $E(y)$ and weight, one line for each species.

c. Write the equation of a model that proposes nonparallel straight-line relationships between mean DDT level $E(y)$ and weight, one line for each species.

d. Fit the model, part **b**, to the data saved in the file. Give the least squares prediction equation.

e. Refer to part **d**. Interpret the value of the least squares estimate of the beta coefficient multiplied by weight.

f. Fit the model, part **c**, to the data saved in the file. Give the least squares prediction equation.

g. Refer to part **f**. Find the estimated slope of the line relating DDT level (y) to weight for the channel catfish species.

12.94 Personality traits and job performance. Refer to the *Journal of Applied Psychology* (Jan. 2011) study of the relationship between task performance and conscientiousness, Exercise 12.54 (p. 704). Recall that the researchers used a quadratic model to relate $y =$ task performance score (measured on a 30-point scale) to $x_1 =$ conscientiousness score (measured on a scale of -3 to $+3$). In addition, the researchers included job complexity in the model, where $x_2 = \{1$ if highly complex job, 0 if not$\}$. The complete model took the form

$$E(y) = \beta_0 + \beta_1 x_1 + \beta_2 (x_1)^2 + \beta_3 x_2 + \beta_4 x_1 x_2 + \beta_5 (x_1)^2 x_2$$

a. For jobs that are not highly complex, write the equation of the model for $E(y)$ as a function of x_1. (Substitute $x_2 = 0$ into the equation.)

b. Refer to part **a.** What do each of the β's represent in the model?

c. For highly complex jobs, write the equation of the model for $E(y)$ as a function of x_1. (Substitute $x_2 = 1$ into the equation.)

d. Refer to part **c.** What do each of the β's represent in the model?

e. Does the model support the researchers' theory that the curvilinear relationship between task performance score (y) and conscientiousness score (x_1) depends on job complexity (x_2)? Explain.

12.95 Recently sold, single-family homes. The National Association of Realtors maintains a database consisting of sales information on homes sold in the United States. The next table lists the sale prices for a sample of 28 recently sold, single-family homes. The table also identifies the region of the country in which the home is located and the total number of homes sold in the region during the month the home sold.

Home Price	Region	Sales Volume
$218,200	NE	55,156
235,900	NE	61,025
192,888	NE	48,991
200,990	NE	55,156
345,300	NE	60,324
178,999	NE	51,446
240,855	NW	61,025
183,200	NW	94,166
165,225	NW	92,063
160,633	NW	89,485
173,900	NW	91,772
241,000	NW	99,025
188,950	NW	94,166
192,880	NW	95,688
193,000	S	155,666
211,980	S	160,000
179,500	S	153,540
185,650	S	148,668
250,900	S	163,210
190,990	S	141,822
242,790	S	163,611
258,900	W	109,083
202,420	W	101,111
365,900	W	116,983
219,900	W	108,773
228,250	W	105,106
235,300	W	107,839
269,800	W	109,026

Source: Based on information from National Association of Realtors, www.realtor.org.

a. Propose a complete second-order model for the sale price of a single-family home as a function of region and sales volume.

b. Give the equation of the curve relating sale price to sales volume for homes sold in the West.

c. Repeat part **b** for homes sold in the Northwest.

d. Which β's in the model, part **a**, allow for differences among the mean sale prices for homes in the four regions?

e. Fit the model, part **a**, to the data using an available statistical software package. Is the model statistically useful for predicting sale price? Test using $\alpha = .01$.

12.96 Volatility of foreign stocks. The relationship between country credit ratings and the volatility of the countries' stock markets was examined in the *Journal of Portfolio Management* (Spring 1996). The researchers point out that this volatility can be explained by two factors: the countries' credit ratings and whether the countries in question have developed or emerging markets. Data on the volatility (measured as the standard deviation of stock returns), credit rating (measured as a percentage), and market type (developed or emerging) for a sample of 30 fictitious countries are saved in the file. (Selected observations are shown in the table below.)

a. Write a model that describes the relationship between volatility (y) and credit rating (x_1) as two nonparallel lines, one for each type of market. Specify the dummy variable coding scheme you use.

b. Plot volatility y against credit rating x_1 for all the developed markets in the sample. On the same graph, plot y against x_1 for all emerging markets in the sample. Does it appear that the model specified in part **a** is appropriate? Explain.

c. Fit the model, part **a**, to the data using a statistical software package. Report the least squares prediction equation for each of the two types of markets.

d. Plot the two prediction equations of part **c** on a scatterplot of the data.

e. Is there evidence to conclude that the slope of the linear relationship between volatility y and credit rating x_1 depends on market type? Test using $\alpha = .01$.

Country	Volatility (standard deviation of return), y	Credit Rating, x_1	Developed (D) or Emerging (E), x_2
1	56.9	9.5	E
2	25.1	72.4	D
3	28.4	58.2	E
4	56.2	9.9	E
5	21.5	92.1	D
⋮	⋮	⋮	⋮
26	47.5	16.9	E
27	22.0	89.0	D
28	21.5	91.9	D
29	38.1	30.7	E
30	37.4	32.2	E

12.9 Comparing Nested Models

To be successful model builders, we require a statistical method that will allow us to determine (with a high degree of confidence) which one among a set of candidate models best fits the data. In this section, we present such a technique for *nested models*.

> Two models are **nested** if one model contains all the terms of the second model and at least one additional term. The more complex of the two models is called the **complete** (or **full**) model, and the simpler of the two is called the **reduced** model.

To illustrate the concept of nested models, consider the straight-line interaction model for the mean auction price $E(y)$ of a grandfather clock as a function of two quantitative variables: age of the clock (x_1) and number of bidders (x_2). The interaction model, fit in Example 12.6, is

$$E(y) = \beta_0 + \beta_1 x_1 + \beta_2 x_2 + \beta_3 x_1 x_2$$

If we assume that the relationship between auction price (y), age (x_1), and bidders (x_2) is curvilinear, then the complete second-order model is more appropriate:

$$E(y) = \overbrace{\beta_0 + \beta_1 x_1 + \beta_2 x_2 + \beta_3 x_1 x_2}^{\text{Terms in interaction model}} + \overbrace{\beta_4 x_1^2 + \beta_5 x_2^2}^{\text{Quadratic terms}}$$

Note that the curvilinear model contains quadratic terms for x_1 and x_2, as well as the terms in the interaction model. Therefore, the models are nested models. In this case, the interaction model is nested within the more complex curvilinear model. Thus, the curvilinear model is the *complete* model, and the interaction model is the *reduced* model.

Suppose we want to know whether the more complex curvilinear model contributes more information for the prediction of y than the straight-line interaction model. This is equivalent to determining whether the quadratic terms β_4 and β_5 should be retained in the model. To test whether these terms should be retained, we test the null hypothesis

$H_0: \beta_4 = \beta_5 = 0$ (i.e., quadratic terms are not important for predicting y)

against the alternative hypothesis

H_a: At least one of the parameters β_4 and β_5 is nonzero (i.e., at least one of the quadratic terms is useful for predicting y).

Note that the terms being tested are those additional terms in the complete (curvilinear) model that are not in the reduced (straight-line interaction) model.

In Section 12.3, we presented the *t*-test for a single β coefficient and the global *F*-test for *all* the β parameters (except β_0) in the model. We now need a test for a *subset* of the β parameters in the complete model. The test procedure is intuitive. First, we use the method of least squares to fit the reduced model and calculate the corresponding sum of squares for error, SSE_R (the sum of squares of the deviations between observed and predicted y-values). Next, we fit the complete model and calculate its sum of squares for error, SSE_C. Then we compare SSE_R to SSE_C by calculating the difference, $SSE_R - SSE_C$. If the additional terms in the complete model are significant, then SSE_C should be much smaller than SSE_R, and the difference $SSE_R - SSE_C$ will be large.

Because SSE will always decrease when new terms are added to the model, the question is whether the difference $SSE_R - SSE_C$ is large enough to conclude that it is due to more than just an increase in the number of model terms and to chance. The formal statistical test uses an *F*-statistic, as shown in the box.

When the assumptions listed in Section 12.1 about the random error term are satisfied, this *F*-statistic has an *F*-distribution with ν_1 and ν_2 df. Note that ν_1 is the number of

β parameters being tested, and ν_2 is the number of degrees of freedom associated with s^2 in the complete model.

F-Test for Comparing Nested Models

Reduced model: $E(y) = \beta_0 + \beta_1 x_1 + \cdots + \beta_g x_g$

Complete model: $E(y) = \beta_0 + \beta_1 x_1 + \cdots + \beta_g x_g + \beta_{g+1} x_{g+1} + \cdots + \beta_k x_k$

$H_0: \beta_{g+1} = \beta_{g+2} = \cdots = \beta_k = 0$

$H_a:$ At least one of the β parameters under test is nonzero.

$$\text{Test statistic: } F = \frac{(\text{SSE}_R - \text{SSE}_C)/(k - g)}{\text{SSE}_C/[n - (k + 1)]}$$

$$= \frac{(\text{SSE}_R - \text{SSE}_C)/\#\beta\text{'s tested in } H_0}{\text{MSE}_C}$$

where

SSE_R = Sum of squared errors for the reduced model

SSE_C = Sum of squared errors for the complete model

MSE_C = Mean square error (s^2) for the complete model

$k - g$ = Number of β parameters specified in H_0 (i.e., number of β parameters tested)

$k + 1$ = Number of β parameters in the complete model (including β_0)

n = Total sample size

Rejection region: $F > F_\alpha$

where F is based on $\nu_1 = k - g$ numerator degrees of freedom and $\nu_2 = n - (k + 1)$ denominator degrees of freedom.

Example 12.12

Analyzing a Complete Second-Order Model— Auction Price Data

Problem Refer to the problem of modeling the auction price (y) of an antique grandfather clock, Examples 12.1–12.6. In these examples, we discovered that price was related to both age (x_1) of the clock and number of bidders (x_2), and age and number of bidders had an interactive effect on price. Both the first-order model of Example 12.1 and the interaction model of Example 12.6, however, propose only straight-line (linear) relationships. We did not consider the possibility that the relationship between price (y) and age (x_1) is curvilinear, or that the relationship between price (y) and number of bidders (x_2) is curvilinear.

a. Propose a complete second-order model for price (y) as a function of age (x_1) and number of bidders (x_2).

b. Fit the model to the data for the 32 clocks in Table 12.1 and give the least squares prediction equation.

c. Do the data provide sufficient evidence to indicate that the quadratic terms in the model contribute information for the prediction of price (y)? That is, is there evidence of curvature in the price-age and price-bidders relationships?

Solution

a. Because both age (x_1) and number of bidders (x_2) are quantitative variables, we write the complete second-order model as follows:

$$E(y) = \beta_0 + \beta_1 x_1 + \beta_2 x_2 + \beta_3 x_1 x_2 + \beta_4 (x_1)^2 + \beta_5 (x_2)^2$$

Note that we have added two quadratic terms, $\beta_4(x_1)^2$ and $\beta_5(x_2)^2$, to the interaction model of Example 12.6.

Regression Analysis: PRICE versus AGE, NUMBIDS, AGE-BID, AGESQ, NUMBIDSQ

```
The regression equation is
PRICE = - 332 + 3.21 AGE + 14.8 NUMBIDS + 1.12 AGE-BID - 0.0030 AGESQ
        - 4.18 NUMBIDSQ

Predictor      Coef  SE Coef       T      P
Constant     -331.9    764.9   -0.43  0.668
AGE           3.208    8.947    0.36  0.723
NUMBIDS       14.81    62.21    0.24  0.814
AGE-BID      1.1232   0.2316    4.85  0.000
AGESQ      -0.00300  0.02748   -0.11  0.914
NUMBIDSQ     -4.179    2.145   -1.95  0.062

S = 86.1019   R-Sq = 96.0%   R-Sq(adj) = 95.2%

Analysis of Variance

Source          DF       SS      MS       F      P
Regression       5  4607038  921408  124.29  0.000
Residual Error  26   192752    7414
Total           31  4799790
```

Figure 12.29

Minitab analysis of complete second-order model for auction price

b. We used Minitab to fit the model to the data in Table 12.2. The Minitab output is shown in Figure 12.29. The least squares prediction equation, highlighted on the printout, is

$$\hat{y} = -332 + 3.21x_1 + 14.8x_2 + 1.12x_1x_2 - .003(x_1)^2 - 4.18(x_2)^2$$

Note that the estimates of the quadratic terms, β_4 and β_5, are both negative, implying downward curvature in both the price-age and price-bidders relationships.

c. To determine whether the quadratic terms are useful for predicting price (y), we want to test

$$H_0: \beta_4 = \beta_5 = 0$$

H_a: At least one of the parameters, β_4 and β_5, differs from 0.

Because the null hypothesis involves a subset of β's, we will need to perform a nested model F-test. The complete model is the complete second-order model of part **a.** The reduced model is obtained by dropping the quadratic terms out of the complete model. Doing so yields:

Reduced model: $E(y) = \beta_0 + \beta_1x_1 + \beta_2x_2 + \beta_3x_1x_2$

We fit this model in Example 12.6. The Minitab printout for this reduced model is reproduced in Figure 12.30.

To conduct this test, we first obtain the SSE values for the complete and reduced models. These values (highlighted, respectively, on Figures 12.29 and 12.30) are

$$\text{SSE}_C = 192,752 \text{ and } \text{SSE}_R = 221,362$$

Also, s^2 for the complete model (highlighted on Figure 12.29) is

$$s^2 = \text{MSE}_C = 7,414$$

Recall that $n = 32$ and that there are $k = 5$ terms in the complete model and $g = 3$ terms in the reduced model. Therefore, the calculated value of the test statistic is

$$\text{Test statistic: } F = \frac{(\text{SSE}_R - \text{SSE}_C)/(k - g)}{\text{MSE}_C} = \frac{(221,362 - 192,752)/2}{7,414} = 1.93$$

The critical F-value for the rejection region is based on $\nu_1 = (k - g) = 2$ numerator df and $\nu_2 = [n - (k + 1)] = 26$ denominator df. If we choose $\alpha = .05$, this critical value is $F_{.05} = 3.37$ and the rejection region is

Rejection region: $F > 3.37$

Because the test statistic, $F = 1.93$, falls outside the rejection region, we fail to reject H_0. That is, there is insufficient evidence (at $\alpha = .05$) to conclude that at least one

Regression Analysis: PRICE versus AGE, NUMBIDS, AGEBID

```
The regression equation is
PRICE = 320 + 0.88 AGE - 93.3 NUMBIDS + 1.30 AGEBID


Predictor     Coef   SE Coef      T      P
Constant     320.5     295.1   1.09  0.287
AGE          0.878     2.032   0.43  0.669
NUMBIDS     -93.26     29.89  -3.12  0.004
AGEBID      1.2978    0.2123   6.11  0.000


S = 88.9145   R-Sq = 95.4%   R-Sq(adj) = 94.9%


Analysis of Variance

Source          DF        SS       MS       F      P
Regression       3   4578427  1526142  193.04  0.000
Residual Error  28    221362     7906
Total           31   4799790
```

Figure 12.30

Minitab analysis of reduced model for auction price

of the quadratic terms contributes information for the prediction of auction price (y). Consequently, there is no evidence of curvature in either the price-age or price-bidders relationship. It appears that the first-order, interaction (reduced) model is adequate for predicting auction price.

Look Back Some statistical software packages will perform the desired nested model F-test if requested. The test statistic and p-value for the test above are highlighted on the SPSS printout, Figure 12.31. Note that p-value = .165 exceeds α = .05; thus, there is insufficient evidence to reject H_0.

◼ **Now Work Exercise 12.100**

Model Summary

Mode l	R	R Square	Adjusted R Square	Std. Error of the Estimate	Change Statistics				
					R Square Change	F Change	df1	df2	Sig. F Change
1	.977[a]	.954	.949	88.915	.954	193.041	3	28	.000
2	.980[b]	.960	.952	86.102	.006	1.930	2	26	.165

a. Predictors: (Constant), AGE_BID, AGE, NUMBIDS

b. Predictors: (Constant), AGE_BID, AGE, NUMBIDS, NUMBIDSQ, AGESQ

Figure 12.31

SPSS printout of nested model F-test for auction price

The nested model F-test can be used to determine whether *any* subset of terms should be included in a complete model by testing the null hypothesis that a particular set of β parameters simultaneously equals 0. For example, we may want to test to determine whether a set of interaction terms for quantitative variables or a set of main effect terms for a qualitative variable should be included in a model. If we reject H_0, the complete model is the better of the two nested models. If we fail to reject H_0, as in Example 12.12, we favor the reduced model. Although we must be cautious about accepting H_0, most practitioners of regression analysis adopt the principle of *parsimony*—that is, in situations where two competing models are found to have essentially the same predictive power (as in Example 12.12), the model with the fewer number of β's (i.e., the more parsimonious model) is selected. Based on this principle, we would drop the two quadratic terms and select the first-order, interaction (reduced) model over the second-order (complete) model.

A **parsimonious model** is a general linear model with a small number of β parameters. In situations where two competing models have essentially the same predictive power (as determined by an F-test), choose the more parsimonious of the two.

> **Guidelines for Selecting Preferred Model in a Nested Model *F*-Test**
>
> | *Conclusion* | | *Preferred Model* |
> |---|---|---|
> | Reject H_0 | → | Complete Model |
> | Fail to reject H_0 | → | Reduced Model |

When the candidate models in model building are nested models, the *F*-test developed in this section is the appropriate procedure to apply to compare the models. However, if the models are not nested, this *F*-test is not applicable. In this situation, the analyst must base the choice of the best model on statistics such as R_a^2 and *s*. It is important to remember that decisions based on these and other numerical descriptive measures of model adequacy cannot be supported with a measure of reliability and are often very subjective in nature.

Exercises 12.97–12.110

Learning the Mechanics

12.97 Determine which pairs of the following models are "nested" models. For each pair of nested models, identify the complete and reduced model.
  a. $E(y) = \beta_0 + \beta_1 x_1 + \beta_2 x_2$
  b. $E(y) = \beta_0 + \beta_1 x_1$
  c. $E(y) = \beta_0 + \beta_1 x_1 + \beta_2 x_1^2$
  d. $E(y) = \beta_0 + \beta_1 x_1 + \beta_2 x_2 + \beta_3 x_1 x_2$
  e. $E(y) = \beta_0 + \beta_1 x_1 + \beta_2 x_2 + \beta_3 x_1 x_2 + \beta_4 x_1^2 + \beta_5 x_2^2$

12.98 Suppose you fit the regression model

$$y = \beta_0 + \beta_1 x_1 + \beta_2 x_2 + \beta_3 x_1 x_2 + \beta_4 x_1^2 + \beta_5 x_2^2 + \varepsilon$$

to $n = 30$ data points and wish to test

$$H_0: \beta_3 = \beta_4 = \beta_5 = 0$$

  a. State the alternative hypothesis H_a.
  b. Give the reduced model appropriate for conducting the test.
  c. What are the numerator and denominator degrees of freedom associated with the *F*-statistic?
  d. Suppose the SSE's for the reduced and complete models are $SSE_R = 1{,}250.2$ and $SSE_C = 1{,}125.2$. Conduct the hypothesis test and interpret the results of your test. Test using $\alpha = .05$.

12.99 The complete model

$$y = \beta_0 + \beta_1 x_1 + \beta_2 x_2 + \beta_3 x_3 + \beta_4 x_4 + \varepsilon$$

was fit to $n = 20$ data points, with SSE = 152.66. The reduced model, $y = \beta_0 + \beta_1 x_1 + \beta_2 x_2 + \varepsilon$, was also fit, with SSE = 160.44.
  a. How many β parameters are in the complete model? The reduced model?
  b. Specify the null and alternative hypotheses you would use to investigate whether the complete model contributes more information for the prediction of *y* than the reduced model.
  c. Conduct the hypothesis test of part **b**. Use $\alpha = .05$.

Applying the Concepts—Basic

12.100 Mental health of a community. An article in the *Community Mental Health Journal* (Aug. 2000) used multiple regression analysis to model the level of community adjustment of clients of the Department of Mental Health and Addiction Services in Connecticut. The dependent variable, community adjustment (*y*), was measured quantitatively based on staff ratings of the clients. (Lower scores indicate better adjustment.) The complete model was a first-order model with 21 independent variables. The independent variables were categorized as Demographic (4 variables), Diagnostic (7 variables), Treatment (4 variables), and Community (6 variables).
  a. Write the equation of $E(y)$ for the complete model.
  b. Give the null hypothesis for testing whether the 7 Diagnostic variables contribute information for the prediction of *y*.
  c. Give the equation of the reduced model appropriate for the test, part **b**.
  d. The test, part **b**, resulted in a test statistic of $F = 59.3$ and *p*-value < .0001. Interpret this result in the words of the problem.

12.101 Buy-side vs. sell-side analysts' earnings forecasts. Refer to the *Financial Analysts Journal* (Jul./Aug. 2008) comparison of earnings forecasts of buy-side and sell-side analysts, Exercise 12.90 (p. 721). Recall that the Harvard Business School professors used regression to model the relative optimism (*y*) of the analysts' 3-month horizon forecasts as a function of $x_1 = \{1$ if the analyst worked for a buy-side firm, 0 if the analyst worked for a sell-side firm$\}$ and $x_2 = $ number of days between forecast and fiscal year-end (i.e., forecast horizon). Consider the complete second-order model

$$E(y) = \beta_0 + \beta_1 x_1 + \beta_2 x_2 + \beta_3 x_1 x_2 + \beta_4 (x_2)^2 + \beta_5 x_1 (x_2)^2$$

  a. What null hypothesis would you test to determine whether the quadratic terms in the model are statistically useful for predicting relative optimism (*y*)?

b. Give the complete and reduced models for conducting the test, part **a.**

c. What null hypothesis would you test to determine whether the interaction terms in the model are statistically useful for predicting relative optimism (y)?

d. Give the complete and reduced models for conducting the test, part **c.**

e. What null hypothesis would you test to determine whether the dummy variable terms in the model are statistically useful for predicting relative optimism (y)?

f. Give the complete and reduced models for conducting the test, part **e.**

12.102 Workplace bullying and intention to leave. Refer to the *Human Resource Management Journal* (Oct. 2008) study of workplace bullying, Exercise 12.91 (p. 722). Recall that multiple regression was used to model an employee's intention to leave (y) as a function of bullying (x_1, measured on a quantitative scale) and perceived organizational support (measured qualitatively as "low POS," "neutral POS," or "high POS"). In Exercise 12.91b, you wrote a model for $E(y)$ as a function of bullying and POS that hypothesizes three parallel straight lines, one for each level of POS. In Exercise 12.91c, you wrote a model for $E(y)$ as a function of bullying and POS that hypothesizes three nonparallel straight lines, one for each level of POS.

a. Explain why the two models are nested. Which is the complete model? Which is the reduced model?

b. Give the null hypothesis for comparing the two models.

c. If you reject H_0 in part **b,** which model do you prefer? Why?

d. If you fail to reject H_0 in part **b,** which model do you prefer? Why?

12.103 Cooling method for gas turbines. Refer to the *Journal of Engineering for Gas Turbines and Power* (Jan. 2005) study of a high-pressure inlet fogging method for a gas turbine engine, Exercise 12.19 (p. 683). Consider a model for heat rate (kilojoules per kilowatt per hour) of a gas turbine as a function of cycle speed (revolutions per minute) and cycle pressure ratio. The data are saved in the file.

a. Write a complete second-order model for heat rate (y).

b. Give the null and alternative hypotheses for determining whether the curvature terms in the complete second-order model are statistically useful for predicting heat rate (y).

c. For the test in part **b,** identify the complete and reduced model.

d. Portions of the Minitab printouts for the two models are shown below. Find the values of SSE_R, SSE_C, and MSE_C on the printouts.

e. Compute the value of the test statistics for the test of part **b.**

f. Find the rejection region for the test of part **b** using $\alpha = .10$.

g. State the conclusion of the test in the words of the problem.

12.104 Personality traits and job performance. Refer to the *Journal of Applied Psychology* (Jan. 2011) study of the relationship between task performance and conscientiousness, Exercise 12.94 (p. 722). Recall that y = task performance score (measured on a 30-point scale) was modeled as a function of x_1 = conscientiousness score (measured on a scale of -3 to $+3$) and x_2 = {1 if highly complex job, 0 if not} using the complete model

$$E(y) = \beta_0 + \beta_1 x_1 + \beta_2 (x_1)^2 + \beta_3 x_2 + \beta_4 x_1 x_2 + \beta_5 (x_1)^2 x_2$$

a. Specify the null hypothesis for testing the overall adequacy of the model.

Complete Model

```
The regression equation is
HEATRATE = 15583 + 0.078 RPM - 523 CPRATIO + 0.00445 RPM_CPR - 0.000000 RPMSQ
           + 8.84 CPRSQ

S = 563.513   R-Sq = 88.5%   R-Sq(adj) = 87.5%

Analysis of Variance

Source          DF        SS        MS      F      P
Regression       5  148526859  29705372  93.55  0.000
Residual Error  61   19370350    317547
Total           66  167897208
```

Reduced Model

```
The regression equation is
HEATRATE = 12065 + 0.170 RPM - 146 CPRATIO - 0.00242 RPM_CPR

S = 633.842   R-Sq = 84.9%   R-Sq(adj) = 84.2%

Analysis of Variance

Source          DF        SS        MS      F      P
Regression       3  142586570  47528857  118.30  0.000
Residual Error  63   25310639    401756
Total           66  167897208
```

Minitab output for Exercise 12.103

b. Specify the null hypothesis for testing whether task performance score (y) and conscientiousness score (x_1) are curvilinearly related.

c. Specify the null hypothesis for testing whether the curvilinear relationship between task performance score (y) and conscientiousness score (x_1) depends on job complexity (x_2).

d. Explain how each of the tests, parts **a–c**, should be conducted (i.e., give the forms of the test statistic and the reduced model).

Applying the Concepts—Intermediate

12.105 Reality TV and cosmetic surgery. Refer to the *Body Image: An International Journal of Research* (March 2010) study of the influence of reality TV shows on one's desire to undergo cosmetic surgery, Exercise 12.17 (p. 682). Recall that psychologists modeled desire to have cosmetic surgery (y) as a function of gender (x_1), self-esteem (x_2), body satisfaction (x_3), and impression of reality TV (x_4). The psychologists theorized that one's impression of reality TV will "moderate" the impact that each of the first three independent variables has on one's desire to have cosmetic surgery. If so, then x_4 will interact with each of the other independent variables.

a. Give the equation of the model for $E(y)$ that matches the theory.

b. Fit the model, part **a**, to the simulated data saved in the file. Evaluate the overall utility of the model.

c. Give the null hypothesis for testing the psychologists' theory.

d. Conduct a nested model F-test to test the theory. What do you conclude?

12.106 Study of supervisor-targeted aggression. "Moonlighters" are workers who hold two jobs at the same time. What are the factors that impact the likelihood of a moonlighting worker becoming aggressive toward his/her supervisor? This was the research question of interest in the *Journal of Applied Psychology* (July 2005). Completed questionnaires were obtained from $n = 105$ moonlighters, and the data were used to fit several multiple regression models for supervisor-directed aggression score (y). Two of the models (with R^2 values in parentheses) are given below:

Model 1: $E(y) = \beta_0 + \beta_1(\text{Age}) + \beta_2(\text{Gender}) + \beta_3(\text{Interatctional injustice at 2nd job}) + \beta_4(\text{Abusive supervisor at 2nd job})$
($R^2 = .101$)

Model 2: $E(y) = \beta_0 + \beta_1(\text{Age}) + \beta_2(\text{Gender}) + \beta_3(\text{Interactional injustice at 2nd job}) + \beta_4(\text{Abusive supervisor at 2nd job}) + \beta_5(\text{Self-esteem}) + \beta_6(\text{History of aggression}) + \beta_7(\text{Interactional injustice at primary job}) + \beta_8(\text{Abusive supervisor at primary job})$
($R^2 = .555$)

a. Interpret the R^2 values for the models.

b. Give the null and alternative hypotheses for comparing the fits of models 1 and 2.

c. Are the two models nested? Explain.

d. The nested F-test for comparing the two models resulted in $F = 42.13$ and p-value $< .001$. What can you conclude from these results?

e. A third model was fit, one that hypothesizes all possible pairs of interactions between self-esteem, history of aggression, interactional injustice at primary job, and abusive supervisor at primary job. Give the equation of this model (model 3).

f. A nested F-test to compare models 2 and 3 resulted in a p-value $> .10$. What can you conclude from this result?

12.107 Agreeableness, gender, and wages. Refer to the *Journal of Personality and Social Psychology* (Feb. 2012) study of on-the-job agreeableness and wages, Exercise 12.92 (p. 722). The researchers modeled mean income, $E(y)$, as a function of both agreeableness score (x_1) and a dummy variable for gender ($x_2 = 1$ if male, 0 if female). Suppose the researchers theorize that for either gender, income will decrease at a decreasing rate as agreeableness score increases. Consequently, they want to fit a second-order model.

a. Consider the model, $E(y) = \beta_0 + \beta_1 x_1 + \beta_2 (x_1)^2 + \beta_3 x_2$. If the researchers' belief is true, what is the expected sign of β_2 in the model?

b. Draw a sketch of the model, part **a**, showing how gender impacts the income-agreeableness score relationship.

c. Write a complete second-order model for $E(y)$ as a function of x_1 and x_2.

d. Draw a sketch of the model, part **c**, showing how gender impacts the income-agreeableness score relationship.

e. What null hypothesis would you test in order to compare the two models, parts **a** and **c**?

f. Fit the models to the sample data saved in the file and carry out the test, part **e**. What do you conclude? (Test using $\alpha = .10$.)

12.108 Recently sold, single-family homes. Refer to the National Association of Realtors data on sales price (y), region (NE, NW, S, or W), and sales volume for 28 recently sold, single-family homes, Exercise 12.95 (p. 723). You fit a complete second-order model for $E(y)$ as a function of region and sales volume.

a. Conduct a nested-model F-test to determine whether the quadratic terms in the model are statistically useful for predicting sales price (y). Use $\alpha = .05$.

b. Based on the result, part **a**, which of the nested models (the complete or the reduced model) do you prefer to use in predicting sales price (y)? Explain.

c. Refer to part **b**. Treat the preferred model as the complete model and conduct a nested model F-test to determine whether region and sales volume interact to affect sales price (y). Use $\alpha = .05$.

d. Based on the result, part **c**, which of the nested models (the complete or the reduced model) do you prefer to use in predicting sales price (y)? Explain.

12.109 Glass as a waste encapsulant. Because glass is not subject to radiation damage, encapsulation of waste in glass is considered to be one of the most promising solutions to the problem of low-level nuclear waste in the environment. However, chemical reactions may weaken the glass.

This concern led to a study undertaken jointly by the Department of Materials Science and Engineering at the University of Florida and the U.S. Department of Energy to assess the utility of glass as a waste encapsulant.* Corrosive chemical solutions (called *corrosion baths*) were prepared and applied directly to glass samples containing one of three types of waste (TDS-3A, FE, and AL); the chemical reactions were observed over time. A few of the key variables measured were

y = Amount of silicon (in parts per million) found in solution at end of experiment. (This is both a measure of the degree of breakdown in the glass and a proxy for the amount of radioactive species released into the environment.)

x_1 = Temperature (°C) of the corrosion bath

x_2 = 1 if waste type TDS-3A, 0 if not

x_3 = 1 if waste type FE, 0 if not

(Waste type AL is the base level.) Suppose we want to model amount y of silicon as a function of temperature (x_1) and type of waste (x_2, x_3).

a. Write a model that proposes parallel straight-line relationships between amount of silicon and temperature, one line for each of the three waste types.

b. Add terms for the interaction between temperature and waste type to the model of part **a.**

c. Refer to the model of part **b.** For each waste type, give the slope of the line relating amount of silicon to temperature.

d. Explain how you could test for the presence of temperature–waste type interaction.

Applying the Concepts—Advanced

12.110 Emotional distress in firefighters. The *Journal of Human Stress* (Summer 1987) reported on a study of "psychological response of firefighters to chemical fire." It is thought that the following complete second-order model will be adequate to describe the relationship between emotional distress and years of experience for two groups of firefighters—those exposed to a chemical fire and those unexposed:

$$E(y) = \beta_0 + \beta_1 x_1 + \beta_2 x_1^2 + \beta_3 x_2 + \beta_4 x_1 x_2 + \beta_5 x_1^2 x_2$$

where

y = Emotional distress

x_1 = Experience (years)

x_2 = 1 if exposed to chemical fire, 0 if not

a. How would you determine whether the *rate* of increase of emotional distress with experience is different for the two groups of firefighters?

b. How would you determine whether there are differences in mean emotional distress levels that are attributable to exposure group?

12.10 Stepwise Regression

Consider the problem of predicting the salary y of an executive. Perhaps the biggest problem in building a model to describe executive salaries is choosing the important independent variables to be included in the model. The list of potentially important independent variables is extremely long (e.g., age, experience, tenure, education level, etc.), and we need some objective method of screening out those that are not important.

The problem of deciding which of a large set of independent variables to include in a model is a common one. Trying to determine which variables influence the profit of a firm, affect blood pressure of humans, or are related to a student's performance in college are only a few examples.

A systematic approach to building a model with a large number of independent variables is difficult because the interpretation of multivariable interactions and higher-order terms is tedious. We therefore turn to a screening procedure, available in most statistical software packages, known as **stepwise regression.**

The most commonly used stepwise regression procedure works as follows. The user first identifies the response, y, and the set of potentially important independent variables, $x_1, x_2, \ldots, x_k$, where k is generally large. [*Note:* This set of variables could include both first-order and higher-order terms. However, we may often include only the main effects of both quantitative variables (first-order terms) and qualitative variables (dummy variables) because the inclusion of second-order terms greatly increases the number of independent variables.] The response and independent variables are then entered into the computer software, and the stepwise procedure begins.

Step 1: The software program fits all possible one-variable models of the form

$$E(y) = \beta_0 + \beta_1 x_i$$

*The background information for this exercise was provided by Dr. David Clark, Department of Materials Science and Engineering, University of Florida.

to the data, where x_i is the ith independent variable, $i = 1, 2, \ldots, k$. For each model, the test of the null hypothesis

$$H_0: \beta_1 = 0$$

against the alternative hypothesis

$$H_a: \beta_1 \neq 0$$

is conducted using the t-test (or the equivalent F-test) for a single β parameter. The independent variable that produces the largest (absolute) t-value is declared the best one-variable predictor of y.* Call this independent variable x_1.

Step 2: The stepwise program now begins to search through the remaining $(k - 1)$ independent variables for the best two-variable model of the form

$$E(y) = \beta_0 + \beta_1 x_1 + \beta_2 x_i$$

This is done by fitting all two-variable models containing x_1 and each of the other $(k - 1)$ options for the second variable x_i. The t-values for the test $H_0: \beta_2 = 0$ are computed for each of the $(k - 1)$ models (corresponding to the remaining independent variables, $x_i, i = 2, 3, \ldots, k$), and the variable having the largest t is retained. Call this variable x_2.

At this point, some software packages diverge in methodology. The better packages now go back and check the t-value of $\hat{\beta}_1$ after $\hat{\beta}_2 x_2$ has been added to the model. If the t-value has become nonsignificant at some specified α level (say $\alpha = .10$), the variable x_1 is removed and a search is made for the independent variable with a β parameter that will yield the most significant t-value in the presence of $\hat{\beta}_2 x_2$. Other packages do not recheck the significance of $\hat{\beta}_1$ but proceed directly to step 3.†

The reason the t-value for x_1 may change from step 1 to step 2 is that the meaning of the coefficient $\hat{\beta}_1$ changes. In step 2, we are approximating a complex response surface in two variables with a plane. The best-fitting plane may yield a different value for $\hat{\beta}_1$ than that obtained in step 1. Thus, both the value of $\hat{\beta}_1$ and its significance usually change from step 1 to step 2. For this reason, the software packages that recheck the t-values at each step are preferred.

Step 3: The stepwise procedure now checks for a third independent variable to include in the model with x_1 and x_2—that is, we seek the best model of the form

$$E(y) = \beta_0 + \beta_1 x_1 + \beta_2 x_2 + \beta_3 x_i$$

To do this, we fit all the $(k - 2)$ models using x_1, x_2, and each of the $(k - 2)$ remaining variables, x_i, as a possible x_3. The criterion is again to include the independent variable with the largest t-value. Call this best third variable x_3.

The better programs now recheck the t-values corresponding to the x_1 and x_2 coefficients, removing the variables with t-values that have become nonsignificant. This procedure is continued until no further independent variables can be found that yield significant t-values (at the specified α level) in the presence of the variables already in the model.

The result of the stepwise procedure is a model containing only those terms with t-values that are significant at the specified α level. Thus, in most practical situations, only several of the large number of independent variables remain. However, it is very important *not* to jump to the conclusion that all the independent variables important for predicting y have been identified or that the unimportant independent variables have been eliminated. Remember, the stepwise procedure is using only *sample estimates* of the true model coefficients (β's) to select the important variables. An extremely large

---

*In step 1, note that the variable with the largest t-value is also the one with the largest (absolute) Pearson product moment correlation, r (Section 11.5), with y.

†*Forward selection* is the name given to stepwise routines that *do not* recheck the significance of each previously entered independent variable. This is in contrast to *stepwise selection* routines, which perform the rechecks. A third approach is to use *backward selection,* where initially, all terms are entered and then eliminated one by one.

number of single β parameter t-tests have been conducted, and the probability is very high that one or more errors have been made in including or excluding variables—that is, we have very probably included some unimportant independent variables in the model (Type I errors) and eliminated some important ones (Type II errors).

There is a second reason why we might not have arrived at a good model. When we choose the variables to be included in the stepwise regression, we may often omit higher-order terms (to keep the number of variables manageable). Consequently, we may have initially omitted several important terms from the model. Thus, we should recognize stepwise regression for what it is: an **objective variable screening procedure.**

Successful model builders will now consider second-order terms (for quantitative variables) and other interactions among variables screened by the stepwise procedure. It would be best to develop this response surface model with a second set of data independent of that used for the screening, so that the results of the stepwise procedure can be partially verified with new data. This is not always possible, however, because in many modeling situations only a small amount of data is available.

Do not be deceived by the impressive-looking t-values that result from the stepwise procedure—it has retained only the independent variables with the largest t-values. Also, be certain to consider second-order terms in systematically developing the prediction model. Finally, if you have used a first-order model for your stepwise procedure, remember that it may be greatly improved by the addition of higher-order terms.

⚠ **CAUTION** Be wary of using the results of stepwise regression to make inferences about the relationship between $E(y)$ and the independent variables in the resulting first-order model. First, an extremely large number of t-tests have been conducted, leading to a high probability of making one or more Type I or Type II errors. Second, the stepwise model does not include any higher-order or interaction terms. Stepwise regression should be used only when necessary—that is, when you want to determine which of a large number of potentially important independent variables should be used in the model-building process.

Example 12.13

Running a Stepwise Regression—Modeling Executive Salary

Problem An international management consulting company develops multiple regression models for executive salaries of its client firms. The consulting company has found that models that use the natural logarithm of salary as the dependent variable have better predictive power than those using salary as the dependent variable.* A preliminary step in the construction of these models is the determination of the most important independent variables. For one firm, 10 potential independent variables (7 quantitative and 3 qualitative) were measured in a sample of 100 executives. The data, described in Table 12.5, are

Table 12.5	Independent Variables in the Executive Salary Example	
Independent Variable	Description	Type
x_1	Experience (years)	Quantitative
x_2	Education (years)	Quantitative
x_3	Bonus eligibility (1 if yes, 0 if no)	Qualitative
x_4	Number of employees supervised	Quantitative
x_5	Corporate assets (millions of dollars)	Quantitative
x_6	Board member (1 if yes, 0 if no)	Qualitative
x_7	Age (years)	Quantitative
x_8	Company profits (past 12 months, millions of dollars)	Quantitative
x_9	Has international responsibility (1 if yes, 0 if no)	Qualitative
x_{10}	Company's total sales (past 12 months, millions of dollars)	Quantitative

Data Set: EXSAL

---

*This is probably because salaries tend to be incremented in *percentages* rather than dollar values. When a response variable undergoes percentage changes as the independent variables are varied, the logarithm of the response variable will be more suitable as a dependent variable.

saved in the file. Because it would be very difficult to construct a complete second-order model with all of the 10 independent variables, use stepwise regression to decide which of the 10 variables should be included in the building of the final model for the natural log of executive salaries.

Solution We will use stepwise regression with the main effects of the 10 independent variables to identify the most important variables. The dependent variable y is the natural logarithm of the executive salaries. The Minitab stepwise regression printout is shown in Figure 12.32.

```
     Alpha-to-Enter: 0.15   Alpha-to-Remove: 0.15


Response is Y on 10 predictors, with N = 100


Step              1       2       3       4       5
Constant     11.091  10.968  10.783  10.278   9.962

X1           0.0278  0.0273  0.0273  0.0273  0.0273
T-Value       12.62   15.13   18.80   24.68   26.50
P-Value       0.000   0.000   0.000   0.000   0.000

X3                   0.197   0.233   0.232   0.225
T-Value                7.10   10.17   13.30   13.74
P-Value               0.000   0.000   0.000   0.000

X4                          0.00048 0.00055 0.00052
T-Value                        7.32   10.92   11.06
P-Value                       0.000   0.000   0.000

X2                                  0.0300  0.0291
T-Value                               8.38    8.72
P-Value                              0.000   0.000

X5                                          0.00196
T-Value                                        3.95
P-Value                                       0.000

S            0.161   0.131   0.106  0.0807  0.0751
R-Sq         61.90   74.92   83.91   90.75   92.06
R-Sq(adj)    61.51   74.40   83.41   90.36   91.64
Mallows C-p  343.9   195.5    93.8    16.8     3.6
```

Figure 12.32

Minitab stepwise regression printout for executive salary data

Note that the first variable included in the model is x_1, years of experience. At the second step, x_3, a dummy variable for the qualitative variable, bonus eligibility or not, is brought into the model. In steps 3, 4, and 5, the variables x_4 (number of employees supervised), x_2 (years of education), and x_5 (corporate assets), respectively, are selected for model inclusion. Minitab stops after five steps because no other independent variables met the criterion for admission into the model. As a default, Minitab uses $\alpha = .15$ in the t-tests conducted. In other words, if the p-value associated with a β coefficient exceeds $\alpha = .15$, the variable is *not* included in the model.

The results of the stepwise regression suggest that we should concentrate on these five independent variables. Models with second-order terms and interactions should be proposed and evaluated to determine the best model for predicting executive salaries.

■ **Now Work Exercise 12.113**

 RECOMMENDATION Do *not* use the stepwise regression model as the *final* model for predicting y. Recall that the stepwise procedure tends to perform a large number of t-tests, inflating the overall probability of a Type I error, and does not automatically include higher-order terms (e.g., interactions and squared terms) in the final model. Use stepwise regression as a variable screening tool when there exists a large number of potentially important independent variables. Then begin building models for y using the variables identified by stepwise.

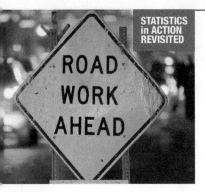

Variable Screening and Model Building

In the previous Statistics in Action Revisited section (p. 687), we used all eight of the independent variables in Table SIA12.1 to fit a first-order model for the cost (y) of a road construction contract awarded using the sealed-bid system. Although the model was deemed statistically useful for predicting y, the standard deviation of the model ($s = 305$ thousand dollars) was probably too large for the model to be practically useful. A more complex model—one involving higher-order terms (interactions and squared terms)—needs to be considered. A complete second-order model involving all eight of the independent variables, however, would require over 100 terms! Consequently, we'll use stepwise regression to select the best subset of independent variables and then form a complete second-order model with just these variables.

Figure SIA12.4 is a Minitab printout of the stepwise regression. You can see that the DOT engineer's cost estimate (DOTEST) is the first variable selected, followed by bid status (STATUS), estimated work days (DAYSEST), and bids to plan holders ratio (BTPRATIO). Recall that Minitab uses a default α level of .15. If we reduce the significance level for entry to $\alpha = .05$, only DOTEST and STATUS are selected because the p-values (highlighted on the printout) for DAYSEST and BTPRATIO are both greater than .05.

```
  Alpha-to-Enter: 0.15   Alpha-to-Remove: 0.15


Response is COST on 8 predictors, with N = 235


Step              1        2        3        4
Constant      20.91   -20.54   -55.22  -212.85

DOTEST       0.9263   0.9308   0.9110   0.9132
T-Value       93.89    95.52    56.86    57.11
P-Value       0.000    0.000    0.000    0.000

STATUS                    166      167      171
T-Value                  3.38     3.40     3.50
P-Value                 0.001    0.001    0.001

DAYSEST                            0.27     0.33
T-Value                            1.55     1.85
P-Value                           0.122    0.065

BTPRATIO                                    241
T-Value                                    1.81
P-Value                                   0.072

S               313      306      305      304
R-Sq          97.42    97.55    97.57    97.60
R-Sq(adj)     97.41    97.52    97.54    97.56
Mallows C-p    15.2      5.7      5.2      4.0
```

Figure SIA12.4

Minitab stepwise regression for the road cost data

Because bid status is a qualitative variable ($x_2 = 1$ if fixed and 0 if competitive), a complete second-order model for contract cost (y) using DOTEST (x_1) and STATUS (x_2) is given by the equation

$$E(y) = \beta_0 + \beta_1 x_1 + \beta_2 (x_1)^2 + \beta_3 x_2 + \beta_4 x_1 x_2 + \beta_5 (x_1)^2 x_2$$

The Minitab printout for this model is shown in Figure SIA12.5. Note that the global F-test for the model is statistically significant (p-value $= .000$), and the model standard deviation, $s = 296.6$, is smaller than the standard deviation of the first-order model.

Are the second-order terms in the model, $\beta_2 (x_1)^2$ and $\beta_5 (x_1)^2 x_2$, necessary? If not, we can simplify the model by dropping these curvature terms. The hypothesis of interest is $H_0: \beta_2 = \beta_5 = 0$. To test this subset of β's, we compare the complete second-order model to a model without the curvilinear terms. The reduced model takes the form

$$E(y) = \beta_0 + \beta_1 x_1 + \beta_3 x_2 + \beta_4 x_1 x_2$$

```
The regression equation is
COST = - 3.0 + 0.916 DOTEST + 0.000001 DOTEST2 - 36.7 STATUS + 0.324 STA_DOT
        - 0.000036 STA_DOT2


Predictor        Coef      SE Coef        T       P
Constant        -2.98        30.89    -0.10   0.923
DOTEST        0.91553      0.02917    31.39   0.000
DOTEST2    0.00000072   0.00000340     0.21   0.833
STATUS        -36.72        74.77    -0.49   0.624
STA_DOT       0.3242       0.1192     2.72   0.007
STA_DOT2  -0.00003576   0.00002478    -1.44   0.150


S = 296.646   R-Sq = 97.7%   R-Sq(adj) = 97.7%


Analysis of Variance

Source           DF          SS          MS        F       P
Regression        5   866723202   173344640  1969.85   0.000
Residual Error  229    20151771       87999
Total           234   886874973
```

Figure SIA12.5

Minitab regression printout for the complete second-order model of contract cost

The results of this nested model (or partial) F-test are shown at the bottom of the SPSS printout, Figure SIA12.6. The p-value of the test (highlighted on the SPSS printout) is .355. Because this p-value is greater than $\alpha = .05$, there is insufficient evidence to reject H_0—that is, there is no evidence to indicate that the two curvature terms are useful predictors of road construction cost. Consequently, the reduced model is selected as the better predictor of cost.

Model Summary

Model	R	R Square	Adjusted R Square	Std. Error of the Estimate	R Square Change	F Change	df1	df2	Sig. F Change
					Change Statistics				
1	.988ᵃ	.977	.977	296.69515	.977	3281.312	3	231	.000
2	.989ᵇ	.977	.977	296.64238	.000	1.041	2	229	.355

a. Predictors: (Constant), STA_DOT, DOTEST, STATUS
b. Predictors: (Constant), STA_DOT, DOTEST, STATUS, DOTEST2, STA_DOT2

Figure SIA12.6

SPSS printout of test to compare the complete second-order model of contract cost to the reduced model

The Minitab printout for the reduced model is shown in Figure SIA12.7. The overall model is statistically useful (p-value = .000 for global F-test), explaining about 98% of the sample variation in contract costs. The model standard deviation, $s = 296.7$, implies that we can predict costs to within about 593 thousand dollars. Also, the t-test for the interaction term, $\beta_4 x_1 x_2$, is significant (p-value = .000), implying that the relationship between contract cost (y) and DOT cost estimate depends on bid status (fixed or competitive).

```
The regression equation is
COST = - 6.4 + 0.921 DOTEST + 28.7 STATUS + 0.163 STA_DOT


Predictor        Coef     SE Coef        T       P
Constant        -6.43       26.21    -0.25   0.806
DOTEST       0.921336    0.009723    94.75   0.000
STATUS         28.67       58.66     0.49   0.625
STA_DOT       0.16328     0.04043     4.04   0.000


S = 296.699   R-Sq = 97.7%   R-Sq(adj) = 97.7%


Analysis of Variance

Source           DF          SS          MS        F       P
Regression        3   866540004   288846668  3281.22   0.000
Residual Error  231    20334968       88030
Total           234   886874973
```

Figure SIA12.7

Minitab regression printout for the reduced model of contract cost

The nature of the interaction is illustrated in the Minitab graph of the least squares prediction equation for the reduced model, Figure SIA12.8. You can see that the rate of increase of contract cost (y) with the DOT engineer's estimate of cost (x_1) is steeper for fixed contracts than for competitive contracts.

Figure SIA12.8

Minitab plot of least squares prediction equation for the reduced model of contract cost

Exercises 12.111–12.118

Learning the Mechanics

12.111 There are six independent variables, x_1, x_2, x_3, x_4, x_5, and x_6, that might be useful in predicting a response y. A total of $n = 50$ observations is available, and it is decided to employ stepwise regression to help in selecting the independent variables that appear to be useful. The software fits all possible one-variable models of the form

$$E(y) = \beta_0 + \beta_1 x_i$$

where x_i is the ith independent variable, $i = 1, 2, \ldots, 6$. The information in the table is provided from the computer printout.

Independent Variable	$\hat{\beta}_i$	$s_{\hat{\beta}_i}$
x_1	1.6	.42
x_2	−.9	.01
x_3	3.4	1.14
x_4	2.5	2.06
x_5	−4.4	.73
x_6	.3	.35

a. Which independent variable is declared the best one-variable predictor of y? Explain.
b. Would this variable be included in the model at this stage? Explain.
c. Describe the next phase that a stepwise procedure would execute.

Applying the Concepts—Basic

12.112 Teacher pay and pupil performance. In *Economic Policy* (January 2011), researchers from the London School of Economics conducted a cross-country analysis of the relationship between teacher's pay and pupils' performance. Data collected for 39 countries were used to model y = the country's average standardized score of its pupils. The independent variables under consideration were: x_1 = country's total teaching staff as a percentage of the country's labor force, x_2 = percentage of women on country's total teaching staff, x_3 = country's

pupil-teacher ratio, x_4 = average teacher's salary after 15 years on staff, x_5 = average teaching hours per year, x_6 = GDP growth of country (%), x_7 = country's educational spending per year, and x_8 = percentile position of country's teachers' salaries after 15 years on staff. Consider a stepwise regression run on the data.

a. What is the form of the model fit in step 1? How many models are fit? How is the "best" independent variable selected in this step?
b. What is the form of the model fit in step 2? How many models are fit? How is the "best" independent variable selected in this step?
c. What is the form of the model fit in step 3? How many models are fit? How is the "best" independent variable selected in this step?
d. The variables x_3, x_4, and x_6 were deemed the best variables for predicting y. How do you recommend the researchers proceed from here? Why?

12.113 Entry-level job preferences. *Benefits Quarterly* (First Quarter, 1995) published a study of entry-level job preferences. A number of independent variables were used to model the job preferences (measured on a 10-point scale) of 164 business school graduates. Suppose stepwise regression is used to build a model for job preference score (y) as a function of the following independent variables:

$$x_1 = \begin{cases} 1 & \text{if flextime position} \\ 0 & \text{if not} \end{cases}$$

$$x_2 = \begin{cases} 1 & \text{if day care support required} \\ 0 & \text{if not} \end{cases}$$

$$x_3 = \begin{cases} 1 & \text{if spousal transfer support required} \\ 0 & \text{if not} \end{cases}$$

x_4 = Number of sick days allowed

$$x_5 = \begin{cases} 1 & \text{if applicant married} \\ 0 & \text{if not} \end{cases}$$

x_6 = Number of children of applicant

$$x_7 = \begin{cases} 1 & \text{if male applicant} \\ 0 & \text{if female applicant} \end{cases}$$

a. How many models are fit to the data in step 1? Give the general form of these models.

b. How many models are fit to the data in step 2? Give the general form of these models.

c. How many models are fit to the data in step 3? Give the general form of these models.

d. Explain how the procedure determines when to stop adding independent variables to the model.

e. Describe two major drawbacks to using the final stepwise model as the best model for job preference score y.

12.114 Accuracy of software effort estimates. Periodically, software engineers must provide estimates of their effort in developing new software. In the *Journal of Empirical Software Engineering* (Vol. 9, 2004), multiple regression was used to predict the accuracy of these effort estimates. The dependent variable, defined as the relative error in estimating effort,

$$y = \text{(Actual effort} - \text{Estimated effort)/(Actual effort)}$$

was determined for each in a sample of $n = 49$ software development tasks. Eight independent variables were evaluated as potential predictors of relative error using stepwise regression. Each of these was formulated as a dummy variable, as shown in the table.

Company role of estimator:	$x_1 = 1$ if developer, 0 if project leader
Task complexity:	$x_2 = 1$ if low, 0 if medium/high
Contract type:	$x_3 = 1$ if fixed price, 0 if hourly rate
Customer importance:	$x_4 = 1$ if high, 0 if low/medium
Customer priority:	$x_5 = 1$ if time of delivery, 0 if cost or quality
Level of knowledge:	$x_6 = 1$ if high, 0 if low/medium
Participation:	$x_7 = 1$ if estimator participates in work, 0 if not
Previous accuracy:	$x_8 = 1$ if more than 20% accurate, 0 if less than 20% accurate

a. In step 1 of the stepwise regression, how many different one-variable models are fit to the data?

b. In step 1, the variable x_1 is selected as the best one-variable predictor. How is this determined?

c. In step 2 of the stepwise regression, how many different two-variable models (where x_1 is one of the variables) are fit to the data?

d. The only two variables selected for entry into the stepwise regression model were x_1 and x_8. The stepwise regression yielded the following prediction equation:

$$\hat{y} = .12 - .28x_1 + .27x_8$$

Give a practical interpretation of the β estimates multiplied by x_1 and x_8.

e. Why should a researcher be wary of using the model, part **d**, as the final model for predicting effort (y)?

Applying the Concepts—Intermediate

12.115 Diet of ducks bred for broiling. Corn is high in starch content; consequently, it is considered excellent feed for domestic chickens. Does corn possess the same potential in feeding ducks bred for broiling? This was the subject of research published in *Animal Feed Science and Technology* (April 2010). The objective of the study was to establish a prediction model for the true metabolizable energy (TME) of corn regurgitated from ducks. The researchers considered 11 potential predictors of TME: dry matter (DM), crude protein (CP), ether extract (EE), ash (ASH), crude fiber (CF), neutral detergent fiber (NDF), acid detergent fiber (ADF), gross energy (GE), amylose (AM), amylopectin (AP), and amylopectin/amylose (AMAP). Stepwise regression was used to find the best subset of predictors. The final stepwise model yielded the following results:

$$\widehat{TME} = 7.70 + 2.14(\text{AMAP}) + .16(\text{NDF}), R^2 = .988,$$
$$s = .07, \text{Global } F \text{ } p\text{-value} = .001$$

a. Determine the number of t-tests performed in step 1 of the stepwise regression.

b. Determine the number of t-tests performed in step 2 of the stepwise regression.

c. Give a full interpretation of the final stepwise model regression results.

d. Explain why it is dangerous to use the final stepwise model as the "best" model for predicting TME.

e. Using the independent variables selected by the stepwise routine, write a complete second-order model for TME.

f. Refer to part **e**. How would you determine if the terms in the model that allow for curvature are statistically useful for predicting TME?

12.116 Reality TV and cosmetic surgery. Refer to the *Body Image: An International Journal of Research* (March 2010) study of the influence of reality TV shows on one's desire to undergo cosmetic surgery, Exercise 12.17 (p. 682). Recall that psychologists modeled desire to have cosmetic surgery (y) as a function of gender (x_1), self-esteem (x_2), body satisfaction (x_3), and impression of reality TV (x_4). Suppose you want to determine which subset of these four independent variables is best for predicting one's desire to have cosmetic surgery. Consequently, you will run a stepwise regression.

a. In step 1 of the stepwise regression, how many t-tests will be performed?

b. In step 2 of the stepwise regression, how many t-tests will be performed?

c. Access the data saved in the file and run the stepwise regression. Which independent variables comprise the best subset of variables for predicting one's desire to have cosmetic surgery?

d. Do you recommend using the resulting stepwise regression model for predicting one's desire to have cosmetic surgery or do you recommend further analysis? Explain your reasoning.

12.117 Bus Rapid Transit study. Bus Rapid Transit (BRT) is a rapidly growing trend in the provision of public transportation in America. The Center for Urban Transportation Research (CUTR) at the University of South Florida conducted a survey of BRT customers in Miami (*Transportation Research Board* Annual Meeting, Jan. 2003). Data on the following variables (all measured on a 5-point scale, where 1 = very unsatisfied and 5 = very satisfied) were collected for a sample of over 500 bus riders: overall satisfaction with BRT (y), safety on bus (x_1), seat availability (x_2), dependability (x_3), travel time (x_4), cost (x_5), information/maps (x_6), convenience of routes (x_7), traffic signals (x_8), safety at bus stops (x_9), hours of service (x_{10}), and frequency of service (x_{11}). CUTR analysts used stepwise regression to model overall satisfaction (y).

a. How many models are fit at step 1 of the stepwise regression?

b. How many models are fit at step 2 of the stepwise regression?

c. How many models are fit at step 11 of the stepwise regression?

d. The stepwise regression selected the following eight variables to include in the model (in order of selection): $x_{11}, x_4, x_2, x_7, x_{10}, x_1, x_9$, and x_3. Write the equation for $E(y)$ that results from stepwise regression.

e. The model, part **d,** resulted in $R^2 = .677$. Interpret this value.

f. Explain why the CUTR analysts should be cautious in concluding that the best model for $E(y)$ has been found.

12.118 **Adverse effects of hot-water runoff.** A marine biologist was hired by the EPA to determine whether the hot-water runoff from a particular power plant located near a large gulf is having an adverse effect on the marine life in the area. The biologist's goal is to acquire a prediction equation for the number of marine animals located at certain designated areas, or stations, in the gulf. Based on past experience, the EPA considered the following environmental factors as predictors for the number of animals at a particular station:

$x_1 =$ Temperature of water (TEMP)

$x_2 =$ Salinity of water (SAL)

$x_3 =$ Dissolved oxygen content of water (DO)

$x_4 =$ Turbidity index, a measure of the turbidity of the water (TI)

$x_5 =$ Depth of the water at the station (ST_DEPTH)

$x_6 =$ Total weight of sea grasses in sampled area (TGRSWT)

As a preliminary step in the construction of this model, the biologist used a stepwise regression procedure to identify the most important of these six variables. A total of 716 samples were taken at different stations in the gulf, producing the SPSS printout shown below. (The response measured was y, the logarithm of the number of marine animals found in the sampled area.)

a. According to the SPSS printout, which of the six independent variables should be used in the model? (Use $\alpha = .10$.)

b. Are we able to assume that the marine biologist has identified all the important independent variables for the prediction of y? Why?

c. Using the variables identified in part **a,** write the first-order model with interaction that may be used to predict y.

d. How would the marine biologist determine whether the model specified in part **c** is better than the first-order model?

e. Note the small value of R^2. What action might the biologist take to improve the model?

Variables Entered/Removed[a]

Model	Variables Entered	Variables Removed	Method
1	ST_DEPTH	.	Stepwise (Criteria: Probability-of-F-to-enter <= .050, Probability-of-F-to-remove >= .100).
2	TGRSWT	.	Stepwise (Criteria: Probability-of-F-to-enter <= .050, Probability-of-F-to-remove >= .100).
3	TI	.	Stepwise (Criteria: Probability-of-F-to-enter <= .050, Probability-of-F-to-remove >= .100).

a. Dependent Variable: LOGNUM

Model Summary

Model	R	R Square	Adjusted R Square	Std. Error of the Estimate
1	.329[a]	.122	.121	.7615773
2	.427[b]	.182	.180	.7348470
3	.432[c]	.187	.184	.7348469

a. Predictors: (Constant), ST_DEPTH

b. Predictors: (Constant), ST_DEPTH, TGRSWT

c. Predictors: (Constant), ST_DEPTH, TGRSWT, TI

PART III: MULTIPLE REGRESSION DIAGNOSTICS

12.11 Residual Analysis: Checking the Regression Assumptions

When we apply regression analysis to a set of data, we never know for certain whether the assumptions of Section 12.1 are satisfied. How far can we deviate from the assumptions and still expect regression analysis to yield results that will have the reliability stated in this chapter? How can we detect departures (if they exist) from the assumptions, and what can we do about them? We provide some answers to these questions in this section.

Recall from Section 12.1 that for any given set of values of $x_1, x_2, \ldots, x_k$, we assume that the random error term ε has the following properties:

1. mean equal to 0

2. constant variance (σ^2)

3. normal probability distribution

4. probabilistically independent

It is unlikely that these assumptions are ever satisfied exactly in a practical application of regression analysis. Fortunately, experience has shown that least squares regression analysis produces reliable statistical tests, confidence intervals, and prediction intervals as long as the departures from the assumptions are not too great. In this section, we present some methods for determining whether the data indicate significant departures from the assumptions.

Because the assumptions all concern the random error component, ε, of the model, the first step is to estimate the random error. Because the actual random error associated with a particular value of y is the difference between the actual y value and its unknown mean, we estimate the error by the difference between the actual y-value and the *estimated* mean. This estimated error is called the *regression residual*, or simply the **residual,** and is denoted by $\hat{\varepsilon}$. The actual error ε and residual $\hat{\varepsilon}$ are shown in Figure 12.33.

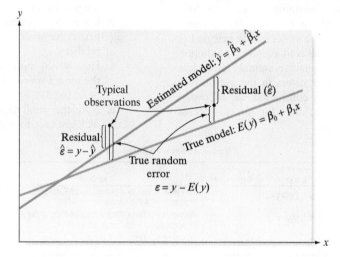

Figure 12.33

Actual random error ε and regression residual $\hat{\varepsilon}$

A **regression residual,** $\hat{\varepsilon}$, is defined as the difference between an observed y value and its corresponding predicted value:

$$\hat{\varepsilon} = (y - \hat{y}) = y - (\hat{\beta}_0 + \hat{\beta}_1 x_1 + \hat{\beta}_2 x_2 + \cdots + \hat{\beta}_k x_k)$$

Because the true mean of y (that is, the true regression model) is not known, the actual random error cannot be calculated. However, because the residual is based on the estimated mean (the least squares regression model), it can be calculated and used to estimate the random error and to check the regression assumptions. Such checks are generally referred to as **residual analyses.** Two useful properties of residuals are given in the next box.

Properties of Regression Residuals

1. The mean of the residuals is equal to 0. This property follows from the fact that the sum of the differences between the observed y values and their least squares predicted $\hat{y}$ values is equal to 0.

$$\sum(\text{Residuals}) = \sum(y - \hat{y}) = 0$$

2. The standard deviation of the residuals is equal to the standard deviation of the fitted regression model, s. This property follows from the fact that the sum of the squared residuals is equal to SSE, which when divided by the error degrees of freedom is equal to the variance of the fitted regression model, s^2. The square root of the variance is both the standard deviation of the residuals and the standard deviation of the regression model.

$$\sum (\text{Residuals})^2 = \sum (y - \hat{y})^2 = \text{SSE}$$

$$s = \sqrt{\frac{\sum (\text{Residuals})^2}{n - (k + 1)}} = \sqrt{\frac{\text{SSE}}{n - (k + 1)}}$$

BIOGRAPHY

FRANCIS J. ANSCOMBE (1918–2001)
Anscombe's Data

British citizen Frank Anscombe grew up in a small town near the English Channel. He attended Trinity College in Cambridge, England, on a merit scholarship, graduating with first class honors in mathematics in 1939. He later earned his master's degree in 1943. During World War II, Anscombe worked for the British Ministry of Supply, developing a mathematical solution for aiming antiaircraft rockets at German bombers and buzz bombs. Following the war, Anscombe worked at the Rothamsted Experimental Station, applying statistics to agriculture. There, he formed his appreciation for solving problems with social relevance. During his career as a professor of statistics, Anscombe served on the faculty of Cambridge, Princeton, and Yale universities. He was a pioneer in the application of computers to statistical analysis and was one of the original developers of residual analysis in regression. Anscombe is famous for a paper he wrote in 1973, in which he showed that one regression model could be fit by four very different data sets ("Anscombe's data"). While Anscombe published 50 research articles on statistics, he also had serious interests in classical music, poetry, and art.

The following examples show how a graphical analysis of regression residuals can be used to verify the assumptions associated with the model and to support improvements to the model when the assumptions do not appear to be satisfied. We rely on statistical software to generate the appropriate graphs in the examples and exercises.

Checking Assumption #1: Mean $\varepsilon = 0$

First, we demonstrate how a residual plot can detect a model in which the hypothesized relationship between $E(y)$ and an independent variable x is misspecified. The assumption of mean error of 0 is violated in these types of models.*

Example 12.14

Analyzing Residuals— Electrical Usage Model

Problem Refer to the problem of modeling the relationship between home size (x) and electrical usage (y) in Example 12.7 (p. 698). The data for $n = 15$ homes are repeated in Table 12.6. Minitab printouts for a straight-line model and a quadratic model fitted to the data are shown in Figures 12.34a and 12.34b, respectively. The residuals from these models are highlighted in the printouts. The residuals are then plotted on the vertical axis against the variable x, size of home, on the horizontal axis in Figures 12.35a and 12.35b, respectively.

a. Verify that each residual is equal to the difference between the observed y value and the estimated mean value, $\hat{y}$.

b. Analyze the residual plots.

---

*For a misspecified model, the hypothesized mean of y, denoted by $E_h(y)$, will not equal the true mean of y, $E(y)$. Because $y = E_h(y) + \varepsilon$, then $\varepsilon = y - E_h(y)$ and $E(\varepsilon) = E[y - E_h(y)] = E(y) - E_h(y) \neq 0$.

Table 12.6	Home Size–Electrical Usage Data
Size of Home, x (sq. ft.)	Monthly Usage, y (kilowatt-hours)
1,290	1,182
1,350	1,172
1,470	1,264
1,600	1,493
1,710	1,571
1,840	1,711
1,980	1,804
2,230	1,840
2,400	1,956
2,710	2,007
2,930	1,984
3,000	1,960
3,210	2,001
3,240	1,928
3,520	1,945

Solution

a. For the straight-line model, the residual is calculated for the first y value as follows:

$$\hat{\varepsilon} = (y - \hat{y}) = 1,182 - 1,362.2 = -180.2$$

where $\hat{y}$ is the first number in the column labeled **Fit** on the Minitab printout in Figure 12.34a. Similarly, the residual for the first y value using the quadratic model (Figure 12.34b) is

$$\hat{\varepsilon} = 1,182 - 1,157.2 = 24.8$$

Both residuals agree with the first values given in the column labeled **Residual** in Figures 12.34a and 12.34b, respectively. Although the residuals both correspond to the same observed y value, 1,182, they differ because the predicted mean value changes depending on whether the straight-line model or quadratic model is used. Similar calculations produce the remaining residuals.

Regression Analysis: USAGE versus SIZE

```
The regression equation is
USAGE = 903 + 0.356 SIZE

Predictor     Coef    SE Coef     T       P
Constant      903.0   132.1       6.83    0.000
SIZE          0.35594 0.05477     6.50    0.000

S = 155.251   R-Sq = 76.5%   R-Sq(adj) = 74.7%

Analysis of Variance

Source          DF      SS        MS       F       P
Regression      1       1017803   1017803  42.23   0.000
Residual Error  13      313338    24103
Total           14      1331140

Obs   SIZE   USAGE    Fit     SE Fit   Residual   St Resid
 1    1290   1182.0   1362.2  68.3     -180.2     -1.29
 2    1350   1172.0   1383.5  65.6     -211.5     -1.50
 3    1470   1264.0   1426.2  60.6     -162.2     -1.13
 4    1600   1493.0   1472.5  55.4       20.5      0.14
 5    1710   1571.0   1511.7  51.4       59.3      0.41
 6    1840   1711.0   1557.9  47.3      153.1      1.04
 7    1980   1804.0   1607.8  43.7      196.2      1.32
 8    2230   1840.0   1696.8  40.3      143.2      0.96
 9    2400   1956.0   1757.3  40.5      198.7      1.33
10    2710   2007.0   1867.6  46.0      139.4      0.94
11    2930   1984.0   1945.9  52.9       38.1      0.26
12    3000   1960.0   1970.8  55.5      -10.8     -0.07
13    3210   2001.0   2045.6  64.0      -44.6     -0.32
14    3240   1928.0   2056.3  65.3     -128.3     -0.91
15    3520   1945.0   2155.9  78.0     -210.9     -1.57
```

Figure 12.34a

Minitab printout for straight-line model of electrical usage

Regression Analysis: USAGE versus SIZE, SIZESQ

```
The regression equation is
USAGE = - 807 + 1.96 SIZE - 0.000340 SIZESQ

Predictor          Coef      SE Coef        T       P
Constant         -806.7        166.9    -4.83   0.000
SIZE            1.9616        0.1525    12.86   0.000
SIZESQ      -0.00034044   0.00003212   -10.60   0.000

S = 50.1998    R-Sq = 97.7%    R-Sq(adj) = 97.3%

Analysis of Variance

Source           DF        SS       MS       F       P
Regression        2   1300900   650450   258.11   0.000
Residual Error   12     30240     2520
Total            14   1331140

Obs   SIZE   USAGE      Fit   SE Fit   Residual   St Resid
  1   1290  1182.0   1157.2     29.3       24.8       0.61
  2   1350  1172.0   1221.0     26.2      -49.0      -1.14
  3   1470  1264.0   1341.2     21.2      -77.2      -1.70
  4   1600  1493.0   1460.3     18.0       32.7       0.70
  5   1710  1571.0   1552.2     17.1       18.8       0.40
  6   1840  1711.0   1650.1     17.6       60.9       1.30
  7   1980  1804.0   1742.6     19.0       61.4       1.32
  8   2230  1840.0   1874.7     21.2      -34.7      -0.76
  9   2400  1956.0   1940.2     21.7       15.8       0.35
 10   2710  2007.0   2009.0     20.0       -2.0      -0.04
 11   2930  1984.0   2018.2     18.4      -34.2      -0.73
 12   3000  1960.0   2014.1     18.4      -54.1      -1.16
 13   3210  2001.0   1982.1     21.5       18.9       0.42
 14   3240  1928.0   1975.1     22.5      -47.1      -1.05
 15   3520  1945.0   1880.0     36.2       65.0       1.87
```

Figure 12.34b

Minitab printout for quadratic model of electrical usage

b. The Minitab plot of the residuals for the straight-line model (Figure 12.35a) reveals a nonrandom pattern. The residuals exhibit a curved shape, with the residuals for the small values of x below the horizontal 0 (mean of the residuals) line, the residuals corresponding to the middle values of x above the 0 line, and the residuals for the largest values of x again below the 0 line. The indication is that the mean value of the random error ε *within* each of these ranges of x (small, medium, large) may not be equal to 0. Such a pattern usually indicates that curvature needs to be added to the model.

When the second-order term is added to the model, the nonrandom pattern disappears. In Figure 12.35b, the residuals appear to be randomly distributed around the 0 line, as expected. Note, too, that the residuals on the quadratic residual plot vary between −75 and 50, compared to between −200 and 200 on the straight-line plot. In fact, $s \approx 50$ for the quadratic model is much smaller than $s \approx 155$ for the straight-line model. The implication is that the quadratic model provides a considerably better model for predicting electrical usage.

Figure 12.35a

Minitab residual plot for straight-line model of electrical usage

Figure 12.35b

Minitab residual plot for quadratic
model of electrical usage

Look Back The residual analysis verifies our conclusions from Example 12.7, where we
found the t-test for the quadratic term, $\beta_2 x^2$, to be statistically significant.

■ **Now Work Exercise 12.120a**

Checking Assumption #2: Constant Error Variance

Residual plots can also be used to detect violations of the assumption of constant
error variance. For example, a plot of the residuals versus the predicted value $\hat{y}$ may
display one of the patterns shown in Figure 12.36. In these figures, the range in values of the residuals increases (or decreases) as $\hat{y}$ increases, thus indicating that the
variance of the random error, ε, becomes larger (or smaller) as the estimate of $E(y)$
increases in value. Because $E(y)$ depends on the x values in the model, this implies
that the variance of ε is not constant for all settings of the x's.

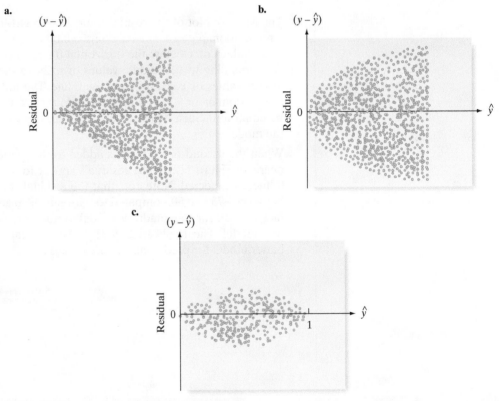

Figure 12.36

Residual plots showing changes in the variance of ε

In the next example, we demonstrate how to use this plot to detect a nonconstant
variance and suggest a useful remedy.

Example 12.15

Using Residuals to Check Equal Variances—Social Workers' Salaries

Problem The data in Table 12.7 are the salaries, y, and years of experience, x, for a sample of 50 social workers. The first-order model $E(y) = \beta_0 + \beta_1 x$ was fitted to the data using SPSS. The SPSS printout is shown in Figure 12.37, followed by a plot of the residuals versus $\hat{y}$ in Figure 12.38. Interpret the results. Make model modifications, if necessary.

Solution The SPSS printout, Figure 12.37, suggests that the first-order model provides an adequate fit to the data. The R^2-value indicates that the model explains 78.7% of the sample variation in salaries. The t-value for testing β_1, 13.31, is highly significant (p-value $\approx$ 0) and indicates that the model contributes information for the prediction of y. However, an examination of the residuals plotted against $\hat{y}$ (Figure 12.38) reveals

Table 12.7	Salary Data for Example 12.15				
Years of Experience, x	Salary, y	Years of Experience, x	Salary, y	Years of Experience, x	Salary, y
7	$26,075	21	$43,628	28	$99,139
28	79,370	4	16,105	23	52,624
23	65,726	24	65,644	17	50,594
18	41,983	20	63,022	25	53,272
19	62,308	20	47,780	26	65,343
15	41,154	15	38,853	19	46,216
24	53,610	25	66,537	16	54,288
13	33,697	25	67,447	3	20,844
2	22,444	28	64,785	12	32,586
8	32,562	26	61,581	23	71,235
20	43,076	27	70,678	20	36,530
21	56,000	20	51,301	19	52,745
18	58,667	18	39,346	27	67,282
7	22,210	1	24,833	25	80,931
2	20,521	26	65,929	12	32,303
18	49,727	20	41,721	11	38,371
11	33,233	26	82,641		

Data Set: SOCIAL

Model Summary[b]

Model	R	R Square	Adjusted R Square	Std. Error of the Estimate
1	.887[a]	.787	.782	8642.441

a. Predictors: (Constant), ESP

b. Dependent Variable: SALARY

ANOVA[b]

Model		Sum of Squares	df	Mean Square	F	Sig.
1	Regression	1.3E+10	1	1.324E+10	177.257	.000[a]
	Residual	3.6E+09	48	74691793.28		
	Total	1.7E+10	49			

a. Predictors: (Constant), ESP

b. Dependent Variable: SALARY

Coefficients[a]

Model		Unstandardized Coefficients		Standardized Coefficients	t	Sig.
		B	Std. Error	Beta		
1	(Constant)	11368.72	3160.317		3.597	.001
	ESP	2141.381	160.839	.887	13.314	.000

a. Dependent Variable: SALARY

Figure 12.37

SPSS regression printout for first-order model of salary

a potential problem. Note the "cone" shape of the residual variability; the size of the residuals increases as the estimated mean salary increases, implying that the constant variance assumption is violated.

One way to stabilize the variance of ε is to refit the model using a transformation on the dependent variable y. With economic data (e.g., salaries), a useful **variance-stabilizing transformation** is the natural logarithm of y, denoted $\ln(y)$.* We fit the model

$$\ln(y) = \beta_0 + \beta_1 x + \varepsilon$$

to the data of Table 12.7. Figure 12.39 shows the SPSS regression analysis printout for the $n = 50$ measurements, while Figure 12.40 shows a plot of the residuals from the log model.

Figure 12.38

SPSS residual plot for first-order model of salary

Model Summary[b]

Model	R	R Square	Adjusted R Square	Std. Error of the Estimate
1	.929[a]	.864	.861	.1541127

a. Predictors: (Constant), ESP

b. Dependent Variable: LNSALARY

ANOVA[b]

Model		Sum of Squares	df	Mean Square	F	Sig.
1	Regression	7.212	1	7.212	303.660	.000[a]
	Residual	1.140	48	.024		
	Total	8.352	49			

a. Predictors: (Constant), ESP

b. Dependent Variable: LNSALARY

Coefficients[a]

Model		Unstandardized Coefficients		Standardized Coefficients	t	Sig.
		B	Std. Error	Beta		
1	(Constant)	9.841	.056		174.631	.000
	ESP	.050	.003	.929	17.426	.000

a. Dependent Variable: LNSALARY

Figure 12.39

SPSS regression printout for model of log salary

Figure 12.40

SPSS residual plot for model of ln(salary)

*Other variance-stabilizing transformations that are used successfully in practice are $\sqrt{y}$ and $\sin^{-1}\sqrt{y}$. Consult the references for more details on these transformations.

You can see that the logarithmic transformation has stabilized the error variances. Note that the cone shape is gone; there is no apparent tendency of the residual variance to increase as mean salary increases. We therefore are confident that inferences using the $\ln(y)$ model are more reliable than those using the untransformed model.

Look Back With transformed models, the analyst should be wary when interpreting model statistics such as $\hat{\beta}_1$ and s. These interpretations must take into account that the dependent variable is not some function of y. For example, the antilogarithm of $\hat{\beta}_1$ in the $\ln(y)$ model for salary (y) represents the percentage change in salary for every 1 year increase in experience (x).

■ **Now Work Exercise 12.120b**

Checking Assumption #3: Errors Normally Distributed

Several graphical methods are available for assessing whether the random error ε has an approximate normal distribution. Recall (Section 4.7) that stem-and-leaf displays, histograms, and normal probability plots are useful for checking whether the data are normally distributed. We illustrate these techniques in an example. But first, we discuss a related problem—using residuals to check for *outliers*.

If the assumption of normally distributed errors is satisfied, then we expect approximately 95% of the residuals to fall within 2 standard deviations of the mean of 0, and almost all of the residuals to lie within 3 standard deviations of the mean of 0. Residuals that are extremely far from 0 and disconnected from the bulk of the other residuals are called **regression outliers** and should receive special attention from the analyst.

A **regression outlier** is a residual that is larger than $3s$ (in absolute value).

Example 12.16

Identifying Outliers— Grandfather Clock Price Model

Problem Refer to Example 12.6 (p. 692) in which we modeled the auction price (y) of a grandfather clock as a function of age (x_1) and number of bidders (x_2). The data for this example are repeated in Table 12.8, with one important difference: The auction price of the clock at the top of the sixth column has been changed from $2,131 to $1,131 (highlighted in Table 12.8). The interaction model

$$E(y) = \beta_0 + \beta_1 x_1 + \beta_2 x_2 + \beta_3 x_1 x_2$$

is again fit to these (modified) data, with the Minitab printout shown in Figure 12.41. The residuals are shown highlighted in the printout and then plotted against the number of bidders, x_2, in Figure 12.42. Analyze the residual plot.

Table 12.8	Altered Auction Price Data				
Age, x_1 (years)	Number of Bidders, x_2	Auction Price, y ($)	Age, x_1 (years)	Number of Bidders, x_2	Auction Price, y ($)
127	13	1,235	170	14	1,131
115	12	1,080	182	8	1,550
127	7	845	162	11	1,884
150	9	1,522	184	10	2,041
156	6	1,047	143	6	845
182	11	1,979	159	9	1,483
156	12	1,822	108	14	1,055
132	10	1,253	175	8	1,545
137	9	1,297	108	6	729
113	9	946	179	9	1,792
137	15	1,713	111	15	1,175
117	11	1,024	187	8	1,593
137	8	1,147	111	7	785
153	6	1,092	115	7	744
117	13	1,152	194	5	1,356
126	10	1,336	168	7	1,262

Data Set: CLOCK2

```
The regression equation is
PRICE = - 513 + 8.17 AGE + 19.9 NUMBIDS + 0.320 AGE_BIDS


Predictor    Coef    SE Coef     T      P
Constant    -512.8    665.9    -0.77  0.448
AGE          8.165    4.585     1.78  0.086
NUMBIDS     19.89     67.44     0.29  0.770
AGE_BIDS     0.3196    0.4790   0.67  0.510


S = 200.598   R-Sq = 72.9%   R-Sq(adj) = 70.0%


Analysis of Variance

Source          DF       SS        MS       F      P
Regression       3   3033587   1011196   25.13  0.000
Residual Error  28   1126703     40239
Total           31   4160290

Obs  AGE   PRICE     Fit   SE Fit   Residual   St Resid
  1  127  1235.0  1310.4    59.3      -75.4      -0.39
  2  115  1080.0  1105.9    62.1      -25.9      -0.14
  3  127   845.0   947.5    61.1     -102.5      -0.54
  4  150  1522.0  1322.5    37.1      199.5       1.01
  5  156  1047.0  1179.5    60.3     -132.5      -0.69
  6  182  1979.0  1831.9    82.9      147.1       0.81
  7  156  1822.0  1598.0    61.9      224.0       1.17
  8  132  1253.0  1185.8    39.7       67.2       0.34
  9  137  1297.0  1178.9    39.0      118.1       0.60
 10  113   946.0   913.9    58.6       32.1       0.17
 11  137  1713.0  1561.0    78.4      152.0       0.82
 12  117  1024.0  1072.6    53.1      -48.6      -0.25
 13  137  1147.0  1115.2    44.3       31.8       0.16
 14  153  1092.0  1149.2    59.0      -57.2      -0.30
 15  117  1152.0  1187.2    69.7      -35.2      -0.19
 16  126  1336.0  1117.6    43.4      218.4       1.12
 17  170  1131.0  1914.4   116.7     -783.4      -4.80R
 18  182  1550.0  1597.7    62.8      -47.7      -0.25
 19  162  1884.0  1598.3    57.0      285.7       1.49
 20  184  2041.0  1776.6    70.7      264.4       1.41
 21  143   845.0  1048.4    58.9     -203.4      -1.06
 22  159  1483.0  1421.8    40.6       61.2       0.31
 23  108  1055.0  1130.7    97.9      -75.7      -0.43
 24  175  1545.0  1522.7    55.4       22.3       0.12
 25  108   729.0   695.5    99.6       33.5       0.19
 26  179  1792.0  1642.7    57.6      149.3       0.78
 27  111  1175.0  1224.0   107.2      -49.0      -0.29
 28  187  1593.0  1651.3    68.6      -58.3      -0.31
 29  111   785.0   781.1    80.9        3.9       0.02
 30  115   744.0   822.7    75.5      -78.7      -0.42
 31  194  1356.0  1480.7   133.6     -124.7      -0.83 X
 32  168  1262.0  1374.0    57.7     -112.0      -0.58
```

Figure 12.41

Minitab regression printout for altered grandfather clock data

R denotes an observation with a large standardized residual.
X denotes an observation whose X value gives it large influence.

Figure 12.42

Minitab residual plot for altered grandfather clock data

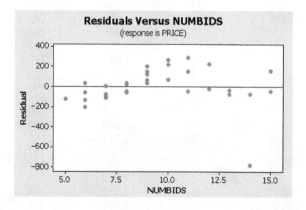

Solution The residual plot dramatically reveals the one altered measurement. Note that one of the two residuals at $x_2 = 14$ bidders falls more than 3 standard deviations below 0. (This observation is highlighted on Figure 12.41.) Note that no other residual falls more than 2 standard deviations from 0.

What do we do with outliers once we identify them? First, we try to determine the cause. Were the data entered into the computer incorrectly? Was the observation recorded incorrectly when the data were collected? If so, we correct the observation and rerun the analysis. Another possibility is that the observation is not representative of the conditions we are trying to model. For example, in this case the low price may be attributable to extreme damage to the clock or to a clock of inferior quality compared to the others. In these cases, we probably would exclude the observation from the analysis. In many cases, you may not be able to determine the cause of the outlier. Even so, you may want to rerun the regression analysis excluding the outlier in order to assess the effect of that observation on the results of the analysis.

Figure 12.43 shows the printout when the outlier observation is excluded from the grandfather clock analysis, and Figure 12.44 shows the new plot of the residuals against the number of bidders. Now only one of the residuals lies beyond 2 standard deviations from 0, and none of them lies beyond 3 standard deviations. Also, the model statistics indicate a much better model without the outlier. Most notably, the s has decreased from 200.6 to 85.83, indicating a model that will provide more precise estimates and predictions (narrower confidence and prediction intervals) for clocks that are similar to those in the reduced sample.

Figure 12.43

Minitab regression printout when outlier is deleted

```
The regression equation is
PRICE = 474 - 0.46 AGE - 114 NUMBIDS + 1.48 AGE_BIDS


Predictor      Coef   SE Coef      T      P
Constant      474.0     298.2   1.59  0.124
AGE          -0.465     2.107  -0.22  0.827
NUMBIDS     -114.12     31.23  -3.65  0.001
AGE_BIDS     1.4781    0.2295   6.44  0.000


S = 85.8286    R-Sq = 95.2%    R-Sq(adj) = 94.7%


Analysis of Variance

Source          DF       SS       MS       F      P
Regression       3  3933417  1311139  177.99  0.000
Residual Error  27   198897     7367
Total           30  4132314
```

Figure 12.44

Minitab residual plot when outlier is deleted

Residuals Versus NUMBIDS
(response is PRICE)

ETHICS in STATISTICS

Removing observations from a sample data set for the sole purpose of improving the fit of a regression model without investigating whether the observations are outliers or legitimate data points is considered *unethical statististical practice.*

Look Back Remember that if the outlier is removed from the analysis when in fact it belongs to the same population as the rest of the sample, the resulting model may provide misleading estimates and predictions.

■ **Now Work Exercise 12.120c**

The next example checks the assumption of the normality of the random error component.

Example 12.17
Using Residuals to Check for Normal Errors— Grandfather Clock Prices

Problem Refer to Example 12.16. Analyze the distribution of the residuals in the grandfather clock example, both before and after the outlier residual is removed. Determine whether the assumption of a normally distributed error term is reasonable.

Solution A histogram and normal probability plot for the two sets of residuals are constructed using Minitab and are shown in Figures 12.45 and 12.46. Note that the outlier appears to skew the histogram in Figure 12.45, whereas the histogram in Figure 12.46 appears to be more mound-shaped. Similarly, the pattern of residuals in the normal probability plot in Figure 12.46 (outlier deleted) is more nearly a straight line than the pattern in Figure 12.45 (outlier included). Thus, the normality assumption appears to be more plausible after the outlier is removed.

Figure 12.45

Minitab graphs of regression residuals for grandfather clock model (outlier included)

Figure 12.46

Minitab graphs of regression residuals for grandfather clock model (outlier deleted)

Look Back Although graphs do not provide formal statistical tests of normality, they do provide a descriptive display. Consult the references for methods to conduct statistical tests of normality using the residuals.

◼ **Now Work Exercise 12.120d**

Of the four assumptions in Section 12.1, the assumption that the random error is normally distributed is the least restrictive when we apply regression analysis in practice—that is, moderate departures from a normal distribution have very little effect on the validity of the statistical tests, confidence intervals, and prediction intervals presented in this chapter. In this case, we say that regression analysis is **robust** with respect to nonnormal errors. However, great departures from normality cast doubt on any inferences derived from the regression analysis.

Checking Assumption #4: Errors Independent

The assumption of independent errors is violated when successive errors are correlated. This typically occurs when the data for both the dependent and independent variables are observed sequentially over a period of time—called **time series data.** Time series data have a unique characteristic; the experimental unit represents a unit of time (e.g., a year, a month, a quarter). There are both graphical and formal statistical tests available for checking the assumption of independent regression errors. For example, a simple graph is to plot the residuals against time. If the residuals tend to group alternately into positive and negative clusters (as shown in Figure 12.47), then it is likely that the errors are correlated and the assumption is violated. If correlated errors are detected, one solution is to construct a **time series model** for $E(y)$. These methods are discussed in detail in Chapter 14.

Figure 12.47

Hypothetical residual plot for time series data

Summary

Residual analysis is a useful tool for the regression analyst, not only to check the assumptions but also to provide information about how the model can be improved. A summary of the residual analyses presented in this section to check the assumption that the random error ε is normally distributed with mean 0 and constant variance is presented in the next box.

Steps in a Residual Analysis

1. Check for a misspecified model by plotting the residuals against each of the quantitative independent variables. Analyze each plot, looking for a curvilinear trend. This shape signals the need for a quadratic term in the model. Try a second-order term in the variable against which the residuals are plotted.

2. Examine the residual plots for outliers. Draw lines on the residual plots at 2- and 3-standard-deviation distances below and above the 0 line. Examine residuals outside the 3-standard-deviation lines as potential outliers and check to see that no more than 5% of the residuals exceed the 2-standard-deviation lines. Determine whether each outlier can be explained as an error in data collection or transcription, corresponds to a member of a population different from that of the remainder of the sample, or simply represents an unusual observation. If the observation is determined to be an error, fix it or remove it. Even if you cannot determine the cause, you may want to rerun the regression analysis without the observation to determine its effect on the analysis.

3. Check for nonnormal errors by plotting a frequency distribution of the residuals, using a stem-and-leaf display or a histogram. Check to see if obvious departures from normality exist. Extreme skewness of the frequency distribution may be due to outliers or could indicate the need for a transformation of the dependent variable. (Normalizing transformations are beyond the scope of this book, but you can find information in the references.)

4. Check for unequal error variances by plotting the residuals against the predicted values, $\hat{y}$. If you detect a cone-shaped pattern or some other pattern that indicates that the variance of ε is not constant, refit the model using an appropriate variance-stabilizing transformation on y, such as $\ln(y)$. (Consult the references for other useful variance-stabilizing transformations.)

A Residual Analysis

In the previous Statistics in Action Revisited section (p. 735), we found the interaction model, $E(y) = \beta_0 + \beta_1 x_1 + \beta_3 x_2 + \beta_4 x_1 x_2$, to be both a statistically and practically useful model for predicting the cost (y) of a road construction contract. Recall that the two independent variables are the DOT engineer's estimate of cost (x_1) and bid status, where $x_2 = 1$ if a fixed bid and $x_2 = 0$ if a competitive bid. Before actually using the model in practice, we need to examine the residuals to be sure that the standard regression assumptions are reasonably satisfied.

Figures SIA12.9 and SIA12.10 are Minitab graphs of the residuals from the interaction model. The histogram shown in Figure SIA12.9 appears to be approximately normally distributed; consequently the assumption of normal errors is reasonably satisfied. The scatterplot of the residuals against $\hat{y}$ shown in Figure SIA12.10, however, shows a distinct "funnel" pattern; this indicates that the assumption of a constant error variance is likely to be violated. One way to modify the model to satisfy this assumption is to use a variance-stabilizing transformation (such as the natural log) on cost (y). When both the y and x variables in a regression equation are economic variables (prices, costs, salaries, etc.), it is often advantageous to transform the x variable also. Consequently, we'll modify the model by making a log transform on both cost (y) and DOTEST (x_1).

Figure SIA12.9

Minitab histogram of residuals from interaction model for road cost

Figure SIA12.10

Minitab plot of residuals versus predicted values from interaction model for road cost

Our modified (log-log) interaction model takes the form

$$E(y^*) = \beta_0 + \beta_1 x_1^* + \beta_2 x_2 + \beta_3 (x_1^*) x_2$$

where $y^* = \ln(\text{COST})$ and $x_1^* = \ln(\text{DOTEST})$. The Minitab printout for this model is shown in Figure SIA12.11, followed by graphs of the residuals in Figures SIA12.12 and SIA12.13. The histogram shown in Figure SIA12.12 is approximately normal, and, more important, the scatterplot of the residuals shown in Figure SIA12.13 has no distinct trend. It appears that the log transformations successfully stabilized the error variance. Note, however, that the t-test for the interaction term in the model (highlighted in Figure SIA12.11) is no longer statistically significant (p-value = .420).

Consequently, we will drop the interaction term from the model and use the simpler modified model,

$$E(y^*) = \beta_0 + \beta_1 x_1^* + \beta_2 x_2$$

to predict road construction cost.

Figure SIA12.11

Minitab regression printout for modified (log-log) model of road construction cost

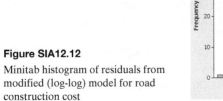

```
The regression equation is
LNCOST = - 0.162 + 1.01 LNDOTEST + 0.324 STATUS - 0.0176 STA_LNDOT


Predictor       Coef   SE Coef        T      P
Constant    -0.16188   0.05193    -3.12  0.002
LNDOTEST     1.00780   0.00798   126.23  0.000
STATUS        0.3243    0.1356     2.39  0.018
STA_LNDOT   -0.01762   0.02181    -0.81  0.420


S = 0.154922   R-Sq = 98.8%   R-Sq(adj) = 98.7%


Analysis of Variance

Source           DF       SS      MS       F      P
Regression        3   439.64  146.55  6105.87  0.000
Residual Error  231     5.54    0.02
Total           234   445.18
```

Figure SIA12.12

Minitab histogram of residuals from modified (log-log) model for road construction cost

Figure SIA12.13

Minitab plot of residuals versus predicted values from modified (log-log) model for road construction cost

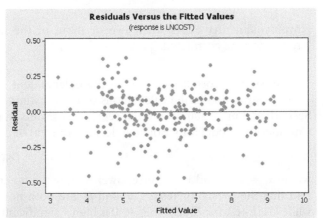

12.12 Some Pitfalls: Estimability, Multicollinearity, and Extrapolation

You should be aware of several potential problems when constructing a prediction model for some response y. A few of the most important are discussed in this final section.

Problem 1: Parameter Estimability

Suppose you want to fit a model relating annual crop yield y to the total expenditure for fertilizer x. We propose the first-order model

$$E(y) = \beta_0 + \beta_1 x$$

Now suppose we have 3 years of data and $1,000 is spent on fertilizer each year. The data are shown in Figure 12.48. You can see the problem: The parameters of the model cannot be estimated when all the data are concentrated at a single x-value. Recall that it takes two points (x-values) to fit a straight line. Thus, the parameters are not estimable when only one x is observed.

A similar problem would occur if we attempted to fit the quadratic model

$$E(y) = \beta_0 + \beta_1 x + \beta_2 x^2$$

to a set of data for which only one or two different x-values were observed (see Figure 12.49). At least three different x-values must be observed before a quadratic model can be fit to a set of data (that is, before all three parameters are estimable).

In general, the number of levels of observed x-values must be one more than the order of the polynomial in x that you want to fit.

For controlled experiments, the researcher can select one of the experimental designs in Chapter 9 that will permit estimation of the model parameters. Even when the values of the independent variables cannot be controlled by the researcher, the independent variables are almost always observed at a sufficient number of levels to permit estimation of the model parameters. When the statistical software you use suddenly refuses to fit a model, however, the problem is probably inestimable parameters.

Figure 12.48

Yield and fertilizer expenditure data: Three years

Problem 2: Multicollinearity

Often, two or more of the independent variables used in a regression model contribute redundant information—that is, the independent variables are correlated with each other. For example, suppose we want to construct a model to predict the gas mileage rating of a truck as a function of its load, x_1 (in tons), and the horsepower, x_2 (in foot-pounds per second), of its engine. We would expect heavy loads to require greater horsepower and to result in lower mileage ratings. Thus, although both x_1 and x_2 contribute information for the prediction of mileage rating, y, some of the information is overlapping because x_1 and x_2 are correlated.

When the independent variables are correlated, we say *multicollinearity* exists. In practice, it is not uncommon to observe correlations among the independent variables. However, a few problems arise when serious multicollinearity is present in the regression variables.

Figure 12.49

Only two x values observed: Quadratic model not estimable

> **Multicollinearity** exists when two or more of the independent variables used in regression are correlated.

First, high correlations among the independent variables increase the likelihood of rounding errors in the calculations of the β estimates, standard errors, and so forth. Second, and more important, the regression results may be confusing and misleading. Consider the model for gasoline mileage rating (y) of a truck:

$$E(y) = \beta_0 + \beta_1 x_1 + \beta_2 x_2$$

where $x_1 = $ load and $x_2 = $ horsepower. Fitting the model to a sample data set, we might find that the t-tests for testing β_1 and β_2 are both nonsignificant at the $\alpha = .05$ level, while the F-test for H_0: $\beta_1 = \beta_2 = 0$ is highly significant ($p = .001$). The tests may seem to be contradictory, but really they are not. The t-tests indicate that the contribution of one variable, say $x_1 = $ load, is not significant after the effect of $x_2 = $ horsepower has been accounted for (because x_2 is also in the model). The significant F-test, on the other hand, tells us that at least one of the two variables is making a contribution to the prediction of y (i.e., either β_1 or β_2 or both differ from 0). In fact, both are probably contributing, but the contribution of one overlaps with that of the other.

Multicollinearity can also have an effect on the signs of the parameter estimates. More specifically, a value of β_i may have the opposite sign from what is expected. In the truck gasoline mileage example, we expect heavy loads to result in lower mileage ratings, and we expect higher horsepowers to result in lower mileage ratings; consequently, we expect the signs of both the parameter estimates to be negative. Yet we may actually see a positive value of β_1 and be tempted to claim that heavy loads result in *higher* mileage ratings. This is the danger of interpreting a β coefficient when the independent variables are correlated. Because the variables contribute redundant information, the effect of x_1 = load on y = mileage rating is measured only partially by β_1.

How can you avoid the problems of multicollinearity in regression analysis? One way is to conduct a designed experiment (Chapter 9) so that the levels of the x variables are uncorrelated. Unfortunately, time and cost constraints may prevent you from collecting data in this manner. Consequently, most data are collected observationally. Because observational data frequently consist of correlated independent variables, you will need to recognize when multicollinearity is present and, if necessary, make modifications in the regression analysis.

Several methods are available for detecting multicollinearity in regression. A simple technique is to calculate the coefficient of correlation, r, between each pair of independent variables in the model and use the procedure outlined in Section 11.5 to test for significantly correlated variables. If one or more of the r-values are statistically different from 0, the variables in question are correlated, and a multicollinearity problem may exist.* The degree of multicollinearity will depend on the magnitude of the value of r, as shown in the box.

Using the Correlation Coefficient r to Detect Multicollinearity

Extreme multicollinearity: $|r| \geq .8$

Moderate multicollinearity: $.2 \leq |r| < .8$

Low multicollinearity: $|r| < .2$

Other indications of the presence of multicollinearity include those mentioned above—namely, nonsignificant t-tests for the individual parameter estimates when the F-test for overall model adequacy is significant and estimates with opposite signs from what is expected.[†]

Detecting Multicollinearity in the Regression Model

1. Significant correlations between pairs of independent variables (see box above)
2. Nonsignificant t-tests for all (or nearly all) of the individual β parameters when the F-test for overall model adequacy is significant
3. Signs opposite from what is expected in the estimated β parameters

---

| Example | 12.18 | |

Detecting Multicollinearity— Modeling Carbon Monoxide in Cigarette Smoke

Problem The Federal Trade Commission (FTC) annually ranks varieties of domestic cigarettes according to their tar, nicotine, and carbon monoxide contents. The U.S. Surgeon General considers each of these three substances hazardous to a smoker's health. Past studies have shown that increases in the tar and nicotine contents of a cigarette are accompanied by an increase in the carbon monoxide emitted from the cigarette smoke. Table 12.9 presents data on tar, nicotine, and carbon monoxide contents (in milligrams) and weight (in grams) for a sample of 25 (filter) brands tested in a recent

---

*Remember that r measures only the pairwise correlation between x-values. Three variables, $x_1, x_2,$ and x_3, may be highly correlated as a group but may not exhibit large pairwise correlations. Thus, multicollinearity may be present even when all pairwise correlations are not significantly different from 0.

[†]More formal methods for detecting multicollinearity, such as variance-inflation factors (VIFs), are available. Independent variables with a VIF of 10 or above are usually considered to be highly correlated with one or more of the other independent variables in the model. Calculation of VIFs are beyond the scope of this introductory text. Consult the chapter references for a discussion of VIFs and other formal methods of detecting multicollinearity.

year. Suppose we want to model carbon monoxide content, y, as a function of tar content, x_1, nicotine content, x_2, and weight, x_3, using the model

$$E(y) = \beta_0 + \beta_1 x_1 + \beta_2 x_2 + \beta_3 x_3$$

The model is fit to the 25 data points in Table 12.9, and a portion of the Minitab printout is shown in Figure 12.50. Examine the printout. Do you detect any signs of multicollinearity?

Table 12.9	FTC Cigarette Data for Example 12.18		
Tar, x_1	Nicotine, x_2	Weight, x_3	Carbon Monoxide, y
14.1	.86	.9853	13.6
16.0	1.06	1.0938	16.6
29.8	2.03	1.1650	23.5
8.0	.67	.9280	10.2
4.1	.40	.9462	5.4
15.0	1.04	.8885	15.0
8.8	.76	1.0267	9.0
12.4	.95	.9225	12.3
16.6	1.12	.9372	16.3
14.9	1.02	.8858	15.4
13.7	1.01	.9643	13.0
15.1	.90	.9316	14.4
7.8	.57	.9705	10.0
11.4	.78	1.1240	10.2
9.0	.74	.8517	9.5
1.0	.13	.7851	1.5
17.0	1.26	.9186	18.5
12.8	1.08	1.0395	12.6
15.8	.96	.9573	17.5
4.5	.42	.9106	4.9
14.5	1.01	1.0070	15.9
7.3	.61	.9806	8.5
8.6	.69	.9693	10.6
15.2	1.02	.9496	13.9
12.0	.82	1.1184	14.9

Source: Federal Trade Commission

Data Set: FTC

Regression Analysis: CO versus TAR, NICOTINE, WEIGHT

```
The regression equation is
CO = 3.20 + 0.963 TAR - 2.63 NICOTINE - 0.13 WEIGHT


Predictor   Coef   SE Coef     T      P
Constant    3.202   3.462    0.93  0.365
TAR         0.9626  0.2422   3.97  0.001
NICOTINE   -2.632   3.901   -0.67  0.507
WEIGHT     -0.130   3.885   -0.03  0.974


S = 1.44573   R-Sq = 91.9%   R-Sq(adj) = 90.7%


Analysis of Variance

Source         DF     SS      MS      F      P
Regression      3   495.26  165.09  78.98  0.000
Residual Error 21    43.89    2.09
```

Correlations: TAR, NICOTINE, WEIGHT

```
            TAR    NICOTINE
NICOTINE   0.977
           0.000

WEIGHT     0.491    0.500
           0.013    0.011


Cell Contents: Pearson correlation
               P-Value
```

Figure 12.50

Minitab printout for model of carbon monoxide content, Example 12.18

Solution First, note that the F-test for overall model utility is highly significant. The test statistic ($F = 78.98$) and observed significance level (p-value $= .000$) are highlighted on the Minitab printout, Figure 12.50. Therefore, at, say $\alpha = .01$, we can conclude that at least one of the parameters—β_1, β_2, or β_3—in the model is nonzero. The t-tests for two of three individual β's, however, are nonsignificant. (The p-values for these tests are highlighted on the printout.) Unless tar (x_1) is the only one of the three variables useful for predicting carbon monoxide content, these results are the first indication of a potential multicollinearity problem.

The negative values for β_2 and β_3 (highlighted on the printout) are a second clue to the presence of multicollinearity. From past studies, the FTC expects carbon monoxide content (y) to increase when either nicotine content (x_2) or weight (x_3) increases—that is, the FTC expects *positive* relationships between y and x_2 and between y and x_3, not negative ones.

All signs indicate that a serious multicollinearity problem exists.

Look Back To confirm our suspicions, we had Minitab produce the coefficient of correlation, r, for each of the three pairs of independent variables in the model. The resulting output is shown (highlighted) at the bottom of Figure 12.50. You can see that tar (x_1) and nicotine (x_2) are highly correlated ($r = .977$), while weight (x_3) is moderately correlated with the other two x's ($r \approx .5$). All three correlations have p-values $\approx .01$ or less; consequently, all three are significantly different from 0 at, say, $\alpha = .05$.

■ Now Work Exercise 12.119

Once you have detected that multicollinearity exists, there are several alternative measures available for solving the problem. The appropriate measure to take depends on the severity of the multicollinearity and the ultimate goal of the regression analysis.

Some researchers, when confronted with highly correlated independent variables, choose to include only one of the correlated variables in the final model. If you are interested in using the model only for estimation and prediction (step 6), you may decide not to drop any of the independent variables from the model. In the presence of multicollinearity, we have seen that it is dangerous to interpret the individual β parameters. However, confidence intervals for $E(y)$ and prediction intervals for y generally remain unaffected *as long as the values of the x's used to predict* y *follow the same pattern of multicollinearity exhibited in the sample data*—that is, you must take strict care to ensure that the values of the x variables fall within the range of the sample data.

Solutions to Some Problems Created by Multicollinearity in Regression*

1. Drop one or more of the correlated independent variables from the model. One way to decide which variables to keep in the model is to employ stepwise regression (Section 12.10).

2. If you decide to keep all the independent variables in the model,

   a. Avoid making inferences about the individual β parameters based on the t-tests.

   b. Restrict inferences about $E(y)$ and future y values to values of the x's that fall within the range of the sample data.

Problem 3: Prediction Outside the Experimental Region

Many research economists had developed highly technical models to relate the state of the economy to various economic indices and other independent variables. Many of these models were multiple regression models, where, for example, the dependent

---

*Several other solutions are available. For example, in the case where higher-order regression models are fit, the analyst may want to code the independent variables so that higher-order terms (e.g., x^2) for a particular x variable are not highly correlated with x. One transformation that works is $z = (x - \bar{x})/s$. Other, more sophisticated procedures for addressing multicollinearity (such as *ridge regression*) are beyond the scope of the text. Consult the references at the end of this chapter.

Figure 12.51

Using a regression model outside the experimental region

variable y might be next year's gross domestic product (GDP) and the independent variables might include this year's rate of inflation, this year's consumer price index (CPI), and so on. In other words, the model might be constructed to predict next year's economy using this year's knowledge.

Unfortunately, these models were almost all unsuccessful in predicting the recession in the early 1970s and the late 1990s. What went wrong? One of the problems was that many of the regression models were used to **extrapolate** (i.e., predict y-values of the independent variables that were outside the region in which the model was developed). For example, the inflation rate in the late 1960s, when the models were developed, ranged from 6% to 8%. When the double-digit inflation of the early 1970s became a reality, some researchers attempted to use the same models to predict future growth in GDP. As you can see in Figure 12.51, the model may be very accurate for predicting y when x is in the range of experimentation, but using the model outside that range is a dangerous practice.

Exercises 12.119–12.131

Learning the Mechanics

12.119 Consider fitting the multiple regression model

$$E(y) = \beta_0 + \beta_1 x_1 + \beta_2 x_2 + \beta_3 x_3 + \beta_4 x_4 + \beta_5 x_5$$

A matrix of correlations for all pairs of independent variables is given below. Do you detect a multicollinearity problem? Explain.

	x_1	x_2	x_3	x_4	x_5
x_1	—	.17	.02	−.23	.19
x_2		—	.45	.93	.02
x_3			—	.22	−.01
x_4				—	.86
x_5					—

12.120 Identify the problem(s) in each of the residual plots shown below.

a.

c.

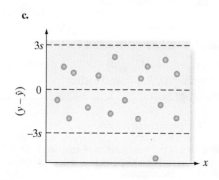

Applying the Concepts—Basic

12.121 **State casket sales restrictions.** Some states permit only licensed firms to sell funeral goods (e.g., caskets, urns) to the consumer, while other states have no restrictions. States with casket sales restrictions are being challenged in court to lift these monopolistic restrictions. A paper in the *Journal of Law and Economics* (Feb. 2008) used multiple regression to investigate the impact of lifting casket sales restrictions on the cost of a funeral. Data collected for a sample of 1,437 funerals were used to fit the model. A simpler version of the model estimated by the researchers is $E(y) = \beta_0 + \beta_1 x_1 + \beta_2 x_2 + \beta_3 x_1 x_2$, where y is the price (in dollars) of a direct burial, $x_1 = \{1$ if funeral home is in a restricted state, 0 if not$\}$, and $x_2 = \{1$ if price includes a basic wooden casket, 0 if no casket$\}$. The estimated equation (with standard errors in parentheses) is:

$$\hat{y} = 1{,}432 + 793 x_1 - 252 x_2 + 261 x_1 x_2, \quad R^2 = .78$$
$$\qquad\quad (70) \qquad (134) \qquad (109)$$

b.

d.

a. Calculate the predicted price of a direct burial with a basic wooden casket at a funeral home in a restricted state.

b. The data include a direct burial funeral with a basic wooden casket at a funeral home in a restricted state that costs $2,200. Assuming the standard deviation of the model is $50, is this data value an outlier?

c. The data also include a direct burial funeral with a basic wooden casket at a funeral home in a restricted state that costs $2,500. Again, assume that the standard deviation of the model is $50. Is this data value an outlier?

12.122 Personality traits and job performance. Refer to the *Journal of Applied Psychology* (Jan. 2011) study of the determinants of task performance, Exercise 12.94 (p. 722). In addition to x_1 = conscientiousness score and x_2 = {1 if highly complex job, 0 if not}, the researchers also used x_3 = emotional stability score, x_4 = organizational citizenship behavior score, and x_5 = counterproductive work behavior score to model y = task performance score. One of their concerns is the level of multicollinearity in the data. Below is a matrix of correlations for all possible pairs of independent variables. Based on this information, do you detect a moderate or high level of multicollinearity? If so, what are your recommendations?

	x_1	x_2	x_3	x_4
Conscientiousness (x_1)				
Job complexity (x_2)	.13			
Emotional stability (x_3)	.62	.14		
Organizational citizenship (x_4)	.24	.03	.24	
Counterproductive work (x_5)	−.23	−.02	−.25	−.62

12.123 Women in top management. Refer to the *Journal of Organizational Culture, Communications and Conflict* (July 2007) study on women in upper management positions at U.S. firms, Exercise 11.67 (p. 639). Monthly data (n = 252 months) were collected for several variables in an attempt to model the number of females in managerial positions (y). The independent variables included the number of females with a college degree (x_1), the number of female high school graduates with no college degree (x_2), the number of males in managerial positions (x_3), the number of males with a college degree (x_4), and the number of male high school graduates with no college degree (x_5). The correlations provided in Exercise 11.67 are given in each part. Determine which of the correlations results in a potential multicollinearity problem for the regression analysis.

a. The correlation relating number of females in managerial positions and number of females with a college degree: r = .983.

b. The correlation relating number of females in managerial positions and number of female high school graduates with no college degree: r = .074.

c. The correlation relating number of males in managerial positions and number of males with a college degree: r = .722.

d. The correlation relating number of males in managerial positions and number of male high school graduates with no college degree: r = .528.

12.124 Factors identifying urban counties. The *Professional Geographer* (Feb. 2000) published a study of urban and rural counties in the western United States. Six independent variables—total county population (x_1), population density (x_2), population concentration (x_3), population growth (x_4), proportion of county land in farms (x_5), and 5-year change in agricultural land base (x_6)—were used to model the urban/rural rating (y) of a county, where rating was recorded on a scale of 1 (most rural) to 10 (most urban). Prior to running the multiple regression analysis, the researchers were concerned about possible multicollinearity in the data. Below is a correlation matrix for data collected on n = 256 counties.

Independent Variable	x_1	x_2	x_3	x_4	x_5
x_1: Total population					
x_2: Population density	.20				
x_3: Population concentration	.45	.43			
x_4: Population growth	−.05	−.14	−.01		
x_5: Farm land	−.16	−.15	−.07	−.20	
x_6: Agricultural change	−.12	−.12	−.22	−.06	−.06

Source: Based on Berry, K. A., et al. "Interpreting what is rural and urban for western U.S. counties," *Professional Geographer*, Vol. 52, No. 1, Feb. 2000, pp. 93–105 (Table 2).

a. Based on the correlation matrix, is there any evidence of extreme multicollinearity?

b. The first-order model with all six independent variables was fit, and the results are shown in the next table. Based on the reported tests, is there any evidence of extreme multicollinearity?

Independent Variable	β Estimate	p-value
x_1: Total population	0.110	0.045
x_2: Population density	0.065	0.230
x_3: Population concentration	0.540	0.000
x_4: Population growth	−0.009	0.860
x_5: Farm land	−0.150	0.003
x_6: Agricultural change	−0.027	0.580

Overall model:
R^2 = .44 $\qquad R_a^2$ = .43 F = 32.47 $\quad p$-value < .001

Source: Berry, K. A., et al. "Interpreting what is rural and urban for western U.S. counties," *Professional Geographer*, Vol. 52, No. 1, Feb. 2000 (Table 2).

12.125 Accuracy of software effort estimates. Refer to the *Journal of Empirical Software Engineering* (Vol. 9, 2004) study of the accuracy of new software effort estimates, Exercise 12.114 (p. 738). Recall that stepwise regression was used to develop a model for the relative error in estimating effort (y) as a function of company role of estimator (x_1 = 1 if developer, 0 if project leader) and previous accuracy (x_8 = 1 if more than 20% accurate, 0 if less than 20% accurate). The stepwise regression yielded the prediction equation $\hat{y}$ = .12 − .28x_1 + .27x_8. The researcher is concerned that the sign of the estimated β multiplied by x_1 is the opposite from what is expected. (The researcher expects a project leader to have a smaller relative error of estimation than a developer.) Give at least one reason why this phenomenon occurred.

Applying the Concepts—Basic

12.126 Reality TV and cosmetic surgery. Refer to the *Body Image: An International Journal of Research* (March 2010) study of the influence of reality TV shows on one's desire to undergo cosmetic surgery, Exercise 12.17 (p. 682). Simulated data for the study is saved in the file. In Exercise 12.17, you fit the first-order model, $E(y) = \beta_0 + \beta_1 x_1 + \beta_2 x_2 + \beta_3 x_3 + \beta_4 x_4$, where y = desire to have cosmetic surgery, x_1 is a dummy variable for gender, x_2 = level of self-esteem, x_3 = level of body satisfaction, and x_4 = impression of reality TV.

a. Check the data for multicollinearity. If you detect multicollinearity, what modifications to the model do you recommend?

b. Conduct a complete residual analysis for the model. Do you detect any violations of the assumptions? If so, what modifications to the model do you recommend?

12.127 Arsenic in groundwater. Refer to the *Environmental Science & Technology* (Jan. 2005) study of the reliability of a commercial kit to test for arsenic in groundwater, Exercise 12.16 (p. 682). Recall that you fit a first-order model for arsenic level (y) as a function of latitude (x_1), longitude (x_2), and depth (x_3) to data saved in the file. Conduct a residual analysis of the data. Based on the results, comment on each of the following:

a. assumption of mean error = 0

b. assumption of constant error variance

c. outliers

d. assumption of normally distributed errors

e. multicollinearity

12.128 Contamination from a plant's discharge. Refer to the U.S. Army Corps of Engineers data on fish contaminated from the toxic discharges of a chemical plant located on the banks of the Tennessee River in Alabama. In Exercise 12.18 (p. 683), you fit the first-order model, $E(y) = \beta_0 + \beta_1 x_1 + \beta_2 x_2 + \beta_3 x_3$, where y = DDT level in captured fish, x_1 = miles captured upstream, x_2 = fish length, and x_3 = fish weight. Conduct a complete residual analysis for the model. Do you recommend any model modifications be made? Explain.

12.129 Failure times of silicon wafer microchips. Refer to the National Semiconductor study of manufactured silicon wafer integrated circuit chips, Exercise 12.63 (p. 706). Recall that the failure times of the microchips (in hours) was determined at different solder temperatures (degrees Celsius). The data are repeated in the table in the next column.

a. Fit the straight-line model $E(y) = \beta_0 + \beta_1 x$ to the data, where y = failure time and x = solder temperature.

b. Compute the residual for a microchip manufactured at a temperature of 149°C.

c. Plot the residuals against solder temperature (x). Do you detect a trend?

Temperature (°C)	Time to Failure (hours)
165	200
162	200
164	1,200
158	500
158	600
159	750
156	1,200
157	1,500
152	500
147	500
149	1,100
149	1,150
142	3,500
142	3,600
143	3,650
133	4,200
132	4,800
132	5,000
134	5,200
134	5,400
125	8,300
123	9,700

Source: Gee, S., and Nguyen, L. "Mean time to failure in wafer level-CSP packages with SnPb and SnAgCu solder bmps," International Wafer Level Packaging Conference, San Jose, CA, Nov. 3–4, 2005 (adapted from Figure 7).

d. In Exercise 12.63c, you determined that failure time (y) and solder temperature (x) were curvilinearly related. Does the residual plot, part c, support this conclusion?

12.130 Cooling method for gas turbines. Refer to the *Journal of Engineering for Gas Turbines and Power* (Jan. 2005) study of a high-pressure inlet fogging method for a gas turbine engine, Exercise 12.103 (p. 729). Now consider the interaction model for heat rate (y) of a gas turbine as a function of cycle speed (x_1) and cycle pressure ratio (x_2), $E(y) = \beta_0 + \beta_1 x_1 + \beta_2 x_2 + \beta_3 x_1 x_2$. Use the data saved in the file to conduct a complete residual analysis for the model. Do you recommend making model modifications?

12.131 Agreeableness, gender, and wages. Refer to the *Journal of Personality and Social Psychology* (Feb. 2012) study of on-the-job agreeableness and wages, Exercise 12.107 (p. 730). Recall that the researchers modeled mean income, $E(y)$, as a function of both agreeableness score (x_1) and a dummy variable for gender ($x_2 = 1$ if male, 0 if female). Use the data saved in the file to analyze the residuals of the model,

$$E(y) = \beta_0 + \beta_1 x_1 + \beta_2 (x_1)^2 + \beta_3 x_2$$

What model modifications, if any, do you recommend?

◼ Chapter Notes

Key Terms

Adjusted multiple coefficient of determination 677
Base level 707
Categorical variable 707
Coded variable 667
Complete model 724
Complete second-order model 701
Dummy variable 707
Extrapolation 758
First-order model 669
Full model 724
General multiple regression model 668
Higher-order term 667
Indicator variable 707
Interaction 691
Interaction model 691
Interaction term 691
Least squares prediction equation 670
Level of a variable 707
Main effect terms 715
Mean square for error (MSE) 670
Method of least squares 669
Model building 668
Multicollinearity 754

Multiple coefficient of determination (R^2) 676
Multiple regression model 667
Nested model 724
Nested model F-test 725
Objective variable screening procedure 733
Paraboloid 702
Parameter estimability 753
Parsimonious model 727
Quadratic model 698
Quadratic term 698
Qualitative variable 707
Reduced model 724
Regression outlier 747
Regression residual 740
Residual analysis 740
Response surface 702
Robust method 750
Saddle-shaped surface 702
Second-order model 698
Second-order term 698
Stepwise regression 731
Time series data 750
Time series model 751
Variance-stabilizing transformation 746

Key Formulas

$$s^2 = \text{MSE} = \frac{\text{SSE}}{n - (k + 1)}$$

Estimator of σ^2 for a model with k independent variables

$$t = \frac{\hat{\beta}_i}{s_{\hat{\beta}_i}}$$

Test statistic for testing H_0: β_i

$\hat{\beta}_i \pm (t_{\alpha/2})s_{\hat{\beta}_i}$, where $t_{\alpha/2}$ depends on $n - (k + 1)$ df

$100(1 - \alpha)\%$ confidence interval for β_i

$$R^2 = \frac{\text{SS}_{yy} - \text{SSE}}{\text{SS}_{yy}}$$

Multiple coefficient of determination

$$R_a^2 = 1 - \left[\frac{(n - 1)}{n - (k + 1)}\right](1 - R^2)$$

Adjusted multiple coefficient of determination

$$F = \frac{\text{MS (Model)}}{\text{MSE}}$$
$$= \frac{R^2/k}{(1 - R^2)/[n - (k + 1)]}$$

Test statistic for testing H_0: $\beta_1 = \beta_2 = \cdots = \beta_k = 0$

$$F = \frac{(\text{SSE}_R - \text{SSE}_C)/\text{number of } \beta\text{'s tested}}{\text{MSE}_C}$$

Test statistic for comparing reduced and complete models

$y - \hat{y}$

Regression residual

Key Symbols

x_1^2	Quadratic form for a quantitative x
$x_1 x_2$	Interaction term
MSE	Mean square for error (estimates σ^2)
$\hat{\varepsilon}$	Estimated random error (residual)
SSE_R	Sum of squared errors, reduced model
SSE_C	Sum of squared errors, complete model
MSE_C	Mean squared error, complete model
$\ln(y)$	Natural logarithm of dependent variable

Key Ideas

Multiple regression variables
$y = $ **Dependent** variable (quantitative)
$x_1, x_2, \ldots, x_k$ are **independent** variables (quantitative or qualitative)

First-order model in k quantitative x's
$$E(y) = \beta_0 + \beta_1 x_1 + \beta_2 x_2 + \cdots + \beta_k x_k$$
Each β_i represents the change in $E(y)$ for every 1-unit increase in x_i, holding all other x's fixed.

Interaction model in 2 quantitative x's
$E(y) = \beta_0 + \beta_1 x_1 + \beta_2 x_2 + \beta_3 x_1 x_2$
$(\beta_1 + \beta_3 x_2)$ represents the change in $E(y)$ for every 1-unit increase in x_1, for fixed value of x_2
$(\beta_2 + \beta_3 x_1)$ represents the change in $E(y)$ for every 1-unit increase in x_2, for fixed value of x_1

Quadratic model in 1 quantitative x
$E(y) = \beta_0 + \beta_1 x + \beta_2 x^2$
β_2 represents the rate of curvature in $E(y)$ for x
$(\beta_2 > 0$ implies *upward* curvature)
$(\beta_2 < 0$ implies *downward* curvature)

Complete second-order model in 2 quantitative x's
$E(y) = \beta_0 + \beta_1 x_1 + \beta_2 x_2 + \beta_3 x_1 x_2 + \beta_4 x_1^2 + \beta_5 x_2^2$
β_4 represents the rate of curvature in $E(y)$ for x_1, holding x_2 fixed
β_5 represents the rate of curvature in $E(y)$ for x_2, holding x_1 fixed

Dummy variable model for 1 qualitative x
$E(y) = \beta_0 + \beta_1 x_1 + \beta_2 x_2 + \cdots + \beta_{k-1} x_{k-1}$
$x_1 = \{1$ if level 1, 0 if not$\}$
$x_2 = \{1$ if level 2, 0 if not$\}$
$x_{k-1} = \{1$ if level $k - 1$, 0 if not$\}$
$\beta_0 = E(y)$ for level k (base level) $= \mu_k$
$\beta_1 = \mu_1 - \mu_k$
$\beta_2 = \mu_2 - \mu_k$

Complete second-order model in 1 quantitative x and 1 qualitative x (two levels, A and B)
$E(y) = \beta_0 + \beta_1 x_1 + \beta_2 x_1^2 + \beta_3 x_2 + \beta_4 x_1 x_2 + \beta_5 x_1^2 x_2$
$x_2 = \{1$ if level A, 0 if level B$\}$

Adjusted coefficient of determination, R_a^2
Cannot be "forced" to 1 by adding independent variables to the model.

Interaction between x_1 and x_2
Implies that the relationship between y and one x depends on the other x.

Parsimonious model
A model with a small number of β parameters.

Recommendation for Assessing Model Adequacy
1. Conduct global F-test; if significant, then:
2. Conduct t-tests on only the most important β's (*interaction* or *squared terms*)
3. Interpret value of $2s$
4. Interpret value of R_a^2

Recommendation for Testing Individual β's
1. If *curvature* (x^2) deemed important, do not conduct test for first-order (x) term in the model.
2. If *interaction* (x_1x_2) deemed important, do not conduct tests for first-order terms (x_1 and x_2) in the model.

Extrapolation
Occurs when you predict y for values of x's that are outside of range of sample data.

Nested models
Are models where one model (the *complete model*) contains all the terms of another model (the *reduced model*) plus at least one additional term.

Multicollinearity
Occurs when two or more x's are correlated.
Indicators of multicollinearity:
1. Highly correlated x's
2. Significant global F-test, but all t-tests nonsignificant
3. Signs on β's opposite from expected

Problems with Using Stepwise Regression Model as the "Final" Model
1. *Extremely large number of* t-*tests* inflate overall probability of at least one Type I error.
2. *No higher-order terms* (interactions or squared terms) are included in the model.

Analysis of Residuals
1. Detect **misspecified model:** *plot residuals vs. quantitative x* (look for trends, e.g., curvilinear trend)
2. Detect **nonconstant error variance:** *plot residuals vs.* $\hat{y}$ (look for patterns, e.g., cone shape)
3. Detect **nonnormal errors:** *histogram, stem-leaf, or normal probability plot of residuals* (look for strong departures from normality)
4. Identify **outliers:** *residuals greater than 3s in absolute value* (investigate outliers before deleting)

Guide to Multiple Regression

Supplementary Exercises 12.132–12.170

Learning the Mechanics

12.132 Suppose you have developed a regression model to explain the relationship between y and x_1, x_2, and x_3. The ranges of the variables you observed were as follows: $10 \le y \le 100$, $5 \le x_1 \le 55$, $.5 \le x_2 \le 1$, and $1,000 \le x_3 \le 2,000$. Will the error of prediction be smaller when you use the least squares equation to predict y when $x_1 = 30$, $x_2 = .6$, and $x_3 = 1,300$, or when $x_1 = 60$, $x_2 = .4$, and $x_3 = 900$? Why?

12.133 When a multiple regression model is used for estimating the mean of the dependent variable and for predicting a new value of y, which will be narrower—the confidence interval for the mean or the prediction interval for the new y value? Why?

12.134 Suppose you fit the model

$$y = \beta_0 + \beta_1 x_1 + \beta_2 x_1^2 + \beta_3 x_2 + \beta_4 x_1 x_2 + \varepsilon$$

to $n = 25$ data points with the following results:

$$\hat{\beta}_0 = 1.26 \quad \hat{\beta}_1 = -2.43 \quad \hat{\beta}_2 = .05 \quad \hat{\beta}_3 = .62 \quad \hat{\beta}_4 = 1.81$$

$$s_{\hat{\beta}_1} = 1.21 \quad s_{\hat{\beta}_2} = .16 \quad s_{\hat{\beta}_3} = .26 \quad s_{\hat{\beta}_4} = 1.49$$

$$\text{SSE} = .41 \quad R^2 = .83$$

a. Is there sufficient evidence to conclude that at least one of the parameters β_1, β_2, β_3, or β_4 is nonzero? Test using $\alpha = .05$.

b. Test H_0: $\beta_1 = 0$ against H_a: $\beta_1 < 0$. Use $\alpha = .05$.

c. Test H_0: $\beta_2 = 0$ against H_a: $\beta_2 > 0$. Use $\alpha = .05$.

d. Test H_0: $\beta_3 = 0$ against H_a: $\beta_3 \ne 0$. Use $\alpha = .05$.

12.135 Suppose you used Minitab to fit the model

$$y = \beta_0 + \beta_1 x_1 + \beta_2 x_2 + \varepsilon$$

to $n = 15$ data points and obtained the printout shown below.

```
The regression equation is
Y = 90.1 - 1.84 X1 + .285 X2


Predictor    Coef   SE Coef      T       P
Constant    90.10    23.10     3.90   0.002
X1          -1.836    0.367    -5.01   0.001
X2           0.285    0.231     1.24   0.465


S = 10.68    R-Sq = 91.6%    R-Sq(adj) = 90.2%

Analysis of Variance

Source          DF     SS      MS      F       P
Regression       2   14801    7400   64.91   0.001
Residual Error  12    1364     114
Total           14   16165
```

a. What is the least squares prediction equation?

b. Find R^2 and interpret its value.

c. Is there sufficient evidence to indicate that the model is useful for predicting y? Conduct an F-test using $\alpha = .05$.

d. Test the null hypothesis H_0: $\beta_1 = 0$ against the alternative hypothesis H_a: $\beta_1 \ne 0$. Test using $\alpha = .05$. Draw the appropriate conclusions.

e. Find the standard deviation of the regression model and interpret it.

12.136 The first-order model $E(y) = \beta_0 + \beta_1 x_1$ was fit to $n = 19$ data points. A residual plot for the model is provided below. Is the need for a quadratic term in the model evident from the residual plot? Explain.

12.137 Write a model relating $E(y)$ to one qualitative independent variable that is at four levels. Define all the terms in your model.

12.138 It is desired to relate $E(y)$ to a quantitative variable x_1 and a qualitative variable at three levels.

a. Write a first-order model.

b. Write a model that will graph as three different second-order curves—one for each level of the qualitative variable.

12.139 Explain why stepwise regression is used. What is its value in the model-building process?

12.140 Consider relating $E(y)$ to two quantitative independent variables x_1 and x_2.

a. Write a first-order model for $E(y)$.

b. Write a complete second-order model for $E(y)$.

12.141 To model the relationship between y, a dependent variable, and x, an independent variable, a researcher has taken one measurement on y at each of three different x values. Drawing on his mathematical expertise, the researcher realizes that he can fit the second-order model

$$E(y) = \beta_0 + \beta_1 x + \beta_2 x^2$$

and it will pass exactly through all three points, yielding $\text{SSE} = 0$. The researcher, delighted with the excellent fit of the model, eagerly sets out to use it to make inferences. What problems will he encounter in attempting to make inferences?

12.142 Suppose you fit the regression model

$$E(y) = \beta_0 + \beta_1 x_1 + \beta_2 x_2 + \beta_3 x_2^2 + \beta_4 x_1 x_2 + \beta_5 x_1 x_2^2$$

to $n = 35$ data points and wish to test the null hypothesis H_0: $\beta_4 = \beta_5 = 0$.

a. State the alternative hypothesis.

b. Explain in detail how to compute the F-statistic needed to test the null hypothesis.

c. What are the numerator and denominator degrees of freedom associated with the F-statistic in part **b**?

d. Give the rejection region for the test if $\alpha = .05$.

Applying the Concepts—Basic

12.143 Comparing private and public college tuition. According to the *Chronicle of Higher Education Almanac*, 4-year private colleges charge, on average, five times as much for tuition and fees than 4-year public colleges. In order to estimate the true difference in the mean amounts charged for an academic year, random samples of 40 private colleges and 40 public colleges were contacted and questioned about their tuition structures.

a. Which of the procedures described in Chapter 8 could be used to estimate the difference in mean charges between private and public colleges?

b. Propose a regression model involving the qualitative independent variable type of college that could be used to investigate the difference between the means. Be sure to specify the coding scheme for the dummy variable in the model.

c. Explain how the regression model you developed in part **b** could be used to estimate the difference between the population means.

12.144 GPAs of business students. Research scientists at the Educational Testing Service (ETS) used multiple regression analysis to model y, the final grade point average (GPA) of business and management doctoral students. A list of the potential independent variables measured for each doctoral student in the study follows:

(1) Quantitative Graduate Management Aptitude Test (GMAT) score
(2) Verbal GMAT score
(3) Undergraduate GPA
(4) First-year graduate GPA
(5) Student cohort (i.e., year in which student entered doctoral program: year 1, year 3, or year 5)

a. Identify the variables as quantitative or qualitative.

b. For each quantitative variable, give your opinion on whether the variable is positively or negatively related to final GPA.

c. For each of the qualitative variables, set up the appropriate dummy variable.

d. Write a first-order, main effects model relating final GPA, y, to the five independent variables.

e. Interpret the β's in the model, part **d**.

f. Write a first-order model for final GPA, y, that allows for a different slope for each student cohort.

g. For each quantitative independent variable in the model, part **f**, give the slope of the line (in terms of the β's) for the year 1 cohort.

12.145 Comparing two orange juice extractors. The Florida Citrus Commission is interested in evaluating the performance of two orange juice extractors, brand A and brand B. It is believed that the size of the fruit used in the test may influence the juice yield (amount of juice per pound of oranges) obtained by the extractors. The commission wants to develop a regression model relating the mean juice yield $E(y)$ to the type of orange juice extractor (brand A or brand B) and the size of orange (diameter), x_1.

a. Identify the independent variables as qualitative or quantitative.

b. Write a model that describes the relationship between $E(y)$ and size of orange as two parallel lines, one for each brand of extractor.

c. Modify the model of part **b** to permit the slopes of the two lines to differ.

d. Sketch typical response lines for the model of part **b**. Do the same for the model of part **c**. Carefully label your graphs.

e. Specify the null and alternative hypotheses you would use to determine whether the model in part **c** provides more information for predicting yield than does the model in part **b**.

f. Explain how you would obtain the quantities necessary to compute the F-statistic that would be used in testing the hypotheses you described in part **e**.

12.146 Global warming and foreign investments. Scientists believe that a major cause of global warming is higher levels of carbon dioxide (CO_2) in the atmosphere. In the *Journal of World-Systems Research* (Summer 2003), sociologists examined the impact of foreign investment dependence on CO_2 emissions in $n = 66$ developing countries. In particular, the researchers modeled the level of CO_2 emissions in 1996 based on foreign investments made 16 years earlier and several other independent variables. The variables and the model results are listed in the table below.

a. Interpret the value of R^2.

b. Use the value of R^2 to test the null hypothesis, $H_0: \beta_1 = \beta_2 = \cdots = \beta_7 = 0$, at $\alpha = .01$.

Results for Exercise 12.146

$y = \ln(\text{level of } CO_2 \text{ emissions in 1996})$	β Estimate	t-value	p-value
$x_1 = \ln(\text{foreign investments in 1980})$	.79	2.52	$< .05$
$x_2 = $ gross domestic investment in 1980	.01	.13	$> .10$
$x_3 = $ trade exports in 1980	$-.02$	-1.66	$> .10$
$x_4 = \ln(\text{GNP in 1980})$	$-.44$	$-.97$	$> .10$
$x_5 = $ agricultural production in 1980	$-.03$	$-.66$	$> .10$
$x_6 = 1$ if African country, 0 if not	-1.19	-1.52	$> .10$
$x_7 = \ln(\text{level of } CO_2 \text{ emissions in 1980})$	.56	3.35	$< .001$

$R^2 = .31$

Source: Based on Grimes, P., & Kentor, J. "Exporting the greenhouse: Foreign capital penetration and CO_2 emissions 1980–1996," *Journal of World-Systems Research*, Vol. IX, No. 2, Summer 2003 (Table 1).

Correlation matrix for Exercise 12.147

Independent Variable	x_2	x_3	x_4	x_5	x_6	$x_7 =$ ln(level of CO_2 emissions in 1980)
$x_1 =$ ln(foreign investments in 1980)	.13	.57	.30	−.38	.14	−.14
$x_2 =$ gross domestic investment in 1980		.49	.36	−.47	−.14	.25
$x_3 =$ trade exports in 1980			.43	−.47	−.06	−.07
$x_4 =$ ln(GNP in 1980)				−.84	−.53	.42
$x_5 =$ agricultural production in 1980					.45	−.50
$x_6 =$ 1 if African country, 0 if not						−.47

Source: Grimes, P., & Kentor, J. "Exporting the greenhouse: Foreign capital penetration and CO_2 emissions 1980–1996," *Journal of World-Systems Research,* Vol. IX, No. 2, Summer 2003 (Appendix B).

c. What null hypothesis would you test to determine if foreign investments in 1980 is a statistically useful predictor of CO_2 emissions in 1996?

d. Conduct the test, part **c**, at $\alpha = .05$.

12.147 Global warming and foreign investments (cont'd). Refer to Exercise 12.146. A matrix giving the correlation (r) for each pair of independent variables is shown above. Identify the independent variables that are highly correlated. What problems may result from including these highly correlated variables in the regression model?

12.148 Accuracy of software effort estimates. Refer to the *Journal of Empirical Software Engineering* (Vol. 9, 2004) study of the accuracy of software effort estimates, Exercise 12.73 (p. 712). Recall that the dependent variable (y) is measured as relative error of the effort estimate of a software development task. A total of eight independent variables were evaluated as potential predictors of relative error. Each of these was formulated as a dummy variable, as shown in the table below.

a. The eight independent variables were entered into a stepwise regression, and the following two variables were selected for entry into the model: x_1 and x_8. Write the main effects model for $E(y)$ as a function of these two variables.

b. The stepwise regression yielded the following prediction equation:

$$\hat{y} = .12 - .28x_1 + .27x_8$$

Give a practical interpretation of the β estimates multiplied by x_1 and x_8.

c. The researcher is concerned that the sign of $\hat{\beta}_1$ in the model is the opposite from what is expected. (The researcher expects a project leader to have a smaller relative error of estimation than a developer.) Give at least one reason why this phenomenon occurred.

Company role of estimator:	$x_1 =$ 1 if developer, 0 if project leader
Task complexity:	$x_2 =$ 1 if low, 0 if medium/high
Contract type:	$x_3 =$ 1 if fixed price, 0 if hourly rate
Customer importance:	$x_4 =$ 1 if high, 0 if low/medium
Customer priority:	$x_5 =$ 1 if time of delivery, 0 if cost or quality
Level of knowledge:	$x_6 =$ 1 if high, 0 if low/medium
Participation:	$x_7 =$ 1 if estimator participates in work, 0 if not
Previous accuracy:	$x_8 =$ 1 if more than 20% accurate, 0 if less than 20% accurate

12.149 Urban population estimation using satellite images. Can the population of an urban area be estimated without taking a census? In *Geographical Analysis* (January, 2007) geography professors at the University of Wisconsin–Milwaukee and Ohio State University demonstrated the use of satellite image maps for estimating urban population. A portion of Columbus, Ohio, was partitioned into $n = 125$ census block groups, and satellite imagery was obtained. For each census block, the following variables were measured: population density (y), proportion of block with low-density residential areas (x_1), and proportion of block with high-density residential areas (x_2). A first-order model for y was fit to the data with the following results:

$$\hat{y} = -.0304 + 2.006x_1 + 5.006x_2, \quad R^2 = .686$$

a. Give a practical interpretation of each β estimate in the model.

b. Give a practical interpretation of the coefficient of determination, R^2.

c. State H_0 and H_a for a test of overall model adequacy.

d. Refer to part **c**. Compute the value of the test statistic.

e. Refer to parts **c** and **d**. Make the appropriate conclusion at $\alpha = .01$.

12.150 Trust in e-retailers. Electronic commerce (or "e-commerce") describes the use of electronic networks to simplify a business operation. With e-commerce, retailers now can advertise and sell their products easily over the Web. In *Internet Research: Electronic Networking Applications and Policy* (Vol. 11, 2001), Canadian researchers investigated the factors that impact the level of trust in Web e-retailers. Five quantitative independent variables were used to model level of trust (y):

$x_1 =$ ease of navigation on the Web site

$x_2 =$ consistency of the Web site

$x_3 =$ ease of learning the Web interface

$x_4 =$ perception of the interface design

$x_5 =$ level of support available to the user

a. Write a first-order model for level of trust as a function of the five independent variables.

b. The model, part **a**, was fit to data collected for $n = 66$ visitors to e-retailers' Web sites and yielded a coefficient of determination of $R^2 = .58$. Interpret this result.

c. Compute the F-statistic used to test the global utility of the model.

d. Using $\alpha = .10$, give the appropriate conclusion for the test, part **c.**

12.151 **Prototyping new software.** To meet the increasing demand for new software products, many systems development experts have adopted a prototyping methodology. The effects of prototyping on the system development life cycle (SDLC) was investigated in the *Journal of Computer Information Systems* (Spring 1993). A survey of 500 randomly selected corporate-level MIS managers was conducted. Three potential independent variables were (1) *importance* of prototyping to each phase of the SDLC; (2) degree of *support* prototyping provides for the SDLC; and (3) degree to which prototyping *replaces* each phase of the SDLC. The table below gives the pairwise correlations of the three variables in the survey data for one particular phase of the SDLC. Use this information to assess the degree of multicollinearity in the survey data. Would you recommend using all three independent variables in a regression analysis? Explain.

Variable Pairs	Correlation Coefficient, r
Importance–Replace	.2682
Importance–Support	.6991
Replace–Support	−.0531

Source: Hardgrave, B. C., Doke, E. R., & Swanson, N. E. "Prototyping effects of the system development life cycle: An empirical study," *Journal of Computer Information Systems,* Vol. 33, No. 3, Spring 1993, p. 16 (Table 1). Copyright © 1993 by IACIS. Reprinted by permission of the author.

12.152 **A CEO's impact on corporate profits.** Can a corporation's annual profit be predicted from information about the company's CEO? Each year *Forbes* publishes data on company profit (in $ millions), CEO's annual income (in $ thousands), and percentage of the company's stock owned by the CEO. Consider a model relating company profit (y) to CEO income (x_1) and stock percentage (x_2). Explain what it means to say that "CEO income x_1 and stock percentage x_2 interact to affect company profit y."

12.153 **"Sun safety" study.** Numerous "sun safety" products exist on the market to prevent excessive exposure to solar radiation. But many people do not practice "sun safety" or recognize the effectiveness of these products. A group of University of Arizona researchers examined the feasibility of educating preschool (4- to 5-year-old) children about sun safety (*American Journal of Public Health,* July 1995). A sample of 122 preschool children was divided into two groups, the control group and the intervention group. Children in the intervention group received a *Be Sun Safe* curriculum in preschool, while the control group did not. All children were tested for their knowledge, comprehension, and application of sun safety at two points in time: prior to the sun safety curriculum (pretest, x_1) and 7 weeks following the curriculum (posttest, y).

a. Write a first-order model for mean posttest score, $E(y)$, as a function of pretest score, x_1, and group. Assume that no interaction exists between pretest score and group.

b. For the model, part **a,** show that the slope of the line relating posttest score to pretest score is the same for both groups of children.

c. Repeat part **a** but assume that pretest score and group interact.

d. For the model, part **c,** show that the slope of the line relating posttest score to pretest score differs for the two groups of children.

Applying the Concepts—Intermediate

12.154 **Promotion of supermarket vegetables.** A supermarket chain is interested in exploring the relationship between the sales of its store-brand canned vegetables (y), the amount spent on promotion of the vegetables in local newspapers (x_1), and the amount of shelf space allocated to the brand (x_2). One of the chain's supermarkets was randomly selected, and over a 20-week period x_1 and x_2 were varied, as reported in the table.

🔵 CANVEG

Week	Sales ($)	Advertising Expenditures ($)	Shelf Space (sq. ft.)
1	2,010	201	75
2	1,850	205	50
3	2,400	355	75
4	1,575	208	30
5	3,550	590	75
6	2,015	397	50
7	3,908	820	75
8	1,870	400	30
9	4,877	997	75
10	2,190	515	30
11	5,005	996	75
12	2,500	625	50
13	3,005	860	50
14	3,480	1,012	50
15	5,500	1,135	75
16	1,995	635	30
17	2,390	837	30
18	4,390	1,200	50
19	2,785	990	30
20	2,989	1,205	30

a. Fit the following model to the data:

$$y = \beta_0 + \beta_1 x_1 + \beta_2 x_2 + \beta_3 x_1 x_2 + \varepsilon$$

b. Conduct an F-test to investigate the overall usefulness of this model. Use $\alpha = .05$.

c. Test for the presence of interaction between advertising expenditures and shelf space. Use $\alpha = .05$.

d. Explain what it means to say that advertising expenditures and shelf space interact.

e. Explain how you could be misled by using a first-order model instead of an interaction model to explain how advertising expenditures and shelf space influence sales.

f. Based on the type of data collected, comment on the assumption of independent errors.

12.155 **Yield strength of steel alloy.** Industrial engineers at the University of Florida used regression modeling as a tool to reduce the time and cost associated with developing new metallic alloys (*Modelling and Simulation in Materials Science and Engineering,* Vol. 13, 2005). To illustrate, the engineers built a regression model for the tensile yield strength (y) of a new steel alloy.

The potentially important predictors of yield strength are listed in the accompanying table.

x_1 = Carbon amount (% weight)
x_2 = Manganese amount (% weight)
x_3 = Chromium amount (% weight)
x_4 = Nickel amount (% weight)
x_5 = Molybdenum amount (% weight)
x_6 = Copper amount (% weight)
x_7 = Nitrogen amount (% weight)
x_8 = Vanadium amount (% weight)
x_9 = Plate thickness (millimeters)
x_{10} = Solution treating (milliliters)
x_{11} = Aging temperature (degrees, Celsius)

a. The engineers discovered that the variable Nickel (x_4) was highly correlated with the other potential independent variables. Consequently, Nickel was dropped from the model. Do you agree with this decision? Explain.

b. The engineers used stepwise regression on the remaining 10 potential independent variables in order to search for a parsimonious set of predictor variables. Do you agree with this decision? Explain.

c. The stepwise regression selected the following independent variables: x_1 = Carbon, x_2 = Manganese, x_3 = Chromium, x_5 = Molybdenum, x_6 = Copper, x_8 = Vanadium, x_9 = Plate thickness, x_{10} = Solution treating, and x_{11} = Aging temperature. All these variables were statistically significant in the stepwise model, with R^2 = .94. Consequently, the engineers used the estimated stepwise model to predict yield strength. Do you agree with this decision? Explain.

12.156 Optimizing semiconductor material processing. Fluorocarbon plasmas are used in the production of semiconductor materials. In the *Journal of Applied Physics* (Dec. 1, 2000), electrical engineers at Nagoya University (Japan) studied the kinetics of fluorocarbon plasmas in order to optimize material processing. In one portion of the study, the surface production rate of fluorocarbon radicals emitted from the production process was measured at various points in time (in milliseconds) after the radio frequency power was turned off. The data are given in the next table. Consider a model relating surface production rate (*y*) to time (*x*).

Rate	Time	Rate	Time
1.00	0.1	0.00	1.7
0.80	0.3	−0.10	1.9
0.40	0.5	−0.15	2.1
0.20	0.7	−0.05	2.3
0.05	0.9	−0.13	2.5
0.00	1.1	−0.08	2.7
−0.05	1.3	0.00	2.9
−0.02	1.5		

Source: Takizawa, K., et al. "Characteristics of C_3 radicals in high-density C_4F_8 plasmas studied by laser-induced fluorescence spectroscopy," *Journal of Applied Physics,* Vol. 88, No. 11, Dec. 1, 2000 (Figure 7). Copyright © 2000 by American Institute of Physics. Reprinted with permission.

a. Graph the data in a scatterplot. What trend do you observe?

b. Fit a quadratic model to the data. Give the least squares prediction equation.

c. Is there sufficient evidence of upward curvature in the relationship between surface production rate and time after turnoff? Use α = .05.

12.157 Modeling peak-hour roadway traffic. Traffic forecasters at the Minnesota Department of Transportation (MDOT) use regression analysis to estimate weekday peak-hour traffic volumes on existing and proposed roadways. In particular, they model *y*, the peak-hour volume (typically, the volume between 7:00 and 8:00 A.M.), as a function of x_1, the road's total volume for the day. For one project involving the redesign of a section of Interstate 494, the forecasters collected *n* = 72 observations of peak-hour traffic volume and 24-hour weekday traffic volume using electronic sensors that count vehicles. The data are saved in the file. (The first and last five observations are listed in the table.)

Observation Number	Peak-Hour Volume	24-Hour Volume	I-35
1	1,990.94	20,070	0
2	1,989.63	21,234	0
3	1,986.96	20,633	0
4	1,986.96	20,676	0
5	1,983.78	19,818	0
⋮	⋮	⋮	
68	2,147.93	22,948	1
69	2,147.85	23,551	1
70	2,144.23	21,637	1
71	2,142.41	23,543	1
72	2,137.39	22,594	1

Source: Traffic and Commodities Studies Section, Minnesota Department of Transportation, St. Paul, Minnesota.

a. Construct a scatterplot for the data, plotting peak-hour volume *y* against 24-hour volume x_1. Note the isolated group of observations at the top of the scatterplot. Investigators discovered that all of these data points were collected at the intersection of Interstate 35W and 46th Street. (These are observations 55–72 in the table.) While all other locations in the sample were three-lane highways, this location was unique in that the highway widens to four lanes just north of the electronic sensor. Consequently, the forecasters decided to include a dummy variable to account for a difference between the I-35W location and all other locations.

b. Knowing that peak-hour traffic volumes have a theoretical upper bound, the forecasters hypothesized that a second-order model should be used to explain the variation in *y*. Propose a complete second-order model for $E(y)$ as a function of 24-hour volume x_1 and the dummy variable for location.

c. Using an available statistical software package, fit the model of part **b** to the data. Interpret the results. Specifically, is the curvilinear relationship between peak-hour volume and 24-hour volume different at the two locations?

d. Conduct a residual analysis of the model, part **b**. Evaluate the assumptions of normality and constant error variance and determine whether any outliers exist.

12.158 Improving Math SAT scores. Refer to the *Chance* (Winter 2001) study of students who paid a private tutor (or coach) to help them improve their Scholastic Assessment Test (SAT) scores, Exercise 2.88 (p. 86). Multiple regression was used to estimate the effect of coaching on SAT–Mathematics scores. Data on 3,492 students (573 of whom were coached) were used to fit the model, $E(y) = \beta_0 + \beta_1 x_1 + \beta_2 x_2$, where y = SAT–Math score, x_1 = score on PSAT, and x_2 = {1 if student was coached, 0 if not}.

a. The fitted model had an adjusted R^2 value of .76. Interpret this result.

b. The estimate of β_2 in the model was 19, with a standard error of 3. Use this information to form a 95% confidence interval for β_2. Interpret the interval.

c. Based on the interval, part **b**, what can you say about the effect of coaching on SAT–Math scores?

d. As an alternative model, the researcher added several "control" variables, including dummy variables for student ethnicity (x_3, x_4, and x_5), a socioeconomic status index variable (x_6), two variables that measured high school performance (x_7 and x_8), the number of math courses taken in high school (x_9), and the overall GPA for the math courses (x_{10}). Write the hypothesized equation for $E(y)$ for the alternative model.

e. Give the null hypothesis for a nested model F-test comparing the initial and alternative models.

f. The nested model F-test, part **e**, was statistically significant at α = .05. Practically interpret this result.

g. The alternative model, part **d**, resulted in R_a^2 = .79, $\hat{\beta}_2$ = 14, and $s_{\hat{\beta}_2}$ = 3. Interpret the value of R_a^2.

h. Refer to part **g**. Find and interpret a 95% confidence interval for β_2.

i. The researcher concluded that "the estimated effect of SAT coaching decreases from the baseline model when control variables are added to the model." Do you agree? Justify your answer.

j. As a modification to the model of part **d**, the researcher added all possible interactions between the coaching variable (x_2) and the other independent variables in the model. Write the equation for $E(y)$ for this modified model.

k. Give the null hypothesis for comparing the models, parts **d** and **j**. How would you perform this test?

12.159 Impact of advertising on market share. The audience for a product's advertising can be divided into four segments according to the degree of exposure received as a result of the advertising. These segments are groups of consumers who receive very high (VH), high (H), medium (M), or low (L) exposure to the advertising. A company is interested in exploring whether its advertising effort affects its product's market share. Accordingly, the company identifies 24 sample groups of consumers who have been exposed to its advertising, six groups at each exposure level. Then, the company determines its product's market share within each group.

Market Share within Group	Exposure Level	Market Share within Group	Exposure Level
10.1	L	12.2	H
10.3	L	12.1	H
10.0	L	11.8	H
10.3	L	12.6	H
10.2	L	11.9	H
10.5	L	12.9	H
10.6	M	10.7	VH
11.0	M	10.8	VH
11.2	M	11.0	VH
10.9	M	10.5	VH
10.8	M	10.8	VH
11.0	M	10.6	VH

a. Write a regression model that expresses the company's market share as a function of advertising exposure level. Define all terms in your model and list any assumptions you make about them.

b. Did you include interaction terms in your model? Why or why not?

c. The data in the table above were obtained by the company. Fit the model in part **a** to the data.

d. Is there evidence to suggest that the firm's expected market share differs for different levels of advertising exposure? Test using α = .05.

12.160 Downtime of a production process. An operations manager is interested in modeling $E(y)$, the expected length of time per month (in hours) that a machine will be shut down for repairs, as a function of the type of machine (001 or 002) and the age of the machine (in years). The manager has proposed the following model:

$$E(y) = \beta_0 + \beta_1 x_1 + \beta_2 x_1^2 + \beta_3 x_2$$

where

x_1 = Age of machine

x_2 = 1 if machine type 001, 0 if machine type 002

The following data were obtained for n = 20 machine breakdowns.

Downtime (hours per month)	Machine Age, x_1 (years)	Machine Type	x_2
10	1.0	001	1
20	2.0	001	1
30	2.7	001	1
40	4.1	001	1
9	1.2	001	1
25	2.5	001	1
19	1.9	001	1
41	5.0	001	1
22	2.1	001	1
12	1.1	001	1
10	2.0	002	0
20	4.0	002	0
30	5.0	002	0
44	8.0	002	0
9	2.4	002	0
25	5.1	002	0
20	3.5	002	0
42	7.0	002	0
20	4.0	002	0
13	2.1	002	0

a. Use the data (saved in the file) to estimate the parameters of this model.

b. Do these data provide sufficient evidence to conclude that the second-order term (x_1^2) in the model proposed by the operations manager is necessary? Test using $\alpha = .05$.

c. Test the null hypothesis that $\beta_1 = \beta_2 = 0$ using $\alpha = .10$. Interpret the results of the test in the context of the problem.

12.161 Forecasting daily admission of a water park. To determine whether extra personnel are needed for the day, the owners of a water adventure park would like to find a model that would allow them to predict the day's attendance each morning before opening based on the day of the week and weather conditions. The model is of the form

$$E(y) = \beta_0 + \beta_1 x_1 + \beta_2 x_2 + \beta_3 x_3$$

where

y = Daily admission

$x_1 = \begin{cases} 1 & \text{if weekend} \\ 0 & \text{otherwise} \end{cases}$ (dummy variable)

$x_2 = \begin{cases} 1 & \text{if sunny} \\ 0 & \text{if overcast} \end{cases}$ (dummy variable)

x_3 = predicted daily high temperature (°F)

These data were recorded for a random sample of 30 days, and a regression model was fitted to the data. The least squares analysis produced the following results:

$$\hat{y} = -105 + 25x_1 + 100x_2 + 10x_3$$

with

$$s_{\hat{\beta}_1} = 10 \quad s_{\hat{\beta}_2} = 30 \quad s_{\hat{\beta}_3} = 4 \quad R^2 = .65$$

a. Interpret the estimated model coefficients.

b. Is there sufficient evidence to conclude that this model is useful for the prediction of daily attendance? Use $\alpha = .05$.

c. Is there sufficient evidence to conclude that the mean attendance increases on weekends? Use $\alpha = .10$.

d. Use the model to predict the attendance on a sunny weekday with a predicted high temperature of 95°F.

e. Suppose the 90% prediction interval for part **d** is (645, 1,245). Interpret this interval.

12.162 Forecasting daily admission of a water park (cont'd). Refer to Exercise 12.161. The owners of the water adventure park are advised that the prediction model could probably be improved if interaction terms were added. In particular, it is thought that the *rate* at which mean attendance increases as predicted high temperature increases will be greater on weekends than on weekdays. The following model is therefore proposed:

$$E(y) = \beta_0 + \beta_1 x_1 + \beta_2 x_2 + \beta_3 x_3 + \beta_4 x_1 x_3$$

The same 30 days of data used in Exercise 12.161 are again used to obtain the least squares model

$$\hat{y} = 250 - 700x_1 + 100x_2 + 5x_3 + 15x_1 x_3$$

with

$$s_{\hat{\beta}_4} = 3.0 \quad R^2 = .96$$

a. Graph the predicted day's attendance, y, against the day's predicted high temperature, x_3, for a sunny weekday and for a sunny weekend day. Plot both on the same graph for x_3 between 70°F and 100°F. Note the increase in slope for the weekend day. Interpret this.

b. Do the data indicate that the interaction term is a useful addition to the model? Use $\alpha = .05$.

c. Use this model to predict the attendance for a sunny weekday with a predicted high temperature of 95°F.

d. Suppose the 90% prediction interval for part **c** is (800, 850). Compare this result with the prediction interval for the model without interaction in Exercise 12.161, part **e**. Do the relative widths of the confidence intervals support or refute your conclusion about the utility of the interaction term (part **b**)?

e. The owners, noting that the coefficient $\hat{\beta}_1 = -700$, conclude the model is ridiculous because it seems to imply that the mean attendance will be 700 less on weekends than on weekdays. Explain why this is *not* the case.

12.163 Sale prices of apartments. A Minneapolis, Minnesota, real estate appraiser used regression analysis to explore the relationship between the sale prices of apartment buildings and various characteristics of the buildings. The file contains data for a random sample of 25 apartment buildings. *Note:* Physical condition of each apartment building is coded E (excellent), G (good), or F (fair). Data for selected observations are shown in the table below.

Data for Exercise 12.163 (selected observations)

Code No.	Sale Price, y ($)	No. of Apartments, x_1	Age of Structure, x_2 (years)	Lot Size, x_3 (sq. ft.)	No. of On-Site Parking Spaces, x_4	Gross Building Area, x_5 (sq. ft.)	Condition of Apartment Building
0229	90,300	4	82	4,635	0	4,266	F
0094	384,000	20	13	17,798	0	14,391	G
0043	157,500	5	66	5,913	0	6,615	G
0079	676,200	26	64	7,750	6	34,144	E
0134	165,000	5	55	5,150	0	6,120	G
⋮	⋮	⋮	⋮	⋮	⋮	⋮	⋮
0019	93,600	4	82	6,864	0	3,840	F
0074	110,000	4	50	4,510	0	3,092	G
0057	573,200	14	10	11,192	0	23,704	E
0104	79,300	4	82	7,425	0	3,876	F
0024	272,000	5	82	7,500	0	9,542	E

Source: Robinson Appraisal Co., Inc., Mankato, Minnesota.

a. Write a model that describes the relationship between sale price and number of apartment units as three parallel lines, one for each level of physical condition. Besure to specify the dummy variable coding scheme you use.

b. Plot y against x_1 (number of apartment units) for all buildings in excellent condition. On the same graph, plot y against x_1 for all buildings in good condition. Do this again for all buildings in fair condition. Does it appear that the model you specified in part **a** is appropriate? Explain.

c. Fit the model from part **a** to the data. Report the least squares prediction equation for each of the three building condition levels.

d. Plot the three prediction equations of part **c** on a scatterplot of the data.

e. Do the data provide sufficient evidence to conclude that the relationship between sale price and number of units differs depending on the physical condition of the apartments? Test using $\alpha = .05$.

f. Check the data set for multicollinearity. How does this impact your choice of independent variables to use in a model for sale price?

g. Conduct a complete residual analysis for the model to check the assumptions on ε.

12.164 Light output of a bulb. A firm that has developed a new type of lightbulb is interested in evaluating its performance in order to decide whether to market it. It is known that the light output of the bulb depends on the cleanliness of its surface area and the length of time the bulb has been in operation. Use the data in the next table and the procedures you learned in this chapter to build a regression model that relates drop in light output to bulb surface cleanliness and length of operation. Be sure to conduct a residual analysis also.

Drop in Light Output (% original output)	Bulb Surface (C = clean) (D = dirty)	Length of Operation (hours)
0	C	0
16	C	400
22	C	800
27	C	1,200
32	C	1,600
36	C	2,000
38	C	2,400
0	D	0
4	D	400
6	D	800
8	D	1,200
9	D	1,600
11	D	2,000
12	D	2,400

12.165 Forecasting a job applicant's merit rating. A large research and development firm rates the performance of each member of its technical staff on a scale of 0 to 100, and this merit rating is used to determine the size of the person's pay raise for the coming year. The firm's personnel department is interested in developing a regression model to help them forecast the merit rating that an applicant for a technical position will receive after being employed 3 years. The firm proposes to use the following second-order model to forecast the merit ratings of applicants who have just completed their graduate studies and have no prior related job experience:

$$E(y) = \beta_0 + \beta_1 x_1 + \beta_2 x_2 + \beta_3 x_1 x_2 + \beta_4 x_1^2 + \beta_5 x_2^2$$

where

$y =$ Applicant's merit rating after 3 years
$x_1 =$ Applicant's GPA in graduate school
$x_2 =$ Applicant's total score (verbal plus quantitative) on the Graduate Record Examination (GRE)

The model, fit to data collected for a random sample of $n = 40$ employees, resulted in SSE $= 1,830.44$ and SS(model) $= 4,911.5$. The reduced model $E(y) = \beta_0 + \beta_1 x_1 + \beta_2 x_2$ is also fit to the same data, resulting in SSE $= 3,197.16$.

a. Identify the appropriate null and alternative hypotheses to test whether the complete (second-order) model contributes information for the prediction of y.

b. Conduct the test of hypothesis given in part **a**. Test using $\alpha = .05$. Interpret the results in the context of this problem.

c. Identify the appropriate null and alternative hypotheses to test whether the complete model contributes more information than the reduced (first-order) model for the prediction of y.

d. Conduct the test of hypothesis given in part **c**. Test using $\alpha = .05$. Interpret the results in the context of this problem.

e. Which model, if either, would you use to predict y? Explain.

12.166 Household food consumption. The data in the table on the next page were collected for a random sample of 26 households in Washington, D.C. An economist wants to relate household food consumption, y, to household income, x_1, and household size, x_2, with the first-order model

$$E(y) = \beta_0 + \beta_1 x_1 + \beta_2 x_2$$

a. Fit the model to the data. Do you detect any signs of multicollinearity in the data? Explain.

b. Is there visual evidence (from a residual plot) that a second-order model may be more appropriate for predicting household food consumption? Explain.

c. Comment on the assumption of constant error variance, using a residual plot. Does it appear to be satisfied?

d. Are there any outliers in the data? If so, identify them.

e. Based on a graph of the residuals, does the assumption of normal errors appear to be reasonably satisfied? Explain.

12.167 State casket sales restrictions. Refer to the *Journal of Law and Economics* (Feb. 2008) study of the impact of lifting casket sales restrictions on the cost of a funeral, Exercise 12.121 (p. 758). Recall that data collected for a sample of 1,437 funerals were used to fit the model, $E(y) = \beta_0 + \beta_1 x_1 + \beta_2 x_2 + \beta_3 x_1 x_2$, where y is the price (in dollars) of a direct burial, $x_1 = $ {1 if funeral home is

Data for Exercise 12.166

Household	Food Consumption ($1,000s)	Income ($1,000s)	Household Size	Household	Food Consumption ($1,000s)	Income ($1,000s)	Household Size
1	4.2	41.1	4	14	4.1	95.2	2
2	3.4	30.5	2	15	5.5	45.6	9
3	4.8	52.3	4	16	4.5	78.5	3
4	2.9	28.9	1	17	5.0	20.5	5
5	3.5	36.5	2	18	4.5	31.6	4
6	4.0	29.8	4	19	2.8	39.9	1
7	3.6	44.3	3	20	3.9	38.6	3
8	4.2	38.1	4	21	3.6	30.2	2
9	5.1	92.0	5	22	4.6	48.7	5
10	2.7	36.0	1	23	3.8	21.2	3
11	4.0	76.9	3	24	4.5	24.3	7
12	2.7	69.9	1	25	4.0	26.9	5
13	5.5	43.1	7	26	7.5	7.3	5

in a restricted state, 0 if not}, and $x_2 = $ {1 if price includes a basic wooden casket, 0 if no casket}. The estimated equation (with standard errors in parentheses) is:

$$\hat{y} = 1,432 + 793x_1 - 252x_2 + 261x_1x_2, \quad R^2 = .78$$

$$(70) \quad (134) \quad (109)$$

a. Interpret the reported value of R^2.
b. Use the value of R^2 to compute the F-statistic for testing the overall adequacy of the model. Test at $\alpha = .05$.
c. Compute the predicted price of a direct burial with a basic wooden casket for a funeral home in a restrictive state.
d. Estimate the difference between the mean price of a direct burial with a basic wooden casket and the mean price of a burial with no casket for a funeral home in a restrictive state.
e. Estimate the difference between the mean price of a direct burial with a basic wooden casket and the mean price of a burial with no casket for a funeral home in a nonrestrictive state.
f. Is there sufficient evidence to indicate that the difference between the mean price of a direct burial with a basic wooden casket and the mean price of a burial with no casket depends on whether the funeral home is in a restrictive state? Test using $\alpha = .05$.

Applying the Concepts—Advanced

12.168 Modeling monthly collision claims. A medium-sized automobile insurance company is interested in developing a regression model to help predict the monthly collision claims of its policyholders. A company analyst has proposed modeling monthly collision claims (y) in the middle Atlantic states as a function of the percentage of claims by drivers under age 30 (x_1) and the average daily temperature during the month (x_2). She believes that as the percentage of claims by drivers under age 30 increases, claims will rise because younger drivers are usually involved in more serious accidents than older drivers. She also believes that claims will rise as the average daily temperature decreases because lower temperatures are associated with icy, hazardous driving conditions. In order to develop a preliminary model, data were collected for the state of New Jersey over a 3-year period. The data are saved in the file. (The first and last five observations are listed in the table below.)

a. Use a statistical software package to fit the complete second-order model
$$E(y) = \beta_0 + \beta_1x_1 + \beta_2x_2 + \beta_3x_1x_2 + \beta_4x_1^2 + \beta_5x_2^2$$
b. Test the hypothesis $H_0: \beta_4 = \beta_5 = 0$ using $\alpha = .05$. Interpret the results in practical terms.
c. Do the results support the analysts' beliefs? Explain. (You may need to conduct further tests of hypotheses to answer this question.)

Data for Exercise 12.168 (first and last 5 months)

Month	Monthly Collision Claims, y ($)	Percentage of Monthly Claimants under the Age of 30, x_1	Newark, N.J., Average Daily Temperature during the Month, x_2 (°F)
1	116,250	50.0	31.5
2	217,180	60.8	33.0
3	43,436	45.1	45.0
4	159,265	56.4	53.9
5	130,308	53.3	63.9
⋮	⋮	⋮	⋮
44	136,528	53.1	76.6
45	193,608	59.8	68.6
46	38,722	45.6	62.4
47	212,309	63.9	50.0
48	118,796	52.3	42.3

Sources: New Jersey Department of Insurance; *Weather of U.S. Cities,* 4th ed., Gale Research Inc., Detroit, 1992.

12.169 Developing a model for college GPA. Many colleges and universities develop regression models for predicting the GPA of incoming freshmen. This predicted GPA can then be used to make admission decisions. Although most models use many independent variables to predict GPA, we will illustrate by choosing two variables:

x_1 = Verbal score on college entrance examination (percentile)

x_2 = Mathematics score on college entrance examination (percentile)

The file contains data on these variables for a random sample of 40 freshmen at one college. (Selected observations are shown in the table.) Use the data to develop a useful prediction equation for college freshman GPA (y). Be sure to conduct a residual analysis for the model.

Verbal, x_1	Mathematics, x_2	GPA, y
81	87	3.49
68	99	2.89
57	86	2.73
100	49	1.54
54	83	2.56
⋮	⋮	⋮
74	67	2.83
87	93	3.84
90	65	3.01
81	76	3.33
84	69	3.06

Critical Thinking Challenge

12.170 IQs and *The Bell Curve*. *The Bell Curve* (Free Press, 1994), written by Richard Herrnstein and Charles Murray (H&M), is a controversial book about race, genes, IQ, and economic mobility. The book heavily employs statistics and statistical methodology in an attempt to support the authors' positions on the relationships among these variables and their social consequences. The main theme of *The Bell Curve* can be summarized as follows:

(1) Measured intelligence (IQ) is largely genetically inherited.
(2) IQ is correlated positively with a variety of socioeconomic status success measures, such as prestigious job, high annual income, and high educational attainment.
(3) From 1 and 2, it follows that socioeconomic successes are largely genetically caused and therefore resistant to educational and environmental interventions (such as affirmative action).

The statistical methodology (regression) employed by the authors and the inferences derived from the statistics were critiqued in *Chance* (Summer 1995) and *The Journal of the American Statistical Association* (Dec. 1995). The following are just a few of the problems with H&M's use of regression that are identified:

Problem 1 H&M consistently use a trio of independent variables—IQ, socioeconomic status, and age—in a series of first-order models designed to predict dependent social outcome variables such as income and

unemployment. (Only on a single occasion are interaction terms incorporated.) Consider, for example, the model

$$E(y) = \beta_0 + \beta_1 x_1 + \beta_2 x_2 + \beta_3 x_3$$

where y = income, x_1 = IQ, x_2 = socioeconomic status, and x_3 = age. H&M employ t-tests on the individual β parameters to assess the importance of the independent variables. As with most of the models considered in *The Bell Curve*, the estimate of β_1 in the income model is positive and statistically significant at $\alpha = .05$, and the associated t-value is larger (in absolute value) than the t-values associated with the other independent variables. Consequently, *H&M claim that IQ is a better predictor of income than the other two independent variables.* No attempt was made to determine whether the model was properly specified or whether the model provides an adequate fit to the data.

Problem 2 In an appendix, the authors describe multiple regression as a "mathematical procedure that yields coefficients for each of [the independent variables], indicating how much of a change in [the dependent variable] can be anticipated for a given change in any particular [independent] variable, with all the others held constant." Armed with this information and the fact that the estimate of β_1 in the model above is positive, *H&M infer that a high IQ necessarily implies (or causes) a high income, and a low IQ inevitably leads to a low income.* (Cause-and-effect inferences like this are made repeatedly throughout the book.)

Problem 3 The title of the book refers to the normal distribution and its well-known "bell-shaped" curve. There is a misconception among the general public that scores on intelligence tests (IQ) are normally distributed. In fact, most IQ scores have distributions that are decidedly skewed. Traditionally, psychologists and psychometricians have transformed these scores so that the resulting numbers have a precise normal distribution. H&M make a special point to do this. Consequently, *the measure of IQ used in all the regression models is normalized (i.e., transformed so that the resulting distribution is normal), despite the fact that regression methodology does not require predictor (independent) variables to be normally distributed.*

Problem 4 A variable that is not used as a predictor of social outcome in any of the models in *The Bell Curve* is level of education. H&M purposely omit education from the models, arguing that IQ causes education, not the other way around. Other researchers who have examined H&M's data report that *when education is included as an independent variable in the model, the effect of IQ on the dependent variable (say, income) is diminished.*

a. Comment on each of the problems identified. Why do each of these problems cast a shadow on the inferences made by the authors?

b. Using the variables specified in the model above, describe how you would conduct the multiple regression analysis. (Propose a more complex model and describe the appropriate model tests, including a residual analysis.)

Activity 12.1 *Insurance Premiums:* Collecting Data for Several Variables

Premiums for life insurance, health insurance, homeowners insurance, and car insurance are based on more than one factor. In this activity, you will consider factors that influence the price that an individual pays for insurance and how you might collect data that would be useful in studying insurance premiums. You may wish to look over statements from your own insurance policies to determine how much coverage you have and how much it costs you.

1. Suppose that you host an independent Web site that provides information about insurance coverage and costs. You would like to add a feature to your site where a person answers a few simple questions in order to receive an estimate of what that person should expect to pay for insurance with a major carrier. Pick one type of insurance and determine what five questions you would most like to ask the person in order to prepare an estimate.

2. Use your five questions from Exercise 1 to define five independent variables. What is the dependent variable in this situation? What would a first-order model for this situation look like?

3. The estimates provided on your Web site will be based on a random sample of policies recently purchased through major carriers. Because insurance rates change frequently, your Web site will need to be frequently updated through new samples. Design a sampling method that can easily be repeated as needed. Be specific as to how you will identify people who have recently purchased policies, how you will choose your sample, what data you will gather, and what method you will use to gather the data.

4. Once the data are collected, describe how you will organize them and use them to complete the model in Exercise 3.

Activity 12.2 Collecting Data and Fitting a Multiple Regression Model

Note: The use of statistical software is required for this project. This is a continuation of the Activity section in Chapter 11, in which you selected three independent variables as predictors of a dependent variable of your choice and obtained at least 25 data values. Now, by means of an available software package, fit the multiple regression model

$$y = \beta_0 + \beta_1 x_1 + \beta_2 x_2 + \beta_3 x_3 + \varepsilon$$

where

y = Dependent variable you chose

x_1 = First independent variable you chose

x_2 = Second independent variable you chose

x_3 = Third independent variable you chose

1. Compare the coefficients $\hat{\beta}_1$, $\hat{\beta}_2$, and $\hat{\beta}_3$ with their corresponding slope coefficients in the Activity of Chapter 11, where you fit three separate straight-line models. How do you account for the differences?

2. Calculate the coefficient of determination, R^2, and conduct the F-test of the null hypothesis H_0: $\beta_1 = \beta_2 = \beta_3 = 0$. What is your conclusion?

3. Check the data for multicollinearity. If multicollinearity exists, how sould you proceed?

4. Now increase your list of 3 variables to include approximately 10 that you think would be useful in predicting the dependent variable. With the aid of statistical software, employ a stepwise regression program to choose the important variables among those you have listed. To test your intuition, list the variables in the order you think they will be selected before you conduct the analysis. How does your list compare with the stepwise regression results?

5. After the group of 10 variables has been narrowed to a smaller group of variables by the stepwise analysis, try to improve the model by including interactions and quadratic terms. Be sure to consider the meaning of each interaction or quadratic term before adding it to the model. (A quick sketch can be very helpful.) See if you can systematically construct a useful model for prediction. If you have a large data set, you might want to hold out the last observations to test the predictive ability of your model after it is constructed. (As noted in Section 12.10, using the same data to construct *and* to evaluate predictive ability can lead to invalid statistical tests and a false sense of security.)

References

Barnett, V., & Lewis, T. *Outliers in Statistical Data.* New York: Wiley, 1978.

Belsley, D. A., Kuh, E., & Welsch, R. E. *Regression Diagnostics: Identifying Influential Data and Sources of Collinearity.* New York: Wiley, 1980.

Chatterjee, S., & Price, B. *Regression Analysis by Example,* 2nd ed. New York: Wiley, 1991.

Draper, N., & Smith, H. *Applied Regression Analysis,* 2nd ed. New York: Wiley, 1981.

Graybill, F. *Theory and Application of the Linear Model.* North Scituate, Mass.: Duxbury, 1976.

Kutner, M., Nachtsheim, C., Neter, J., & Li, W. *Applied Linear Statistical Models,* 5th ed. New York: McGraw. Hill/Irwin, 2005.

Mendenhall, W. *Introduction to Linear Models and the Design and Analysis of Experiments.* Belmont, Calif.: Wadsworth, 1968.

Mendenhall, W., & Sincich, T. *A Second Course in Statistics: Regression Analysis,* 7th ed. Upper Saddle River, N.J.: Prentice Hall, 2011.

Mosteller, F., & Tukey, J. W. *Data Analysis and Regression: A Second Course in Statistics.* Reading, Mass.: Addison-Wesley, 1977.

Rousseeuw, P. J., & Leroy, A. M. *Robust Regression and Outlier Detection.* New York: Wiley, 1987.

Weisberg, S. *Applied Linear Regression,* 2nd ed. New York: Wiley, 1985.

Note: Automated commands for generating combinations and permutations are not available in SPSS.

SPSS: Multiple Regression

Step 1 Access the SPSS spreadsheet file that contains the dependent and independent variables.

Step 2 Click on the "Analyze" button on the SPSS menu bar and then click on "Regression" and "Linear," as shown in Figure 12.S.1. The resulting dialog box appears as shown in Figure 12.S.2.

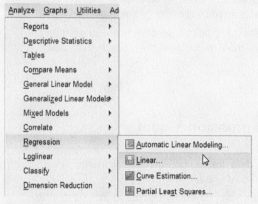

Figure 12.S.1 SPSS menu options for regression

Figure 12.S.2 SPSS linear regression dialog box

Step 3 Specify the dependent variable in the "Dependent" box and the independent variables in the "Independent(s)" box. [*Note:* If your model includes interaction and/or squared terms, you must create and add these higher-order variables to the SPSS spreadsheet file *prior* to running a regression analysis. You can do this by clicking the "Transform" button on the SPSS main menu and selecting the "Compute" option.]

Step 4 To perform a standard regression analysis, select "Enter" in the "Method" box. To perform a stepwise regression analysis, select "Stepwise" in the "Method" box.

Step 5 To perform a nested model *F*-test for additional model terms, click the "Next" button and enter the terms you want to test in the "Independent(s)" box. [*Note:* These terms, plus the terms you entered initially, form the complete model for the

nested *F*-test.] Next, click the "Statistics" button and select "R squared change." Click "Continue" to return to the main SPSS regression dialog box.

Step 6 To produce confidence intervals for the model parameters, click the "Statistics" button and check the appropriate menu items in the resulting menu list (see Figure 12.S.3).

Figure 12.S.3 SPSS linear regression save options

Step 7 To obtain prediction intervals for *y* and confidence intervals for *E(y)*, click the "Save" button and check the appropriate items in the resulting menu list. (The prediction intervals will be added as new columns to the SPSS data spreadsheet.)

Step 8 Residual plots are obtained by clicking the "Plots" button and making the appropriate selections on the resulting menu (see Figure 12.S.4).

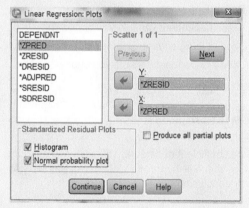

Figure 12.S.4 SPSS linear regression plots options

Step 9 To return to the main Regression dialog box from any of these optional screens, click "Continue." Click "OK" on the Regression dialog box to view the multiple regression results.

Minitab: Multiple Regression

Multiple Regression

Step 1 Access the Minitab worksheet file that contains the dependent and independent variables.

Step 2 Click on the "Stat" button on the Minitab menu bar and then click on "Regression" and "Regression" again, as shown in Figure 12.M.1.

Figure 12.M.1 Minitab menu options for regression

Step 3 The resulting dialog box appears as shown in Figure 12.M.2. Specify the dependent variable in the "Response" box and the independent variables in the "Predictors" box. [*Note:* If your model includes interaction and/or squared terms, you must create and add these higher-order variables to the Minitab worksheet *prior* to running a regression analysis. You can do this by clicking the "Calc" button on the Minitab main menu and selecting the "Calculator" option.]

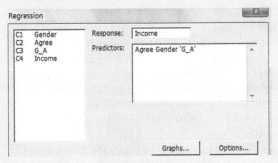

Figure 12.M.2 Minitab regression dialog box

Step 4 To produce prediction intervals for y and confidence intervals for E(y), click the "Options" button and then enter the values of the x's in the appropriate box on the resulting menu list (see Figure 12.M.3).

Figure 12.M.3 Minitab regression options

Step 5 Residual plots are obtained by clicking the "Graphs" button and making the appropriate selections on the resulting menu (see Figure 12.M.4).

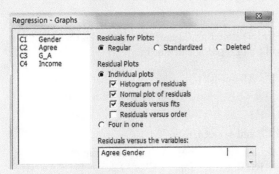

Figure 12.M.4 Minitab regression graphs options

Step 6 To return to the main Regression dialog box from any of these optional screens, click "OK."

Step 7 When you have made all your selections, click "OK" on the main Regression dialog box to produce the Minitab multiple regression printout.

Stepwise Regression

Step 1 Click on the "Stat" button on the main menu bar; then click on "Regression" and click on "Stepwise" (see Figure 12.M.1). The resulting dialog box appears like the one in Figure 12.M.2.

Step 2 Specify the dependent variable in the "Response" box and the independent variables in the stepwise model in the "Predictors" box.

Step 3 As an option, you can select the value of α to use in the analysis by clicking on the "Methods" button and specifying the value. (The default is $\alpha = .15$.)

Step 4 Click "OK" to view the stepwise regression results.

Excel: Multiple Regression

Multiple Regression in Excel

Step 1 Access the Excel worksheet file that contains the dependent and independent variables. [*Note:* If your model includes interaction and/or squared terms, you must create and add these higher-order variables to the Excel worksheet *prior* to running a regression analysis.]

Step 2 Click "Data" from the Excel menu bar and then select "Data Analysis." The resulting menu is shown in Figure 12.E.1.

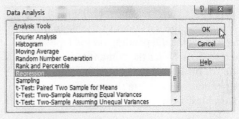

Figure 12.E.1 Excel data analysis menu options for regression

Step 3 Select "Regression" from the drop-down menu and then click "OK." The resulting dialog box is shown in Figure 12.E.2.

Figure 12.E.2 Excel regression dialog box

Step 4 Specify the cell ranges for the y and x variables in the "Input" area of the Multiple Regression dialog box. [*Note:* The x variables must be in adjacent columns on the Excel worksheet.]

Step 5 Select the confidence level for confidence intervals for the model parameters.

Step 6 To produce graphs of the regression residual, select the "Residual Plots" and "Normal probability plots" options.

Step 7 After making all your selections, click "OK" to produce the multiple regression results.

Multiple Regression with Excel/XLSTAT

Step 1 Within XLSTAT, open the Excel spreadsheet with the data for the dependent and independent variables.

Step 2 Click the "XLSTAT" button on the Excel main menu bar, select "Modeling data," then click "Linear regression," as shown in Figure 12.E.3.

Figure 12.E.3 XLSTAT menu options for multiple regression

Step 3 When the resulting dialog box appears (Figure 12.E.4), enter the column containing the dependent variable in the "Y / Dependent variables" box. Depending on the type of independent variables, check either the "Quantitative" or "Qualitative" option (or both) and then enter the columns containing the independent variables in the appropriate "X / Explanatory variables" boxes.

Figure 12.E.4 XLSTAT dialog box for linear regression

Step 4 To obtain prediction/confidence intervals, select the "Prediction" tab, then enter the column with the values of the independent variables for which you want to make predictions in the "X / Explanatory variables" and "Quantitative" or "Qualitative" boxes, as shown in Figure 12.E.5.

Step 5 Click "OK," then "Continue" to display the test results.

Figure 12.E.5 XLSTAT dialog box for predictions

Stepwise Regression with Excel/XLSTAT

Step 1 Within XLSTAT, open the Excel spreadsheet with the data for the dependent and independent variables.

Step 2 Click the "XLSTAT" button on the Excel main menu bar, select "Modeling data," then click "Linear regression," as shown in Figure 12.E.3.

Step 3 When the resulting dialog box appears (Figure 12.E.4), enter the column containing the dependent variable in the "Y / Dependent variables" box. Depending on the type of independent variables, check either the "Quantitative" or "Qualitative" option (or both) and then enter the columns containing the independent variables in the appropriate "X / Explanatory variables" boxes.

Step 4 Select the "Options" tab, then check the "Stepwise" option under "Model selection," as shown in Figure 12.E.6.

Figure 12.E.6 XLSTAT regression options dialog box

Step 5 Click "OK," then "Continue" to display the stepwise results.

TI-84 Graphing Calculator:
Multiple Regression

Note: Only simple linear and quadratic regression models can be fit using the TI-84 graphing calculator.

Quadratic Regression
I. Finding the Quadratic Regression Equation

Step 1 *Enter the data*

• Press **STAT** and select **1:Edit**

   Note: If the list already contains data, clear the old data. Use the up **ARROW** to highlight "**L1**" or "**L2**."

- Press **CLEAR ENTER**
- Use the **ARROW** and **ENTER** keys to enter the data set into **L1** and **L2**

Step 2 *Find the quadratic regression equation*

- Press **STAT** and highlight **CALC**
- Press **5** for **QuadReg**
- Press **ENTER**
- The screen will show the values for a, b, and c in the equation
- If the diagnostics are on, the screen will also give the value for r^2
- To turn the diagnostics feature on:
- Press **2nd 0** for **CATALOG**
- Press the **ALPHA** key and x^{-1} for **D**
- Press the down **ARROW** until **DiagnosticsOn** is high-lighted
- Press **ENTER** twice

II. Graphing the Quadratic Curve with the Scatterplot

Step 1 *Enter the data as shown in part I above*

Step 2 *Set up the data plot*

- Press **Y =** and **CLEAR** all functions from the Y registers
- Press **2nd Y =** for **STAT PLOT**
- Press **1** for **Plot1**
- Set the cursor so that **ON** is flashing and press **ENTER**
- For **Type,** use the **ARROW** and **ENTER** keys to highlight and select the scatterplot (first icon in the first row)
- For **Xlist,** choose the column containing the x-data
- For **Freq,** choose the column containing the y-data

Step 3 *Find the regression equation and store the equation in Y1*

- Press **STAT** and highlight **CALC**
- Press **5** for **QuadReg** (*Note:* Don't press ENTER here because you want to store the regression equation in Y1)
- Press **VARS**
- Use the right **ARROW** to highlight **Y-VARS**
- Press **ENTER** to select **1:Function**
- Press **ENTER** to select **1:Y1**
- Press **ENTER**

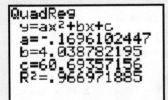

Step 4 *View the scatterplot and regression line*

- Press **ZOOM** and then press **9** to select **9:ZoomStat**

Plotting Residuals

When computing a regression equation on the TI-84, the residuals are automatically computed and saved to a list called **RESID. RESID** can be found under the **LIST menu** (**2nd STAT**).

Step 1 *Enter the data*

- Press **STAT** and select **1:Edit**
- *Note:* If the list already contains data, clear the old data. Use the up **ARROW** to highlight "**L1**" or "**L2**."
- Press **CLEAR ENTER**
- Use the **ARROW** and **ENTER** keys to enter the data set into **L1** and **L2**

Step 2 *Compute the regression equation*

- Press **STAT** and highlight **CALC**
- Press **4** for **LinReg(ax + b)**
- Press **ENTER**

Step 3 *Set up the data plot*

- Press **Y=** and **CLEAR** all functions from the Y registers
- Press **2nd Y =** for **STAT-PLOT**
- Press **1** for **Plot1**
- Set the cursor so that **ON** is flashing and press **ENTER**
- For **Type,** use the **ARROW** and **ENTER** keys to highlight and select the scatterplot (first icon in the first row).
- Move the cursor to **Xlist** and choose the column containing the x-data
- Move the cursor to **Ylist** and press **2nd STAT** for **LIST**
- Use the down **ARROW** to highlight the listname **RESID** and press **ENTER**

Step 4 *View the scatterplot of the residuals*

- Press **ZOOM 9** for **ZoomStat**

The Condo Sales Case

This case involves an investigation of the factors that affect the sale price of oceanside condominium units. It represents an extension of an analysis of the same data by Herman Kelting. Although condo sale prices have increased dramatically over the past 20 years, the relationship between these factors and sale price remains about the same. Consequently, the data provide valuable insight into today's condominium sales market.

The sales data were obtained for a new oceanside condominium complex consisting of two adjacent and connected eight-floor buildings. The complex contains 200 units of equal size (approximately 500 square feet each). The locations of the buildings relative to the ocean, the swimming pool, the parking lot, etc., are shown in the accompanying figure. There are several features of the complex that you should note:

1. The units facing south, called *ocean view*, face the beach and ocean. In addition, units in building 1 have a good view of the pool. Units to the rear of the building, called *bay-view*, face the parking lot and an area of land that ultimately borders a bay. The view from the upper floors of these units is primarily of wooded, sandy terrain. The bay is very distant and barely visible.

2. The only elevator in the complex is located at the east end of building 1, as are the office and the game room. People moving to or from the higher floor units in building 2 would likely use the elevator and move through the passages to their units. Thus, units on the higher floors and at a greater distance from the elevator would be less convenient; they would require greater effort in moving baggage, groceries, and so on and would be farther away from the game room, the office, and the swimming pool. These units also possess an advantage: there would be the least amount of traffic through the hallways in the area and hence they are the most private.

3. Lower-floor oceanside units are most suited to active people; they open onto the beach, ocean,

and pool. They are within easy reach of the game room, and they are easily reached from the parking area.

4. Checking the layout of the condominium complex, you discover that some of the units in the center of the complex, units ending in numbers 11 and 14, have part of their view blocked.

5. The condominium complex was completed at the time of the 1975 recession; sales were slow, and the developer was forced to sell most of the units at auction approximately 18 months after opening. Consequently, the auction data are completely buyer specified and hence consumer oriented in contrast to most other real estate sales data that are, to a high degree, seller and broker specified.

6. Many unsold units in the complex were furnished by the developer and rented prior to the auction. Consequently, some of the units bid on and sold at auction had furniture, others did not.

This condominium complex is obviously unique. For example, the single elevator located at one end of the complex produces a remarkably high level of both inconvenience and privacy for the people occupying units on the top floors in building 2. Consequently, the developer is unsure of how the height of the unit (floor number), distance of the unit from the elevator, presence or absence of an ocean view, etc., affect the prices of the units sold at auction. To investigate these relationships, the following data (saved in the data file) were recorded for each of the 106 units sold at the auction:

1. *Sale price.* Measured in hundreds of dollars (adjusted for inflation).

2. *Floor height.* The floor location of the unit; the variable levels are 1, 2, . . . , 8.

3. *Distance from elevator.* This distance, measured along the length of the complex, is expressed in number of condominium units. An additional two units of distance was added to the units in building 2 to account for the walking distance in the connecting area between the two buildings. Thus, the distance of unit 105 from the elevator would be 3, and the distance between unit 113 and the elevator would be 9. The variable levels are 1, 2, . . . , 15.

4. *View of ocean.* The presence or absence of an ocean view is recorded for each unit and specified

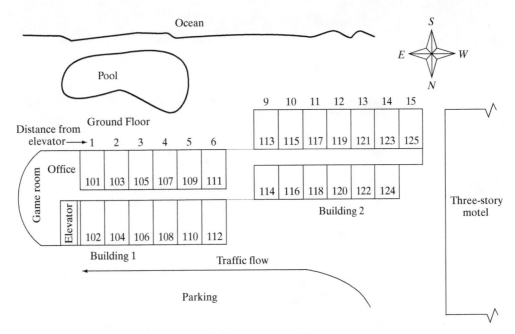

Figure C5.1 Layout of condominium complex

with a dummy variable (1 if the unit possesses an ocean view and 0 if not). Note that units not possessing an ocean view face the parking lot.

5. *End unit.* We expect the partial reduction of view of end units on the ocean side (numbers ending in 11) to reduce their sale price. The ocean view of these end units is partially blocked by building 2. This qualitative variable is also specified with a dummy variable (1 if the unit has a unit number ending in 11 and 0 if not).

6. *Furniture.* The presence or absence of furniture is recorded for each unit and is represented with a single dummy variable (1 if the unit was furnished and 0 if not).

Your objective for this case is to build a regression model that accurately predicts the sale price

of a condominium unit sold at auction. Prepare a professional document that presents the results of your analysis. Include graphs that demonstrate how each of the independent variables in your model affects auction price. A layout of the data file is described below.

Variable	Type
PRICE	QN
FLOOR	QN
DISTANCE	QN
VIEW	QL
ENDUNIT	QL
FURNISH	QL

(Number of Observations: 106)   *Data Set:* CONDO

14

Where We've Been

- Discovered that variation in the output of processes is inevitable.
- Presented both managerial and statistical methods for continuously improving processes and the quality of their output.
- Learned how to use control charts to monitor process variation and determine when action should be taken to improve a process.

Where We're Going

- Focus on methods for analyzing data generated by a process over time (i.e., *time series data*).
- Present descriptive methods for characterizing time series data (14.1–14.2)
- Present inferential methods for forecasting future values of time series data (14.3–14.9)

■ Time Series *Descriptive Analyses,*

Models, and Forecasting

STATISTICS in ACTION

Forecasting the Monthly Sales of a New Cold Medicine

In the pharmaceutical industry, sales forecasting is critical to the success of a company. Accurate forecasts aid sales managers in improving decision making, the finance department in controlling and scheduling its operating costs and capital budget, the human resources department in projecting staffing, and the purchasing department in controlling inventories and production schedules. Due to the critical, life-and-death nature of the industry, pharmaceutical manufacturers rely on sophisticated analytical techniques to build their forecasts.

Several years ago, a major pharmaceutical company based in New Jersey introduced a new cold medicine called Coldex. (For proprietary reasons, the actual name of the product is withheld.) Coldex is now sold regularly in drugstores and supermarkets across the United States. Prior to launching the product nationally, the company hired consultants from the Graduate School of Management at Rutgers University (The State University of New Jersey) to help the company build a monthly forecast model for Coldex. This Statistics in Action involves a portion of the analysis conducted by the consultants.

Consider the task of forecasting the sales of Coldex for the first 3 months of the third year of the product's existence. The company provided data on the monthly sales (in thousands of dollars) for the first 2 years of the product's life. The data, saved in the **COLDEX** file, are listed in Table SIA14.1. In the Statistics in Action Revisited sections in this chapter, we demonstrate several forecasting methods used by the consultants.

Table SIA14.1			Coldex Monthly Sales Data				
Year	Month	Time	Sales	Year	Month	Time	Sales
1	Jan	1	3,394	2	Jan	13	4,568
	Feb	2	4,010		Feb	14	3,710
	Mar	3	924		Mar	15	1,675
	Apr	4	205		Apr	16	999
	May	5	293		May	17	986
	Jun	6	1,130		Jun	18	1,786
	Jul	7	1,116		Jul	19	2,253
	Aug	8	4,009		Aug	20	5,237
	Sep	9	5,692		Sep	21	6,679
	Oct	10	3,458		Oct	22	4,116
	Nov	11	2,849		Nov	23	4,109
	Dec	12	3,470		Dec	24	5,124

Source: Based on personal communication from Carol Cowley, Carla Marchesini, and Ginny Wilson. Rutgers University Graduate School of Management.   *Data Set:* COLDEX

STATISTICS in ACTION REVISITED

□ Forecasting with Exponential Smoothing **(p. 14-28)**

□ Forecasting with Simple Linear Regression **(p. 14-31)**

□ Forecasting with a Seasonal Regression Model **(p. 14-35)**

In the previous chapter, we were concerned with improving processes. In this chapter, our concern is not with the improvement of the internal workings of processes but with describing and predicting the output of processes. The process outputs on which we focus are the streams of data generated by processes over time. Recall from Chapters 2 and 13 that such data streams are called **time series** or **time series data.** For example, businesses generate time series data such as weekly sales, quarterly earnings, and yearly profits that can be used to describe and evaluate the performance of the business. The U.S. economy can be thought of as a system that generates streams of data that include the gross domestic product, the Consumer Price Index, and the unemployment rate.

The methods of this chapter focus exclusively on the time series data generated by a process. Properly analyzed, these data reveal much about the past and future behavior of the process. Time series data, like other types of data we have discussed in previous chapters, are subjected to two kinds of analyses: **descriptive** and **inferential.** Descriptive analyses use graphical and numerical techniques to provide a clear understanding of any patterns that are present in the time series. After graphing the data, you will often want to use them to make inferences about the future values of the time series (i.e., you will want to **forecast** future values). For example, once you understand the past and present trends of the Dow Jones Industrial Average, you would probably want to forecast its future trend before making decisions about buying and selling stocks. Because significant amounts of money may be riding on the accuracy of your forecasts, you would be interested in measures of their reliability. Forecasts and their measures of reliability are examples of **inferential techniques** in time series analysis.

14.1   Descriptive Analysis: Index Numbers

A common technique for characterizing a business or economic time series is to compute *index numbers.* Index numbers measure how time series values change relative to a preselected time period, called the *base period.*

> An **index number** measures the change in a variable over time relative to the value of the variable during a specific **base period.**

Two types of indexes dominate business and economic applications: **price** and **quantity indexes.** Price indexes measure changes in the price of a commodity or group of commodities over time. The Consumer Price Index (CPI) is a price index because it measures price changes of a group of commodities that are intended to reflect typical purchases of American consumers. On the other hand, an index constructed to measure the change in the total number of automobiles produced annually by American manufacturers would be an example of a quantity index.

Methods of calculating index numbers range from very simple to extremely complex, depending on the numbers and types of commodities represented by the index. Several important types of index numbers are described in this section.

Simple Index Numbers

When an index number is based on the price or quantity of a single commodity, it is called a *simple index number.*

> A **simple index number** is based on the relative changes (over time) in the price or quantity of a single commodity.

For example, consider the price of silver (in dollars per fine ounce) between 1975 and 2011, shown in Table 14.1. To construct a simple index to describe the relative changes in silver prices, we must first choose a *base period.* The choice is important because the price for all other periods will be compared with the price during the base period. We select 1975 as the base period, a time just preceding the period of rapid economic inflation associated with dramatic oil price increases.

Table 14.1	Silver Prices, 1975–2011				
Year	Price ($/oz.)	Year	Price ($/oz.)	Year	Price ($/oz.)
1975	4.43	1988	6.53	2001	4.37
1976	4.35	1989	5.50	2002	4.60
1977	4.63	1990	4.83	2003	4.85
1978	5.42	1991	4.06	2004	6.65
1979	11.08	1992	3.95	2005	7.22
1980	20.98	1993	4.31	2006	11.57
1981	10.49	1994	5.29	2007	13.39
1982	7.92	1995	5.20	2008	15.02
1983	11.43	1996	5.20	2009	14.66
1984	8.14	1997	4.90	2010	20.16
1985	6.13	1998	5.54	2011	35.11
1986	5.46	1999	5.22		
1987	7.02	2000	4.95		

Source: Reprinted with permission of The Silver Institute.   *Data Set:* SILVER

To calculate the simple index number for a particular year, we divide that year's price by the price during the base year and multiply the result by 100. Thus, for the 1992 silver price index number, we calculate

$$1992 \text{ index number} = \left(\frac{1992 \text{ silver price}}{1975 \text{ silver price}}\right)100 = \left(\frac{3.95}{4.43}\right)100 = 89.2$$

Similarly, the index number for 2011 is

$$2011 \text{ index number} = \left(\frac{2011 \text{ silver price}}{1975 \text{ silver price}}\right)100 = \left(\frac{35.11}{4.43}\right)100 = 792.6$$

The index number for the base period is always 100. In our example, we have

$$1975 \text{ index number} = \left(\frac{1975 \text{ silver price}}{1975 \text{ silver price}}\right)100 = 100$$

	A	B	C
1	YEAR	PRICE	INDEX
2	1975	4.43	100.00
3	1976	4.35	98.19
4	1977	4.63	104.51
5	1978	5.42	122.35
6	1979	11.08	250.11
7	1980	20.98	473.59
8	1981	10.49	236.79
9	1982	7.92	178.78
10	1983	11.43	258.01
11	1984	8.14	183.75
12	1985	6.13	138.37
13	1986	5.46	123.25
14	1987	7.02	158.47
15	1988	6.53	147.40
16	1989	5.50	124.15
17	1990	4.83	109.03
18	1991	4.06	91.65
19	1992	3.95	89.16
20	1993	4.31	97.29
21	1994	5.29	119.41
22	1995	5.20	117.38
23	1996	5.20	117.38
24	1997	4.90	110.61
25	1998	5.54	125.06
26	1999	5.22	117.83
27	2000	4.95	111.74
28	2001	4.37	98.65
29	2002	4.60	103.84
30	2003	4.85	109.48
31	2004	6.65	150.11
32	2005	7.22	162.98
33	2006	11.57	261.17
34	2007	13.39	302.26
35	2008	15.02	339.05
36	2009	14.66	330.93
37	2010	20.16	455.08
38	2011	35.11	792.55

Figure 14.1

Excel workbook with simple
index numbers for silver prices
(base = 1975)
Source: The Silver Institute.

Index numbers below 100 indicate a decrease in the time series value; in contrast, index numbers above 100 indicate an increase. Thus, the silver price decreased by 11% (the difference between the 1992 and 1975 index numbers) between 1975 and 1992 and increased by 693% between 1975 and 2011. The simple index numbers for all silver prices between 1975 and 2011 were computed using Excel and are shown in the Excel spreadsheet, Figure 14.1. The index is also portrayed graphically in Figure 14.2. The steps for calculating simple index numbers are summarized in the next box.

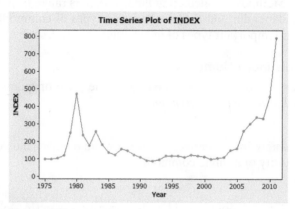

Figure 14.2

Minitab time series graph of simple silver price index
Source: The Silver Institute.

Steps for Calculating a Simple Index Number

1. Obtain the prices or quantities for the commodity over the time period of interest.

2. Select a base period.

3. Calculate the index number for each period according to the formula

$$\text{Index number at time } t = \left(\frac{\text{Time series value at time } t}{\text{Time series value at base period}} \right) 100$$

Symbolically,

$$I_t = \left(\frac{Y_t}{Y_0} \right) 100$$

where I_t is the index number at time t, Y_t is the time series value at time t, and Y_0 is the time series value at the base period.

Composite Index Numbers

A **composite index number** represents combinations of the prices or quantities of several commodities. For example, suppose you want to construct an index for the total number of sales of the two major automobile manufacturers in the United States: General Motors and Ford. The first step is to collect data on the sales of each manufacturer during the period in which you are interested, say 2000–2012. To summarize the information from both time series in a single index, we add the sales of each manufacturer for each year—that is, we form a new time series consisting of the total number of automobiles sold by the two manufacturers. Then we construct a simple index for the *total* of the two series. The resulting index is called a *simple composite index*. We illustrate the construction of a simple composite index in Example 14.1.

A **simple composite index** is a simple index for a time series consisting of the total price or total quantity of two or more commodities.

Example 14.1

Constructing a Simple Composite Index—High-Tech Stocks

Problem One of the primary uses of index numbers is to characterize changes in stock prices over time. Stock market indexes have been constructed for many different types of companies and industries, and several composite indexes have been developed to characterize all stocks. These indexes are reported on a daily basis in the news media (e.g., Standard and Poor's 500 Stocks Index and Dow Jones 65 Stocks Index).

Consider the 2011 monthly closing prices (i.e., closing prices on the last day of each month) given in Table 14.2 for three high-technology company stocks listed on the New York Stock Exchange. To see how this type of stock fared over the year, construct a simple composite index using January 2011 as the base period. Graph the index and comment on its implications.

Table 14.2	Monthly Closing Prices of Three High-Technology Company Stocks				
Year	Month	Time	IBM	Intel	Microsoft
2011	Jan	1	162.00	21.46	27.73
	Feb	2	161.88	21.47	26.58
	Mar	3	164.27	19.72	25.48
	Apr	4	165.05	23.15	25.92
	May	5	167.50	21.73	23.91
	Jun	6	181.85	22.53	26.02
	Jul	7	127.98	22.33	27.40
	Aug	8	166.98	19.64	25.80
	Sep	9	174.87	21.34	24.89
	Oct	10	186.38	23.74	26.25
	Nov	11	189.66	24.64	25.22
	Dec	12	183.88	24.25	26.96

Source: www.msn.com.

Data Set: HITECH

Solution First, we calculate the total for the three stock prices each month. These totals are shown in the "TOTAL" column in the Excel workbook displayed in Figure 14.3. Then the simple composite index is calculated by dividing each monthly total by the January 2011 total. The index values are given in the last column of Figure 14.3, and a graph of the simple composite index is shown in Figure 14.4.

Figure 14.3

Excel workbook with simple composite index for high-tech stock prices

Source: www.msn.com.

	A	B	C	D	E	F	G	H
1	YEAR	MONTH	TIME	IBM	INTEL	MICROSOFT	TOTAL	INDEX
2	2011	JAN	1	162.00	21.46	27.73	211.19	100.00
3	2011	FEB	2	161.88	21.47	26.58	209.93	99.40
4	2011	MAR	3	164.27	19.72	25.48	209.47	99.19
5	2011	APR	4	165.05	23.15	25.92	214.12	101.39
6	2011	MAY	5	167.50	21.73	23.91	213.14	100.92
7	2011	JUN	6	181.85	22.53	26.02	230.40	109.10
8	2011	JUL	7	127.98	22.33	27.40	177.71	84.15
9	2011	AUG	8	166.98	19.64	25.80	212.42	100.58
10	2011	SEP	9	174.87	21.34	24.89	221.10	104.69
11	2011	OCT	10	186.38	23.74	26.25	236.37	111.92
12	2011	NOV	11	189.66	24.64	25.22	239.52	113.41
13	2011	DEC	12	183.88	24.25	26.96	235.09	111.32

Figure 14.4

Minitab time series graph of simple composite index for high-tech stock prices

Source: www.msn.com.

Time Series Plot of Simple Composite Stock Price Index

The plot of the 2011 simple composite index for these high-technology stocks shows a dramatic drop in the stock market in July 2011, followed by an increasing trend. Overall, the composite price of these high-technology stocks increased about 11% from January (Index = 100) to December (Index = 111.32).

Look Back The difference between two index numbers gives the percentage change in the value of the time series variable between the two time periods.

■ **Now Work Exercise 14.10c, d**

A simple composite price index has a major drawback: The quantity of the commodity that is purchased during each period is not taken into account. Only the price totals are used to calculate the index. We can remedy this situation by constructing a *weighted composite price index*.

> A **weighted composite price index** weights the prices by quantities purchased prior to calculating totals for each time period. The weighted totals are then used to compute the index in the same way that the unweighted totals are used for simple composite indexes.

Because the quantities purchased change from time period to time period, the choice of which time period's quantities to use as the basis for the weighted composite index is an important one. A **Laspeyres index** uses the *base period quantities as weights*. The rationale is that the prices at each time period should be compared as if the same quantities were purchased each period as were purchased during the base period. This method measures price inflation (or deflation) by fixing the purchase quantities at their base period values. The method for calculating a Laspeyres index is given in the box below.

> **Steps for Calculating a Laspeyres Index**
>
> 1. Collect price information for each of the k price series to be used in the composite index. Denote these series by $P_{1t}, P_{2t}, \ldots, P_{kt}$.
> 2. Select a base period. Call this time period t_0.
> 3. Collect purchase quantity information for the base period. Denote the k quantities by $Q_{1t_0}, Q_{2t_0}, \ldots, Q_{kt_0}$.
> 4. Calculate the weighted totals for each time period according to the formula
>
> $$\sum_{i=1}^{k} Q_{it_0} P_{it}$$
>
> 5. Calculate the Laspeyres index, I_t, at time t by taking the ratio of the weighted total at time t to the base period weighted total and multiplying by 100—that is,
>
> $$I_t = \frac{\sum_{i=1}^{k} Q_{it_0} P_{it}}{\sum_{i=1}^{k} Q_{it_0} P_{it_0}} \times 100$$

Example 14.2

Constructing a Laspeyres Index—High-Tech Stocks

Problem The 2011 January and December prices for the three high-technology company stocks are given in Table 14.3. Suppose that, in January 2011, an investor purchased the quantities shown in the table. [*Note:* Only two prices are used to simplify the example. The same methods can be applied to calculate the index for other months.] Calculate the Laspeyres index for the investor's portfolio of high-technology stocks using January 2011 as the base period.

Table 14.3	Prices of High-Technology Stocks with Quantities Purchased		
	IBM	Intel	Microsoft
Shares purchased	500	100	1,000
January price	162.00	21.46	27.73
December price	183.88	24.25	26.96

Source: www.msn.com.

Solution First, we calculate the weighted price totals for each time period, using the January quantities as weights. Thus,

$$\text{January weighted total} = \sum_{i=1}^{3} Q_{i, \text{Jan.}} \, P_{i, \text{Jan.}}$$

$$= 500(162.00) + 100(21.46) + 1,000(27.73)$$

$$= 110,876$$

$$\text{December weighted total} = \sum_{i=1}^{3} Q_{i, \text{Jan.}} \, P_{i, \text{Dec.}}$$

$$= 500(183.88) + 100(24.25) + 1,000(26.96)$$

$$= 121,325$$

Then the Laspeyres index is calculated by multiplying the ratio of each weighted total to the base period weighted total by 100. Thus,

$$I_{\text{Jan.}} = \frac{\sum_{i=1}^{3} Q_{i, \text{Jan.}} \, P_{i, \text{Jan.}}}{\sum_{i=1}^{3} Q_{i, \text{Jan.}} \, P_{i, \text{Jan.}}} \times 100 = \frac{110,876}{110,876} \times 100 = 100$$

$$I_{\text{Dec.}} = \frac{\sum_{i=1}^{3} Q_{i, \text{Jan.}} \, P_{i, \text{Dec.}}}{\sum_{i=1}^{3} Q_{i, \text{Jan.}} \, P_{i, \text{Jan.}}} \times 100 = \frac{121,325}{110,876} \times 100 = 109.42$$

Look Back The implication is that when weighted by quantities purchased, the total value of these stocks increased by about $(109 - 100)\% = 9\%$ from January to December in 2011.

■ **Now Work Exercise 14.14b**

The Laspeyres index is appropriate when the base period quantities are reasonable weights to apply to all time periods. This is the case in applications such as that described in Example 14.2, where the base period quantities represent actual quantities of stock purchased and held for some period of time. Laspeyres indexes are also appropriate when the base period quantities remain reasonable approximations of purchase quantities in subsequent periods. However, it can be misleading when the relative purchase quantities change significantly from those in the base period.

Probably the best-known Laspeyres index is the all-items Consumer Price Index (CPI). This monthly composite index is made up of hundreds of item prices, and the U.S. Bureau of Labor Statistics (BLS) sampled over 30,000 families' purchases in 1982–1984 to determine the base period quantities. Thus, beginning in 1988, the all-items CPI published each month reflects quantities purchased in 1982–1984 by a sample of families across the United States. However, as prices increase for some commodities more quickly than for others, consumers tend to substitute less expensive commodities where possible. For example, as gasoline prices rapidly inflated in the mid-2000s, consumers began to purchase more fuel efficient cars. The net effect of using the base period quantities for the CPI is to overestimate the effect of inflation on consumers because the quantities are fixed at levels that will actually change in response to price changes.

There are several solutions to the problem of purchase quantities that change relative to those of the base period. One is to change the base period regularly, so that the quantities are regularly updated. A second solution is to compute the index at each time period by using the purchase quantities of that period, rather than those of the base period. A **Paasche index** is calculated by using price totals *weighted by the purchase quantities of the period the index value represents*. The steps for calculating a Paasche index are given in the box.

Steps for Calculating a Paasche Index

1. Collect price information for each of the k price series to be used in the composite index. Denote these series by $P_{1t}, P_{2t}, \ldots, P_{kt}$.
2. Select a base period. Call this time period t_0.
3. Collect purchase quantity information for every period. Denote the k quantities for period t by $Q_{1t}, Q_{2t}, \ldots, Q_{kt}$.
4. Calculate the Paasche index for time t by multiplying the ratio of the weighted total at time t to the weighted total at time t_0 (base period) by 100, where the weights used are the purchase quantities for time period t. Thus,

$$I_t = \frac{\sum_{i=1}^{k} Q_{it} P_{it}}{\sum_{i=1}^{k} Q_{it} P_{it_0}} \times 100$$

Example 14.3

Constructing a Paasche Index—High-Tech Stocks

Problem The 2011 January and December prices and volumes (actual quantities purchased) in millions of shares for three high-technology company stocks are shown in Table 14.4. Calculate and interpret the Paasche index, using January 2011 as the base period.

Table 14.4	Prices and Volumes of High-Technology Stocks					
	IBM		Intel		Microsoft	
	Price	Volume	Price	Volume	Price	Volume
January	162.00	7	21.46	91	27.73	65
December	183.88	12	24.25	92	26.96	101

Source: S&P Daily Stock Price Record, moneycentral.msn.com.

Solution The key to calculating a Paasche index is to remember that the weights (purchase quantities) change for each time period. Thus,

$$I_{\text{Jan.}} = \frac{\sum_{i=1}^{3} Q_{i,\,\text{Jan.}} P_{i,\,\text{Jan.}}}{\sum_{i=1}^{3} Q_{i,\,\text{Jan.}} P_{i,\,\text{Jan.}}} \times 100 = 100$$

$$I_{\text{Dec.}} = \frac{\sum_{i=1}^{3} Q_{i,\,\text{Dec.}} P_{i,\,\text{Dec.}}}{\sum_{i=1}^{3} Q_{i,\,\text{Dec.}} P_{i,\,\text{Jan.}}} \times 100$$

$$= \frac{(12)(183.88) + (92)(24.25) + (101)(26.96)}{(12)(162.00) + (92)(21.46) + (101)(27.73)} \times 100 = \frac{7,160.52}{6,719.05} \times 100$$

$$= 106.6$$

The implication is that in 2011, December prices represent a $(106.6 - 100)\% = 6.6\%$ increase from January prices, assuming the purchase quantities were at December levels for *both* periods.

■ **Now Work Exercise 14.14d**

The Paasche index is most appropriate when you want to compare current prices to base period prices at *current* purchase levels. However, there are several major problems associated with the Paasche index. First, it requires that purchase quantities be known for every time period. This rules out a Paasche index for applications such as the CPI because the time and monetary resource expenditures required to collect quantity information are considerable. (Recall that more than 30,000 families were sampled to estimate purchase quantities in 1982–1984.) A second problem is that although each period is compared to the base period, it is difficult to compare the index at two other periods because the quantities used are different for each period. Consequently, the change in the index is affected by changes in both prices *and* quantities. This fact makes it difficult to interpret the change in a Paasche index between periods when neither is the base period.

Although there are other types of indexes that use different weighting factors, the Laspeyres and Paasche indexes are the most popular composite indexes. Depending on the primary objective in constructing an index, one of them will probably be suitable for most purposes.

ETHICS in STATISTICS

Intentionally selecting a base period in order to inflate or deflate an index number, without reporting the base period, is considered *unethical statistical practice*.

Exercises 14.1–14.14

Learning the Mechanics

14.1 Explain in words how to construct a simple index.

14.2 Explain in words how to calculate the following types of indexes:
 a. Simple composite index
 b. Weighted composite index
 c. Laspeyres index
 d. Paasche index

14.3 Explain in words the difference between Laspeyres and Paasche indexes.

14.4 The table below gives the prices for three products (A, B, and C) for the four quarters of last year.

Quarter	A	B	C
1	3.25	1.75	8.00
2	3.50	1.25	9.35
3	3.90	1.20	9.70
4	4.25	1.00	10.50

 a. Compute a simple index for the Quarter 4 price of product A, using Quarter 1 as the base period.
 b. Compute a simple index for the Quarter 2 price of product B, using Quarter 1 as the base period.
 c. Compute a simple composite index for the Quarter 4 price of all three products, using Quarter 1 as the base period.
 d. Compute a simple composite index for the Quarter 4 price of all three products, using Quarter 2 as the base period.

14.5 Refer to Exercise 14.4. The next table gives the quantities purchased for three products (A, B, and C) for the four quarters of last year.

Quarter	A	B	C
1	100	20	50
2	200	25	35
3	250	50	25
4	300	100	20

 a. Compute a Laspeyres index for the Quarter 4 price of all three products, using Quarter 1 as the base period.
 b. Compute a Paasche index for the Quarter 4 price of all three products, using Quarter 2 as the base period.

Applying the Concepts—Basic

14.6 **Annual median family income.** The table below lists the U.S. median annual family income every 5 years during the period 1975–2010. It also contains several values for each of two simple indexes for median family income.
 a. Calculate the missing values of each simple index.
 b. Interpret the index for 1990.

Year	Income ($)	Base 1975 Index	Base 1980 Index
1975	13,719	–	65.26
1980	21,023	153.24	–
1985	27,735	202.16	–
1990	35,353	257.69	–
1995	40,611	–	–
2000	50,732	–	–
2005	56,194	–	–
2010	60,363	–	–

Source: U.S. Census Bureau, 2012.

14.7 Annual U.S. beer production. The table below describes U.S. beer production (in millions of barrels) for the period 1980–2010.

USBEER

a. Use 1980 as the base period to compute the simple index for this time series. Interpret the value for 2010.

b. Refer to part **a.** Is this an example of a quantity index or a price index?

c. Recompute the simple index using 1990 as the base period. Plot the two indexes on the same graph. What pattern do you observe?

Year	Beer	Year	Beer	Year	Beer
1980	188	1991	203	2002	200
1981	194	1992	202	2003	195
1982	194	1993	203	2004	198
1983	195	1994	202	2005	197
1984	193	1995	199	2006	198
1985	193	1996	201	2007	199
1986	195	1997	199	2008	200
1987	195	1998	198	2009	196
1988	198	1999	198	2010	194
1989	200	2000	199		
1990	204	2001	199		

Source: 2011 BREWER'S ALMANAC. Copyright © 2011 by The Beer Institute. Reprinted with permission.

14.8 Quarterly single-family housing starts. The quarterly numbers of single-family housing starts (in thousands of dwellings) in the United States from 2007 through 2011 are recorded below.

HSTART

a. Using Quarter 1, 2007, as a base period, calculate the simple index for this quarterly time series.

b. Interpret the simple index for Quarter 2, 2010.

c. By what percentage did the number of housing starts change between Quarter 1, 2007, and Quarter 4, 2011?

d. By what percentage did the number of housing starts increase between Quarter 1, 2009, and Quarter 4, 2011?

Year	Quarter	Housing Starts
2007	1	260
	2	333
	3	265
	4	188
2008	1	162
	2	194
	3	163
	4	103
2009	1	78
	2	124
	3	138
	4	105
2010	1	114
	2	142
	3	119
	4	96
2011	1	90
	2	123
	3	118
	4	100

Source: United States Census Bureau.

14.9 Price of natural gas. The table below lists the price of natural gas (in dollars per 1,000 cubic feet) between 1980 and 2010.

NATGAS

Year	Price	Year	Price	Year	Price
1980	3.68	1997	6.94	2005	12.70
1990	5.80	1998	6.82	2006	13.73
1991	5.82	1999	6.69	2007	13.08
1992	5.89	2000	7.76	2008	13.89
1993	6.16	2001	9.63	2009	12.14
1994	6.41	2002	7.89	2010	11.20
1995	6.06	2003	9.63		
1996	6.34	2004	10.75		

Source: United States Census Bureau.

a. Using 1980 as the base period, calculate and plot the simple index for the price of natural gas from 1990 through 2010.

b. Use the simple index to interpret the trend in the price of natural gas.

c. Is the index you constructed in part **a** a price or quantity index? Explain.

Applying the Concepts—Intermediate

14.10 Employment in farm and nonfarm categories. Civilian employment is broadly classified by the federal government into two categories—agricultural and nonagricultural. Employment figures (in thousands of workers) for farm and nonfarm categories for selected years from 1980 to 2010 are given in the table below.

CVEMP

Year	Farm	Nonfarm	Year	Farm	Nonfarm
1980	3,364	95,938	2000	2,464	134,427
1985	3,179	103,971	2005	2,197	139,532
1990	3,223	115,570	2010	2,206	136,858
1995	3,440	121,460			

Source: United States Census Bureau.

a. Compute simple indexes for each of the two time series using 1980 as the base period.

b. Which segment has shown the greater percentage change in employment over the period shown?

NW c. Compute a simple composite index for total employment for the years 1980–2010. Use 1980 as a base period.

NW d. Refer to part **c.** Interpret the composite index value for 2010.

14.11 GDP personal consumption expenditures. The gross domestic product (GDP) is the total national output of goods and services valued at market prices. As such, the GDP is a commonly used barometer of the U.S. economy. One component of the GDP is personal consumption expenditures, which is itself the sum of expenditures for durable goods, nondurable goods, and services. The GDP for these components (in billions of dollars) is shown in the next table, in 5-year increments from 1970 to 2010.

GDP

a. Using these three component values, construct a simple composite index for the personal consumption component of GDP. Use 1970 as the base year.

b. Suppose we want to update the index by using 1980 as the base year. Update the index using only the index values you calculated in part **a,** without referring to the original data.

c. Graph the personal consumption expenditure index for the years 1960–2010, first using 1970 as the base year and then using 1980 as the base year. What effect does changing the base year have on the graph of this index?

Year	Durables	Nondurables	Services
1970	90	229	330
1975	134	416	475
1980	226	573	956
1985	353	919	1,395
1990	497	994	2,344
1995	636	1,180	3,172
2000	916	1,543	4,371
2005	1,106	1,968	5,745
2010	1,089	2,336	6,923

Source: United States Census Bureau.

14.12 GDP personal consumption expenditures (cont'd). Refer to Exercise 14.11. Suppose the output quantities in 1970, measured in billions of units purchased, are as follows:

Durable goods: 10.9

Nondurable goods: 14.02

Services: 42.6

a. Use the outputs to calculate the Laspeyres index from 1960 to 2010 (same increments as in Exercise 14.11) with 1970 as the base period.

b. Plot the simple composite index of Exercise 14.11 and the Laspeyres index of part **a** on the same graph. Comment on the differences between the two indexes.

14.13 Hourly earnings for workers. The table below lists the average hourly earnings (in dollars) and the average number

HOURS

of hours worked per week for selected years from 1990 to 2010 for workers in three different industries.

a. Compute a simple index for average hourly earnings for manufacturing workers over the period 1990 to 2010. Use 1990 as the base year. Do the same for information and food services workers.

b. Plot the three simple indexes on the same graph and interpret the results.

c. Compute simple composite indexes for hourly earnings and weekly hours over the 40-year period. Use 1990 as the base year.

d. Plot the two composite indexes, part **c,** on the same graph and interpret the results.

14.14 Production and price of metals. The level of price and production of metals in the United States is one measure of the

METALS strength of an industrial economy. The table at the bottom of the page lists the annual prices (in dollars per ton) and production (in millions of tons) for three metals—copper, aluminum, and iron scrap—from 2006 to 2010.

a. Compute the simple composite price and quantity indexes for the 5-year period, using 2006 as the base period.

NW b. Compute the Laspeyres price index for the 5-year period, using 2006 as the base period.

c. Plot the simple composite and Laspeyres indexes on the same graph. Comment on the differences.

NW d. Compute the Paasche price index for the 5-year period, using 2006 as the base period.

e. Plot the Paasche and Laspeyres indexes on the same graph. Comment on the differences.

f. Compare the Paasche and Laspeyres index values for 2008 and 2010. Which index is more appropriate for describing the change in this 2-year period? Explain.

Data for Exercise 14.13

	Manufacturing		Information		Food Services	
Year	Earnings	Hours	Earnings	Hours	Earnings	Hours
1990	10.78	40.5	13.40	35.8	5.70	25.9
2000	14.32	41.3	19.07	36.8	7.92	26.2
2005	16.56	40.7	22.06	36.5	8.80	25.7
2007	17.26	41.2	23.96	36.5	9.82	25.6
2008	17.75	40.8	24.78	36.7	10.23	25.4
2009	18.24	39.8	25.45	36.6	10.49	25.0
2010	18.61	41.1	25.86	36.3	10.68	25.0

Source: United States Census Bureau.

Data for Exercise 14.14

	Copper		Iron Scrap		Aluminum	
Year	Price	Production	Price	Production	Price	Production
2006	6,940	1.21	214	71	2,680	2.28
2007	7,230	1.27	249	77	2,690	2.55
2008	7,040	1.22	349	74	2,660	2.66
2009	5,320	1.11	208	80	1,750	1.73
2010	7,680	1.06	319	76	2,300	1.73

Source: US Geological Survey.

14.2 Descriptive Analysis: Exponential Smoothing

As you have seen in the previous section, index numbers are useful for describing trends and changes in time series. However, time series often have such irregular fluctuations that trends are difficult to describe. Index numbers can be misleading in such cases because the series is changing so rapidly. Methods for removing the rapid fluctuations in a time series so the general trend can be seen are called *smoothing* techniques.

Exponential smoothing is one type of weighted average that assigns positive weights to past and current values of the time series. A single weight, w, called the **exponential smoothing constant,** is selected so that w is between 0 and 1. Then the exponentially smoothed series, E_t, is calculated as follows:

$$E_1 = Y_1$$
$$E_2 = wY_2 + (1 - w)E_1$$
$$E_3 = wY_3 + (1 - w)E_2$$
$$\vdots$$
$$E_t = wY_t + (1 - w)E_{t-1}$$

Thus, the exponentially smoothed value at time t assigns the weight w to the current series value and the weight $(1 - w)$ to the previous smoothed value.

For example, consider the silver price time series in Table 14.1 (p. 14-3). Suppose we want to calculate the exponentially smoothed series for the years 1982 through 2011 using a smoothing constant of $w = .3$. The calculations proceed as follows:

$$E_{1982} = Y_{1982} = 7.92$$
$$E_{1983} = .3Y_{1983} + (1 - .3)E_{1982} = .3(11.43) + .7(7.92) = 8.97$$
$$E_{1984} = .3Y_{1984} + (1 - .3)E_{1983} = .3(8.14) + .7(8.97) = 8.72$$
$$\vdots$$
$$E_{2011} = .3Y_{2011} + (1 - .3)E_{2010} = .3(35.11) + .7(14.54) = 20.71$$

All the exponentially smoothed values corresponding to $w = .3$ are given in the Minitab worksheet, Figure 14.5. (*Note:* Minitab gives the value of E_t in row $t + 1$.)

The actual silver prices and exponentially smoothed prices are graphed in Figure 14.6. Like many averages, the exponentially smoothed series changes less rapidly than the time series itself. The choice of w affects the smoothness of E_t. The smaller (closer to 0) is the value of w, the smoother is E_t. Because small values of w give more weight to the past values of the time series, the smoothed series is not affected by rapid changes in the current values and, therefore, appears smoother than the original series. Conversely, choosing w near 1 yields an exponentially smoothed series that is much like the original series—that is, large values of w give more weight to the current value of the time series, so the smoothed series looks like the original series. This concept is illustrated in Figure 14.7. The steps for calculating an exponentially smoothed series are given in the box on the next page.

SILVER2.MTP ***

	C1	C2	C3
↓	YEAR	PRICE	SMOOTH3
1	1982	7.92	7.9200
2	1983	11.43	8.9730
3	1984	8.14	8.7231
4	1985	6.13	7.9452
5	1986	5.46	7.1996
6	1987	7.02	7.1457
7	1988	6.53	6.9610
8	1989	5.50	6.5227
9	1990	4.83	6.0149
10	1991	4.06	5.4284
11	1992	3.95	4.9849
12	1993	4.31	4.7824
13	1994	5.29	4.9347
14	1995	5.20	5.0143
15	1996	5.20	5.0700
16	1997	4.90	5.0190
17	1998	5.54	5.1753
18	1999	5.22	5.1887
19	2000	4.95	5.1171
20	2001	4.37	4.8930
21	2002	4.60	4.8051
22	2003	4.85	4.8186
23	2004	6.65	5.3680
24	2005	7.22	5.9236
25	2006	11.57	7.6175
26	2007	13.39	9.3493
27	2008	15.02	11.0505
28	2009	14.66	12.1333
29	2010	20.16	14.5413
30	2011	35.11	20.7119

Figure 14.5

Minitab worksheet with exponentially smoothed ($w = .3$) silver prices

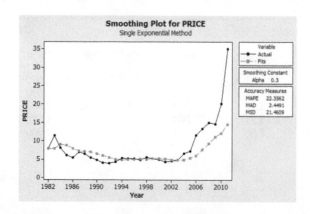

Figure 14.6

Minitab graph of exponentially smoothed ($w = .3$) silver prices

Figure 14.7

Minitab graph of exponentially smoothed ($w = .3$ and $w = .7$) silver prices

---

Steps for Calculating an Exponentially Smoothed Series

1. Select an exponential smoothing constant, w, between 0 and 1. Remember that small values of w give less weight to the current value of the series and yield a smoother series. Larger choices of w assign more weight to the current value of the series and yield a more variable series.

2. Calculate the exponentially smoothed series E_t from the original time series Y_t as follows:

$$E_1 = Y_1$$
$$E_2 = wY_2 + (1 - w)E_1$$
$$E_3 = wY_3 + (1 - w)E_2$$
$$\vdots$$
$$E_t = wY_t + (1 - w)E_{t-1}$$

Example 14.4

Exponential Smoothing— Annual Sales Revenue

Problem Annual sales data (recorded in thousands of dollars) for a firm's first 35 years of operation are provided in Table 14.5. Create an exponentially smoothed series for the sales time series using $w = .7$ and plot both series.

Table 14.5	A Firm's Annual Sales Revenues ($ thousands)		
Year	Sales Revenue	Year	Sales Revenue
1	5.8	19	103.2
2	4.0	20	85.4
3	5.5	21	86.2
4	15.6	22	89.9
5	25.1	23	89.2
6	20.3	24	99.1
7	31.4	25	100.3
8	48.0	26	111.7
9	46.1	27	102.2
10	35.9	28	115.5
11	35.5	29	119.2
12	53.5	30	125.2
13	48.4	31	136.3
14	61.6	32	146.8
15	65.6	33	150.1
16	71.4	34	151.4
17	83.4	35	150.9
18	93.6		

Data Set: SALE35

SALES35.MTW ***

↓	C1	C2	C3
	T	SALES	EXP7
1	1	5.8	5.800
2	2	4.0	4.540
3	3	5.5	5.212
4	4	15.6	12.484
5	5	25.1	21.315
6	6	20.3	20.605
7	7	31.4	28.161
8	8	48.0	42.048
9	9	46.1	44.885
10	10	35.9	38.595
11	11	35.5	36.429
12	12	53.5	48.379
13	13	48.4	48.394
14	14	61.6	57.638
15	15	65.6	63.211
16	16	71.4	68.943
17	17	83.4	79.063
18	18	93.6	89.239
19	19	103.2	99.012
20	20	85.4	89.484
21	21	86.2	87.185
22	22	89.9	89.086
23	23	89.2	89.166
24	24	99.1	96.120
25	25	100.3	99.046
26	26	111.7	107.904
27	27	102.2	103.911
28	28	115.5	112.023
29	29	119.2	117.047
30	30	125.2	122.754
31	31	136.3	132.236
32	32	146.8	142.431
33	33	150.1	147.799
34	34	151.4	150.320
35	35	150.9	150.726

Figure 14.8

Minitab worksheet with exponentially smoothed ($w = .7$) sales revenues

Solution To find the exponentially smoothed series with $w = .7$, we calculate

$$E_1 = Y_1 = 5.8$$
$$E_2 = wY_2 + (1 - w)E_1 = .7(4.0) + .3(5.8) = 4.54$$
$$E_3 = wY_3 + (1 - w)E_2 = .7(5.5) + .3(4.54) = 5.21$$

etc.

We obtained the exponentially smoothed values for all 35 years using Minitab. The values are shown on the Minitab worksheet, Figure 14.8, in the column labeled *EXP7*. A plot of the original time series and exponentially smoothed series is shown in the Minitab graph, Figure 14.9. You can see that the smoothed series provides a good picture of the general trend of the original series. Note, too, that the exponentially smoothed series is less sensitive to short-term deviations of the sales revenues from the trend that occurred in years 10, 11, and 19.

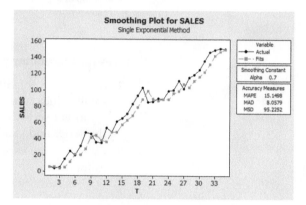

Figure 14.9

Minitab graph of exponentially smoothed ($w = .7$) sales revenues

Look Back If you desire a less variable exponentially smoothed series, then select a smoothing constant closer to 0 (e.g., $w = .5$ or $w = .2$).

■ **Now Work Exercise 14.16**

One of the primary uses of exponential smoothing is to forecast future values of a time series. Because only current and past values of the time series are used in exponential smoothing, it is easily adapted to forecasting. We demonstrate this application of exponentially smoothed series in Section 14.4.

Exercises 14.15–14.22

Learning the Mechanics

14.15 Describe the effect of selecting an exponential constant of $w = .2$. Of $w = .8$. Which will produce a smoother trend?

14.16 A monthly time series is shown in the table to the right.
L14016
NW
  a. Calculate the missing values in the exponentially smoothed series using $w = .5$.
  b. Graph the time series and the exponentially smoothed series on the same graph.

Applying the Concepts—Basic

14.17 Annual U.S. beer production. Refer to the annual U.S. beer production time series, Exercise 14.7 (p. 14-10).
USBEER
  a. Calculate the exponentially smoothed series for U.S. beer production for the period 1980–2010 using $w = .2$.
  b. Calculate the exponentially smoothed series using $w = .8$.

Month	t	Y_t	Exponentially Smoothed Series ($w = .5$)
Jan	1	280	—
Feb	2	281	—
Mar	3	250	265.3
Apr	4	246	255.6
May	5	239	—
Jun	6	218	—
Jul	7	218	—
Aug	8	210	—
Sep	9	205	—
Oct	10	206	—
Nov	11	200	—
Dec	12	200	—

  c. Plot the two exponentially smoothed series ($w = .2$ and $w = .8$) on the same graph. Which smoothed series best portrays the long-term trend?

14.18 Foreign fish production. Overfishing and pollution of U.S. coastal waters have resulted in an increased dependence FFTONS by the United States on the fishing grounds of other countries. The table below describes the annual fish catch (in thousands of metric tons) in all fishing areas of Peru and Chile for the years 2000 to 2008.

Year	Chile	Peru
2000	4,692	10,665
2001	4,363	7,990
2002	4,817	8,775
2003	4,176	6,100
2004	5,584	9,627
2005	5,029	9,416
2006	4,971	7,046
2007	4,636	7,250
2008	4,398	7,406

Source: United States Census Bureau.

a. Compute an exponentially smoothed series for both Chile and Peru, using a smoothing coefficient of $w = .5$.

b. Plot both actual series and both smoothed series on the same graph. Describe the differences in variation of catches over time between the two countries. For example, do they move up and down together over time?

Applying the Concepts—Intermediate

14.19 Yearly price of gold. The price of gold is used by some financial analysts as a barometer of investors' expectations GOLDYR of inflation, with the price of gold tending to increase as concerns about inflation increase. The table below shows the average annual price of gold (in dollars per ounce) from 1990 through 2011.

Year	Price	Year	Price
1990	384	2001	271
1991	362	2002	310
1992	344	2003	363
1993	360	2004	410
1994	384	2005	445
1995	384	2006	603
1996	388	2007	695
1997	331	2008	872
1998	294	2009	972
1999	279	2010	1,225
2000	279	2011	1,572

Source: Data from the London Bullion Market Association (LMBA). Copyright © 2012 by the World Gold Council. Reprinted with permission. www.kitco.com.

a. Compute an exponentially smoothed series for the gold price time series for the period from 1990 to 2011, using a smoothing coefficient of $w = .8$.

b. Plot the original series and the exponentially smoothed series on the same graph. Comment on the trend observed.

14.20 Personal consumption in transportation. There has been phenomenal growth in the transportation sector of the economy TRNEXP since 1990. The personal consumption expenditure figures (in billions of dollars) are given in the table in the next column.

a. Compute exponentially smoothed values of this personal consumption time series, using the smoothing constants $w = .2$ and $w = .8$.

b. Plot the actual series and the two smoothed series on the same graph. Comment on the trend in personal consumption expenditure on transportation in the 2000s as compared to the 1990s.

Year	Expenditure on Transportation
1990	593.6
1991	553.2
1992	585.1
1993	611.4
1994	646.3
1995	658.6
1996	690.8
1997	730.7
1998	781.3
1999	832.1
2000	853.5
2001	872.1
2002	891.1
2003	913.0
2004	926.3
2005	905.9
2006	922.1
2007	925.2
2008	1,033.5
2009	890.7

Source: U.S. Census Bureau. *Statistical Abstract of the United States,* 2012.

14.21 OPEC crude oil imports. The data in the table below are the amounts of crude oil (millions of barrels) imported OPEC into the United States from the Organization of Petroleum Exporting Countries (OPEC) for the years 1990–2010.

Year	t	Imports, Y_t
1990	1	1,283
1991	2	1,233
1992	3	1,247
1993	4	1,339
1994	5	1,307
1995	6	1,219
1996	7	1,258
1997	8	1,378
1998	9	1,522
1999	10	1,543
2000	11	1,659
2001	12	1,770
2002	13	1,490
2003	14	1,671
2004	15	1,948
2005	16	1,738
2006	17	1,745
2007	18	1,969
2008	19	1,984
2009	20	1,594
2010	21	1,654

Source: United States Census Bureau.

a. Construct two exponentially smoothed series for this time series, using $w = .1$ and $w = .9$.

b. Plot the original series and the two smoothed series on the same graph. Which smoothed series looks more like the original series? Why?

14.22 S&P 500 Stock Index. Standard & Poor's 500 Composite Stock Index (S&P 500) is a stock market index. Like the Dow Jones Industrial Average, it is an indicator of stock market activity. The data in the table are end-of-quarter values of the S&P 500 for the years 2004–2011.

SP500

a. Calculate and plot the exponentially smoothed series for the quarterly S&P 500 using a smoothing constant of $w = .3$.

b. Repeat part a but use $w = .7$.

c. Which exponentially smoothed series do you prefer for describing trends in the series? Explain.

Year	Quarter	S&P 500	Year	Quarter	S&P 500
2004	1	1,126.2	2008	1	1,322.7
	2	1,140.8		2	1,280.0
	3	1,114.6		3	1,164.7
	4	1,211.9		4	903.3
2005	1	1,180.6	2009	1	797.9
	2	1,191.3		2	919.3
	3	1,228.8		3	1,057.1
	4	1,248.3		4	1,115.1
2006	1	1,294.9	2010	1	1,169.4
	2	1,270.2		2	1,030.7
	3	1,335.8		3	1,141.2
	4	1,418.3		4	1,257.6
2007	1	1,420.9	2011	1	1,325.8
	2	1,503.3		2	1,320.6
	3	1,526.7		3	1,131.4
	4	1,468.4		4	1,257.6

Source: Standard & Poor's.

14.3 Time Series Components

In the previous two sections, we showed how to use various *descriptive* techniques to obtain a picture of the behavior of a time series. Now we want to expand our coverage to include techniques that will let us make statistical inferences about the time series. These *inferential techniques* are generally focused on the problem of *forecasting* future values of the time series.

Before forecasts of future values of a time series can be made, some type of model that can be projected into the future must be used to describe the series. Time series models range in complexity from **descriptive models,** such as the exponential smoothing models discussed in the previous section, to **inferential models,** such as the combinations of regression and specialized time series models to be discussed later in this chapter. Whether the model is simple or complex, the objective is the same: to produce accurate forecasts of future values of the time series.

Many different algebraic representations of time series models have been proposed. One of the most widely used is an **additive model*** of the form

$$Y_t = T_t + C_t + S_t + R_t$$

The **secular trend,** T_t, also known as the **long-term trend,** is a time series component that describes the long-term movements of Y_t. For example, if you want to characterize the secular trend of the production of automobiles since 1930, you would show T_t as an upward-moving time series over the period from 1930 to the present. This does not imply that the automobile production series has always moved upward from month to month and from year to year, but it does mean the long-term trend has been an increase over that period of time.

The **cyclical effect,** C_t, generally describes fluctuations of the time series about the secular trend that are attributable to business and economic conditions. For example, refer back to the monthly closing prices of three high-technology stocks for 2011, Table 14.2 (p. 14-5). Recall that a plot of the simple composite index (Figure 14.4) showed a generally decreasing secular trend. However, during periods of recession, the index tends to lie below the secular trend, while in times of general economic expansion, it lies above the long-term trend line.

---

*Another useful form is the *multiplicative model:* $Y_t = T_t C_t S_t R_t$. This can be changed to an additive form by taking natural logarithms (i.e., $\ln Y_t = \ln T_t + \ln C_t + \ln S_t + \ln R_t$). See Section 14.8.

The **seasonal effect,** S_t, describes the fluctuations in the time series that recur during specific time periods. For example, quarterly power loads for a Florida utility company tend to be highest in the summer months (Quarter III), with another, smaller peak in the winter months (Quarter I). The spring and fall (Quarters II and IV) seasonal effects are negative, meaning that the series tends to lie below the long-term trend line during those quarters.

The **residual effect,** R_t, is what remains of Y_t after the secular, cyclical, and seasonal components have been removed. Part of the residual effect may be attributable to unpredictable rare events (earthquake, presidential assassination, etc.) and part to the randomness of human actions. In any case, the presence of the residual component makes it impossible to forecast the future values of a time series without error. Thus, the presence of the residual effect emphasizes a point we first made in Chapter 11 in connection with regression models: No business phenomena should be described by deterministic models. All realistic business models, time series or otherwise, should include a residual component.

Each of the four components contributes to the determination of the value of Y_t at each time period. Although it will not always be possible to characterize each component separately, the component model provides a useful theoretical formulation that helps the time series analyst achieve a better understanding of the phenomena affecting the path followed by the time series.

14.4 Forecasting: Exponential Smoothing

In Section 14.2, we discussed exponential smoothing as a method for describing a time series that involves removing the irregular fluctuations. In terms of the time series components discussed in the previous section, exponential smoothing tends to de-emphasize (or "smooth") most of the residual effects. This, coupled with the fact that exponential smoothing uses only past and current values of the series, makes it a useful tool for forecasting time series.

Recall that the formula for exponential smoothing is

$$E_t = wY_t + (1 - w)E_{t-1}$$

where w, the *exponential smoothing constant*, is a number between 0 and 1. We learned that the selection of w controls the smoothness of E_t. A choice near 0 places more emphasis (weight) on *past* values of the time series and therefore yields a smoother series; a choice near 1 gives more weight to *current* values of the series.

Suppose the objective is to forecast the next value of the time series, Y_{t+1}. The **exponentially smoothed forecast** for Y_{t+1} is simply the smoothed value at time t:

$$F_{t+1} = E_t$$

where F_{t+1} is the **forecast** of Y_{t+1}. To help interpret this forecast formula, substitute the smoothing formula for E_t:

$$F_{t+1} = E_t = wY_t + (1 - w)E_{t-1}$$
$$= wY_t + (1 - w)F_t$$
$$= F_t + w(Y_t - F_t)$$

Note that we have substituted F_t for E_{t-1} because the forecast for time t is the smoothed value for time $(t - 1)$. The final equation provides insight into the exponential smoothing forecast: The forecast for time $(t + 1)$ is equal to the forecast for time t, F_t, plus a correction for the error in the forecast for time t, $(Y_t - F_t)$. This is why the exponentially smoothed forecast is called an **adaptive forecast**—the forecast for time $(t + 1)$ is explicitly adapted for the error in the forecast for time t.

Because exponential smoothing consists of averaging past and present values, the smoothed values will tend to lag behind the series when a long-term trend exists. In addition, the averaging tends to smooth any seasonal component. Therefore, exponentially smoothed forecasts are appropriate only when the trend and seasonal components are relatively insignificant. Because the exponential smoothing model assumes that the time series has little or no trend or seasonal component, the forecast F_{t+1} is used to forecast not only Y_{t+1}, but also all future values of Y_{t+1}, that is, the forecast for two time periods ahead is

$$F_{t+2} = F_{t+1}$$

and for three time periods ahead is

$$F_{t+3} = F_{t+2} = F_{t+1}$$

The exponential smoothing forecasting technique is summarized in the next box.

Calculation of Exponentially Smoothed Forecasts

1. Given the observed time series $Y_1, Y_2, \ldots, Y_t$, first calculate the exponentially smoothed values $E_1, E_2, \ldots, E_t$, using

$$E_1 = Y_1$$
$$E_2 = wY_2 + (1 - w)E_1$$
$$\vdots$$
$$E_t = wY_t + (1 - w)E_{t-1}$$

2. Use the last smoothed value to forecast the next time series value:

$$F_{t+1} = E_t$$

3. Assuming that Y_t is relatively free of trend and seasonal components, use the same forecast for all future values of Y_t:

$$F_{t+2} = F_{t+1}$$
$$F_{t+3} = F_{t+1}$$
$$\vdots$$

Two important points must be made about exponentially smoothed forecasts:

1. The choice of w is crucial. If you decide that w will be small (near 0), you will obtain a smooth, slowly changing series of forecasts. On the other hand, the selection of a large value of w (near 1) will yield more rapidly changing forecasts that depend mostly on the current values of the series. In general, several values of w should be tried to determine how sensitive the forecast series is to the choice of w. Forecasting experience will provide the best basis for the choice of w for a particular application.

2. The farther into the future you forecast, the less certain you can be of accuracy. Because the exponentially smoothed forecast is constant for all future values, any changes in trend or seasonality are not taken into account. However, the uncertainty associated with future forecasts applies not only to exponentially smoothed forecasts but also to all methods of forecasting. In general, time series forecasting should be confined to the short term.

Example	14.5

Forecasting with Exponential Smoothing— Sales Revenue

Problem Refer to Example 14.4 (p. 14-13). The annual sales data (recorded in thousands of dollars) for a firm's first 35 years of operation are reproduced in the Minitab worksheet, Figure 14.10. Apply the exponential smoothing technique to the data for years 1 to 32 in order to forecast sales revenue in years 33, 34, and 35. Make forecasts using both $w = .3$ and $w = .7$ and compare the results.

↓	C1	C2	C3	C4
	T	SALES	EXP3	EXP7
1	1	5.8	5.800	5.800
2	2	4.0	5.260	4.540
3	3	5.5	5.332	5.212
4	4	15.6	8.412	12.484
5	5	25.1	13.419	21.315
6	6	20.3	15.483	20.605
7	7	31.4	20.258	28.161
8	8	48.0	28.581	42.048
9	9	46.1	33.836	44.885
10	10	35.9	34.456	38.595
11	11	35.5	34.769	36.429
12	12	53.5	40.388	48.379
13	13	48.4	42.792	48.394
14	14	61.6	48.434	57.638
15	15	65.6	53.584	63.211
16	16	71.4	58.929	68.943
17	17	83.4	66.270	79.063
18	18	93.6	74.469	89.239
19	19	103.2	83.088	99.012
20	20	85.4	83.782	89.484
21	21	86.2	84.507	87.185
22	22	89.9	86.125	89.086
23	23	89.2	87.048	89.166
24	24	99.1	90.663	96.120
25	25	100.3	93.554	99.046
26	26	111.7	98.998	107.904
27	27	102.2	99.959	103.911
28	28	115.5	104.621	112.023
29	29	119.2	108.995	117.047
30	30	125.2	113.856	122.754
31	31	136.3	120.589	132.236
32	32	146.8	128.453	142.431

Figure 14.10

Minitab worksheet with actual and exponentially smoothed ($w = .3$ and $w = .7$) sales revenues, years 1–32

Solution First, we used Minitab to calculate the exponentially smoothed series for years 1–32 using both $w = .3$ and $w = .7$. These smoothed values are shown in Figure 14.10 in the columns labeled *EXP3* and *EXP7*, respectively.

Now, the forecast for year 33 is simply the smoothed sales revenue value in the last year of the smoothed series, year 32. Consequently, we have

$$F_{33} = E_{32} = 128.45 \text{ for } w = .3 \quad \text{(values highlighted on Figure 14.10)}$$
$$142.43 \text{ for } w = .7$$

With exponential smoothing, the same forecasts are made for any future year. Thus, we have

$$F_{34} = E_{32} = 128.45 \text{ for } w = .3$$
$$142.43 \text{ for } w = .7$$

and

$$F_{35} = E_{32} = 128.45 \text{ for } w = .3$$
$$142.43 \text{ for } w = .7$$

Both sets of forecasts are shown in Table 14.6. Also shown are the actual sales revenue values and corresponding forecast errors for years 33–35. The **forecast error** is defined as the actual value minus the forecast value, i.e.,

$$\text{Forecast error} = (\text{Actual} - \text{Forecast})$$

Table 14.6		Sales Revenues (Years 33–35): Actual vs. Forecast Values			
Year	Actual	Forecast ($w = .3$)	Forecast Error	Forecast ($w = .7$)	Forecast Error
33	150.1	128.45	21.65	142.43	7.67
34	151.4	128.45	22.95	142.43	8.97
35	150.9	128.45	22.45	142.43	8.47

You can see that the forecast errors using $w = .7$ are considerably smaller than the forecast errors for $w = .3$. Consequently, future forecasts of the sales revenue time series will likely have a smaller forecast error when a smoothing constant of .7 is employed.

Look Back Note that both the $w = .3$ and $w = .7$ forecasts underestimate the sales revenues for years 33–35. This is because exponentially smoothed forecasts implicitly assume no trend exists in the time series. This example illustrates the risk associated with anything other than very short-term forecasting.

◾ Now Work Exercise 14.25a

Many time series have long-term, or secular, trends. For such series, the exponentially smoothed forecast is inappropriate for all but the very short term. In the next section, we present an extension of the exponentially smoothed forecast—*Holt's method*—that allows for secular trend in the forecasts.

14.5 Forecasting Trends: Holt's Method

The exponentially smoothed forecasts for the sales revenue values in the previous section have large forecast errors, in part because they do not recognize the trend in the time series. In this section, we present an extension of the exponential smoothing method of forecasting that explicitly recognizes the trend in a time series. The **Holt forecasting model** consists of both an exponentially smoothed component (E_t) and a trend component (T_t).* The trend component is used in the calculation of the exponentially smoothed value. The following equations show that both E_t and T_t are weighted averages:

$$E_t = wY_t + (1 - w)(E_{t-1} + T_{t-1})$$
$$T_t = v(E_t - E_{t-1}) + (1 - v)T_{t-1}$$

Note that the equations require *two* smoothing constants, w and v, each of which is between 0 and 1. As before, w controls the smoothness of E_t; a choice near 0 places more emphasis on past values of the time series, while a value of w near 1 gives more weight to current values of the series and de-emphasizes the past.

The trend component of the series is estimated *adaptively,* using a weighted average of the most recent change in the level, represented by ($E_t - E_{t-1}$), and the trend estimate, represented by T_{t-1}, from the previous period. A choice of the weight v near 0 places more emphasis on the past estimates of trend, while a choice of v near 1 gives more weight to the current change in level.

The calculation of the components for Holt's model, which proceeds much like the exponential smoothing calculations, is summarized in the box.

Steps for Calculating Components of the Holt Forecasting Model

1. Select an exponential smoothing constant w between 0 and 1. Small values of w give less weight to the current values of the time series and more weight to the past. Larger choices assign more weight to the current value of the series.

---

*In some statistical sofware packages (e.g., Minitab), Holt's method is called *double exponential smoothing.*

2. Select a trend smoothing constant v between 0 and 1. Small values of v give less weight to the current changes in the level of the series and more weight to the past trend. Larger values assign more weight to the most recent trend of the series and less to past trends.

3. Calculate the two components, E_t and T_t, from the time series Y_t beginning at time $t = 2$ as follows:*

$$E_2 = Y_2$$
$$T_2 = Y_2 - Y_1$$
$$E_3 = wY_3 + (1 - w)(E_2 + T_2)$$
$$T_3 = v(E_3 - E_2) + (1 - v)T_2$$
$$\vdots$$
$$E_t = wY_t + (1 - w)(E_{t-1} + T_{t-1})$$
$$T_t = v(E_t - E_{t-1}) + (1 - v)T_{t-1}$$

[*Note:* E_1 and T_1 are not defined.]

Example	14.6

Applying Holt's Smoothing Method—Annual Sales Data

Problem Refer to the yearly sales data, Example 14.4 (p. 14-13). Using $w = .7$ and $v = .5$, apply Holt's smoothing method to the data for years 1 through 30. Give the values of the smoothed and trend components each year, then plot the data and the smoothing component, E_t, on the same graph.

Solution We used Minitab to perform Holt's calculations and generate the values of E_t and T_t for the annual series. The E_t and T_t values for each year are listed under the *SMOOTH* and *TREND* columns, respectively, on the Minitab worksheet, Figure 14.11.

↓	C1	C2	C3	C4
	T	SALES	SMOOTH	TREND
1	1	5.8	5.800	4.14658
2	2	4.0	5.784	2.06525
3	3	5.5	6.205	1.24302
4	4	15.6	13.154	4.09629
5	5	25.1	22.745	6.84357
6	6	20.3	23.087	3.59251
7	7	31.4	29.984	5.24481
8	8	48.0	44.169	9.71482
9	9	46.1	48.435	6.99063
10	10	35.9	41.758	0.15666
11	11	35.5	37.424	-2.08837
12	12	53.5	48.051	4.26906
13	13	48.4	49.576	2.89711
14	14	61.6	58.862	6.09154
15	15	65.6	65.406	6.31783
16	16	71.4	71.497	6.20448
17	17	83.4	81.690	8.19890
18	18	93.6	92.487	9.49762
19	19	103.2	102.835	9.92306
20	20	85.4	93.608	0.34763
21	21	86.2	88.527	-2.36667
22	22	89.9	88.778	-1.05763
23	23	89.2	88.756	-0.53974
24	24	99.1	95.835	3.26953
25	25	100.3	99.941	3.68798
26	26	111.7	109.279	6.51272
27	27	102.2	106.277	1.75569
28	28	115.5	113.260	4.36909
29	29	119.2	118.729	4.91893
30	30	125.2	124.734	5.46225

Figure 14.11

Minitab worksheet with actual and Holt's smoothed ($w = .7$ and $v = .5$) sales revenues, years 1–30

*The calculation begins at time $t = 2$ rather than at $t = 1$ because the first two observations are needed to obtain the first estimate of trend, T_2. As an option, some statistical software packages use simple linear regression to estimate E_1 and T_1; for the model $E(Y_t) = \beta_0 + \beta_1 t$, $E_1 = \hat{\beta}_0$ and $T_1 = \hat{\beta}_1$.

A graph of Y_t and E_t is shown in Figure 14.12. Note that the trend component T_t measures the general upward trend in Y_t.*

Figure 14.12

Minitab graph of Holt's smoothed ($w = .7$ and $v = .5$) sales data

Look Back The choice of $v = .5$ gives equal weight to the most recent trend and to past trends in the sales of the firm. The result is that the exponential smoothing component, E_t, provides a smooth, upward-trending description of the firm's sales.

Our objective is to use Holt's exponentially smoothed series to forecast the future values of the time series. For the one-step-ahead forecast, this is accomplished by adding the most recent exponentially smoothed component to the most recent trend component—that is, the forecast at time $(t + 1)$, given observed values up to time t, is

$$F_{t+1} = E_t + T_t$$

The idea is that we are constructing the forecast by combining the most recent smoothed estimate, E_t, with the estimate of the expected increase (or decrease) attributable to trend, T_t.

The forecast for two steps ahead is similar, except that we add estimated trend for *two* periods:

$$F_{t+2} = E_t + 2T_t$$

Similarly, for the k-step-ahead forecast, we add the estimated increase (or decrease) in trend over k periods:

$$F_{t+k} = E_t + kT_t$$

Holt's forecasting methodology is summarized in the box.

Holt's Forecasting Methodology

1. Calculate the exponentially smoothed and trend components, E_t and T_t, for each observed value of $Y_t (t \geq 2)$ using the formulas given in the previous box.

2. Calculate the one-step-ahead forecast using

$$F_{t+1} = E_t + T_t$$

3. Calculate the k-step-ahead forecast using

$$F_{t+k} = E_t + kT_t$$

---

*Minitab uses simple linear regression to calculate the initial smoothed and trend values. See the footnote on page 14-21.

Example	14.7

Forecasting with Holt's Method—Annual Sales

Problem Refer to Example 14.6 and Figure 14.11, which lists the sales revenue for years 1–30 along with Holt's smoothing components using $w = .7$ and $v = .5$. Apply Holt's forecasting methodology to forecast the firm's annual sales in years 31–35. Compute the forecast errors for each of these five years.

Solution From Figure 14.11 the smoothed and trend values (highlighted) for the last year (year 30) are $E_{30} = 124.73$ and $T_{30} = 5.46$. Consequently, the forecast for year 31 (the 1-year-ahead forecast) is

$$F_{31} = E_{30} + T_{30} = 124.73 + 5.46 = 130.19$$

The forecast 2 years ahead is

$$F_{32} = E_{30} + 2T_{30} = 124.73 + 2(5.46) = 135.65$$

For years 33–35 we find

$$F_{33} = E_{30} + 3T_{30} = 124.73 + 3(5.46) = 141.11$$
$$F_{34} = E_{30} + 4T_{30} = 124.73 + 4(5.46) = 146.57$$
$$F_{35} = E_{30} + 5T_{30} = 124.73 + 5(5.46) = 152.03$$

The forecasts and forecast errors for these five years are shown in Table 14.7. Note that unlike the constant exponential smoothing forecasts, Holt's forecast values increase from year 31 to year 35. This upward trend in the forecast is a result of Holt's estimated trend component. Note, also, that the forecast errors fluctuate in magnitude and in sign. This is due to the fact that the actual time series value (sales revenue) does not necessarily increase at the same rate as Holt's forecasted values.

Table 14.7	Sales Revenues (Years 31–35): Actual vs. Forecast Values		
Year	Actual	Forecast ($w = .7$, $v = .5$)	Forecast Error
31	136.3	130.19	6.11
32	146.8	135.65	11.15
33	150.1	141.11	8.99
34	151.4	146.57	4.83
35	150.9	152.03	−1.13

Look Back The selection of $w = .7$ and $v = .5$ as the smoothing and trend weights for the sales forecasts was based on the objectives of assigning more weight to recent series values in the exponentially smoothed component and of assigning equal weights to the recent and past trend estimates. Most forecasters will try several different combinations of weights when using Holt's forecasting model in order to assess the sensitivity of the forecasts to the choice of weights. The values of w and v that lead to the smallest forecast errors are typically used to make future forecasts.

■ **Now Work Exercise 14.25b**

In the following section, we demonstrate how to use the forecast errors to develop a single measure of forecast accuracy. These measures can then be used to compare and contrast different forecasting methodologies.

Exercises 14.23–14.31

Learning the Mechanics

14.23 How does the choice of the smoothing constant w impact an exponentially smoothed forecast?

14.24 Refer to Exercise 14.4 (p. 14-9). The table with the prices
NW for product A for the four quarters of last year is reproduced at right. Holt's smoothing method with $w = .2$ and $v = .6$ was applied to the data.

a. Find the missing trend value for Quarter 3.

Quarter	A	Smoothed Value	Trend
1	3.25	—	—
2	3.50	3.50	0.25
3	3.90	3.78	?
4	4.25	?	0.29

b. Find the missing smoothed value for Quarter 4.

c. Give the Holt's forecast for the price in Quarter 5.

Applying the Concepts—Basic

14.25 Annual U.S. beer production. Refer to Exercise 14.7 [NW] (p. 14-10) and the data on U.S. beer production (in millions of barrels) for the years 1980–2010.

USBEER **a.** Use the 1980–2007 values to forecast the 2008–2010 production, using simple exponential smoothing with $w = .3$. Repeat with $w = .7$.

b. Use Holt's model with $w = .7$ and $v = .3$ to forecast the 2008–2010 production. Repeat with $w = .3$ and $v = .7$.

14.26 Quarterly single-family housing starts. Refer to the quarterly housing start series, Exercise 14.8 (p. 14-10). Suppose HSTART you want to forecast the number of new housing starts in 2012 using data for 2010 and 2011.

a. Calculate the exponentially smoothed values for 2010 and 2011 using $w = .6$.

b. Plot the housing starts series and the exponentially smoothed series on the same graph.

c. Use the exponentially smoothed data from 2010–2011 to forecast the quarterly number of housing starts in 2012.

14.27 Consumer Price Index. The CPI measures the increase (or decrease) in the prices of goods and services relative to a CPI base year. The CPI for the years 1990–2010 (using 1984 as a base period) is shown in the table below.

a. Graph the time series. Do you detect a long-term trend?

b. Calculate and plot the exponentially smoothed series for the CPI using a smoothing constant of $w = .4$. Use the exponentially smoothed values to forecast the CPI in 2011.

c. Use Holt's forecasting model with trend to forecast the CPI in 2011. Use smoothing constants $w = .4$ and $v = .5$.

14.28 OPEC crude oil imports. Refer to the annual OPEC oil import data, Exercise 14.21 (p. 14-15).

OPEC **a.** Use the exponentially smoothed ($w = .9$) series you constructed in Exercise 14.21a to forecast OPEC oil imports in 2010.

b. Forecast OPEC oil imports in 2010 using the Holt's forecasting model with smoothing constants $w = .3$ and $v = .8$.

c. Calculate the errors of the forecasts, parts **a** and **b**. Which method yields the smallest forecast error?

Applying the Concepts—Intermediate

14.29 S&P 500 Stock Index. Refer to the quarterly Standard & Poor's 500 stock market index, Exercise 14.22 (p. 14-16).

SP500 **a.** Use exponential smoothing with $w = .7$ to smooth the series from 2004 through 2010. Then forecast the quarterly values in 2011 using *only* the information through the fourth quarter of 2010.

b. Repeat part **a** using $w = .3$.

14.30 S&P 500 Stock Index (cont'd). Refer to Exercise 14.29. Suppose you want to use only the 2009–2010 S&P values to forecast the quarterly 2011 values. Calculate the forecasts using Holt's model with $w = .3$ and $v = .5$. Repeat with $w = .7$ and $v = .5$.

14.31 Monthly gold prices. The fluctuation of gold prices is a reflection of the strength or weakness of the U.S. dollar. The GOLDMN table below shows monthly gold prices from January 2005 to December 2011.

a. Use exponential smoothing with $w = .5$ to calculate monthly smoothed values from 2005 to 2010. Then forecast the monthly gold prices for 2011.

b. Calculate 12 one-step-ahead forecasts for 2011 by updating the exponentially smoothed values with each month's actual value and then forecasting the next month's value.

c. Repeat parts **a–b** using Holt's method with $w = .5$ and $v = .5$.

Year	CPI	Year	CPI
1990	125.8	2001	177.1
1991	129.1	2002	179.9
1992	132.8	2003	184.0
1993	136.8	2004	188.9
1994	147.8	2005	195.3
1995	152.4	2006	201.6
1996	156.9	2007	207.3
1997	160.5	2008	215.3
1998	163.0	2009	214.5
1999	166.6	2010	218.1
2000	171.5		

Source: US Department of Commerce.

Data for Exercise 14.31

Month	2005	2006	2007	2008	2009	2010	2011
Jan	424.2	549.9	631.2	889.6	858.7	1,118.0	1,356.4
Feb	423.4	555.0	664.7	922.3	943.2	1,095.4	1,372.7
Mar	434.2	557.1	654.9	968.4	924.3	1,113.3	1,424.0
Apr	428.9	610.6	679.4	909.7	890.2	1,148.7	1,473.8
May	421.9	676.5	666.9	888.7	928.6	1,205.4	1,510.4
Jun	430.7	596.2	655.5	889.5	945.7	1,232.9	1,528.7
Jul	424.5	633.8	665.3	939.8	934.2	1,193.0	1,572.8
Aug	437.9	632.6	665.4	839.0	949.4	1,215.8	1,755.8
Sep	456.0	598.2	712.7	829.9	996.6	1,271.1	1,771.9
Oct	469.9	585.8	754.6	806.6	1,043.2	1,342.0	1,665.2
Nov	476.7	627.8	806.3	760.9	1,127.0	1,369.9	1,739.0
Dec	509.8	629.8	803.2	816.1	1,134.7	1,390.6	1,652.3

Sources: Standard & Poor's.

14.6 Measuring Forecast Accuracy: MAD and RMSE

As demonstrated in Example 14.5, forecast error (i.e., the difference between the actual time series value and its forecast) can be used to evaluate the accuracy of the forecast. Knowledge of a forecast's accuracy aids in the selection of both the forecasting methodology to be utilized and the parameters of the forecast formula (e.g., the weights in the exponentially smoothed or Holt forecasts). Three popular measures of forecast accuracy, all based on forecast errors, are the *mean absolute deviation (MAD)*, the *mean absolute percentage error (MAPE)*, and the *root mean squared error (RMSE)* of the forecasts. Their formulas are given in the box.

Measures of Forecast Accuracy for *m* Forecasts

Assume time series data for $t = 1, 2, 3, \ldots, n$ are used to make forecasts for the periods $t = n + 1, n + 2, \ldots, n + m$.

1. **Mean absolute deviation (MAD)**

$$\text{MAD} = \frac{\sum_{t=n+1}^{n+m} |Y_t - F_t|}{m}$$

2. **Mean absolute percentage error (MAPE)**

$$\text{MAPE} = \frac{\sum_{t=n+1}^{n+m} \left| \frac{(Y_t - F_t)}{Y_t} \right|}{m} \times 100$$

3. **Root mean squared error (RMSE)**

$$\text{RMSE} = \sqrt{\frac{\sum_{t=n+1}^{n+m} (Y_t - F_t)^2}{m}}$$

Note that all three measures require one or more actual values of the time series against which to compare the forecasts. Thus, we can either wait several time periods until the observed values are available, or we can hold out several of the values at the end of the time series, not using them to model the time series, but saving them for evaluating the forecasts obtained from the model.

Example 14.8 **Comparing Measures of Forecast Accuracy— Annual Sales**	**Problem** Refer to the annual sales data of Examples 14.6 and 14.7 (pp. 14-21 and 14-23). We want to use the data for all 35 years to forecast annual sales for years 36–40. Consider three alternative forecasting models: exponential smoothing with $w = .3$, exponential smoothing with $w = .7$, and Holt's method with $w = .7$ and $v = .5$. Minitab was used to obtain the forecasts for these alternative models. The Minitab printouts shown in Figures 14.13a–c give the forecasts (highlighted) for all three models. Suppose the actual sales values (in thousands of dollars) for years 36–40 are 150.2, 161.7, 159.3, 168.5, and 170.4, respectively. Find measures of forecast accuracy (MAD, MAPE, and RMSE) for each of the three forecasting models and use this information to evaluate the models. **Solution** For ease of notation, we will number the forecasting models as follows. *Model 1:* Exponential smoothing ($w = .3$) *Model 2:* Exponential smoothing ($w = .7$) *Model 3:* Holt's method ($w = .7, v = .5$)

Single Exponential Smoothing for SALES

```
Data      SALES
Length    35

Smoothing Constant
Alpha   0.3

Accuracy Measures
MAPE    21.485
MAD     13.187
MSD    249.068

Forecasts
Period  Forecast    Lower    Upper
36       143.188   110.879  175.497
37       143.188   110.879  175.497
38       143.188   110.879  175.497
39       143.188   110.879  175.497
40       143.188   110.879  175.497
```

Figure 14.13a

Minitab forecasts of annual sales—exponential smoothing ($w = .3$)

Single Exponential Smoothing for SALES

```
Data      SALES
Length    35

Smoothing Constant
Alpha   0.7

Accuracy Measures
MAPE    15.1498
MAD      8.0579
MSD     95.2252

Forecasts
Period  Forecast    Lower    Upper
36       150.726   130.985  170.467
37       150.726   130.985  170.467
38       150.726   130.985  170.467
39       150.726   130.985  170.467
40       150.726   130.985  170.467
```

Figure 14.13b

Minitab forecasts of annual sales—exponential smoothing ($w = .7$)

Double Exponential Smoothing for SALES

```
Data      SALES
Length    35

Smoothing Constants
Alpha (level)  0.7
Gamma (trend)  0.5

Accuracy Measures
MAPE    19.3874
MAD      7.0010
MSD     81.4953

Forecasts
Period  Forecast    Lower    Upper
36       155.474   138.322  172.626
37       157.713   136.058  179.368
38       159.952   133.404  186.501
39       162.192   130.539  193.844
40       164.431   127.552  201.310
```

Figure 14.13c

Minitab forecasts of annual sales—Holt's method ($w = .7$ and $v = .5$)

The forecasts for the three models as well as forecast errors are listed in the Excel workbook, Figure 14.14. These forecast errors are used to find the MAD, MAPE, and RMSE measures of forecast accuracy for each of the three models.

For example, for Model 1:

$$\text{MAD}_1 = \frac{|7.01| + |18.51| + |16.11| + |25.31| + |27.21|}{5} = 18.83$$

$$\text{MAPE}_1 = \left\{ \frac{\left|\frac{7.01}{150.2}\right| + \left|\frac{18.51}{161.7}\right| + \left|\frac{16.11}{159.3}\right| + \left|\frac{25.31}{168.5}\right| + \left|\frac{27.21}{170.4}\right|}{5} \right\} \times 100 = 11.44$$

$$\text{RMSE}_1 = \sqrt{\frac{(7.01)^2 + (18.51)^2 + (16.11)^2 + (25.31)^2 + (27.21)^2}{5}} = 20.16$$

	A	B	C	D	E	F	G	H	I	J	K
1	T	SALES	MODEL 1	ERROR 1		MODEL 2	ERROR 2		MODEL 3	ERROR 3	
2	36	150.2	143.19	7.01		150.73	-0.53		155.47	-5.27	
3	37	161.7	143.19	18.51		150.73	10.97		157.71	3.99	
4	38	159.3	143.19	16.11		150.73	8.57		159.95	-0.65	
5	39	168.5	143.19	25.31		150.73	17.77		162.19	6.31	
6	40	170.4	143.19	27.21		150.73	19.67		164.43	5.97	
7											
8		MAD	18.83			11.50			4.44		
9		MAPE	11.44			6.92			2.73		
10		RMSE	20.16			13.39			4.89		
11											
12											

Figure 14.14

Excel workbook with measures of annual sales forecast accuracy

The formulas for MAD, MAPE, and RMSE were programmed into Excel. The results are shown (highlighted) in Figure 14.14. For Model 2, $MAD_2 = 11.50$, $MAPE_2 = 6.92$, and $RMSE_2 = 13.39$. For Model 3, $MAD_3 = 4.44$, $MAPE_3 = 2.73$, and $RMSE_3 = 4.89$.

You can see that Model 3 has the smallest MAD as well as the smallest MAPE and the smallest RMSE. Of the three forecasting models, then, Model 3 (Holt's method with $w = .7$ and $v = .5$) yields the most accurate predictions of future annual sales.

Look Back We expect Holt's method to yield more accurate forecasts for annual sales because it explicitly accounts for trends in the sales data. The exponential smoothing forecasts do not account for any increasing or decreasing trends in the data; hence, they are the same for all five forecasted years. The accuracy of all three forecasting methods, however, will decrease the further we forecast into the future.

■ **Now Work Exercise 14.32**

ETHICS in STATISTICS

Intentionally selecting time periods with small forecast errors and omitting time periods with large forecast errors in the calculations of MAPE, MAD, and RMSE for the purpose of evaluating forecast accuracy is considered *unethical statistical practice*.

[*Note*: Most statistical software packages will automatically compute the values of MAPE, MAD, and RMSE (equivalent to the square root of the *mean squared deviation, MSD*) for all n observations in the data set. For example, these statistics are shown in the middle of the Minitab printouts, Figures 14.13a–c.]

Criteria such as MAPE, MAD, and RMSE for assessing forecast accuracy require special care in interpretation. The number of time periods included in the evaluation is critical to the decision about which forecasting model is preferred. The choice depends on how many time periods ahead the analyst plans to forecast. With N time periods in your data, a good rule of thumb is to forecast ahead no more than $N/2$ time periods. Remember, however, that long-term forecasts are generally less accurate than short-term forecasts.

We conclude this section with a comment. A major disadvantage of forecasting with smoothing techniques (exponential smoothing or Holt's model) is that no measure of the forecast error (or reliability) is known *prior* to observing the future value. Although forecast errors can be calculated *after* the future values of the time series have been observed (as in Example 14.8), we prefer to have some measure of the accuracy of the forecast *before* the actual values are observed. One option is to compute forecasts and forecast errors for all n observations in the data set and use these "past" forecast errors to estimate the standard deviation of all forecast errors (i.e., the *standard error of the forecast*). A rough estimate of this standard error is the value of RMSE, and an approximate 95% prediction interval for any future forecast is

$$F_t \pm 2(\text{RMSE})$$

[An interval like this is shown at the bottom of the Minitab printouts, Figures 14.13a–c.] However, because the theoretical distributional properties of the forecast errors with smoothing methods (exponential smoothing or Holt's method) are unknown, many analysts regard smoothing methods as descriptive procedures rather than as inferential ones.

In the preceding chapters, we learned that predictions with inferential regression models are accompanied by well-known measures of reliability. The standard errors of the predicted values allow us to construct 95% prediction intervals. We discuss an inferential time series forecasting model in the next section.

Forecasting with Exponential Smoothing

Recall that a pharmaceutical company hired consultants at Rutgers University to forecast monthly sales of a new brand of cold medicine called Coldex. The company provided monthly data on Coldex sales for the first 2 years of the product's life and desires forecasts of sales for the first 3 months of the third year. (The data are saved in the **COLDEX** file.) One forecasting model considered by the consultants was an exponential smoothing model with a smoothing constant of $w = .7$. Minitab was used to find the smoothed values of the monthly series. The Minitab plot of both the actual monthly sales and smoothed sales values is shown in Figure SIA14.1, followed by the exponentially smoothed forecasts in Figure SIA14.2.

Figure SIA14.1

Minitab plot of monthly Coldex sales with exponentially smoothed values ($w = .7$)

The exponentially smoothed sales forecast for each of the first 3 months of year 3 is the smoothed value for the last month of the series (month 24). This value, highlighted on Figure SIA14.2, is 4,870 thousand dollars. Minitab also gives approximate 95% confidence bounds around the forecast. The interval (highlighted on the printout) is (1,750, 7,989). Thus, we are (approximately) 95% confident that the actual sales for the month will be between 1,750 and 7,989 thousand dollars. This wide interval was deemed unusable by the pharmaceutical company; consequently, the consultants searched for a better forecasting model. One of these models is presented in the next Statistics in Action Revisited (p. 14-31).

Single Exponential Smoothing for SALES

```
Data     SALES
Length   24


Smoothing Constant

Alpha  0.7


Accuracy Measures

MAPE       88
MAD      1273
MSD   2512726


Forecasts
```

Period	Forecast	Lower	Upper
25	4869.91	1750.49	7989.34
26	4869.91	1750.49	7989.34
27	4869.91	1750.49	7989.34

Figure SIA14.2

Minitab forecasts of monthly Coldex sales using exponential smoothing ($w = .7$)

Data Set: COLDEX

Exercises 14.32–14.37

Applying the Concepts—Basic

14.32 Annual U.S. beer production. Refer to the beer production forecasts, Exercise 14.25 (p. 14-24). In part **a** you obtained forecasts of 2008–2010 beer production using exponential smoothing with $w = .3$ and $w = .7$.

    a. Calculate the forecast errors for the $w = .3$ exponentially smoothed forecasts.

    b. Calculate the forecast errors for the $w = .7$ exponentially smoothed forecasts.

    c. Calculate MAD, MAPE, and RMSE for the exponential smoothing forecasts using $w = .3$.

    d. Calculate MAD, MAPE, and RMSE for the exponential smoothing forecasts using $w = .7$.

    e. Refer to parts **c** and **d.** Which forecast method do you recommend?

14.33 Annual U.S. beer production (cont'd). Refer to the beer production forecasts, Exercise 14.25 (p. 14-24). In part **b** you obtained forecasts of 2008–2010 beer production using Holt's method with $(w = .3, v = .7)$ and $(w = .7, v = .3)$.

    a. Calculate the forecast errors for the $w = .3, v = .7$ Holt forecasts.

    b. Calculate the forecast errors for the $w = .7, v = .3$ Holt forecasts.

    c. Calculate MAD, MAPE, and RMSE for the $w = .3, v = .7$ Holt forecasts.

    d. Calculate MAD, MAPE, and RMSE for the $w = .7, v = .3$ Holt forecasts.

    e. Refer to parts **c** and **d.** Which forecast method do you recommend?

14.34 S&P 500 Stock Index. Refer to your exponential smoothing forecasts of the quarterly S&P 500 for 2011, Exercise 14.29 (p. 14-24).

    a. Calculate MAD, MAPE, and RMSE for the forecasts with $w = .7$.

    b. Calculate MAD, MAPE, and RMSE for the forecasts with $w = .3$.

    c. Compare MAD, MAPE, and RMSE for the two simple exponential smoothing forecast models. Which model leads to more accurate forecasts?

14.35 S&P 500 Stock Index (cont'd). Refer to your Holt forecasts of the quarterly S&P 500 for 2011, Exercise 14.30 (p. 14-24).

    a. Calculate MAD, MAPE, and RMSE for the forecasts with $w = .3$ and $v = .5$.

    b. Calculate MAD, MAPE, and RMSE for the forecasts with $w = .7$ and $v = .5$.

    c. Compare MAD, MAPE, and RMSE for the two Holt forecasts models. Which model leads to more accurate forecasts?

Applying the Concepts—Intermediate

14.36 Monthly gold prices. Refer to the monthly gold prices, Exercise 14.31 (p. 14-24). Two models were used to forecast the monthly 2011 gold prices: an exponential smoothing model with $w = .5$ and a Holt model with $w = .5$ and $v = .5$.

    a. Use MAD, MAPE, and RMSE criteria to evaluate the two models' accuracy for forecasting the monthly 2011 values using the 2005–2010 data.

    b. Use the MAD, MAPE, and RMSE criteria to evaluate the two models' accuracy when making the 12 one-step-ahead forecasts, updating the models with each month's actual value before forecasting the next month's value.

14.37 U.S. school enrollments. The next table reports annual U.S. school enrollment (in thousands) for the period 1990–2010.

Year	Enrollment	Year	Enrollment
1990	60,267	2001	69,936
1991	61,605	2002	71,215
1992	62,686	2003	71,442
1993	63,241	2004	71,688
1994	63,986	2005	72,075
1995	64,764	2006	73,318
1996	65,743	2007	73,685
1997	66,470	2008	74,079
1998	66,983	2009	77,288
1999	67,667	2010	78,519
2000	68,146		

Source: United States Census Bureau.

    a. Use the 1990 to 2007 enrollments and simple exponential smoothing to forecast the 2008–2010 school enrollments. Use $w = .8$.

    b. Use Holt's method with $w = .8$ and $v = .7$ to forecast the 2008–2010 enrollments.

    c. Apply the MAD, MAPE, and RMSE criteria to evaluate the two forecasting models of parts **a** and **b.** Which model is better? Why?

14.7 Forecasting Trends: Simple Linear Regression

Perhaps the simplest **inferential forecasting model** is one with which you are familiar: the simple linear regression model. A straight-line model is used to relate the time series, Y_t, to time, t, and the least squares line is used to forecast future values of Y_t.

    Suppose a firm is interested in forecasting its sales revenues for each of the next 5 years. To make such forecasts and assess their reliability, a time series model must be constructed. Refer again to the yearly sales data for a firm's 35 years of operation

Figure 14.15

Minitab scatterplot of annual sales with least squares line

given in Table 14.5 (p. 14-13). A Minitab plot of the data (Figure 14.15) reveals a linearly increasing trend, so the model

$$E(Y_t) = \beta_0 + \beta_1 t$$

seems plausible for the secular trend. We fit the model to the data using SPSS; the resulting printout is shown in Figure 14.16. The least squares model (highlighted on the printout) is

$$\hat{Y}_t = \hat{\beta}_0 + \hat{\beta}_1 t = -.333 + 4.325t \quad \text{with} \quad R^2 = .969$$

(This least squares line is shown on Figure 14.15.)

We can now forecast sales for years 36–40. The forecasts of sales and the corresponding 95% prediction intervals are shown on the SPSS spreadsheet, Figure 14.17. For example, for $t = 36$, we have

$$\hat{Y}_{36} = 155.38$$

Model Summary

Model	R	R Square	Adjusted R Square	Std. Error of the Estimate
1	.985[a]	.969	.969	7.9863

a. Predictors: (Constant), T

ANOVA[b]

Model		Sum of Squares	df	Mean Square	F	Sig.
1	Regression	66789.029	1	66789.029	1047.172	.000[a]
	Residual	2104.753	33	63.780		
	Total	68893.782	34			

a. Predictors: (Constant), T
b. Dependent Variable: SALES

Coefficients[a]

Model		Unstandardized Coefficients		Standardized Coefficients		
		B	Std. Error	Beta	t	Sig.
1	(Constant)	-.333	2.759		-.121	.905
	T	4.325	.134	.985	32.360	.000

a. Dependent Variable: SALES

Figure 14.16

SPSS least squares regression of annual sales

	T	PRED_SALES	LOWER95CLI	UPPER95CLI
1	36	155.38	138.19	172.57
2	37	159.70	142.43	176.97
3	38	164.03	146.68	181.38
4	39	168.35	150.91	185.79
5	40	172.68	155.15	190.21

Figure 14.17

SPSS spreadsheet with 95% prediction intervals for annual sales with the 95% prediction interval (138.2, 172.6). Similarly, we can obtain the forecasts and prediction intervals for years 37–40. Although it is not easily perceptible in the printout, the prediction intervals widen as we attempt to forecast further into the future. This agrees with the intuitive notion that short-term forecasts should be more reliable than long-term forecasts.

There are two problems associated with forecasting time series using a least squares model.

Problem 1

We are using the least squares model to forecast values outside the region of observation of the independent variable, t — that is, we are forecasting for values of t between 36 and 40, but the observed sales are for t-values between 1 and 35. As we noted in Chapters 11 and 12, it is risky to use a least squares regression model for prediction outside the experimental region.

Problem 1 obviously cannot be avoided. Because forecasting always involves predictions about the future values of a time series, some or all of the independent variables will probably be outside the region of observation on which the model was developed. It is important that the forecaster recognize the dangers of this type of prediction. If underlying conditions change drastically after the model is estimated (e.g., if federal price controls are imposed on the firm's products during the 36th year of operation), then for any forecasting model the forecasts and their confidence intervals are probably useless.

Problem 2

Although the straight-line model may adequately describe the secular trend of the sales, we have not attempted to build any cyclical effects into the model. Thus, the effect of inflationary and recessionary periods will be to increase the error of the forecasts because the model does not anticipate such periods.

Fortunately, the forecaster often has some degree of control over problem 2, as we demonstrate in the remainder of the chapter.

In forming the prediction intervals for the forecasts, we made the standard regression assumptions (Chapters 11 and 12) about the random error component of the model. We assumed the errors have mean 0, constant variance, and normal probability distributions, and are *independent*. The latter assumption is dubious in time series models, especially in the presence of short-term trends. Often, if a year's value lies above the secular trend line, the next year's value has a tendency to be above the line also — that is, the errors tend to be correlated (see Figure 14.15).

We discuss how to deal with correlated errors in Section 14.9. For now, we can characterize the simple linear regression forecasting method as useful for discerning secular trends, but it is probably too simplistic for most time series. And, as with all forecasting methods, the simple linear regression forecasts should be applied only over the short term.

STATISTICS in ACTION REVISITED

Forecasting with Simple Linear Regression

A second model considered by consultants to forecast monthly sales of a new cold medicine (Coldex) was a simple linear regression model with time (t) as the independent variable, where $t = 1, 2, 3, \ldots, 24$. The Minitab graph of the least squares line is shown in Figure SIA14.3, followed by the simple linear regression printout in Figure SIA14.4.

Note that the p-value for testing the slope coefficient is .047. Thus, at $\alpha = .05$, the model is statistically useful for predicting monthly sales. However, the coefficient of determination is low ($R^2 = .168$); only about 17% of the sample variation in monthly sales can be explained by the linear time trend.

The simple linear forecasts for each of the first 3 months of year 3 are shown on the Minitab worksheet, Figure SIA14.5. Minitab also gives a 95% prediction interval for

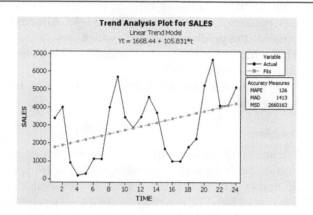

Figure SIA14.3

Minitab plot of least squares line for forecasting monthly Coldex sales

---

Regression Analysis: SALES versus TIME

```
The regression equation is
SALES = 1668 + 106 TIME


Predictor    Coef   SE Coef     T      P
Constant    1668.4    717.8   2.32   0.030
TIME        105.83    50.23   2.11   0.047


S = 1703.52    R-Sq = 16.8%    R-Sq(adj) = 13.0%


Analysis of Variance
```

Figure SIA14.4

Minitab simple linear regression printout for the linear trend forecasting model

```
Source          DF         SS         MS      F      P
Regression       1   12880305   12880305   4.44   0.047
Residual Error  22   63843919    2901996
Total           23   76724223
```

Figure SIA14.5

Minitab worksheet with simple linear regression forecasts of monthly sales

↓	C1	C2	C3	C4	C5	C6
	YEAR	MONTH	TIME	FORECAST	PL95LOW	PL95UPP
1	3	1	25	4314.22	480.528	8147.92
2	3	2	26	4420.06	549.731	8290.38
3	3	3	27	4525.89	616.500	8435.27

each forecast. The intervals for months 25, 26, and 27 are (480.5, 8,147.9), (549.7, 8,290.4), and (616.5, 8,435.3), respectively. For the first month of year 3 (i.e., month 25), we are 95% confident that the actual sales will fall between 480.5 and 8,147.9 thousand dollars. Similar interpretations are made for the other two forecasts.

As with the exponential smoothing model, these intervals were too wide to be of practical use by the pharmaceutical company. How can the forecasting model be improved? Examine Figure SIA14.3 and note the cyclical trends in the monthly sales data. Neither the exponential smoothing model nor the linear regression model account for this cyclical variation. A forecasting model is needed that explicitly accounts for such trends. Such a model is presented in the next Statistics in Action Revisited (p. 14-35).

💿 *Data Set:* COLDEX

14.8 Seasonal Regression Models

Many time series have distinct seasonal patterns. Retail sales are usually highest around Christmas, spring, and fall, with lulls in the winter and summer periods. Energy usage is highest in summer and winter, and lowest in spring and fall. Teenage unemployment rises in summer months when schools are not in session and falls near Christmas when many businesses hire part-time help.

Multiple regression models can be used to forecast future values of a time series with strong seasonal components. To accomplish this, the mean value of the time series,

$E(Y_t)$, is given a mathematical form that describes both the secular trend and seasonal components of the time series. Although the **seasonal model** can assume a wide variety of mathematical forms, the use of dummy variables to describe seasonal differences is common.

For example, consider the power load data for a Southern utility company shown in Table 14.8. Data were obtained for each quarter from 2001 through 2012. A model that combines the expected growth in usage and the seasonal component is

$$E(Y_t) = \beta_0 + \beta_1 t + \beta_2 Q_1 + \beta_3 Q_2 + \beta_4 Q_3$$

where

$$t = \text{Time period, ranging from } t = 1 \text{ for Quarter 1 of 2001 to}$$

$$t = 48 \text{ for Quarter 4 of 2012}$$

$$Q_1 = \begin{cases} 1 & \text{if Quarter 1} \\ 0 & \text{if Quarter 2, 3, or 4} \end{cases}$$

$$Q_2 = \begin{cases} 1 & \text{if Quarter 2} \\ 0 & \text{if Quarter 1, 3, or 4} \end{cases}$$

$$Q_3 = \begin{cases} 1 & \text{if Quarter 3} \\ 0 & \text{if Quarter 1, 2, or 4} \end{cases}$$

The Minitab printout in Figure 14.18 shows the least squares fit of this model to the data in Table 14.8.

Note that the model appears to fit well, with $R^2 = .914$, indicating that the model accounts for about 91% of the sample variability in power loads over the 12-year period. The global $F = 114.88$ (p-value $= .000$) strongly supports the hypothesis that the model has predictive utility. The model standard deviation of 7.86 indicates that the

Table 14.8	Quarterly Power Loads (megawatts) for a Southern Utility Company, 2001–2012				
Year	Quarter	Power Load	Year	Quarter	Power Load
2001	1	68.8	2007	1	130.6
	2	65.0		2	116.8
	3	88.4		3	144.2
	4	69.0		4	123.3
2002	1	83.6	2008	1	142.3
	2	69.7		2	124.0
	3	90.2		3	146.1
	4	72.5		4	135.5
2003	1	106.8	2009	1	147.1
	2	89.2		2	119.3
	3	110.7		3	138.2
	4	91.7		4	127.6
2004	1	108.6	2010	1	143.4
	2	98.9		2	134.0
	3	120.1		3	159.6
	4	102.1		4	135.1
2005	1	113.1	2011	1	149.5
	2	94.2		2	123.3
	3	120.5		3	154.4
	4	107.4		4	139.4
2006	1	116.2	2012	1	151.6
	2	104.4		2	133.7
	3	131.7		3	154.5
	4	117.9		4	135.1

Data Set: POWER

Regression Analysis: LOAD versus T, Q1, Q2, Q3

```
The regression equation is
LOAD = 70.5 + 1.64 T + 13.7 Q1 - 3.74 Q2 + 18.5 Q3

Predictor      Coef   SE Coef       T      P
Constant     70.509     3.116   22.63  0.000
T           1.63621   0.08214   19.92  0.000
Q1           13.659     3.217    4.25  0.000
Q2           -3.736     3.212   -1.16  0.251
Q3           18.470     3.209    5.76  0.000

S = 7.85795    R-Sq = 91.4%   R-Sq(adj) = 90.6%

Analysis of Variance

Source           DF        SS       MS       F      P
Regression        4   28375.0   7093.7  114.88  0.000
Residual Error   43    2655.1     61.7
Total            47   31030.1
```

Figure 14.18

Minitab least squares fit to quarterly power load model

---

model predictions will usually be accurate to within approximately $\pm 2(7.86)$, or about ± 16 megawatts. Furthermore, $\hat{\beta}_1 = 1.64$ indicates an estimated average growth in load of 1.64 megawatts per quarter. Finally, the seasonal dummy variables have the following interpretations (refer to Chapter 12):*

$\hat{\beta}_2 = 13.66$ Quarter 1 loads average 13.66 megawatts more than Quarter 4 loads.

$\hat{\beta}_3 = -3.74$ Quarter 2 loads average 3.74 megawatts less than Quarter 4 loads.

$\hat{\beta}_4 = 18.47$ Quarter 3 loads average 18.47 megawatts more than Quarter 4 loads.

Thus, as expected, winter and summer loads exceed spring and fall loads, with the peak occurring during the summer months.

In order to forecast the 2013 power loads, we calculate the predicted value $\hat{Y}_k$ for $k = 49, 50, 51,$ and 52, at the same time substituting the dummy variable appropriate for each quarter. Thus, for 2013,

$$\hat{Y}_{\text{Quarter 1}} = \hat{\beta}_0 + \hat{\beta}_1(49) + \hat{\beta}_2 = 70.51 + 1.636(49) + 13.66 = 164.3$$

$$\hat{Y}_{\text{Quarter 2}} = \hat{\beta}_0 + \hat{\beta}_1(50) + \hat{\beta}_3 = 148.6$$

$$\hat{Y}_{\text{Quarter 3}} = \hat{\beta}_0 + \hat{\beta}_1(51) + \hat{\beta}_4 = 172.4$$

$$\hat{Y}_{\text{Quarter 4}} = \hat{\beta}_0 + \hat{\beta}_1(52) = 155.6$$

The predicted values and 95% prediction intervals (highlighted) are given on the Minitab worksheet, Figure 14.19a, and graphed in Figure 14.19b. Also shown in Figure 14.19a are the actual 2013 quarterly power loads. Notice that all 2013 power loads fall inside the forecast intervals.

The seasonal model used to forecast the power loads is an **additive model** because the secular trend component ($\beta_1 t$) is added to the seasonal component ($\beta_2 Q_1 + \beta_3 Q_2 + \beta_4 Q_3$) to form the model. A **multiplicative model** would have the same form, except that the dependent variable would be the natural logarithm of power load; that is,

$$\ln Y_t = \beta_0 + \beta_1 t + \beta_2 Q_1 + \beta_3 Q_2 + \beta_4 Q_3 + \varepsilon$$

Figure 14.19a

Minitab worksheet with quarterly power load forecasts

	C1	C2	C3	C4	C5	C6	C7	C8	C9	C10
	T	YEAR	QTR	LOAD	Q1	Q2	Q3	PRED	LOWER95CLI	UPPER95CLI
1	49	2013	1	151.3	1	0	0	164.341	147.294	181.389
2	50	2013	2	132.9	0	1	0	148.583	131.536	165.630
3	51	2013	3	160.5	0	0	1	172.425	155.378	189.472
4	52	2013	4	161.0	0	0	0	155.591	138.544	172.639

QTRPOWERFORECASTS.MTP ***

*These interpretations assume a fixed value of t. In practical terms this is unrealistic, because each quarter is associated with a different value of t. Nevertheless, the coefficients of the seasonal dummy variables provide insight into the seasonality of these time series data.

Figure 14.19b

Minitab graph of quarterly power loads with forecasts

To see the multiplicative nature of this model, we take the antilogarithm of both sides of the equation to get

$$Y_t = \exp\{\beta_0 + \beta_1 t + \beta_2 Q_1 + \beta_3 Q_2 + \beta_4 Q_3 + \varepsilon\}$$
$$= \underbrace{\exp\{\beta_0\}}_{\text{Constant}} \underbrace{\exp\{\beta_1 t\}}_{\substack{\text{Secular} \\ \text{trend}}} \underbrace{\exp\{\beta_2 Q_1 + \beta_3 Q_2 + \beta_4 Q_3\}}_{\substack{\text{Seasonal} \\ \text{component}}} \underbrace{\exp\{\varepsilon\}}_{\substack{\text{Residual} \\ \text{component}}}$$

The multiplicative model often provides a better forecasting model when the time series is changing at an increasing rate over time.

When time series data are observed monthly, a regression forecasting model needs 11 dummy variables to describe monthly seasonality; three dummy variables can be used (as in the previous models) if the seasonal changes are hypothesized to occur quarterly. In general, this approach to seasonal modeling requires one dummy variable fewer than the number of seasonal changes expected to occur.

There are approaches besides the regression dummy variable method for forecasting seasonal time series. Trigonometric (sine and cosine) terms can be used in regression models to model periodicity. Other time series models, such as Holt's exponential smoothing model, do not use the regression approach at all, and there are various methods for adding seasonal components to these models. For example, the **Holt-Winters forecasting model** is a modification of Holt's model that includes a seasonality component.

We have chosen to discuss the regression approach because it makes use of the important modeling concepts covered in Chapter 12 and because the regression forecasts are accompanied by prediction intervals that provide some measure of the forecast reliability. While most other methods do not have explicit measures of reliability, many have proved their merit by providing good forecasts for particular applications. Consult the references at the end of the chapter for details of other seasonal models.

STATISTICS in ACTION REVISITED

Forecasting with a Seasonal Regression Model

The consultants hired by the pharmaceutical company detected a cyclical trend in the monthly sales data. They noted that sales of the cold medicine were higher during the winter and summer months as compared to the other months over the 2-year period. To account for this seasonal trend, they created 11 dummy variables ($x_1, x_2, \ldots, x_{11}$) for the 12 months of the year. The seasonal forecasting model takes the form

$$E(Y_t) = \beta_0 + \beta_1 t + \beta_2 x_1 + \beta_3 x_2 + \beta_4 x_3 + \beta_5 x_4 + \beta_6 x_5 + \beta_7 x_6 + \beta_8 x_7 + \beta_9 x_8 + \beta_{10} x_9 + \beta_{11} x_{10} + \beta_{12} x_{11}$$

The Minitab regression printout for the model is shown in Figure SIA14.6, followed by the model forecasts in Figure SIA14.7. The global F-test (p-value = .000) indicates that the model is statistically useful for predicting monthly sales, and the model

STATISTICS in ACTION REVISITED CONTINUED

The regression equation is
SALES = 2961 + 74.2 TIME + 501 JAN + 306 FEB - 2329 MAR - 3101 APR - 3138 MAY
        - 2393 JUN - 2241 JUL + 623 AUG + 2111 SEP - 361 OCT - 744 NOV

Predictor	Coef	SE Coef	T	P
Constant	2960.5	320.2	9.25	0.000
TIME	74.25	11.65	6.38	0.000
JAN	500.8	365.5	1.37	0.198
FEB	305.5	361.6	0.84	0.416
MAR	-2329.2	358.0	-6.51	0.000
APR	-3101.0	354.8	-8.74	0.000
MAY	-3137.7	351.9	-8.92	0.000
JUN	-2393.5	349.4	-6.85	0.000
JUL	-2241.2	347.2	-6.45	0.000
AUG	623.0	345.5	1.80	0.099
SEP	2111.3	344.1	6.14	0.000
OCT	-361.5	343.1	-1.05	0.315
NOV	-743.7	342.5	-2.17	0.053

S = 342.314   R-Sq = 98.3%   R-Sq(adj) = 96.5%

Analysis of Variance

Source	DF	SS	MS	F	P
Regression	12	75435259	6286272	53.65	0.000
Residual Error	11	1288964	117179		
Total	23	76724223			

Figure SIA14.6

Minitab printout for seasonal regression model of monthly Coldex sales

Figure SIA14.7

Minitab worksheet with seasonal regression forecasts of monthly sales

↓	C1	C2	C3	C4	C5	C6
	YEAR	MONTH	TIME	FORECAST	PL95LOW	PL95UPP
1	3	1	25	5317.5	4285.83	6349.17
2	3	2	26	5196.5	4164.83	6228.17
3	3	3	27	2636.0	1604.33	3667.67

coefficient of determination ($R^2 = .983$) indicates that over 98% of the sample variation in monthly sales can be explained by the seasonal model. Statistically, this model is a tremendous improvement over the linear trend model.

The 95% prediction intervals for sales in months 25, 26, and 27 (highlighted on Figure SIA14.7) are (4,285.8, 6,349.2), (4,164.8, 6,228.2), and (1,604.3, 3,667.7), respectively. Thus, for the first month of year 3 (month 25), we are 95% confident that the actual sales will fall between 4,285.8 and 6,349.2 thousand dollars. (Similar interpretations are made for the other two forecasts.) These intervals are much narrower than those for the previous two forecasting models, and they also reflect the expected drop in sales in March (month 3) from the winter months. This seasonal model was used successfully by the pharmaceutical firm to forecast monthly sales.

Data Set: COLDEX

Exercises 14.38–14.46

Learning the Mechanics

14.38 The annual price of a finished product (in cents per pound) from 1997 to 2012 is given in the table below. The time variable t begins with $t = 1$ in 1997 and is incremented by 1 for each additional year. L14038

Year	t	Price, Y_t	Year	t	Price, Y_t
1997	1	21.73	2005	9	24.42
1998	2	24.32	2006	10	25.49
1999	3	25.31	2007	11	26.19
2000	4	26.36	2008	12	27.31
2001	5	27.31	2009	13	24.40
2002	6	27.58	2010	14	24.24
2003	7	24.79	2011	15	25.87
2004	8	25.36	2012	16	26.86

a. Fit the straight-line model, $E(Y_t) = \beta_0 + \beta_1 t$, to the data.
b. Give the least squares estimates of the β's.

c. Use the least squares prediction equation to obtain the forecasts for 2013 and 2014.
d. Find 95% forecast intervals for 2013 and 2014.

14.39 Retail sales in Quarters 1–4 over a 10-year period for a department store are shown (in hundreds of thousands of dollars) in the table below. L14039

Year	Quarter			
	1	2	3	4
1	8.3	10.3	8.7	13.5
2	9.8	12.1	10.1	15.4
3	12.1	14.5	12.7	17.1
4	13.7	16.0	14.2	19.2
5	17.4	19.7	18.0	23.1
6	18.2	20.5	18.6	24.0
7	20.0	22.2	20.5	25.1
8	22.3	25.1	22.9	27.7
9	24.7	26.9	25.1	29.8
10	25.8	28.7	26.0	32.2

a. Write a regression model that contains trend and seasonal components to describe the sales data.

b. Use least squares regression to fit the model. Evaluate the fit of the model.

c. Use the regression model to forecast the quarterly sales during year 11. Give 95% prediction intervals for the forecasts.

14.40 What advantage do regression forecasts have over exponentially smoothed forecasts? Does this advantage ensure that regression forecasts will prove to be more accurate? Explain.

Applying the Concepts—Basic

14.41 Mortgage interest rates. The level at which commercial lending institutions set mortgage interest rates has a significant effect on the volume of buying, selling, and construction of residential and commercial real estate. The data in the table are the annual average mortgage interest rates for conventional, fixed-rate, 30-year loans for the period 1987–2010.

MRJ30

Year	Interest Rate (%)	Year	Interest Rate (%)
1987	10.46	1999	7.46
1988	10.86	2000	8.08
1989	12.07	2001	7.01
1990	9.97	2002	6.56
1991	11.14	2003	5.89
1992	8.27	2004	5.86
1993	7.17	2005	5.93
1994	8.28	2006	6.47
1995	7.86	2007	6.40
1996	7.76	2008	6.23
1997	7.57	2009	5.38
1998	6.92	2010	4.86

Source: United States Census Bureau.

a. Fit the simple regression model

$$E(Y_t) = \beta_0 + \beta_1 t$$

where t is the number of years since 1987 (i.e., $t = 0, 1, \ldots, 23$).

b. Forecast the average mortgage interest rate in 2013. Find a 95% prediction interval for this forecast.

14.42 Price of natural gas. Refer to Exercise 14.9 (p. 14-10) and the annual prices of natural gas from 1990 to 2010. A simple linear regression model, $E(Y_t) = \beta_0 + \beta_1 t$, where t is the number of years since 1990, is proposed to forecast the annual price of natural gas.

NATGAS

a. Give the least squares estimates of the β's and interpret their values.

b. Evaluate the model's fit.

c. Find and interpret 95% prediction intervals for the years 2011 and 2012.

d. Describe the problems associated with using a simple linear regression model to predict time series data.

14.43 A gasoline tax on carbon emissions. In an effort to reduce gasoline consumption and curb carbon emissions, policymakers have proposed raising gasoline taxes. In the *Journal of Applied Econometrics* (Vol. 26, 2011), a group of economists investigated the effect of a gasoline tax

on gas consumption. The researchers used least squares regression to model gasoline consumption in month t (Y_t) as a function of the average inflation-adjusted after-tax price of gasoline in month t (X_t) and dummy variables for months.

a. Write a model for Y_t as a function of X_t that proposes a linear relationship between gasoline consumption and after-tax gasoline price.

b. Add dummy variables for months to the model, part **a.** Use December as the base level.

c. What statistical test would you conduct to determine whether mean gasoline consumption varies from month to month? Give the null hypothesis for the test.

d. Monthly data from January 1998 to March 2008 ($n = 123$ months) were used to fit the model, part **b.** In terms of the β's of the model, what is the forecast of gasoline consumption in January 2013?

Applying the Concepts—Intermediate

14.44 Predicting presidential elections. Researchers at the University of West Florida used regression analysis to build a model for predicting the outcome of presidential elections (*Political Analysis*, Vol. 17, 2009). The dependent variable of interest was Y_t = percentage of the two-party vote won by the incumbent party's candidate in election year t. Independent variables included in the model are similar to those listed below.

Fiscal policy of incumbent party in election year t: $X_{1t} = \{1$ if expansion, 0 if not$\}$

Duration of incumbent party: X_{2t} = number of consecutive terms served prior to election year t

Party of incumbent in election year t: $X_{3t} = \{1$ if Democrat, 0 if Republican$\}$

GDP trend in election year t: X_{4t} = number of quarters of the previous administration where the GDP > 3.2%

GDP growth rate: X_{5t} = growth rate of the GDP in the first three quarters of election year t

a. Write a first-order regression model for $E(Y_t)$ as a function of the five independent variables.

b. The model, part **a**, was fit to data collected for $n = 24$ election years (from 1916 to 2008). The coefficient of determination was reported as $R^2 = .91$. Interpret this result, practically.

c. Use the value of R^2 to compute the F-statistic for testing the global adequacy of the model. Carry out the test using $\alpha = .05$.

d. The estimated β for X_{1t} was reported as -4.08 (p-value $< .05$). Interpret this result, practically.

e. The estimated β for X_{2t} was reported as -3.41 (p-value $< .05$). Interpret this result, practically.

f. The estimated β for X_{3t} was reported as -4.84 (p-value $< .05$). Interpret this result, practically.

g. The estimated β for X_{4t} was reported as $.92$ (p-value $< .05$). Interpret this result, practically.

h. The estimated β for X_{5t} was reported as $.66$. Interpret this result, practically.

i. The standard deviation of the model was reported as $s = 2.36$. Interpret this result, practically.

j. Do you recommend that the researchers use the model to predict the outcome of a future presidential election? Explain.

14.45 Life insurance policies in force. The table below represents all life insurance policies (in millions) in force on the lives of U.S. residents for the years 1980 through 2009.

Year	No. of Policies (in millions)	Year	No. of Policies (in millions)
1980	402	1995	370
1981	400	1996	355
1982	390	1997	351
1983	387	1998	358
1984	385	1999	367
1985	386	2000	369
1986	391	2001	377
1987	395	2002	375
1988	391	2003	379
1989	394	2004	373
1990	389	2005	373
1991	375	2006	375
1992	366	2007	374
1993	363	2008	335
1994	366	2009	291

Source: U.S. Census Bureau. *Statistical Abstract of the United States,* 2012.

a. Use the method of least squares to fit a simple regression model to the data.

b. Forecast the number of life insurance policies in force for 2010 and 2011.

c. Construct 95% prediction intervals for the forecasts of part **b.**

d. Check the accuracy of your forecasts by looking up the actual number of life insurance policies in force for 2010 and 2011 in the *Statistical Abstract of the United States.*

14.46 Graphing calculator sales. The next table presents the quarterly sales index for one brand of graphing calculator

GCALC

Year	First Quarter	Second Quarter	Third Quarter	Fourth Quarter
2008	438	398	252	160
2009	464	429	376	216
2010	523	496	425	318
2011	593	576	456	398
2012	636	640	526	498

at a campus bookstore. The quarters are based on an academic year, so the first quarter represents fall; the second, winter; the third, spring; and the fourth, summer.

Define the time variable as $t = 1$ for the first quarter of 2008, $t = 2$ for the second quarter of 2008, etc. Consider the following seasonal dummy variables:

$$Q_1 = \begin{cases} 1 & \text{if Quarter 1} \\ 0 & \text{otherwise} \end{cases}$$

$$Q_2 = \begin{cases} 1 & \text{if Quarter 2} \\ 0 & \text{otherwise} \end{cases}$$

$$Q_3 = \begin{cases} 1 & \text{if Quarter 3} \\ 0 & \text{otherwise} \end{cases}$$

a. Write a regression model for $E(Y_t)$ as a function of t, Q_1, Q_2, and Q_3.

b. Find and interpret the least squares estimates and evaluate the usefulness of the model.

c. Which of the assumptions about the random error component is in doubt when a regression model is fit to time series data?

d. Find the forecasts and the 95% prediction intervals for the 2013 quarterly sales. Interpret the result.

14.9 Autocorrelation and the Durbin-Watson Test

Recall that one of the assumptions we make when using a regression model for predictions is that the errors are independent. However, with time series data, this assumption is questionable. The cyclical component of a time series may result in deviations from the secular trend that tend to cluster alternately on the positive and negative sides of the trend, as shown in Figure 14.20.

The observed errors between the time series and the regression model for the secular trend (and seasonal component, if present) are called **time series residuals.** Thus, if the time series Y_t has an estimated trend of $\hat{Y}_t$, then the time series residual* is

$$\hat{R}_t = Y_t - \hat{Y}_t$$

Note that time series residuals are defined just as the residuals for any regression model. However, we will usually plot time series residuals versus time to determine whether a cyclical component is apparent.

For example, consider the sales forecasting data in Table 14.5 (p. 14-13), to which we fit a simple straight-line regression model. The Minitab plot of the data and model is repeated in Figure 14.21, and a plot of the time series residuals is shown in Figure 14.22.

Notice the tendency of the residuals to group alternately into positive and negative clusters—that is, if the residual for year t is positive, there is a tendency for the residual

Figure 14.20
Illustration of cyclical errors

---

*We use $\hat{R}_t$ rather than $\hat{\varepsilon}$ to denote a time series residual because, as we shall see, time series residuals often do not satisfy the regression assumptions associated with the random component ε.

Figure 14.21

Minitab scatterplot of annual sales with least squares line

Figure 14.22

Minitab plot of residuals versus time

for year $(t + 1)$ to be positive. These cycles are indicative of possible positive correlation between neighboring residuals. The correlation between time series residuals at different points in time is called *autocorrelation,* and the autocorrelation of neighboring residuals (time periods t and $t + 1$) is called *first-order autocorrelation.*

> The correlation between time series residuals at different points in time is called **autocorrelation.** Correlation between neighboring residuals (at times t and $t + 1$) is called **first-order autocorrelation.** In general, correlation between residuals at times t and $t + d$ is called dth-order autocorrelation.

Rather than speculate about the presence of autocorrelation among time series residuals, we prefer to test for it. For most business and economic time series, the relevant test is for first-order autocorrelation. Other higher-order autocorrelations may indicate seasonality (e.g., fourth-order autocorrelation in a quarterly time series). However, when we use the term *autocorrelation* in this text, we are referring to first-order autocorrelation unless otherwise specified. So, we test

H_0: No first-order autocorrelation of residuals

H_a: Positive first-order autocorrelation of residuals

The **Durbin-Watson d-statistic** is used to test for the presence of first-order autocorrelation. The statistic is given by the formula

$$d = \frac{\sum_{t=2}^{n}(\hat{R}_t - \hat{R}_{t-1})^2}{\sum_{t=1}^{n}\hat{R}_t^2}$$

where n is the number of observations (time periods) and $(\hat{R}_t - \hat{R}_{t-1})$ represents the difference between a pair of successive time series residuals. The value of d always falls in the interval from 0 to 4. The interpretations of the values of d are given in the box. Most statistical software packages include a routine that calculates d for time series residuals.

Interpretation of Durbin-Watson d-Statistic

$$d = \frac{\sum_{t=2}^{n}(\hat{R}_t - \hat{R}_{t-1})^2}{\sum_{t=1}^{n}\hat{R}_t^2} \qquad \text{Range of } d: 0 \le d \le 4$$

1. If the residuals are uncorrelated, then $d \approx 2$.
2. If the residuals are positively autocorrelated, then $d < 2$, and if the autocorrelation is very strong, $d \approx 0$.
3. If the residuals are negatively autocorrelated, then $d > 2$, and if the autocorrelation is very strong, $d \approx 4$.

Durbin and Watson (1951) give tables for the lower-tail values of the d-statistic, which are shown in Tables X ($\alpha = .05$) and XI ($\alpha = .01$) of Appendix D. Part of Table X is reproduced in Table 14.9. For the sales example, we have $k = 1$ independent variable and $n = 35$ observations. Using $\alpha = .05$ for the one-tailed test for positive autocorrelation, we obtain the tabled values $d_L = 1.40$ and $d_U = 1.52$. The meaning of these values is illustrated in Figure 14.23. Because of the complexity of the sampling distribution of d, it is not possible to specify a single point that acts as a boundary between the rejection and nonrejection regions, as we did for the z, t, F, and other test statistics. Instead, an upper (d_U) and lower (d_L) bound are specified. Thus a d-value less than d_L *does* provide strong evidence of positive autocorrelation at $\alpha = .05$ (recall that small d values indicate positive autocorrelation); a d value greater than d_U does *not* provide evidence of positive autocorrelation at $\alpha = .05$; and a value of d between d_L and d_U might or might not be significant at the $\alpha = .05$ level. If $d_L < d < d_U$, more information is needed before we can reach any conclusion about the presence of autocorrelation.

Table 14.9	Reproduction of Part of Table X of Appendix D: Critical Values for the Durbin-Watson d-Statistic, $\alpha = .05$								
	$k = 1$		$k = 2$		$k = 3$		$k = 4$		$k = 5$	
n	d_L	d_U	d_L	d_U	d_L	d_U	d_L	d_U	d_L	d_U
31	1.36	1.50	1.30	1.57	1.23	1.65	1.16	1.74	1.09	1.83
32	1.37	1.50	1.31	1.57	1.24	1.65	1.18	1.73	1.11	1.82
33	1.38	1.51	1.32	1.58	1.26	1.65	1.19	1.73	1.13	1.81
34	1.39	1.51	1.33	1.58	1.27	1.65	1.21	1.73	1.15	1.81
35	1.40	1.52	1.34	1.58	1.28	1.65	1.22	1.73	1.16	1.80
36	1.41	1.52	1.35	1.59	1.29	1.65	1.24	1.73	1.18	1.80
37	1.42	1.53	1.36	1.59	1.31	1.66	1.25	1.72	1.19	1.80
38	1.43	1.54	1.37	1.59	1.32	1.66	1.26	1.72	1.21	1.79
39	1.43	1.54	1.38	1.60	1.33	1.66	1.27	1.72	1.22	1.79
40	1.44	1.54	1.39	1.60	1.34	1.66	1.29	1.72	1.23	1.79

Tests for negative autocorrelation and two-tailed tests can be conducted by making use of the symmetry of the sampling distribution of the d-statistic about its mean. The test procedure is summarized in the next box.

GEOFFREY S. WATSON (1921–1998)
The Durbin-Watson Test

Australian Geoff Watson was educated at the University of Melbourne, where he earned a mathematics degree in 1942. Following World War II, Watson moved to North Carolina State University to begin work on a graduate degree in statistics. He eventually earned his PhD in 1951. During his illustrious career as a statistics professor and researcher, Watson had appointments at Cambridge University, Australian National University, the University of Toronto, Johns Hopkins University, and Princeton University (where he was chairman of the statistics department). While visiting Cambridge in the late 1940s, Watson collaborated with James Durbin of the London School of Economics to develop their well-known Durbin-Watson test for serial correlation. His research interests covered a wide spectrum of statistical applications all across the world, including estimating the size of the penguin population (Antarctica), paleontology problems (Sweden), probability in quantum mechanics (Rome), molecular biology (Italy), and ozone depletion (U.S. Energy Information Administration). Outside his professional life, Watson was a serious painter (landscapes and hills) and an accomplished tennis player (effective lob).

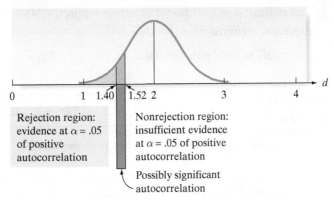

Figure 14.23

Rejection region for the Durbin-Watson *d* test: Sales example

Durbin-Watson *d*-Test for Autocorrelation

One-Tailed Test	Two-Tailed Test
H_0: No first-order autocorrelation	H_0: No first-order autocorrelation
H_a: Positive first-order autocorrelation (or H_a: Negative first-order autocorrelation)	H_a: Positive or negative first-order autocorrelation

Test statistic:

$$d = \frac{\sum_{t=2}^{n}(\hat{R}_t - \hat{R}_{t-1})^2}{\sum_{t=1}^{n}\hat{R}_t^2}$$

Rejection region:

$d < d_{L,\alpha}$
[or $(4 - d) < d_{L,\alpha}$
if H_a: Negative first-order autocorrelation]

where $d_{L,\alpha}$ is the lower tabled value corresponding to k independent variables and n observations. The corresponding upper value $d_{U,\alpha}$ defines a "possibly significant" region between $d_{L,\alpha}$ and $d_{U,\alpha}$ (see Figure 14.23).

Rejection region:

$d < d_{L,\alpha/2}$ or $(4 - d) < d_{L,\alpha/2}$

where $d_{L,\alpha/2}$ is the lower tabled value corresponding to k independent variables and n observations. The corresponding upper value $d_{U,\alpha/2}$ defines a "possibly significant" region between $d_{L,\alpha/2}$ and $d_{U,\alpha/2}$ (see Figure 14.23).

Requirements for the Validity of the *d*-Test

The residuals are normally distributed.

Example 14.9

Conducting the Durbin–Watson Test—Sales Revenue Model

Problem Refer to the straight-line regression model relating annual sales revenue, Y_t, to year t. Figures 14.21 and 14.22 provide graphical evidence of a potential residual correlation problem. Conduct a formal test for positive first-order autocorrelation by applying the Durbin-Watson test. Use $\alpha = .05$.

Solution We used SPSS to conduct the Durbin-Watson test. A portion of the SPSS printout for the least squares regression of annual sales is shown in Figure 14.24. The elements of the test follow:

H_0: No first-order autocorrelation

H_a: Positive first-order autocorrelation

Test statistic: $d = 1.02$ (highlighted on Figure 14.24)

Rejection region: $d < d_L = 1.40$

(where d_L is highlighted in Table 14.9 for $n = 35, \alpha = .05$, and $k = 1$).

Figure 14.24

SPSS regression printout with Durbin-Watson statistic for annual SALES model

Model Summary[b]

Model	R	R Square	Adjusted R Square	Std. Error of the Estimate	Durbin-Watson
1	.985[a]	.969	.969	7.9863	1.020

a. Predictors: (Constant), T
b. Dependent Variable: SALES

Conclusion: Because $d = 1.02$ is below the critical d_L value of 1.40, we reject H_0. Thus, there is sufficient evidence (at $\alpha = .05$) to conclude that the residuals of the straight-line model for sales are positively autocorrelated.

Look Back In the presence of autocorrelated residuals, the regression analysis tends to produce inflated t-statistics. Consequently, an analyst has a greater than α probability of committing a Type I error when testing a model parameter. For example, if a t-test is conducted on a β-parameter using $\alpha = .05$, the analyst will falsely reject H_0 more than 5% of the time when the regression errors are autocorrelated.

■ **Now Work Exercise 14.49**

Once strong evidence of autocorrelation has been established, as in the case of the sales example, doubt is cast on the least squares results and any inferences drawn from them. Under these conditions, a time series model that accounts for the autocorrelation of the random errors is required. Such time series models take the form

$$Y_t = E(Y_t) + R_t$$

where $E(Y_t)$ is the usual deterministic portion of the model and R_t is a term that represents autocorrelated error at time t. Consequently, the analyst must not only model the deterministic component but also the error component. For example, a model that is useful when the errors have first-order autocorrelation (called a *first-order autoregressive model*) is

$$R_t = \phi R_{t-1} + \varepsilon_t$$

where ε_t represents the usual independent error term. If the deterministic component can be modeled as a straight-line function of t, then the full model is

$$Y_t = \underbrace{\beta_0 + \beta_1 t}_{E(Y_t)} + \underbrace{\phi R_{t-1} + \varepsilon_t}_{R_t}$$

Consult the references at the end of this chapter for how to analyze these sophisticated time series models.

Exercises 14.47–14.56

Learning the Mechanics

14.47 Define autocorrelation. Explain why it is important in time series modeling and forecasting.

14.48 What do the following Durbin-Watson statistics suggest about the autocorrelation of the time series residuals from which each was calculated?

  a. $d = 3.9$
  b. $d = .2$
  c. $d = 1.99$

14.49 For each case, indicate the decision regarding the test of the null hypothesis of no first-order autocorrelation against the alternative hypothesis of positive first-order autocorrelation.

  a. $k = 2, n = 20, \alpha = .05, d = 1.1$
  b. $k = 2, n = 20, \alpha = .01, d = 1.1$
  c. $k = 5, n = 65, \alpha = .05, d = .95$
  d. $k = 1, n = 31, \alpha = .01, d = 1.35$

Applying the Concepts—Basic

14.50 Forecasting monthly car and truck sales. Forecasts of automotive vehicle sales in the United States provide the basis for financial and strategic planning at large automotive corporations. The following forecasting model was developed for Y_t, total monthly passenger car and light truck sales (in thousands):

$$E(Y_t) = \beta_0 + \beta_1 x_1 + \beta_2 x_2 + \beta_3 x_3 + \beta_4 x_4 + \beta_5 x_5$$

where x_1 = average monthly retail price of regular gasoline, x_2 = annual percentage change in GDP per quarter, x_3 = monthly consumer confidence index, x_4 = total number of vehicles scrapped (millions) per month, and x_5 = vehicle seasonality. The model was fit to monthly data collected over a 12-year period (i.e., $n = 144$ months), with the following results: $R^2 = .856$, Durbin-Watson $d = 1.01$.

a. Is there sufficient evidence to indicate that the overall model contributes information for the prediction of monthly passenger car and light truck sales? Test using $\alpha = .05$.

b. Is there sufficient evidence to indicate that the regression errors are positively correlated? Test using $\alpha = .05$.

c. Comment on the validity of the inference concerning model adequacy in light of the result of part **b**.

14.51 Predicting presidential elections. Refer to the *Political Analysis* (Vol. 17, 2009) study on predicting presidential elections, Exercise 14.44 (p. 14-37). Recall that a regression model with five independent variables was fit to data collected for $n = 24$ election years in order to predict Y_t = percentage of the two-party vote won by the incumbent party's candidate in election year t. The Durbin-Watson d-statistic for the model was reported as $d = 1.77$. Is there evidence (at $\alpha = .05$) of positively correlated errors in the model? Explain.

14.52 The consumer purchasing value of the dollar, Y_t, from 1970 to 2010 is illustrated by the data in the table in the next **DOLLAR** column. The buying power of the dollar (compared with 1982) is listed for each year. The first-order model

$$Y_t = \beta_0 + \beta_1 t + \varepsilon$$

was fit to the data using the method of least squares. The Minitab printout and a plot of the regression residuals follow.

a. Examine the plot of the regression residuals against t. Is there a tendency for the residuals to have long positive and negative runs? To what do you attribute this phenomenon?

Regression Analysis: VALUE versus T

```
The regression equation is
VALUE = 1.90 - 0.0393 T

Predictor      Coef    SE Coef       T      P
Constant    1.89596    0.08948   21.19  0.000
T          -0.039274   0.003712  -10.58  0.000

S = 0.281263   R-Sq = 74.2%   R-Sq(adj) = 73.5%

Analysis of Variance

Source          DF      SS       MS       F      P
Regression       1   8.8534   8.8534  111.91  0.000
Residual Error  39   3.0852   0.0791
Total           40  11.9387

Durbin-Watson statistic = 0.0555155
```

b. Locate the Durbin-Watson d-statistic on the printout and test the null hypothesis that the time series residuals are uncorrelated. Use $\alpha = .10$.

c. What assumption(s) must be satisfied in order for the test of part **b** to be valid?

Year	t	Value, Y_t	Year	t	Value, Y_t
1970	1	2.545	1991	22	0.822
1971	2	2.469	1992	23	0.812
1972	3	2.392	1993	24	0.802
1973	4	2.193	1994	25	0.797
1974	5	1.901	1995	26	0.782
1975	6	1.718	1996	27	0.762
1976	7	1.645	1997	28	0.759
1977	8	1.546	1998	29	0.765
1978	9	1.433	1999	30	0.752
1979	10	1.289	2000	31	0.725
1980	11	1.136	2001	32	0.711
1981	12	1.041	2002	33	0.720
1982	13	1.000	2003	34	0.698
1983	14	0.984	2004	35	0.673
1984	15	0.964	2005	36	0.642
1985	16	0.955	2006	37	0.623
1986	17	0.969	2007	38	0.600
1987	18	0.949	2008	39	0.565
1988	19	0.926	2009	40	0.580
1989	20	0.880	2010	41	0.556
1990	21	0.839			

Source: United States Census Bureau.

Applying the Concepts—Intermediate

14.53 Mortgage interest rates. Refer to the data on annual mortgage interest rate (Y_t), Exercise 14.41 (p. 14-37). You fit the **MJR30** simple linear regression model, $E(Y_t) = \beta_0 + \beta_1 t$, to the data for the years 1987 to 2010 ($t = 0, 1, 2, \ldots, 23$).

a. Find and plot the regression residuals against t. Does the plot suggest the presence of autocorrelation? Explain.

b. Conduct the Durbin-Watson test (at $\alpha = .05$) to test formally for the presence of positively autocorrelated regression errors.

c. Comment on the validity of the inference concerning model adequacy in light of the result of part **b**.

14.54 Price of natural gas. Refer to the annual data on natural gas price (Y_t), Exercise 14.42 (p. 14-37). You fit the simple **NATGAS** linear regression model, $E(Y_t) = \beta_0 + \beta_1 t$, to the data for the years 1990 to 2010 ($t = 1, 2, \ldots, 21$).

Residuals Versus T
(response is VALUE)

a. Find and plot the regression residuals against t. Does the plot suggest the presence of autocorrelation? Explain.

b. Conduct the Durbin-Watson test (at $\alpha = .05$) to test formally for the presence of positively autocorrelated regression errors.

c. Comment on the validity of the inference concerning model adequacy in light of the result of part **b**.

14.55 Modeling the deposit share of a retail bank. Exploratory research published in the *Journal of Professional Services Marketing* (Vol. 5, 1990) examined the relationship between deposit share of a retail bank and several marketing variables. Quarterly deposit share data were collected for 5 consecutive years for each of nine retail banking institutions. The model analyzed took the following form:

$$E(Y_t) = \beta_0 + \beta_1 P_{t-1} + \beta_2 S_{t-1} + \beta_3 D_{t-1}$$

where Y_t = deposit share of a bank in quarter t ($t = 1, 2, \ldots, 20$), P_{t-1} = expenditures on promotion-related activities in quarter $t - 1$, S_{t-1} = expenditures on service-related activities in quarter $t - 1$, and D_{t-1} = expenditures on distribution-related activities in quarter $t - 1$. A separate model was fit for each bank with the results shown in the table.

a. Interpret the values of R^2 for each bank.

b. Test the overall adequacy of the model for each bank using $\alpha = .01$.

c. Conduct the Durbin-Watson d-test for positive residual correlation for each bank at $\alpha = .01$. What conclusions do you draw about autocorrelation?

Bank	R^2	p-Value for Global F-Test	Durbin-Watson d
1	.914	.000	1.3
2	.721	.004	3.4
3	.926	.000	2.7
4	.827	.000	1.9
5	.270	.155	.85
6	.616	.012	1.8
7	.962	.000	2.5
8	.495	.014	2.3
9	.500	.011	1.1

14.56 Life insurance policies in force. Refer to the annual data on number of life insurance policies in force (Y_t), Exercise 14.45 (p. 14-38). You fit the simple linear regression model, $E(Y_t) = \beta_0 + \beta_1 t$, to the data for the years 1980 to 2009 ($t = 1, 2, \ldots, 30$).

LIFE

a. Find and plot the regression residuals against t. Does the plot suggest the presence of autocorrelation? Explain.

b. Conduct the Durbin-Watson test (at $\alpha = .05$) to test formally for the presence of positively autocorrelated regression errors.

c. Comment on the validity of the inference concerning model adequacy in light of the result of part **b**.

▫ Chapter Notes

Key Terms

Adaptive forecast 14-18
Additive model 14-34
Autocorrelation 14-39
Base period 14-2
Composite index number 14-4
Cyclical effect 14-16
Descriptive 14-2
Descriptive models 14-16
Durbin-Watson d-statistic 14-39
Durbin-Watson test 14-41
Exponentially smoothed forecast 14-17
Exponential smoothing 14-12
Exponential smoothing constant 14-12
First-order autocorrelation 14-39
Forecast 14-2
Forecast error 14-19
Holt forecasting model 14-20
Holt-Winters forecasting model 14-35
Index number 14-2
Inferential 14-2
Inferential forecasting model 14-29

Inferential models 14-16
Inferential techniques 14-2
Laspeyres index 14-6
Long-term trend 14-16
Mean absolute deviation 14-25
Mean absolute percentage error 14-25
Multiplicative model 14-34
Paasche index 14-8
Price 14-3
Quantity indexes 14-3
Residual effect 14-17
Root mean squared error 14-25
Seasonal effect 14-17
Seasonal model 14-33
Secular trend 14-16
Simple composite index 14-4
Simple index number 14-3
Time series or time series data 14-2
Time series residuals 14-38
Weighted composite price index 14-6

Key Formulas

$$I_t = \left(\frac{Y_t}{Y_0}\right)100 \qquad \text{Simple index}$$

$$I_t = \left(\frac{\text{Total of all } Y\text{-values at time } t}{\text{Total of all } Y\text{-values at time } t_0}\right)100 \qquad \text{Simple composite index}$$

Weighted composite price indexes:

$$I_t = \left(\frac{\sum_{i=1}^{k} Q_{it_0}P_{it}}{\sum_{i=1}^{k} Q_{it_0}P_{it_0}}\right)100 \qquad \text{Laspeyres}$$

$$I_t = \left(\frac{\sum_{i=1}^{k} Q_{it}P_{it}}{\sum_{i=1}^{k} Q_{it}P_{it_0}}\right)100 \qquad \text{Paasche}$$

Exponential smoothing:

$$E_t = wY_t + (1 - w)E_{t-1}, \text{where } E_1 = Y_1$$

Forecast: $F_{t+k} = E_t$

Holt's method:

$$E_t = wY_t + (1 - w)(E_{t-1} + T_{t-1}),$$
$$\text{where } E_2 = Y_2, T_2 = Y_2 - Y_1$$

$$T_t = v(E_t - E_{t-1}) + (1 - v)T_{t-1}$$

Forecast: $F_{t+k} = E_t + kT_t$

$$MAD = \frac{\sum_{t=n+1}^{n+m} |Y_t - F_t|}{m}$$

Mean absolute deviation

$$MAPE = \frac{\sum_{t=n+1}^{n+m} \left| \frac{Y_t - F_t}{Y_t} \right|}{m} \times 100$$

Mean absolute percentage error

$$RMSE = \sqrt{\frac{\sum_{t=n+1}^{n+m} (Y_t - F_t)^2}{m}}$$

Root mean squared error

$$d = \frac{\sum_{t=2}^{n} \left(\hat{R}_t - \hat{R}_{t-1} \right)^2}{\sum_{t=1}^{n} \hat{R}_t^2}$$

Durbin-Watson test statistic

Key Symbols

Y_t	. . . Time series value at time t
I_t	. . . Index at time t
P_t	. . . Price series at time t
Q_t	. . . Quantity series at time t
E_t	. . . Exponentially smoothed value at time t
T_t	. . . Smoothed trend at time t
F_{t+k}	. . . k-step-ahead forecast value
MAD	. . . Mean absolute deviation
MAPE	. . . Mean absolute percentage error
RMSE	. . . Root mean squared error
$\hat{R}_t$	. . . Residual at time t
d	. . . Value of Durbin-Watson test statistic
d_L	. . . Lower critical value of d
d_U	. . . Upper critical value of d

Key Ideas

Time Series Data

Data generated by processes over time.

Index Number

Measures the change in a variable over time relative to a base period.

Types of index numbers:

1. **simple index number**
2. **simple composite index number** and
3. **weighted composite number (Laspeyres index or Paasche index)**

Time Series Components

1. **secular (long-term) trend**
2. **cyclical effect**
3. **seasonal effect** and
4. **residual effect**

Time Series Forecasting

Descriptive methods of forecasting with smoothing:

1. **exponential smoothing** and
2. **Holt's method**

An *inferential* forecasting method: **least squares regression**

Measures of forecast accuracy:

1. **mean absolute deviation (MAD)**
2. **mean absolute percentage error (MAPE)** and
3. **root mean squared error (RMSE)**

Problems with least squares regression forecasting:

1. *prediction outside the experimental region* and
2. *regression errors are autocorrelated*

Autocorrelation

Correlation between time series residuals at different points in time. A test for first-order autocorrelation: **Durbin-Watson test**

Guide to Time Series Analysis

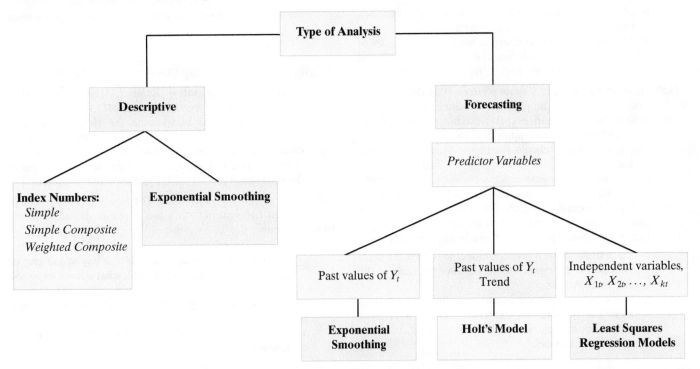

Supplementary Exercises 14.57–14.71

Applying the Concepts—Basic

14.57 Insured Social Security workers. Workers insured under the Social Security program are categorized as fully and permanently insured, fully but not permanently insured, or insured in the event of disability. The number of workers (in millions) in each insured category from 2000 to 2011 are provided in the accompanying table.

Year	Fully, Permanent	Fully, not Permanent	Event of Disability
2000	140.9	44.9	139.5
2001	142.9	45.2	141.7
2002	144.9	45.3	143.5
2003	147.0	45.0	144.9
2004	149.0	44.8	146.2
2005	151.1	44.7	147.7
2006	153.3	45.1	150.1
2007	155.4	45.6	152.3
2008	157.4	46.0	154.5
2009	159.2	44.8	150.6
2010	161.1	44.6	151.7
2011	163.1	44.3	152.6

Source: The Social Security Administration.

a. Compute a simple composite index for the number of workers in the three insured categories using 2000 as the base period.

b. Is the index, part **a,** a price index or a quantity index?

c. Refer to part **a.** Interpret the index value for 2011.

14.58 Insured Social Security workers (cont'd). Refer to Exercise 14.57.

a. Compute the exponentially smoothed series for the annual number of workers who are fully and permanently insured for Social Security. Use the smoothing constant $w = .5$.

b. Plot the number of workers and the exponentially smoothed values on the same graph.

c. Use exponential smoothing to forecast the number of fully and permanently insured workers in 2012 and 2013. What is the drawback to these forecasts?

14.59 Demand for emergency room services. With the advent of managed care, U.S. hospitals have begun to operate like businesses. More than ever before, hospital administrators need to know and apply the theories and methods taught in business schools. Richmond Memorial Hospital in Richmond, Virginia, uses regression analysis to forecast the demand for emergency room services. Specifically, Richmond Memorial uses data on patient visits to the emergency room during each of the past 10 Augusts to forecast next August's demand. Data for the month of August in a recent 10-year period are shown in the next table.

a. Use a straight-line regression model to construct a point forecast for emergency room demand for each of the next three Augusts.

b. Provide 95% prediction intervals around the forecasts.

c. Describe the potential dangers associated with using simple linear regression to forecast demand for emergency room services.

Year t	Visits	Daily Average Y_t	Year t	Visits	Daily Average Y_t
1	1,367	44.09	6	3,019	97.38
2	1,642	52.96	7	2,794	90.12
3	1,780	57.41	8	2,846	91.80
4	2,060	66.45	9	3,001	96.80
5	2,257	72.80	10	3,548	114.45

d. Which other method described in this chapter would be appropriate for forecasting patient visits to the emergency room?

14.60 Retail prices of food items. In 1990, the average weekly food cost for a suburban family of four was estimated to be $154.40. The table below presents the retail prices of four food items for selected years from 1990 to 2010. Assume a typical suburban family of four purchased the following quantities of food, on average, each week during 1990:

Spaghetti	Ground Beef	Eggs	Potatoes
2 lb.	5 lb.	1 doz.	10 lb.

Year	Spaghetti ($/lb.)	Ground Beef ($/lb.)	Eggs ($/doz.)	Potatoes ($/lb.)
1990	.85	1.63	1.00	.32
1995	.88	1.40	1.16	.38
2000	.88	1.63	.96	.35
2005	.87	2.30	1.35	.50
2010	1.19	2.38	1.79	.58

Source: United States Census Bureau.

a. Calculate a Laspeyres price index for 1990 to 2010, using 1990 as the base year.

b. According to your index, how much did the above "basket" of foods increase or decrease in price from 1990 to 2010?

Applying the Concepts—Intermediate

14.61 Mortgage interest rates. Refer to the annual interest rate time series, Exercise 14.41 (p. 14-37). Use $w = .3$ and $v = .7$ to compute the Holt forecasts for 2011–2013. Compare these to the linear regression forecasts obtained in Exercise 14.41 using MAD, MAPE, and RMSE. [*Note:* You will need to obtain the actual values of the time series for 2011–2013 to complete this exercise.]

14.62 Price of Abbott Labs stock. The yearly closing prices of Abbott Laboratories stock are shown in the table on the next page.

a. Use exponential smoothing with $w = .8$ to forecast the 2012 and 2013 closing prices. If you buy at the end of 2011 and sell at the end of 2013, what is your expected gain (loss)?

b. Repeat part **a** using Holt's method with $w = .8$ and $v = .5$.

c. In which forecast do you have more confidence? Explain.

Data for Exercise 14.62

Year	Closing Price	Year	Closing Price
1990	45.00	2001	55.75
1991	68.07	2002	40.00
1992	30.03	2003	46.60
1993	29.05	2004	46.65
1994	32.05	2005	39.43
1995	41.05	2006	48.71
1996	50.75	2007	56.15
1997	65.50	2008	53.37
1998	49.00	2009	53.99
1999	36.31	2010	47.91
2000	48.44	2011	56.23

Source: Yahoo.com.

14.63 Price of Abbott Labs stock (cont'd). Refer to Exercise 14.62.

ABBLAB
  a. Fit a simple linear regression model to the stock price data.
  b. Plot the fitted regression line on a scatterplot of the data.
  c. Forecast the 2012 and 2013 closing prices using the regression model.
  d. Construct 95% prediction intervals for the forecasts of part **c.** Interpret the intervals in the context of the problem.
  e. Obtain the time series residuals for the simple linear model and use the Durbin-Watson d-statistic to test for the presence of autocorrelation.

14.64 Retirement assets. Annual retirement assets (in billions of dollars) for two fund types are given in the table below.

RETIRE
  a. Compute simple indexes for each of the two time series using 2000 as the base period.
  b. Construct a time series plot that displays both indexes.
  c. Using the results of parts **a** and **b,** compare and contrast the two types of funds.

Year	IRA	401(k)
2000	2,629	1,725
2004	3,299	2,189
2005	3,652	2,396
2006	4,207	2,768
2007	4,784	2,982
2008	3,759	2,275
2009	4,230	2,754

Source: United States Census Bureau.

14.65 Quarterly GDP values. The gross domestic product (GDP) is the total U.S. output of goods and services valued at market prices. The quarterly GDP values (in billions of dollars)

QTRGDP

Year	Quarter	GDP	Year	Quarter	GDP
2007	1	13,511		3	13,921
	2	13,738		4	14,087
	3	13,951	2010	1	14,278
	4	14,031		2	14,468
2008	1	14,151		3	14,606
	2	14,295		4	14,755
	3	14,413	2011	1	14,868
	4	14,200		2	15,013
2009	1	13,894		3	15,176
	2	13,854		4	15,319

Source: US Department of Commerce.

for the period 2007–2011 are given in the accompanying table. Using weights $w = .5$ and $v = .5$, calculate Holt forecasts for the four quarters of 2012.

14.66 Quarterly GDP values (cont'd). Refer to Exercise 14.65.
QTRGDP
  a. Use the simple linear regression model fit to the 2007–2011 data to forecast the 2012 quarterly GDP. Place 95% prediction limits on the forecasts.
  b. The GDP values given are *seasonally adjusted,* which means that an attempt to remove seasonality has been made prior to reporting the figures. Add quarterly dummy variables to the model. Use the partial F-test (discussed in Section 12.9) to determine whether the data indicate the significance of the seasonal component. Does the test support the assertion that the GDP figures are seasonally adjusted?
  c. Use the seasonal model to forecast the 2012 quarterly GDP values.
  d. Calculate the time series residuals for the seasonal model and use the Durbin-Watson test to determine whether the residuals are autocorrelated. Use $\alpha = .10$.

14.67 Quarterly GDP values (cont'd). Refer to Exercises 14.65 and 14.66. For each of the forecasting models, apply the MAD, MAPE, and RMSE criteria to evaluate the forecasts for the four quarters of 2012. Which of the forecasting models performs best according to each criterion? (You will need to obtain the actual 2012 GDP values to complete this exercise.)
QTRGDP

14.68 Revolving credit loans. A major portion of total consumer credit extended is in the category of revolving credit loans. Amounts outstanding (in billions of dollars) for the period 1990–2010 are given in the table.
LOANS

Year	Revolving	Year	Revolving
1990	239	2001	716
1991	264	2002	749
1992	278	2003	771
1993	310	2004	800
1994	366	2005	825
1995	444	2006	875
1996	508	2007	942
1997	538	2008	958
1998	579	2009	866
1999	609	2010	801
2000	683		

Source: United States Census Bureau.

  a. Use a simple linear regression model to forecast the 2011 and 2012 values. Place 95% prediction limits on each forecast.
  b. Calculate the Holt forecasts for 2011 and 2011 using $w = .7$ and $v = .7$. Compare the results with the simple linear regression forecasts of part **a.**

14.69 Using the CPI to compute real income. The number of dollars a person receives in a year is referred to as his or her *monetary* (or *money*) *income.* This figure can be adjusted to reflect the purchasing power of the dollars received relative to the purchasing power of dollars in some base period. The result is called a person's *real income.* The CPI can be used to adjust monetary income to obtain real income (in terms of 1984 dollars). To compute your real income for a specific year, simply divide your monetary
CPI

income for that year by that year's CPI and multiply by 100. In Exercise 14.27 (p. 14-24), we listed the CPI for 1990 and 2010 as 125.8 and 218.1, respectively.

a. Suppose your monetary income increased from $50,000 in 1990 to $95,000 in 2010. What were your real incomes in 1990 and 2010? Were you able to buy more goods and services in 1990 or 2010? Explain.

b. What monetary income would have been required in 2010 to provide equivalent purchasing power to a 1990 monetary income of $20,000?

14.70 IBM stock prices. Refer to Example 14.1 (p. 14-5) and the 2011 monthly IBM stock prices.

HITECH a. Use the exponentially smoothed series (with $w = .5$) from January to September 2011 to forecast the monthly values of the IBM stock price from October to December 2011. Calculate the forecast errors.

b. Use a simple linear regression model fit to the IBM stock prices from January to September 2011. Let time t range from 1 to 9, representing the 9 months in the sample. Interpret the least squares estimates.

c. With what approximate precision do you expect to be able to predict the IBM stock price using the regression model?

d. Give the simple linear regression forecasts and the 95% forecast intervals for the October–December 2011 prices. How does the precision of these forecasts agree with the approximation obtained in part **c**?

e. Compare the exponential smoothing forecasts, part **a**, to the regression forecasts, part **d**, using MAD, MAPE, and RMSE.

f. What assumptions does the random error component of the regression model have to satisfy in order to make

the model inferences (such as the forecast intervals in part **c**) valid?

g. Test to determine whether there is evidence of first-order positive autocorrelation in the random error component of the regression model. Use $\alpha = .05$. What can you infer about the validity of the model inferences?

14.71 Forecasting foreign exchange rates. T. C. Chiang considered several time series forecasting models of future foreign exchange rates for U.S. currency (*The Journal of Financial Research*, Summer 1986). One popular theory among financial analysts is that the forward (90-day) exchange rate is a useful predictor of the future spot exchange rate. Using monthly data on exchange rates for the British pound for $n = 81$ months, Chiang fit the model $E(Y_t) = \beta_0 + \beta_1 x_{t-1}$, where $Y_t = \ln(\text{spot rate})$ in month t, and $x_{i=1} = \ln(\text{forward rate})$ in month $t - 1$. The analysis yielded the following results:

$$t\text{-value} = 47.9, \quad s = .025, \quad R^2 = .957,$$
$$\text{Durbin-Watson } d = .962$$

a. Is the model statistically useful for forecasting future spot exchange rates for the British pound? Test using $\alpha = .05$.

b. Interpret the values of s and R^2.

c. Is there evidence of positive autocorrelation among the residuals? Test using $\alpha = .05$.

d. Based on the results of parts **a–c**, would you recommend using the model to forecast spot exchange rates?

Activity 14.1 Time Series

For this activity select a recurring quantity from your own life for which you have monthly records for at least 2 years. This might be the cost of a utility bill, the number of cell phone minutes used, or even your income. If you do not have access to such records, use the Internet to find similar data, such as median monthly home prices in your area for at least 2 years.

1. Which methods from this chapter might apply to your data? Does there appear to be a seasonal component affecting the data? If so, can you explain the seasonal effect in simple terms?

2. Use methods from this chapter to predict the value of your quantity for the next year. Be prepared to defend your choice of methods.

References

Abraham, B., & Ledholter, J. *Statistical Methods for Forecasting*. New York: Wiley, 1983 (paperback, 2005; online, 2008).

Anderson, T. W. *The Statistical Analysis of Time Series*. New York: Wiley, 1971 (paperback, 1994).

Box, G. E. P., Jenkins, G. M., & Reinsel, G. C. *Time Series Analysis: Forecasting and Control*, 4th ed. New York: Wiley, 2008.

Chipman, J. S. "Efficiency of Least Squares Estimation of Linear Trend When Residuals Are Autocorrelated." *Econometrica*, Vol. 47, 1979.

Durbin, J., & Watson, G. S. "Testing for Serial Correlation in Least Squares Regression, I." *Biometrika*, Vol. 37, 1950, pp. 409–428.

Durbin, J., & Watson, G. S. "Testing for Serial Correlation in Least Squares Regression, II." *Biometrika*, Vol. 38, 1951, pp. 159–178.

Durbin, J., & Watson, G. S. "Testing for Serial Correlation in Least Squares Regression, III." *Biometrika*, Vol. 58, 1971, pp. 1–19.

Evans, M. *Practical Business Forecasting*. New York: Wiley-Blackwell, 2002.

Fuller, W. A. *Introduction to Statistical Time Series*, 2nd ed. New York: Wiley, 1996 (online, 2008).

Granger, C. W. J., & Newbold, P. *Forecasting Economic Time Series*, 2nd ed. New York: Academic Press, 1986.

Greene, W. H. *Econometric Analysis*, 7th ed. Upper Saddle River, N.J.: Prentice Hall, 2008.

Hamilton, J. D. *Time Series Analysis*. Princeton: Princeton University Press, 1994.

Harvey, A. *Time Series Models*, 2nd ed. Cambridge: MIT Press, 1993.

Maddala, G. S., & Lahiri, K. *Introduction to Econometrics*, 4th ed. New York: Wiley, 2010.

Makridakis, S., et al. *The Forecasting Accuracy of Major Time Series Methods*. New York: Wiley, 1984.

Nelson, C. R. *Applied Time Series Analysis for Managerial Forecasting*. San Francisco: Holden-Day, 1990.

Shively, T. S. "Fast Evaluation of the Distribution of the Durbin-Watson and Other Invariant Test Statistics in Time Series Regression." *Journal of the American Statistical Association*, Vol. 85, 1990.

Theil, H. *Principles of Econometrics*. New York: Wiley, 1971.

White, K. J. "The Durbin-Watson Test for Autocorrelation in Nonlinear Models." *Review of Economics and Statistics*, Vol. 74, 1992.

Willis, R. E. *A Guide to Forecasting for Planners*. Englewood Cliffs, N.J.: Prentice Hall, 1987.

USING TECHNOLOGY	Technology images shown here are taken from SPSS Statistics Professional 20.0, Minitab 16, XLSTAT for Pearson, and Excel 2010.

SPSS: Forecasting

Exponential Smoothing or Holt's Method

Step 1 Within SPSS, open the data file containing the time series data.

Step 2 There are no point-and-click options for exponential smoothing in SPSS. Rather, you must enter the appropriate program commands (called syntax) to generate the results. Click the "File" button on the Excel main menu bar, then "New," and click "Syntax," as shown in Figure 14.S.1.

Figure 14.S.1 SPSS menu options for creating program commands

Step 3 On the resulting dialog box, enter the commands for exponential smoothing (see Figure 14.S.2) or Holt's method (see Figure 14.S.3). In both programs, the time series variable to be forecasted (e.g., SALES) follows the "EXSMOOTH" command. Use "MODEL=SINGLE" for exponential smoothing and "MODEL=HOLT" for Holt's method. "ALPHA" represents the smoothing constant, and "GAMMA" represents the trend smoothing constant. Use the "INITIAL" command to specify the initial value in the forecast (this is usually the value of the time series variable at time 1).

Figure 14.S.2 SPSS program commands for forecasting with exponential smoothing

Step 4 Click "Run," then "All" to generate the forecasts. (These forecasts will be added to the SPSS data file.)

Figure 14.S.3 SPSS program commands for Holt's forecasting method

Regression

Step 1 Click the "Analyze" button on the SPSS main menu bar, then click on "Regression" and "Linear." (See Using Technology, Chapter 12.)

Step 2 Specify the dependent time series variable in the "Dependent" box and the independent variables in the model in the "Independent(s)" box. Click "Save" and make the appropriate menu selections to save the forecasted values as well as 95% prediction intervals.

Step 3 To conduct the Durbin-Watson test for autocorrelated errors, click on the "Statistics" button to obtain the menu shown in Figure 14.S.4. Check the "Durbin-Watson" box and then click "Continue" to return to the "Linear Regression" dialog box. Click "OK" to view the results.

Figure 14.S.4 SPSS linear regression statistics menu

Minitab: Forecasting

Exponential Smoothing or Holt's method

Step 1 Click the "Stat" button on the Minitab main menu bar and then click on "Time Series." This will produce the menu list shown in Figure 14.M.1.

Figure 14.M.1 Minitab options for time series analysis

Step 2 Click on "Single Exp Smoothing" for the exponential smoothing method or "Double Exp Smoothing" for Holt's method with trend. For example, clicking "Single Exp Smoothing" will result in the dialog box shown in Figure 14.M.2.

Figure 14.M.2 Minitab exponential smoothing dialog box

Step 3 Select the quantitative variable to be smoothed and place it in the "Variable" box and set the value of the smoothing constant in the "Weight to Use in Smoothing" box.

Step 4 Select the "Options" box and specify "1" where Minitab asks for the number of observations to use for the initial smoothed value. As an option, you can store the forecast values by selecting "Storage" and making the appropriate selections.

Step 5 Click "OK" to view the results.

Regression

Step 1 Click the "Stat" button on the Minitab main menu bar and then click on "Regression" and "Regression" again. (See Using Technology, Chapter 12.)

Step 2 Specify the dependent time series variable in the "Response" box and the independent variables in the model in the "Predictors" box.

Step 3 Click "Options" to display the Regression Options dialog box. As shown in Figure 14.M.3, you may select "Durbin-Watson statistic" to conduct a test for autocorrelated errors and/or make selections for producing a prediction interval for a future value of the time series variable.

Figure 14.M.3 Minitab regression options

Step 4 Click "Storage" and make the appropriate menu selections to save the forecasted values as well as 95% prediction intervals. (These values will appear on the Minitab worksheet.)

Step 5 Click "OK" on the Linear Regression dialog box to produce the forecasts.

Note: Time series forecasting methods are not yet available in the student version of Excel/XLSTAT.

☐ Appendix A: Summation Notation

Denote the measurements of a quantitative data set as follows: $x_1, x_2, x_3, \ldots, x_n$, where x_1 is the first measurement in the data set, x_2 is the second measurement in the data set, x_3 is the third measurement in the data set, . . . , and x_n is the nth (and last) measurement in the data set. Thus, if we have five measurements in a set of data, we will write x_1, x_2, x_3, x_4, x_5 to represent the measurements. If the actual numbers are 5, 3, 8, 5, and 4, we have $x_1 = 5$, $x_2 = 3, x_3 = 8, x_4 = 5$, and $x_5 = 4$.

Most of the formulas used in this text require a summation of numbers. For example, one sum is the sum of all the measurements in the data set, or $x_1 + x_2 + x_3 + \cdots + x_n$. To shorten the notation, we use the symbol Σ for the summation–that is, $x_1 + x_2 + x_3 + \cdots + x_n = \sum_{i=1}^{n} x_i$. Verbally translate $\sum_{i=1}^{n} x_i$ as follows: "The sum of the measurements, whose typical member is x_i, beginning with the member x_1 and ending with the member x_n."

Suppose, as in our earlier example, that $x_1 = 5, x_2 = 3, x_3 = 8, x_4 = 5$, and $x_5 = 4$. Then the sum of the five measurements, denoted $\sum_{i=1}^{n} x_i$, is obtained as follows:

$$\sum_{i=1}^{5} x_i = x_1 + x_2 + x_3 + x_4 + x_5$$
$$= 5 + 3 + 8 + 5 + 4 = 25$$

Another important calculation requires that we square each measurement and then sum the squares. The notation for this sum is $\sum_{i=1}^{n} x_i^2$. For the preceding five measurements, we have

$$\sum_{i=1}^{5} x_i^2 = x_1^2 + x_2^2 + x_3^2 + x_4^2 + x_5^2$$
$$= 5^2 + 3^2 + 8^2 + 5^2 + 4^2$$
$$= 25 + 9 + 64 + 25 + 16 = 139$$

In general, the symbol following the summation sign represents the variable (or function of the variable) that is to be summed.

The Meaning of Summation Notation $\sum_{i=1}^{n} x_i$

Sum the measurements on the variable that appears to the right of the summation symbol, beginning with the 1st measurement and ending with the nth measurement.

Example A.1
Finding a Sum

Problem A sample data set contains the following six measurements: 5, 1, 3, 0, 2, 1. Find

$$\sum_{i=1}^{n} x_i$$

Solution For these data, the sample size $n = 6$. The measurements are denoted $x_1 = 5$, $x_2 = 1, x_3 = 3, x_4 = 0, x_5 = 2$, and $x_6 = 5$. Then

$$\sum_{i=1}^{n} x_i = x_1 + x_2 + x_3 + x_4 + x_5 + x_6 = 5 + 1 + 3 + 0 + 2 + 1 = 12$$

Example A.2

Finding a Sum of Squares

Problem Refer to Example A.1. Find

$$\sum_{i=1}^{n} x_i^2$$

Solution Now we desire the sum of squares of the six measurements.

$$\sum_{i=1}^{n} x_i^2 = x_1^2 + x_2^2 + x_3^2 + x_4^2 + x_5^2 + x_6^2 = 5^2 + 1^2 + 3^2 + 0^2 + 2^2 + 1^2$$

$$= 25 + 1 + 9 + 0 + 4 + 1 = 40$$

Example A.3

Finding a Sum of Differences

Problem Refer to Example A.1. Find

$$\sum_{i=1}^{n} (x_i - 2)$$

Solution Here, we subtract 2 from each measurement, then sum the six differences.

$$\sum_{i=1}^{n} (x_i - 2) = (x_1 - 2) + (x_2 - 2) + (x_3 - 2) + (x_4 - 2) + (x_5 - 2) + (x_6 - 2)$$

$$= (5 - 2) + (1 - 2) + (3 - 2) + (0 - 2) + (2 - 2) + (1 - 2)$$

$$= 3 + (-1) + 1 + (-2) + 0 + (-1) = 0$$

☐ Appendix B: Basic Counting Rules

Sample points associated with many experiments have identical characteristics. If you can develop a counting rule to count the number of sample points, it can be used to aid in the solution of many probability problems. For example, many experiments involve sampling n elements from a population of N. Then, as explained in Section 3.1, we can use the formula

$$\binom{N}{n} = \frac{N!}{n!(N-n)!}$$

to find the number of different samples of n elements that could be selected from the total of N elements. This gives the number of sample points for the experiment.

Here, we give you a few useful counting rules. You should learn the characteristics of the situation to which each rule applies. Then, when working a probability problem, carefully examine the experiment to see whether you can use one of the rules.

Learning how to decide whether a particular counting rule applies to an experiment takes patience and practice. If you want to develop this skill, try to use the rules to solve some of the exercises in Chapter 3. Proofs of the rules below can be found in the text by W. Feller listed in the references to Chapter 3.

Multiplicative Rule

You have k sets of different elements, n_1 in the first set, n_2 in the second set,..., and n_k in the kth set. Suppose you want to form a sample of k elements by *taking one element from each of the* k *sets*. The number of different samples that can be formed is the product

$$n_1 \cdot n_2 \cdot n_3 \cdot \, \cdots \, \cdot n_k$$

Example B.1

Applying the Multiplicative Rule

Problem A product can be shipped by four airlines, and each airline can ship via three different routes. How many distinct ways exist to ship the product?

Solution A method of shipment corresponds to a pairing of one airline and one route. Therefore, $k = 2$, the number of airlines is $n_1 = 4$, the number of routes is $n_2 = 3$, and the number of ways to ship the product is

$$n_1 \cdot n_2 = (4)(3) = 12$$

Look Back How the multiplicative rule works can be seen by using a tree diagram, introduced in Section 3.6. The airline choice is shown by three branching lines in Figure B.1.

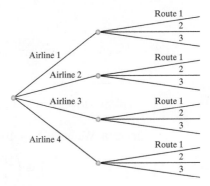

Figure B.1

Tree diagram for airline example

783

Example B.2	**Problem** You have 20 candidates for three different executive positions, E_1, E_2, and E_3. How many different ways could you fill the positions?
Applying the Multiplicative Rule	

Solution For this example, there are $k = 3$ sets of elements:

  Set 1: The candidates available to fill position E_1
  Set 2: The candidates remaining (after filling E_1) that are available to fill E_2
  Set 3: The candidates remaining (after filling E_1 and E_2) that are available to fill E_3

The numbers of elements in the sets are $n_1 = 20$, $n_2 = 19$, and $n_3 = 18$. Thus, the number of different ways to fill the three positions is

$$n_1 \cdot n_2 \cdot n_3 = (20)(19)(18) = 6{,}480$$

Partitions Rule

You have a *single* set of N distinctly different elements, and you want to partition it into k sets, the first set containing n_1 elements, the second containing n_2 elements,..., and the kth containing n_k elements. The number of different partitions is

$$\frac{N!}{n_1! n_2! \cdot \cdots \cdot n_k!} \quad \text{where } n_1 + n_2 + n_3 + \cdots + n_k = N$$

Example B.3	**Problem** You have 12 construction workers available for 3 job sites. Suppose you want to assign 3 workers to job 1, 4 to job 2, and 5 to job 3. How many different ways could you make this assignment?
Applying the Partitions Rule	

Solution For this example, $k = 3$ (corresponding to the $k = 3$ job sites), $N = 12$, and $n_1 = 3$, $n_2 = 4$, $n_3 = 5$. Then the number of different ways to assign the workers to the job sites is

$$\frac{N!}{n_1! n_2! n_3!} = \frac{12!}{3!4!5!} = \frac{12 \cdot 11 \cdot 10 \cdot \cdots \cdot 3 \cdot 2 \cdot 1}{(3 \cdot 2 \cdot 1)(4 \cdot 3 \cdot 2 \cdot 1)(5 \cdot 4 \cdot 3 \cdot 2 \cdot 1)} = 27{,}720$$

Combinations Rule

The combinations rule given in Chapter 3 is a special case ($k = 2$) of the partitions rule—that is, sampling is equivalent to partitioning a set of N elements into $k = 2$ groups: elements that appear in the sample and those that do not. Let $n_1 = n$, the number of elements in the sample, and $n_2 = N - n$, the number of elements remaining. Then the number of different samples of n elements that can be selected from N is

$$\frac{N!}{n_1! n_2!} = \frac{N!}{n!(N - n)!} = \binom{N}{n}$$

This formula was given in Section 3.1.

Example B.4	**Problem** How many samples of 4 firefighters can be selected from a group of 10?
Applying the Combinations Rule	

Solution We have $N = 10$ and $n = 4$; then

$$\binom{N}{n} = \binom{10}{4} = \frac{10!}{4!6!} = \frac{10 \cdot 9 \cdot 8 \cdot \cdots \cdot 3 \cdot 2 \cdot 1}{(4 \cdot 3 \cdot 2 \cdot 1)(6 \cdot 5 \cdot \cdots \cdot 2 \cdot 1)} = 210$$

Permutations Rule

The permutations rule is a generalization of the combinations rule where the order of the elements selected from the sample is important. (It can also be viewed as a special cases of the multiplicative rule.) A particular order is called a *permutation*. The number of different permutations of n elements that can be selected from a population of N elements is

$$\frac{N!}{(N - n)!} = N(N - 1)(N - 2) \cdots (N - n + 1)$$

Example   B.5

Applying the Permutations Rule

Problem There are three different entrances to a burning building. A fire captain must select three firefighters to enter the building, one for each entrance. The first firefighter selected will enter through the front door, the second through the back door, and the third one through a hole in the roof. How many permutations of three firefighters can be selected from a crew of 10 firefighters?

Solution Here we have $N = 10$ and $n = 3$. Since the order of selection is important, we apply the permutations rule:

$$\frac{N!}{(N - n)!} = \frac{10!}{(10 - 3)!} = \frac{10!}{7!} = \frac{10 \cdot 9 \cdot 8 \cdot 7 \cdot 6 \cdot 5 \cdot 4 \cdot 3 \cdot 2 \cdot 1}{7 \cdot 6 \cdot 5 \cdot 4 \cdot 3 \cdot 2 \cdot 1} = 10 \cdot 9 \cdot 8 = 720$$

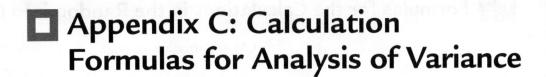

Appendix C: Calculation Formulas for Analysis of Variance

C.1 Formulas for the Calculations in the Completely Randomized Design

$$CM = \text{Correction for mean}$$

$$= \frac{(\text{Total of all observations})^2}{\text{Total number of observations}} = \frac{\left(\sum\limits_{i=1}^{n} y_i\right)^2}{n}$$

$$SS(\text{Total}) = \text{Total sum of squares}$$

$$= (\text{Sum of squares of all observations}) - CM = \sum_{i=1}^{n} y_i^2 - CM$$

$$SST = \text{Sum of squares for treatments}$$

$$= \left(\begin{array}{c}\text{Sum of squares of treatment totals with}\\\text{each square divided by the number of}\\\text{observations for that treatment}\end{array}\right) - CM$$

$$= \frac{T_1^2}{n_1} + \frac{T_2^2}{n_2} + \cdots + \frac{T_k^2}{n_k} - CM$$

$$SSE = \text{Sum of squares for error} = SS(\text{Total}) - SST$$

$$MST = \text{Mean square for treatments} = \frac{SST}{k-1}$$

$$MSE = \text{Mean square for error} = \frac{SSE}{n-k}$$

$$F = \text{Test statistic} = \frac{MST}{MSE}$$

where

$$n = \text{Total number of observations}$$
$$k = \text{Number of treatments}$$
$$T_i = \text{Total for treatment } i \ (i = 1, 2, \ldots, k)$$

C.2 Formulas for the Calculations in the Randomized Block Design

$$CM = \text{Correction for mean}$$

$$= \frac{(\text{Total of all observations})^2}{\text{Total number of observations}} = \frac{\left(\sum y_i\right)^2}{n}$$

$$SS(\text{Total}) = \text{Total sum of squares}$$

$$= (\text{Sum of squares of all observations}) - CM = \sum y_i^2 - CM$$

$$SST = \text{Sum of squares for treatments}$$

$$= \left(\begin{array}{c}\text{Sum of squares of treatment totals with} \\ \text{each square divided by } b, \text{ the number of} \\ \text{observations for that treatment}\end{array}\right) - CM$$

$$= \frac{T_1^2}{b} + \frac{T_2^2}{b} + \cdots + \frac{T_p^2}{b} - CM$$

$$SST = \text{Sum of squares for blocks}$$

$$= \left(\begin{array}{c}\text{Sum of squares of block totals with} \\ \text{each square divided by } k, \text{ the number} \\ \text{of observations in that block}\end{array}\right) - CM$$

$$= \frac{B_1^2}{k} + \frac{B_2^2}{k} + \cdots + \frac{B_b^2}{k} - CM$$

$$SSE = \text{Sum of squares for error} = SS(\text{Total}) - SST - SSB$$

$$MST = \text{Mean square for treatments} = \frac{SST}{k-1}$$

$$MSB = \text{Mean square for blocks} = \frac{SSB}{b-1}$$

$$MSE = \text{Mean square for error} = \frac{SSE}{n-k-b+1}$$

$$F = \text{Test statistic} = \frac{MST}{MSE}$$

where

$$n = \text{Total number of observations}$$

$$b = \text{Number of blocks}$$

$$k = \text{Number of treatments}$$

$$T_i = \text{Total for treatment } i \ (i = 1, 2, \ldots, k)$$

$$B_i = \text{Total for block } i \ (i = 1, 2, \ldots, b)$$

C.3 Formulas for the Calculations for a Two-Factor Factorial Experiment

$$
\text{CM} = \text{Correction for mean}
$$

$$
= \frac{(\text{Total of all } n \text{ measurements})^2}{n} = \frac{\left(\sum_{i=1}^{n} y_i\right)^2}{n}
$$

$$
\text{SS(Total)} = \text{Total sum of squares}
$$

$$
= (\text{Sum of squares of all } n \text{ measurements}) - \text{CM} = \sum_{i=1}^{n} y_i^2 - \text{CM}
$$

$$
\text{SS}(A) = \text{Sum of squares for main effects, factor } A
$$

$$
= \left(\begin{array}{c} \text{Sum of squares of the totals } A_1, A_2, \ldots, A_a \\ \text{divided by the number of measurements} \\ \text{in a single total, namely } br \end{array}\right) - \text{CM}
$$

$$
= \frac{\sum_{i=1}^{a} A_i^2}{br} - \text{CM}
$$

$$
\text{SS}(B) = \text{Sum of squares for main effects, factor } B
$$

$$
= \left(\begin{array}{c} \text{Sum of squares of the totals } B_1, B_2, \ldots, B_b \\ \text{divided by the number of measurements} \\ \text{in a single total, namely } ar \end{array}\right) - \text{CM}
$$

$$
= \frac{\sum_{i=1}^{b} B_i^2}{ar} - \text{CM}
$$

$$
\text{SS}(AB) = \text{Sum of squares for } AB \text{ interaction}
$$

$$
= \left(\begin{array}{c} \text{Sum of squares of the cell totals} \\ AB_{11}, AB_{12}, \ldots, AB_{ab} \text{ divided by} \\ \text{the number of measurements} \\ \text{in a single total, namely } r \end{array}\right) - \text{SS}(A) - \text{SS}(B) - \text{CM}
$$

$$
= \frac{\sum_{j=1}^{b} \sum_{i=1}^{a} AB_{ij}^2}{r} - \text{SS}(A) - \text{SS}(B) - \text{CM}
$$

where

$a = $ Number of levels of factor A

$b = $ Number of levels of factor B

$r = $ Number of replicates (observations per treatment)

$A_i = $ Total for level i of factor A ($i = 1, 2, \ldots, a$)

$B_j = $ Total for level j of factor B ($j = 1, 2, \ldots, b$)

$AB_{ij} = $ Total for treatment (i, j), i.e., for ith level of factor A and jth level of factor B

C.4 Tukey's Multiple Comparisons Procedure (Equal Sample Sizes)

Step 1 Select the desired experimentwise error rate, α

Step 2 Calculate

$$\omega = q_\alpha(k, v) \frac{s}{\sqrt{n_t}}$$

where

k = Number of sample means (i.e., number of treatments)

$s = \sqrt{\text{MSE}}$

v = Number of degress of freedom associated with MSE

n_t = Number of observations in each of the k samples (i.e., number of observations per treatment)

$q_\alpha(k, v)$ = Critical value of the Studentized range (Table XV in Appendix D)

Step 3 Calculate and rank the k sample means.

Step 4 Place a bar over those pairs of treatment means that differ by less than ω. A pair of treatments not connected by an overbar (i.e., differing by more than ω) implies a difference in the corresponding population means.

Note: The confidence level associated with all inferences drawn from the analysis is $(1 - \alpha)$.

C.5 Bonferroni Multiple Comparisons Procedure (Pairwise Comparisons)

Step 1 Calculate for each treatment pair (i, j)

$$B_{ij} = t_{\alpha/(2c)} s \sqrt{\frac{1}{n_i} + \frac{1}{n_j}}$$

where

k = Number of sample (treatment) means in the experiment

c = Number of pairwise comparisons

[*Note:* If all pairwise comparisons are to be made, then $c = k(k - 1)/2$]

$s = \sqrt{\text{MSE}}$

v = Number of degrees of freedom associated with MSE

n_i = Number of observations in sample for treatment i

n_j = Number of observations in sample for treatment j

$t_{\alpha/(2c)}$ = Critical value of t distribution with v df and tail area $\alpha/(2c)$ (Table III in Appendix D)

Step 2 Rank the sample means and place a bar over any treatment pair (i, j) whose sample means differ by less than B_{ij}. Any pair of means not connected by an overbar implies a difference in the corresponding population means.

Note: The level of confidence associated with all inferences drawn from the analysis is at least $(1 - \alpha)$.

C.6 Scheffé's Multiple Comparisons Procedure (Pairwise Comparisons)

Step 1   Calculate Scheffé's critical difference for each pair of treatments (i, j):

$$S_{ij} = \sqrt{(k - 1)(F_\alpha)(\text{MSE})\left(\frac{1}{n_1} + \frac{1}{n_j}\right)}$$

where

k = Number of sample (treatment) means

MSE = Mean squared error

n_i = Number of observations in sample for treatment i

n_j = Number of observations in sample for treatment j

F_α = Critical value of F-distribution with $k - 1$ numerator df and v denominator df (Tables V, VI, VII, and VIII in Appendix D)

v = Number of degrees of freedom associated with MSE

Step 2   Rank the k sample means and place a bar over any treatment pair (i, j) that differs by less than S_{ij}. Any pair of sample means not connected by an overbar implies a difference in the corresponding population means.

◻ Appendix D: Tables

Table I	Binomial Probabilities

Tabulated values are $\sum_{x=0}^{k} p(x)$. *(Computations are rounded at the third decimal place.)*

a. *n* = 5

p k	.01	.05	.10	.20	.30	.40	.50	.60	.70	.80	.90	.95	.99
0	.951	.774	.590	.328	.168	.078	.031	.010	.002	.000	.000	.000	.000
1	.999	.977	.919	.737	.528	.337	.188	.087	.031	.007	.000	.000	.000
2	1.000	.999	.991	.942	.837	.683	.500	.317	.163	.058	.009	.001	.000
3	1.000	1.000	1.000	.993	.969	.913	.812	.663	.472	.263	.081	.023	.001
4	1.000	1.000	1.000	1.000	.998	.990	.969	.922	.832	.672	.410	.226	.049

b. *n* = 6

p k	.01	.05	.10	.20	.30	.40	.50	.60	.70	.80	.90	.95	.99
0	.941	.735	.531	.262	.118	.047	.016	.004	.001	.000	.000	.000	.000
1	.999	.967	.886	.655	.420	.233	.109	.041	.011	.002	.000	.000	.000
2	1.000	.998	.984	.901	.744	.544	.344	.179	.070	.017	.001	.000	.000
3	1.000	1.000	.999	.983	.930	.821	.656	.456	.256	.099	.016	.002	.000
4	1.000	1.000	1.000	.998	.989	.959	.891	.767	.580	.345	.114	.033	.001
5	1.000	1.000	1.000	1.000	.999	.996	.984	.953	.882	.738	.469	.265	.059

c. *n* = 7

p k	.01	.05	.10	.20	.30	.40	.50	.60	.70	.80	.90	.95	.99
0	.932	.698	.478	.210	.082	.028	.008	.002	.000	.000	.000	.000	.000
1	.998	.956	.850	.577	.329	.159	.063	.019	.004	.000	.000	.000	.000
2	1.000	.996	.974	.852	.647	.420	.227	.096	.029	.005	.000	.000	.000
3	1.000	1.000	.997	.967	.874	.710	.500	.290	.126	.033	.003	.000	.000
4	1.000	1.000	1.000	.995	.971	.904	.773	.580	.353	.148	.026	.004	.000
5	1.000	1.000	1.000	1.000	.996	.981	.937	.841	.671	.423	.150	.044	.002
6	1.000	1.000	1.000	1.000	1.000	.998	.992	.972	.918	.790	.522	.302	.068

d. *n* = 8

p k	.01	.05	.10	.20	.30	.40	.50	.60	.70	.80	.90	.95	.99
0	.923	.663	.430	.168	.058	.017	.004	.001	.000	.000	.000	.000	.000
1	.997	.943	.813	.503	.255	.106	.035	.009	.001	.000	.000	.000	.000
2	1.000	.994	.962	.797	.552	.315	.145	.050	.011	.001	.000	.000	.000
3	1.000	1.000	.995	.944	.806	.594	.363	.174	.058	.010	.000	.000	.000
4	1.000	1.000	1.000	.990	.942	.826	.637	.406	.194	.056	.005	.000	.000
5	1.000	1.000	1.000	.999	.989	.950	.855	.685	.448	.203	.038	.006	.000
6	1.000	1.000	1.000	1.000	.999	.991	.965	.894	.745	.497	.187	.057	.003
7	1.000	1.000	1.000	1.000	1.000	.999	.996	.983	.942	.832	.570	.337	.077

(continued)

Table I	(continued)

e. $n = 9$

k \ p	.01	.05	.10	.20	.30	.40	.50	.60	.70	.80	.90	.95	.99
0	.914	.630	.387	.134	.040	.010	.002	.000	.000	.000	.000	.000	.000
1	.997	.929	.775	.436	.196	.071	.020	.004	.000	.000	.000	.000	.000
2	1.000	.992	.947	.738	.463	.232	.090	.025	.004	.000	.000	.000	.000
3	1.000	.999	.992	.914	.730	.483	.254	.099	.025	.003	.000	.000	.000
4	1.000	1.000	.999	.980	.901	.733	.500	.267	.099	.020	.001	.000	.000
5	1.000	1.000	1.000	.997	.975	.901	.746	.517	.270	.086	.008	.001	.000
6	1.000	1.000	1.000	1.000	.996	.975	.910	.768	.537	.262	.053	.008	.000
7	1.000	1.000	1.000	1.000	1.000	.996	.980	.929	.804	.564	.225	.071	.003
8	1.000	1.000	1.000	1.000	1.000	1.000	.998	.990	.960	.866	.613	.370	.086

f. $n = 10$

k \ p	.01	.05	.10	.20	.30	.40	.50	.60	.70	.80	.90	.95	.99
0	.904	.599	.349	.107	.028	.006	.001	.000	.000	.000	.000	.000	.000
1	.996	.914	.736	.376	.149	.046	.011	.002	.000	.000	.000	.000	.000
2	1.000	.988	.930	.678	.383	.167	.055	.012	.002	.000	.000	.000	.000
3	1.000	.999	.987	.879	.650	.382	.172	.055	.011	.001	.000	.000	.000
4	1.000	1.000	.998	.967	.850	.633	.377	.166	.047	.006	.000	.000	.000
5	1.000	1.000	1.000	.994	.953	.834	.623	.367	.150	.033	.002	.000	.000
6	1.000	1.000	1.000	.999	.989	.945	.828	.618	.350	.121	.013	.001	.000
7	1.000	1.000	1.000	1.000	.998	.988	.945	.833	.617	.322	.070	.012	.000
8	1.000	1.000	1.000	1.000	1.000	.998	.989	.954	.851	.624	.264	.086	.004
9	1.000	1.000	1.000	1.000	1.000	1.000	.999	.994	.972	.893	.651	.401	.096

g. $n = 15$

k \ p	.01	.05	.10	.20	.30	.40	.50	.60	.70	.80	.90	.95	.99
0	.860	.463	.206	.035	.005	.000	.000	.000	.000	.000	.000	.000	.000
1	.990	.829	.549	.167	.035	.005	.000	.000	.000	.000	.000	.000	.000
2	1.000	.964	.816	.398	.127	.027	.004	.000	.000	.000	.000	.000	.000
3	1.000	.995	.944	.648	.297	.091	.018	.002	.000	.000	.000	.000	.000
4	1.000	.999	.987	.838	.515	.217	.059	.009	.001	.000	.000	.000	.000
5	1.000	1.000	.998	.939	.722	.403	.151	.034	.004	.000	.000	.000	.000
6	1.000	1.000	1.000	.982	.869	.610	.304	.095	.015	.001	.000	.000	.000
7	1.000	1.000	1.000	.996	.950	.787	.500	.213	.050	.004	.000	.000	.000
8	1.000	1.000	1.000	.999	.985	.905	.696	.390	.131	.018	.000	.000	.000
9	1.000	1.000	1.000	1.000	.996	.966	.849	.597	.278	.061	.002	.000	.000
10	1.000	1.000	1.000	1.000	.999	.991	.941	.783	.485	.164	.013	.001	.000
11	1.000	1.000	1.000	1.000	1.000	.998	.982	.909	.703	.352	.056	.005	.000
12	1.000	1.000	1.000	1.000	1.000	1.000	.996	.973	.873	.602	.184	.036	.000
13	1.000	1.000	1.000	1.000	1.000	1.000	1.000	.995	.965	.833	.451	.171	.010
14	1.000	1.000	1.000	1.000	1.000	1.000	1.000	1.000	.995	.965	.794	.537	.140

(continued)

Table I	(continued)

h. $n = 20$

k \ p	.01	.05	.10	.20	.30	.40	.50	.60	.70	.80	.90	.95	.99
0	.818	.358	.122	.012	.001	.000	.000	.000	.000	.000	.000	.000	.000
1	.983	.736	.392	.069	.008	.001	.000	.000	.000	.000	.000	.000	.000
2	.999	.925	.677	.206	.035	.004	.000	.000	.000	.000	.000	.000	.000
3	1.000	.984	.867	.411	.107	.016	.001	.000	.000	.000	.000	.000	.000
4	1.000	.997	.957	.630	.238	.051	.006	.000	.000	.000	.000	.000	.000
5	1.000	1.000	.989	.804	.416	.126	.021	.002	.000	.000	.000	.000	.000
6	1.000	1.000	.998	.913	.608	.250	.058	.006	.000	.000	.000	.000	.000
7	1.000	1.000	1.000	.968	.772	.416	.132	.021	.001	.000	.000	.000	.000
8	1.000	1.000	1.000	.990	.887	.596	.252	.057	.005	.000	.000	.000	.000
9	1.000	1.000	1.000	.997	.952	.755	.412	.128	.017	.001	.000	.000	.000
10	1.000	1.000	1.000	.999	.983	.872	.588	.245	.048	.003	.000	.000	.000
11	1.000	1.000	1.000	1.000	.995	.943	.748	.404	.113	.010	.000	.000	.000
12	1.000	1.000	1.000	1.000	.999	.979	.868	.584	.228	.032	.000	.000	.000
13	1.000	1.000	1.000	1.000	1.000	.994	.942	.750	.392	.087	.002	.000	.000
14	1.000	1.000	1.000	1.000	1.000	.998	.979	.874	.584	.196	.011	.000	.000
15	1.000	1.000	1.000	1.000	1.000	1.000	.994	.949	.762	.370	.043	.003	.000
16	1.000	1.000	1.000	1.000	1.000	1.000	.999	.984	.893	.589	.133	.016	.000
17	1.000	1.000	1.000	1.000	1.000	1.000	1.000	.996	.965	.794	.323	.075	.001
18	1.000	1.000	1.000	1.000	1.000	1.000	1.000	.999	.992	.931	.608	.264	.017
19	1.000	1.000	1.000	1.000	1.000	1.000	1.000	1.000	.999	.988	.878	.642	.182

i. $n = 25$

k \ p	.01	.05	.10	.20	.30	.40	.50	.60	.70	.80	.90	.95	.99
0	.778	.277	.072	.004	.000	.000	.000	.000	.000	.000	.000	.000	.000
1	.974	.642	.271	.027	.002	.000	.000	.000	.000	.000	.000	.000	.000
2	.998	.873	.537	.098	.009	.000	.000	.000	.000	.000	.000	.000	.000
3	1.000	.966	.764	.234	.033	.002	.000	.000	.000	.000	.000	.000	.000
4	1.000	.993	.902	.421	.090	.009	.000	.000	.000	.000	.000	.000	.000
5	1.000	.999	.967	.617	.193	.029	.002	.000	.000	.000	.000	.000	.000
6	1.000	1.000	.991	.780	.341	.074	.007	.000	.000	.000	.000	.000	.000
7	1.000	1.000	.998	.891	.512	.154	.022	.001	.000	.000	.000	.000	.000
8	1.000	1.000	1.000	.953	.677	.274	.054	.004	.000	.000	.000	.000	.000
9	1.000	1.000	1.000	.983	.811	.425	.115	.013	.000	.000	.000	.000	.000
10	1.000	1.000	1.000	.994	.902	.586	.212	.034	.002	.000	.000	.000	.000
11	1.000	1.000	1.000	.998	.956	.732	.345	.078	.006	.000	.000	.000	.000
12	1.000	1.000	1.000	1.000	.983	.846	.500	.154	.017	.000	.000	.000	.000
13	1.000	1.000	1.000	1.000	.994	.922	.655	.268	.044	.002	.000	.000	.000
14	1.000	1.000	1.000	1.000	.998	.966	.788	.414	.098	.006	.000	.000	.000
15	1.000	1.000	1.000	1.000	1.000	.987	.885	.575	.189	.017	.000	.000	.000
16	1.000	1.000	1.000	1.000	1.000	.996	.946	.726	.323	.047	.000	.000	.000
17	1.000	1.000	1.000	1.000	1.000	.999	.978	.846	.488	.109	.002	.000	.000
18	1.000	1.000	1.000	1.000	1.000	1.000	.993	.926	.659	.220	.009	.000	.000
19	1.000	1.000	1.000	1.000	1.000	1.000	.998	.971	.807	.383	.033	.001	.000
20	1.000	1.000	1.000	1.000	1.000	1.000	1.000	.991	.910	.579	.098	.007	.000
21	1.000	1.000	1.000	1.000	1.000	1.000	1.000	.998	.967	.766	.236	.034	.000
22	1.000	1.000	1.000	1.000	1.000	1.000	1.000	1.000	.991	.902	.463	.127	.002
23	1.000	1.000	1.000	1.000	1.000	1.000	1.000	1.000	.998	.973	.729	.358	.026
24	1.000	1.000	1.000	1.000	1.000	1.000	1.000	1.000	1.000	.996	.928	.723	.222

Table II	Normal Curve Areas

z	.00	.01	.02	.03	.04	.05	.06	.07	.08	.09
.0	.0000	.0040	.0080	.0120	.0160	.0199	.0239	.0279	.0319	.0359
.1	.0398	.0438	.0478	.0517	.0557	.0596	.0636	.0675	.0714	.0753
.2	.0793	.0832	.0871	.0910	.0948	.0987	.1026	.1064	.1103	.1141
.3	.1179	.1217	.1255	.1293	.1331	.1368	.1406	.1443	.1480	.1517
.4	.1554	.1591	.1628	.1664	.1700	.1736	.1772	.1808	.1844	.1879
.5	.1915	.1950	.1985	.2019	.2054	.2088	.2123	.2157	.2190	.2224
.6	.2257	.2291	.2324	.2357	.2389	.2422	.2454	.2486	.2517	.2549
.7	.2580	.2611	.2642	.2673	.2704	.2734	.2764	.2794	.2823	.2852
.8	.2881	.2910	.2939	.2967	.2995	.3023	.3051	.3078	.3106	.3133
.9	.3159	.3186	.3212	.3238	.3264	.3289	.3315	.3340	.3365	.3389
1.0	.3413	.3438	.3461	.3485	.3508	.3531	.3554	.3577	.3599	.3621
1.1	.3643	.3665	.3686	.3708	.3729	.3749	.3770	.3790	.3810	.3830
1.2	.3849	.3869	.3888	.3907	.3925	.3944	.3962	.3980	.3997	.4015
1.3	.4032	.4049	.4066	.4082	.4099	.4115	.4131	.4147	.4162	.4177
1.4	.4192	.4207	.4222	.4236	.4251	.4265	.4279	.4292	.4306	.4319
1.5	.4332	.4345	.4357	.4370	.4382	.4394	.4406	.4418	.4429	.4441
1.6	.4452	.4463	.4474	.4484	.4495	.4505	.4515	.4525	.4535	.4545
1.7	.4554	.4564	.4573	.4582	.4591	.4599	.4608	.4616	.4625	.4633
1.8	.4641	.4649	.4656	.4664	.4671	.4678	.4686	.4693	.4699	.4706
1.9	.4713	.4719	.4726	.4732	.4738	.4744	.4750	.4756	.4761	.4767
2.0	.4772	.4778	.4783	.4788	.4793	.4798	.4803	.4808	.4812	.4817
2.1	.4821	.4826	.4830	.4834	.4838	.4842	.4846	.4850	.4854	.4857
2.2	.4861	.4864	.4868	.4871	.4875	.4878	.4881	.4884	.4887	.4890
2.3	.4893	.4896	.4898	.4901	.4904	.4906	.4909	.4911	.4913	.4916
2.4	.4918	.4920	.4922	.4925	.4927	.4929	.4931	.4932	.4934	.4936
2.5	.4938	.4940	.4941	.4943	.4945	.4946	.4948	.4949	.4951	.4952
2.6	.4953	.4955	.4956	.4957	.4959	.4960	.4961	.4962	.4963	.4964
2.7	.4965	.4966	.4967	.4968	.4969	.4970	.4971	.4972	.4973	.4974
2.8	.4974	.4975	.4976	.4977	.4977	.4978	.4979	.4979	.4980	.4981
2.9	.4981	.4982	.4982	.4983	.4984	.4984	.4985	.4985	.4986	.4986
3.0	.4987	.4987	.4987	.4988	.4988	.4989	.4989	.4989	.4990	.4990
3.1	.49903	.49906	.49910	.49913	.49916	.49918	.49921	.49924	.49926	.48829
3.2	.49931	.49934	.49936	.49938	.49940	.49942	.49944	.49946	.49948	.49950
3.3	.49952	.49953	.49955	.49957	.49958	.49960	.49961	.49962	.49964	.49965
3.4	.49966	.49968	.49969	.49970	.49971	.49972	.49973	.49974	.49975	.49976
3.5	.49977	.49978	.49978	.49979	.49980	.49981	.49981	.49982	.49983	.49983
3.6	.49984	.49985	.49985	.49986	.49986	.49987	.49987	.49988	.49988	.49989
3.7	.49989	.49990	.49990	.49990	.49991	.49991	.49992	.49992	.49992	.49992
3.8	.49993	.49993	.49993	.49994	.49994	.49994	.49994	.49995	.49995	.49995
3.9	.49995	.49995	.49996	.49996	.49996	.49996	.49996	.49996	.49997	.49997

Source: Abridged from Table I of A. Hald. *Statistical Tables and Formulas* (New York: Wiley), 1952. Reproduced by permission of A. Hald.

Table III | Critical Values of *t*

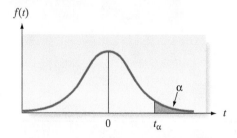

Degrees of Freedom	$t_{.100}$	$t_{.050}$	$t_{.025}$	$t_{.010}$	$t_{.005}$	$t_{.001}$	$t_{.0005}$
1	3.078	6.314	12.706	31.821	63.657	318.31	636.62
2	1.886	2.920	4.303	6.965	9.925	22.326	31.598
3	1.638	2.353	3.182	4.541	5.841	10.213	12.924
4	1.533	2.132	2.776	3.747	4.604	7.173	8.610
5	1.476	2.015	2.571	3.365	4.032	5.893	6.869
6	1.440	1.943	2.447	3.143	3.707	5.208	5.959
7	1.415	1.895	2.365	2.998	3.499	4.785	5.408
8	1.397	1.860	2.306	2.896	3.355	4.501	5.041
9	1.383	1.833	2.262	2.821	3.250	4.297	4.781
10	1.372	1.812	2.228	2.764	3.169	4.144	4.587
11	1.363	1.796	2.201	2.718	3.106	4.025	4.437
12	1.356	1.782	2.179	2.681	3.055	3.930	4.318
13	1.350	1.771	2.160	2.650	3.012	3.852	4.221
14	1.345	1.761	2.145	2.624	2.977	3.787	4.140
15	1.341	1.753	2.131	2.602	2.947	3.733	4.073
16	1.337	1.746	2.120	2.583	2.921	3.686	4.015
17	1.333	1.740	2.110	2.567	2.898	3.646	3.965
18	1.330	1.734	2.101	2.552	2.878	3.610	3.922
19	1.328	1.729	2.093	2.539	2.861	3.579	3.883
20	1.325	1.725	2.086	2.528	2.845	3.552	3.850
21	1.323	1.721	2.080	2.518	2.831	3.527	3.819
22	1.321	1.717	2.074	2.508	2.819	3.505	3.792
23	1.319	1.714	2.069	2.500	2.807	3.485	3.767
24	1.318	1.711	2.064	2.492	2.797	3.467	3.745
25	1.316	1.708	2.060	2.485	2.787	3.450	3.725
26	1.315	1.706	2.056	2.479	2.779	3.435	3.707
27	1.314	1.703	2.052	2.473	2.771	3.421	3.690
28	1.313	1.701	2.048	2.467	2.763	3.408	3.674
29	1.311	1.699	2.045	2.462	2.756	3.396	3.659
30	1.310	1.697	2.042	2.457	2.750	3.385	3.646
40	1.303	1.684	2.021	2.423	2.704	3.307	3.551
50	1.299	1.676	2.009	2.403	2.678	3.261	3.496
60	1.296	1.671	2.000	2.390	2.660	3.232	3.460
70	1.294	1.667	1.994	2.381	2.648	3.211	3.435
80	1.292	1.664	1.990	2.374	2.639	3.195	3.416
90	1.291	1.662	1.987	2.369	2.632	3.183	3.402
100	1.290	1.660	1.984	2.364	2.629	3.174	3.390
120	1.289	1.658	1.980	2.358	2.617	3.160	3.373
150	1.287	1.655	1.976	2.351	2.609	3.145	3.357
∞	1.282	1.645	1.960	2.326	2.576	3.090	3.291

Source: This table is reproduced with the kind permission of the Trustees of Biometrika from E. S. Pearson and H. O. Hartley (eds.). *The Biometrika Tables for Statisticians,.* Vol. 1, 3rd ed., Biometrika, 1966.

Table IV	Critical Values of χ^2

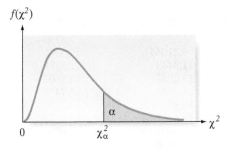

Degrees of Freedom	$\chi^2_{.995}$	$\chi^2_{.990}$	$\chi^2_{.975}$	$\chi^2_{.950}$	$\chi^2_{.900}$
1	.0000393	.0001571	.0009821	.0039321	.0157908
2	.0100251	.0201007	.0506356	.102587	.210720
3	.0717212	.114832	.215795	.351846	.584375
4	.206990	.297110	.484419	.710721	1.063623
5	.411740	.554300	.831211	1.145476	1.61031
6	.675727	.872085	1.237347	1.63539	2.20413
7	.989265	1.239043	1.68987	2.16735	2.83311
8	1.344419	1.646482	2.17973	2.73264	3.48954
9	1.734926	2.087912	2.70039	3.32511	4.16816
10	2.15585	2.55821	3.24697	3.94030	4.86518
11	2.60321	3.05347	3.81575	4.57481	5.57779
12	3.07382	3.57056	4.40379	5.22603	6.30380
13	3.56503	4.10691	5.00874	5.89186	7.04150
14	4.07468	4.66043	5.62872	6.57063	7.78953
15	4.60094	5.22935	6.26214	7.26094	8.54675
16	5.14224	5.81221	6.90766	7.96164	9.31223
17	5.69724	6.40776	7.56418	8.67176	10.0852
18	6.26481	7.01491	8.23075	9.39046	10.8649
19	6.84398	7.63273	8.90655	10.1170	11.6509
20	7.43386	8.26040	9.59083	10.8508	12.4426
21	8.03366	8.89720	10.28293	11.5913	13.2396
22	8.64272	9.54249	10.9823	12.3380	14.0415
23	9.26042	10.19567	11.6885	13.0905	14.8479
24	9.88623	10.8564	12.4011	13.8484	15.6587
25	10.5197	11.5240	13.1197	14.6114	16.4734
26	11.1603	12.1981	13.8439	15.3791	17.2919
27	11.8076	12.8786	14.5733	16.1513	18.1138
28	12.4613	13.5648	15.3079	16.9279	18.9392
29	13.1211	14.2565	16.0471	17.7083	19.7677
30	13.7867	14.9535	16.7908	18.4926	20.5992
40	20.7065	22.1643	24.4331	26.5093	29.0505
50	27.9907	29.7067	32.3574	34.7642	37.6886
60	35.5346	37.4848	40.4817	43.1879	46.4589
70	43.2752	45.4418	48.7576	51.7393	55.3290
80	51.1720	53.5400	57.1532	60.3915	64.2778
90	59.1963	61.7541	65.6466	69.1260	73.2912
100	67.3276	70.0648	74.2219	77.9295	82.3581
150	109.142	112.668	117.985	122.692	128.275
200	152.241	156.432	162.728	168.279	174.835
300	240.663	245.972	253.912	260.878	269.068
400	330.903	337.155	346.482	354.641	364.207
500	422.303	429.388	439.936	449.147	459.926

(continued)

Table IV	(continued)				
Degrees of Freedom	$\chi^2_{.100}$	$\chi^2_{.050}$	$\chi^2_{.025}$	$\chi^2_{.010}$	$\chi^2_{.005}$
1	2.70554	3.84146	5.02389	6.63490	7.87944
2	4.60517	5.99147	7.37776	9.21034	10.5966
3	6.25139	7.81473	9.34840	11.3449	12.8381
4	7.77944	9.48773	11.1433	13.2767	14.8602
5	9.23635	11.0705	12.8325	15.0863	16.7496
6	10.6446	12.5916	14.4494	16.8119	18.5476
7	12.0170	14.0671	16.0128	18.4753	20.2777
8	13.3616	15.5073	17.5346	20.0902	21.9550
9	14.6837	16.9190	19.0228	21.6660	23.5893
10	15.9871	18.3070	20.4831	23.2093	25.1882
11	17.2750	19.6751	21.9200	24.7250	26.7569
12	18.5494	21.0261	23.3367	26.2170	28.2995
13	19.8119	22.3621	24.7356	27.6883	29.8194
14	21.0642	23.6848	26.1190	29.1413	31.3193
15	22.3072	24.9958	27.4884	30.5779	32.8013
16	23.5418	26.2962	28.8454	31.9999	34.2672
17	24.7690	27.5871	30.1910	33.4087	35.7185
18	25.9894	28.8693	31.5264	34.8053	37.1564
19	27.2036	30.1435	32.8523	36.1908	38.5822
20	28.4120	31.4104	34.1696	37.5662	39.9968
21	29.6151	32.6705	35.4789	38.9321	41.4010
22	30.8133	33.9244	36.7807	40.2894	42.7956
23	32.0069	35.1725	38.0757	41.6384	44.1813
24	33.1963	36.4151	39.3641	42.9798	45.5585
25	34.3816	37.6525	40.6465	44.3141	46.9278
26	35.5631	38.8852	41.9232	45.6417	48.2899
27	36.7412	40.1133	43.1944	46.9630	49.6449
28	37.9159	41.3372	44.4607	48.2782	50.9933
29	39.0875	42.5569	45.7222	49.5879	52.3356
30	40.2560	43.7729	46.9792	50.8922	53.6720
40	51.8050	55.7585	59.3417	63.6907	66.7659
50	63.1671	67.5048	71.4202	76.1539	79.4900
60	74.3970	79.0819	83.2976	88.3794	91.9517
70	85.5271	90.5312	95.0231	100.425	104.215
80	96.5782	101.879	106.629	112.329	116.321
90	107.565	113.145	118.136	124.116	128.299
100	118.498	124.342	129.561	135.807	140.169
150	172.578	179.581	185.800	193.208	198.360
200	226.021	233.994	241.058	249.445	255.264
300	331.789	341.395	349.874	359.906	366.844
400	436.649	447.632	457.305	468.724	476.606
500	540.930	553.127	563.852	576.493	585.207

Table V	Percentage Points of the *F*-Distribution, $\alpha = .10$

ν_1				Numerator Degrees of Freedom					
ν_2	1	2	3	4	5	6	7	8	9
1	39.86	49.50	53.59	55.83	57.24	58.20	58.91	59.44	59.86
2	8.53	9.00	9.16	9.24	9.29	9.33	9.35	9.37	9.38
3	5.54	5.46	5.39	5.34	5.31	5.28	5.27	5.25	5.24
4	4.54	4.32	4.19	4.11	4.05	4.01	3.98	3.95	3.94
5	4.06	3.78	3.62	3.52	3.45	3.40	3.37	3.34	3.32
6	3.78	3.46	3.29	3.18	3.11	3.05	3.01	2.98	2.96
7	3.59	3.26	3.07	2.96	2.88	2.83	2.78	2.75	2.72
8	3.46	3.11	2.92	2.81	2.73	2.67	2.62	2.59	2.56
9	3.36	3.01	2.81	2.69	2.61	2.55	2.51	2.47	2.44
10	3.29	2.92	2.73	2.61	2.52	2.46	2.41	2.38	2.35
11	3.23	2.86	2.66	2.54	2.45	2.39	2.34	2.30	2.27
12	3.18	2.81	2.61	2.48	2.39	2.33	2.28	2.24	2.21
13	3.14	2.76	2.56	2.43	2.35	2.28	2.23	2.20	2.16
14	3.10	2.73	2.52	2.39	2.31	2.24	2.19	2.15	2.12
15	3.07	2.70	2.49	2.36	2.27	2.21	2.16	2.12	2.09
16	3.05	2.67	2.46	2.33	2.24	2.18	2.13	2.09	2.06
17	3.03	2.64	2.44	2.31	2.22	2.15	2.10	2.06	2.03
18	3.01	2.62	2.42	2.29	2.20	2.13	2.08	2.04	2.00
19	2.99	2.61	2.40	2.27	2.18	2.11	2.06	2.02	1.98
20	2.97	2.59	2.38	2.25	2.16	2.09	2.04	2.00	1.96
21	2.96	2.57	2.36	2.23	2.14	2.08	2.02	1.98	1.95
22	2.95	2.56	2.35	2.22	2.13	2.06	2.01	1.97	1.93
23	2.94	2.55	2.34	2.21	2.11	2.05	1.99	1.95	1.92
24	2.93	2.54	2.33	2.19	2.10	2.04	1.98	1.94	1.91
25	2.92	2.53	2.32	2.18	2.09	2.02	1.97	1.93	1.89
26	2.91	2.52	2.31	2.17	2.08	2.01	1.96	1.92	1.88
27	2.90	2.51	2.30	2.17	2.07	2.00	1.95	1.91	1.87
28	2.89	2.50	2.29	2.16	2.06	2.00	1.94	1.90	1.87
29	2.89	2.50	2.28	2.15	2.06	1.99	1.93	1.89	1.86
30	2.88	2.49	2.28	2.14	2.05	1.98	1.93	1.88	1.85
40	2.84	2.44	2.23	2.09	2.00	1.93	1.87	1.83	1.79
60	2.79	2.39	2.18	2.04	1.95	1.87	1.82	1.77	1.74
120	2.75	2.35	2.13	1.99	1.90	1.82	1.77	1.72	1.68
∞	2.71	2.30	2.08	1.94	1.85	1.77	1.72	1.67	1.63

(continued)

| Table V | (continued) |

| | | | | | Numerator Degrees of Freedom | | | | | |

ν_2	10	12	15	20	24	30	40	60	120	∞
1	60.19	60.71	61.22	61.74	62.00	62.26	62.53	62.79	63.06	63.33
2	9.39	9.41	9.42	9.44	9.45	9.46	9.47	9.47	9.48	9.49
3	5.23	5.22	5.20	5.18	5.18	5.17	5.16	5.15	5.14	5.13
4	3.92	3.90	3.87	3.84	3.83	3.82	3.80	3.79	3.78	3.76
5	3.30	3.27	3.24	3.21	3.19	3.17	3.16	3.14	3.12	3.10
6	2.94	2.90	2.87	2.84	2.82	2.80	2.78	2.76	2.74	2.72
7	2.70	2.67	2.63	2.59	2.58	2.56	2.54	2.51	2.49	2.47
8	2.54	2.50	2.46	2.42	2.40	2.38	2.36	2.34	2.32	2.29
9	2.42	2.38	2.34	2.30	2.28	2.25	2.23	2.21	2.18	2.16
10	2.32	2.28	2.24	2.20	2.18	2.16	2.13	2.11	2.08	2.06
11	2.25	2.21	2.17	2.12	2.10	2.08	2.05	2.03	2.00	1.97
12	2.19	2.15	2.10	2.06	2.04	2.01	1.99	1.96	1.93	1.90
13	2.14	2.10	2.05	2.01	1.98	1.96	1.93	1.90	1.88	1.85
14	2.10	2.05	2.01	1.96	1.94	1.91	1.89	1.86	1.83	1.80
15	2.06	2.02	1.97	1.92	1.90	1.87	1.85	1.82	1.79	1.76
16	2.03	1.99	1.94	1.89	1.87	1.84	1.81	1.78	1.75	1.72
17	2.00	1.96	1.91	1.86	1.84	1.81	1.78	1.75	1.72	1.69
18	1.98	1.93	1.89	1.84	1.81	1.78	1.75	1.72	1.69	1.66
19	1.96	1.91	1.86	1.81	1.79	1.76	1.73	1.70	1.67	1.63
20	1.94	1.89	1.84	1.79	1.77	1.74	1.71	1.68	1.64	1.61
21	1.92	1.87	1.83	1.78	1.75	1.72	1.69	1.66	1.62	1.59
22	1.90	1.86	1.81	1.76	1.73	1.70	1.67	1.64	1.60	1.57
23	1.89	1.84	1.80	1.74	1.72	1.69	1.66	1.62	1.59	1.55
24	1.88	1.83	1.78	1.73	1.70	1.67	1.64	1.61	1.57	1.53
25	1.87	1.82	1.77	1.72	1.69	1.66	1.63	1.59	1.56	1.52
26	1.86	1.81	1.76	1.71	1.68	1.65	1.61	1.58	1.54	1.50
27	1.85	1.80	1.75	1.70	1.67	1.64	1.60	1.57	1.53	1.49
28	1.84	1.79	1.74	1.69	1.66	1.63	1.59	1.56	1.52	1.48
29	1.83	1.78	1.73	1.68	1.65	1.62	1.58	1.55	1.51	1.47
30	1.82	1.77	1.72	1.67	1.64	1.61	1.57	1.54	1.50	1.46
40	1.76	1.71	1.66	1.61	1.57	1.54	1.51	1.47	1.42	1.38
60	1.71	1.66	1.60	1.54	1.51	1.48	1.44	1.40	1.35	1.29
120	1.65	1.60	1.55	1.48	1.45	1.41	1.37	1.32	1.26	1.19
∞	1.60	1.55	1.49	1.42	1.38	1.34	1.30	1.24	1.17	1.00

Source: From Merrington, M., & Thompson, C. M. "Tables of percentage points of the inverted beta (*F*)-distribution," *Biometrika*, 1943, 33, 73–88. Reproduced by permission of the *Biometrika* Trustees.

Table VI	Percentage Points of the *F*-Distribution, $\alpha = .05$

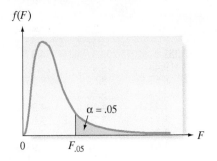

ν_1				Numerator Degrees of Freedom					
ν_2	1	2	3	4	5	6	7	8	9
1	161.4	199.5	215.7	224.6	230.2	234.0	236.8	238.9	240.5
2	18.51	19.00	19.16	19.25	19.30	19.33	19.35	19.37	19.38
3	10.13	9.55	9.28	9.12	9.01	8.94	8.89	8.85	8.81
4	7.71	6.94	6.59	6.39	6.26	6.16	6.09	6.04	6.00
5	6.61	5.79	5.41	5.19	5.05	4.95	4.88	4.82	4.77
6	5.99	5.14	4.76	4.53	4.39	4.28	4.21	4.15	4.10
7	5.59	4.74	4.35	4.12	3.97	3.87	3.79	3.73	3.68
8	5.32	4.46	4.07	3.84	3.69	3.58	3.50	3.44	3.39
9	5.12	4.26	3.86	3.63	3.48	3.37	3.29	3.23	3.18
10	4.96	4.10	3.71	3.48	3.33	3.22	3.14	3.07	3.02
11	4.84	3.98	3.59	3.36	3.20	3.09	3.01	2.95	2.90
12	4.75	3.89	3.49	3.26	3.11	3.00	2.91	2.85	2.80
13	4.67	3.81	3.41	3.18	3.03	2.92	2.83	2.77	2.71
14	4.60	3.74	3.34	3.11	2.96	2.85	2.76	2.70	2.65
15	4.54	3.68	3.29	3.06	2.90	2.79	2.71	2.64	2.59
16	4.49	3.63	3.24	3.01	2.85	2.74	2.66	2.59	2.54
17	4.45	3.59	3.20	2.96	2.81	2.70	2.61	2.55	2.49
18	4.41	3.55	3.16	2.93	2.77	2.66	2.58	2.51	2.46
19	4.38	3.52	3.13	2.90	2.74	2.63	2.54	2.48	2.42
20	4.35	3.49	3.10	2.87	2.71	2.60	2.51	2.45	2.39
21	4.32	3.47	3.07	2.84	2.68	2.57	2.49	2.42	2.37
22	4.30	3.44	3.05	2.82	2.66	2.55	2.46	2.40	2.34
23	4.28	3.42	3.03	2.80	2.64	2.53	2.44	2.37	2.32
24	4.26	3.40	3.01	2.78	2.62	2.51	2.42	2.36	2.30
25	4.24	3.39	2.99	2.76	2.60	2.49	2.40	2.34	2.28
26	4.23	3.37	2.98	2.74	2.59	2.47	2.39	2.32	2.77
27	4.21	3.35	2.96	2.73	2.57	2.46	2.37	2.31	2.25
28	4.20	3.34	2.95	2.71	2.56	2.45	2.36	2.29	2.24
29	4.18	3.33	2.93	2.70	2.55	2.43	2.35	2.28	2.22
30	4.17	3.32	2.92	2.69	2.53	2.42	2.33	2.27	2.21
40	4.08	3.23	2.84	2.61	2.45	2.34	2.25	2.18	2.12
60	4.00	3.15	2.76	2.53	2.37	2.25	2.17	2.10	2.04
120	3.92	3.07	2.68	2.45	2.29	2.17	2.09	2.02	1.96
∞	3.84	3.00	2.60	2.37	2.21	2.10	2.01	1.94	1.88

(continued)

Table VI	(continued)									
ν_1					Numerator Degrees of Freedom					
ν_2	10	12	15	20	24	30	40	60	120	∞
1	241.9	243.9	245.9	248.0	249.1	250.1	251.1	252.2	253.3	254.3
2	19.40	19.41	19.43	19.45	19.45	19.46	19.47	19.48	19.49	19.50
3	8.79	8.74	8.70	8.66	8.64	8.62	8.59	8.57	8.55	8.53
4	5.96	5.91	5.86	5.80	5.77	5.75	5.72	5.69	5.66	5.63
5	4.74	4.68	4.62	4.56	4.53	4.50	4.46	4.43	4.40	4.36
6	4.06	4.00	3.94	3.87	3.84	3.81	3.77	3.74	3.70	3.67
7	3.64	3.57	3.51	3.44	3.41	3.38	3.34	3.30	3.27	3.23
8	3.35	3.28	3.22	3.15	3.12	3.08	3.04	3.01	2.97	2.93
9	3.14	3.07	3.01	2.94	2.90	2.86	2.83	2.79	2.75	2.71
10	2.98	2.91	2.85	2.77	2.74	2.70	2.66	2.62	2.58	2.54
11	2.85	2.79	2.72	2.65	2.61	2.57	2.53	2.49	2.45	2.40
12	2.75	2.69	2.62	2.54	2.51	2.47	2.43	2.38	2.34	2.30
13	2.67	2.60	2.53	2.46	2.42	2.38	2.34	2.30	2.25	2.21
14	2.60	2.53	2.46	2.39	2.35	2.31	2.27	2.22	2.18	2.13
15	2.54	2.48	2.40	2.33	2.29	2.25	2.20	2.16	2.11	2.07
16	2.49	2.42	2.35	2.28	2.24	2.19	2.15	2.11	2.06	2.01
17	2.45	2.38	2.31	2.23	2.19	2.15	2.10	2.06	2.01	1.96
18	2.41	2.34	2.27	2.19	2.15	2.11	2.06	2.02	1.97	1.92
19	2.38	2.31	2.23	2.16	2.11	2.07	2.03	1.98	1.93	1.88
20	2.35	2.28	2.20	2.12	2.08	2.04	1.99	1.95	1.90	1.84
21	2.32	2.25	2.18	2.10	2.05	2.01	1.96	1.92	1.87	1.81
22	2.30	2.23	2.15	2.07	2.03	1.98	1.94	1.89	1.84	1.78
23	2.27	2.20	2.13	2.05	2.01	1.96	1.91	1.86	1.81	1.76
24	2.25	2.18	2.11	2.03	1.98	1.94	1.89	1.84	1.79	1.73
25	2.24	2.16	2.09	2.01	1.96	1.92	1.87	1.82	1.77	1.71
26	2.22	2.15	2.07	1.99	1.95	1.90	1.85	1.80	1.75	1.69
27	2.20	2.13	2.06	1.97	1.93	1.88	1.84	1.79	1.73	1.67
28	2.19	2.12	2.04	1.96	1.91	1.87	1.82	1.77	1.71	1.65
29	2.18	2.10	2.03	1.94	1.90	1.85	1.81	1.75	1.70	1.64
30	2.16	2.09	2.01	1.93	1.89	1.84	1.79	1.74	1.68	1.62
40	2.08	2.00	1.92	1.84	1.79	1.74	1.69	1.64	1.58	1.51
60	1.99	1.92	1.84	1.75	1.70	1.65	1.59	1.53	1.47	1.39
120	1.91	1.83	1.75	1.66	1.61	1.55	1.50	1.43	1.35	1.25
∞	1.83	1.75	1.67	1.57	1.52	1.46	1.39	1.32	1.22	1.00

Source: From Merrington, M., & Thompson, C. M. "Tables of percentage points of the inverted beta (*F*)-distribution," *Biometrika*, 1943, 33, 73–88. Reproduced by permission of the *Biometrika* Trustees.

Table VII	Percentage Points of the *F*-Distribution, $\alpha = .025$

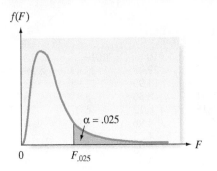

ν_1	Numerator Degrees of Freedom								
ν_2	1	2	3	4	5	6	7	8	9
1	647.8	799.5	864.2	899.6	921.8	937.1	948.2	956.7	963.3
2	38.51	39.00	39.17	39.25	39.30	39.33	39.36	39.37	39.39
3	17.44	16.04	15.44	15.10	14.88	14.73	14.62	14.54	14.47
4	12.22	10.65	9.98	9.60	9.36	9.20	9.07	8.98	8.90
5	10.01	8.43	7.76	7.39	7.15	6.98	6.85	6.76	6.68
6	8.81	7.26	6.60	6.23	5.99	5.82	5.70	5.60	5.52
7	8.07	6.54	5.89	5.52	5.29	5.12	4.99	4.90	4.82
8	7.57	6.06	5.42	5.05	4.82	4.65	4.53	4.43	4.36
9	7.21	5.71	5.08	4.72	4.48	4.32	4.20	4.10	4.03
10	6.94	5.46	4.83	4.47	4.24	4.07	3.95	3.85	3.78
11	6.72	5.26	4.63	4.28	4.04	3.88	3.76	3.66	3.59
12	6.55	5.10	4.47	4.12	3.89	3.73	3.61	3.51	3.44
13	6.41	4.97	4.35	4.00	3.77	3.60	3.48	3.39	3.31
14	6.30	4.86	4.24	3.89	3.66	3.50	3.38	3.29	3.21
15	6.20	4.77	4.15	3.80	3.58	3.41	3.29	3.20	3.12
16	6.12	4.69	4.08	3.73	3.50	3.34	3.22	3.12	3.05
17	6.04	4.62	4.01	3.66	3.44	3.28	3.16	3.06	2.98
18	5.98	4.56	3.95	3.61	3.38	3.22	3.10	3.01	2.93
19	5.92	4.51	3.90	3.56	3.33	3.17	3.05	2.96	2.88
20	5.87	4.46	3.86	3.51	3.29	3.13	3.01	2.91	2.84
21	5.83	4.42	3.82	3.48	3.25	3.09	2.97	2.87	2.80
22	5.79	4.38	3.78	3.44	3.22	3.05	2.93	2.84	2.76
23	5.75	4.35	3.75	3.41	3.18	3.02	2.90	2.81	2.73
24	5.72	4.32	3.72	3.38	3.15	2.99	2.87	2.78	2.70
25	5.69	4.29	3.69	3.35	3.13	2.97	2.85	2.75	2.68
26	5.66	4.27	3.67	3.33	3.10	2.94	2.82	2.73	2.65
27	5.63	4.24	3.65	3.31	3.08	2.92	2.80	2.71	2.63
28	5.61	4.22	3.63	3.29	3.06	2.90	2.78	2.69	2.61
29	5.59	4.20	3.61	3.27	3.04	2.88	2.76	2.67	2.59
30	5.57	4.18	3.59	3.25	3.03	2.87	2.75	2.65	2.57
40	5.42	4.05	3.46	3.13	2.90	2.74	2.62	2.53	2.45
60	5.29	3.93	3.34	3.01	2.79	2.63	2.51	2.41	2.33
120	5.15	3.80	3.23	2.89	2.67	2.52	2.39	2.30	2.22
∞	5.02	3.69	3.12	2.79	2.57	2.41	2.29	2.19	2.11

(continued)

Table VII	**(continued)**									
ν_1					Numerator Degrees of Freedom					
ν_2	10	12	15	20	24	30	40	60	120	∞
1	968.6	976.7	984.9	993.1	997.2	1,001	1,006	1,010	1,014	1,018
2	39.40	39.41	39.43	39.45	39.46	39.46	39.47	39.48	39.49	39.50
3	14.42	14.34	14.25	14.17	14.12	14.08	14.04	13.99	13.95	13.90
4	8.84	8.75	8.66	8.56	8.51	8.46	8.41	8.36	8.31	8.26
5	6.62	6.52	6.43	6.33	6.28	6.23	6.18	6.12	6.07	6.02
6	5.46	5.37	5.27	5.17	5.12	5.07	5.01	4.96	4.90	4.85
7	4.76	4.67	4.57	4.47	4.42	4.36	4.31	4.25	4.20	4.14
8	4.30	4.20	4.10	4.00	3.95	3.89	3.84	3.78	3.73	3.67
9	3.96	3.87	3.77	3.67	3.61	3.56	3.51	3.45	3.39	3.33
10	3.72	3.62	3.52	3.42	3.37	3.31	3.26	3.20	3.14	3.08
11	3.53	3.43	3.33	3.23	3.17	3.12	3.06	3.00	2.94	2.88
12	3.37	3.28	3.18	3.07	3.02	2.96	2.91	2.85	2.79	2.72
13	3.25	3.15	3.05	2.95	2.89	2.84	2.78	2.72	2.66	2.60
14	3.15	3.05	2.95	2.84	2.79	2.73	2.67	2.61	2.55	2.49
15	3.06	2.96	2.86	2.76	2.70	2.64	2.59	2.52	2.46	2.40
16	2.99	2.89	2.79	2.68	2.63	2.57	2.51	2.45	2.38	2.32
17	2.92	2.82	2.72	2.62	2.56	2.50	2.44	2.38	2.32	2.25
18	2.87	2.77	2.67	2.56	2.50	2.44	2.38	2.32	2.26	2.19
19	2.82	2.72	2.62	2.51	2.45	2.39	2.33	2.27	2.20	2.13
20	2.77	2.68	2.57	2.46	2.41	2.35	2.29	2.22	2.16	2.09
21	2.73	2.64	2.53	2.42	2.37	2.31	2.25	2.18	2.11	2.04
22	2.70	2.60	2.50	2.39	2.33	2.27	2.21	2.14	2.08	2.00
23	2.67	2.57	2.47	2.36	2.30	2.24	2.18	2.11	2.04	1.97
24	2.64	2.54	2.44	2.33	2.27	2.21	2.15	2.08	2.01	1.94
25	2.61	2.51	2.41	2.30	2.24	2.18	2.12	2.05	1.98	1.91
26	2.59	2.49	2.39	2.28	2.22	2.16	2.09	2.03	1.95	1.88
27	2.57	2.47	2.36	2.25	2.19	2.13	2.07	2.00	1.93	1.85
28	2.55	2.45	2.34	2.23	2.17	2.11	2.05	1.98	1.91	1.83
29	2.53	2.43	2.32	2.21	2.15	2.09	2.03	1.96	1.89	1.81
30	2.51	2.41	2.31	2.20	2.14	2.07	2.01	1.94	1.87	1.79
40	2.39	2.29	2.18	2.07	2.01	1.94	1.88	1.80	1.72	1.64
60	2.27	2.17	2.06	1.94	1.88	1.82	1.74	1.67	1.58	1.48
120	2.16	2.05	1.94	1.82	1.76	1.69	1.61	1.53	1.43	1.31
∞	2.05	1.94	1.83	1.71	1.64	1.57	1.48	1.39	1.27	1.00

Denominator Degrees of Freedom

Table VIII	Percentage Points of the *F*-Distribution, $\alpha = .01$

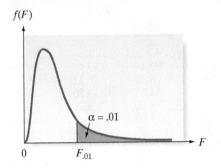

ν_1	Numerator Degrees of Freedom								
ν_2	1	2	3	4	5	6	7	8	9
1	4,052	4,999.5	5,403	5,625	5,764	5,859	5,928	5,982	6,022
2	98.50	99.00	99.17	99.25	99.30	99.33	99.36	99.37	99.39
3	34.12	30.82	29.46	28.71	28.24	27.91	27.67	27.49	27.35
4	21.20	18.00	16.69	15.98	15.52	15.21	14.98	14.80	14.66
5	16.26	13.27	12.06	11.39	10.97	10.67	10.46	10.29	10.16
6	13.75	10.92	9.78	9.15	8.75	8.47	8.26	8.10	7.98
7	12.25	9.55	8.45	7.85	7.46	7.19	6.99	6.84	6.72
8	11.26	8.65	7.59	7.01	6.63	6.37	6.18	6.03	5.91
9	10.56	8.02	6.99	6.42	6.06	5.80	5.61	5.47	5.35
10	10.04	7.56	6.55	5.99	5.64	5.39	5.20	5.06	4.94
11	9.65	7.21	6.22	5.67	5.32	5.07	4.89	4.74	4.63
12	9.33	6.93	5.95	5.41	5.06	4.82	4.64	4.50	4.39
13	9.07	6.70	5.74	5.21	4.86	4.62	4.44	4.30	4.19
14	8.86	6.51	5.56	5.04	4.69	4.46	4.28	4.14	4.03
15	8.68	6.36	5.42	4.89	4.56	4.32	4.14	4.00	3.89
16	8.53	6.23	5.29	4.77	4.44	4.20	4.03	3.89	3.78
17	8.40	6.11	5.18	4.67	4.34	4.10	3.93	3.79	3.68
18	8.29	6.01	5.09	4.58	4.25	4.01	3.84	3.71	3.60
19	8.18	5.93	5.01	4.50	4.17	3.94	3.77	3.63	3.52
20	8.10	5.85	4.94	4.43	4.10	3.87	3.70	3.56	3.46
21	8.02	5.78	4.87	4.37	4.04	3.81	3.64	3.51	3.40
22	7.95	5.72	4.82	4.31	3.99	3.76	3.59	3.45	3.35
23	7.88	5.66	4.76	4.26	3.94	3.71	3.54	3.41	3.30
24	7.82	5.61	4.72	4.22	3.90	3.67	3.50	3.36	3.26
25	7.77	5.57	4.68	4.18	3.85	3.63	3.46	3.32	3.22
26	7.72	5.53	4.64	4.14	3.82	3.59	3.42	3.29	3.18
27	7.68	5.49	4.60	4.11	3.78	3.56	3.39	3.26	3.15
28	7.64	5.45	4.57	4.07	3.75	3.53	3.36	3.23	3.12
29	7.60	5.42	4.54	4.04	3.73	3.50	3.33	3.20	3.09
30	7.56	5.39	4.51	4.02	3.70	3.47	3.30	3.17	3.07
40	7.31	5.18	4.31	3.83	3.51	3.29	3.12	2.99	2.89
60	7.08	4.98	4.13	3.65	3.34	3.12	2.95	2.82	2.72
120	6.85	4.79	3.95	3.48	3.17	2.96	2.79	2.66	2.56
∞	6.63	4.61	3.78	3.32	3.02	2.80	2.64	2.51	2.41

(continued)

Table VIII	(continued)									
ν_1	Numerator Degrees of Freedom									
ν_2	10	12	15	20	24	30	40	60	120	∞
1	6,056	6,106	6,157	6,209	6,235	6,261	6,287	6,313	6,339	6,366
2	99.40	99.42	99.43	99.45	99.46	99.47	99.47	99.48	99.49	99.50
3	27.23	27.05	26.87	26.69	26.60	26.50	26.41	26.32	26.22	26.13
4	14.55	14.37	14.20	14.02	13.93	13.84	13.75	13.65	13.56	13.46
5	10.05	9.89	9.72	9.55	9.47	9.38	9.29	9.20	9.11	9.02
6	7.87	7.72	7.56	7.40	7.31	7.23	7.14	7.06	6.97	6.88
7	6.62	6.47	6.31	6.16	6.07	5.99	5.91	5.82	5.74	5.65
8	5.81	5.67	5.52	5.36	5.28	5.20	5.12	5.03	4.95	4.86
9	5.26	5.11	4.96	4.81	4.73	4.65	4.57	4.48	4.40	4.31
10	4.85	4.71	4.56	4.41	4.33	4.25	4.17	4.08	4.00	3.91
11	4.54	4.40	4.25	4.10	4.02	3.94	3.86	3.78	3.69	3.60
12	4.30	4.16	4.01	3.86	3.78	3.70	3.62	3.54	3.45	3.36
13	4.10	3.96	3.82	3.66	3.59	3.51	3.43	3.34	3.25	3.17
14	3.94	3.80	3.66	3.51	3.43	3.35	3.27	3.18	3.09	3.00
15	3.80	3.67	3.52	3.37	3.29	3.21	3.13	3.05	2.96	2.87
16	3.69	3.55	3.41	3.26	3.18	3.10	3.02	2.93	2.84	2.75
17	3.59	3.46	3.31	3.16	3.08	3.00	2.92	2.83	2.75	2.65
18	3.51	3.37	3.23	3.08	3.00	2.92	2.84	2.75	2.66	2.57
19	3.43	3.30	3.15	3.00	2.92	2.84	2.76	2.67	2.58	2.49
20	3.37	3.23	3.09	2.94	2.86	2.78	2.69	2.61	2.52	2.42
21	3.31	3.17	3.03	2.88	2.80	2.72	2.64	2.55	2.46	2.36
22	3.26	3.12	2.98	2.83	2.75	2.67	2.58	2.50	2.40	2.31
23	3.21	3.07	2.93	2.78	2.70	2.62	2.54	2.45	2.35	2.26
24	3.17	3.03	2.89	2.74	2.66	2.58	2.49	2.40	2.31	2.21
25	3.13	2.99	2.85	2.70	2.62	2.54	2.45	2.36	2.27	2.17
26	3.09	2.96	2.81	2.66	2.58	2.50	2.42	2.33	2.23	2.13
27	3.06	2.93	2.78	2.63	2.55	2.47	2.38	2.29	2.20	2.10
28	3.03	2.90	2.75	2.60	2.52	2.44	2.35	2.26	2.17	2.06
29	3.00	2.87	2.73	2.57	2.49	2.41	2.33	2.23	2.14	2.03
30	2.98	2.84	2.70	2.55	2.47	2.39	2.30	2.21	2.11	2.01
40	2.80	2.66	2.52	2.37	2.29	2.20	2.11	2.02	1.92	1.80
60	2.63	2.50	2.35	2.20	2.12	2.03	1.94	1.84	1.73	1.60
120	2.47	2.34	2.19	2.03	1.95	1.86	1.76	1.66	1.53	1.38
∞	2.32	2.18	2.04	1.88	1.79	1.70	1.59	1.47	1.32	1.00

Source: From Merrington, M., & Thompson, C. M. "Tables of percentage points of the inverted beta (*F*)-distribution," *Biometrika*, 1943, 33, 73–88. Reproduced by permission of the *Biometrika* Trustees.

Table IX	Control Chart Constants				
Number of Observations in Subgroup, n	A_2	d_2	d_3	D_3	D_4
2	1.880	1.128	.853	.000	3.267
3	1.023	1.693	.888	.000	2.574
4	.729	2.059	.880	.000	2.282
5	.577	2.326	.864	.000	2.114
6	.483	2.534	.848	.000	2.004
7	.419	2.704	.833	.076	1.924
8	.373	2.847	.820	.136	1.864
9	.337	2.970	.808	.184	1.816
10	.308	3.078	.797	.223	1.777
11	.285	3.173	.787	.256	1.744
12	.266	3.258	.778	.283	1.717
13	.249	3.336	.770	.307	1.693
14	.235	3.407	.762	.328	1.672
15	.223	3.472	.755	.347	1.653
16	.212	3.532	.749	.363	1.637
17	.203	3.588	.743	.378	1.622
18	.194	3.640	.738	.391	1.608
19	.187	3.689	.733	.403	1.597
20	.180	3.735	.729	.415	1.585
21	.173	3.778	.724	.425	1.575
22	.167	3.819	.720	.434	1.566
23	.162	3.858	.716	.443	1.557
24	.157	3.895	.712	.451	1.548
25	.153	3.931	.709	.459	1.541

Source: ASTM Manual on the Presentation of Data and Control Chart Analysis, Philadelphia, PA: American Society for Testing Materials, pp. 134–136, 1976.

Table X	Critical Values for the Durbin-Watson d-Statistic, $\alpha = .05$									
	$k = 1$		$k = 2$		$k = 3$		$k = 4$		$k = 5$	
n	d_L	d_U	d_L	d_U	d_L	d_U	d_L	d_U	d_L	d_U
15	1.08	1.36	.95	1.54	.82	1.75	.69	1.97	.56	2.21
16	1.10	1.37	.98	1.54	.86	1.73	.74	1.93	.62	2.15
17	1.13	1.38	1.02	1.54	.90	1.71	.78	1.90	.67	2.10
18	1.16	1.39	1.05	1.53	.93	1.69	.92	1.87	.71	2.06
19	1.18	1.40	1.08	1.53	.97	1.68	.86	1.85	.75	2.02
20	1.20	1.41	1.10	1.54	1.00	1.68	.90	1.83	.79	1.99
21	1.22	1.42	1.13	1.54	1.03	1.67	.93	1.81	.83	1.96
22	1.24	1.43	1.15	1.54	1.05	1.66	.96	1.80	.96	1.94
23	1.26	1.44	1.17	1.54	1.08	1.66	.99	1.79	.90	1.92
24	1.27	1.45	1.19	1.55	1.10	1.66	1.01	1.78	.93	1.90
25	1.29	1.45	1.21	1.55	1.12	1.66	1.04	1.77	.95	1.89
26	1.30	1.46	1.22	1.55	1.14	1.65	1.06	1.76	.98	1.88
27	1.32	1.47	1.24	1.56	1.16	1.65	1.08	1.76	1.01	1.86
28	1.33	1.48	1.26	1.56	1.18	1.65	1.10	1.75	1.03	1.85
29	1.34	1.48	1.27	1.56	1.20	1.65	1.12	1.74	1.05	1.84
30	1.35	1.49	1.28	1.57	1.21	1.65	1.14	1.74	1.07	1.83
31	1.36	1.50	1.30	1.57	1.23	1.65	1.16	1.74	1.09	1.83
32	1.37	1.50	1.31	1.57	1.24	1.65	1.18	1.73	1.11	1.82
33	1.38	1.51	1.32	1.58	1.26	1.65	1.19	1.73	1.13	1.81
34	1.39	1.51	1.33	1.58	1.27	1.65	1.21	1.73	1.15	1.81
35	1.40	1.52	1.34	1.58	1.28	1.65	1.22	1.73	1.16	1.80
36	1.41	1.52	1.35	1.59	1.29	1.65	1.24	1.73	1.18	1.80
37	1.42	1.53	1.36	1.59	1.31	1.66	1.25	1.72	1.19	1.80
38	1.43	1.54	1.37	1.59	1.32	1.66	1.26	1.72	1.21	1.79
39	1.43	1.54	1.38	1.60	1.33	1.66	1.27	1.72	1.22	1.79
40	1.44	1.54	1.39	1.60	1.34	1.66	1.29	1.72	1.23	1.79
45	1.48	1.57	1.43	1.62	1.38	1.67	1.34	1.72	1.29	1.78
50	1.50	1.59	1.46	1.63	1.42	1.67	1.38	1.72	1.34	1.77
55	1.53	1.60	1.49	1.64	1.45	1.68	1.41	1.72	1.38	1.77
60	1.55	1.62	1.51	1.65	1.48	1.69	1.44	1.73	1.41	1.77
65	1.57	1.63	1.54	1.66	1.50	1.70	1.47	1.73	1.44	1.77
70	1.58	1.64	1.55	1.67	1.52	1.70	1.49	1.74	1.46	1.77
75	1.60	1.65	1.57	1.68	1.54	1.71	1.51	1.74	1.49	1.77
80	1.61	1.66	1.59	1.69	1.56	1.72	1.53	1.74	1.51	1.77
85	1.62	1.67	1.60	1.70	1.57	1.72	1.55	1.75	1.52	1.77
90	1.63	1.68	1.61	1.70	1.59	1.73	1.57	1.75	1.54	1.78
95	1.64	1.69	1.62	1.71	1.60	1.73	1.58	1.75	1.56	1.78
100	1.65	1.69	1.63	1.72	1.61	1.74	1.59	1.76	1.57	1.78

Table XI	Critical Values for the Durbin-Watson d-Statistic, $\alpha = .01$									
	$k = 1$		$k = 2$		$k = 3$		$k = 4$		$k = 5$	
n	d_L	d_U	d_L	d_U	d_L	d_U	d_L	d_U	d_L	d_U
15	.81	1.07	.70	1.25	.59	1.46	.49	1.70	.39	1.96
16	.84	1.09	.74	1.25	.63	1.44	.53	1.66	.44	1.90
17	.87	1.10	.77	1.25	.67	1.43	.57	1.3	.48	1.85
18	.90	1.12	.80	1.26	.71	1.42	.61	1.60	.52	1.80
19	.93	1.13	.83	1.26	.74	1.41	.65	1.58	.56	1.77
20	.95	1.15	.86	1.27	.77	1.41	.68	1.57	.60	1.74
21	.97	1.16	.89	1.27	.80	1.41	.72	1.55	.63	1.71
22	1.00	1.17	.91	1.28	.83	1.40	.75	1.54	.66	1.69
23	1.02	1.19	.94	1.29	.86	1.40	.77	1.53	.70	1.67
24	1.04	1.20	.96	1.30	.88	1.41	.80	1.53	.72	1.66
25	1.05	1.21	.98	1.30	.90	1.41	.83	1.52	.75	1.65
26	1.07	1.22	1.00	1.31	.93	1.41	.85	1.52	.78	1.64
27	1.09	1.23	1.02	1.32	.95	1.41	.88	1.51	.81	1.63
28	1.10	1.24	1.04	1.32	.97	1.41	.90	1.51	.83	1.62
29	1.12	1.25	1.05	1.33	.99	1.42	.92	1.51	.85	1.61
30	1.13	1.26	1.07	1.34	1.01	1.42	.94	1.51	.88	1.61
31	1.15	1.27	1.08	1.34	1.02	1.42	.96	1.51	.90	1.60
32	1.16	1.28	1.10	1.35	1.04	1.43	.98	1.51	.92	1.60
33	1.17	1.29	1.11	1.36	1.05	1.43	1.00	1.51	.94	1.59
34	1.18	1.30	1.13	1.36	1.07	1.43	1.01	1.51	.95	1.59
35	1.19	1.31	1.14	1.27	1.08	1.44	1.03	1.51	.97	1.59
36	1.21	1.32	1.15	1.38	1.10	1.44	1.04	1.51	.99	1.59
37	1.22	1.32	1.16	1.38	1.11	1.45	1.06	1.51	1.00	1.59
38	1.23	1.33	1.18	1.39	1.12	1.45	1.07	1.52	1.02	1.58
39	1.24	1.34	1.19	1.39	1.14	1.45	1.09	1.52	1.03	1.58
40	1.25	1.34	1.20	1.40	1.15	1.46	1.10	1.52	1.05	1.58
45	1.29	1.38	1.24	1.42	1.20	1.48	1.16	1.53	1.11	1.58
50	1.32	1.40	1.28	1.45	1.24	1.49	1.20	1.54	1.16	1.59
55	1.36	1.43	1.32	1.47	1.28	1.51	1.25	1.55	1.21	1.59
60	1.38	1.45	1.35	1.48	1.32	1.52	1.28	1.56	1.25	1.60
65	1.41	1.47	1.38	1.50	1.35	1.53	1.31	1.57	1.28	1.61
70	1.43	1.49	1.40	1.52	1.37	1.55	1.34	1.58	1.31	1.61
75	1.45	1.50	1.42	1.53	1.39	1.56	1.37	1.59	1.34	1.62
80	1.47	1.52	1.44	1.54	1.42	1.57	1.39	1.60	1.36	1.62
85	1.48	1.53	1.46	1.55	1.43	1.58	1.41	1.60	1.39	1.63
90	1.50	1.54	1.47	1.56	1.45	1.59	1.43	1.61	1.41	1.64
95	1.51	1.55	1.49	1.57	1.47	1.60	1.45	1.62	1.42	1.64
100	1.52	1.56	1.50	1.58	1.48	1.60	1.46	1.63	1.44	1.65

Source: From Durbin, J., & Watson, G. S. "Testing for serial correlation in least squares regression, II," *Biometrika*, 1951, 30, 159–178. Reproduced by permission of the *Biometrika* Trustees.

| Table XII | Critical Values of T_L and T_U for the Wilcoxon Rank Sum Test: Independent Samples |

Test statistic is the rank sum associated with the smaller sample (if equal sample sizes, either rank sum can be used).

a. $\alpha = .025$ one-tailed; $\alpha = .05$ two-tailed

n_2 \ n_1	3 T_L	3 T_U	4 T_L	4 T_U	5 T_L	5 T_U	6 T_L	6 T_U	7 T_L	7 T_U	8 T_L	8 T_U	9 T_L	9 T_U	10 T_L	10 T_U
3	5	16	6	18	6	21	7	23	7	26	8	28	8	31	9	33
4	6	18	11	25	12	28	12	32	13	35	14	38	15	41	16	44
5	6	21	12	28	18	37	19	41	20	45	21	49	22	53	24	56
6	7	23	12	32	19	41	26	52	28	56	29	61	31	65	32	70
7	7	26	13	35	20	45	28	56	37	68	39	73	41	78	43	83
8	8	28	14	38	21	49	29	61	39	73	49	87	51	93	54	98
9	8	31	15	41	22	53	31	65	41	78	51	93	63	108	66	114
10	9	33	16	44	24	56	32	70	43	83	54	98	66	114	79	131

b. $\alpha = .05$ one-tailed; $\alpha = .10$ two-tailed

n_2 \ n_1	3 T_L	3 T_U	4 T_L	4 T_U	5 T_L	5 T_U	6 T_L	6 T_U	7 T_L	7 T_U	8 T_L	8 T_U	9 T_L	9 T_U	10 T_L	10 T_U
3	6	15	7	17	7	20	8	22	9	24	9	27	10	29	11	31
4	7	17	12	24	13	27	14	30	15	33	16	36	17	39	18	42
5	7	20	13	27	19	36	20	40	22	43	24	46	25	50	26	54
6	8	22	14	30	20	40	28	50	30	54	32	58	33	63	35	67
7	9	24	15	33	22	43	30	54	39	66	41	71	43	76	46	80
8	9	27	16	36	24	46	32	58	41	71	52	84	54	90	57	95
9	10	29	17	39	25	50	33	63	43	76	54	90	66	105	69	111
10	11	31	18	42	26	54	35	67	46	80	57	95	69	111	83	127

Source: From Wilcoxon, F., & Wilcox, R. A. "Some rapid approximate statistical procedures," 1964, 20–23. Courtesy of Lederle Laboratories Division of American Cyanamid Company, Madison, NJ.

Table XIII	Critical Values of T_0 in the Wilcoxon Paired Difference Signed Rank Test						
One-Tailed	Two-Tailed	$n = 5$	$n = 6$	$n = 7$	$n = 8$	$n = 9$	$n = 10$
$\alpha = .05$	$\alpha = .10$	1	2	4	6	8	11
$\alpha = .025$	$\alpha = .05$		1	2	4	6	8
$\alpha = .01$	$\alpha = .02$			0	2	3	5
$\alpha = .005$	$\alpha = .01$				0	2	3
		$n = 11$	$n = 12$	$n = 13$	$n = 14$	$n = 15$	$n = 16$
$\alpha = .05$	$\alpha = .10$	14	17	21	26	30	36
$\alpha = .025$	$\alpha = .05$	11	14	17	21	25	30
$\alpha = .01$	$\alpha = .02$	7	10	13	16	20	24
$\alpha = .005$	$\alpha = .01$	5	7	10	13	16	19
		$n = 17$	$n = 18$	$n = 19$	$n = 20$	$n = 21$	$n = 22$
$\alpha = .05$	$\alpha = .10$	41	47	54	60	68	75
$\alpha = .025$	$\alpha = .05$	35	40	46	52	59	66
$\alpha = .01$	$\alpha = .02$	28	33	38	43	49	56
$\alpha = .005$	$\alpha = .01$	23	28	32	37	43	49
		$n = 23$	$n = 24$	$n = 25$	$n = 26$	$n = 27$	$n = 28$
$\alpha = .05$	$\alpha = .10$	83	92	101	110	120	130
$\alpha = .025$	$\alpha = .05$	73	81	90	98	107	117
$\alpha = .01$	$\alpha = .02$	62	69	77	85	93	102
$\alpha = .005$	$\alpha = .01$	55	61	68	76	84	92
		$n = 29$	$n = 30$	$n = 31$	$n = 32$	$n = 33$	$n = 34$
$\alpha = .05$	$\alpha = .10$	141	152	163	175	188	201
$\alpha = .025$	$\alpha = .05$	127	137	148	159	171	183
$\alpha = .01$	$\alpha = .02$	111	120	130	141	151	162
$\alpha = .005$	$\alpha = .01$	100	109	118	128	138	149
		$n = 35$	$n = 36$	$n = 37$	$n = 38$	$n = 39$	
$\alpha = .05$	$\alpha = .10$	214	228	242	256	271	
$\alpha = .025$	$\alpha = .05$	195	208	222	235	250	
$\alpha = .01$	$\alpha = .02$	174	186	198	211	224	
$\alpha = .005$	$\alpha = .01$	160	171	183	195	208	
		$n = 40$	$n = 41$	$n = 42$	$n = 43$	$n = 44$	$n = 45$
$\alpha = .05$	$\alpha = .10$	287	303	319	336	353	371
$\alpha = .025$	$\alpha = .05$	264	279	295	311	327	344
$\alpha = .01$	$\alpha = .02$	238	252	267	281	297	313
$\alpha = .005$	$\alpha = .01$	221	234	248	262	277	292
		$n = 46$	$n = 47$	$n = 48$	$n = 49$	$n = 50$	
$\alpha = .05$	$\alpha = .10$	389	408	427	446	466	
$\alpha = .025$	$\alpha = .05$	361	379	397	415	434	
$\alpha = .01$	$\alpha = .02$	329	345	362	380	398	
$\alpha = .005$	$\alpha = .01$	307	323	339	356	373	

Source: From Wilcoxon, F., & Wilcox, R. A. "Some rapid approximate statistical procedures," 1964, p. 28. Courtesy of Lederle Laboratories Division of American Cyanamid Company, Madison, NJ.

Table XIV	Critical Values of Spearman's Rank Correlation Coefficient

The values correspond to a one-tailed test of $H_0: p = 0$. The value should be doubled for two-tailed tests.

n	$\alpha = .05$	$\alpha = .025$	$\alpha = .01$	$\alpha = .005$	n	$\alpha = .05$	$\alpha = .025$	$\alpha = .01$	$\alpha = .005$
5	.900	–	–	–	18	.399	.476	.564	.625
6	.829	.886	.943	–	19	.388	.462	.549	.608
7	.714	.786	.893	–	20	.377	.450	.534	.591
8	.643	.738	.833	.881	21	.368	.438	.521	.576
9	.600	.683	.783	.833	22	.359	.428	.508	.562
10	.564	.648	.745	.794	23	.351	.418	.496	.549
11	.523	.623	.736	.818	24	.343	.409	.485	.537
12	.497	.591	.703	.780	25	.336	.400	.475	.526
13	.475	.566	.673	.745	26	.329	.392	.465	.515
14	.457	.545	.646	.716	27	.323	.385	.456	.505
15	.441	.525	.623	.689	28	.317	.377	.448	.496
16	.425	.507	.601	.666	29	.311	.370	.440	.487
17	.412	.490	.582	.645	30	.305	.364	.432	.478

Source: From Olds, E. G. "Distribution of sums of squares of rank differences for small samples," *Annals of Mathematical Statistics*, 1938, 9. Reproduced with the permission of the editor, *Annals of Mathematical Statistics*.

| Table XV | Critical Values of the Studentized Range, $\alpha = .05$ |

k / v	2	3	4	5	6	7	8	9	10	11
1	17.97	26.98	32.82	37.08	40.41	43.12	45.40	47.36	49.07	50.59
2	6.08	8.33	9.80	10.88	11.74	12.44	13.03	13.54	13.99	14.39
3	4.50	5.91	6.82	7.50	8.04	8.48	8.85	9.18	9.46	9.72
4	3.93	5.04	5.76	6.29	6.71	7.05	7.35	7.60	7.83	8.03
5	3.64	4.60	5.22	5.67	6.03	6.33	6.58	6.80	6.99	7.17
6	3.46	4.34	4.90	5.30	5.63	5.90	6.12	6.32	6.49	6.65
7	3.34	4.16	4.68	5.06	5.36	5.61	5.82	6.00	6.16	6.30
8	3.26	4.04	4.53	4.89	5.17	5.40	5.60	5.77	5.92	6.05
9	3.20	3.95	4.41	4.76	5.02	5.24	5.43	5.59	5.74	5.87
10	3.15	3.88	4.33	4.65	4.91	5.12	5.30	5.46	5.60	5.72
11	3.11	3.82	4.26	4.57	4.82	5.03	5.20	5.35	5.49	5.61
12	3.08	3.77	4.20	4.51	4.75	4.95	5.12	5.27	5.39	5.51
13	3.06	3.73	4.15	4.45	4.69	4.88	5.05	5.19	5.32	5.43
14	3.03	3.70	4.11	4.41	4.64	4.83	4.99	5.13	5.25	5.36
15	3.01	3.67	4.08	4.37	4.60	4.78	4.94	5.08	5.20	5.31
16	3.00	3.65	4.05	4.33	4.56	4.74	4.90	5.03	5.15	5.26
17	2.98	3.63	4.02	4.30	4.52	4.70	4.86	4.99	5.11	5.21
18	2.97	3.61	4.00	4.28	4.49	4.67	4.82	4.96	5.07	5.17
19	2.96	3.59	3.98	4.25	4.47	4.65	4.79	4.92	5.04	5.14
20	2.95	3.58	3.96	4.23	4.45	4.62	4.77	4.90	5.01	5.11
24	2.92	3.53	3.90	4.17	4.37	4.54	4.68	4.81	4.92	5.01
30	2.89	3.49	3.85	4.10	4.30	4.46	4.60	4.72	4.82	4.92
40	2.86	3.44	3.79	4.04	4.23	4.39	4.52	4.63	4.73	4.82
60	2.83	3.40	3.74	3.98	4.16	4.31	4.44	4.55	4.65	4.73
120	2.80	3.36	3.68	3.92	4.10	4.24	4.36	4.47	4.56	4.64
∞	2.77	3.31	3.63	3.86	4.03	4.17	4.29	4.39	4.47	4.55

k / v	12	13	14	15	16	17	18	19	20
1	51.96	53.20	54.33	55.36	56.32	57.22	58.04	58.83	59.56
2	14.75	15.08	15.38	15.65	15.91	16.14	16.37	16.57	16.77
3	9.95	10.15	10.35	10.52	10.69	10.84	10.98	11.11	11.24
4	8.21	8.37	8.52	8.66	8.79	8.91	9.03	9.13	9.23
5	7.32	7.47	7.60	7.72	7.83	7.93	8.03	8.12	8.21
6	6.79	6.92	7.03	7.14	7.24	7.34	7.43	7.51	7.59
7	6.43	6.55	6.66	6.76	6.85	6.94	7.02	7.10	7.17
8	6.18	6.29	6.39	6.48	6.57	6.65	6.73	6.80	6.87
9	5.98	6.09	6.19	6.28	6.36	6.44	6.51	6.58	6.64
10	5.83	5.93	6.03	6.11	6.19	6.27	6.34	6.40	6.47
11	5.71	5.81	5.90	5.98	6.06	6.13	6.20	6.27	6.33
12	5.61	5.71	5.80	5.88	5.95	6.02	6.09	6.15	6.21
13	5.53	5.63	5.71	5.79	5.86	5.93	5.99	6.05	6.11
14	5.46	5.55	5.64	5.71	5.79	5.85	5.91	5.97	6.03
15	5.40	5.49	5.57	5.65	5.72	5.78	5.85	5.90	5.96
16	5.35	5.44	5.52	5.59	5.66	5.73	5.79	5.84	5.90
17	5.31	5.39	5.47	5.54	5.61	5.67	5.73	5.79	5.84
18	5.27	5.35	5.43	5.50	5.57	5.63	5.69	5.74	5.79
19	5.23	5.31	5.39	5.46	5.53	5.59	5.65	5.70	5.75
20	5.20	5.28	5.36	5.43	5.49	5.55	5.61	5.66	5.71
24	5.10	5.18	5.25	5.32	5.38	5.44	5.49	5.55	5.59
30	5.00	5.08	5.15	5.21	5.27	5.33	5.38	5.43	5.47
40	4.90	4.98	5.04	5.11	5.16	5.22	5.27	5.31	5.36
60	4.81	4.88	4.94	5.00	5.06	5.11	5.15	5.20	5.24
120	4.71	4.78	4.84	4.90	4.95	5.00	5.04	5.09	5.13
∞	4.62	4.68	4.74	4.80	4.85	4.89	4.93	4.97	5.01

Source: Biometrika Tables for Statisticians, Vol. I, 3rd ed., edited by E. S. Pearson and H. O. Hartley (Cambridge University Press, 1996). Reproduced by permission of Professor E. S. Pearson and the *Biometrika* Trustees.

Answers to Selected Exercises

Chapter 1

1.3 Population/sample; variable(s); collect data; describe **1.5** Published source; designed experiment; observationally **1.13** Qualitative; qualitative **1.15 a.** Single-family residential property **b.** Sale price and the Zillow estimated value; quantitative **c.** If the 2,045 properties were all the properties sold in Arlington, Texas, in the past 6 months **d.** All the singe-family residential properties sold in the last 6 months in Arlington, Texas **e.** No **1.17 a.** All U.S. citizens **b.** President's job performance; qualitative **c.** 2000 polled individuals **d.** Estimate the proportion of all citizens who believe the president is doing a good job. **e.** Survey **f.** Not very likely **1.19 a.** Qualitative **b.** Quantitative **c.** Qualitative **d.** Qualitative **e.** Qualitative **f.** Quantitative **1.21 a.** Sample, if interested in CEOs of all U.S. companies; population, if interested in only the 500 CEOs in the 2011 Scoreboard **b.** (1) qualitative; (2) quantitative; (3) quantitative; (4) quantitative; (5) quantitative; (6) quantitative **1.23** Descriptive **1.25 a.** All who took the GMAT between 1990 and 1997 **b.** Survey **c.** No; self-selection **1.27 a.** Quantitative **b.** Quantitative **c.** Qualitative **d.** Quantitative **e.** Qualitative **f.** Quantitative **g.** Qualitative **1.29 a.** Speed of the deliveries; accuracy of the invoices; quality of the packaging **b.** Total numbers of questionnaires received **1.31 a.** All accounting alumni of the large university **b.** Quantitative: age, income, job satisfaction score, Machiavellian rating; qualitative: gender, education level **c.** 198 alumni who returned the questionnaire **d.** Survey **e.** Machiavellian behavior is not required to achieve success in business. **f.** Nonrespondents may be more Machiavellian in nature, biasing the results. **1.33 a.** Engaged couples who used a particular Web site **b.** Price of the engagement ring (quantitative) and the level of appreciation (qualitative) **c.** All engaged couples **d.** No **1.35 a.** All bank presidents in the United States **1.37 a.** All persons over 14 in United States **b.** Unemployment status; qualitative **c.** Inferential

Chapter 2

2.1 16; .18, .45, .15, .14 **2.3 a.** Bar graph **b.** Type of robotic limb **c.** Legs only **d.** None: .142; both: .075; legs only: .594; wheels only: .189 **2.5** Most (84%) malls have small or small standard tenants **2.7 a.** Qualitative **2.9** Companies and employees created 73% of blogs/forums **2.11 a.** .712 **b.** .195 **c.** Medical: .707; surgical: .721 **d.** Medical: .173; surgical: .233 **2.13** If team behind, goalie is likely to dive right **2.15 a.** Response time **c.** 3,570 **2.17 d.** Most aquifers are bedrock; most MTBE levels are below the limit; 79% of private wells and 60% of public wells are not contaminated **2.19** 50, 75, 125, 100, 25, 50, 50, 25 **2.21 a.** Frequency histogram **b.** 14 **c.** 49 **2.23 a.** Relative frequency **b.** 12% **2.25 b.** Years 1996–2000 had the highest number of firms with at least one acquisition **2.27 a.** Very little change **b.** Higher scores in 2011 **d.** 32; Michigan **2.29** Yes **2.31** More than 20 years of experience: "no"—38%, "yes"—19% **2.33** "Inside job" not likely since histogram appears similar to frequency distribution **2.35** $\bar{x} = 2.72, m = 2.65$ **2.37** mean > median: skewed right; mean < median: skewed left; mean = median: symmetric **2.39** mode = 15; $\bar{x} = 14.55; m = 15$ **2.41 a.** mean < median **b.** mean > median **c.** Equal **2.43 a.** mean = 653; average amount of sparkling wine exported by the 30 countries is $653,000 **b.** median = 231; half the 30 export values are above $231,000 **c.** mean = 481; average change in amount exported by the 30 countries is 481% **d.** median = 156; half the 30 percentage changes are above 156% **2.45 a.** 759,601; average research expenditures of top 20 ranked universities is $759,601 thousand **b.** 695,408.5; half of top 20 ranked universities have research expenditures less than $695,405.8 thousand **c.** No; sample not representative of all American universities **2.47 a.** 11 **b.** 9 **c.** 7 **d.** Honey dosage leads to greatest improvement **2.49 a.** Skewed right **b.** Skewed left **c.** Skewed right **d.** Skewed right **e.** Symmetric **f.** Skewed left **2.51** Average semester hours taken by sample of candidates is 141.31 hours; half of the sampled candidates take less than 140 semester hours; data likely to be symmetric **2.53** Joint: $\bar{x} = 2.65, m = 1.5$; no prefiling: $\bar{x} = 4.24, m = 3.2$; prepack: $\bar{x} = 1.82, m = 1.4$; 3 centers **2.55 a.** Median **b.** Mean **2.57 a.** R = 4, $s^2 = 2.3, s = 1.52$ **b.** R = 6, $s^2 = 3.619, s = 1.90$ **c.** R = 10, $s^2 = 7.111$, $s = 2.67$ **d.** R = 5, $s^2 = 1.624, s = 1.274$ **2.59 a.** $\bar{x} = 5.6, s^2 = 17.3, s = 4.16$ **b.** $\bar{x} = 13.75$ feet, $s^2 = 152.25$ square feet, $s = 12.34$ feet **c.** $\bar{x} = -2.5, s^2 = 4.3, s = 2.07$ **d.** $\bar{x} = .33$ ounce, $s^2 = .0587$ square ounce, $s = .24$ ounce **2.61** Data set 1: 0, 1, 2, 3, 4, 5, 6, 7, 8, 9; data set 2: 0, 0, 1, 1, 2, 2, 3, 3, 9, 9 **2.63 a.** R = 3, $s^2 = 1.3, s = 1.14$ **b.** R = 3, $s^2 = 1.3, s = 1.14$ **c.** R = 3, $s^2 = 1.3, s = 1.14$ **d.** No effect **2.65 a.** R = $4,882 thousand **b.** s = $1,113 thousand **c.** $s^2 = 1,238,769$ **2.67 a.** 155; accurate **b.** 722.036; inaccurate **c.** 26.871; less **d.** standard deviation **2.69 a.** R = 10, $s^2 = 7.67, s = 2.77$ **b.** R = 8, $s^2 = 5.15, s = 2.27$ **c.** R = 8, $s^2 = 5.06, s = 2.25$ **2.71 a.** Dollars; quantitative **b.** At least $\frac{3}{4}$; at least $\frac{8}{9}$; nothing; nothing **2.73** Approx. 68%; approx. 95%; essentially all **2.75** Between R/6 = 104.17 and R/4 = 156.25; no **2.77 a.** (1.79, 4.43) **b.** No **2.79 a.** (105.77, 176.85) **b.** At least $\frac{3}{4}$ **c.** Nothing **2.81 a.** $\bar{x} = 95.7$, $s = 4.96$ **b.** (90.74, 100.66), (85.78, 105.62), (80.82, 110.58) **c.** 89.2%, 96.2%, 97.8%; Chebyshev's Rule **2.83** $\bar{x} = 234.74, s = 9.91$; (205.0, 264.5) **2.85 a.** Flexed: $\bar{x} \pm 2s = (51, 67)$; extended: $\bar{x} \pm 2s = (39, 47)$; yes **b.** Flexed: $\bar{x} \pm 2s = (39, 79)$; extended: $\bar{x} \pm 2s = (13, 73)$; no **2.87** Do not buy **2.89** 11:30 and 4:00 **2.91 a.** 25%, 75% **b.** 50%, 50% **c.** 80%, 20% **d.** 16%, 84% **2.93 a.** z = 2 **b.** z = -3 **c.** z = -2 **d.** z = 1.67 **2.95** Average score is 283; 25% score below 259; 75% score below 308; 90% score below 329 **2.97** Half the graduates had starting salaries less than $41,100; half the graduates had mid-career salaries less than $71,100; 90% of the graduates had mid-career salaries less than $131,000 **2.99** No **2.101 a.** 0 **b.** 21 **c.** $\bar{x} = 5.24, s = 7.24; z = 5.90$ **d.** Yes **2.103 a.** Harvard's productivity score falls 5.08 standard deviations above the mean **b.** Howard's productivity score falls .81 standard deviation below the mean **c.** Yes **2.105** Not necessarily, since the standard deviation will be large for right-skewed data **2.107** IQR = 25 **2.109 a.** Sample A: IQR = 22; sample B: IQR = 15 **b.** Sample A: 84; sample B: 140 and 206 **2.111 a.** 50% of expenditures are less than $6,232; 25% are less than $5,309; 75% are less than $7,216 **b.** $1,907 **c.** .75 - .25 = .50 **2.113 a.** z = 1.05, no **b.** greater than 194.6 or less than 88 **2.115 b.** Joint: 1.5; none firms: 3.2; prepack: 1.4 **d.** No **e.** Yes **2.117 a.** 10 outliers: 69, 73, 74, 78, 83, 84, 84, 86, 86, and 86 **b.** 7 outliers: 69, 73, 74, 78, 83, 84, and 84 **c.** No **2.119** No outliers; agree with claim **2.123** Yes; yes, negative association between punishment use and average payoff **2.125** No **2.127 a.** No **b.** Positive trend **c.** Positive trend **2.129 a.** Yes

b. USAID and State   **2.131 a.** Weak association   **b.** 1,000   **c.** Negative association   **2.133** Vertical axis is cut off; width of bars increases   **2.135 a.** Scales on two vertical axes differ   **b.** Craigslist revenue much lower than newspaper ad sales   **2.139 a.** $-1, 1, 2$ **b.** $0, 4, 6$ **c.** $1, 3, 4$ **d.** $.1, .3, .4$ **2.141 a.** $6, 27, 5.20$ **b.** $6.25, 28.25, 5.32$ **c.** $7, 37.67, 6.14$ **d.** $3, 0, 0$ **2.147 a.** .082, .173, .167, .174, .139, .098, .074, .046, .048; 16.7% of articles published were in the Buyer Behavior area   **b.** Lower percentage for Marketing Research   **2.149** 60% of cars with 4-star rating   **2.151 a.** Body defect   **b.** Paint or dents   **2.153 a.** At most 25%   **b.** $\approx 2.5\%$ **2.155 c.** Penalties for CAA tend to be smaller   **2.157 d.** HRD group   **e.** $\bar{x} = .63$; average number of carats of 308 diamonds is .63   **f.** $m = .62$; 50% of the diamonds weigh less than .62 carat   **g.** Mode = 1.0; carat value of 1.0 occurred the most often   **h.** Mean or median   **i.** $(.077, 1.185)$ **2.159 a.** Grounding and fire   **b.** $\bar{x} = 66.19, s = 56.05; (0, 234.34)$ **2.161 a.** At least $\frac{8}{9}$ of the velocities fall within $(906, 966)$ **b.** No   **2.163 a.** No scale on vertical axis   **b.** Add vertical axis scale   **2.165 a.** Skewed right   **c.** ≈ 38 **d.** No, $z = 3.333$ **2.167 a.** both height and width of bars change   **2.169** Laid off: $m = 40.5$; not laid off: $m = 40$; company probably not vulnerable   **2.171** Yes; no observations were recorded in the interval just below the interval centered at 1.000 cm

Chapter 3

3.1 a. .5   **b.** .3   **c.** .6   **3.3** $P(A) = .55, P(B) = .50, P(C) = .70$ **3.5 a.** 10   **b.** 20   **c.** 15,504   **3.7 a.** $(B_1, B_2), (B_1, R_1), (B_1, R_2), (B_1, R_3),$ $(B_2, R_1), (B_2, R_2), (B_2, R_3), (R_1, R_2), (R_1, R_3), (R_2, R_3)$ **b.** $P(E_i) = \frac{1}{10}$ **c.** $P(A) = \frac{1}{10}, P(B) = \frac{3}{5}, P(C) = \frac{3}{10}$ **3.9 a.** Brown, yellow, red, blue, orange, and green   **b.** $P(\text{Br}) = 0.13, P(\text{Y}) = 0.14, P(\text{R}) = 0.13, P(\text{Bl}) = 0.24, P(\text{O}) = 0.2, P(\text{G}) = 0.16$ **c.** .13   **d.** .43   **e.** .76   **3.11** .0057   **3.13 a.** None, 1 or 2, 3–5, 6–9, 10 or more   **b.** $P(\text{none}) = 0.19, P(1 \text{ or } 2) = 0.31, P(3-5) = 0.26, P(6-9) = 0.05, P(10 \text{ or more}) = 0.19$ **c.** .50   **3.15 a.** Certification mark on label   **b.** .60   **c.** .16   **d.** .94   **3.17 a.** $\frac{1}{100} = .01$ **b.** .0095; yes   **3.19 a.** $\frac{1}{8}$ **b.** 70   **c.** .5   **3.21** 455   **3.23 a.** 6; $(G_1G_2G_3), (G_1G_2G_4), (G_1G_2G_5), (G_2G_3G_4), (G_2G_3G_5), (G_2G_4G_5)$ **b.** .282, .065, .339, .032, .008, .274   **c.** .686   **3.25 a.** 1 to 2   **b.** $\frac{1}{2}$ **c.** $\frac{2}{5}$ **3.27 a.** 32   **b.** $\frac{1}{32}$ **c.** 12   **d.** $\frac{12}{32} = .375$ **e.** .5   **3.29 b.** $P(A) = \frac{7}{8}, P(B) = \frac{1}{2}, P(A \cup B) = \frac{7}{8},$ $P(A^c) = \frac{1}{8}, P(A \cap B) = \frac{1}{2}$ **3.31 a.** $\frac{3}{4}$ **b.** $\frac{13}{20}$ **c.** 1   **d.** $\frac{2}{5}$ **e.** $\frac{1}{4}$ **f.** $\frac{7}{20}$ **g.** 1   **h.** $\frac{1}{4}$ **3.33 a.** .65   **b.** .72   **c.** .25   **d.** .08   **e.** .35   **f.** .72   **g.** 0   **h.** A and C, B and C, C and D **3.35 a.** $A \cap B$ **b.** A^c **c.** $C \cup B$ **d.** $B^c \cap A^c$ **3.37 a.** $\{L, W, B, N\}$ **b.** .594, .189, .075, .142   **c.** .264   **d.** .669   **e.** .858   **3.39 a.** AC, AW, AF, IC, IW, and IF   **b.** .148, .066, .426, .176, .052, .132   **c.** .640   **d.** .118   **e.** .176   **f.** .786   **g.** .676   **3.41 a.** $\frac{127}{244}$ **b.** $\frac{7}{244}$ **c.** $\frac{117}{244}$ **d.** $\frac{148}{244}$ **3.43 a.** $P \cap S \cap A$ **b.** $\frac{1}{5}$ **c.** $A \cup S; \frac{4}{5}$ **d.** $P \cap S; \frac{3}{10}$ **3.45 a.** .531   **b.** .75   **c.** .094   **3.47 a.** .09   **b.** .09   **c.** .84   **d.** No   **e.** Column events not mutually exclusive   **3.49 a.** .5   **b.** .25   **c.** No   **3.51 a.** .08   **b.** .4   **c.** .52   **3.53 a.** .8, .7, .6   **b.** .25, .375, .375   **d.** No   **3.55 a.** .37   **b.** .68   **c.** .15   **d.** .2206   **e.** 0   **f.** 0   **g.** No   **3.57 a.** A and C, B and C **b.** None   **c.** .65, .90   **3.59** .444   **3.61** .135   **3.63 a.** .055   **b.** .139   **c.** No   **3.65 a.** .371   **b.** .209   **c.** Yes   **3.67 a.** .406   **b.** .294   **3.69 a.** $P(A|I) = .9, P(B|I) = .95, P(A|I^c) = .2, P(B|I^c) = .1$ **b.** .855   **c.** .02   **d.** .995   **3.71 a.** .23   **b.** .729   **3.73** .60   **3.75 a.** $(.5)^{10} = .000977$ **b.** .00195   **c.** .99805   **3.77 a.** .225   **b.** .125   **c.** .35   **d.** .643   **e.** .357   **3.81 a.** .0788   **b.** .2545   **c.** Novice   **3.83 a.** .52, .39, .09   **b.** .516   **3.85** No; $P(D|G > 60) = .1075$ **3.87 a.** Supplier 4; $P(S_4|D) = .7147$ **b.** Suppliers 4 or 6   **3.91 b.** .6   **3.93 a.** 0   **b.** No   **3.95** .5   **3.97 a.** 0, .2, .9, 1, .7, .3, .4, 0   **b.** No; yes   **c.** No; no   **3.99 a.** E and D, P and P, M and O, T and C **b.** .325   **c.** .711   **3.101** .73   **3.103 a.** False   **b.** True   **c.** True   **d.** False   **3.105 a.** $B \cap C$ **b.** A^c **c.** $C \cup B$ **d.** $A \cap C^c$ **3.107 b.** .95   **c.** .25   **d.** .5   **3.109 a.** .684   **b.** .124   **c.** No   **d.** .316   **e.** .717   **f.** .091   **3.111 a.** .00000625   **b.** .0135   **c.** Doubt validity of the manufacturer's claim   **d.** No   **3.113 a.** .006   **b.** .012   **c.** .018   **3.115 a.** .157   **b.** .029   **c.** .291   **d.** .222   **e.** .183   **3.117** .79   **3.119 a.** LLLL, LLLU, LLUL, LULL, ULLL, LLUU, LULU, LUUL, ULLU, ULUL, UULL, LUUU, ULUU, UULU, UUUL, UUUU   **b.** $\frac{1}{16}$ **c.** $\frac{5}{16}$ **3.121 a.** .7127   **b.** .2873   **c.** .9639   **d.** .3078   **e.** .0361   **f.** 3   **3.123** $P(A|B) = 0$ **3.125** .526   **3.127 a.** .0362   **b.** .0352   **3.129** Marilyn

Chapter 4

4.1 a. Discrete   **b.** Continuous   **c.** Continuous   **d.** Discrete   **e.** Discrete   **4.3** Discrete   **4.5** Discrete   **4.7** Inflation rate   **4.9** Number of returns per day; number of new salespeople hired   **4.11 a.** .25   **b.** .35   **d.** .80   **4.13 a.** .25   **b.** .40   **c.** .75   **4.15 a.** $p(x) = \frac{1}{6}$ for all x values   **4.17 a.** $\mu = 0, \sigma^2 = 2.94, \sigma = 1.72$ **c.** .96   **4.19 a.** 1; 1   **b.** x **c.** $\mu = 1, \sigma^2 = .6; \mu = 1, \sigma^2 = .2$ **4.21 a.** $p(1) = 0, p(2) = .0408,$ $p(3) = .1735, p(4) = .6020, p(5) = .1837$ **b.** .1837   **c.** .0408   **d.** 3.93   **4.23 b.** .14   **c.** $\mu = 4.655, \sigma^2 = 19.856$ **d.** $(-4.26, \quad 13.57)$ **4.25 a.** 0, 2, 3, 4   **b.** $p(0) = .3302, p(2) = .5472, p(3) = .0472, p(4) = .0755$ **c.** 1.538   **4.27 b.** $p(0) = .1160, p(1) = .3124, p(2) = .3364,$ $p(3) = .1811, p(4) = .0488, p(5) = .0053$ **d.** .0541   **4.29 a.** .23   **b.** .0809   **c.** .77   **4.31 a.** .508   **b.** .391   **c.** .094   **d.** .007   **4.33** $p(8.5) = .4622,$ $p(9) = .2888, p(9.5) = .1417, p(10) = .0700, p(10.5) = .0252, p(11) = .0117, p(12) = .00052$ **4.35 a.** $p(\$300,000) = .3, p(\$0) = .7$ **b.** $\$90,000$ **4.37 a.** $p(x) = .05$ for all x-values   **b.** 52.5   **c.** $(-5.16, \quad 110.16)$ **f.** 33.25, 38.3577   **g.** .525   **i.** .20   **j.** .65   **4.39** $\$.25$ **4.41 a.** Discrete   **b.** Binomial   **d.** 3.5; 1.02   **4.43 a.** .4096   **b.** .3456   **c.** .027   **d.** .0081   **e.** .3456   **f.** .027   **4.45 a.** 12.5, 6.25, 2.5   **b.** 16, 12.8, 3.578   **c.** 60, 24, 4.899   **d.** 63, 6.3, 2.510   **e.** 48, 9.6, 3.098   **f.** 40, 38.4, 6.197   **4.47 a.** Adult who does not work in the summer   **c.** .35   **d.** .2522   **e.** .2616   **4.49 b.** .5   **c.** 125   **4.51** .677   **4.53 a.** .6591   **b.** .2373   **4.55 a.** .055   **b.** In 2020, more than 9% of Denver bridges will have a rating of 4 or below   **4.57 a.** $\mu = 520, \sigma = 13.49$ **b.** No, $z = -8.90$ **4.59 b.** $\mu = 2.4, \sigma = 1.47$ **c.** $p = .90, q = .10, n = 24, \mu = 21.60, \sigma = 1.47$ **4.61 a.** Discrete   **b.** Poisson   **d.** $\mu = 3, \sigma = 1.73$ **4.63 a.** .3   **b.** .119   **c.** .167   **d.** .167   **4.65 a.** .9197   **b.** .6767   **c.** .4232   **d.** Decreases   **4.67 a.** Hypergeometric   **b.** Binomial   **4.69 c.** $\mu = 1.415, \sigma = 1.054$ **d.** .280   **4.71 a.** .0111   **b.** .05   **c.** $\mu = 4.5, \sigma = 2.12$ **4.73** .2693   **4.75** .1848   **4.77** .1931   **4.79** .5507   **4.81 a.** ≈ 0 **b.** ≈ 0 **c.** Yes   **4.83** No; probability of only 5 females selected is ≈ 0 **4.85 a.** .0721   **b.** .0594   **c.** .2434   **d.** .3457   **e.** .5   **f.** .9233   **4.87 a.** .6826   **b.** .9500   **c.** .90   **d.** .9544   **4.89 a.** $-.81$ **b.** .55   **c.** 1.43   **d.** .21   **e.** -2.05 **f.** .50   **4.91 a.** -2.5 **b.** 0   **c.** -6.81 **d.** -3.75 **e.** 1.25   **f.** -1.25 **4.93 a.** .3830   **b.** .3023   **c.** .1525   **d.** .7333   **e.** .1314   **f.** .9545   **4.95 a.** Yes   **b.** 10, 6   **c.** .726   **d.** .7291   **4.97 a.** .0331   **b.** .4677   **c.** 99.9   **4.99 a.** .4207   **b.** .000337   **4.101 a.** .2743   **b.** .008   **4.103 a.** 125   **b.** 7.91   **c.** 9.49   **d.** 1   **4.105 a.** .3413   **b.** .0026   **c.** .3830   **4.107 a.** 69.2   **b.** 42.2   **4.109 a.** 25.14%   **b.** 90.375   **4.111** .703   **4.113 b.** 50; 9   **c.** .5398; 0   **4.115** $z = -.588$ if no coaching, $z = 2.4$ if coaching; more likely that leader did not receive coaching   **4.117 a.** .68   **b.** .95   **c.** 1.00   **4.119** Plot c   **4.121 b.** $\bar{x} = 67.76,$ $s = 26.87; 94.5\%$ of observations within $\bar{x} \pm 2s$ **c.** IQR = 37, IQR/s = 1.38   **4.123 a.** Approx. normal   **b.** Approx. normal   **4.125** No   **4.127** IQR/s = 1.3   **4.129** None   **4.131** $z = -.75$ for minimum value of 128   **4.133 a.** $f(x) = .04$ $(20 \leq x \leq 45)$, 0 otherwise   **b.** 32.5, 7.22   **4.135 a.** .367879   **b.** .950213   **c.** .223130   **d.** .993262   **4.137 a.** 0   **b.** 1   **c.** 1   **4.139** .25   **4.141 a.** .133; .571   **b.** .267; 0   **4.143 a.** .449329

b. .864665   **4.145 a.** .5   **b.** .3   **c.** Only 1 possible connection   **4.147 a.** Continuous   **c.** 7, .2887, (6.422, 7.577)   **d.** .5   **e.** 0   **f.** .75   **g.** .0002
4.149 a. .753403   **b.** .667   **c.** .811   **4.151** .4444   **4.153** $-\theta \ln(.5) = .6931470$ **4.157 a.** .2734   **b.** .4096   **c.** .3432   **4.159 a.** .192   **b.** .228   **c.** .772
d. .987   **e.** .960   **f.** 14, 4.2, 2.049   **g.** .975   **4.161 a.** Poisson   **b.** Binomial   **c.** Binomial   **4.163 a.** Discrete   **b.** Continuous   **c.** Continuous
d. Continuous   **4.165 a.** .9821   **b.** .0179   **c.** .9505   **d.** .3243   **e.** .9107   **f.** .0764   **4.167 a.** Exponential   **b.** Uniform   **c.** Normal   **4.169 a.** .6915
b. .1587   **c.** .1915   **d.** .3085   **e.** 0   **f.** 1   **4.171 a.** 47.68   **b.** 47.68   **c.** 30.13   **d.** 41.5   **e.** 30.13   **4.173 b.** .2592   **c.** .0870   **d.** .6826   **e.** 3.00   **4.175 a.** .5, .289
b. .2   **c.** No, $p = .005$ **4.177 a.** .221199   **b.** .002394   **c.** .082085   **4.179 b.** $n = 20$, $p = .8$.   **c.** .175   **d.** .804   **e.** 16   **4.181 a.** .367869   **b.** .606531
c. .135335; .135335   **d.** .814046   **4.183 a.** .383   **b.** .0002   **4.185** No   **4.187 a.** .8264   **b.** 17 times   **c.** .6217   **d.** 0, −157   **4.189 a.** 1.25, 1.09; no
b. .007   **c.** Not applicable   **4.191 a.** $\mu = 113.24$, $\sigma = 4.19$ **b.** $z = 6.38$ **4.193 b.** .85   **c.** .6, .7, 0   **d.** A_1: 2.4; A_2: 1.5; A_3: 1.65; A_4: .10
e. A_1: .86; A_2: .67; A_3: .57; A_4: .3   **4.195 a.** .125   **b.** 5   **4.197** .2676; no   **4.199 a.** .8106   **b.** .1894   **c.** \$1,246,100   **4.201** 292   **4.203** 5,102
4.205 a. $\sigma = 1$: .6826; $\sigma = 2$: .4260; $\sigma = 4$: .3734   **b.** $\sigma = 1$: .6945; $\sigma = 2$: .42; $\sigma = 4$: .3709   **c.** $\sigma = 1$; $\sigma = 2$

Chapter 5

5.1 a. $(0,0), (0,2), (0,4), (0,6), (2,0), (2,2), (2,4), (2,6), (4,0), (4,2), (4,4), (4,6), (6,0), (6,2), (6,4), (6,6)$ **b.** $0, 1, 2, 3, 1, 2, 3, 4, 2, 3, 4, 5,$
$3, 4, 5, 6$ **c.** $\frac{1}{16}$ **d.** $p(0) = \frac{1}{16}, p(1) = \frac{2}{16}, p(2) = \frac{3}{16}, p(3) = \frac{4}{16}, p(4) = \frac{3}{16}, p(5) = \frac{2}{16}, p(6) = \frac{1}{16}$ **5.3 a.** $p(1) = .04, p(1.5) = .12,$
$p(2) = .17, p(2.5) = .20, p(3) = .20, p(3.5) = .14, p(4) = .08, p(4.5) = .04, p(5) = .01$ **c.** .05   **d.** No   **5.5 a.** Same as Exercise 5.3a
5.9 a. 5   **b.** $E(\bar{x}) = 5$ **c.** $E(m) = 4.778$ **d.** $\bar{x}$ **5.11 a.** yes   **b.** median   **5.13 b.** 1.61   **c.** $E(s^2) = 1.61$ **e.** $E(s) = 1.004$ **5.15** No
5.17 a. 100, 5   **b.** 100, 2   **c.** 100, 1   **d.** 100, 1.414   **e.** 100, .447   **f.** 100, .316   **5.19 a.** .0228   **b.** .0668   **c.** .0062   **d.** .8185   **e.** .0013   **5.21 a.** .8944
b. .0228   **c.** .1292   **d.** .9699   **5.23 a.** Skewed right   **b.** $\mu = 95.52$, $\sigma = 91.45$ **c.** Normal; $\mu_{\bar{x}} = 95.52$ and $\sigma_{\bar{x}} = 14.47$ **d.** .3520   **5.25 a.** 68
b. 4.02   **c.** Approx. normal   **d.** .7734   **5.27** No; $P(\bar{x} < 103) = .0107$ **5.29 a.** $\approx$ normal with $\mu_{\bar{x}} = .53$ and $\sigma_{\bar{x}} = .0273$ **b.** .0336
c. Before: $p = .0139$; after: $p = .3557$; after   **5.31 a.** .0034   **b.** ≈ 0; true mean is larger than 6 ppb   **5.33** Not likely; $P(\bar{x} > 42) \approx 0$
5.35 Handrubbing: $p = .2743$; handwashing: $p = .0047$; handrubbing   **5.37 a.** $\mu_{\hat{p}} = .1, \sigma_{\hat{p}} = .0134$ **b.** $\mu_{\hat{p}} = .5, \sigma_{\hat{p}} = .0224$ **c.** $\mu_{\hat{p}} = .7$,
$\sigma_{\hat{p}} = .0205$ **5.39 a.** $E(\hat{p}) = .85, \sigma_{\hat{p}} = .0226$ **b.** Approx. normal   **c.** .9864   **5.41 d.** As n increases, $\sigma_{\hat{p}}$ decreases; distributions all approx.
normal   **5.43 a.** .67   **b.** .0149   **c.** Approx. normal   **d.** 1   **e.** 1   **5.45 a.** Approx. normal with $\mu_{\hat{p}} = .03$ and $\sigma_{\hat{p}} = .0054$ **b.** .9999   **c.** .8238
5.47 a. .0019   **b.** True $p > .4$ **c.** Sample not representative of target population   **5.49 a.** .92   **b.** .0099   **5.51 b.** $E(A) = \theta$ **c.** Choose
estimator with smaller variance   **5.53 a.** .5   **b.** .0606   **c.** .0985   **d.** .8436   **5.55 a.** .9032   **b.** .9850   **c.** .3328   **5.61** .0838   **5.63 a.** .6   **b.** .0566
c. Approx. normal   **d.** .0384   **5.65 a.** $\approx$ normal   **b.** .0091   **c.** .9544   **5.67** .9772   **5.69 a.** $\mu_{\hat{p}} = .2, \sigma_{\hat{p}} = .0253$ **b.** (.1494, .2596)   **c.** .9544
5.71 a. .01; .002   **b.** (.00164, .00236)   **5.73 a.** 60; 6   **b.** Normal   **c.** 0

Chapter 6

6.1 a. 1.645   **b.** 2.576   **c.** 1.96   **d.** 1.282   **6.3 a.** $28 \pm .784$ **b.** $102 \pm .65$ **c.** $15 \pm .0588$ **d.** $4.05 \pm .163$ **e.** No   **6.5 a.** $26.2 \pm .96$ **b.** In
repeated sampling, 95% of all confidence intervals constructed will include μ.   **c.** 26.2 ± 1.26 **d.** Increases   **e.** Yes   **6.7** Point
estimator is a single number   **6.9** Yes   **6.11 a.** 3.11   **b.** (3.02, 3.30)   **c.** Incorrect   **d.** No impact—CLT applies   **6.13** $6,563 \pm 97.65$
6.15 a. (2.55, 3.98)   **b.** 99% confident that true mean number of wheels on all social robots is between 2.55 and 3.98   **c.** .99
6.17 a. μ = mean salary of all 500 CEOs   **6.19 a.** 99.6   **b.** 99.6 ± 2.24 **c.** 95% confident that true Mach rating score of all purchasing
managers is between 97.36 and 101.84.   **d.** Yes   **6.21** SAT–Math   **6.23 a.** $z_{.10} = 1.282$, $t_{.10} = 1.533$ **b.** $z_{.05} = 1.645$, $t_{.05} = 2.132$
c. $z_{.025} = 1.96$, $t_{.025} = 2.776$ **d.** $z_{.01} = 2.326$, $t_{.01} = 3.747$ **e.** $z_{.005} = 2.576$, $t_{.005} = 4.604$ **6.25 a.** 2.228   **b.** 2.228   **c.** −1.812   **d.** 1.725
e. 4.032   **6.27 a.** 5 ± 1.88 **b.** 5 ± 2.39 **c.** 5 ± 3.75 **d.** $5 \pm .78, 5 \pm .94, 5 \pm 1.28$; decreased width   **6.29 a.** μ = mean trap spacing
for the population of red spiny lobster fishermen   **b.** 89.86   **c.** Sampling distribution of $\bar{x}$ is unknown   **d.** (79.10, 100.62)   **e.** 95% confident that true mean trap spacing is between 79.10 and 100.62 meters   **f.** Population of trap spacings is normally distributed
6.31 (71.67, 79.13)   **6.33 a.** (1.64, 2.13)   **b.** No   **6.35 a.** (303.4, 413.6)   **b.** 95% confident that true mean skidding distance falls between
303.4 and 413.6 meters   **c.** $\approx$ normal   **d.** No   **6.37 a.** (.09, .94)   **b.** (1.49, 3.69)   **c.** Mean is lower in water containing oil   **6.39 a.** All 212
firms in *Forbes* Largest Private Companies list   **b.** (2.10, 8.68)   **c.** 98% confident that true mean revenue is between \$2.10 and
\$8.68 billion.   **d.** $\approx$ normal   **e.** Yes   **6.41 a.** Yes   **b.** No   **c.** No   **d.** No   **6.43 a.** Yes   **b.** $.46 \pm .065$ **c.** 95% confident p is between .395
and .525   **d.** 95% of all similarly constructed intervals contain the true value of p **6.45 a.** .4   **b.** Approx. normal   **c.** (.38, .42)   **d.** 95%
confident that true proportion of Arlington homes with market values that are overestimated by more than 10% falls between .38 and
.42   **e.** No   **6.47 a.** All American adults   **b.** 1,000 adults surveyed   **c.** Proportion of all American adults who think Starbucks coffee is
overpriced   **d.** $.73 \pm .028$ **6.49 a.** .60   **b.** (.58, .62)   **c.** 95% confident that true proportion of all adults who use cell phones while
driving falls between .58 and .62   **6.51** (.367, .453)   **6.53** $.269 \pm .014$; 90% confident that true percentage of all firms with acquisitions
is between 25.5% and 28.3%   **6.55 a.** No   **b.** (0, .019)   **6.57 a.** True proportion of all fillets that are red snapper   **c.** $.27 \pm .17$
d. 95% confident that true proportion of all fillets that are red snapper is between .10 and .44   **6.59** 95% CI for p: (.849, .851);
actual performance is below claim of $p = .95$ **6.61 a.** 68   **b.** 31   **6.63** 34   **6.65 a.** .098, 0.784, 0.56, 0.392, 0.196   **6.67** 84   **6.69** 21
6.71 1,692   **6.73** 14,735   **6.75** 43; 171; 385   **6.77** No   **6.79 a.** .7746   **b.** .8944   **c.** .9487   **d.** .995   **6.81 a.** 1.00   **b.** .6124   **c.** 0   **d.** As n
increases, standard error decreases.   **6.83** $.42 \pm .021$ **6.85 a.** 36.03 ± 3.40 **b.** $.7 \pm .16$ **6.87 a.** $.56 \pm .012$ **c.** 95% confident that
true proportion of active NFL players who select a professional coach as most influential is between .548 and .572   **6.89 a.** 156.46
b. 18.70   **c.** 156.46 ± 37.405 **d.** Not reasonable   **6.91** No; $.086 \pm .041$ **6.93 a.** (4.54, 8.81)   **b.** (.00024, .00085)   **c.** (641.86, 1809.09)
d. (.95, 12.66)   **6.95** (4.27, 65.90)   **6.97 a.** (.13, .19); 95% confident that true standard deviation of facial WHR for CEOs is between
.13 and .19   **b.** Approx. normal   **6.99** (3178.6, 7618.4); 95% confident that true standard deviation of radon levels in tombs is between
3,178.6 and 7,618.4 Bq/m³   **6.101** (6.25, 17.74); 99% confident that true variance in drug concentrations is between 6.67 and 17.74
6.103 (43.72, 1199.95)   **6.105 a.** −1.725   **b.** 3.250   **c.** 1.860   **d.** 2.898   **6.107 a.** 32.5 ± 5.15 **b.** 23,871   **c.** (714.2, 1163.7)   **6.109 a.** 19.0228;
2.70039   **b.** 32.8523; 8.90655   **c.** 79.49; 27.9907   **6.111 (1)** p = proportion with excellent health; **(2), (3),** and **(4)** μ = mean number

of days health not good   **6.113 a.** .11   **b.** .11 $\pm$ .050   **6.115** 97   **6.117** .694 $\pm$ .092   **6.119 a.** 4.25 $\pm$ 4.14   **b.** 99% confident that true mean number of blogs/forums falls between .11 and 8.39   **c.** No; apply the Central Limit Theorem   **6.121** .667 $\pm$ .065   **6.123 a.** 49.3 $\pm$ 8.6   **b.** 99% confident that mean amount removed from all soil specimens is between 40.70% and 57.90%   **c.** Normal distribution   **d.** Possible   **e.** (.75, 45)   **6.125 a.** 66.83 $\pm$ 6.17   **c.** 45.31 $\pm$ 4.15   **6.127 a.** .867   **b.** (.781, .953)   **c.** 95% confident that true proportion of Wal-Mart stores with more than 2 inaccurately scanned items is between .781 and .953   **d.** Not believable   **e.** No   **f.** 126   **6.129 a.** .833 $\pm$ .149   **b.** No   **c.** 1,337   **6.131** 818   **6.137 a.** Yes   **b.** Missing measure of reliability   **c.** 95% CI for μ: .932 $\pm$ .037

Chapter 7

7.1 Null; alternative   **7.3** α **7.5** Reject H_0 when H_0 is true; accept H_0 when H_0 is true; Reject H_0 when H_0 is false; accept H_0 when H_0 is false   **7.7** No   **7.9 a.** H_0: $p = .68$ **b.** $|z| > 2.576$ **7.11** H_0: $p = .07$, H_a: $p < .07$ **7.13** H_0: $\mu = 863$, H_a: $\mu < 863$ **7.15 a.** Unsafe; safe   **c.** α **7.17 c.** α **e.** Decrease   **f.** Increase   **7.19 a.** .1151   **b.** .1151   **c.** .2302   **7.21 a.** Do not reject H_0 **b.** Reject H_0 **c.** Reject H_0 **d.** Do not reject H_0 **e.** Do not reject H_0 **7.23** .0150   **7.25** .03   **7.27** .06   **7.29 a.** $z > 2.14$ **b.** .0162   **7.31 a.** $z = -1.61$, reject H_0 **b.** $z = -1.61$, do not reject H_0 **7.33 a.** $z = 5.71$, reject H_0 **b.** Test valid due to CLT   **7.35** H_0: $\mu = 2.2$, H_a: $\mu \neq 2.2$, p-value ≈ 0, reject H_0 for any reasonable α **7.37 a.** H_0: $\mu = .250$, H_a: $\mu \neq .250$ **b.** $\bar{x} = .25248$, $s = .00223$ **c.** $z = 7.03$ **d.** p-value ≈ 0 **e.** $|z| > 2.576$ **f.** Yes, reject H_0 **7.39 a.** Yes; $z = 1.85$, p-value $= .0322$, reject H_0 **b.** Yes; $z = -1.85$, p-value $= .0322$, reject H_0 **c.** No; apply CLT   **7.41** $z = -1.86$, do not reject H_0 **7.43 a.** $z = 26.15$, p-value ≈ 0, reject H_0 **b.** $z = -14.24$, p-value ≈ 0, reject H_0 **7.45 a.** $z = 2.73$, reject H_0 **c.** No   **7.47 a.** Small n, data normal   **b.** Mound-shaped and symmetric; t is flatter than z **7.49 a.** $|t| > 2.160$ **b.** $t > 2.500$ **c.** $t > 1.397$ **d.** $t < -2.718$ **e.** $|t| > 1.729$ **f.** $t < -2.353$ **7.51 a.** Population is normally distributed   **b.** Reject H_0 at $\alpha = .05$ **c.** .076   **7.53** H_0: $\mu = 6{,}000$, H_a: $\mu < 6{,}000$, p-value $= .096/2 = .048$, $\alpha = .10$, reject H_0 **7.55 a.** H_0: $\mu = 2$, H_a: $\mu \neq 2$ **b.** $t = -1.02$ **c.** $|t| > 2.093$ **d.** Do not reject H_0 **e.** .322   **7.57 a.** H_0: $\mu = 1.4$, H_a: $\mu > 1.4$ **b.** Chance of concluding $\mu > 1.4$ when $\mu = 1.4$ is .10   **c.** $\bar{x} = 5.243$, $s = .192$ **d.** $t = 34.67$ **e.** p-value $= 0$ **f.** Reject H_0 **7.59** Yes, $t = -2.53$ **7.61** No, $t = 2.97$ **7.63** Yes, using $\alpha = .05$; Plant 1: p-value $= .197$; Plant 2: p-value $= .094$ **7.65 a.** -2.33 **c.** Reject H_0 **d.** .0099   **7.67 a.** $z = 1.13$, do not reject H_0 **b.** .1292   **7.69 a.** $\hat{p} = .67$ **b.** H_0: $p = .7$, H_a: $p > .7$ **c.** $z = -1.80$ **d.** $z > 2.326$ **e.** p-value $= .9641$ **f.** Do not reject H_0 **g.** Do not reject H_0 **7.71** Yes, $z = -3.54$ **7.73 a.** H_0: $p = .5$, H_a: $p < .5$ **b.** .231   **c.** Do not reject H_0 **7.75** No; $z = -.89$ **7.77 a.** No, $z = 1.49$ **b.** .0681   **7.79** Population: all U.S. households with TVs; experimental unit: individual household with a TV; variable: whether or not the household has a DVR; parameter: $p = $ proportion all households with DVRs; H_0: $p = .41$, H_a: $p \neq .41$; test statistic: $z = (\hat{p} - .41)/\sqrt{(.41)(.59)/n}$ **7.81** $z = 1.20$, do not reject H_0 **7.83 a.** $\chi^2 < 6.26214$ or $\chi^2 > 27.4884$ **b.** $\chi^2 > 40.2894$ **c.** $\chi^2 > 21.0642$ **d.** $\chi^2 < 3.57056$ **e.** $\chi^2 < 1.63539$ or $\chi^2 > 12.5916$ **f.** $\chi^2 < 13.8484$ **7.85 a.** $\chi^2 = 479.16$, reject H_0 **7.87 a.** H_0: $\sigma^2 = 100$, H_a: $\sigma^2 < 100$ **b.** $\chi^2 < 167.361$ **c.** Chance of concluding $\sigma < 10$ when $\sigma = 10$ is .05   **d.** $\chi^2 = 154.81$, p-value $= .009$ **e.** Reject H_0 **f.** Rates of return $\approx$ normal   **7.89 a.** H_0: $\sigma^2 = .000004$, H_a: $\sigma^2 \neq .000004$ **b.** $\chi^2 = 48.49$, do not reject H_0 **c.** Tee weights $\approx$ normal   **7.91** No, $\chi^2 = 13.77$ **7.93** At $\alpha = .05$, yes; $\chi^2 = 133.90$ **7.95 a.** With large s, test statistic will be small   **b.** 1.76   **c.** Yes; $\chi^2 = 99$ **7.97 b.** 532.9   **d.** .1949   **e.** .8051   **7.99 a.** Approx. normal with $\mu_{\bar{x}} = 75$ and $\sigma_{\bar{x}} = 2.14$ **b.** Approx. normal with $\mu_{\bar{x}} = 70$ and $\sigma_{\bar{x}} = 2.14$ **c.** .1469   **d.** .8531   **7.101 a.** Approx. normal with $\mu_{\hat{p}} = .7$ and $\sigma_{\hat{p}} = .046$ **b.** Approx. normal with $\mu_{\hat{p}} = .65$ and $\sigma_{\hat{p}} = .048$ **c.** .7979   **d.** .9469   **7.103 a.** .1949, Type II error   **b.** .05, Type I error   **c.** .8051   **7.105** .7764   **7.107** .1075   **7.109** Alternative   **7.111** Large   **7.113 a.** $t = -7.51$, reject H_0 **b.** $t = -7.51$, reject H_0 **7.115 a.** $z = -1.78$, reject H_0 **b.** $z = -1.78$, do not reject H_0 **7.117 a.** $\chi^2 = 63.48$, reject H_0 **b.** $\chi^2 = 63.48$, reject H_0 **7.119 a.** $\chi^2 < 24.3$ or $\chi^2 > 73.1$ **b.** $\chi^2 = 63.72$ **c.** Do not reject H_0 **7.121 a.** H_0: $\mu = 1$, H_a: $\mu > 1$ **b.** Reject H_0 if $t > 1.345$ **d.** $t = 2.41$ **e.** $.01 < $ p-value $< .025$, reject H_0 **f.** $\chi^2 = 12.78$, do not reject H_0 **7.123 a.** H_0: $p = .75$ **b.** Type I error: conclude p differs from .75 when $p = .75$; Type II error: conclude $p = .75$ when p differs from .75   **7.125 a.** H_0: $\mu = 100$, H_a: $\mu \neq 100$ **b.** Random sample; population of cost-of-living indexes $\approx$ normal   **c.** $t = -1.89$, do not reject H_0 **d.** p-value $= .108$ **7.127 a.** H_0: No disease, H_a: Disease   **b.** Type I error = false positive; Type II error = false negative   **c.** Type II error; β **7.129** $\chi^2 = 187.9$, do not reject H_0 **7.131 a.** $z = -3.22$, do not reject H_0 **b.** p-value ≈ 1 **c.** .8159   **7.133 a.** Concluding that percentage of shoplifters turned over to police is 50% when, in fact, the percentage is higher than 50%   **b.** .8461   **c.** Decreases to .7389   **7.135 a.** No, $z = 1.41$ **b.** Small   **c.** .0793   **7.137 a.** No   **b.** $\beta = .5910$, power $= .4090$ **c.** Increases   **7.139 a.** No, $z = 1.37$ **b.** Yes, $z = -4.58$ **7.141** Yes; $z = 2.50$, do not reject H_0: $\mu = 220$ **7.143 a.** $z = 2.73$, reject H_0 **c.** Sampling distribution of $\bar{x}$ is approx. normal by CLT   **7.145** $z = 7.83$, reject H_0

Chapter 8

8.1 a. 150 $\pm$ 6   **b.** 150 $\pm$ 8   **c.** 0; 5   **d.** 0 $\pm$ 10   **e.** Variability of the difference is greater   **8.3 a.** 35 $\pm$ 24.5   **b.** $z = 2.8$, p-value $= .0052$, reject H_0 **c.** p-value $= .0026$ **d.** $z = .8$, p-value $= .4238$, do not reject H_0 **e.** Independent random samples   **8.5 a.** No   **b.** No   **c.** No   **d.** Yes   **e.** No   **8.7 a.** .5989   **b.** Yes, $t = -2.39$ **c.** $-1.24 \pm .98$ **d.** Confidence interval   **8.9 a.** Do not reject H_0 **b.** .0575   **8.11 a.** $t = -1.646$, do not reject H_0 **b.** -2.50 ± 3.12 **8.13 a.** 5.70 $\pm$ 5.07   **b.** R–Z group; yes   **8.15 a.** H_0: $\mu_1 - \mu_2 = 0$, H_a: $\mu_1 - \mu_2 \neq 0$ **b.** $t = .62$ **c.** $|t| > 1.684$ **d.** Do not reject H_0 **e.** Do not reject H_0 **f.** Independent random samples, both populations normal, $\sigma_1^2 = \sigma_2^2$ **8.17 a.** .90 $\pm$ .064   **b.** Buy-side   **c.** Large, independent random samples   **8.19 a.** $t = 1.56$, do not reject H_0: $\mu_T = \mu_I$ **b.** $t = -.50$, do not reject H_0: $\mu_W = \mu_I$ **c.** No differences   **8.21** $z = -2.81$, reject H_0: $\mu_C = \mu_R$ **8.23** Yes, $z = 3.20$, sufficient evidence to conclude $\mu_{\text{Honey}} > \mu_{\text{DM}}$ **8.25 a.** No sample variances   **b.** s_1^2 and s_2^2 **c.** $z < -2.326$ **d.** .24   **e.** Smaller   **8.27 a.** $t > 1.796$ **b.** $t > 1.319$ **c.** $t > 3.182$ **d.** $t > 2.374$ **8.29 a.** H_0: $\mu_d = 0$, H_a: $\mu_d < 0$ **b.** $t = -5.29$, p-value $= .0003$, reject H_0 **c.** $(-4.98, -2.42)$ **d.** Population of differences is normal   **8.31 a.** H_0: $\mu_d = 0$, H_a: $\mu_d > 0$ **b.** Paired test   **c.** $z = 3.10$ **d.** $z = 19.18$ **e.** Paired test   **f.** Reject H_0 **g.** No   **h.** (2.86, 3.74)   **8.33 a.** Two hole measurements at each location   **c.** $\bar{d} = .14$, $s_d = 1.26$ **d.** $(-.435, .715)$ **e.** Yes   **8.35 a.** Response rates observed twice for each survey   **b.** No, $t = .53$ **c.** Reject H_0 **8.37 a.** Yes, $t = 2.864$ **8.39** (.036, .224); Huffman-coding   **8.41** $t = .46$,

p-value $= 0.65$, do not reject H_0 **8.43 a.** Binomial distributions **b.** Distribution is approx. normal for large n's   **8.45 a.** No **b.** No **c.** No **d.** No **e.** No   **8.47 a.** $z = -4.02$, reject H_0 **b.** $z = -4.02$, reject H_0 **c.** $z = -4.02$, reject H_0 **d.** $-.1 \pm .041$ **8.49 a.** .153 **b.** .215 **c.** $(-.132, .008)$ **d.** No evidence of a difference   **8.51 a.** $p_1 - p_2$ **b.** $H_0: p_1 - p_2 = 0, H_a: p_1 - p_2 \neq 0$ **c.** $z = -2.67$ **d.** $|z| > 2.576$ **e.** .008 **f.** Reject H_0 **8.53 a.** All January patients; all May patients **b.** .083 **c.** $(.033, .133)$ **d.** Yes   **8.55** No, $z = 1.68$ **8.57** Yes; 95% CI for $(p_{AA} - p_{White}) = (.089, .131), z = 14.64$ **8.59 a.** 500, 46 **b.** Sample may not be representative   **8.61 a.** 29,954 **b.** 2,165 **c.** 1,113   **8.63** 34   **8.65** 156   **8.67** 13,531 for each survey   **8.69** 1,729   **8.71 a.** 5,051   **8.73 a.** 4.10 **b.** 3.57 **c.** 8.81 **d.** 3.21   **8.75 a.** $F > 1.74$ **b.** $F > 2.04$ **c.** $F > 2.35$ **d.** $F > 2.78$ **8.77 a.** $F > 2.11$ **b.** $F > 3.01$ **c.** $F > 2.04$ **d.** $F > 2.30$ **e.** $F > 5.27$ **8.79 a.** $F = 4.29$, do not reject H_0 **b.** $.05 < p$-value $< .10$ **8.81 a.** $H_0: \sigma_1^2 = \sigma_2^2, H_a: \sigma_1^2 \neq \sigma_2^2$ **b.** $F = 1.16$ **c.** $F > 2.16$ **d.** Fail to reject H_0 **e.** Valid   **8.83** $F = .844$, p-value $= .681$, fail to reject H_0 **8.85 a.** No, $F = 2.27$ **b.** $.05 < p$-value $< .10$ **8.87 a.** Yes, $F = 8.29$ **b.** No   **8.91 a.** $t = .78$, do not reject H_0 **b.** 2.50 ± 8.99 **c.** 225   **8.93 a.** $3.90 \pm .31$ **b.** $z = 20.60$, reject H_0 **c.** 346   **8.95 a.** $\mu_1 - \mu_2$ **b.** $p_1 - p_2$ **c.** μ_d **8.97 a.** $.29 \pm 1.45$ **b.** $F = 1.06$, do not reject H_0 **c.** No significant difference   **8.99 a.** Yes **b.** $z = 4.58$, reject H_0 **8.101 b.** $H_0: \mu_d = 0, H_a: \mu_d \neq 0$ **c.** Reject H_0 **8.103 a.** $H_0: \mu_1 = \mu_2, H_a: \mu_1 \neq \mu_2$ **b.** Reject H_0 **c.** Do not reject H_0 **d.** No practical difference   **8.105 a.** $p_1 - p_2$ **b.** $H_0: p_1 - p_2 = 0, H_a: p_1 - p_2 \neq 0$ **c.** $z = -5.16$ **d.** $|z| > 2.58$ **e.** Yes **f.** Reject H_0 **8.107 a.** All male and all female cell phone users **b.** .32; .25 **c.** $.07 \pm .04$ **d.** Yes **e.** .71; .77 **f.** $z = -2.45$, reject H_0 **8.109 a.** Yes, $t = -1.96$ **c.** .058 **d.** -7.4 ± 6.38 **8.111 a.** $z = 94.35$, reject H_0 **b.** $(-.155, -.123)$ **8.113** 4,802   **8.115** No, $F = 2.79$ **8.117 a.** $H_0: \mu_1 = \mu_2, H_a: \mu_1 > \mu_2$ **c.** Reject H_0; yes **d.** $H_0: \mu_1 = \mu_2, H_a: \mu_1 \neq \mu_2$ **e.** Do not reject H_0; yes   **8.119** Aad: no, at $\alpha = .05$; Ab: yes, at $\alpha = .05$; Intention: no, at $\alpha = .05$ **8.121 a.** yes, $z = -2.79$ **b.** 95% CI: $-.011 \pm .0077$ **8.123** Yes; 95% confidence interval for μ_d: $(-242.29, -106.96)$

Chapter 11

11.3 $\beta_1 = \frac{1}{3}, \beta_0 = \frac{14}{3}, y = \frac{14}{3} + (1/3)x$ **11.9** No   **11.11 a.** $\Sigma(y - \hat{y}) = 0.02$, SSE $= 1.2204$ **c.** SSE $= 108.00$ **11.13 b.** Negative linear relationship **c.** $8.54, -.994$ **11.15 a.** $y = \beta_0 + \beta_1 x + \varepsilon$ **b.** $\hat{y} = -97.41 + 1.19x$ **c.** No practical interpretation **d.** For every 1-point increase in 2001 Math SAT score, estimate 2011 Math SAT score to increase 1.19 points   **11.17 a.** $\hat{y} = 7.21 + 35.92x$ **b.** y-intercept: no practical interpretation; slope: for each unit change in surface area to volume, estimate drug release rate to increase by 35.92 **c.** 25.17 **d.** Not reliable; $x = .50$ is outside range   **11.19 a.** $\hat{y} = -14.14 + .63x$ **b.** For each additional 1 million births, estimate number of software millionaire birthdays to increase by .63 **c.** 7.83 **d.** $\hat{y} = 2.72 + .31x$ **e.** For each additional CEO birthday, estimate number of software millionaire birthdays to increase by .63 **f.** 5.79   **11.21 a.** $E(y) = \beta_0 + \beta_1 x$ **b.** $\hat{y} = 250.14 - .629x$ **c.** No practical interpretation **d.** For every 1-yard increase in driving distance, driving accuracy to decrease .629% **e.** Slope   **11.23** $7.88 million   **11.27** Plot b   **11.29 a.** .3475 **b.** 1.179   **11.31 a.** .2 **b.** About 95% of the observed payoffs fall within .4 unit of their predicted values   **11.33 a.** 2.01 **b.** About 95% of the observed release rates fall within 4% of their predicted values   **11.35 a.** SSE $= 44.16$, $s^2 = 11.04, s = 3.32$ **b.** SSE $= 9.69, s^2 = 2.42, s = 1.56$ **c.** $x =$ CEO birthdays   **11.37 a.** SSE $= 1.017, s^2 = .0462, s = .215$ **c.** About 95% of the observed sweetness index values fall within .43 units of their predicted values   **11.39 a.** $s = 5.37$; about 95% of the observed FCAT-Math scores fall within 10.74 points of their predicted values **b.** $s = 3.42$; about 95% of the observed FCAT-Reading scores fall within 6.84 points of their predicted values **c.** Reading score   **11.41 a.** 95% CI: 31 ± 1.13; 90% CI: $31 \pm .92$ **b.** 95% CI: 64 ± 4.28; 90% CI: 64 ± 3.53 **c.** 95% CI: $-8.4 \pm .67$; 90% CI: $-8.4 \pm .55$ **11.43** 80% CI: $.82 \pm .33$; 98% CI: $.82 \pm .76$ **11.45 a.** $H_0: \beta_1 = 0, H_a: \beta_1 > 0$ **b.** Reject H_0, p-value ≈ 0 **c.** $(1.09, 1.29)$ **11.47 a.** Positive **b.** $(-1.18, 1.72)$ **c.** Insufficient evidence of a linear relationship   **11.49** $(30.17, 41.67)$; 90% confident that for each additional unit increase in surface area to volume, the increase in the drug release rate is between 30.17 and 41.67   **11.51 a.** $(-.048, 1.304)$ **b.** $(.179, .434)$ **c.** No; yes   **11.53 a.** $H_0: \beta_1 = 0, H_a: \beta_1 < 0$ **b.** $t = -13.23$, p-value ≈ 0 **c.** Reject H_0 **11.55** No, $t = .66$ **11.57 a.** Yes, p-value $= \frac{.008}{2} = .004$ **b.** Possible outlier **c.** p-value $= \frac{.332}{2} = .166$, do not reject H_0 **11.59 a.** Positive **b.** Negative **c.** 0 slope **d.** Positive or negative   **11.61 a.** .944 **b.** .802   **11.63 a.** 18% of sample variation in points scored is explained by the linear relationship with yards from goal line **b.** $-.424$; negative   **11.65 a.** $E(y) = \beta_0 + \beta_1 x$ **b.** Moderately strong positive linear relationship between RMP and SET ratings **c.** Positive **d.** Reject $H_0: \rho = 0$ **e.** .4624   **11.67 a.** Strong positive linear relationship between number of females in managerial positions and number of females with college degree **b.** Very weak positive linear relationship between number of females in managerial positions and number of female HS graduates with no college **c.** Moderately strong positive linear relationship between number of males in managerial positions and number of males with college degree **d.** Moderate positive linear relationship between number of males in managerial positions and number of male HS graduates with no college   **11.69 a.** .624; 62.4% of sample variation in software millionaire birthdays is explained by the linear relationship with number of U.S. births **b.** .917; 91.7% of sample variation in software millionaire birthdays is explained by the linear relationship with number of CEO births **c.** Yes   **11.71** $r^2 = .2286, r = -.478$ **11.73** $r = .243, r^2 = .059$ **11.75** Yes, reject $H_0: \rho = 0$ for all occupations; no   **11.77 c.** 4.64 ± 1.12 **d.** $2.28 \pm .63$; $-.41 \pm 1.17$ **11.79 a.** $\hat{y} = 1.375 + .875x$ **c.** 1.5 **d.** .1875 **e.** $(3.23, 3.89)$ **f.** $(3.81, 5.94)$ **11.81 a.** $(4783, 6792)$ **b.** $(2643, 8933)$ **11.83** For run $= 1$:90% confident that mean sweetness index of all runs with pectin value of 220 falls between 5.65 and 5.84   **11.85 a.** $(5.44, 15.32)$ **b.** Narrower   **11.87 a.** $(2.955, 4.066)$; 99% confident that the mean mass of all spills with elapsed time of 15 minutes is between 2.995 and 4.066 **b.** $(1.02, 6.00)$; 99% confident that the actual mass of a single spill with elapsed time of 15 minutes is between 1.02 and 6.0 **c.** Prediction interval for y; yes   **11.89 a.** Yes, $t = -5.91$; negative **b.** $(.656, 2.829)$ **c.** $(1.467, 2.018)$ **11.91** $\hat{y} = -32.35 + 4.82x; t = 16.60$, p-value $= 0$, reject H_0; $r^2 = .69$ **11.93** $\hat{y} = 62.449 - .34673x; t = -12.56$, p-value $= 0$, reject H_0; $r^2 = .07$ **11.95 a.** $\hat{y} = 37.08 - 1.6x$ **c.** 57.2 **d.** 4.4 **e.** $-1.6 \pm .5$ **f.** 13.08 ± 6.93 **g.** 13.08 ± 7.86

11.97 a. Moderately strong positive linear relationship between skill level and goal-setting ability **b.** Reject H_0 at $\alpha = .01$ **c.** .49
11.99 b. $\hat{y} = 569.58 - .0019x$ **e.** Range of x: \$15,100 to \$70,000 **f.** $t = -.82$, do not reject H_0 **11.101 a.** $E(y) = \beta_0 + \beta_1 x$
b. $\hat{y} = -2,298.4 + 11,598.9x$ **c.** No practical interpretation **d.** (11,146.1, 12,051.7) **e.** 1,117.6 **f.** $H_0: \beta_1 = 0$, $H_a: \beta_1 > 0$
g. p-value $< .0001$ **h.** .8925 **i.** .9447 **j.** (1,297.6, 5,704.6) **k.** (3,362.5, 3,639.7) **11.103 b.** $\hat{y} = 44.13 + .237x$ **c.** 19.40 **d.** Possibly
e. $t = 1.27$, do not reject H_0 **f.** (−.16, .63) **g.** 57.143 ± 34.818 **h.** $x = 110$ outside range **i.** $\bar{x} = 44.1579$ **11.105 a.** Increasing trend
b. Positive **c.** Support; $t = 4.60$, reject H_0 **11.107 c.** $r_1 = .965, r_2 = .996$ **d.** Yes **11.109 a.** Yes, $t = -4.37$ **11.111** Machine-hours:
$t = 3.30, p = .008$, reject $H_0, r^2 = .521$; labor-hours: $t = 1.43, p = .183$, do not reject $H_0, r^2 = .170$

Chapter 12

12.1 a. $E(y) = \beta_0 + \beta_1 x_1 + \beta_2 x_2$ **b.** $E(y) = \beta_0 + \beta_1 x_1 + \beta_2 x_2 + \beta_3 x_3 + \beta_4 x_4$ **c.** $E(y) = \beta_0 + \beta_1 x_1 + \beta_2 x_2 + \beta_3 x_3 + \beta_4 x_4 + \beta_5 x_5$
12.3 a. $t = 1.45$, do not reject H_0 **b.** $t = 3.21$, reject H_0 **12.5** $n - (k + 1)$ **12.7 a.** Yes, $s = .117$ **b.** Yes, $F = 55.2$ **12.9 a.** \$93,002
b. \$98,774 **c.** 32% of sample variation in salary is explained by the model **d.** 95% confident that for each additional year of experience,
mean salary will increase between \$2,700 to \$3,200, holding PhD status and manager status constant **e.** 95% confident that mean salary
of PhDs will be \$11,500 to \$22,300 higher than salaries for non-PhDs, holding years of experience and manager status constant
f. 95% confident that mean salary of managers will be \$7,600 to \$14,600 higher than salaries for nonmanagers, holding years of
experience and PhD status constant **12.11 a.** $F = 4.74$, p-value $< .01$, reject H_0 **b.** 13% of sample variation in Mach score
can be explained by the model **c.** No **12.13 a.** $\hat{y} = 1.81231 + 0.10875x_1 + 0.00017x_2$ **c.** (.027, .190) **d.** (.00009, .00025)
e. $\hat{y} = 1.20785 + 0.06343x_1 + 0.00056x_2$; (.016, .111); (.00024, .00088) **12.15 a.** $E(y) = \beta_0 + \beta_1 x_1 + \beta_2 x_2 + \beta_3 x_3 + \beta_4 x_4$
b. Reject H_0 **c.** Yes **d.** $H_0: \beta_1 = \beta_2 = \beta_3 = \beta_4 = 0$ **e.** $F > 3.37$ **f.** Thrill: reject H_0; Change: do not reject H_0; Surprise: do not reject H_0
12.17 a. $\hat{y} = 14.0107 - 2.1865x_1 - .04794x_2 - .3223x_3 + .493x_4$ **c.** Yes, $F = 40.85$ **d.** R_a^2 **e.** $t = -2.25$, reject H_0 **f.** (.24, .74)
12.19 a. $E(y) = \beta_0 + \beta_1 x_1 + \beta_2 x_2 + \beta_3 x_3 + \beta_4 x_4 + \beta_5 x_5$ **b.** $\hat{y} = 13,614.5 + 0.0888x_1 - 9.201x_2 + 14.394x_3 + 0.35x_4 - 0.848x_5$
d. 458.83 **e.** $F = 147.3, p < .001$, reject H_0 **f.** .917 **g.** Yes, $t = -6.14$ **12.21 b.** $F = 5.11$, reject H_0 **12.23 a.** Model 1: $t = 2.58$,
reject $H_0: \beta_1 = 0$; Model 2: $t = 3.32$, reject $H_0: \beta_1 = 0, t = 6.47$, reject $H_0: \beta_2 = 0, t = -4.77$, reject $H_0: \beta_3 = 0, t = 0.24$, do not reject
$H_0: \beta_4 = 0$; Model 3: $t = 3.21$, reject $H_0: \beta_1 = 0, t = 5.24$, reject $H_0: \beta_2 = 0, t = -4.00$, reject $H_0: \beta_3 = 0, t = 2.28$, reject $H_0: \beta_4 = 0$,
$t = .014$, do not reject $H_0: \beta_5 = 0$ **c.** Model 2 **12.25 a.** 3.78 **b.** 4.68 **12.27 a.** 95% confident that mean desire is between 13.42 and
14.31 for all females with a self-esteem of 24, body satisfaction of 3, and impression of reality TV of 4 **b.** 95% confident that mean
desire is between 8.79 and 10.89 for all males with a self-esteem of 22, body satisfaction of 9, and impression of reality TV of 4
12.29 a. (11,599.6, 13,665.5) **b.** (12,157.9, 13,107.1) **c.** Yes **12.31 a.** $\hat{y} = 130.22 + .169x_1 + .0259x_2 - 1.1115x_3$ **b.** $F = 100.06$,
reject H_0 **c.** (−5.76, 198.85) **12.33 a.** $\hat{y} = -3783 + .00875x_1 + 1.93x_2 + 3444x_3 + 2093x_4$ **b.** $F = 72.11$, reject H_0 **c.** (1,449, 2,424)
12.35 c. Interaction is present **12.37 a.** $\hat{y} = -2.55 + 3.82x_1 + 2.63x_2 - 1.29x_1 x_2$ **b.** Twisted plane **c.** $x_2 = 1$: $\hat{y} = .08 + 2.53x_1$;
$x_2 = 3$: $\hat{y} = 5.34 - .05x_1$; $x_2 = 5$: $\hat{y} = 10.6 - 2.63x_1$ **e.** $H_0: \beta_3 = 0$ vs. $H_a: \beta_3 \neq 0$ **f.** $t = -8.06$, reject H_0 **12.39 a.** $E(y) = \beta_0 + \beta_1 x_1 + $
$\beta_2 x_2 + \beta_3 x_1 x_2$ **b.** $(\beta_1 + 2.5\beta_3)$ **c.** $(\beta_1 + 5\beta_3)$ **d.** $(\beta_2 + 100\beta_3)$ **e.** $H_0: \beta_3 = 0$ **12.41 a.** $E(y) = \beta_0 + \beta_1 x_1 + \beta_2 x_2 + \beta_3 x_1 x_2$
b. $\beta_3 < 0$ **12.43 a.** $\hat{y} = 11.779 - 1.972x_1 + .585x_4 - .553x_1 x_4$ **b.** 9.97 **c.** $F = 45.1$, reject H_0 **d.** .439 **e.** 2.35 **f.** $t = -2.00$, reject H_0
12.45 a. $E(y) = \beta_0 + \beta_1 x_1 + \beta_2 x_2 + \beta_3 x_3 + \beta_4 x_1 x_3 + \beta_5 x_2 x_3$ **b.** $\hat{y} = 10,769 - 1,288x_1 + 218.8x_2 - 1,550.1x_3 - 10.99x_1 x_3 + 19.99x_2 x_3$
c. $t = -.93$, do not reject H_0 **d.** $t = 1.78$, do not reject H_0 **12.47 b.** $\hat{y} = .906 - .023x_1 + .305x_2 + .275x_5 - .003x_1 x_2 + .002x_1 x_5$; yes
12.49 a. $E(y) = \beta_0 + \beta_1 x + \beta_2 x^2$ **b.** $E(y) = \beta_0 + \beta_1 x_1 + \beta_2 x_2 + \beta_3 x_1 x_2 + \beta_4 x_1^2 + \beta_5 x_2^2$ **c.** $E(y) = \beta_0 + \beta_1 x_1 + \beta_2 x_2 + \beta_3 x_3 + \beta_4 x_1 x_2 + $
$\beta_5 x_1 x_3 + \beta_6 x_2 x_3 + \beta_7 x_1^2 + \beta_8 x_2^2 + \beta_9 x_3^2$ **12.51 a.** Yes, $F = 85.94$ **b.** $H_0: \beta_2 = 0$ vs. $H_a: \beta_2 > 0$ **c.** $H_0: \beta_2 = 0$ vs. $H_a: \beta_2 < 0$ **12.53 a.** Yes,
$F = 25.93$ **b.** $t = -10.74$, reject H_0 **c.** $t = .60$, do not reject H_0 **12.55 b.** 22.6% of the sample variation in points scored is explained
by the quadratic model **c.** No **d.** $H_0: \beta_2 = 0$ **12.57 b.** First-order model; first-order model; second-order model **12.59 a.** $E(y) = \beta_0 + $
$\beta_1 x_1 + \beta_2 x_2 + \beta_3 x_1 x_2 + \beta_4 x_1^2 + \beta_5 x_2^2$ **b.** 14% of sample variation in attitude toward improving efficiency can be explained by the
model **c.** Downward curvature in the relationship between attitude and congruence **d.** Evidence of interaction
12.61 a. $E(y) = \beta_0 + \beta_1 x$ **b.** $E(y) = \beta_0 + \beta_1 x + \beta_2 x^2$ **c.** Quadratic model **d.** $F = 57.75$, overall model is statistically useful; $t = 3.98$,
sufficient evidence of curvature **e.** Quadratic model **12.63 a.** Curvilinear **b.** $\hat{y} = 154,243 - 1,908.9x + 5.93x^2$ **c.** $t = 5.66$, reject
H_0 **12.65 b.** Possibly **c.** $\hat{y} = 2,802.4 + 122.95x$ **d.** $\hat{y} = 4,944.2 - 183.03x + 7.46x^2$ **e.** $t = 3.38$, reject $H_0: \beta_2 = 0$; 2nd-order
12.67 $E(y) = \beta_0 + \beta_1 x_1 + \beta_2 x_2$, where $x_1 = \{1$ level 1, 0 if not$\}$, $x_2 = \{1$ level 2, 0 if not$\}$; $\beta_0 = \mu_3, \beta_1 = \mu_1 - \mu_3, \beta_2 = \mu_2 - \mu_3$
12.69 a. Level 1: 10.2; Level 2: 6.2; Level 3: 22.2; Level 4: 12.2 **b.** $H_0: \beta_1 = \beta_2 = \beta_3 = 0$ **12.71 a.** Method: $x_1 = \{1$ manual, 0 if automated$\}$;
Soil: $x_2 = \{1$ if clay, 0 if not$\}$, $x_3 = \{1$ if gravel, 0 if not$\}$; Slope: $x_4 = \{1$ if East, 0 if not$\}$, $x_5 = \{1$ if South, 0 if not$\}$, $x_6 = \{1$ if West, 0 if not$\}$,
$x_7 = \{1$ if Southeast, 0 if not$\}$ **b.** $E(y) = \beta_0 + \beta_1 x_1$ **c.** $E(y) = \beta_0 + \beta_1 x_2 + \beta_2 x_3$ **d.** $E(y) = \beta_0 + \beta_1 x_4 + \beta_2 x_5 + \beta_3 x_6 + \beta_4 x_7$
12.73 a. $E(y) = \beta_0 + \beta_1 x, x = \{1$ if developer, 0 if not$\}$ **b.** $E(y) = \beta_0 + \beta_1 x_1 + \beta_2 x_2, x_1 = \{1$ if low, 0 if not$\}, x_2 = \{1$ if medium, 0 if not$\}$
c. $E(y) = \beta_0 + \beta_1 x, x = \{1$ if fixed price, 0 if not$\}$ **d.** $E(y) = \beta_0 + \beta_1 x_1 + \beta_2 x_2, x_1 = \{1$ if time-of-delivery, 0 if not$\}$,
$x_2 = \{1$ if cost, 0 if not$\}$ **12.75 a.** $x_1 = \{1$ if blond Caucasian, 0 if not$\}, x_2 = \{1$ if brunette Caucasian, 0 if not$\}$ **b.** $E(y) = \beta_0 + $
$\beta_1 x_1 + \beta_2 x_2$ **c.** β_0 **d.** β_1 **e.** $\beta_0 > 0; \beta_1 > 0; \beta_2 \approx 0$ **f.** Yes **12.77 a.** $x_1 = \{1$ if large/private, 0 if not$\}, x_2 = \{1$ if small/public, 0 if not$\}$,
$x_3 = \{1$ if small/private, 0 if not$\}$ **b.** $E(y) = \beta_0 + \beta_1 x_1 + \beta_2 x_2 + \beta_3 x_3$ **c.** Differences in mean likelihood of reporting sustainability
policies among the four groups **d.** $x_1 = \{1$ if small, 0 if large$\}, x_2 = \{1$ if private, 0 if public$\}$ **e.** $E(y) = \beta_0 + \beta_1 x_1 + \beta_2 x_2$ **f.** Large/pub-
lic: β_0; large/private: $\beta_0 + \beta_2$; small/public: $\beta_0 + \beta_1$; small/private: $\beta_0 + \beta_1 + \beta_2$ **g.** Public: $\mu_S - \mu_L = \beta_1$; private: $\mu_S - \mu_L = \beta_1$
h. $E(y) = \beta_0 + \beta_1 x_1 + \beta_2 x_2 + \beta_3 x_1 x_2$ **i.** Large/public: β_0; large/private: $\beta_0 + \beta_2$; small/public: $\beta_0 + \beta_1$; small/private: $\beta_0 + \beta_1 + $

$\beta_2 + \beta_3$ **j.** Public: $\mu_S - \mu_L = \beta_1$; private: $\mu_S - \mu_L = \beta_1 + \beta_3$ **12.79 a.** $E(y) = \beta_0 + \beta_1 x$, where $x = \{1$ if Lotion/Cream, 0 if not$\}$
b. $\hat{y} = .7775 + .1092x$ **c.** $H_0: \beta_1 = 0$ **d.** $t = .24$, do not reject H_0 **e.** $\hat{y} = 7.56 - 1.65x$; $t = -.46$, do not reject H_0 **12.81 a.** $E(y) = \beta_0 +$
$\beta_1 x_1 + \beta_2 x_2$, $x_1 = \{1$ if group V, 0 if not$\}$, $x_2 = \{1$ if group S, 0 if not$\}$ **b.** $\hat{y} = 3.1667 - 1.0833x_1 - 1.4537x_2$ **c.** $F = 20.45$, reject H_0
12.83 a. $E(y) = \beta_0 + \beta_1 x_1 + \beta_2 x_1^2$ **b.** $E(y) = \beta_0 + \beta_1 x_1 + \beta_2 x_1^2 + \beta_3 x_2 + \beta_4 x_3$, where x_2 and x_3 are dummy variables **c.** add terms:
$\beta_5 x_1 x_2 + \beta_6 x_1 x_3 + \beta_7 x_1^2 x_2 + \beta_8 x_1^2 x_3$ **d.** $\beta_5 = \beta_6 = \beta_7 = \beta_8 = 0$ **e.** $\beta_2 = \beta_5 = \beta_6 = \beta_7 = \beta_8 = 0$ **f.** $\beta_3 = \beta_4 = \beta_5 = \beta_6 = \beta_7 = \beta_8 = 0$
12.85 a. $\hat{y} = 48.8 - 3.4x_1 + .07x_1^2$; $\hat{y} = 46.44 + .3x_1 + .05x_1^2$; $\hat{y} = 41.3 - .7x_1 + .03x_1^2$ **12.87 a.** .58 **b.** .03 **12.89 a.** Model is statisti-
cally useful; reject $H_0: \beta_1 = \beta_2 = \cdots = \beta_{12} = 0$ **b.** No significant impact; do not reject $H_0: \beta_1 = 0$ **c.** Positive impact; reject
$H_0: \beta_3 = 0$ **d.** $E(y) = \beta_0 + \beta_1 x_3 + \beta_2 x_5 + \beta_3 x_6 + \cdots + \beta_9 x_{12} + \beta_{10} x_3 x_5 + \beta_{11} x_3 x_6 + \cdots + \beta_{17} x_3 x_{12}$ **12.91 a.** $x_2 = \{1$ if low, 0 if not$\}$,
$x_3 = \{1$ if neutral, 0 if not$\}$ **b.** $E(y) = \beta_0 + \beta_1 x_1 + \beta_2 x_2 + \beta_3 x_3$ **c.** $E(y) = \beta_0 + \beta_1 x_1 + \beta_2 x_2 + \beta_3 x_3 + \beta_4 x_1 x_2 + \beta_5 x_1 x_3$
d. Part c **12.93 a.** $x_1 = \{1$ if channel catfish, 0 if not$\}$, $x_2 = \{1$ if largemouth bass, 0 if not$\}$ **b.** $E(y) = \beta_0 + \beta_1 x_1 + \beta_2 x_2 + \beta_3 x_3$,
where $x_3 =$ weight **c.** $E(y) = \beta_0 + \beta_1 x_1 + \beta_2 x_2 + \beta_3 x_3 + \beta_4 x_1 x_3 + \beta_5 x_2 x_3$ **d.** $\hat{y} = 3.1 + 26.5x_1 - 4.1x_2 + 0.0037x_3$
f. $\hat{y} = 3.5 + 25.6x_1 - 3.47x_2 + 0.0034x_3 + 0.0008x_1 x_3 - .0013x_2 x_3$ **g.** .0042 **12.95 a.** $E(y) = \beta_0 + \beta_1 x_1 + \beta_2 x_1^2 + \beta_3 x_2 +$
$\beta_4 x_3 + \beta_5 x_4 + \beta_6 x_1 x_2 + \beta_7 x_1 x_3 + \beta_8 x_1 x_4 + \beta_9 x_1^2 x_2 + \beta_{10} x_1^2 x_3 + \beta_{11} x_1^2 x_4$, where $x_1 =$ sales volume and $x_2 - x_4$ are dummy variables for
region **b.** $E(y) = (\beta_0 + \beta_5) + (\beta_1 + \beta_8)x_1 + (\beta_2 + \beta_{11})x_1^2$ **c.** $E(y) = (\beta_0 + \beta_3) + (\beta_1 + \beta_6)x_1 + (\beta_2 + \beta_9)x_1^2$ **d.** β_3 through β_{11}
e. Yes, $F = 8.21$, $p = .000$ **12.97** a and b, a and d, a and e, b and c, b and d, b and e, c and e, d and e **12.99 a.** 5; 3 **b.** $H_0: \beta_3 = \beta_4 = 0$
c. $F = .38$, do not reject H_0 **12.101 a.** $H_0: \beta_4 = \beta_5 = 0$ **b.** Complete model: $E(y) = \beta_0 + \beta_1 x_1 + \beta_2 x_2 + \beta_3 x_1 x_2 + \beta_4 x_2^2 + \beta_5 x_1 x_2^2$;
reduced model: $E(y) = \beta_0 + \beta_1 x_1 + \beta_2 x_2 + \beta_3 x_1 x_2$ **c.** $H_0: \beta_3 = \beta_5 = 0$ **d.** Complete model: $E(y) = \beta_0 + \beta_1 x_1 + \beta_2 x_2 + \beta_3 x_1 x_2 +$
$\beta_4 x_2^2 + \beta_5 x_1 x_2^2$; reduced model: $E(y) = \beta_0 + \beta_1 x_1 + \beta_2 x_2 + \beta_4 x_2^2$ **e.** $H_0: \beta_1 = \beta_3 = \beta_5 = 0$ **f.** Complete model: $E(y) = \beta_0 + \beta_1 x_1 +$
$\beta_2 x_2 + \beta_3 x_1 x_2 + \beta_4 x_2^2 + \beta_5 x_1 x_2^2$; reduced model: $E(y) = \beta_0 + \beta_2 x_2 + \beta_4 x_2^2$ **12.103 a.** $E(y) = \beta_0 + \beta_1 x_1 + \beta_2 x_2 + \beta_3 x_1 x_2 + \beta_4 x_1^2 + \beta_5 x_2^2$
b. $H_0: \beta_4 = \beta_5 = 0$ **c.** Complete model: $E(y) = \beta_0 + \beta_1 x_1 + \beta_2 x_2 + \beta_3 x_1 x_2 + \beta_4 x_1^2 + \beta_5 x_2^2$; reduced model: $E(y) = \beta_0 + \beta_1 x_1 + \beta_2 x_2 +$
$\beta_3 x_1 x_2$ **d.** $SSE_R = 25,310,639$, $SSE_C = 19,370,350$, $MSE_C = 317,547$ **e.** $F = 9.35$ **f.** $F > 2.39$ **g.** reject H_0 **12.105 a.** $E(y) = \beta_0 +$
$\beta_1 x_1 + \beta_2 x_2 + \beta_3 x_3 + \beta_4 x_4 + \beta_5 x_1 x_4 + \beta_6 x_2 x_4 + \beta_7 x_3 x_4$ **b.** $F = 24.40$, reject H_0 **c.** $H_0: \beta_5 = \beta_6 = \beta_7 = 0$ **d.** $F = 1.74$, do not reject H_0
12.107 a. Positive **c.** $E(y) = \beta_0 + \beta_1 x_1 + \beta_2 x_1^2 + \beta_3 x_2 + \beta_4 x_1 x_2 + \beta_5 x_1^2 x_2$ **e.** $H_0: \beta_4 = \beta_5 = 0$ **f.** $F = .83$, do not reject H_0
12.109 a. $E(y) = \beta_0 + \beta_1 x_1 + \beta_2 x_2 + \beta_3 x_3$ **b.** Add terms: $\beta_4 x_1 x_2 + \beta_5 x_1 x_3$ **c.** AL: β_1; TDS-3A: $\beta_1 + \beta_4$; FE: $\beta_1 + \beta_5$
d. Test $H_0: \beta_4 = \beta_5 = 0$ using a nested model F-test **12.111 a.** x_2 **b.** Yes **c.** Fit all models of the form $E(y) = \beta_0 + \beta_1 x_2 + \beta_2 x_i$
12.113 a. 7; $E(y) = \beta_0 + \beta_1 x_i$ **b.** 6; $E(y) = \beta_0 + \beta_1 x_1 + \beta_2 x_i$ **c.** 5; $E(y) = \beta_0 + \beta_1 x_1 + \beta_2 x_2 + \beta_3 x_i$ **12.115 a.** 11 **b.** 10
d. No interactions or squared terms; inflated Type I error rate **e.** $E(y) = \beta_0 + \beta_1(\text{AMAP}) + \beta_2(\text{NDF}) + \beta_3(\text{AMAP})(\text{NDF}) +$
$\beta_4(\text{AMAP})^2 + \beta_5(\text{NDF})^2$ **f.** Test $H_0: \beta_3 = \beta_4 = \beta_5 = 0$ **12.117 a.** 11 **b.** 10 **c.** 1 **d.** $E(y) = \beta_0 + \beta_1 x_{11} + \beta_2 x_4 +$
$\beta_3 x_2 + \beta_4 x_7 + \beta_5 x_{10} + \beta_6 x_1 + \beta_7 x_9 + \beta_8 x_3$ **e.** 67.7% of sample variation in overall satisfaction can be explained by the model
f. No interactions or squared terms in model; high probability of making at least one Type I error **12.119** Yes **12.121 a.** 2,234
b. No **c.** Yes, $z = 5.32$ **12.123 a.** No **b.** No **c.** Yes **d.** Possibly **12.125** Multicollinearity **12.127 a.** Satisfied **b.** Violated
c. Some outliers **d.** Violated **e.** No **12.129 a.** $\hat{y} = 30,856 - 191.57x$ **b.** -1162.07 **c.** Yes, curvilinear trend **d.** Yes
12.131 Nonconstant error variance **12.133** Confidence interval **12.135 a.** $\hat{y} = 90.1 - 1.836x_1 + .285x_2$ **b.** .916 **c.** Yes, $F = 64.91$
d. $t = -5.01$, reject H_0 **e.** 10.68 **12.137** $E(y) = \beta_0 + \beta_1 x_1 + \beta_2 x_2 + \beta_3 x_3$, where $x_1 = \{1$ if level 2, 0 otherwise$\}$,
$x_2 = \{1$ if level 3, 0 otherwise$\}$, $x_3 = \{1$ if level 4, 0 otherwise$\}$ **12.141** No degrees of freedom for error **12.143 a.** Confidence
interval for $(\mu_1 - \mu_2)$ **b.** $E(y) = \beta_0 + \beta_1 x$, $x = \{1$ if public college, 0 if private college$\}$ **12.145 a.** Type of extractor is qualitative; size
is quantitative **b.** $E(y) = \beta_0 + \beta_1 x_1 + \beta_2 x_2$, where $x_1 =$ diameter of orange, $x_2 = \{1$ if brand B, 0 if not$\}$ **c.** $E(y) = \beta_0 + \beta_1 x_1 +$
$\beta_2 x_2 + \beta_3 x_1 x_2$ **e.** $H_0: \beta_3 = 0$ **12.147** x_4 and x_5 **12.149 a.** β_0: no practical interpretation; β_1: for every 1-unit increase in proportion of
block with low-density areas, estimate density to increase 2.006 units; β_2: for every 1-unit increase in proportion of block with high-density
areas, estimate density to increase 5.006 units **b.** 68.6% of sample variation in population density can be explained by the model
c. $H_0: \beta_1 = \beta_2 = 0$ **d.** $F = 133.3$ **e.** reject H_0 **12.151** Importance and Support are correlated at .6991; no **12.153 a.** $E(y) = \beta_0 +$
$\beta_1 x_1 + \beta_2 x_2$, where $x_2 = \{1$ if intervention group, 0 if control group$\}$ **b.** Slope $= \beta_1$ **c.** $E(y) = \beta_0 + \beta_1 x_1 + \beta_2 x_2 + \beta_3 x_1 x_2$
d. Intervention slope $= (\beta_1 + \beta_3)$; control slope $= \beta_1$ **12.155 a.** Possibly **b.** Yes **c.** No **12.157 b.** $E(y) = \beta_0 + \beta_1 x_1 +$
$\beta_2 x_1^2 + \beta_3 x_2 + \beta_4 x_1 x_2 + \beta_5 x_1^2 x_2$, where $x_2 = \{1$ if 1-35W, 0 if not$\}$ **c.** Yes, $F = 457.73$ **d.** Assumptions satisfied
12.159 a. $E(y) = \beta_0 + \beta_1 x_1 + \beta_2 x_2 + \beta_3 x_3$, where $x_1 = \{1$ if VH, 0 otherwise$\}$, $x_2 = \{1$ if H, 0 otherwise$\}$, $x_3 = \{1$ if M, 0 otherwise$\}$
b. No **c.** $\hat{y} = 10.2 + .5x_1 + 2.02x_2 + .683x_3$ **d.** Yes, $F = 63.09$ **12.161 b.** Yes, $F = 16.10$ **c.** Yes, $t = 2.5$ **d.** 945
12.163 a. $E(y) = \beta_0 + \beta_1 x_1 + \beta_2 x_6 + \beta_3 x_7$, where $x_6 = \{1$ if good, 0 otherwise$\}$, $x_7 = \{1$ if fair, 0 otherwise$\}$ **c.** Excellent:
$\hat{y} = 188,875 + 15,617x_1$; good: $\hat{y} = 85,829 + 15,617x_1$; fair: $\hat{y} = 36,388 + 15,617x_1$ **e.** Yes, $F = 8.43$ **f.** $(x_1$ and $x_3)$, $(x_1$ and $x_5)$, $(x_3$
and $x_5)$ highly correlated **g.** Assumptions satisfied **12.165 a.** $H_0: \beta_1 = \beta_2 = \beta_3 = \beta_4 = \beta_5 = 0$ **b.** $F = 18.24$, reject H_0
c. $H_0: \beta_3 = \beta_4 = \beta_5 = 0$ **d.** $F = 8.46$, reject H_0 **e.** Second-order model **12.167 a.** 78% of sample variation in price is explained
by the model **b.** $F = 1,693.55$, reject H_0 **c.** \$2,234 **d.** \$9 **e.** $-\$252$ **f.** yes, $t = 2.39$ **12.169** $\hat{y} = -11.5 + 0.189x_1$
$+ 0.159x_2 - 0.00114x_1^2 - 0.000871x_2^2$

Chapter 14

14.5 a. 127.63 **b.** 116.37 **14.7 a.** $I_{2010} = 103.19$; beer production in 2010 increased by 3.19% over the beer production in 1980
b. Quantity **c.** $I_{2010} = 95.10$ **14.9 a.** $I_{1980} = 100.00$, $I_{1981} = 157.61, \ldots, I_{2010} = 304.35$ **c.** Price **14.11 a.** $I_{1970} = 100.00$,
$I_{1975} = 157.94, \ldots, I_{2010} = 1,594.45$ **b.** $I_{1970} = 36.98$, $I_{1975} = 58.40, \ldots, I_{2010} = 589.62$ **c.** Flattens the graph
14.13 a. Manufacturing: $I_{1990} = 100.00$, $I_{2000} = 132.84, \ldots, I_{2010} = 172.63$; Information: $I_{1990} = 100.00$,

$I_{2000} = 142.31, \ldots, I_{2010} = 192.99$; Food: $I_{1990} = 100.00$, $I_{2000} = 138.95, \ldots, I_{2010} = 187.37$ **c.** Earnings: $I_{1990} = 100.00$, $I_{2000} = 138.25, \ldots, I_{2010} = 184.57$; Hours: $I_{1990} = 100.00$, $I_{2000} = 102.1, \ldots, I_{2010} = 100.2$ **14.15** $w = .2$ **14.17 a.** $E_{1980} = 188.0$, $E_{1981} = 189.2, \ldots, E_{2009} = 198.1$, $E_{2010} = 197.3$ **b.** $E_{1980} = 188.0$, $E_{1981} = 192.8, \ldots, E_{2009} = 196.8$, $E_{2010} = 194.6$ **c.** $w = .2$ series **14.19 a.** $E_{1990} = 384.00$, $E_{1991} = 366.40, \ldots, E_{2010} = 1168.78$, $E_{2011} = 1491.36$ **14.21 a.** $w = .1$: $E_{1990} = 1{,}283.0$, $E_{1991} = 1{,}278.0, \ldots, E_{2009} = 1{,}618.9$, $E_{2010} = 1{,}622.4$; $w = .9$: $E_{1990} = 1{,}283.0$, $E_{1991} = 1{,}238.0, \ldots, E_{2009} = 1{,}632.6$, $E_{2010} = 1{,}651.9$ **b.** $w = .9$ series **14.25 a.** $w = .3$: $F_{2008} = F_{2009} = F_{2010} = 198.16$; $w = .7$: $F_{2008} = F_{2009} = F_{2010} = 198.62$ **b.** $w = .7$ and $v = .3$: $F_{2008} = 198.84$, $F_{2009} = 199.11$, $F_{2010} = 199.38$; $w = .3$ and $v = .7$: $F_{2008} = 198.46$, $F_{2009} = 198.88$, $F_{2010} = 199.30$ **14.27 a.** Yes **b.** $F_{2011} = 212.67$ **c.** $F_{2011} = 225.62$ **14.29 a.** Forecast for all four quarters $= 1{,}215.8$ **b.** Forecast for all four quarters $= 1{,}413.0$ **14.31 a.** Forecast for all 12 months $= 1{,}360.35$ **b.** $F_{\text{Jan}} = 1{,}360.35$, $F_{\text{Feb}} = 1{,}358.38$, $F_{\text{Mar}} = 1{,}365.54, \ldots, F_{\text{Dec}} = 1{,}713.46$ **c.** Forecasts: $F_{\text{Jan}} = 1{,}436.48$, $F_{\text{Feb}} = 1{,}477.19$, $F_{\text{Mar}} = 1{,}517.88, \ldots, F_{\text{Dec}} = 1{,}884.14$; one-step-ahead forecasts: $F_{\text{Jan}} = 1{,}436.49$, $F_{\text{Feb}} = 1{,}477.12$, $F_{\text{Mar}} = 1{,}404.48, \ldots, F_{\text{Dec}} = 1{,}781.32$ **14.33 a.** $1.54, -2.88, -5.30$ **b.** $1.16, -3.11, -5.38$ **c.** MAD $= 3.24$, MAPE $= 1.66$, RMSE $= 3.59$ **d.** MAD $= 3.22$, MAPE $= 1.65$, RMSE $= 3.65$ **14.35 a.** MAD $= 94.9$, MAPE $= 8.0$, RMSE $= 128.6$ **b.** MAD $= 119.9$, MAPE $= 10.0$, RMSE $= 153.7$ **c.** Holt's model with $w = .3$ and $v = .5$ **14.37 a.** Forecasts for all 3 years $= 73{,}558.2$ **b.** $F_{2008} = 74{,}402.6$, $F_{2009} = 75{,}068.8$, $F_{2011} = 75{,}735.0$ **c.** Exponential smoothing: MAD $= 3{,}070.5$, MAPE $= 3.9$, RMSE $= 3{,}595.9$; Holt's: MAD $= 1{,}775.6$, MAPE $= 2.29$, RMSE $= 2{,}064.0$; Holt's model **14.39 a.** $E(Y_t) = \beta_0 + \beta_1 t + \beta_2 x_1 + \beta_3 x_2 + \beta_4 x_3$, where $x_1 = \{1$ if Qtr. 1, 0 if not$\}$, $x_2 = \{1$ if Qtr. 2, 0 if not$\}$, $x_3 = \{1$ if Qtr. 3, 0 if not$\}$ **b.** $\hat{Y}_t = 11.49 + .51t - 3.95x_1 - 2.09x_2 - 4.52x_3$; $F = 1{,}275.44$, reject H_0 **c.** Qtr. 1: $(27.22, 29.67)$; Qtr. 2: $(29.59, 32.04)$; Qtr. 3: $(27.67, 30.12)$; Qtr. 4: $(32.70, 35.15)$ **14.41 a.** $\hat{Y}_t = 10.50 - .245t$ **b.** 4.14; $(2.12, 6.16)$ **14.43 a.** $E(Y_t) = \beta_0 + \beta_1 X_t$ **b.** $E(Y_t) = \beta_0 + \beta_1 X_t + \beta_2 x_1 + \beta_3 x_2 + \cdots + \beta_{12} x_{11}$, where $x_1 = \{1$ if Jan., 0 if not$\}$, $x_2 = \{1$ if Feb., 0 if not$\}, \ldots, x_{11} = \{1$ if Nov., 0 if not$\}$ **c.** subset F-test; $H_0: \beta_2 = \beta_3 = \cdots = \beta_{12} = 0$ **d.** $\hat{\beta}_0 + \hat{\beta}_1(180) + \hat{\beta}_2$ **14.45 a.** $\hat{Y}_t = 399.34 - 1.67t$ **b.** $F_{2010} = 347.46$, $F_{2011} = 345.79$ **c.** F_{2010}: $(311.85, 383.08)$; F_{2011}: $(309.95, 381.63)$ **14.47** Regression errors are correlated **14.49 a.** Inconclusive **b.** Inconclusive **c.** Reject H_0 **d.** Fail to reject H_0 **14.51** No; do not reject H_0 **14.53 a.** Yes **b.** $d = 1.24$, reject H_0 **c.** Not valid **14.55 b.** Models statistically useful for Banks 1, 2, 3, 4, and 7 **c.** No evidence of positive autocorrelation for all nine banks **14.57 a.** $I_{2000} = 100$, $I_{2001} = 101.4, \ldots, I_{2010} = 109.9$, $I_{2011} = 110.7$ **b.** Quantity **c.** Number of insured workers increased by 10.7% between 2000 and 2011 **14.59 a.** $\hat{Y}_t = 38.17 + 7.32t$; forecasts: 118.68, 126.00, 133.32 **b.** Year 11: $(100.61, 136.75)$; Year 12: $(107.06, 144.94)$; Year 13: $(113.40, 153.24)$ **14.61** $F_{2011} = 5.19$, $F_{2012} = 4.94$, $F_{2013} = 4.69$; Holt's forecast errors are larger **14.63 a.** $\hat{Y}_t = 42.56 + .449t$ **c.** $F_{2012} = 52.44$, $F_{2013} = 52.89$ **d.** F_{2012}: $(29.30, 75.57)$; F_{2013}: $(24.49, 76.28)$ **e.** $d = 1.75$, do not reject H_0 **14.65** $F_{2012,1} = 15{,}481.1$; $F_{2012,2} = 15{,}629.0$; $F_{2012,3} = 15{,}776.9$; $F_{2012,4} = 15{,}924.8$ **14.69 a.** \$39,746; \$43,558; 2010 **b.** \$34,674 **14.71 a.** Yes **c.** Yes **d.** No

☐ Index

☐ Credits

Photos

Chapter 1
pp. 1, 9, 20, 23 Sergej Khakimullin/Shutterstock; **p. 8** Nitr/Fotolia; **p. 12** Kevin Russ/iStockphoto; **p. 19** AVAVA/Fotolia

Chapter 2
pp. 37, 44, 57, 83, 97, 103 Pryzmat/Shutterstock; **p. 42** Dorling Kindersley, Ltd.; **p. 88** Wavebreakmedia ltd/Shutterstock; **p. 96** Jeffrey Smith/iStockphoto; **p. 110** Dorling Kindersley, Ltd.; **p. 126** Dorling Kindersley, Ltd.

Chapter 3
pp. 128, 138, 150, 163 Simon Askham/iStockphoto; **p. 133** Shariff Che'Lah/Fotolia; **p. 144** Dorling Kindersley, Ltd.; **p. 156** ArrowStudio, LLC/Shutterstock; **p. 170** Ronald Hudson/Fotolia

Chapter 4
pp. 184, 208, 216 Mario Beauregard/Fotolia; **p. 186** Soupstock/Fotolia; **p. 193** Shock/Fotolia; **p. 215** Michaeljung/Shutterstock; **p. 226** Andrea Lehmkuhl/Fotolia; **p. 228** Sebastian Duda/iStockphoto

Chapter 5
pp. 265, 282 Terex/Fotolia; **p. 269** Juan R. Velasco/Shutterstock; **p. 288** Christian42/Fotolia; **p. 297** Duncan Noakes/Fotolia

Chapter 6
pp. 299, 316, 324, 331 Jacquelyn Martin/AP Images; **p. 306** Pressmaster/Fotolia; **p. 320** Svetlana Lukienko/Shutterstock; **p. 323** Iofoto/Fotolia; **p. 338** DIGIcal/iStockphoto

Chapter 7
pp. 355, 365, 375, 391 Jeff Chiu/AP Images; **p. 364** Ellen Creager/KRT/Newscom; **p. 374** Wavebreakmedia Ltd./Shutterstock; **p. 381** Michael Shake/Fotolia; **p. 389** Dorling Kindersley, Ltd.

Chapter 8
pp. 419, 430, 452 NAN/Fotolia; **p. 421** Thinkstock Images; **p. 442** WavebreakMediaMicro/Fotolia; **p. 456** Vasko Miokovic Photography/iStockphoto; **p. 461** Kenneth Sponsler/Shutterstock; **p. 485** Dorling Kindersley, Ltd.

Chapter 11
pp. 601, 612, 627, 637, 645 JustASC/Shutterstock; **p. 608** Scott Leigh/iStockphoto

Chapter 12
pp. 666, 687, 735, 752 Fotosav/Shutterstock; **p. 669** David Stockman/iStockphoto; **p. 674** Tina Fineberg/AP Images; **p. 698** LeahKat/Shutterstock; **p. 709** Marie C. Fields/Shutterstock; **p. 741** Harry Hu/iStockphoto; **p. 778** Roberto A. Sanchez/iStockphoto

Chapter 14
pp. 14-1, 14-28, 14-31, 14-35 Varuka/Shutterstock; **p. 14-3** Bettmann/Corbis

Technology Images

Portions of information contained in this publication/book are printed with permission of Minitab Inc. All such material remains the exclusive property and copyright of Minitab Inc. All rights reserved. MINITAB® and all other trademarks and logos for the Company's products and services are the exclusive property of Minitab Inc. All other marks referenced remain the property of their respective owners. See minitab.com for more information. In this publication, screen shots of Minitab software were generated using Minitab 16.

All images showing usage of TI83/84 Plus calculator are copyright © Texas Instruments Inc. Reproduced by permission.

Charts generated using SPSS Statistics Professional 20.0 software have been reprinted courtesy of International Business Machines Corporation, © SPSS, Inc., and IBM Company. IBM, the IBM logo, ibm.com, and SPSS are trademarks of International Business Machines Corp., registered in many jurisdictions worldwide. Other product and service names might be trademarks of IBM or other companies. A current list of IBM trademarks is available on the Web at "IBM copyright and trademark information" at www.ibm.com/legal/copytrade.shtml.

StatCrunch for Pearson screenshots appearing in this book are copyright 2007–2012 by Integrated Analytics LLC. Reproduced by permission of Pearson Education.

MICROSOFT® WINDOWS®, and MICROSOFT OFFICE® ARE REGISTERED TRADEMARKS OF THE MICROSOFT CORPORATION IN THE U.S.A. AND OTHER COUNTRIES. THIS BOOK IS NOT SPONSORED OR ENDORSED BY OR AFFILIATED WITH THE MICROSOFT CORPORATION. Examples in this text have been taken from Microsoft Excel 2010, Professional Office version. The concepts and theory being taught are applicable in other, similar versions of software.

MICROSOFT AND/OR ITS RESPECTIVE SUPPLIERS MAKE NO REPRESENTATIONS ABOUT THE SUITABILITY OF THE INFORMATION CONTAINED IN THE DOCUMENTS AND RELATED GRAPHICS PUBLISHED AS PART OF THE SERVICES FOR ANY PURPOSE. ALL SUCH DOCUMENTS AND RELATED GRAPHICS ARE PROVIDED "AS IS" WITHOUT WARRANTY OF ANY KIND. MICROSOFT AND/OR ITS RESPECTIVE SUPPLIERS HEREBY DISCLAIM ALL WARRANTIES AND CONDITIONS WITH REGARD TO THIS INFORMATION, INCLUDING ALL WARRANTIES AND CONDITIONS OF MERCHANTABILITY, WHETHER EXPRESS, IMPLIED OR STATUTORY, FITNESS FOR A PARTICULAR PURPOSE, TITLE AND NON-INFRINGEMENT. IN NO EVENT SHALL MICROSOFT AND/OR ITS RESPECTIVE SUPPLIERS BE LIABLE FOR ANY SPECIAL, INDIRECT OR CONSEQUENTIAL DAMAGES OR ANY DAMAGES WHATSOEVER RESULTING FROM LOSS OF USE, DATA OR PROFITS, WHETHER IN AN ACTION OF CONTRACT, NEGLIGENCE OR OTHER TORTIOUS ACTION, ARISING OUT OF OR IN CONNECTION WITH THE USE OR PERFORMANCE OF INFORMATION AVAILABLE FROM THE SERVICES. THE DOCUMENTS AND RELATED GRAPHICS CONTAINED HEREIN COULD INCLUDE TECHNICAL INACCURACIES OR TYPOGRAPHICAL ERRORS. CHANGES ARE PERIODICALLY ADDED TO THE INFORMATION HEREIN. MICROSOFT AND/OR ITS RESPECTIVE SUPPLIERS MAY MAKE IMPROVEMENTS AND/OR CHANGES IN THE PRODUCT(S) AND/OR THE PROGRAM(S) DESCRIBED HEREIN AT ANY TIME. PARTIAL SCREEN SHOTS MAY BE VIEWED IN FULL WITHIN THE SOFTWARE VERSION SPECIFIED.

Selected Formulas

CHAPTER 2

Relative Frequency $=$ (frequency)$/n$

$$\bar{x} = \frac{\Sigma x}{n}$$

$$s^2 = \frac{\Sigma(x - \bar{x})^2}{n - 1} = \frac{\Sigma x^2 - \frac{(\Sigma x)^2}{n}}{n - 1}$$

$$s = \sqrt{s^2}$$

$$z = \frac{x - \mu}{\sigma} = \frac{x - \bar{x}}{s}$$

Chebyshev $=$ At least $\left(1 - \frac{1}{k^2}\right)100\%$

$$\text{IQR} = Q_U - Q_L$$

CHAPTER 3

$$P(A^c) = 1 - P(A)$$

$$P(A \cup B) = P(A) + P(B) - P(A \cap B)$$

$$= P(A) + P(B) \text{ if } A \text{ and } B \text{ mutually exclusive}$$

$$P(A \cap B) = P(A|B) \cdot P(B) = P(B|A) \cdot P(A)$$

$$= P(A) \cdot P(B) \text{ if } A \text{ and } B \text{ independent}$$

$$P(A|B) = \frac{P(A \cap B)}{P(B)}$$

$$\binom{N}{n} = \frac{N!}{n!(N - n)!}$$

Bayes's: $P(S_i|A) =$

$$\frac{P(S_i)P(A|S_i)}{P(S_1)P(A|S_1) + P(S_2)P(A|S_2) + \cdots + P(S_k)P(A|S_k)}$$

CHAPTER 5

CI for μ: $\bar{x} \pm (z_{\alpha/2})\sigma/\sqrt{n}$ (large n)

$$\bar{x} \pm (t_{\alpha/2})s/\sqrt{n} \text{ (small } n, \sigma \text{ unknown)}$$

CI for p: $\hat{p} \pm z_{\alpha/2}\sqrt{\dfrac{\hat{p}\hat{q}}{n}}$

Estimating μ: $n = (z_{\alpha/2})^2(\sigma^2)/(\text{SE})^2$

Estimating p: $n = (z_{\alpha/2})^2(pq)/(\text{SE})^2$

CHAPTER 4

Key Formulas

Random Variable	Prob. Dist'n	Mean	Variance
General Discrete:	Table, formula, or graph for $p(x)$	$\displaystyle\sum_{\text{all } x} x \cdot p(x)$	$\displaystyle\sum_{\text{all } x} (x - \mu)^2 \cdot p(x)$
Binomial:	$p(x) = \binom{n}{x}p^x q^{n-x}$ $x = 0, 1, 2, \ldots, n$	np	npq
Poisson:	$p(x) = \dfrac{\lambda^x e^{-\lambda}}{x!}$ $x = 0, 1, 2, \ldots$	λ	λ
Uniform:	$f(x) = 1/(d - c)$ $(c \le x \le d)$	$(c + d)/2$	$(d - c)^2/12$
Normal:	$f(x) = \dfrac{1}{\sigma\sqrt{2\pi}} e^{-\frac{1}{2}[(x-\mu)/\sigma]^2}$	μ	σ^2
Standard Normal:	$f(z) = \dfrac{1}{\sqrt{2\pi}} e^{-\frac{1}{2}(z)^2}$ $z = (x - \mu)/\sigma$	$\mu = 0$	$\sigma^2 = 1$
Sample Mean:(large n)	$f(\bar{x}) = \dfrac{1}{\sigma_{\bar{x}}\sqrt{2\pi}} e^{-\frac{1}{2}[(\bar{x}-\mu)/\sigma_{\bar{x}}]^2}$	$\mu_{\bar{x}} = \mu$	$\sigma_{\bar{x}}^2 = \sigma^2/n$

CHAPTER 6

Test for μ: $z = \dfrac{\bar{x} - \mu_0}{\sigma/\sqrt{n}}$ (large n)

$t = \dfrac{\bar{x} - \mu_0}{s/\sqrt{n}}$ (small n, σ unknown)

Test for p: $z = \dfrac{\hat{p} - p_0}{\sqrt{p_0 q_0/n}}$

Test for σ^2: $\chi^2 = (n-1)s^2/(\sigma_0)^2$

CHAPTER 7

CI for $\mu_1 - \mu_2$:

$\left.(\bar{x}_1 - \bar{x}_2) \pm z_{\alpha/2}\sqrt{\dfrac{\sigma_1^2}{n_1} + \dfrac{\sigma_2^2}{n_2}}\right\}$ (large n_1 and n_2)

Test for $\mu_1 - \mu_2$:

$\left. z = \dfrac{(\bar{x}_1 - \bar{x}_2) - D_0}{\sqrt{\dfrac{\sigma_1^2}{n_1} + \dfrac{\sigma_2^2}{n_2}}}\right\}$ (large n_1 and n_2)

$s_p^2 = \dfrac{(n_1 - 1)s_1^2 + (n_2 - 1)s_2^2}{n_1 + n_2 - 2}$

CI for $\mu_1 - \mu_2$:

$\left.(\bar{x}_1 - \bar{x}_2) \pm t_{\alpha/2}\sqrt{s_p^2\left(\dfrac{1}{n_1} + \dfrac{1}{n_2}\right)}\right\}$ (small n_1 and/or n_2)

Test for $\mu_1 - \mu_2$:

$\left. t = \dfrac{(\bar{x}_1 - \bar{x}_2) - D_0}{\sqrt{s_p^2\left(\dfrac{1}{n_1} + \dfrac{1}{n_2}\right)}}\right\}$ (small n_1 and/or n_2)

CI for μ_d: $\bar{x}_d \pm t_{\alpha/2}\dfrac{s_d}{\sqrt{n}}$

Test for μ_d: $t = \dfrac{\bar{x}_d - \mu_d}{s_d/\sqrt{n}}$

CI for $p_1 - p_2$: $(\hat{p}_1 - \hat{p}_2) \pm z_{\alpha/2}\sqrt{\dfrac{\hat{p}_1\hat{q}_1}{n_1} + \dfrac{\hat{p}_2\hat{q}_2}{n_2}}$

Test for $p_1 - p_2$: $z = \dfrac{(\hat{p}_1 - \hat{p}_2) - D_0}{\sqrt{\hat{p}\hat{q}\left(\dfrac{1}{n_1} + \dfrac{1}{n_2}\right)}}$

$\hat{p} = \dfrac{x_1 + x_2}{n_1 + n_2}$

Test for (σ_1^2/σ_2^2): $F = (s_1^2/s_2^2)$

Estimating $\mu_1 - \mu_2$: $n_1 = n_2 = (z_{\alpha/2})^2(\sigma_1^2 + \sigma_2^2)/(\text{ME})^2$

Estimating $p_1 - p_2$: $n_1 = n_2 = (z_{\alpha/2})^2(p_1 q_1 + p_2 q_2)/(\text{ME})^2$

CHAPTER 8

ANOVA Test for completely randomized design:
$F = \text{MST/MSE}$

ANOVA Test for randomized block design:
$F = \text{MST/MSE}$

ANOVA Test for factorial design interaction:
$F = \text{MS(A} \times \text{B)/MSE}$

Pairwise comparisons: $c = k(k-1)/2$

CHAPTER 9

Multinomial test: $\chi^2 = \Sigma \dfrac{(n_i - E_i)^2}{E_i}$

$E_i = n(p_{i0})$

Contingency table test: $\chi^2 = \Sigma \dfrac{(n_{ij} - E_{ij})^2}{E_{ij}}$

$E_{ij} = \dfrac{R_i C_j}{n}$

CHAPTER 10

$SS_{xx} = \Sigma x^2 - \dfrac{(\Sigma x)^2}{n}$

$SS_{yy} = \Sigma y^2 - \dfrac{(\Sigma y)^2}{n}$

$SS_{xy} = \Sigma xy - \dfrac{(\Sigma x)(\Sigma y)}{n}$

$\hat{y} = \hat{\beta}_0 + \hat{\beta}_1 x$

$\hat{\beta}_1 = \dfrac{SS_{xy}}{SS_{xx}}$

$\hat{\beta}_0 = \bar{y} - \hat{\beta}_1\bar{x}$

$r = \dfrac{SS_{xy}}{\sqrt{SS_{xx}}\sqrt{SS_{yy}}}$

(*Continued on previous page*)